New York

Prentice Hall
Chemistry

PEARSON

Prentice Hall

Upper Saddle River, New Jersey
Needham, Massachusetts

NEW YORK

PRINT COMPONENTS

New York Student Edition
New York Teacher's Edition
New York Lesson Plans
New York Progress Monitoring Assessments
New York Standardized Test Preparation Workbook
Core Teaching Resources
Guided Reading and Study Workbook
Guided Reading and Study Workbook, ATE
Laboratory Manual
Laboratory Manual, ATE
Laboratory Practicals
Small-Scale Chemistry Laboratory Manual
Small-Scale Chemistry Laboratory Manual, ATE
Graphing Calculator Problems
Test-Taking Tips With Transparencies,
   Grades 9–12 Science
Test Preparation Blackline Masters

TECHNOLOGY COMPONENTS

Interactive Textbook CD-ROM
Interactive Textbook Web Site
Computer Test Bank CD-ROM
Interactive Textbook w/Chem ASAP CD-ROM
Interactive Textbook w/Chem ASAP Online
Transparencies
Presentation Pro CD-ROM
Probeware Lab Manual
Small-Scale Chemistry Lab Video
Chemistry Alive Labs and Chemistry
   Field Trips DVD
Virtual Chem Labs
Exam_View_® Computer Test Bank
Teacher Express CD-ROM
PHSchool.com Web site

About the cover: The sample-well plate filled with colorful solutions illustrates the beauty and excitement of chemistry. Image from Getty Images, Inc.

Acknowledgments appear on page R146, which constitutes an extension of this copyright page.

Pearson Prentice Hall™ is a trademark of Pearson Education, Inc.
Pearson® is a registered trademark of Pearson plc.
Prentice Hall® is a registered trademark of Pearson Education, Inc.

ISBN 0-13-125886-9

1 2 3 4 5 6 7 8 9 10   08 07 06 05 04

About the Authors

ANTONY C. WILBRAHAM

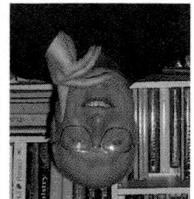

Antony Wilbraham is an Emeritus Professor of Chemistry. He taught college-level chemistry for more than 25 years at Southern Illinois University at Edwardsville, Illinois, where he was also Director of Hazardous Waste Management. In 1978, he received the University Teaching Excellence Award. Dr. Wilbraham has been writing high school and college-level chemistry textbooks and related ancillaries almost 25 years and has published extensively in science journals for over 30 years. He is a member of the American Chemical Society, a member of the National Science Teachers Association, and a Fellow of the Royal Society of Chemistry.

DENNIS D. STALEY

Dennis Staley was an instructor in the Department of Chemistry and the Office of Science and Math Education at Southern Illinois University at Edwardsville, Illinois. He has been teaching high school and college-level chemistry for more than 20 years. In 1981 he received the University Teaching Excellence Award. Mr. Staley has been writing high school and college-level chemistry textbooks and related ancillaries for almost 25 years. He is a member of the American Chemical Society and a member of the National Science Teachers Association.

MICHAEL S. MATTA

Michael Matta is an Emeritus Professor of Chemistry. He was a professor of chemistry at Southern Illinois University at Edwardsville, Illinois, from 1969 to 1996, and served as Department Chair from 1980 to 1983. In 1973, Dr. Matta received the University Teaching Excellence Award. He has been developing and writing high school and college-level chemistry textbooks and related ancillaries for almost 25 years and has published extensively in scientific journals. He is a member of the American Chemical Society, the National Science Teachers Association, and the American Association for the Advancement of Science.

EDWARD L. WATERMAN

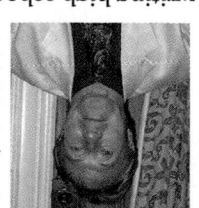

Edward Waterman has taught chemistry, advanced placement chemistry, and organic and biochemistry since 1976 at Rocky Mountain High School in Fort Collins, Colorado. Mr. Waterman conducts workshops for teachers on such topics as small-scale chemistry labs, advanced placement chemistry, block scheduling, Internet for the chemistry classroom, and virtual chemistry on CD-ROM. Mr. Waterman holds a Bachelor of Science degree in chemistry from Montana State University and a Master of Science degree in chemistry from Colorado State University.

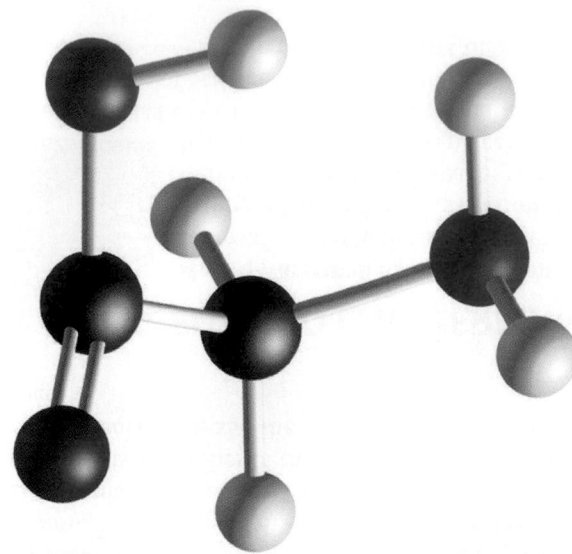

New York Reviewers

KERRY BREINLINGER

Kerry Breinlinger has been a chemistry teacher at Ballston Spa High School in Ballston Spa, NY for the past six years. She has also served as a consultant for the New York State Education Department as an item writer and editor for the past two years. Kerry received her B.S. in Chemistry and her M. Ed. from the University of Massachusetts at Amherst.

COLEEN K. McCAFFERY

Coleen K. McCaffery earned her Bachelors of Science degree in Chemistry from Siena College in 1993 and her Masters of Science degree in curriculum development and instructional technology from Albany University in 2000. Currently she is teaching regents and advanced placement chemistry at Guilderland High School in Guilderland, New York where she has been for seven years. During the past four years she has been an editor and item writer for the New York State Regents chemistry exam.

THOMAS W. SHILAND

Thomas W. Shiland graduated from Cambridge Central High School in upstate New York in 1969, and from Dartmouth College in 1973, majoring in chemistry. He has taught chemistry for 20 years at Saratoga Springs High School in Saratoga Springs, New York, where he is science department chairman and teaches Regents and advanced placement chemistry. He is past president of the New York State Science Education Leadership association and is presently vice president of the Science Teachers Association of New York State. He has published articles on science teaching in The Science Teacher, the Journal of Chemical Education, Science Education and the Journal of Research in Science Teaching. He has worked during the summer for the past five years editing and writing chemistry questions for the New York State Regents chemistry exam.

Reviewers

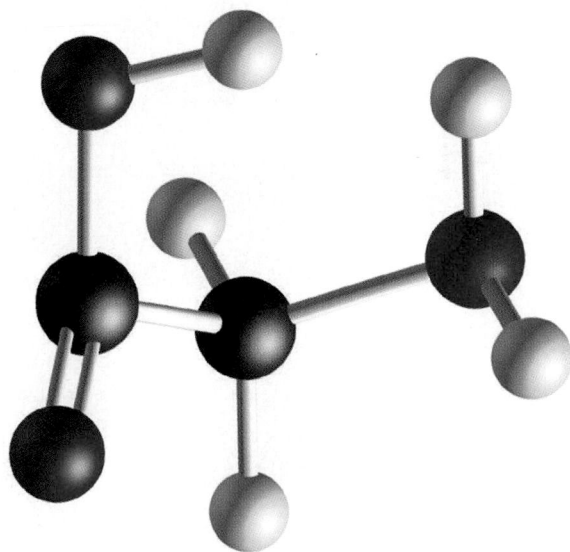

Content Reviewers

Regina M. Barrier
Western Regional Outreach Coordinator
The Science House
North Carolina State University

Martha D. Bruch
Department of Chemistry
SUNY – Oswego
Oswego, New York

Pamela J. Delaney
Department of Chemistry and
Biochemistry
Montclair State University
Upper Montclair, New Jersey

Alison J. Frontier
Department of Chemistry
University of Rochester
Rochester, New York

Patricia L. Lang
Department of Chemistry
Ball State University
Muncie, Indiana

Chi H. Mak
Department of Chemistry
University of Southern California
Los Angeles, California

M. Uljana Mayer, Ph.D.
Pacific Northwest National Lab
Richland, Washington

David J. Merkler, Ph.D.
Department of Chemistry
University of South Florida
Tampa, Florida

Jeffery W. Seyler
Department of Chemistry
University of Southern Indiana
Evansville, Indiana

Harry A. Stern
Postdoctoral Research Scientist
Cornell University
Ithaca, New York

Carey E. Stronach, Ph.D.
Department of Physics
Virginia State University
Petersburg, Virginia

Aaron W. Todd, Ph.D.
Professor of Chemistry, Emeritus
Middle Tennessee State University
Murfreesboro, Tennessee

Mark E. Welker
Department of Chemistry
Wake Forest University
Winston-Salem, North Carolina

Teacher Reviewers

Paulette Berger
Zionsville Community High School
Zionsville, Indiana

Tonia Bonner
Village Christian Academy
Fayetteville, North Carolina

Jeanne M. Dyer
Sickles High School
Tampa, Florida

Amy Fisher
R. Nelson Snider High School
Ft. Wayne, Indiana

Stephen Gerofsky
Lake Weir High School
Ocala, Florida

Rob Larsen
West Orange High School
Winter Garden, Florida

Aimee Pulido
La Joya Senior High School
La Joya, Texas

Michael Richardson
Seymour High School
Seymour, Indiana

Rhonda W. Smith
Enloe High School
Raleigh, North Carolina

Jan Carroll Weir
Science Dept. Chairman
Lawrence Central High School
Indianapolis, Indiana

Thomas C. Zebovitz
Walla Walla Community College
Walla Walla, Washington

Chemistry

PRENTICE HALL ●

NEW YORK

Contents

This overview lists and explains the New York Core Curriculum. Because you will be tested on this content at the end of the course, you'll also find some sample test questions to help you prepare for the exam.

Find out about your state's science safety standards and how the safety features in this book meet the New York safety requirements for laboratory work.

See how the text is organized to help you study and master the New York Core Curriculum for Chemistry. Follow these strategies and you'll have a great year!

Contents

Contents

Contents

Reference Section

Integrated Technology

*i*Interactive Textbook with ChemASAP

- Complete textbook and key art and photos online and on CD-ROM
- Online textbook powered by tried and true teacher resource and student tool, ChemASAP.
- **Animations** illustrate important concepts
- **Simulations** allow students to manipulate variables, observe results, and draw conclusions
- **Assessment** provides over 500 unique test and quiz items
- **Problem-solving** tutorials provide detailed, step-by-step solutions to over 100 practice problems

Go Online

SciLINKS NSTA

- Goes hand-in-hand with the Student Edition for additional support—student activities, chapter assessment, teacher support, and many more resources—with every chapter

PHSchool.com

- Referenced at point-of-use in the Student Edition, these Web links are maintained and updated by the National Science Teachers Association—with accompanying worksheets

*V*irtual **CHEM**Lab

- Inquiry-based lab simulation environment allows students and teachers to perform any chemistry lab accurately and efficiently, without costly equipment and cleanup
- Pre-set labs correspond to specific Small-Scale Labs and Quick Labs
- Virtual ChemLab environment stresses proper procedures, safety, and observable and non-observable results

Probe or sensor versions available in the Probeware Lab Manual.

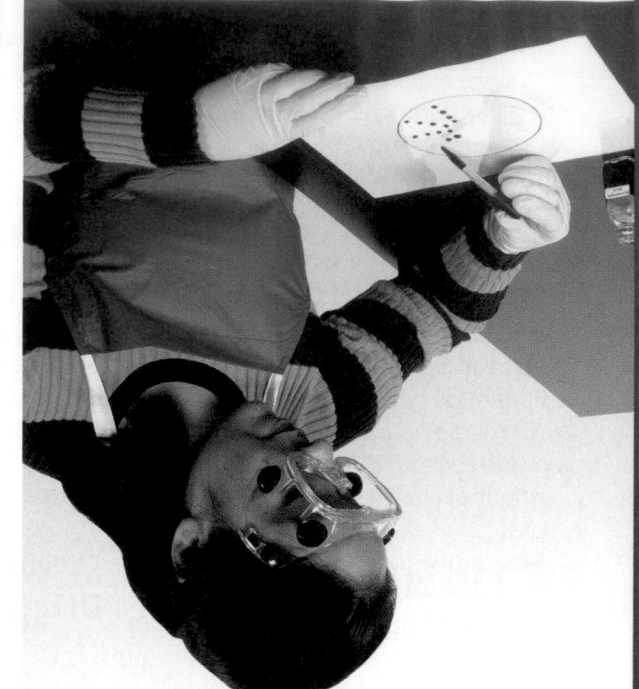

Use everyday materials with easy setup to produce immediate, obvious lab results.

Small-Scale LABS

Quick LABS

Apply chemistry concepts and skills with these quick, effective hands-on opportunities.

 Probe or sensor versions available in the Probeware Lab Manual.

INQUIRY Activities

Begin each chapter with an activity that sets the purpose for reading.

INTERPRETING GRAPHS

Organize and interpret data while building critical thinking skills.

INTERPRETING GRAPHS

a. Analyzing Data Which alkali metal has an atomic radius of 238 pm?

b. Drawing Conclusions Based on the data for alkali metals and noble gases, how does atomic size change within a group?

c. Predicting Is an atom of barium, atomic number 56, smaller or larger than an atom of cesium (Cs)?

Atomic Radius *versus* Atomic Number

CHEMath

Reinforces math concepts needed for problem solving with these point-of-use refreshers.

CHEMath

Logarithms

The common logarithm (log) of a number (N) is the exponent (x) to which the base 10 must be raised to yield the number. If $N = 10^x$, then $\log N = x$

The use of logarithms allows a large range of values to be conveniently expressed as small, nonexponential numbers. For example, $\log (10^3) = 3$ and $\log (10^6) = 6$. Although there is a range of three orders of magnitude (10 × 10 or 1000) between the numbers 10^3 and 10^6, the range of the log values is only 3.

The concentration of hydrogen ions in most aqueous solutions, although small, can vary over many orders of magnitude. Scientists use pH, a logarithmic scale which ranges between 0 and 14, to more conveniently express the hydrogen ion concentration of a solution.

Math Handbook
For help with logarithms, go to page R78.

CHEMath

Conversion Factors

A conversion factor is a ratio of two quantities equal to one another. When working conversion problems, the conversion factors should be written so that the unit of a given measurement cancels, leaving the correct unit for your answer. Note that the equalities needed to write a particular conversion factor may be given in the problem; in other cases, you will need to know or look up the necessary equalities.

Math Handbook
For help with conversion problems, go to page R66.

CHEMath

Significant Figures

The significant figures in a measurement are all the digits known with certainty plus one estimated digit. The number of significant figures in measurements in a calculation, are used to determine the rounded answer of the calculation.

When multiplying and dividing measurements, the rounded answer can have no more significant figures than the least number of significant figures in any measurement in the calculation.
The product of 3.6 m × 2.48 m = 8.928 m² is rounded to 8.9 m² (2 significant figures).

When adding and subtracting measurements, the answer can have no more decimal places than the least number of decimal places in any measurement in the problem. The difference of 8.68 cm − 2.2 cm = 6.58 cm is rounded to 6.6 cm (one decimal place).

Math Handbook
For help with significant figures, go to page R59.

NEW YORK

CONCEPTUAL PROBLEMS

NEW YORK

Technology & Society

Relates content to current technological advances.

Careers in Chemistry

Career opportunities that require an understanding of chemistry.

New York Chemistry
Core Curriculum

The state of New York has established science standards describing science knowledge and skills that you will learn this year. In the following pages we provide examples of what this content means to you and sample problems to help you gain the knowledge and skills you need to be successful.

Learning Standards

Listed below are the seven learning standards for mathematics, science, and technology, upon which your curriculum is based. Standards 2, 6, and 7 address the interconnectedness between chemistry, math, and other science disciplines. Your textbook will cover these three standards by teaching how current technologies affect chemistry and by providing real-world examples of how chemistry, math, and other disciplines are used. Standards 1 and 4 outline the inquiry skills and chemistry content that you are expected

Standard 1

Students will use mathematical analysis, scientific inquiry, and engineering design, as appropriate, to pose questions, seek answers, and develop solutions.

Standard 2

Students will access, generate, process, and transfer information using appropriate technologies.

Standard 3

Students will understand mathematics and become mathematically confident by communicating and reasoning mathematically, by applying mathematics in real-world settings, and by solving problems through the integrated study of number systems, geometry, algebra, data analysis, probability, and trigonometry.

Standard 4

Students will understand and apply scientific concepts, principles, and theories pertaining to the physical setting and living environment and recognize the historical development of ideas in science.

Standard 5

Students will apply technological knowledge and skills to design, construct, use, and evaluate products and systems to satisfy human and environmental needs.

Standard 6

Students will understand the relationships and common themes that connect mathematics, science, and technology and apply the themes to these and other areas of learning.

Standard 7

Students will apply the knowledge and thinking skills of mathematics, science, and technology to address real-life problems and make informed decisions.

to learn. You will find a review of these two standards in depth in the following pages. Standards 3 and 5 are not part of the Physical Setting/Chemistry Core Curriculum.

To check your mastery of your new skills and knowledge, you may use the Regents Practice Exam at the end of most chapters. Also, don't forget to make use of our Take It to the Net feature located at: www.phschool.com

STANDARD 1: Mathematical Analysis

Students will use mathematical analysis, scientific inquiry, and engineering design, as appropriate, to pose questions, seek answers, and develop solutions.

Key Idea 1

Abstraction and symbolic representation are used to communicate mathematically.

M1.1 Use algebraic and geometric representations to describe and compare data.

What It Means To You

Measurements are used to determine experimental data. To be meaningful, these data must be organized and displayed. You will learn to use various scales of measurement to determine data and to create tables and graphs to display data. You will also learn to apply geometry to particles and their behavior.

Where You Will Learn This

Sections 3.3-3.4, 7.3-8.1, 8.3, 13.3, 15.1

EXAMPLE QUESTION

A students is conducting an experiment to determine the effect of temperature on the volume of an inflated balloon. What two measurements could be taken directly and placed in a data table? What measurement would have to be calculated from these data?

Key Idea 2

Deductive and inductive reasoning are used to reach mathematical conclusions.

M2.1 Use deductive reasoning to construct and evaluate conjectures and arguments, recognizing that patterns and relationships in mathematics assist them in arriving at these conjectures and arguments.

What It Means To You

Graphs drawn from experimental data are meaningful only when the variables used and the pattern of data shown are interpreted and applied. You will learn to interpret a graph constructed from experimentally obtained data.

Where You Will Learn This

Sections 1.2, 13.4, 14.2-14.3, 16.4

EXAMPLE QUESTION

Look at the graph on this page. Which of the following generalizations is true, based on this graph?

(1) Atomic radius increases from left to right across a period.
(2) Atomic radius decreases from left to right across a period.
(3) Ionic radius increases from left to right across a period.
(4) Ionic radius decreases from left to right across a period.

Standard Course of Study

NEW YORK

Key Idea 3

Critical thinking skills are used in the solution of mathematical problems.

M3.1 Apply algebraic and geometric concepts and skills to the solution of problems.

What It Means To You

Experimentation is problem solving. Because only one factor can vary in an experiment, it is assumed that other factors are constant. The results of the experiment should make sense, based on data obtained. You will learn to state assumptions and evaluate the situation to see that the assumptions have been met. You will also evaluate the appropriateness of an answer, based on given data.

Where You Will Learn This

Sections 3.1, 14.2–14.3

EXAMPLE QUESTION

In an experiment, the pressure of a gas inside a balloon decreases when the volume of the balloon increases. What assumptions are made about the gas in this balloon?

(1) The amount of gas and the temperature are constant.

(2) The amount of gas and the temperature do not affect pressure or volume.

(3) The relationship shown in this experiment does not apply to all experiments.

(4) The volume increases because the amount of gas increases.

STANDARD 1: Scientific Inquiry

Students will use mathematical analysis, scientific inquiry, and engineering design, as appropriate, to pose questions, seek answers, and develop solutions.

Key Idea 1

The central purpose of scientific inquiry is to develop explanations of natural phenomena in a continuing, creative process.

S1.1 Elaborate on basic scientific and personal explanations of natural phenomena, and develop extended visual models and mathematical formulations to represent thinking.

What It Means To You

Because much of chemistry occurs on the atomic level, models are essential to the study of chemistry. You will learn to develop and use theories and models to represent and explain observations and to make predictions about natural phenomena.

Where You Will Learn This

Sections 4.1–4.2, 11.3, 13.1–13.2

EXAMPLE QUESTION

Use the model shown on this page to explain why metals conduct an electrical current and ionic crystals do not.

Standard Course of Study

S1.2 Hone ideas through reasoning, library research, and discussion with others, including experts.

What It Means To You

The development of theories is based on the observation of repeated patterns. Often, it is impractical to repeat experiments enough times to thoroughly support a theory. You will learn to locate data from published sources to support and explain patterns observed in natural phenomena.

Where You Will Learn This
Section 3.2

EXAMPLE QUESTION

A student looks in the library for sources that help explain why the periodic table is organized the way it is. Which of the following articles would most likely help explain periodicity?

(1) "Refining Elements"
(2) "Uses of Metals"
(3) "Seasons, Tides, and Phases of the Moon"
(4) "Defining Chemical and Physical Properties"

S1.3 Work towards reconciling competing explanations, clarifying points of agreement and disagreement.

What It Means To You

When experiments are performed by different scientists, the possibility exists that differing conclusions are drawn. You will learn to evaluate the merits of different scientific theories and indicate why one theory might be favored over another.

Where You Will Learn This
Section 1.3

EXAMPLE QUESTION

Elements were initially listed on the periodic table according to increasing atomic mass. Why was it concluded that elements should be listed according to increasing atomic number instead of increasing atomic mass?

Key Idea 2

Beyond the use of reasoning and consensus, scientific inquiry involves the testing of proposed explanations involving the use of conventional techniques and procedures and usually requiring considerable ingenuity.

S2.1 Devise ways of making observations to test proposed explanations.

What It Means To You

The solution to a problem does not usually come with predetermined steps to be followed. You will learn to design experiments that use sound scientific methods and can be used to test proposed hypotheses.

Where You Will Learn This

Sections that include Small-Scale Labs, such as 2.4, 3.4, 4.3, 5.2, 7.2, 8.4, 9.2, 10.2, 11.3

EXAMPLE QUESTION

Which of the following choices is not part of designing an experiment?
(1) Use your senses to make observations.
(2) State a testable hypothesis.
(3) Draw conclusions based on observations and measurements.
(4) Adjust data as needed to support your hypothesis.

S2.2 Refine research ideas through library investigations, including information retrieval and reviews of the literature, and through peer feedback obtained from review and discussion.

What It Means To You

Research plans might require modification based on information from other sources. You will learn to gather information from library investigations, technological retrieval, and literature reviews and use this information to improve your experimental design.

Where You Will Learn This

Sections 6.3, 16.1, 17.4

EXAMPLE QUESTION

A student is performing an experiment to determine the relationship between the nitrogen content of fertilizer and plant growth. How many of the following topics might be used to improve the experimental design?
a. percent composition of various fertilizers
b. the effect of sunlight on plant growth
c. the label instructions showing how much fertilizer is recommended
d. the relative amounts of nitrogen and phosphorus in the fertilizer.

(1) 1   (2) 2
(3) 3   (4) 4

S2.3 Develop and present proposals including formal hypotheses to test explanations, i.e.; they predict what should be observed under specific conditions if their explanation is true.

What It Means To You

The development and presentation of research proposals can take different forms. In this course, you will learn to develop research proposals based on given information, a particular test, and a prediction of the results.

Where You Will Learn This
Sections 7.2, 11.3, 14.4, 15.2, 17.4

EXAMPLE QUESTION

Consider the statement, "If X is true and a particular test Y is done, then prediction Z will occur." In an investigation, a white precipitate forms when a student adds silver nitrate to a sample of tap water. The properties of the precipitate identify it as silver chloride. For this investigation, what given information is Z in the statement?

S2.4 Carry out a research plan for testing explanations, including selecting and developing techniques, acquiring and building apparatus, and recording observations as necessary.

What It Means To You

To be effective in the laboratory, techniques must be performed safely and the apparatus used must be safe. You will learn to evaluate a research plan in terms of the safety procedures that must accompany it.

Where You Will Learn This
Section 1.3

EXAMPLE QUESTION

The procedure for an experiment requires the safety symbol shown.

What precautions are indicated by this safety symbol?

(1) Be careful while handling hot objects.
(2) Always use a thermal mitt.
(3) Use caution when working near an open flame.
(4) A laboratory apron should be worn.

Key Idea 3

The observations made while testing proposed explanations, when analyzed using conventional and invented methods, provide new insights into phenomena.

S3.1 Use various means of representing and organizing observations (e.g., diagrams, tables, charts, graphs, equations, and matrices) and insightfully interpret the organized data.

What It Means To You

A data table is one common way to display data and observations. You will learn to use scientific concepts to organize observations in a data table and to analyze and interpret any trends or patterns shown in the table.

Where You Will Learn This

Section 14.4

EXAMPLE QUESTION

An experiment produced the results shown in the table. Compare the table to the location of the elements on the periodic table. Where are the most active metals located on the periodic table?

Activity Series of Metals

Name	Symbol
Lithium	Li
Potassium	K
Calcium	Ca
Sodium	Na
Magnesium	Mg
Aluminum	Al
Zinc	Zn
Iron	Fe
Lead	Pb
(Hydrogen)	(H)*
Copper	Cu
Mercury	Hg
Silver	Ag

Decreasing reactivity →

*Metals from Li to Na will replace H from acids and water; from Mg to Pb they will replace H from acids only.

S3.2 Apply statistical analysis techniques when appropriate to test if chance alone explains the result.

What It Means To You

Increasing the sample size or the number of repetitions in an experiment is a useful way to determine whether results are based on chance or not. You will learn to control sample size and use numerous trials to determine the reliability of certain results.

Where You Will Learn This

Sections 3.4, 4.2–4.3, 18.4

EXAMPLE QUESTION

A student wants to determine the amount of magnesium oxide produced when magnesium is burned in air. She finds the mass of Mg used and also finds the mass of product after the Mg is burned. Which of the following choices will provide the most accurate result?

(1) One 2.4-g sample of Mg is burned in an open container.

(2) One 2.4-g sample of Mg is burned in a small, closed container.

(3) Four different samples of Mg are burned separately in an open container.

(4) Four different samples of Mg are burned separately in a small, closed container.

S3.3 Assess correspondence between the predicted result contained in the hypothesis and the actual result, and reach a conclusion as to whether or not the explanation on which the prediction is supported.

What It Means To You

Not all experimental results are precise and accurate. Human and experimental factors can cause errors in the results. You will learn to determine sources of experimental error and analyze their effects on the results. You will also learn to calculate percent error for quantitative results.

Where You Will Learn This
Sections 3.1, 3.4

EXAMPLE QUESTION

The mass of a container is measured to be 35.6 g. The actual mass of the container is 35.8 g. What is the percent error of the measurement?

(1) 0.559% (2) 0.562%

(3) 5.59% (4) 5.62%

S3.4 Using results of the test and through public discussion, revise the explanation and contemplate additional research.

What It Means To You

Experimental results are subject to public scrutiny. You will learn to revise explanations and do further research based on your results and scientific reaction to them.

Where You Will Learn This
Section 17.4

EXAMPLE QUESTION

You burned completely 1.56 g of magnesium ribbon in air. You predicted the amount of product to be 2.59 g. However, the actual amount of product was 2.54 g. A class discussion pointed out that some of the magnesium might have reacted with an element other than oxygen in the air. How might you revise the experiment to account for this suggestion?

STANDARD 1: Engineering Design

Students will use mathematical analysis, scientific inquiry, and engineering design, as appropriate, to pose questions, seek answers, and develop solutions.

Key Idea 1

Engineering design is an iterative process involving modeling and optimization (finding the best solution within given constraints); this process is used to develop technological solutions to problems within given constraints.

What It Means To You

A scientist should be able to initiate and carry out a thorough investigation that includes how technology can be used to solve a problem. You will learn to perform such a creative investigation using models and working plans.

Where You Will Learn This

See Small-Scale Labs and Technology & Society in each chapter

EXAMPLE QUESTION

A student designed and performed an experiment about bonding, during which he used the following items: calculator, balls and springs, sugar, the Internet, drawings on paper, probeware, salt, metal strips, and a voltmeter. Classify each of these items as technology, model, or neither technology nor model.

S3.5 Develop a written report for public scrutiny that describes the proposed explanation, including a literature review, the research carried out, its results, and suggestions for further research.

What It Means To You

Communication and justification of results are important parts of any experiment. You will learn to accurately and concisely present and defend your explanations by a written report that other people can review.

Where You Will Learn This

Section Assessments that include Writing Activities, such as 2.2, 8.3, 9.1, 16.2

EXAMPLE QUESTION

Explain how a data table could be used in a written report to both communicate and justify experimental results.

Students will understand and apply scientific concepts, principles, and theories pertaining to the physical setting and living environment and recognize the historical development of ideas in science.

Key Idea 3

Matter is made up of particles whose properties determine the observable characteristics of matter and its reactivity.

3.1 Explain the properties of materials in terms of the arrangement and properties of the atoms that compose them.

What It Means To You

Physical and chemical properties of a material are the result of the composition and structure of its atoms. You will learn about atoms and the particles that make them up and how the structure of an atom determines the properties of that element or materials that contain that element.

Where You Will Learn This

Sections 2.1–2.4, 3.4–8.1, 9.1–9.5, 10.3, 13.1–13.4, 15.2–16.4, 18.4, 19.1–19.2, 19.4–19.5, 22.1–23.3, 24.2–24.4, 25.1

EXAMPLE QUESTION

At room temperature, bromine is a liquid, oxygen is a gas, and sodium is a solid. Explain each of these states in terms of how the atoms are arranged in the element.

3.2 Use atomic and molecular models to explain common chemical reactions.

What It Means To You

Substances behave in a manner that is predictable based on the atoms involved. You will learn to predict the results of a chemical reaction and identify different types of reactions, based on the rearrangement of atoms or the transfer of electrons that occurs during the reaction.

Where You Will Learn This

Sections 2.1, 2.3–2.4, 11.2, 20.1–21.3, 23.1–23.4, 24.2, 24.4–24.5

EXAMPLE QUESTION

What type of chemical reaction is shown in the above figure?

(1) combination (synthesis)
(2) decomposition
(3) single-replacement
(4) double-replacement

Standard Course of Study

3.3 Apply the principle of conservation of mass to chemical reactions.

What It Means To You

In all chemical reactions, mass, energy, and charge are conserved. You will learn to balance chemical equations, compare types of formulas, and determine percent composition of a compound.

Where You Will Learn This

Sections 2.4, 10.1–11.1, 11.3, 12.1–12.3, 15.2, 17.4, 20.1

EXAMPLE QUESTION

Balance the following chemical equation.

$$Cu(OH)_2 + H_3PO_4 \rightarrow Cu_3(PO_4)_2 + H_2O$$

3.4 Use kinetic molecular theory (KMT) to explain rates of reactions and the relationships among temperature, pressure, and volume of a substance.

What It Means To You

KMT can be used to explain the behavior of ideal gases and what happens to particles in equilibrium. You will learn to compare a real gas and an ideal gas and describe the relationships among pressure, volume, temperature, and amount of a gas. You will also examine what factors control the rate of a reaction and how a reaction in equilibrium responds to stress.

Where You Will Learn This

Sections 10.2, 11.1, 12.2, 13.1, 14.1–14.4, 18.1–18.3, 18.5, 19.3, 24.3

EXAMPLE QUESTION

How will the following equilibrium be affected by an increase in temperature?

$$2KClO_3(s) + heat \rightarrow 2KCl(s) + 3O_2(g)$$

(1) It will remain as it is.
(2) It will shift to the left.
(3) It will shift to the right.
(4) It will go to completion.

Key Idea 4

Energy exists in many forms, and when these forms change energy is conserved.

4.1 Observe and describe transmission of various forms of energy.

What It Means To You

Energy can exist in several different forms and is either given off or absorbed during chemical reactions. You will learn to interpret energy changes both quantitatively and qualitatively.

Where You Will Learn This

Sections 1.2, 17.1–17.4, 18.4, 24.1

EXAMPLE QUESTION

Which of the following terms describes this chemical reaction?

$$2NaHCO_3(s) + heat \rightarrow Na_2CO_3(s) + H_2O(g) + CO_2(g)$$

(1) equilibrium
(2) combustion
(3) endothermic
(4) exothermic

4.2 Explain heat in terms of kinetic molecular theory.

What It Means To You

Heat is based on the temperature of two objects, but heat and temperature are not the same thing. You will learn to distinguish between heat and temperature and use these concepts to explain changes in state.

Where You Will Learn This

Sections 3.2, 13.2, 17.1–17.3

EXAMPLE QUESTION

While ice is melting

(1) energy is absorbed
(2) energy is released
(3) temperature increases
(4) temperature decreases

4.4 Explain the benefits and risks of radioactivity.

What It Means To You

Radioactive materials spontaneously release either particles or electromagnetic radiation. You will learn about uses and dangers of radioactive materials and the processes of fission and fusion and how to balance a nuclear equation.

Where You Will Learn This

Sections 25.1–25.4

EXAMPLE QUESTION

Using the diagram below explain the difference in fission and fusion.

a. Discuss why one of these processes is currently used as an energy source but the other process is not.
b. Which of these processes is represented by the diagram?

$4\,{}^{1}_{1}H$ $^{4}_{2}He$ $2\,{}^{0}_{+1}e$
hydrogen nuclei   helium nucleus   positrons

Key Idea 5

Energy and matter interact through forces that result in changes in motion.

5.2 Explain chemical bonding in terms of the behavior of electrons.

What It Means To You

Chemical bonds form when valence electrons are either transferred or shared between atoms or are mobile in a metal. You will learn to describe different types of bonds and their formation and the intermolecular forces that occur between particles.

Where You Will Learn This

Sections 6.3–9.1, 9.5, 13.3, 15.1, 24.1, 24.5–24.6

EXAMPLE QUESTION

Explain how each of the following types of bond forms.

a. ionic
b. pure covalent
c. polar covalent
d. metallic

5.3 Compare energy relationships within an atom's nucleus to those outside the nucleus.

What It Means To You

Chemical reactions do not involve the nucleus of an atom, but nuclear reactions involve nuclear changes. You will learn about how transmutations occur and describe energy changes that occur during a nuclear reaction.

Where You Will Learn This

Sections 25.2–25.3

EXAMPLE QUESTION

What process is shown in the diagram below?

(1) fission
(2) fusion
(3) radioactivity
(4) transmutation

$_2^4$He
Alpha
particle

$_7^{14}$N
Nitrogen
nucleus

$_9^{18}$F
Unstable
fluorine

$_1^1$H
Proton

$_8^{17}$O
Oxygen

Lab Safety in Chemistry

North Carolina's *Total Science Safety System* helps your teacher ensure your safety while working in the science lab. However, safety is not only your teacher's responsibility but yours too as Objective 1.03 in your Course of Study.

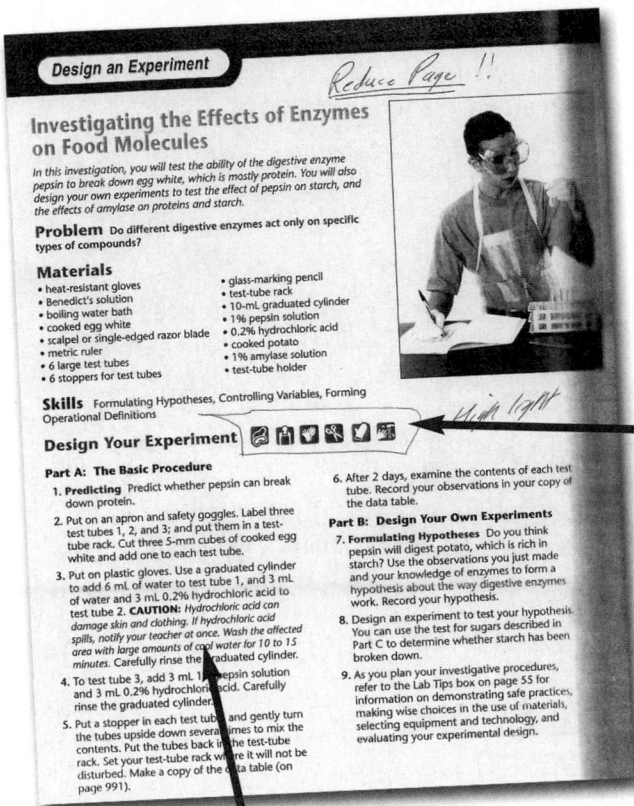

1. Safety Symbols

Safety symbols alert you to possible dangers in the laboratory that remind you to work carefully.

- **Look inside the front cover for a complete list of the symbols and what they stand for.**
- **Find symbols that apply to your tasks on every lab or activity.**
- **Review all the symbols again in Appendix A.**

> "Experimentation allows you to "discover" science concepts and teaches you to conduct investigations safely. You should be aware of the hazards present during the lab and the actions of nearby students. Read instructions carefully before each lab and practice safety plans. Everyone in the lab has a duty to act responsibly!"
>
> Regina M. Barrier
> NC Science Safety Consultant

2. CAUTION Statements

Sometimes you'll find CAUTION statements built into the procedure steps on the labs and activities. They alert you to specific actions that will help you stay safe.

3. Appendix E: Laboratory Safety

This appendix reviews the safety symbols and gives you general instructions on how to stay safe when working with science materials.

In Your Textbook

Look at pages 137, 458, 604, and 746 for more examples.
What safety alerts are on each page?

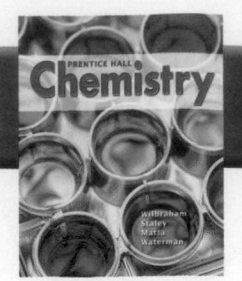

Use This Book for Success

Read for Meaning

17.2 Measuring and Expressing Heat Changes

Connecting to Your World As you know, a burning match gives off heat. When you strike a match, heat is released to the surroundings in all directions. You can classify this reaction as exothermic. In addition to describing the direction of heat flow, you may also want to determine the quantity of heat that is transferred. How much heat does a burning match release to the surroundings? In this section you will learn how you can measure heat changes in chemical and physical processes by applying the concept of specific heat.

Calorimetry

Heat that is released or absorbed during many chemical reactions can be measured by a technique called calorimetry. **Calorimetry** is the precise measurement of heat change for chemical and physical processes. ▶ **In calorimetry, the heat released by the system is equal to the heat absorbed by its surroundings.** In order to measure heat changes precisely, the process being investigated must be carried out in an insulated container. The insulated device used to measure the absorption or release of heat in chemical or physical processes is called a **calorimeter**.

Constant-Pressure Calorimeters Foam cups are excellent heat insulators. Because they do not let much heat in or out, they can be used as simple calorimeters. In fact, the heat change for many chemical reactions can be measured in a constant-pressure calorimeter similar to the one shown in Figure 17.5. Because most chemical reactions and physical changes carried out in the laboratory are open to the atmosphere, these changes occur at constant pressure. For systems at constant pressure, the heat content is the same as a property called the **enthalpy** (H) of the system. Heat reactions carried out at constant pressure are changes in enthalpy, symbolized as ΔH (rea Because the reactions presented in this text constant pressure, the terms *heat* and *enth* interchangeably. In other words, $q = \Delta H$.

Figure 17.5 In a simple constant-press calorimeter, the thermometer measures temperature change as chemicals react water. The substances reacting in soluti constitute the system. The water constit the surroundings.

Guide for Reading

▶ **Key Concepts**
- What basic concept is made use of in calorimetry?
- How can a chemical equation express heat change?

Vocabulary
calorimetry
calorimeter
enthalpy
thermochemical equation
heat of reaction
heat of combustion

Reading Strategy
Relating Text and Visuals As you read, look closely at Figure 17.7 on page 511. Explain how these diagrams help you understand exothermic and endothermic processes.

Thermometer

Stirrer

17.2 Section Assessment

16. ▶ Key Concept Calorimetry is based on what basic concept?

17. ▶ Key Concept How are heat changes treated in chemical equations?

18. When 2 mol of solid magnesium (Mg) combines with 1 mole of oxygen gas (O_2), 2 mol of solid magnesium oxide (MgO) is formed and 1204 kJ of heat is released. Write the thermochemical equation for this combustion reaction.

19. Gasohol contains ethanol (C_2H_5OH)(l), which when burned reacts with oxygen to produce $CO_2(g)$ and $H_2O(g)$. How much heat is released when 12.5 g of ethanol burns?

$$C_2H_5OH(l) + 3O_2(g) \longrightarrow 2CO_2(g) + 3H_2O(g)$$
$$\Delta H = -1235 \text{ kJ}$$

20. Explain the term *heat of combustion*.

Elements ▶ **Handbook**

Representative Elements Look up the important chemical reactions involving the representative elements. Write five chemical equations that describe endothermic reactions, and five equations that describe exothermic reactions.

Interactive Textbook

Assessment Test yourself on the concepts in Section 17.2.
—with **ChemASAP**

Before You Read
The Guide for Reading helps you master concepts by introducing Key Concepts, Vocabulary, and a Reading Strategy.

As You Read
Key Concepts in boldface sentences allow you to focus on the big ideas of chemistry.

After You Read
Section Assessment gives you the opportunity to review Key Concepts at the end of every lesson.

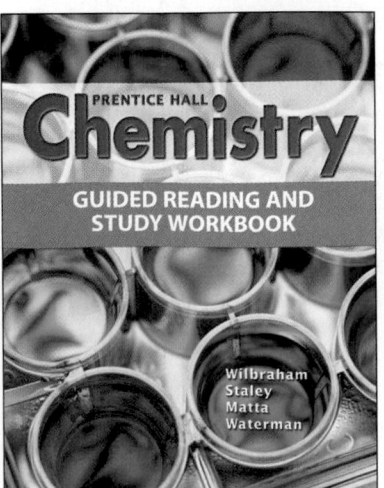

Check Your Understanding
The **Guided Reading and Study Workbook** gives you extra support with vocabulary, reading and math skills, and graphics to enhance your understanding.

Practice Your Math Skills

SAMPLE PROBLEM 17.4

Using the Heat of Reaction to Calculate Heat Change

Using the thermochemical equation in Figure 17.7b on page 511, calculate the amount of heat (in kJ) required to decompose 2.24 mol $NaHCO_3(s)$.

1 **Analyze** *List the knowns and the unknown.*

Knowns
- 2.24 mol $NaHCO_3(s)$ decomposes
- $\Delta H = 129$ kJ

Unknown
- $\Delta H = ?$ kJ

Use the thermochemical equation,

$$2NaHCO_3(s) + 129 \text{ kJ} \longrightarrow Na_2CO_3(s) + H_2O(g) + CO_2(g),$$

to write a conversion factor relating kilojoules of heat and moles of $NaHCO_3$. Then use the conversion factor to determine ΔH for 2.24 mol $NaHCO_3$.

2 **Calculate** *Solve for the unknown.*

The thermochemical equation indicates that 129 kJ are needed to decompose 2 mol $NaHCO_3(s)$. Use this relationship to write the following conversion factor.

$$\frac{129 \text{ kJ}}{2 \text{ mol } NaHCO_3(s)}$$

Using dimensional analysis, calculate ΔH.

$$\Delta H = 2.24 \text{ mol } NaHCO_3(s) \times \frac{129 \text{ kJ}}{2 \text{ mol } NaHCO_3(s)}$$
$$= 144 \text{ kJ}$$

3 **Evaluate** *Does the result make sense?*

Because $\Delta H = 129$ kJ refers to the decomposition of 2 mol $NaHCO_3(s)$, the decomposition of 2.24 mol should absorb about 10% more heat than 129 kJ, or slightly more than 142 kJ. The answer of 144 kJ is consistent with this estimate.

Practice Problems

14. When carbon disulfide is formed from its elements, heat is absorbed. Calculate the amount of heat (in kJ) absorbed when 5.66 g of carbon disulfide is formed.
$$C(s) + 2S(s) \longrightarrow CS_2(l)$$
$$\Delta H = 89.3 \text{ kJ}$$

15. The production of iron and carbon dioxide from iron(III) oxide and carbon monoxide is an exothermic reaction. How many kilojoules of heat are produced when 3.40 mol Fe_2O_3 reacts with an excess of CO?
$$Fe_2O_3(s) + 3CO(g) \longrightarrow$$
$$2Fe(s) + 3CO_2(g) + 26.3 \text{ kJ}$$

CHEMath

Conversion Factors

A conversion factor is a ratio of two quantities that are equal to one another. When doing conversions, write the conversion factors so that the unit of a given measurement cancels, leaving the correct unit for your answer. Note that the equalities needed to write a particular conversion factor may be given in the problem. In other cases, you will need to know or look up the necessary equalities.

Math Handbook

For help with conversion factors go to page 905.

Interactive Textbook

Problem Solving
Solve Problem 15 with the help of an interactive guided tutorial.
with **ChemASAP**

Practice for Test-Taking Success
A variety of problems, utilizing a three-step problem-solving approach, helps you understand chemistry concepts while practicing vital math skills.

Support Where You Need It
You'll find additional help nearby with the **ChemMath** refreshers in the margins and the **Math Handbook** in the Appendix.

Math Support Online
The **Interactive Textbook with ChemASAP** contains practice and problem-solving tutorials to give you extra math reinforcement.

Two-Step Problem Solving
Conceptual Problems encourage you to solve problems using critical thinking and analytical skills.

CONCEPTUAL PROBLEM 17.1

Recognizing Exothermic and Endothermic Processes

On a sunny winter day, the snow on a rooftop begins to melt. As the meltwater drips from the roof, it refreezes into icicles. Describe the direction of heat flow as the water freezes. Is this process endothermic or exothermic?

1 **Analyze** *Identify the relevant concepts.*

Heat always flows from a warmer object to a cooler object. An endothermic process absorbs heat from the surroundings. An exothermic process releases heat to the surroundings.

2 **Solve** *Apply concepts to this situation.*

Define the liquid water as the system and the air as the surroundings. Heat flows from the (warmer) liquid water to the (cooler) air. Because heat is released from the system to the surroundings, this process is exothermic.

Practice Problems

1. A container of melted paraffin wax is allowed to stand at room temperature until the wax solidifies. What is the direction of heat flow as the wax solidifies? Is the process exothermic or endothermic?

2. When solid barium hydroxide octahydrate $(Ba(OH)_2 \cdot 8H_2O)$ is mixed in a beaker with solid ammonium thiocyanate (NH_4SCN), a reaction occurs. The beaker quickly becomes very cold. Is the reaction exothermic or endothermic?

Prepare for Tests

CHAPTER 17 Regents Practice

Reviewing Content

17.1 The Flow of Energy—Heat

38. Explain in your own words the law of conservation of energy.

39. What always happens when two objects of different temperatures come in contact? Give an example from your own experience.

40. Define potential energy in terms of chemistry.

41. What factors determine heat capacity?

42. What is the relationship between a calorie and a Calorie?

43. Make the following conversions.
a. 8.50×10^2 cal to Calories
b. 444 cal to joules
c. 1.8 kJ to joules
d. 4.5×10^{-1} kJ to calories

44. Why do you think it is important to define the system and the surroundings?

45. Describe the sign convention that is used in thermochemical calculations.

46. Two substances in a glass beaker chemically react, and the beaker becomes too hot to touch.
a. Is the reaction exothermic or endothermic?
b. If the two substances are defined as the system, what constitutes the surroundings?

47. Classify these processes as exothermic or endothermic.
a. condensing steam b. evaporating alcohol
c. burning alcohol d. baking a potato

17.2 Measuring and Expressing Heat Changes

48. What name is given to a heat change at constant pressure?

49. What is the function of a calorimeter?

50. There are some obvious sources of error in experiments that use foam cups as calorimeters. Name at least three.

51. What device would you use to measure the heat released at constant volume?

52. Give the standard conditions for heat of combustion.

53. What information is given in a thermochemical equation?

17.3 Heat in Changes of State

54. Explain why ice melts at 0°C without an increase of temperature, even though heat flows from the surroundings to the system (the ice).

55. Calculate the quantity of heat gained or lost in the following changes.
a. 3.50 mol of water freezes at 0°C.
b. 0.44 mol of steam condenses at 100°C.
c. 1.25 mol NaOH(s) dissolves in water.
d. 0.15 mol $C_2H_5OH(l)$ vaporizes at 78.3°C.

56. Sodium acetate dissolves readily in water according to the following equation.

$$NaC_2H_3O_2(s) \longrightarrow NaC_2H_3O_2(aq)$$
$$\Delta H = -17.3 \text{ kJ/mol}$$

Would this process increase or decrease the temperature of the water?

17.4 Calculating Heat Reaction

57. Explain Hess's law of heat summation.

58. A considerable amount of heat is required for the decomposition of aluminum oxide.

$$2Al_2O$$

a. What is the
1 mol of alu
b. Is the react

59. Calculate the
lead(IV) chlori
chloride with

$$PbCl_2($$

Use the follow

$$Pb(s)$$

$$Pb(s$$

60. What is the st
element in its

61. Consider the
value of ΔH_f^o
Is this statem

Check Understanding at Every Step

You'll have many opportunities to assess your understanding with Checkpoint questions and at the end of every section and chapter.

temperature. As you can see from the equation, specific heat may be expressed in terms of joules or calories. Therefore, the units of specific heat are either J/(g × °C) or cal/(g × °C).

 Checkpoint *What is the relationship between specific heat and heat capacity?*

Regents Practice Exam

Test-Taking Tip

Eliminate Wrong Answers If you don't know which response is correct, start by eliminating those you know are wrong. If you can rule out some choices, you'll have fewer left to consider and you'll increase your chances of choosing the correct answer.

Select the choice that best answers each question or completes each statement.

1. The ΔH_{fus} of ethanol (C_2H_5OH) is 4.60 kJ/mol. How many kilojoules are required to melt 24.5 g of ethanol at its freezing point?
a. 2.45 kJ b. 5.33 kJ
c. 245 kJ d. 18.8 kJ

2. How much heat, in kilojoules, must be added to 178 g of water to increase the temperature of the water by 5.0°C?
a. 890 kJ b. 36 kJ
c. 3.7 kJ d. 0.093 kJ

ormation of a free
d state is always
b. positive.
d. higher for solids than
gases.

$2HgO(s) \longrightarrow 2Hg(l) +$
n ΔH for the reaction
$O(s)$ is
b. −90.83 kJ.
d. −181.66 kJ.

city of grain alcohol is ten
pecific heat capacity of
r with a mass of 55 g is
mass of cool alcohol. If
silver bar drops 45 °C,
alcohol
b. decreases 4.5°C.
d. decreases 45°C.

rine gas react to form
. Calculate the heat
onversion of 15.0 g of
tant pressure.
$H_2(g) + F_2(g) \to 2HF(g)$

The lettered choices below refer to Questions 7–10. A lettered choice may be used once, more than once, or not at all.
(A) kJ/mol
(B) (J × °C)/g
(C) J/(g × °C)
(D) kJ
(E) kJ/°C
Which unit is appropriate for each of the following measurements?

7. heat of reaction
8. heat capacity
9. molar heat of fusion
10. specific heat capacity

Use the graph and table to answer Questions 11–14. Assume 1.00 mol of substance in each container.

Substance	Freezing point (K)	ΔH_{fus} (kJ/mol)	Boiling point (K)	ΔH_{vap} (kJ/mol)
Ammonia	195.3	5.65	239.7	23.4
Benzene	278.7	9.87	353.3	30.8
Methanol	175.5	3.16	337.2	35.3
Neon	24.5	0.33	27.1	1.76

11. Calculate heat absorbed in region A for neon.
12. Calculate heat absorbed in region C for benzene.
13. Calculate heat absorbed in regions B and C for methanol. [specific heat = 81.6 J/(g × °C)]
14. Calculate heat absorbed in regions A, B, and C

17.2 Section Assessment

16. **Key Concept** Calorimetry is based on what basic concept?

17. **Key Concept** How are heat changes treated in chemical equations?

18. When 2 mol of solid magnesium (Mg) combines with 1 mole of oxygen gas (O_2), 2 mol of solid magnesium oxide (MgO) is formed and 1204 kJ of heat is released. Write the thermochemical equation for this combustion reaction.

19. Gasohol contains ethanol (C_2H_5OH) (l), which when burned reacts with oxygen to produce $CO_2(g)$ and $H_2O(g)$. How much heat is released when 12.5 g of ethanol burns?

$$C_2H_5OH(l) + 3O_2(g) \longrightarrow 2CO_2(g) + 3H_2O(g)$$
$$\Delta H = -1235 \text{ kJ}$$

20. Explain the term *heat of combustion*.

Elements ➝ Handbook

Representative Elements Look up the important chemical reactions involving the representative elements. Write five chemical equations that describe endothermic reactions, and five equations that describe exothermic reactions.

Interactive Textbook

Assessment Test yourself on the concepts in Section 17.2.
——with **ChemASAP**

Interpreting Graphs

Practice analyzing data in charts and graphs—important skills you'll need to succeed on tests.

Heating Curve for Water

Boiling point

ΔH_{vap}

Vapor

ΔH_{fus}

Liquid

Melting point

Solid

Temperature

Heat Supplied

INTERPRETING GRAPHS

a. Identify In which region(s) of the graph is the slope zero?
b. Describe How does the amount of energy required to melt a given mass of ice compare to the energy required to vaporize the same mass of water? Explain.
c. Apply Concepts Which region of the graph represents the coexistence of solid and liquid? Liquid and solid?

Use the Illustrations and Photos

Art and Text Work Together
As you read the text, you'll find helpful photos and illustrations that make concepts more easily understood. Diagrams simplify complex ideas and demonstrate abstract processes.

Figure 17.2 Heat flow is defined from the point of view of the system. ⓐ In an endothermic process, heat flows into the system from the surroundings. ⓑ In an exothermic process, heat flows from the system to the surroundings. In both cases, energy is conserved. Interpreting Diagrams *In which process does q have a negative value?*

Figure 17.6 Nutritionists use bomb calorimeters to measure the energy content of the foods you eat. To see some of their data (expressed in Calories per serving), you can look at a nutrition label. Calculating *According to the nutrition label below, each serving contains 140 Calories. How many kilojoules is this?*

Nutrition Facts
Serving Size 1 Cookie (26g / 0.9oz.)
Servings Per Container 8

Amount Per Serving		
Calories 140	Calories from Fat 70	
		% Daily Value*
Total Fat 8 g		**12%**
Saturated Fat 2.5 g		**13%**
Polyunsaturated Fat 0 g		
Monounsaturated Fat 3 g		
Cholesterol 10 mg		**3%**
Sodium 80 mg		**3%**
Total Carbohydrate 16 g		**5%**
Dietary Fiber 0 g		**0%**
Sugars 9 g		

Explore the Technology at Your Fingertips

—with **ChemASAP**

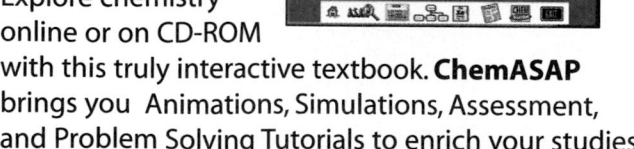

Go Interactive!
Explore chemistry online or on CD-ROM with this truly interactive textbook. **ChemASAP** brings you Animations, Simulations, Assessment, and Problem Solving Tutorials to enrich your studies.

Go Online
For: Links on specific heat
Visit: www.SciLinks.org
Web code: cdn-1171

A World of Resources
Go Online Web links bring you quick access to a variety of chemistry topics. Continuously, updated with current information, these sites show you how chemistry impacts your world.

Virtual **CHEM**Lab

A Simulated Lab Environment
These hands-on lab activities let you perform exciting experiments without the worry of equipment or clean-up.

Chemists use a multi-channel pipette to test many samples at the same time.

INQUIRY Activity

Solid or Liquid?

Materials

tablespoon, cornstarch, small bowl, water

Procedure

1. Add 3 heaping tablespoons of cornstarch to the bowl, and then add 3 tablespoons of water.

2. Use the spoon to thoroughly stir the contents of the bowl. Then let the mixture stand for 5 minutes.

3. Slowly push your finger into the mixture. Repeat with your fist.

4. Quickly jab your finger into the mixture. Repeat with your fist.

5. Take a handful of the mixture and form a ball. Squeeze and release the ball several times.

Think About It

1. What happened when you slowly pushed your finger or fist into the mixture?

2. What happened when you jabbed your finger or fist into the mixture?

3. What happened when you squeezed the ball? When you released the ball?

4. What factor seems to determine whether the mixture behaves like a solid or like a liquid?

Connecting to Your World

The *Galileo* spacecraft was placed in orbit around Jupiter to collect data about the planet and its moons. Instruments aboard *Galileo* analyzed the atmosphere of the moon Io. They found large amounts of sulfur and sulfur dioxide. These chemicals are usually released when volcanoes erupt on Earth. So the presence of these chemicals verified that the volcanoes on Io's surface are active. Chemistry helped scientists to study the geology of a distant object in the solar system. In this section, you will learn about chemistry in general and ways you can use your knowledge of chemistry.

What Is Chemistry?

In autumn thousands of visitors travel to New England to view vivid colors like those in Figure 1.1. These colors appear as the trees approach the winter months when growth no longer takes place. The bright pigments are produced by a complex chemical process, which depends on changes in temperature and hours of daylight. The color pigments in leaves are an example of matter. Matter is the general term for all the things that can be described as materials, or "stuff." **Matter** is anything that has mass and occupies space. You don't have to be able to see something for it to qualify as matter. The air you breathe is an example of "invisible" matter.

Chemistry is the study of the composition of matter and the changes that matter undergoes. **Because living and nonliving things are made of matter, chemistry affects all aspects of life and most natural events.** Chemistry can explain how some creatures survive deep in the ocean where there is no light, or why some foods taste sweet and some taste bitter. It can even explain why there are different shampoos for dry or oily hair.

Guide for Reading

Key Concepts
- Why is the scope of chemistry so vast?
- What are five traditional areas of study in chemistry?
- How are pure and applied chemistry related?
- What are three general reasons to study chemistry?

Vocabulary
matter
chemistry
organic chemistry
inorganic chemistry
biochemistry
analytical chemistry
physical chemistry
pure chemistry
applied chemistry
technology

Reading Strategy
Relating Text and Visuals As you read, look closely at Figure 1.2. Explain how this illustration helps you to understand the traditional areas of study in chemistry.

Figure 1.1 Chemical changes that occur in leaves can cause brilliant displays of color.

Areas of Study

Because the scope of chemistry is vast, chemists tend to focus on one area. 🔑 **Five traditional areas of study are organic chemistry, inorganic chemistry, biochemistry, analytical chemistry, and physical chemistry.**

Most of the chemicals found in organisms contain carbon. Organic chemistry was originally defined as the study of these carbon-based chemicals. Today, with a few exceptions, **organic chemistry** is defined as the study of all chemicals containing carbon. By contrast, **inorganic chemistry** is the study of chemicals that, in general, do not contain carbon. Inorganic chemicals are found mainly in non-living things, such as rocks. The study of processes that take place in organisms is **biochemistry.** These processes include muscle contraction and digestion. **Analytical chemistry** is the area of study that focuses on the composition of matter. A task that would fall into this area of chemistry is measuring the level of lead in drinking water. **Physical chemistry** is the area that deals with the mechanism, the rate, and the energy transfer that occurs when matter undergoes a change.

The boundaries between the five areas are not firm. A chemist is likely to be working in more than one area of chemistry at any given time. For example, an organic chemist uses analytical chemistry to determine the composition of an organic chemical. Figure 1.2 shows how research in these areas of study can be used to keep humans healthy.

Figure 1.2 Chemists study structures and processes in the human body. **Inferring *Does a bone contain mainly organic or inorganic chemicals?***

Physical Chemistry
A physical chemist might study factors that affect breathing rates during exercise.

Organic Chemistry
Athletes inhale chemicals developed by organic chemists to control symptoms of asthma.

Analytical Chemistry
Analytical chemists develop tests to detect chemicals in the blood. The tests help to show if organs in the body are working properly.

Inorganic Chemistry
An inorganic chemist might explain how a lack of calcium can affect the growth and repair of bones.

Biochemistry
A biochemist might study how the energy used for the contraction of muscles is produced and stored.

Pure and Applied Chemistry

Some chemists enjoy doing research on fundamental aspects of chemistry. This type of research is sometimes called pure chemistry. **Pure chemistry** is the pursuit of chemical knowledge for its own sake. The chemist doesn't expect that there will be any immediate practical use for the knowledge. Most chemists do research that is designed to answer a specific question. **Applied chemistry** is research that is directed toward a practical goal or application. In practice, pure chemistry and applied chemistry are often linked. **Pure research can lead directly to an application, but an application can exist before research is done to explain how it works.** Nylon and aspirin provide examples of these two approaches.

Nylon For years, chemists didn't fully understand the structure of materials such as cotton and silk. Hermann Staudinger, a German chemist, proposed that these materials contained small units joined together like links in a chain. In the early 1930s, Wallace Carothers did experiments to test Staudinger's proposal. His results supported the proposal. During his research Carothers produced some materials that don't exist in nature. One of these materials, nylon, can be drawn into long, thin, silk-like fibers, as shown in Figure 1.3. Because the supply of natural silk was limited, a team of scientists and engineers were eager to apply Carother's research to the commercial production of nylon. By 1939, they had perfected a large-scale method for making nylon fibers.

Figure 1.3 Long, thin nylon fibers are woven into the fabric used in this backpack. Other objects that can be made from nylon are jackets, fishing lines, toothbrush bristles, and ropes.

Aspirin Long before researchers figured out how aspirin works, people used it to relieve pain. By 1950, some doctors began to recommend a low daily dose of aspirin for patients who were at risk for a heart attack. Many heart attacks occur when blood clots block the flow of blood through arteries in the heart. Some researchers suspected that aspirin could keep blood clots from forming. In 1971, it was discovered that aspirin can block the production of a group of chemicals that cause pain. These same chemicals are also involved in the formation of blood clots.

Technology The development of nylon and the use of aspirin to prevent heart attacks belong to a system of applied science called technology. **Technology** is the means by which a society provides its members with those things needed and desired. Technology allows humans to do some things more quickly or with less effort. It allows people to do things that would be impossible without technology, such as traveling to the moon. In any technology, scientific knowledge is used in ways that can benefit or harm people and the environment. Debates about how to use scientific knowledge are usually debates about the risks and benefits of technology.

For: Links on Applied Chemistry
Visit: www.SciLinks.org
Web Code: cdn-1011

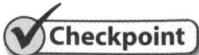 **Checkpoint** *Which material found in nature does nylon resemble?*

Why Study Chemistry?

Should you use hot water or cold water to remove sunblock from a shirt? How could studying chemistry help you to be a better nurse, firefighter, reporter, or chef? If your local government wanted to build a solid waste incinerator in your town, what questions would you ask about the project? Chemistry can have an impact on all aspects of your life. **Chemistry can be useful in explaining the natural world, preparing people for career opportunities, and producing informed citizens.**

Explaining the Natural World You were born with a curiosity about your world. Chemistry can help you satisfy your natural desire to understand how things work. For example, chemistry can be seen in all aspects of food preparation. Chemistry can explain why apples turn brown upon exposure to air. It can explain why the texture of eggs changes from runny to firm as eggs are boiled, scrambled, or fried. Chemistry can explain why water expands as it freezes, sugar dissolves faster in hot water, and adding yeast to bread dough makes the dough rise. After you study this textbook, you will know the answers to these questions and many more.

Preparing For a Career Being a chemist can be rewarding. Section 1.2 will present some examples of how chemists contribute to society. In this book, you will find features on careers that require knowledge of chemistry. Some of the choices may surprise you. You do not need to have the word *chemist* in your job title to benefit from knowing chemistry. For example, a firefighter must know which chemicals to use to fight different types of fires. A reporter may be asked to interview a chemist to gather background for a story. Turf managers are admired for the patterns they produce on a ball field while mowing grass, but their more important task is keeping the grass healthy, which requires an understanding of soil chemistry. A photographer, like the one in Figure 1.4, uses chemical processes to control the development of photographs in a darkroom.

Figure 1.4 Even after the invention of the digital camera, many photographers still work with film. They use chemical processes to develop film in a darkroom. **Inferring** *Why isn't film developed under natural light conditions?*

Being an Informed Citizen Industry, private foundations, and the federal government all provide funds for scientific research. The availability of funding can influence the direction of research. Those who distribute funds have to balance the importance of a goal against the cost. Because there is a limit to the money available, areas of research often compete for funds.

For example, space exploration research could not take place without federal funding. Critics argue that the money spent on space exploration would be better spent on programs such as cancer research. Those who support space exploration point out that NASA research has led to the development of many items used on Earth. These include smoke detectors, scratch-resistant plastic lenses, heart monitors, and flat-screen televisions. What if all the money spent on space exploration was used to find a cure for cancer? Are there enough valid avenues of research to take advantage of the extra funding? Would there be qualified scientists to do the research?

Like the citizens shown in Figure 1.5, you will need to make choices that will influence the development of technology. You may vote directly on some issues through ballot initiatives or indirectly through the officials you elect. You may speak at a public hearing or write a letter to the editor or sign a petition. When it comes to technology, there is no one correct answer. But knowledge of chemistry and other sciences can help you evaluate the data presented, arrive at an informed opinion, and take appropriate action.

Figure 1.5 By registering to vote, these citizens in Chicago, Illinois, can have a say in the decisions made by their government. Those decisions include how much money to provide for scientific research.

1.1 Section Assessment

1. **Key Concept** Explain why chemistry affects all aspects of life and most natural events.

2. **Key Concept** Name the five traditional areas into which chemistry can be divided.

3. **Key Concept** Describe the relationship between pure chemistry and applied chemistry.

4. **Key Concept** List three reasons for studying chemistry.

5. Workers digging a tunnel through a city find some ancient pots decorated with geometric designs. Which of the following tasks might they ask a chemist to do? Explain your answer.
   a. Determine the materials used to make the pots.
   b. Explain what the designs on the pots represent.
   c. Recommend how to store the pots to prevent further damage.

6. Would a geologist ask a biochemist to help identify the minerals in a rock? Explain your answer.

7. Explain how knowledge of chemistry can help you be a more informed citizen.

Writing ▶ Activity

Describing Technology Pick one activity that you can do faster or with less effort because of technology. Write a paragraph in which you describe the activity, identify the technology, and explain how the technology affects the activity.

interactive **Textbook**

Assessment 1.1 Test yourself on the concepts in Section 1.1.

— with **ChemASAP**

1.2 Chemistry Far and Wide

 New York Standards: M2.1a, 4.1a, 7.1

Guide for Reading

Key Concepts

- What impact do chemists have on materials, energy, medicine, agriculture, the environment, and the study of the universe?

Vocabulary

macroscopic
microscopic
biotechnology
pollutant

Reading Strategy

Monitoring Your Understanding
After you read this section, identify something you learned that is important to your life and explain why it is important to you.

Connecting to Your World The first tools were objects such as a stone with a sharp edge. In time, people learned to reshape these objects to produce better tools. Native Americans in what is now Illinois drilled holes in mussel shells and carved lines onto the shells to make them look like small fish. The shells were likely used as lures for ice fishing. People also began to produce materials that did not exist in nature. By weaving plant fibers together, they made cloth, which is softer and dries more quickly than animal skins. Chemistry plays a key role in the production of new materials. In this section, you will learn how chemistry affects many aspects of modern life.

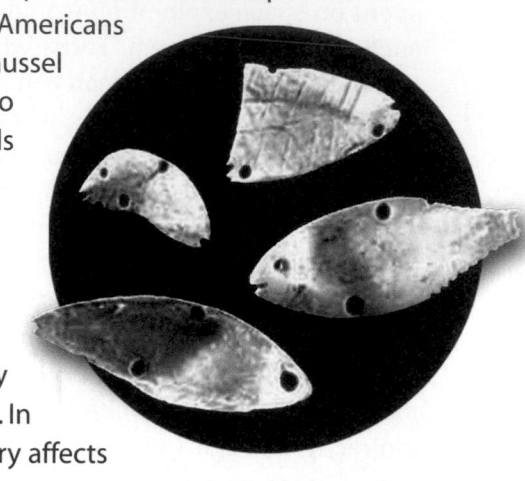

Materials

The search for new materials continues. **Chemists design materials to fit specific needs.** Often they find inspiration in nature. In 1948, while hiking through the woods of his native Switzerland, George de Mestral took a close look at the pesky burrs that stuck to his clothing. When he looked at the burrs under magnification, he saw that each burr was covered with many tiny hooks that could latch on to tiny loops in the woven cloth of his clothing. George had a weaver make two cloth tapes. On the surface of one tape were hooks, and on the surface of the other tape were loops that the hooks could fit into, as shown in Figure 1.6. In 1955 George patented the design for his hook-and-loop tapes. These tapes are used as fasteners for items such as shoes and gloves.

This story illustrates two different ways of looking at the world—the macroscopic view and the microscopic view. The burrs that George de Mestral used as a model for his tapes are small compared to many objects in nature. However, they were large enough for George to see. Burrs belong to the **macroscopic** world, the world of objects that are large enough to see with the unaided eye. George needed more than his own vision to see the hooks on a burr. The hooks belong to the **microscopic** world, or the world of objects that can be seen only under magnification.

Figure 1.6 This is a magnified view of hook-and-loop tape. Color was added to the photo to highlight the structures. **Classifying** *Does the photograph show a macroscopic or a microscopic view of the tape? Explain.*

Energy

Energy is necessary to meet the needs of a modern society. It is used to heat buildings, manufacture goods, and process foods. It is used to transport people and goods between locations. With population growth and more industrialization around the globe, the demands for energy continue to increase. There are two ways to meet the demand for energy—conserve energy resources and produce more energy. **Chemists play an essential role in finding ways to conserve energy, produce energy, and store energy.**

Conservation One of the easiest ways to conserve energy is through the use of insulation. Much of the energy consumed is used to keep houses warm and freezers cold. Insulation acts as a barrier to heat flow from the inside to the outside of a house or from the outside to the inside of a freezer. The foam used in drink cups provides excellent insulation because it contains pockets of trapped air. One of the most exciting modern insulation materials devised by chemists is SEAgel, which is a foam made from seaweed. SEAgel is very lightweight. In fact, SEAgel is so light that it can float on soap bubbles, as shown in Figure 1.7.

Figure 1.7 This insulation is light enough to float on soap bubbles yet is very effective at preventing heat transfer.

Production The burning of coal, petroleum, and natural gas is a major source of energy. These materials are called fossil fuels because they formed from the remains of ancient plants and animals. Scientists are always looking for new sources of energy because the supply of fossil fuels is limited. One intriguing possibility is fuels obtained from plants. Oil from the soybeans shown in Figure 1.8 is used to make biodiesel. Regular diesel fuel is a petroleum product that produces an irritating black exhaust when it burns. When biodiesel burns, the exhaust smells like French fries!

Storage Batteries are devices that use chemicals to store energy that will be released as electric current when the batteries are used. Batteries vary in size, power, and hours of useful operation. For some applications, it is important to have batteries that can be recharged rather than thrown away. One application that benefits from rechargeable batteries is cordless tools. These tools were first developed for NASA. Astronauts in the Apollo program needed a way to drill beneath the Moon's surface to collect samples. Other devices that use rechargeable batteries are digital cameras, wireless phones, and laptop computers.

Figure 1.8 Oil from soybeans can be used in a substitute for regular diesel fuel.
Predicting *The supply of diesel fuel is limited. Is the supply of soybeans limited?*

✓ Checkpoint *What plant is a source of biodiesel?*

Soybean in pod

Medicine and Biotechnology

No field has benefited more from advances in chemistry than medicine. 🔑 **Chemistry supplies the medicines, materials, and technology that doctors use to treat their patients.** Work in the field of medicine is often done by biochemists. Their overall goal is to understand the structure of matter found in the human body and the chemical changes that occur in cells. To accomplish their goal, they work with biologists and doctors.

Medicines There are over 2000 prescription drugs. They are designed to treat various conditions including infections, high blood pressure, and depression. Other drugs, such as aspirin and antacids, can be sold without a prescription. Many drugs are effective because they interact in a specific way with chemicals in cells. Knowledge of the structure and function of these target chemicals helps a chemist design safe and effective drugs.

Materials Chemistry can supply materials to repair or replace body parts. Diseased arteries can be replaced with plastic tubes. Artificial hips and knees made from metals and plastics can replace worn-out joints and allow people to walk again without pain. Burn patients may benefit from a plastic "skin" that can heal itself when the plastic cracks. Chemicals that repair the damage are released from tiny capsules in the plastic.

Biotechnology Figure 1.9a shows a model of a small piece of DNA. Segments of DNA called genes store the information that controls changes that take place in cells. From 1990 to 2003, scientists worldwide worked on the Human Genome Project. They identified the genes that comprise human DNA—about 30,000. They determined the sequence of the genes in DNA. Some tools these scientists developed are used in biotechnology.

Biotechnology applies science to the production of biological products or processes. It uses techniques that can alter the DNA in living organisms. It may depend on the transfer of genes from one organism to another. When genes from humans are inserted into bacteria, the bacteria act as factories. They produce chemicals of importance to humans, such as insulin, which is used to treat some types of diabetes. Production takes place in large versions of the bioreactors in Figure 1.9b. In the future, scientists expect to use gene therapy to treat some diseases. A gene that is not working properly would be replaced with one that will work properly.

Figure 1.9 The discovery of the structure of DNA led to the development of biotechnology. ⓐ This computer graphics model shows a small segment of DNA. ⓑ The conditions in a bioreactor are controlled so that the bacteria produce as much of the product as possible.

Agriculture

The world's population is increasing, but the amount of land available to grow food is decreasing. Land that was once used for agriculture is now used for homes and industries. So it is important to ensure that land used for agriculture is as productive as possible. ⊙ **Chemists help to develop more productive crops and safer, more effective ways to protect crops.**

Productivity One way to track productivity is to measure the amount of edible food that is grown on a given unit of land. Some factors that decrease productivity are poor soil quality, lack of water, weeds, plant diseases, and pests that eat crops. Chemists can help with many of these problems. They test soil to see if it contains the right chemicals to grow a particular crop and recommend ways to improve the soil. They use biotechnology to develop plants that are more likely to survive a drought or insect attack.

Chemists can also help to conserve water. In many regions, water is not an abundant resource. Finding reliable ways to determine when a crop needs water is important. The jellyfish in Figure 1.10 has a gene that causes it to glow. If that gene is inserted into a potato plant, the plant glows when it needs to be watered. These altered plants would be removed from the field before the rest of the crop was harvested.

Crop Protection For years, farmers have used chemicals to attack insect pests. In the past, these chemicals were nonspecific; that is, a chemical designed to kill a pest could also kill useful insects. Today, the trend is toward chemicals that are designed to treat specific problems. These chemicals are often similar to the chemicals that plants produce for protection.

Chemists sometimes use chemicals produced by insects to fight insect pests. Female insects may produce chemicals that attract male insects. This type of chemical has proved effective in combating pinworms. The worms leave holes and black blotches when they tunnel into tomatoes. Pinworms mate when they are in the moth stage of development. The plastic tube wrapped around the stem of the tomato plant in Figure 1.11 contains the chemical that a female pinworm moth emits to attract male moths. When the chemical is released from these tubes, it interferes with the mating process so that fewer pinworms are produced.

✔ **Checkpoint** *What jellyfish gene did scientists transfer to a potato?*

Figure 1.10 If genes from this jellyfish *(Aequaria victoria)* are transferred to a potato plant, the plant glows when it needs to be watered. **Predicting** *How does the modified plant help a farmer to conserve water?*

Plastic tube

Figure 1.11 In the plastic tube wrapped around the tomato stem, there is a chemical that attracts male pinworm moths. This process reduces the rate of mating between female and male moths, and the number of pinworms produced.

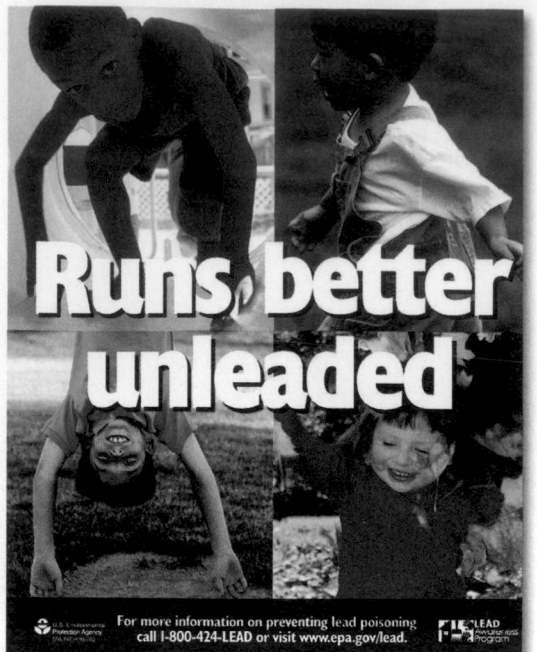

Figure 1.12 This poster was used to warn people about the danger to children from lead-based paint.

The Environment

One unintended consequence of new technologies is the production of pollutants. A **pollutant** is a material found in air, water, or soil that is harmful to humans or other organisms. **Chemists help to identify pollutants and prevent pollution.**

Identify Pollutants Lead is a pollutant with a long history. The Romans used lead pipes for plumbing and stored their wine in lead-glazed vessels. Brain damage from lead poisoning may have caused Roman rulers to make bad decisions, which led to the fall of the Roman Empire. Until the mid-1900s, lead was used in many products, including paints and gasoline. A study done in 1971 showed that the level of lead that is harmful to humans is much lower than had been thought, especially for children. Low levels of lead in the blood can permanently damage the nervous system of a growing child. This damage causes many problems, including a reduced ability to learn.

Prevent Pollution The use of lead paint in houses was banned in 1978. Using lead in gasoline and in public water supply systems was banned in 1986. Today, the major source of lead in children is lead-based paint in about 39 million homes built before 1978. When children play with flakes of peeling paint or touch surfaces covered with paint dust, they can transfer the paint to their mouths with their fingers. The strategies used to prevent lead poisoning include testing children's blood for lead, regulation of home sales to families with young children, and public awareness campaigns with posters like the one in Figure 1.12. The graph in Figure 1.13 shows the results of these efforts.

✔Checkpoint **When was the use of lead paint in houses banned?**

Figure 1.13 This graph shows data on children in the United States with higher than acceptable levels of lead in their blood.

INTERPRETING GRAPHS

a. Analyzing Data What percent of children had elevated lead levels in the 1970s?

b. Calculating If a percentage point equals 200,000 children, how many children had elevated lead levels in 2000?

c. Drawing Conclusions Explain the dramatic drop in the percentage of children affected by lead poisoning between 1980 and 1988.

The Universe

Scientists assume that the methods used to study Earth can be applied to other objects in the universe. 🔑 **To study the universe, chemists gather data from afar and analyze matter that is brought back to Earth.**

In the early 1800s, scientists began to study the composition of stars by analyzing the light they transmitted to Earth. In 1868, Pierre Janssen discovered a gas on the sun's surface that was not known on Earth. Norman Lockyer named the gas helium from the Greek word *helios,* meaning "sun." In 1895, William Ramsay discovered helium on Earth.

Because the moon and the planets do not emit light, scientists must use other methods to gather data about these objects. They depend on matter brought back to Earth by astronauts or on probes that can analyze matter in space. Chemists have analyzed more than 850 pounds of moon rocks that were brought back to Earth. The large rock in Figure 1.14a is similar to rocks formed by volcanoes on Earth, suggesting that vast oceans of molten lava once covered the moon's surface. Figure 1.14b is a drawing of the robotic vehicle *Opportunity*. The vehicle was designed to determine the chemical composition of rocks and soil on Mars. Data collected at the vehicle's landing site indicated that the site was once drenched with water.

Figure 1.14 With help from NASA, chemists study matter from other bodies in the solar system. ⓐ Apollo astronauts brought rocks from the moon back to Earth. ⓑ This artist's drawing shows the robotic vehicle *Opportunity* on the surface of Mars.

1.2 Section Assessment

8. 🔑 **Key Concept** When chemists develop new materials, what is their general goal?

9. 🔑 **Key Concept** Name three ways chemists help meet the demand for energy.

10. 🔑 **Key Concept** How do chemists help doctors treat patients?

11. 🔑 **Key Concept** What role do chemists play in agriculture?

12. 🔑 **Key Concept** How do chemists help protect the environment?

13. 🔑 **Key Concept** Describe two ways that chemists study the universe.

14. Use lead as an example to explain the meaning of the term *pollutant.*

15. Use an example to compare and contrast the terms *macroscopic* and *microscopic.*

Elements ➤ **Handbook**

Cleaning Up Pollutants Read about phytoremediation on page R44. Write a paragraph summarizing this method for dealing with pollutants. Explain how it could be used to clean up soil containing high levels of lead.

Textbook

Assessment 1.2 Test yourself on the concepts in Section 1.2.

with ChemASAP

Nature's Pharmacy

About 40 percent of all modern medicines come from chemicals produced by plants or animals. With any source, chemists must first identify the effective, or active, ingredient. Then they must purify the chemical and show that it is safe for human use. Chemists often modify a chemical to make it more effective or less toxic.

Applying Concepts *Are the chemicals derived from plants and animals organic or inorganic?*

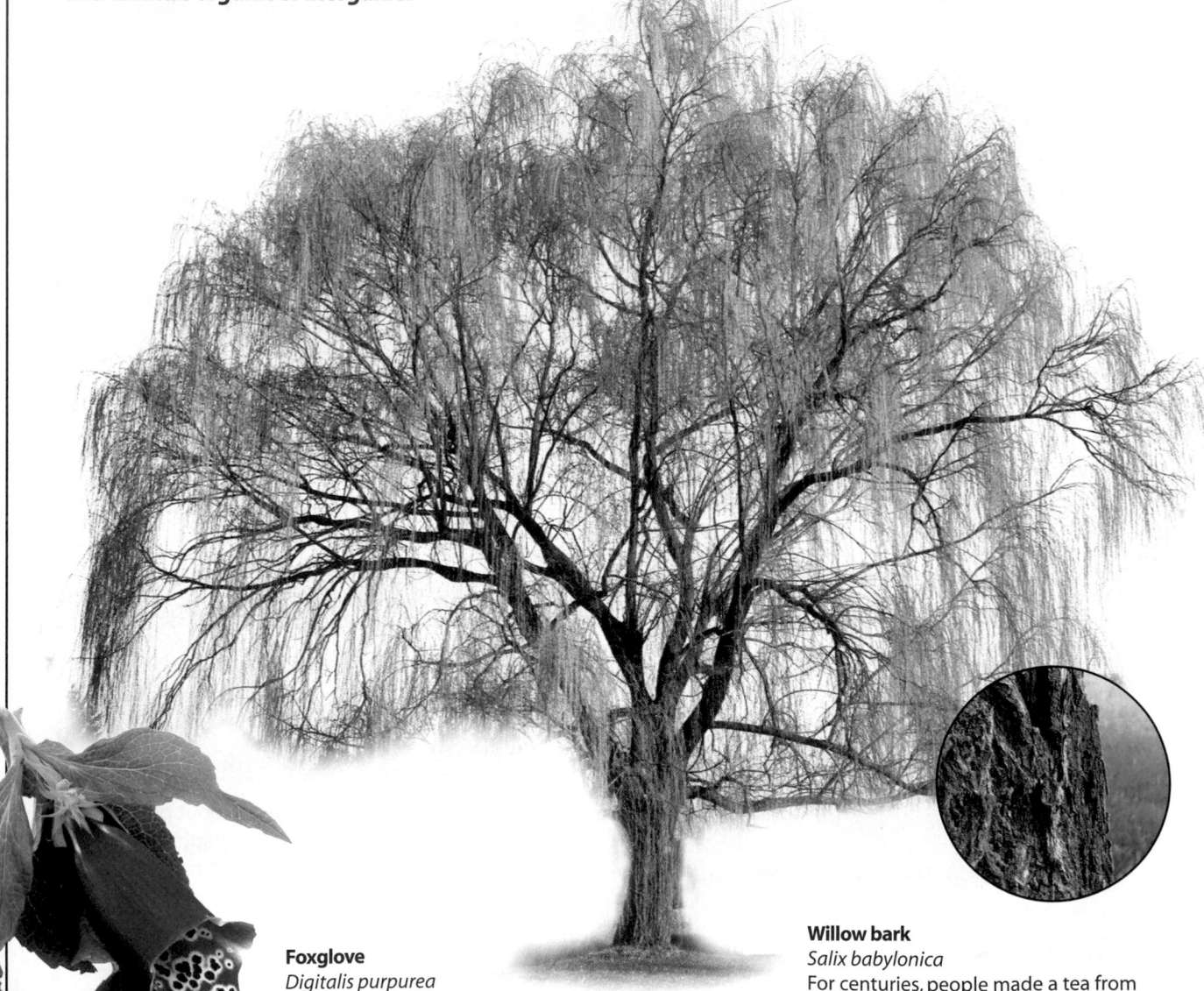

Cinchona tree
Cinchona succirubra
Bark from this tree was used for centuries to treat malaria, a disease with recurring bouts of fever and chills. The active ingredient in the bark is quinine—the chemical that gives tonic water its bitter taste.

Foxglove
Digitalis purpurea
The poison produced by this plant (digitalis) is used in small doses to treat congestive heart failure. It causes heart muscle cells to contract with more power, which increases the ability of the heart to pump blood.

Willow bark
Salix babylonica
For centuries, people made a tea from willow bark to treat headaches and other ailments. By 1828, chemists had isolated the active ingredient in willow bark. For the next 70 years, chemists worked to produce the most effective drug based on this chemical. What they produced is aspirin (acetylsalicylic acid).

Death stalker scorpion
Leiurus quinquestriatus
This scorpion's narrow pincers are weak, but the venom in its tail is very powerful. Scientists have isolated a chemical from this venom, which is used to treat an incurable form of brain cancer.

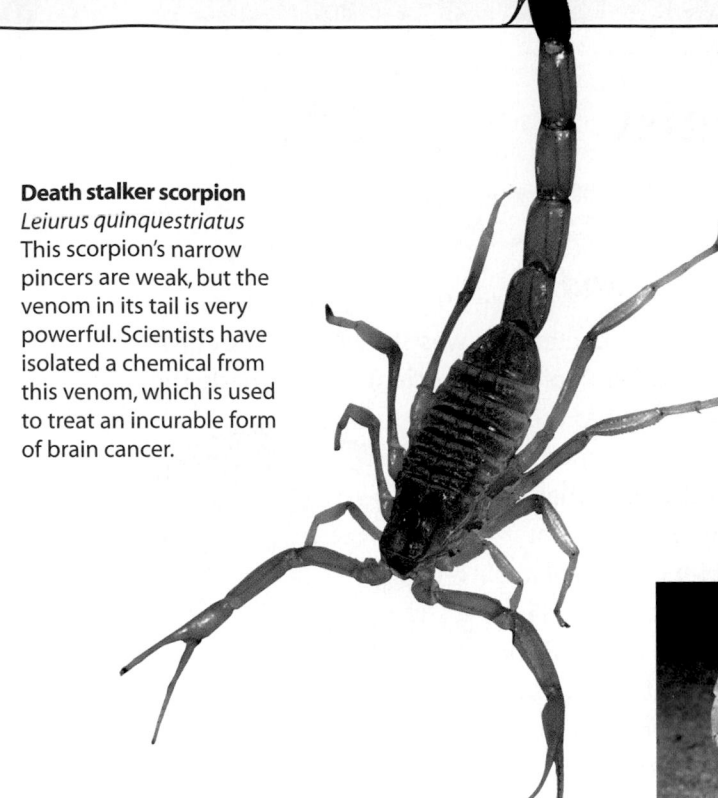

Vampire bat
Desmodus rotundus
After this bat bites an animal with its sharp teeth, it laps up blood from the wound. A chemical in the bat's saliva keeps the blood from clotting. Doctors use this chemical to dissolve blood clots that cause strokes.

Cone snail
Conus striatus
Cone snails produce toxins that paralyze their prey. Chemists are studying these toxins as possible treatments for chronic pain and nervous system disorders, such as Parkinson's disease.

Poison dart frogs
Dendrobates reticulatus
Poisons from the food these tiny (1/2-inch-long) frogs eat collect in their skin. Chemists use these poisons to study the human nervous system. A chemical found in a frog from Ecuador served as a model for a drug that is as powerful a painkiller as morphine but is not addictive.

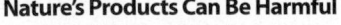

Nature's Products Can Be Harmful
Chemicals from natural sources are not always effective or harmless. In 2004, the FDA banned weight-loss products based on the herb ephedra. This herb contains the chemical ephedrine, which is associated with increased blood pressure, abnormal heart rates, a higher risk of stroke, and even death.

New York Standards: S1.3a, S2.4a, 2.1

Guide for Reading

 Key Concepts

- How did alchemy lay the groundwork for chemistry?
- How did Lavoisier help to transform chemistry?
- What are the steps in the scientific method?
- What role do collaboration and communication play in science?

Vocabulary

scientific method
observation
hypothesis
experiment
manipulated variable
responding variable
theory
scientific law

Reading Strategy

Building Vocabulary After you read this section, explain the difference between a theory and a scientific law.

Connecting to Your World

In 1928, Alexander Fleming, a Scottish scientist, noticed that a bacteria he was studying did not grow in the presence of a yellow-green mold. Other scientists had made the same observation, but Fleming was the first to recognize its importance. He assumed that the mold had released a chemical that prevented the growth of the bacteria. That chemical was penicillin, which can kill a wide range of harmful bacteria. In 1945, Fleming shared a Nobel Prize for Medicine with Howard Florey and Ernst Chain, who led the team that isolated penicillin. In this section you will study the methods scientists use to solve problems.

Alchemy

The word *chemistry* comes from *alchemy*. Long before there were chemists, alchemists were studying matter. Alchemy arose independently in many regions of the world. It was practiced in China and India as early as 400 B.C. In the eighth century, Arabs brought alchemy to Spain, from where it spread quickly to other parts of Europe.

Alchemy had a practical side and a mystical side. Practical alchemy focused on developing techniques for working with metals, glass, and dyes. Mystical alchemy focused on concepts like perfection. Because gold was seen as the perfect metal, alchemists were searching for a way to change other metals, such as lead, into gold. Although alchemists did not succeed in this quest, the work they did spurred the development of chemistry.

Alchemists developed the tools and techniques for working with chemicals. Alchemists developed processes for separating mixtures and purifying chemicals. They designed equipment that is still used today, including beakers, flasks, tongs, funnels, and the mortar and pestle in Figure 1.15. What they did not do was provide a logical set of explanations for the changes in matter that they observed. That task was left for chemists to accomplish.

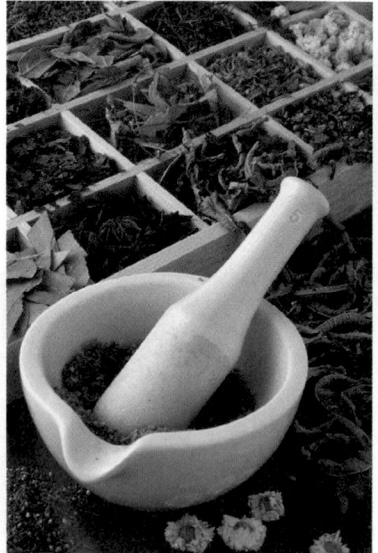

Figure 1.15 A bowl-shaped mortar and a club-shaped pestle are used to grind or crush materials such as herbs, spices, and paint pigments. The mortar and pestle in the photograph is made of porcelain, which is a hard material.

An Experimental Approach to Science

By the 1500s in Europe, there was a shift from alchemy to science. Science flourished in Britain in the 1600s, partly because King Charles II was a supporter of the sciences. With his permission, some scientists formed the Royal Society of London for the Promotion of Natural Knowledge. The scientists met to discuss scientific topics and conduct experiments. The society's aim was to encourage scientists to base their conclusions about the natural world on experimental evidence, not on philosophical debates.

In France, Antoine-Laurent Lavoisier did work in the late 1700s that would revolutionize the science of chemistry. **Lavoisier helped to transform chemistry from a science of observation to the science of measurement that it is today.** To make careful measurements, Lavoisier designed a balance that could measure mass to the nearest 0.0005 gram.

One of the many things Lavoisier accomplished was to settle a long-standing debate about how materials burn. The accepted explanation was that materials burn because they contain phlogiston, which is released into the air as a material burns. To support this explanation, scientists had to ignore the evidence that metals can gain mass as they burn. By the time Lavoisier did his experiments, he knew that there were two main gases in air—oxygen and nitrogen. Lavoisier was able to show that oxygen is required for a material to burn. Lavoisier's wife Marie Anne, shown in Figure 1.16, helped with his scientific work. She made drawings of his experiments and translated scientific papers from English. Figure 1.17 shows a reconstruction of Lavoisier's laboratory in a museum in Paris, France.

At the time of the French Revolution, Lavoisier was a member of the despised royal taxation commission. He took the position to finance his scientific work. Although he was dedicated to improving the lives of the common people, his association with taxation made him a target of the revolution. In 1794 he was arrested, tried, and beheaded.

✓Checkpoint *What long-standing debate did Lavoisier help settle?*

Figure 1.16 This portrait of Antoine Lavoisier and his wife Marie Anne was painted by Jacques Louis David in 1788. The painting includes some equipment that Lavoisier used in his experiments.

Figure 1.17 This reconstruction of Lavoisier's laboratory is in a museum in Paris, France.
Interpreting Photographs *What objects do you recognize that are similar to objects that you use in the laboratory?*

21

Figure 1.18 Observation is an essential step in the scientific method.

The Scientific Method

A Nobel Prize winner in science once said that science is about "ordinary people doing ordinary things." Scientists have a powerful tool that they can use to produce valuable, sometimes spectacular, results. Like all scientists, the biochemist shown in Figure 1.18 is using the scientific method to solve difficult problems. The **scientific method** is a logical, systematic approach to the solution of a scientific problem. ⊂⊃ **Steps in the scientific method include making observations, testing hypotheses, and developing theories.** Figure 1.19 shows how these steps fit together.

Making Observations The scientific method is useful for solving many kinds of problems because it is closely related to ordinary common sense. Suppose you try to turn on a flashlight and you notice that it does not light. When you use your senses to obtain information, you make an **observation.** An observation can lead to a question: What's wrong with the flashlight?

Testing Hypotheses If you guess that the batteries are dead, you are making a hypothesis. A **hypothesis** is a proposed explanation for an observation. You can test your hypothesis by putting new batteries in the flashlight. If the flashlight lights, you can be fairly certain that your hypothesis is true. What if the flashlight does not work after you replace the batteries? A hypothesis is useful only if it accounts for what is actually observed. When experimental data does not fit a hypothesis, the hypothesis must be changed. A new hypothesis might be that the light bulb is burnt out. You can replace the bulb to test this hypothesis.

Replacing the bulb is an **experiment,** a procedure that is used to test a hypothesis. When you design experiments, you deal with variables, or factors that can change. The variable that you change during an experiment is the **manipulated variable,** or independent variable. The variable that is observed during the experiment is the **responding variable,** or dependent variable. If you keep other factors that can affect the experiment from changing during the experiment, you can relate any change in the responding variable to changes in the manipulated variable.

For the results of an experiment to be accepted, the experiment must produce the same result no matter how many times it is repeated, or by whom. This is why scientists are expected to publish a description of their procedures along with their results.

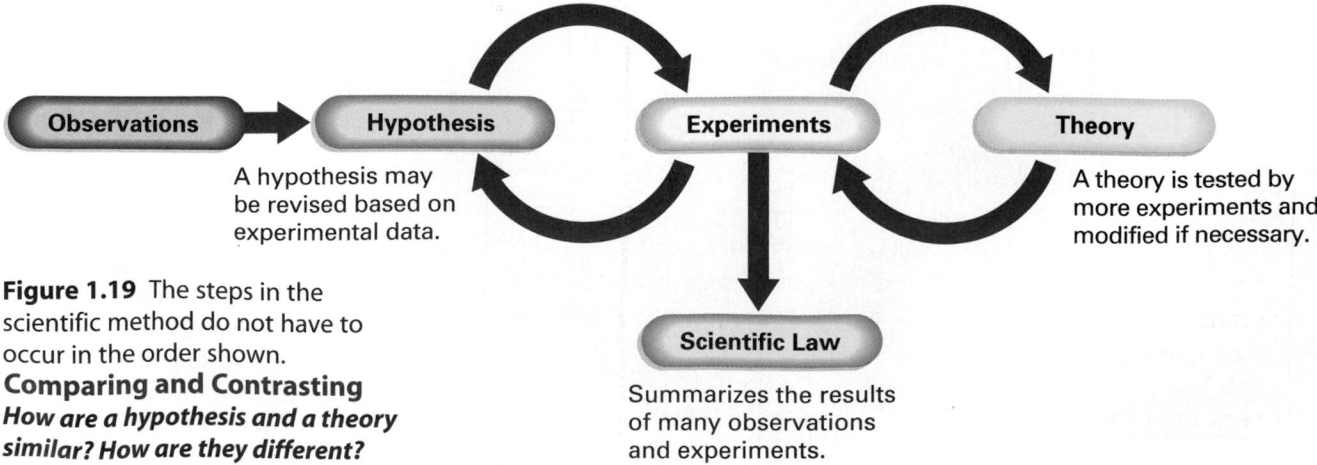

Figure 1.19 The steps in the scientific method do not have to occur in the order shown.
Comparing and Contrasting
How are a hypothesis and a theory similar? How are they different?

Observations → Hypothesis → Experiments → Theory

A hypothesis may be revised based on experimental data.

A theory is tested by more experiments and modified if necessary.

Scientific Law
Summarizes the results of many observations and experiments.

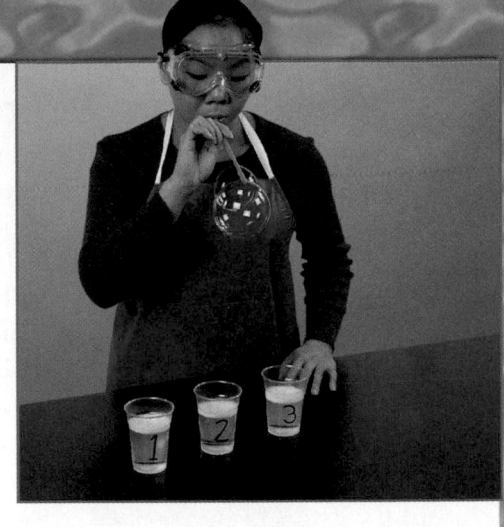

Quick LAB

Bubbles!

Purpose
To test the hypothesis that bubble making can be affected by adding sugar or salt to a bubble-blowing mixture.

Materials
- 3 plastic drinking cups
- liquid dish detergent
- measuring cup and spoons
- water
- table sugar
- table salt
- drinking straw

Procedure
1. Label three drinking cups 1, 2, and 3. Measure and add one teaspoon of liquid dish detergent to each cup. Use the measuring cup to add two thirds of a cup of water to each drinking cup. Then swirl the cups to form a clear mixture. **CAUTION** *Wipe up any spills immediately so that no one will slip and fall.*

2. Add a half teaspoon of table sugar to cup 2 and a half teaspoon of table salt to cup 3. Swirl each cup for one minute.

3. Dip the drinking straw into cup 1, remove it, and blow gently into the straw to make the largest bubble you can. Practice making bubbles until you feel you have reasonable control over your bubble production.

4. Repeat Step 3 with the mixtures in cups 2 and 3.

Analyze and Conclude
1. Did you observe any differences in your ability to produce bubbles using the mixtures in cup 1 and cup 2?

2. Did you observe any differences in your ability to produce bubbles using the mixtures in cup 1 and cup 3?

3. What can you conclude about the effects of table sugar and table salt on your ability to produce bubbles?

4. Propose another hypothesis related to bubble making and design an experiment to test your hypothesis.

Developing Theories Once a hypothesis meets the test of repeated experimentation, it may be raised to a higher level of ideas. It may become a theory. A **theory** is a well-tested explanation for a broad set of observations. In chemistry, one theory addresses the fundamental structure of matter. This theory is very useful because it helps you form mental pictures of objects that you cannot see. Other theories allow you to predict the behavior of matter.

When scientists say that a theory can never be proved, they are not saying that a theory is unreliable. They are simply leaving open the possibility that a theory may need to be changed at some point in the future to explain new observations or experimental results.

Scientific Laws Figure 1.19 shows how scientific experiments can lead to laws as well as theories. A **scientific law** is a concise statement that summarizes the results of many observations and experiments. In Chapter 14, you will study laws that describe how gases behave. One law describes the relationship between the volume of a gas in a container and its temperature. If all other variables are kept constant, the volume of the gas increases as the temperature increases. The law doesn't try to explain the relationship it describes. That explanation requires a theory.

For: Links on Scientific Methods
Visit: www.SciLinks.org
Web Code: cdn-1012

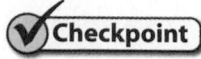 *When can a hypothesis become a theory?*

Figure 1.20 For a volleyball team to win, the players must collaborate, or work together.

Collaboration and Communication

No matter how talented the players on a team, one player cannot ensure victory for the team. Individuals must collaborate, or work together, for the good of the team. Think about the volleyball players in Figure 1.20. In volleyball, the person who spikes the ball depends on the person who sets the ball. Unless the ball is set properly, the spiker will have limited success. Many sports recognize the importance of collaboration by keeping track of assists. During a volleyball game, the players also communicate with one another so it is clear who is going to do which task. Strategies that are successful in sports can work in other fields, such as science. **⊙━ When scientists collaborate and communicate, they increase the likelihood of a successful outcome.**

Collaboration Scientists choose to collaborate for different reasons. For example, some research problems are so complex that no one person could have all the knowledge, skills, and resources to solve the problem. It is often necessary to bring together individuals from different disciplines. Each scientist will typically bring different knowledge and, perhaps, a different approach to bear on a problem. Just talking with a scientist from another discipline may provide insights that are helpful.

There may be a practical reason for collaboration. For example, an industry may give a university funding for pure research in an area of interest to the industry. Scientists at the university get the equipment and the time required to do research. In exchange, the scientists provide ideas and expertise. The industry may profit from its investment by marketing applications based on the research.

Collaboration isn't always a smooth process. Conflicts can arise about use of resources, amount of work, who is to receive credit, and when and what to publish. Like the students in Figure 1.21, you will likely work on a team in the laboratory. If so, you may face some challenges. But you can also experience the benefits of a successful collaboration.

Figure 1.21 Working in a group can be challenging, but it can also be rewarding.
Applying Concepts *What steps in the scientific method are these students using?*

Communication The way that scientists communicate with each other and with the public has changed over the centuries. In earlier centuries, scientists exchanged ideas through letters. They also formed societies to discuss the latest work of their members. When societies began to publish journals, scientists could use the journals to keep up with new discoveries.

Today, many scientists, like those in Figure 1.22, work as a team. They can communicate face to face. They also can exchange ideas with other scientists by e-mail, by phone, and at international conferences. Scientists still publish their results in scientific journals, which are the most reliable source of information about new discoveries. Articles are published only after being reviewed by experts in the author's field. Reviewers may find errors in experimental design or challenge the author's conclusions. This review process is good for science because work that is not well founded is usually not published.

The Internet is a major source of information. One advantage of the Internet is that anyone can get access to its information. One disadvantage is that anyone can post information on the Internet without first having that information reviewed. To judge the reliability of information you find on the Internet, you have to consider the source. This same advice applies to articles in newspapers and magazines or the news you receive from television. If a media outlet has a reporter who specializes in science, chances are better that a report will be accurate.

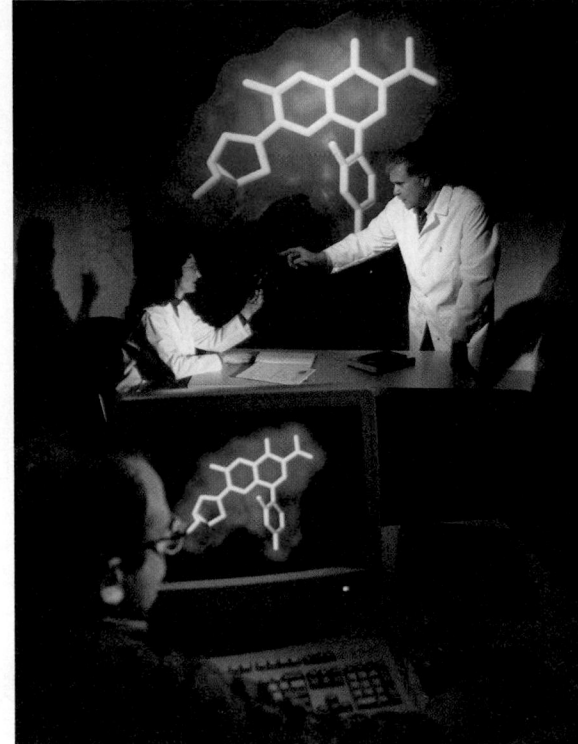

Figure 1.22 Communication between scientists can occur face to face. These chemists are using the model projected on the screen to discuss the merits of a new medicine.

1.3 Section Assessment

16. **Key Concept** What did alchemists contribute to the development of chemistry?

17. **Key Concept** How did Lavoisier revolutionize the science of chemistry?

18. **Key Concept** Name three steps in the scientific method.

19. **Key Concept** Explain why collaboration and communication are important in science.

20. How did Lavoisier's wife help him to communicate the results of his experiments?

21. Why should a hypothesis be developed before experiments take place?

22. Why is it important for scientists to publish a description of their procedures along with the results of their experiments?

23. What is the difference between a theory and a scientific law?

24. What process takes place before an article is published in a scientific journal?

25. In Chapter 2, you will learn that matter is neither created nor destroyed in any chemical change. Is this statement a theory or a law? Explain your answer.

Connecting Concepts

Being an Informed Citizen Write a paragraph explaining how you can learn about the research that is done by scientists. Then explain how this information could help you be an informed citizen.

Textbook

Assessment 1.3 Test yourself on the concepts in Section 1.3.

—— with **ChemASAP**

Laboratory Safety

Purpose
To demonstrate your knowledge of safe laboratory practices.

Procedure
While doing the chemistry experiments in this textbook, you will work with equipment similar to the equipment shown in the photographs. Your success, and your safety, will depend on following instructions and using safe laboratory practices. To test your knowledge of these practices, answer the question after each safety symbol. Refer to the safety rules in Appendix D and any instructions provided by your teacher.

 When should safety goggles be worn?

 What should you do if glassware breaks?

 What precautions should you take when working near an open flame?

 If you accidentally spill water near electrical equipment, what should you do?

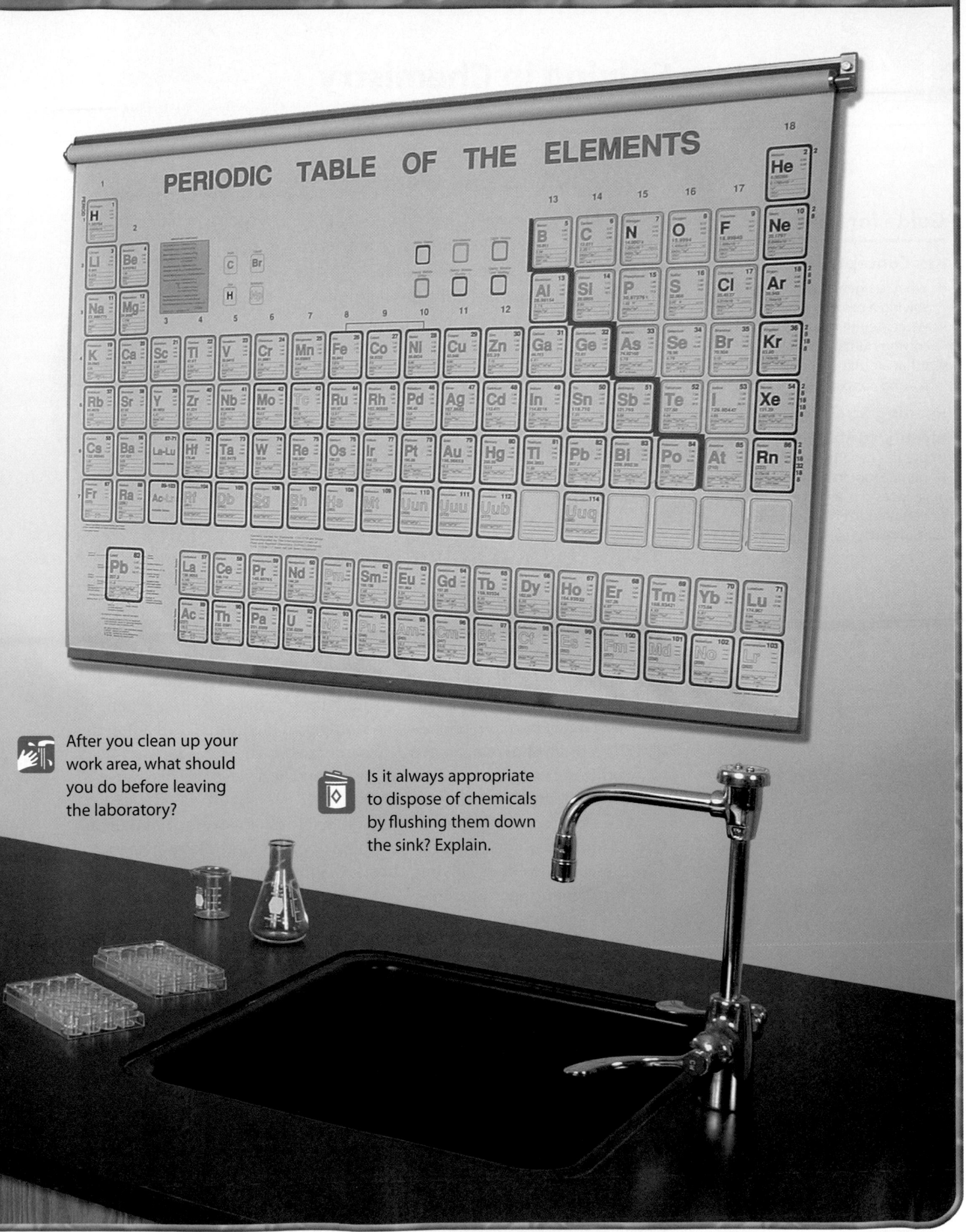

After you clean up your work area, what should you do before leaving the laboratory?

Is it always appropriate to dispose of chemicals by flushing them down the sink? Explain.

Guide for Reading

🔑 Key Concepts

• What is a general approach to solving a problem?
• What are the three steps for solving numeric problems?
• What are the two steps for solving conceptual problems?

Reading Strategy

Identifying Main Idea/Details
Under the heading Solving Numeric Problems, there are three main ideas presented as subheads. As you read, list two details that support each main idea.

Connecting to Your World

Shape-sorter toys fascinate young children. Typically, the children try placing a shape in different holes until they find the right one. They may try to place an incorrect shape in the same hole over and over again. An older child has enough experience to place the correct shape in each hole on the first try. The trial-and-error approach used by young children is one method of problem solving, but it is usually not the best one. In this section, you will learn effective ways to solve problems in chemistry.

Skills Used in Solving Problems

Problem solving is a skill you use all the time. You are in a supermarket. Do you buy a name brand or the store brand of peanut butter? Do you buy the 1-liter bottle or the 2-liter bottle of a carbonated beverage? Do you choose the express line if there are five customers ahead of you or the non-express line with a single shopper who has lots of items?

When you solve a problem you may have a data table, a graph, or another type of visual to refer to. The shopper in Figure 1.23 is reading the label on a can while trying to decide whether to buy the item. She may need to avoid certain ingredients because of a food allergy. Or she may want to know the amount of Calories per serving.

The skills you use to solve a word problem in chemistry are not that different from those you use while shopping or cooking or planning a party. 🔑 **Effective problem solving always involves developing a plan and then implementing that plan.**

Figure 1.23 A shopper must make many decisions. Some of those decisions are based on data, like the information on a food label.

Solving Numeric Problems

Because measurement is such an important part of chemistry, most word problems in chemistry require some math. The techniques used in this book to solve numeric problems are conveniently organized into a three-step, problem-solving approach. This approach has been shown to be very helpful and effective. So we recommend that you follow this approach when working on numeric problems in this textbook. ⊂▸ **The steps for solving a numeric word problem are analyze, calculate, and evaluate.** Figure 1.24 summarizes the three-step process and Sample Problem 1.1 shows how the steps work in a problem.

1 Analyze To solve a word problem, you must first determine where you are starting from (identify what is known) and where you are going (identify the unknown). What is known may be a measurement. Or it may be an equation that shows a relationship between measurements. If you expect the answer (the unknown) to be a number, you need to determine what units the answer should have before you do any calculations.

After you identify the known and the unknown, you need to make a plan for getting from the known to the unknown. Planning is at the heart of successful problem solving. As part of planning, you might draw a diagram that helps you visualize a relationship between the known and the unknown. You might need to use a table or graph to identify data or to identify a relationship between a known quantity and the unknown. You may need to select an equation that you can use to calculate the unknown.

2 Calculate If you make an effective plan, doing the calculations is usually the easiest part of the process. For some problems, you will have to convert a measurement from one unit to another. Or you may need to rearrange an equation before you can solve for an unknown. However, you will be taught these math skills as needed. There will also be reminders throughout the textbook to use the Math Handbook in Appendix C.

3 Evaluate After you calculate an answer, you should evaluate it. Is the answer reasonable? Does it make sense? If not, reread the word problem. Did you copy the data correctly? Did you choose the right equations? It helps to round off the numbers and make an estimate of the answer. If the answer is much larger or much smaller than your estimate, check your calculations.

Check that your answer has the correct unit and the correct number of significant figures. You may need to use scientific notation in your answer. You will study significant figures and scientific notation in Chapter 3.

✓ Checkpoint *How can making an estimate help you evaluate an answer?*

Figure 1.24 This flowchart summarizes the steps for solving a numeric problem. **Predicting** *In which step do you make a plan for getting from what is known to what is unknown?*

This view of Indianapolis, Indiana, shows part of the historic central canal in White River State Park.

SAMPLE PROBLEM 1.1

Estimating Walking Time

You are visiting Indianapolis for the first time. Because it is a nice day, you decide to walk from the Indiana State Capital to the Murat Centre for an afternoon performance. According to the map in Figure 1.25, the shortest route from the capital to the theater is 8 blocks. How many minutes will the trip take if you can walk one mile in 20 minutes? Assume that 10 short city blocks equals one mile.

1 Analyze *List the knowns and the unknown.*

Knowns
- distance to be traveled = 8 blocks
- walking speed = 1 mile/20 minutes
- 1 mile = 10 blocks

Unknown
- time of trip = ? minutes

This problem is an example of what is typically called a conversion problem. In a conversion problem, one unit of measure (in this case, blocks) must be expressed in a different unit (in this case, minutes).

Divide the distance to be traveled (in blocks) by the number of blocks in one mile to get the distance of the trip in miles. Then multiply the number of miles by the time it takes to walk one mile.

2 Calculate *Solve for the unknown*

$$8 \text{ blocks} \times \frac{1 \text{ mile}}{10 \text{ blocks}} = 0.8 \text{ miles}$$

$$0.8 \text{ miles} \times \frac{20 \text{ minutes}}{1 \text{ mile}} = 16 \text{ minutes}$$

3 Evaluate *Does the result make sense?*

The answer seems reasonable, 16 minutes to walk 8 short blocks. The answer has the correct unit. The relationships used are correct.

Practice Problems

26. Using the information in the sample problem, how many short blocks can be walked in 48 minutes?

27. There is an ice cream shop 6 blocks north of your hotel. How many minutes will it take to walk there and back?

Textbook

Problem-Solving 1.27
Solve Problem 27 with the help of an interactive guided tutorial.

with ChemASAP

Figure 1.25 Refer to this map of Indianapolis, Indiana, while you do Sample Problem 1.1.
Interpreting Diagrams
In the section of downtown bounded by north, east, south, and west streets, the main streets and avenues are named for states. What are the five exceptions to this pattern?

Solving Conceptual Problems

Not every word problem in chemistry requires calculations. Some problems ask you to apply the concepts you are studying to a new situation. In this text, these nonnumeric problems are labeled conceptual problems. To solve a conceptual problem, you still need to identify what is known and what is unknown. Most importantly, you still need to make a plan for getting from the known to the unknown. But if your answer is not a number, you do not need to check the units, make an estimate, or check your calculations.

The three-step problem-solving approach is modified for conceptual problems. ☞ **The steps for solving a conceptual problem are analyze and solve.** Figure 1.26 summarizes the process, and Conceptual Problem 1.1 on the next page shows how the steps work in an actual problem.

Figure 1.26 This flowchart shows the two steps used for solving a conceptual problem.
Comparing and Contrasting *With a conceptual problem, why is the second step solve rather than calculate?*

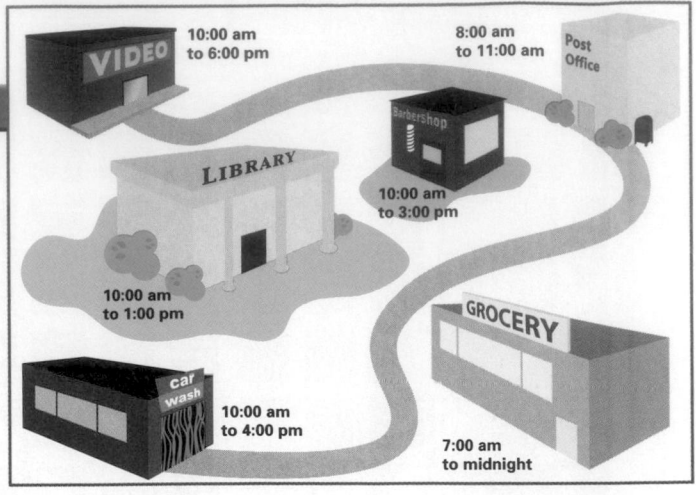

CONCEPTUAL PROBLEM 1.1

Running Errands

Manny has to run 6 errands between 10 and 5 on Saturday. He must get a haircut, wash his car, buy stamps, rent a video, return a library book, and buy some groceries. Assume that each errand will take 30 minutes and that Manny will do only one errand per hour. Manny will stop for a lunch break between 12 and 1. Use the information in the drawing to figure out a way for Manny to accomplish all 6 tasks.

1 Analyze *Identify the relevant concepts.*

Each place that Manny needs to visit is open for a limited number of hours on Saturday. Manny must do his errands between 10 and 12, and between 1 and 5. At a rate of one errand per hour, Manny must do 2 errands before lunch and 4 errands after lunch.

2 Solve *Apply concepts to this situation.*

The post office and library are open only in the morning. The barbershop and the car wash close earlier than the video store. The supermarket is open late. One possible order for the errands is post office, library, barbershop, car wash, video store, and supermarket.

Practice Problems

28. Describe two alternative orders in which Manny could complete his errands.

29. What if Manny had 7 errands instead of 6? What would he need to do to adjust for the extra errand?

Problem-Solving 1.29
Solve Problem 29 with the help of an interactive guided tutorial.

—— with **ChemASAP**

1.4 Section Assessment

30. 🔑 **Key Concept** What are the two general steps in successful problem solving?

31. 🔑 **Key Concept** List the three steps for solving numeric problems.

32. 🔑 **Key Concept** List the two steps for solving conceptual problems.

33. Read the conversion problem and then answer the questions. "There are 3600 seconds in an hour. How many seconds are there in one day?"
  a. Identify the known and the unknown.
  b. What relationship between the known and unknown do you need to solve the problem?
  c. Calculate the answer to the problem.
  d. Evaluate your answer and explain why your answer makes sense.

Writing ▶ Activity

Compare and Contrast Paragraph Write a paragraph comparing the processes for solving numeric problems and conceptual problems. How are the processes similar? In what way are they different?

Assessment 1.4 Test yourself on the concepts in Section 1.4.

—— with **ChemASAP**

CHAPTER 1 Study Guide

Key Concepts

🔑 1.1 Chemistry
- Because living and nonliving things are made of matter, chemistry affects all aspects of life and most natural events.
- Chemistry can be divided into five traditional areas of study: organic chemistry, inorganic chemistry, biochemistry, analytical chemistry, and physical chemistry.
- Pure research can lead directly to an application, but an application can exist before research is done to explain how it works.
- Chemistry can be useful in explaining the natural world, preparing people for career opportunities, and producing informed citizens.

🔑 1.2 Chemistry Far and Wide
- Chemists design materials to fit specific needs. Chemists play an essential role in finding ways to conserve energy, produce energy, and store energy.
- Chemists supply the medicines, materials, and technology that doctors use to treat patients. Chemists help to develop more productive crops and safer, more effective ways to protect crops.
- Chemists help to identify pollutants and prevent pollution.
- To study the universe, chemists gather data from afar and analyze matter that is brought back to Earth.

🔑 1.3 Thinking Like a Scientist
- Alchemists developed tools and techniques for working with chemicals.
- Lavoisier helped to transform chemistry from a science of observation to the science of measurement that it is today.
- Steps in the scientific method include making observations, testing hypotheses, and developing theories.
- When scientists collaborate and communicate, they increase the likelihood of a successful outcome.

🔑 1.4 Problem Solving in Chemistry
- Effective problem solving always involves developing a plan and then implementing the plan.
- The steps for solving a numeric word problem are analyze, calculate, and evaluate. The steps for solving a conceptual problem are analyze and solve.

Vocabulary

- analytical chemistry (p. 8)
- applied chemistry (p. 9)
- biochemistry (p. 8)
- biotechnology (p. 14)
- chemistry (p. 7)
- experiment (p. 22)
- hypothesis (p. 22)
- inorganic chemistry (p. 8)
- macroscopic (p. 12)
- matter (p. 7)
- microscopic (p. 12)
- manipulated variable (p. 22)
- observation (p. 22)
- organic chemistry (p. 8)
- physical chemistry (p. 8)
- pollutant (p. 16)
- pure chemistry (p. 9)
- responding variable (p. 22)
- scientific law (p. 23)
- scientific method (p. 22)
- technology (p. 9)
- theory (p. 23)

Organizing Information

Use these terms to construct a concept map that organizes the major ideas of this chapter.

Concept Map 1 Solve the Concept Map with the help of an interactive guided tutorial.

— with **ChemASAP**

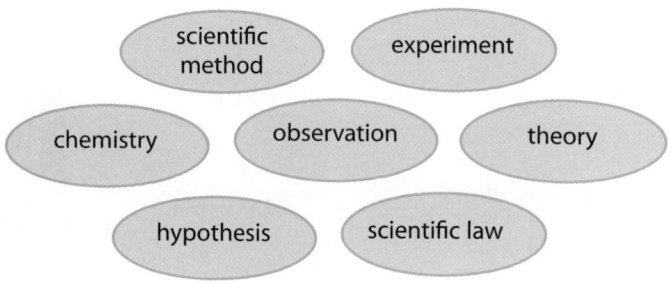

Review and Assessment

Blue questions emphasize Regents Exam content

Chemistry

34. **Explain why air is classified as matter.**

35. The Japanese characters for chemistry literally mean "change study." Why are these appropriate characters to represent chemistry?

36. Describe the main difference between inorganic chemistry and organic chemistry.

37. Was Wallace Carothers doing pure chemistry or applied chemistry when he discovered nylon? Explain your answer.

38. Explain how chemists were able to connect the ability of aspirin to relieve pain to its ability to reduce the risk of a heart attack.

39. Why would a firefighter or a reporter need to understand chemistry?

40. Match each area of chemistry with a numbered statement.
    a. physical chemistry   **b.** organic chemistry
    c. analytical chemistry   **d.** inorganic chemistry
    e. biochemistry

    (1) Measure the level of lead in blood.
    (2) Increase the production of rice per acre.
    (3) Classify minerals based on composition.
    (4) Develop a new way to get energy from coal.
    (5) Explain what happens when a diamond shatters.

41. Explain why chemistry might be useful in a career you are thinking of pursuing.

42. Compare and contrast the study of chemistry with the study of a language.

Chemistry Far and Wide

43. George de Mestral used burrs as a model for his hook-and-loop tapes. Using burrs as an example, explain the difference between a macroscopic and a microscopic view of matter.

44. How does the development of new types of insulation help to conserve energy?

45. What is the overall goal of biochemists?

46. Describe two ways that biotechnology can be used to treat diseases.

47. How can testing soil help to increase the productivity of farmland?

48. What is a pollutant?

49. Why is it important that young children not be exposed to lead-based paint?

50. How can scientists study the composition of distant stars?

Use this photograph of a javelin thrower to answer Questions 51 and 52.

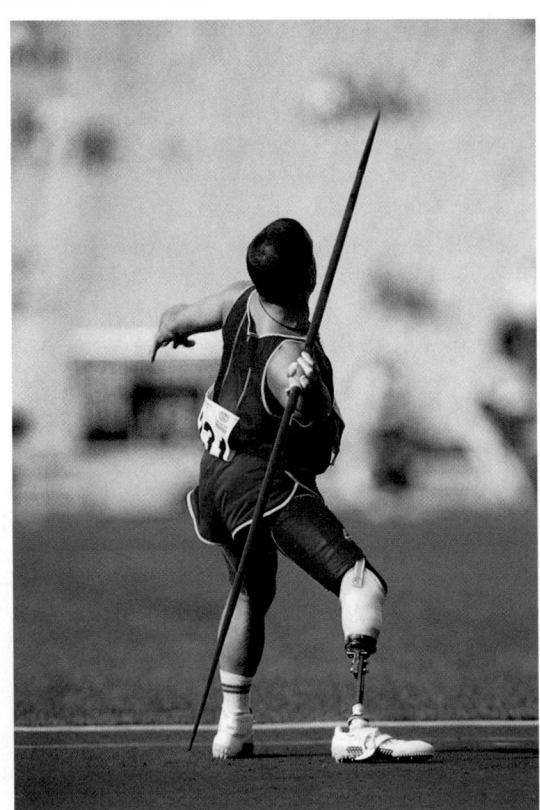

51. Explain how chemistry has affected the ability of this athlete to compete.

52. What type of chemist might study how an athlete uses energy during a competition? Give a reason for your answer.

1.3 Thinking Like a Scientist

53. What did the scientists who founded the Royal Society of London share with Lavoisier?

54. What is the most powerful tool that any scientist can have?

55. What is the purpose of an experiment?

56. Which of the following is *not* a part of the scientific method?
  a. hypothesis   **b.** experiment
  c. guess   **d.** theory

57. How do an independent variable and a dependent variable differ?

58. You perform an experiment and get unexpected results. According to the scientific method, what should you do next?

59. Explain how the results of many experiments can lead to both a scientific law and a theory.

60. List two general reasons why scientists are likely to collaborate.

61. A doctor examines a patient's sore throat and suggests that the patient has strep throat. She takes a sample to test for the bacteria that cause strep throat. What parts of the scientific method is the doctor applying?

62. You perform an experiment and find that the results do not agree with an accepted theory. Should you conclude that you made an error in your procedure? Explain.

63. A student is planning a science fair project called "Does Temperature Affect How High a Basketball Can Bounce?"
  a. Based on the project title, identify the independent variable and the dependent variable.
  b. Name at least two factors that would need to be kept constant during the experiment.

64. Describe a situation in which you used at least two steps in the scientific method to solve a problem.

65. Pure water freezes at 0°C. A student wanted to test the effect of adding salt to the water. The table shows the data that was collected.

Effect of Salt on Freezing Point of Water	
Salt Added	**Freezing Point**
5 g	−4.8°C
10 g	−9.7°C
15 g	−15.1°C
20 g	−15.0°C

  a. What was the independent variable?
  b. What was the dependent variable?
  c. Why must the volume of water be the same for each test?
  d. Based on the data, the student hypothesized, "As more salt is added to water, the freezing point of the water decreases." Is this hypothesis supported by the data? Explain.

66. Comment on the idea that science accepts what works and rejects what does not work.

67. Important discoveries in science are sometimes the result of an accident. Louis Pasteur said, "Chance favors the prepared mind." Explain how both of these statements can be true.

68. Explain what is wrong with the statement, "Theories are proven by experiments."

69. You find a sealed box with strings protruding from three holes, as shown in the diagram. When you tug string A, it becomes longer, and string C becomes shorter. When you tug string B, it becomes longer, but strings A and C are not affected. Make a diagram showing the arrangement of the strings inside the box.

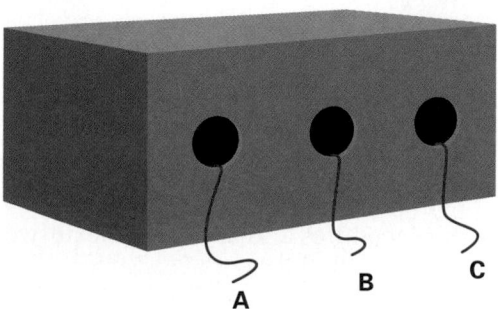

Review and Assessment *continued*

70. You are asked to design an experiment to answer the question: "Which paper towel is the best?"
    a. What is the independent variable in your experiment?
    b. List three possible dependent variables that could be used to define "best."
    c. Pick one of the dependent variables and rewrite the question as a hypothesis.
    d. List at least five factors that must be kept constant when you test the hypothesis.

1.4 Problem Solving in Chemistry

71. Identify the statements that correctly describe good problem solvers.
    a. Read a problem only once.
    b. Check their work.
    c. Look up missing facts.
    d. Look for relationships among the data.

72. What do effective problem-solving strategies have in common?

73. In which step of the three-step problem-solving approach for numeric problems is a problem-solving strategy developed?

74. On the average, a baseball team wins two out of every three games it plays. How many games will this team lose in a 162-game season?

75. If your heart beats at an average rate of 72 times per minute, how many times will your heart beat in an hour? In a day?

76. How many days would it take you to count a million pennies if you could count one penny each second?

77. In the time a person on a bicycle travels 4 miles, a person in a car travels 30 miles. Assuming a constant speed, how far will the car travel while the bicycle travels 40 miles?

78. Four beakers have a total weight of 2.0 lb. Each beaker when full holds 0.5 lb of water. Describe two different procedures you could use to calculate the weight of two full beakers of water. Then try both procedures and compare the answers.

79. The air you breathe is composed of about 20% oxygen and 80% nitrogen. Use your problem solving skills to decide which drawing best represents a sample of air. Explain your choice.

a.   b.

c.   d.

 Oxygen   Nitrogen

80. A certain ball, when dropped from any height, bounces one-half the original height. If the ball was dropped from a height of 60 in. and allowed to bounce freely, what is the total distance the ball has traveled when it hits the ground for the third time? Assume the ball bounces straight up and down.

81. Eggs are shipped from the farm to market by truck. They are packed 12 eggs to a carton and 20 cartons to a box. Four boxes are placed in each crate. Crates are stacked on a truck 5 crates wide, 6 crates deep and 5 crates high. How many eggs are on a truck?

82. An oil tanker containing 4,000,000 barrels is emptied at the rate of 5000 gallons per minute. What information do you need to figure out how long it would take to empty the tanker?

83. A crate of envelopes sells for $576.00. A package of envelopes contains 250 envelopes. Six packages are packed inside a carton. Twelve cartons are packed in a box. Eight boxes are packed in a crate.
    a. What does a package of envelopes cost?
    b. What fact given in the problem was not needed to calculate the answer?

New York Regents Practice Exams

THE NEW YORK CORE CURRICULUM FOR CHEMISTRY

The New York Core Curriculum for Chemistry provides a guideline for what you should know to succeed on the Regents Examination in chemistry. The chemistry topics that you need to know are outlined in these standards. Success in mastering these concepts will lead to success in the Regents Examination.

The Regents Examination consists of Parts A, B, and C, each of which contains a different type of question.

- Part A questions are entirely multiple-choice and test your knowledge of concepts from the core curriculum.

- Part B questions test skills and understandings of concepts outlined in the core curriculum and include both multiple-choice and constructed response questions.

- Part C questions often require an extended constructed response and relate to real-world situations. For these questions, you will often need to provide a more detailed answer, supported with applications or examples and written in complete sentences.

HOW CAN *PRENTICE HALL CHEMISTRY* HELP?

In several ways, *Prentice Hall Chemistry* can help you learn what you need to know to be successful in the part of the Regents Exam that relates to chemistry.

This textbook provides you with chemistry content that corresponds to the content required by the core curriculum. Each standard in the core curriculum is explained in this textbook. In addition, other topics that expand on these standards provide enrichment and show how the topics in the standards relate to each other and to real-life situations.

Prentice Hall Chemistry provides you with practice for each of these types of questions. All chapters in your textbook end with a four- or five-page chapter assessment that helps you review the content of the chapter.

- The first pages of the chapter assessment are general questions grouped according to the section in which they appear. These questions cover some chapter topics that are in the core curriculum and some topics that are not.

  The questions that appear in blue review the core curriculum standards and have the same form as the questions in the Regents Exam. With the exception of Chapters 1 and 24, at least half of the questions in these pages are Regents-type questions.

- The last two pages of the chapter assessment are a Regents Practice Exam. All questions in this practice exam review either the chapter concepts that relate to the core curriculum or core curriculum concepts from previous chapters. They also are in the same format as the questions that appear in the Regents Exam.

Matter and Change

As this Indonesian potter shapes a pot, she causes a physical change in the clay.

INQUIRY Activity

Classifying Matter

Materials

4 clear containers, 4 small cups, tape or self-adhesive labels, pen, half-cup measure, water, half-teaspoon measures, sugar, baking powder, flour, baking soda, stirring rod, clock or watch

Procedure

1. Label the clear containers and the small cups Sugar, Baking powder, Flour, and Baking soda.

2. Use the small cups to collect half a teaspoon of each solid. Be sure to use the half-teaspoon measure that is assigned to each solid.

3. Add half a cup of water to each clear container.

4. Without stirring, add each solid to its corresponding container. Observe and record any change that occurs after the solids are added.

5. Stir the contents of each container for at least 45 seconds. Rinse the rod with water between stirrings. Record what you observe.

Think About It

1. Can you use the appearance of the four solids to distinguish them? Explain your answer.

2. Which solid could you distinguish from the other three after Step 4 of the procedure? How could you distinguish this solid?

3. Can you distinguish completely among the remaining three solids based on the results of Step 5? Explain your answer.

4. Make a list of properties, such as color, that can be used to describe materials.

Connecting to Your World

The more than 1200 species of bamboo belong to a family of grasses that includes wheat and corn. In tropical regions, bamboo plants grow rapidly to great heights. The tender shoots of some bamboo plants are a favorite food of pandas. People use the woody stems of mature plants to make furniture, fishing rods, and flooring. Because bamboo is inexpensive and abundant, disposable chopsticks are usually made from bamboo. Bamboo has properties that make it a good choice for use in chopsticks. It has no noticeable odor or taste. It is hard, yet easy to split, and it is heat resistant. In this section, you will learn how properties can be used to classify and identify matter.

Describing Matter

Understanding matter begins with observation and what you observe when you look at a particular sample of matter is its properties. Is a solid shiny or dull? Does a liquid flow quickly or slowly? Is a gas odorless or does it have a smell? ☞ **Properties used to describe matter can be classified as extensive or intensive.**

Extensive Properties Recall that matter is anything that has mass and takes up space. The **mass** of an object is a measure of the amount of matter the object contains. The mass of a bowling ball with finger holes is five or six times greater than the mass of the bowling ball shown in Figure 2.1, which is used to play a game called candlepins. There is also a difference in the volume of the balls. The **volume** of an object is a measure of the space occupied by the object. Mass and volume are examples of extensive properties. An **extensive property** is a property that depends on the amount of matter in a sample.

Intensive Properties There are properties to consider when selecting a bowling ball other than mass. Beginning bowlers want a bowling ball that is likely to maintain a straight path. They use bowling balls with a hard surface made from polyester. Experienced bowlers want a bowling ball they can curve, or hook, toward the pins. Often, they use a polyurethane ball, which has a softer surface. Hardness is an example of an intensive property. An **intensive property** is a property that depends on the type of matter in a sample, not the amount of matter.

Guide for Reading

Key Concepts
- How can properties used to describe matter be classified?
- Why do all samples of a substance have the same intensive properties?
- What are three states of matter?
- How can physical changes be classified?

Vocabulary
mass
volume
extensive property
intensive property
substance
physical property
solid
liquid
gas
vapor
physical change

Reading Strategy

Using Prior Knowledge Before you read, write a definition for the term *liquid*. After you read this section, compare and contrast the definition of *liquid* in the text with your original definition.

Figure 2.1 This bowling ball and candlepin are used in a game played mainly in New England.

Figure 2.2 This gold falcon standard from Egypt is about 3000 years old. The copper kettles are about 150 years old. **Analyzing Data** *Which of the properties listed in Table 2.1 could not be used to distinguish copper from gold?*

Identifying Substances

Each object in Figure 2.2 has a different chemical makeup, or composition. The sculpture of a falcon is mainly gold. The kettles are mainly copper. Matter that has a uniform and definite composition is called a **substance.** Gold and copper are examples of substances, which are also referred to as pure substances. ⊙ **Every sample of a given substance has identical intensive properties because every sample has the same composition.**

Gold and copper have some properties in common, but there are differences besides their distinctive colors. Pure copper can scratch the surface of pure gold because copper is harder than gold. Copper is better than gold as a conductor of heat or electric current. Both gold and copper are malleable, which means they can be hammered into sheets without breaking. But gold is more malleable than copper. Hardness, color, conductivity, and malleability are examples of physical properties. A **physical property** is a quality or condition of a substance that can be observed or measured without changing the substance's composition.

Table 2.1 lists physical properties for some substances. The states of the substances are given at room temperature. (Although scientists use room temperature to refer to a range of temperatures, in this book it will be used to refer to a specific temperature, 20°C.) Physical properties can help chemists identify substances. For example, a colorless substance that was found to boil at 100°C and melt at 0°C would likely be water. A colorless substance that boiled at 78°C and melted at −117°C would most certainly not be water. Based on Table 2.1, it would likely be ethanol.

✔Checkpoint *Which is a better conductor of electric current—gold or copper?*

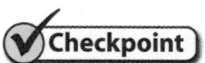

Physical Properties of Some Substances				
Substance	State	Color	Melting point (°C)	Boiling point (°C)
Neon	gas	colorless	−249	−246
Oxygen	gas	colorless	−218	−183
Chlorine	gas	greenish-yellow	−101	−34
Ethanol	liquid	colorless	−117	78
Mercury	liquid	silvery-white	−39	357
Bromine	liquid	reddish-brown	−7	59
Water	liquid	colorless	0	100
Sulfur	solid	yellow	115	445
Sodium chloride	solid	white	801	1413
Gold	solid	yellow	1064	2856
Copper	solid	reddish-yellow	1084	2562

For: Links on Physical Properties of Matter
Visit: www.SciLinks.org
Web Code: cdn-1021

States of Matter

Depending on the circumstances, you use three different words to refer to water—water, ice, and steam. Water, which is a common substance, exists in three different physical states. So can most other substances. 🔑 **Three states of matter are solid, liquid, and gas.** Certain characteristics that can distinguish these three states of matter are summarized in Figure 2.3.

Solids A **solid** is a form of matter that has a definite shape and volume. The shape of a solid doesn't depend on the shape of its container. The particles in a solid are packed tightly together, often in an orderly arrangement, as shown in Figure 2.3a. As a result, solids are almost incompressible; that is, it is difficult to squeeze a solid into a smaller volume. In addition, solids expand only slightly when heated.

Liquids Look at Figure 2.3b. The particles in a liquid are in close contact with one another, but the arrangement of particles in a liquid is not rigid or orderly. Because the particles in a liquid are free to flow from one location to another, a liquid takes the shape of the container in which it is placed. However, the volume of the liquid doesn't change as its shape changes. The volume of a liquid is fixed or constant. Thus, a **liquid** is a form of matter that has an indefinite shape, flows, yet has a fixed volume. Liquids are almost incompressible, but they tend to expand slightly when heated.

𝒾**nteractive Textbook**

Animation 1 Relate the states of matter to the arrangements of their particles.

— with **ChemASAP**

Solid	**Liquid**	**Gas**
Definite shape	Indefinite shape	Indefinite shape
Definite volume	Definite volume	Indefinite volume
Not easily compressed	Not easily compressed	Easily compressed

Figure 2.3 The arrangement of particles is different in solids, liquids, and gases. ❶ In a solid, the particles are packed closely together in a rigid arrangement. ❷ In a liquid, the particles are close together, but they are free to flow past one another. ❸ In a gas, the particles are relatively far apart and can move freely.
Relating Cause and Effect *Use the arrangements of their particles to explain the general shape and volume of solids and gases.*

Figure 2.4 The silvery substance in the photograph is gallium, which has a melting point of 30°C. **Inferring** *What can you infer about the temperature of the hand holding the gallium?*

Gases Like a liquid, a gas takes the shape of its container. But unlike a liquid, a gas can expand to fill any volume. A **gas** is a form of matter that takes both the shape and volume of its container. Look back at Figure 2.3c. As shown in the model, the particles in a gas are usually much farther apart than the particles in a liquid. Because of the space between particles, gases are easily compressed into a smaller volume.

The words *vapor* and *gas* are sometimes used interchangeably. But there is a difference. The term *gas* is used for substances, like oxygen, that exist in the gaseous state at room temperature. (*Gaseous* is the adjective form of *gas*.) **Vapor** describes the gaseous state of a substance that is generally a liquid or solid at room temperature, as in water vapor.

✓ Checkpoint *When should the term vapor be used instead of gas?*

Physical Changes

The melting point of gallium metal is 30°C. Figure 2.4 shows how heat from a person's hand can melt a sample of gallium. The shape of the sample changes during melting as the liquid begins to flow, but the composition of the sample does not change. Melting is an example of a physical change. During a **physical change,** some properties of a material change, but the composition of the material does not change.

Words such as *boil, freeze, melt,* and *condense* are used to describe physical changes. So are words such as *break, split, grind, cut,* and *crush.* However, there is a difference between these two sets of words. Each set describes a different type of physical change. **⊙━ Physical changes can be classified as reversible or irreversible.** Melting is an example of a reversible physical change. If a sample of liquid gallium is cooled below its melting point, the liquid will become a solid. All physical changes that involve a change from one state to another are reversible. Cutting hair, filing nails, and cracking an egg are examples of irreversible physical changes.

2.1 Section Assessment

1. **⊙━ Key Concept** Name two categories used to classify properties of matter.

2. **⊙━ Key Concept** Explain why all samples of a given substance have the same intensive properties.

3. **⊙━ Key Concept** Name three states of matter.

4. **⊙━ Key Concept** Describe the two categories used to classify physical changes.

5. Which property in Table 2.1 can most easily distinguish sodium chloride from the other solids?

6. In what way are liquids and gases alike? In what way are liquids and solids different?

7. Is the freezing of mercury a reversible or irreversible physical change? Explain your answer.

8. Explain why samples of gold and copper can have the same extensive properties, but not the same intensive properties.

Elements ▶ Handbook

Read about the metal indium on page R16. What is the melting point of indium? Which other metal has a similar melting point—gallium or gold? Provide data to support your answer.

ℹ️ Interactive Textbook

Assessment 2.1 Test yourself on the concepts in Section 2.1.

━ with **ChemASAP**

Hanging by a Thread

Strands in a spider web are about one tenth the diameter of a human hair. Yet a golden orb spider web can withstand the impact of a insect, or even a small bird, flying at high speed because the silk in the web's frame and spokes is stronger than steel, more elastic than nylon, and tougher than rubber. Scientists are always looking for lightweight materials with these properties, but they cannot set up farms to harvest spider silk because a spider will fight to defend its territory. Instead, scientists use biotechnology to produce spider silk. **Interpreting Diagrams** *Where are the silk glands located in a spider?*

Spinnerets
(magnification: 110,0003)

Heart

Eyes

Mouth

Stomach

Lung

Silk glands

Spider anatomy A spider releases its silk through spinnerets at the tip of its abdomen. Inside each spinneret are tens or hundreds of spigots. Silk travels from a silk gland through a duct to a spigot. As the silk is released from a spigot, it changes from a liquid to a solid.

Female Golden Orb Spider
Nephila clavipes
Body length: 24 mm to 40 mm

Spider silk from goat's milk
Scientists have identified the spider genes that contain the instructions for producing silk. When these genes are transferred to goats, the goats produce milk containing spider silk. Scientists separate the silk from the milk, purify it, and spin it into fibers.

2.2 Mixtures

New York Standards: 3.1s, 3.1t, 3.1nn, 3.1oo

Guide for Reading

Key Concepts
- How can mixtures be classified?
- How can mixtures be separated?

Vocabulary
mixture
heterogeneous mixture
homogeneous mixture
solution
phase
filtration
distillation

Reading Strategy

Building Vocabulary After you read this section, explain the difference between homogeneous and heterogeneous mixtures.

Connecting to Your World In 1848, gold was discovered in California. This discovery led to a massive migration, or rush, of people to California. Panning is one way to separate gold from a mixture of gold and materials such as sand or gravel. A pan containing the mixture is placed underwater and shaken vigorously from left to right. This motion causes heavier materials, such as gold, to move to the bottom of the pan and lighter materials, such as sand, to move to the top where they can be swept away. In this section, you will learn how to classify and separate mixtures.

Classifying Mixtures

A salad bar, like the one in Figure 2.5, provides a range of items, such as cucumbers and hot peppers. Customers choose which items to use in their salads and how much of each item to use. So each salad has a different composition. A **mixture** is a physical blend of two or more components.

Most samples of matter are mixtures. Some mixtures are easier to recognize than others. You can easily recognize chicken noodle soup as a mixture of chicken, noodles, and broth. Recognizing air as a mixture of gases is more difficult. But the fact that air can be drier or more humid shows that the amount of one component of air—water vapor—can vary. Chicken noodle soup and air represent two different types of mixtures. **Based on the distribution of their components, mixtures can be classified as heterogeneous mixtures or as homogeneous mixtures.**

Figure 2.5 You can choose the amount of each item you select from a salad bar. So your salad is unlikely to have the same composition as other salads containing the same items.

Quick LAB

Separating Mixtures

Purpose
To separate a mixture using paper chromatography.

Materials
- green marking pen
- filter paper strip
- metric ruler
- clear plastic tape
- pencil
- rubbing alcohol
- clear plastic drinking cup
- clear plastic wrap

Procedure

1. Use the marking pen to draw a line across a strip of filter paper, as shown in the drawing. The line should be 2 cm from one end of the strip.
2. Tape the unmarked end of the filter paper to the center of a pencil so that the strip hangs down when the pencil is held horizontally.
3. Working in a well-ventilated room, pour rubbing alcohol into a plastic cup to a depth of 1 cm.
4. Rest the pencil on the rim of the cup so that the ink end of the strip touches the rubbing alcohol, but does not extend below its surface. Use plastic wrap to cover the top of the cup.
5. Observe the setup for 15 minutes.

Filter paper
Ink line
Alcohol

Analyze and Conclude

1. How did the appearance of the filter paper change during the procedure?
2. What evidence is there that green ink is a mixture?
3. How could you use this procedure to identify an unknown type of green ink?

Heterogeneous Mixtures In chicken noodle soup, the ingredients are not evenly distributed throughout the mixture. There is likely to be more chicken in one spoonful than in another spoonful. A mixture in which the composition is not uniform throughout is a **heterogeneous mixture.**

Homogeneous Mixtures The substances in the olive oil and vinegar in Figure 2.6 are evenly distributed throughout these mixtures. So olive oil doesn't look like a mixture. The same is true for vinegar. Vinegar is a mixture of water and acetic acid, which dissolves in the water. Olive oil and vinegar are homogeneous mixtures. A **homogeneous mixture** is a mixture in which the composition is uniform throughout. Another name for a homogeneous mixture is a **solution.** Many solutions are liquids. But some are gases, like air, and some are solids, like stainless steel, which is a mixture of iron, chromium, and nickel.

The term **phase** is used to describe any part of a sample with uniform composition and properties. By definition, a homogeneous mixture consists of a single phase. A heterogeneous mixture consists of two or more phases. When oil and vinegar are mixed, they form layers, or phases, as shown in Figure 2.6. The oil phase floats on the water phase.

✓ Checkpoint *How many phases are there in a homogeneous mixture?*

Olive oil   Vinegar

Oil & vinegar

Figure 2.6 Olive oil and vinegar are homogeneous mixtures. The substances in these mixtures are evenly distributed. When olive oil is mixed with vinegar, they form a heterogeneous mixture with two distinct phases.

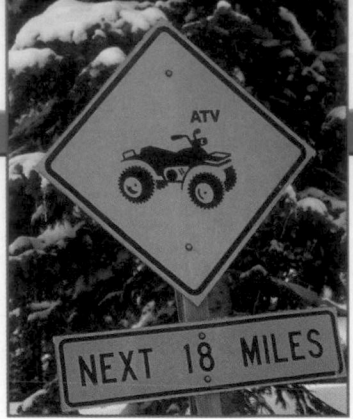

Separating a Heterogeneous Mixture

Sometimes plastic signs are used to mark trails used by hikers or vehicles. The sign in the photo is used to mark locations along a trail where an all terrain vehicle (ATV) is permitted. Aluminum nails are used to attach signs at eye level to trees or posts. How could a mixture of aluminum nails and iron nails be separated?

1 **Analyze** *Identify the relevant concepts.*

List properties of aluminum and iron.

Aluminum:
- metal
- gray color
- doesn't dissolve in water
- not attracted to magnet

Iron:
- metal
- gray color
- doesn't dissolve in water
- attracted to magnet

2 **Solve** *Apply concepts to this situation.*

Identify a property that can be used to separate iron and aluminum objects. The ability to be attracted by a magnet is a property that iron and aluminum do not share. You could use a magnet to remove the iron nails from a mixture of iron and aluminum nails.

9. What physical properties could be used to separate iron filings from table salt?

10. Air is mainly a mixture of nitrogen and oxygen, with small amounts of other gases such as argon and carbon dioxide. What property could you use to separate the gases in air?

Interactive Textbook

Problem Solving 2.10 Solve Problem 10 with the help of an interactive guided tutorial.

with ChemASAP

Separating Mixtures

If you have a salad containing an ingredient you don't like, you can use a fork to remove the pieces of the unwanted ingredient. Many mixtures are not as easy to separate. To separate a mixture of olive oil and vinegar, for example, you could decant, or pour off, the oil layer. Or you might cool the mixture until the oil turned solid. The first method takes advantage of the fact that oil floats on water. The second method takes advantage of a difference in the temperatures at which the olive oil and vinegar freeze. **Differences in physical properties can be used to separate mixtures.**

Filtration The colander in Figure 2.7 can separate cooked pasta from the cooking water. The water passes through the holes in the colander, but the pasta does not. The holes, or pores, in a coffee filter are smaller than the holes in a colander to retain coffee grains. But the holes are not small enough to retain the particles in water. The process that separates a solid from the liquid in a heterogeneous mixture is called **filtration.**

Figure 2.7 A colander is used to separate pasta from the water in which it was cooked. This process is a type of filtration.

Figure 2.8 A distillation can be used to remove impurities from water. As liquid water changes into water vapor, substances dissolved in the water are left behind in the distillation flask. **Inferring** *What can you infer about the boiling points of substances dissolved in the impure water?*

100°C

Cold water out

Condenser

Steam at 100°C

Tap water (mixture)

Cold water in

Receiver flask

Distilled water

Distillation Tap water is a homogeneous mixture of water and substances that dissolved in the water. One way to separate water from the other components in tap water is through a process called distillation. During a **distillation,** a liquid is boiled to produce a vapor that is then condensed into a liquid. Figure 2.8 shows an apparatus that can be used to perform a small-scale distillation.

As water in the distillation flask is heated, water vapor forms, rises in the flask, and passes into a glass tube in the condenser. The tube is surrounded by cold water, which cools the vapor to a temperature at which it turns back into a liquid. The liquid water is collected in a second flask. The solid substances that were dissolved in the water remain in the distillation flask because their boiling points are much higher than the boiling point of water.

2.2 Section Assessment

11. **⚷ Key Concept** How are mixtures classified?

12. **⚷ Key Concept** What type of properties can be used to separate mixtures?

13. Explain the term *phase* as it relates to homogeneous and heterogeneous mixtures.

14. Classify each of the following as a homogeneous or heterogeneous mixture.
    a. food coloring
    b. ice cubes in liquid water
    c. mouthwash
    d. mashed, unpeeled potatoes

15. How are a substance and a solution similar? How are they different?

16. In general, when would you use filtration to separate a mixture? When would you use distillation to separate a mixture?

17. Describe a procedure that could be used to separate a mixture of sand and table salt.

Writing ▸ Activity

Writing to Persuade Write a paragraph in support of this statement: Dry tea is a mixture, not a substance. Include at least two pieces of evidence to support your argument.

Textbook

Assessment 2.2 Test yourself on the concepts in Section 2.2.

── with **ChemASAP**

Guide for Reading

Key Concepts
- How are elements and compounds different?
- How can substances and mixtures be distinguished?
- What do chemists use to represent elements and compounds?

Vocabulary
element
compound
chemical change
chemical symbol

Reading Strategy
Relating Text and Visuals As you read, look at Figure 2.10. Explain how this illustration helps you understand the relationship between different kinds of matter.

Connecting to Your World

Take two pounds of sugar, two cups of boiling water, and one-quarter teaspoon of cream of tartar. You have the ingredients to make spun sugar. Add food coloring and you have the sticky, sweet concoction sold at baseball games and amusement parks as cotton candy. Sugar is a substance that contains three other substances—carbon, hydrogen, and oxygen. In this section, you will learn how substances are classified as elements or compounds.

Distinguishing Elements and Compounds

Substances can be classified as elements or compounds. An **element** is the simplest form of matter that has a unique set of properties. Oxygen and hydrogen are two of the more than 100 known elements. A **compound** is a substance that contains two or more elements chemically combined in a fixed proportion. For example, carbon, oxygen, and hydrogen are chemically combined in the compound sucrose, the sugar in spun sugar. (Sometimes sucrose is referred to as table sugar to distinguish it from other sugar compounds.) In every sample of sucrose there are twice as many hydrogen particles as oxygen particles. The proportion of hydrogen particles to oxygen particles in sucrose is fixed. There is a key difference between elements and compounds. **Compounds can be broken down into simpler substances by chemical means, but elements cannot.**

Breaking Down Compounds Physical methods that are used to separate mixtures cannot be used to break a compound into simpler substances. Boil liquid water and you get water vapor, not the oxygen and hydrogen that water contains. Dissolve a sugar cube in water and you still have sucrose, not oxygen, carbon, and hydrogen. This result does not mean that sucrose or water cannot be broken down into simpler substances. But the methods must involve a chemical change. A **chemical change** is a change that produces matter with a different composition than the original matter. Heating is one of the processes used to break down compounds into simpler substances. The layer of sugar in Figure 2.9 is heated in a skillet until it breaks down into solid carbon and water vapor. Can the substances that are produced also be broken down?

Figure 2.9 When table sugar is heated, it goes through a series of chemical changes. The final products of these changes are solid carbon and water vapor.

There is no chemical process that will break down carbon into simpler substances because carbon is an element. Heating will not cause water to break down, but electricity will. When an electric current passes through water, oxygen gas and hydrogen gas are produced. The following diagram summarizes the overall process.

$$\overbrace{\underset{\text{Compound}}{\text{Sugar}} \xrightarrow{\text{heat}} \underset{\text{Element}}{\text{Carbon}} + \underset{\text{Compound}}{\text{Water}}}^{\text{Chemical change}}$$

$$\downarrow$$

$$\overbrace{\underset{\text{Compound}}{\text{Water}} \xrightarrow{\text{electricity}} \underset{\text{Element}}{\text{Hydrogen}} + \underset{\text{Element}}{\text{Oxygen}}}^{\text{Chemical change}}$$

Properties of Compounds In general, the properties of compounds are quite different from those of their component elements. Sugar is a sweet-tasting, white solid, but carbon is a black, tasteless solid. Hydrogen is a gas that burns in the presence of oxygen—a colorless gas that supports burning. The product of this chemical change is water, a liquid that can stop materials from burning. Figure 2.10 shows samples of table salt (sodium chloride), sodium, and chlorine. When the elements sodium and chlorine combine chemically to form sodium chloride, there is a change in composition and a change in properties. Sodium is a soft, gray metal. Chlorine is a pale yellow-green poisonous gas. Sodium chloride is a white solid.

✓**Checkpoint** *What process can be used to break down water?*

Figure 2.10 Compounds and the elements from which they form have different properties. **Observing** *Based on the photographs, describe two physical properties of sodium and two of chlorine.*

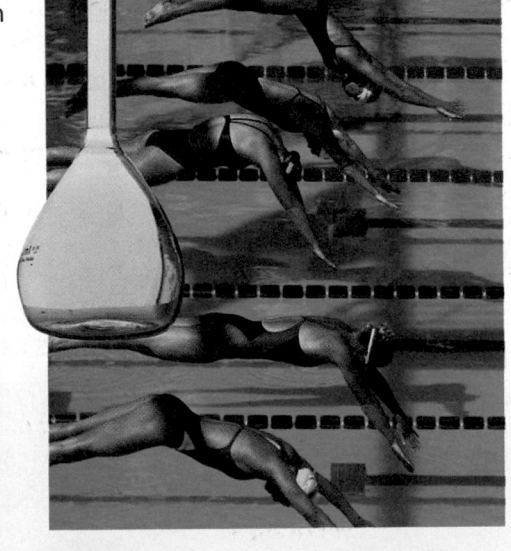

Chlorine is used to kill harmful organisms in swimming pools.

Sodium chloride (commonly known as table salt) is used to season or preserve food.

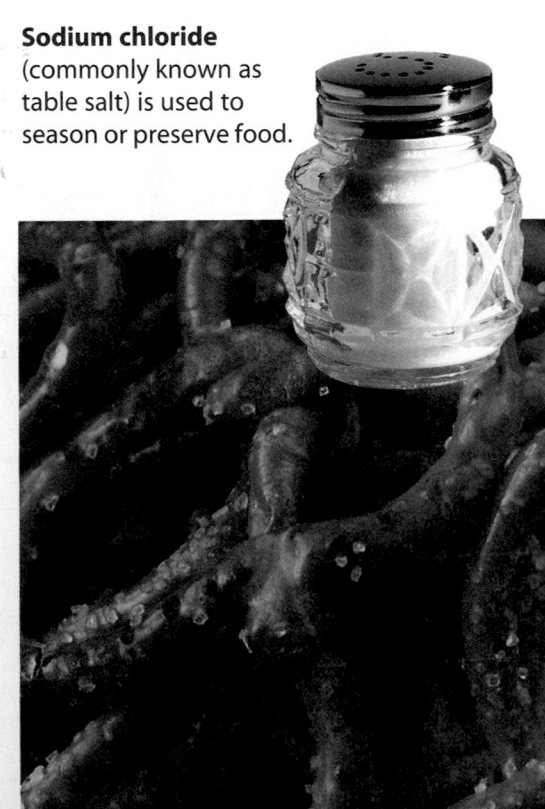

Sodium is stored under oil to keep it from reacting with oxygen or water vapor in air. Sodium vapor produces the light in some street lamps.

Distinguishing Substances and Mixtures

Deciding whether a sample of matter is a substance or a mixture based solely on appearance can be difficult. After all, homogeneous mixtures and substances will both appear to contain only one kind of matter. Sometimes you can decide by considering whether there is more than one version of the material in question. For example, you can buy whole milk, low-fat milk, no-fat milk, light cream, and heavy cream. From this information, you can conclude that milk and cream are mixtures. You might infer that these mixtures differ in the amount of fat they contain. Most gas stations offer at least two blends of gasoline. The blends have different octane ratings and different costs per gallon, with premium blends costing more than regular blends. So gasoline must be a mixture.

You can use their general characteristics to distinguish substances from mixtures. **If the composition of a material is fixed, the material is a substance. If the composition of a material may vary, the material is a mixture.** Figure 2.11 summarizes the general characteristics of elements, compounds, and mixtures.

Figure 2.11 The flow chart summarizes the process for classifying matter. Any sample of matter is either an element, a compound, or a mixture. **Interpreting Diagrams** *What is the key difference between a substance and a solution?*

Matter

Can be separated physically

Substance
Definite composition (homogeneous)

Mixture of substances
Variable composition

Can be separated chemically

Element

Compound

Homogeneous mixture
Uniform; also called a solution

Heterogeneous mixture
Nonuniform; distinct phases

Silver   Beryl   Stainless Steel   Granite

CONCEPTUAL PROBLEM 2.2

Classifying Materials

When the blue-green solid in the photograph is heated, a colorless gas and a black solid form. All three materials are substances. Is it possible to classify these substances as elements or compounds?

1 **Analyze** *Identify the relevant concepts.*

List the known facts and relevant concepts.
- A blue-green solid is heated.
- A colorless gas and a black solid appear.
- A compound can be broken down into simpler substances by a chemical change, but an element cannot.
- Heating can cause a chemical change.

2 **Solve** *Apply concepts to this situation.*

Determine if the substances are elements or compounds. Before heating, there was one substance. After heating there were two substances. The blue-green solid must be a compound. Based on the information given, it isn't possible to know if the colorless gas or black solid are elements or compounds.

Practice Problems

18. Liquid A and Liquid B are clear liquids. They are placed in open containers and allowed to evaporate. When evaporation is complete, there is a white solid in container B, but no solid in container A. From these results, what can you infer about the two liquids?

19. A clear liquid in an open container is allowed to evaporate. After three days, a solid is left in the container. Was the clear liquid an element, a compound, or a mixture? How do you know?

Textbook

Problem Solving 2.19 Solve Problem 19 with the help of an interactive guided tutorial.

— with **ChemASAP**

Symbols and Formulas

The common names water and table salt do not provide information about the chemical composition of these substances. Also, words are not ideal for showing what happens to the composition of matter during a chemical change. 🔑 **Chemists use chemical symbols to represent elements, and chemical formulas to represent compounds.**

Using symbols to represent different kinds of matter is not a new idea. Figure 2.12 shows some symbols that were used in earlier centuries. The symbols used today for elements are based on a system developed by a Swedish chemist, Jöns Jacob Berzelius (1779–1848). He based his symbols on the Latin names of elements. Each element is represented by a one- or two-letter **chemical symbol.** The first letter of a chemical symbol is always capitalized. When a second letter is used, it is lowercase.

Alchemy Symbols

Dalton's Symbols

Figure 2.12 The symbols used to represent elements have changed over time. Alchemists and the English chemist John Dalton (1766–1844) both used drawings to represent chemical elements. Today, elements are represented by one- or two-letter symbols.

Table 2.2

Symbols and Latin Names for Some Elements		
Name	**Symbol**	**Latin name**
Sodium	Na	*natrium*
Potassium	K	*kalium*
Antimony	Sb	*stibium*
Copper	Cu	*cuprum*
Gold	Au	*aurum*
Silver	Ag	*argentum*
Iron	Fe	*ferrum*
Lead	Pb	*plumbum*
Tin	Sn	*stannum*

Go Online

For: Links on Element Names
Visit: www.SciLinks.org
Web Code: cdn-1023

If the English name and the Latin name of an element are similar, the symbol will appear to have been derived from the English name. Examples include Ca for calcium, N for nitrogen, and S for sulfur. Table 2.2 shows examples of elements where the symbols do not match the English names.

Chemical symbols provide a shorthand way to write the chemical formulas of compounds. The symbols for hydrogen, oxygen, and carbon are H, O, and C. The formula for water is H_2O. The formula for sucrose, or table sugar, is $C_{12}H_{22}O_{11}$. Subscripts in chemical formulas are used to indicate the relative proportions of the elements in the compound. For example, the subscript 2 in H_2O indicates that there are always two parts of hydrogen for each part of oxygen in water. Because a compound has a fixed composition, the formula for a compound is always the same.

2.3 Section Assessment

20. 🔑 **Key Concept** How is a compound different from an element?

21. 🔑 **Key Concept** How can you distinguish a substance from a mixture?

22. 🔑 **Key Concept** What are chemical symbols and chemical formulas used for?

23. Name two methods that can be used to break down compounds into simpler substances.

24. Classify each of these samples of matter as an element, a compound, or a mixture.
    a. table sugar   b. tap water
    c. cough syrup   d. nitrogen

25. Write the chemical symbol for each element.
    a. hydrogen   b. oxygen
    c. silver   d. sodium
    e. hydrogen   f. aluminum

26. Name the chemical elements represented by the following symbols.
    a. C   b. Ca   c. K   d. Au   e. Fe   f. Cu

27. What elements make up the pain reliever acetaminophen, chemical formula $C_8H_9O_2N$? Which element is present in the greatest proportion by number of particles?

Writing ▶ Activity

Compare and Contrast Paragraph Compare and contrast elements and compounds. Compare them by saying how they are alike. Contrast them by describing how they are different.

Interactive Textbook

Assessment 2.3 Test yourself on the concepts in Section 2.3.

—— with **ChemASAP**

2.4 Chemical Reactions

New York Standards: 3.1x, 3.2a, 3.3a

Connecting to Your World

Iron is an element with many desirable properties. It is abundant, easy to shape when heated, and relatively strong, especially when mixed with carbon in steel. Iron has one main disadvantage. Over time, objects made of iron will rust if they are left exposed to air. The brittle layer of rust that forms on the surface of the object flakes off, exposing more iron to the air. In this section, you will learn to recognize chemical changes and to distinguish them from physical changes.

Guide for Reading

Key Concepts
- What always happens during a chemical change?
- What are four possible clues that a chemical change has taken place?
- How are the mass of the reactants and the mass of the products of a chemical reaction related?

Vocabulary
chemical property
chemical reaction
reactant
product
precipitate
law of conservation of mass

Reading Strategy
Predicting Before you read, predict what will happen to the mass of a sample of matter that burns. After you read, check the accuracy of your prediction and correct any misconceptions.

Chemical Changes

The compound formed when iron rusts is iron oxide (Fe_2O_3). Words such as *burn, rot, rust, decompose, ferment, explode,* and *corrode* usually signify a chemical change. The ability of a substance to undergo a specific chemical change is called a **chemical property.** Iron is able to combine with oxygen to form rust. So the ability to rust is a chemical property of iron. Chemical properties can be used to identify a substance. But chemical properties can be observed only when a substance undergoes a chemical change.

Figure 2.13 compares a physical change and a chemical change that can occur in a mixture of iron and sulfur. When a magnet is used to separate iron from sulfur, the change is a physical change. The substances present before the change are the same substances present after the change, although they are no longer physically blended. Recall that during a physical change, the composition of matter never changes. **During a chemical change, the composition of matter always changes.** When the mixture of iron and sulfur is heated, a chemical change occurs. The sulfur and iron react and form iron sulfide (FeS).

A chemical change is also called a chemical reaction. One or more substances change into one or more new substances during a **chemical reaction.** A substance present at the start of the reaction is a **reactant.** A substance produced in the reaction is a **product.** In the reaction of iron and sulfur, iron and sulfur are reactants and iron sulfide is a product.

Figure 2.13 A mixture of iron filings and sulfur can be changed. **ⓐ** A magnet separates the iron from the sulfur. **ⓑ** Heat combines iron and sulfur in a compound. **Classifying** *Which change is a chemical change? Explain.*

Figure 2.14 Clues to chemical change often have practical applications. **ⓐ** Bubbles of carbon dioxide gas form when a geologist puts acid on a rock that contains compounds called carbonates. **ⓑ** When a test strip is dipped in urine, the color change is used to estimate the level of the sugar glucose in urine. **ⓒ** One step in the production of cheese is a reaction that causes milk to separate into solid curds and liquid whey.

Recognizing Chemical Changes

How can you tell whether a chemical change has taken place? There are four clues that can serve as a guide. ⟨➡⟩ **Possible clues to chemical change include a transfer of energy, a change in color, the production of a gas, or the formation of a precipitate.**

Every chemical change involves a transfer of energy. For example, energy stored in natural gas is used to cook food. When the methane in natural gas combines with oxygen in the air, energy is given off in the form of heat and light. Some of this energy is transferred to and absorbed by food that is cooking over a lit gas burner. The energy causes chemical changes to take place in the food. The food may brown as it cooks, which is another clue that chemical changes are occurring.

You can observe two other clues to chemical change while cleaning a bathtub. The ring of soap scum that can form in a bathtub is an example of a precipitate. A **precipitate** is a solid that forms and settles out of a liquid mixture. Some bathroom cleaners that you can use to remove soap scum start to bubble when you spray them on the scum. The bubbles are a product of a chemical change that is taking place in the cleaner.

If you observe a clue to chemical change, you cannot be certain that a chemical change has taken place. The clue may be the result of a physical change. For example, energy is always transferred when matter changes from one state to another. Bubbles form when you boil water or open a carbonated drink. The only way to be sure that a chemical change has occurred is to test the composition of a sample before and after the change. Figure 2.14 shows examples of practical situations in which different clues to chemical change are visible.

✓Checkpoint *What energy transfer takes place when food cooks?*

Figure 2.15 When the liquids in photograph A are mixed, they react. None of the products are gases. **Analyzing Data** *How do you know that a reaction took place and that mass was conserved during the reaction?*

Conservation of Mass

When wood burns, substances in the wood combine with oxygen from the air. As the wood burns, a sizable amount of matter is reduced to a small pile of ashes. The reaction seems to involve a reduction in the amount of matter. But appearances can be deceiving. ⚷ **During any chemical reaction, the mass of the products is always equal to the mass of the reactants.** Two of the products of burning wood—carbon dioxide gas and water vapor—are released into the air. When the mass of these gases is considered, the amount of matter is unchanged. Careful measurements show that the total mass of the reactants (wood and the oxygen consumed) equals the total mass of the products (carbon dioxide, water vapor, and ash).

Mass also holds constant during physical changes. For example, when 10 grams of ice melt, 10 grams of liquid water are produced. Similar observations have been recorded for all chemical and physical changes studied. The scientific law that reflects these observations is the law of conservation of mass. The **law of conservation of mass** states that in any physical change or chemical reaction, mass is conserved. Mass is neither created nor destroyed. The conservation of mass is more easily observed when a change occurs in a closed container, as in Figure 2.15.

2.4 Section Assessment

28. ⚷ **Key Concept** How does a chemical change affect the composition of matter?

29. ⚷ **Key Concept** Name four possible clues that a chemical change has taken place.

30. ⚷ **Key Concept** In a chemical reaction, how does the mass of the reactants compare with the mass of the products?

31. What is the main difference between physical changes and chemical changes?

32. Classify the following changes as physical or chemical changes.
    a. Water boils.   **b.** Salt dissolves in water.
    c. Milk turns sour.   **d.** A metal rusts.

33. According to the law of conservation of mass, when is mass conserved?

34. Hydrogen and oxygen react chemically to form water. How much water would form if 4.8 grams of hydrogen reacted with 38.4 grams of oxygen?

Connecting **Concepts**

The Scientific Method Lavoisier proposed the law of conservation of mass in 1789. Write a paragraph describing, in general, what Lavoisier must have done before he proposed this law. Use what you learned about the scientific method in Section 1.3.

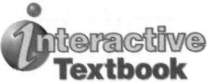
Interactive Textbook

Assessment 2.4 Test yourself on the concepts in Section 2.4.

— with **ChemASAP**

1 + 2 + 3 = Black!

Purpose
To make macroscopic observations of chemical reactions and use them to solve problems.

Materials
- paper
- metric ruler
- reaction surface
- materials shown in grid
- pipette, medicine droppers, and spatulas

Procedure

1. Draw two copies of the grid on separate sheets of paper. Make each square in the grid 2 cm on each side.
2. Place a reaction surface over one of the grids. Use the second grid as a data table to record your observations.
3. Use the column and row labels to determine which materials belong in each square. Depending on the material, add one drop, one piece, or a few grains.
4. Stir each mixture by forcing air from an empty pipette as directed by your teacher.

	NaClO	H$_2$O$_2$	CuSO$_4$
KI			
KI + Starch		FOR	
KI + Paper		REFERENCE	
KI + Cereal		ONLY	

Analyze and Conclude
Using your experimental data, record the answers to the following questions below your data table.

1. What color is a mixture of sodium hypochlorite (NaClO) and potassium iodide (KI)?
2. What happens when you mix NaClO, KI, and starch?
3. What do NaClO, H$_2$O$_2$, and CuSO$_4$ have in common?
4. What substance is found in both paper and cereal? How do you know?
5. If you used NaClO instead of CuSO$_4$ in reactions other than the reaction with KI and starch, would you expect the results to always be identical? Explain your answer.

You're The Chemist
The following small-scale activities allow you to develop your own procedures and analyze the results.

1. **Design It!** Design and carry out an experiment to see which foods contain starch.
2. **Design It!** Read the label on a package of iodized salt. How much KI does iodized salt contain? Design an experiment to demonstrate the presence of KI in iodized salt and its absence in salt that is not iodized.
3. **Design It!** Antacid tablets often contain starch as a binder to hold the ingredients in the tablet together. Design and carry out an experiment to explore various antacid tablets to see if they contain starch.
4. **Analyze It!** NaClO is a bleaching agent. Such agents are used to whiten clothes and remove stains. Use different color marker pens to draw several lines on a piece of white paper. Add one drop of NaClO to each line. What happens? Try inventing a technique that you can use to make "bleach art."

Key Concepts

 2.1 Properties of Matter
- Properties used to describe matter can be classified as extensive or intensive.
- Every sample of a given substance has identical intensive properties because every sample has the same composition.
- Three states of matter are solid, liquid, and gas.
- Physical changes can be classified as reversible or irreversible.

 2.2 Mixtures
- Mixtures can be classified as heterogeneous mixtures or as homogeneous mixtures, based on the distribution of their components.
- Differences in physical properties can be used to separate mixtures.

 2.3 Elements and Compounds
- Compounds can be broken down into simpler substances by chemical means, but elements cannot.
- If the composition of a material is fixed, the material is a substance. If the composition may vary, the material is a mixture.
- Chemists use chemical symbols to represent elements, and chemical formulas to represent compounds.

2.4 Chemical Reactions
- During a chemical change, the composition of matter always changes.
- Four possible clues to chemical change include a transfer of energy, a change in color, the production of a gas, or the formation of a precipitate.
- During any chemical reaction, the mass of the products is always equal to the mass of the reactants.

Vocabulary

- chemical change (p. 48)
- chemical property (p. 53)
- chemical reaction (p. 53)
- chemical symbol (p. 51)
- compound (p. 48)
- distillation (p. 47)
- element (p. 48)
- extensive property (p. 39)
- filtration (p. 46)

- gas (p. 42)
- heterogeneous mixture (p. 45)
- homogeneous mixture (p. 45)
- intensive property (p. 39)
- law of conservation of mass (p. 55)
- liquid (p. 41)
- mass (p. 39)
- mixture (p. 44)
- phase (p. 45)

- physical change (p. 42)
- physical property (p. 40)
- precipitate (p. 54)
- product (p. 53)
- reactant (p. 53)
- solid (p. 41)
- solution (p. 45)
- substance (p. 40)
- vapor (p. 42)
- volume (p. 39)

Organizing Information

Use these terms to construct a concept map that organizes the major ideas of this chapter.

Concept Map 2 Solve the Concept Map with the help of an interactive guided tutorial.

—with **ChemASAP**

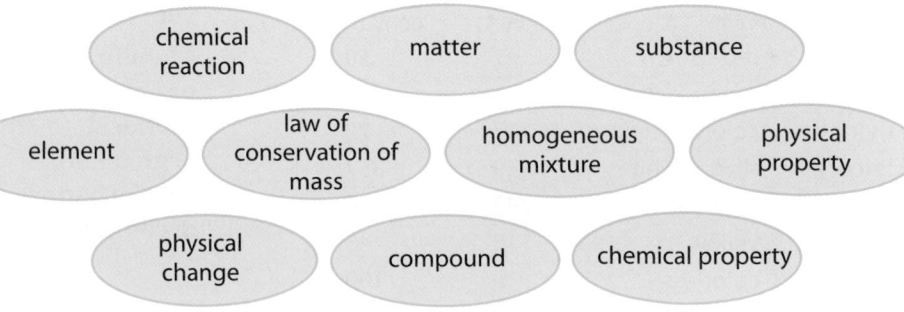

Review and Assessment

Blue questions emphasize Regents Exam content

Properties of Matter

36. Describe the difference between an extensive property and an intensive property and give an example of each.

37. List three physical properties of copper.

38. Name two physical properties that could be used to distinguish between water and ethanol.

39. Name one physical property that could *not* be used to distinguish chlorine from oxygen.

40. What is the physical state of each of these materials at room temperature?
   a. gold   b. gasoline
   c. neon   d. olive oil
   e. oxygen   f. mercury

41. Fingernail-polish remover (mostly acetone) is a liquid at room temperature. Would you describe acetone in the gaseous state as a vapor or a gas? Explain your answer.

42. Compare the arrangements of individual particles in the three states of matter.

43. Use Table 2.1 to identify four substances that undergo a physical change if the temperature is reduced from 50°C to −50°C. What is the physical change that takes place in each case?

44. Explain why sharpening a pencil is a different type of physical change than freezing water to make ice cubes.

45. Explain why mass cannot be used as a property to identify a sample of matter.

46. Is malleability an extensive property or an intensive property? Explain.

Use the data table to answer Questions 47–50.

Substance	Color	Melting point (°C)	Boiling point (°C)
Bromine	red-brown	−7	59
Chlorine	green-yellow	−101	−34
Ethanol	colorless	−117	78
Mercury	silvery-white	−39	357
Neon	colorless	−249	−246
Sulfur	yellow	115	445
Water	colorless	0	100

47. Which colorless substance is a liquid at −30°C?

48. Which colorless substance is a gas at 60°C?

49. Which substance is a solid at 7°C?

50. Which element is a liquid when mercury boils?

51. The state of a substance can change when the substance is heated or cooled. So what does it mean to say that a certain substance is a solid, liquid, or gas?

52. Use the arrangement of particles in solids and gases to explain why solids are not as easy to compress as gases.

53. Discuss the statement "A gas requires a container, but a solid is its own container."

54. Explain why this statement is false. "Because there is no change in composition during a physical change, the appearance of the substance will not change."

55. Use Table 2.1 to answer this question. The states listed in the table are those determined at 20°C and 1 atm pressure.
   a. Which substances in the table are in the liquid state at 125°C?
   b. Use the physical properties of one of these substances to explain how you figured out the answer to Question 55a.
   c. The substances in the table are listed in order of increasing melting point. How would the list differ if the substances were listed in order of increasing boiling point?

Mixtures

56. What is the difference between homogeneous mixtures and heterogeneous mixtures?

57. How many phases does a solution have? Explain your answer.

58. Classify each of the following as homogeneous or heterogeneous mixtures.
   a. chocolate-chip ice cream
   b. green ink
   c. cake batter
   d. cooking oil

59. Devise a way to separate sand from a mixture of charcoal, sand, sugar, and water.

Elements and Compounds

60. How could you distinguish an element from a compound?

61. Explain how the three items in each of the following groups relate to each other. Identify each item as an element, compound, or mixture.
   a. hydrogen, oxygen, and water
   b. nitrogen, oxygen, and air
   c. sodium, chlorine, and table salt
   d. carbon, water, and table sugar

62. What does the formula H_2O tell you about the composition of water?

63. Imagine you are standing in a kitchen and then in the middle of a park. When you view your surroundings in each location do you see mostly elements, compounds, or mixtures?

64. The mass of the elements iron and oxygen in four samples of a rust-colored substance was measured in grams (g). The amount of iron and oxygen in each sample is shown on the graph.

Mass of Elements in Samples

   a. Do you think each sample contains are the same compound? Explain.
   b. Another sample of similar material was found to contain 9.9 grams of iron and 3.4 grams of oxygen. Does this sample contain the same substance as the other four samples? Explain.

Chemical Reactions

65. Use the word equation to explain how a chemical change differs from a physical change.

$$\text{iron} + \text{sulfur} \xrightarrow{heat} \text{iron sulfide}$$

66. Which type of property *cannot* be observed without changing the composition of a substance?

67. When ammonium nitrate (NH_4NO_3) explodes, the products are nitrogen, oxygen, and water. When 40 grams of ammonium nitrate explode, 14 grams of nitrogen and 8 grams of oxygen form. How many grams of water form?

68. How are the items in each of the following pairs similar ? How are they different?
   a. copper and silver
   b. distilled water and saltwater
   c. table sugar and table salt

69. In photograph A, a coil of zinc metal is in a solution of sulfuric acid. In photograph B, a yellow solution of sodium chromate is being added to a colorless solution of silver nitrate. What clues in the photographs indicate that a chemical change is probably occurring?

A.   **B.**

Test-Taking Tip

Using Models To answer some test questions, you will be asked to use visual models. At first the models may look very similar. Decide which information will help you answer the question. The number of particles, their colors, or their shapes may or may not be important.

Regents Practice Exam

Part A

For each statement or question write the number of the word or expression that, of those given, best completes the statement or answers the question.

1. Which of the following choices is a physical change?
   (1) paper being shredded
   (2) steel rusting
   (3) charcoal burning
   (4) a newspaper yellowing in the sun

2. Which phrase best describes an apple?
   (1) heterogeneous mixture
   (2) homogeneous compound
   (3) heterogeneous substance
   (4) homogeneous mixture

3. Which element is paired with the wrong symbol?
   (1) sulfur, S
   (2) potassium, P
   (3) nitrogen, N
   (4) calcium, Ca

4. Which of the following properties would be the same for salt and table sugar?
   (1) boiling point
   (2) melting point
   (3) density
   (4) color

5. The state of matter characterized by a definite volume and an indefinite shape is a
   (1) solid
   (2) liquid
   (3) mixture
   (4) gas

The lettered choices below refer to Questions 6–9. A lettered choice may be used once, more than once, or not at all.

   (1) compound
   (2) heterogeneous mixture
   (3) element
   (4) homogeneous mixture

Which description correctly identifies each of the following materials?

6. air

7. carbon monoxide

8. zinc

9. mushroom pizza

Part B-1

For each statement or question write the number of the word or expression that, of those given, best completes the statement or answers the question.

10. Which of the following choices is an example of a substance?
    (1) copper
    (2) saltwater
    (3) soup
    (4) soil

11. The air in a city probably contains certain gases that air on the top of a mountain would not contain. From this information, you can conclude that air is
    (1) a compound
    (2) an element
    (3) a mixture
    (4) a substance

12. Which of the following statements about a newspaper gives an example of a chemical property of the newspaper?
    (1) The color is black and white.
    (2) The texture is smooth.
    (3) It can be cut into pieces.
    (4) It will burn.

13. Magnesium burns with a white-hot flame. Which of the following statements is true about this chemical reaction?
    (1) The magnesium is the same before and after the reaction.
    (2) A physical change occurs.
    (3) The mass of the magnesium and the oxygen equals the mass of the compound formed.
    (4) The product has less mass than the magnesium and oxygen.

Use the particle diagrams to answer Question 14.

14. The species in diagram A react. Use the law of conservation of mass to determine which choice represents the reaction products.

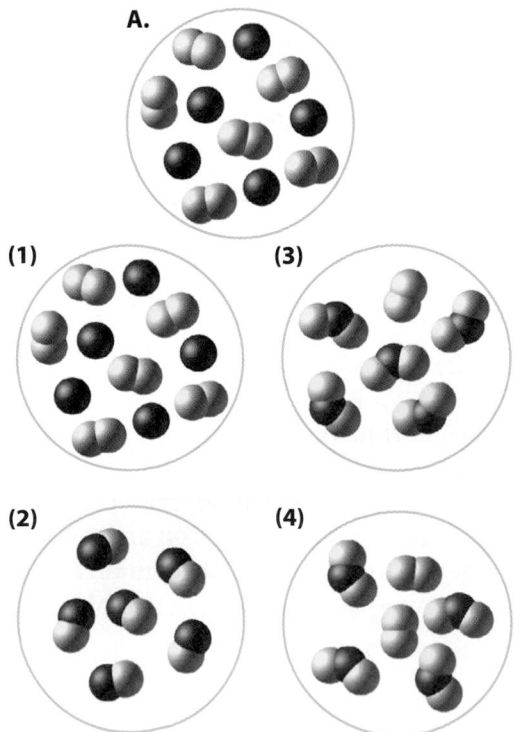

A.

(1)

(3)

(2)

(4)

Part B-2

Answer each of the following questions.
Use the data table to answer Questions 15–18.

Mass of magnesium (g)	Mass of oxygen (g)	Mass of magnesium oxide (g)
5.0	3.3	8.3
6.5	(a)	10.8
13.6	9.0	(b)
(c)	12.5	31.5

15. Magnesium metal burns vigorously in oxygen to produce the compound magnesium oxide. Use the law of conservation of mass to identify the masses labeled (a), (b), and (c) in the table.

16. Use the data in the completed table to construct a graph with mass of magnesium on the *x*-axis and mass of magnesium oxide on the *y*-axis.

17. Using the graph created in the previous question, determine the number of grams of magnesium oxide formed when 8.0 g of magnesium are burned.

18. How many grams of magnesium and oxygen react to form 20.0 g of magnesium oxide?

19. Assume the following substances are all at 40°C. As the temperature drops, which substance will freeze first? Which will be the last to freeze? Use a table of properties of elements to help you.
a. water   **b.** mercury   **c.** gallium

20. When powdered iron is left exposed to the air, it forms iron(III) oxide, or rust. Explain why the mass of the rust is greater than the mass of the powdered iron.

21. Identify each of the following items as a mixture or compound. Classify the mixtures as homogeneous or heterogeneous.
a. raw egg   **c.** ice
b. gasoline   **d.** blood

22. Classify the following properties of the element silicon as chemical or physical properties.
a. blue-gray color
b. brittle
c. doesn't dissolve in water
d. melts at 1410°C
e. reacts vigorously with fluorine

23. Name the elements found in each of the following compounds.

a. ammonia (NH_3)
b. potassium oxide (K_2O)
c. sucrose ($C_{12}H_{22}O_{11}$)
d. calcium sulfide (CaS)

24. Classify each of the following as a physical or chemical change. For any chemical change, list at least one clue to support your answer.
a. A copper wire is bent.
b. Charcoal burns in a grill.
c. Bread dough rises when yeast is added.
d. Sugar dissolves in water.

Part C

Answer each of the following questions.

25. What is the goal of a distillation? Describe briefly how this goal is accomplished.

26. Five elements make up 97.9% of the mass of the human body. These elements are oxygen (64.8%), carbon (18.1%), hydrogen (10.0%), nitrogen (3.1%), and calcium (1.9%). Compare these data with those in the pie graph below, which shows the five most abundant elements by mass in Earth's crust, oceans, and atmosphere.

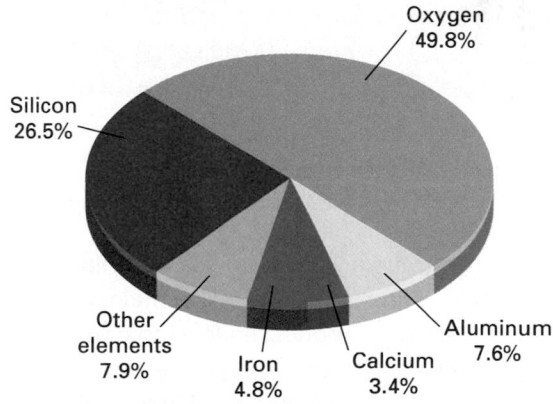

a. Which elements are abundant both in the human body and Earth's crust, oceans, and atmosphere?
b. Which elements are abundant in Earth's crust, oceans, and atmosphere, but not in the human body?
c. Would you expect the compounds found in the human body to be the same as or different from those found in rocks, seawater, and air? Use the data to explain your answer.

Milliliters (mL) are a common metric unit of volume.

INQUIRY Activity

Exploring Density

Materials

three beakers, a 250 mL graduated cylinder, a colorless and clear cylindrical container, shampoo, water, rubbing alcohol, red food coloring, a medicine dropper, a spoon or stirring rod, and small solid objects (such as a paper clip, plastic soda-bottle cap, aluminum nail, or piece of cork).

Procedure

1. Pour about 250 mL each of shampoo, water, and rubbing alcohol into separate beakers.

2. Stir a drop of food coloring into the rubbing alcohol and the shampoo.

3. Carefully pour each liquid (in the following order: shampoo, water, rubbing alcohol) down the inside of the colorless cylindrical container to a depth of 2.5 cm (about 1 in.).

4. Record the positions of the three layers of liquids.

5. Gently add each small solid object to the layered liquids and record its resting location.

Think About It

1. Propose an explanation for the order of layering of the liquids.

2. Do you think it would make any difference if you added the liquids in a different order? Why or why not?

3.1 Measurements and Their Uncertainty

 New York Standards: M3.1b, S3.3b, 6.3

Connecting to Your World

On January 4, 2004, the Mars Exploration Rover Spirit landed on Mars. Equipped with five scientific instruments and a rock abrasion tool (shown at left), Spirit was sent to examine the Martian surface around Gusev Crater, a wide basin that may have once held a lake. Each day of its mission, Spirit recorded measurements for analysis. This data helped scientists learn about the geology and climate on Mars. All measurements have some uncertainty. In the chemistry laboratory, you must strive for accuracy and precision in your measurements.

Guide for Reading

 Key Concepts
- How do measurements relate to science?
- How do you evaluate accuracy and precision?
- Why must measurements be reported to the correct number of significant figures?
- How does the precision of a calculated answer compare to the precision of the measurements used to obtain it?

Vocabulary

measurement
scientific notation
accuracy
precision
accepted value
experimental value
error
percent error
significant figures

Reading Strategy

Building Vocabulary As you read, write a definition of each key term in your own words.

Using and Expressing Measurements

Your height (67 inches), your weight (134 pounds), and the speed you drive on the highway (65 miles/hour) are some familiar examples of measurements. A **measurement** is a quantity that has both a number and a unit. Everyone makes and uses measurements. For instance, you decide how to dress in the morning based on the temperature outside. If you were baking cookies, you would measure the volumes of the ingredients as indicated in the recipe.

Such everyday situations are similar to those faced by scientists. **Measurements are fundamental to the experimental sciences. For that reason, it is important to be able to make measurements and to decide whether a measurement is correct.** The units typically used in the sciences are those of the International System of Measurements (SI).

In chemistry, you will often encounter very large or very small numbers. A single gram of hydrogen, for example, contains approximately 602,000,000,000,000,000,000,000 hydrogen atoms. The mass of an atom of gold is 0.000 000 000 000 000 000 000 327 gram. Writing and using such large and small numbers is very cumbersome. You can work more easily with these numbers by writing them in scientific, or exponential, notation.

In **scientific notation,** a given number is written as the product of two numbers: a coefficient and 10 raised to a power. For example, the number 602,000,000,000,000,000,000,000 written in scientific notation is 6.02×10^{23}. The coefficient in this number is 6.02. In scientific notation, the coefficient is always a number equal to or greater than one and less than ten. The power of 10, or exponent, in this example is 23. Figure 3.1 illustrates how to express the number of stars in a galaxy by using scientific notation. For more practice on writing numbers in scientific notation, refer to page R56 of Appendix C.

$$200,000,000,000. = 2 \times 10^{11}$$

Decimal moves 11 places to the left.   Exponent is 11

Figure 3.1 Expressing very large numbers, such as the estimated number of stars in a galaxy, is easier if scientific notation is used.

Figure 3.2 The distribution of darts illustrates the difference between accuracy and precision. **a** Good accuracy and good precision: The darts are close to the bull's-eye and to one another. **b** Poor accuracy and good precision: The darts are far from the bull's-eye but close to one another. **c** Poor accuracy and poor precision: The darts are far from the bull's-eye and from one another.

a	**b**	**c**
Good accuracy Good precision	Poor accuracy Good precision	Poor accuracy Poor precision

Accuracy, Precision, and Error

Your success in the chemistry lab and in many of your daily activities depends on your ability to make reliable measurements. Ideally, measurements should be both correct and reproducible.

Accuracy and Precision Correctness and reproducibility relate to the concepts of accuracy and precision, two words that mean the same thing to many people. In chemistry, however, their meanings are quite different. **Accuracy** is a measure of how close a measurement comes to the actual or true value of whatever is measured. **Precision** is a measure of how close a series of measurements are to one another. ➤ **To evaluate the accuracy of a measurement, the measured value must be compared to the correct value. To evaluate the precision of a measurement, you must compare the values of two or more repeated measurements.**

Darts on a dartboard illustrate accuracy and precision in measurement. Let the bull's-eye of the dartboard represent the true, or correct, value of what you are measuring. The closeness of a dart to the bull's-eye corresponds to the degree of accuracy. The closer it comes to the bull's-eye, the more accurately the dart was thrown. The closeness of several darts to one another corresponds to the degree of precision. The closer together the darts are, the greater the precision and the reproducibility.

Look at Figure 3.2 as you consider the following outcomes.

a. All of the darts land close to the bull's-eye and to one another. Closeness to the bull's-eye means that the degree of accuracy is great. Each dart in the bull's-eye corresponds to an accurate measurement of a value. Closeness of the darts to one another indicates high precision.

b. All of the darts land close to one another but far from the bull's-eye. The precision is high because of the closeness of grouping and thus the high level of reproducibility. The results are inaccurate, however, because of the distance of the darts from the bull's-eye.

c. The darts land far from one another and from the bull's-eye. The results are both inaccurate and imprecise.

 ✓**Checkpoint** *How does accuracy differ from precision?*

Determining Error Note that an individual measurement may be accurate or inaccurate. Suppose you use a thermometer to measure the boiling point of pure water at standard pressure. The thermometer reads 99.1°C. You probably know that the true or accepted value of the boiling point of pure water under these conditions is actually 100.0°C. There is a difference between the **accepted value,** which is the correct value based on reliable references, and the **experimental value,** the value measured in the lab. The difference between the accepted value and the experimental value is called the **error.**

$$\text{Error} = \text{experimental value} - \text{accepted value}$$

Error can be positive or negative depending on whether the experimental value is greater than or less than the accepted value.

For the boiling-point measurement, the error is 99.1°C − 100.0°C, or −0.9° C. The magnitude of the error shows the amount by which the experimental value differs from the accepted value. Often, it is useful to calculate the relative error, or percent error. The **percent error** is the absolute value of the error divided by the accepted value, multiplied by 100%.

$$\text{Percent error} = \frac{|\text{error}|}{\text{accepted value}} \times 100\%$$

Using the absolute value of the error means that the percent error will always be a positive value. For the boiling-point measurement, the percent error is calculated as follows.

$$\begin{aligned}
\text{Percent error} &= \frac{|99.1°C - 100.0°C|}{100.0°C} \times 100\% \\
&= \frac{0.9°C}{100.0°C} \times 100\% \\
&= 0.009 \times 100\% \\
&= 0.9\%
\end{aligned}$$

Just because a measuring device works doesn't necessarily mean that it is accurate. As Figure 3.3 shows, a weighing scale that does not read zero when nothing is on it is bound to yield error. In order to weigh yourself accurately, you must first make sure that the scale is zeroed.

Word *Origins*

Percent comes from the Latin words *per,* meaning "by" or "through," and *centum,* meaning "100." **What do you think the phrase *per annum* means?**

Figure 3.3 The scale below has not been properly zeroed, so the reading obtained for the person's weight is inaccurate. There is a difference between the person's correct weight and the measured value. **Calculating *What is the percent error of a measured value of 114 lb if the person's actual weight is 107 lb?***

Figure 3.4 The precision of a weighing scale depends on how finely it is calibrated.

Significant Figures in Measurements

Supermarkets often provide scales like the one in Figure 3.4. Customers use these scales to measure the weight of produce that is priced per pound. If you use a scale that is calibrated in 0.1-lb intervals, you can easily read the scale to the nearest tenth of a pound. With such a scale, however, you can also estimate the weight to the nearest hundredth of a pound by noting the position of the pointer between calibration marks.

Suppose you estimate a weight that lies between 2.4 lb and 2.5 lb to be 2.46 lb. The number in this estimated measurement has three digits. The first two digits in the measurement (2 and 4) are known with certainty. But the rightmost digit (6) has been estimated and involves some uncertainty. These three reported digits all convey useful information, however, and are called significant figures. The **significant figures** in a measurement include all of the digits that are known, plus a last digit that is estimated. ⟶ **Measurements must always be reported to the correct number of significant figures because calculated answers often depend on the number of significant figures in the values used in the calculation.**

Instruments differ in the number of significant figures that can be obtained from their use and thus in the precision of measurements. The three meter sticks in Figure 3.5 can be used to make successively more precise measurements of the board.

Textbook

Animation 2 See how the accuracy of a calculated result depends on the sensitivity of the measuring instruments.

—with ChemASAP

Rules for determining whether a digit in a measured value is significant:

1 Every nonzero digit in a reported measurement is assumed to be significant. The measurements 24.7 meters, 0.743 meter, and 714 meters each express a measure of length to three significant figures.

2 Zeros appearing between nonzero digits are significant. The measurements 7003 meters, 40.79 meters, and 1.503 meters each have four significant figures.

3 Leftmost zeros appearing in front of nonzero digits are not significant. They act as placeholders. The measurements 0.0071 meter, 0.42 meter, and 0.000 099 meter each have only two significant figures. The zeros to the left are not significant. By writing the measurements in scientific notation, you can eliminate such placeholding zeros: in this case, 7.1×10^{-3} meter, 4.2×10^{-1} meter, and 9.9×10^{-5} meter.

4 Zeros at the end of a number and to the right of a decimal point are always significant. The measurements 43.00 meters, 1.010 meters, and 9.000 meters each have four significant figures.

ⓐ Measured length = 0.6 m

ⓑ Measured length = 0.61 m

ⓒ Measured length = 0.607 m

Figure 3.5 Three differently calibrated meter sticks are used to measure the length of a board. **ⓐ** A meter stick calibrated in a 1-m interval. **ⓑ** A meter stick calibrated in 0.1-m intervals. **ⓒ** A meter stick calibrated in 0.01-m intervals. **Measuring** *How many significant figures are reported in each measurement?*

5 Zeros at the rightmost end of a measurement that lie to the left of an understood decimal point are not significant if they serve as place-holders to show the magnitude of the number. The zeros in the measurements 300 meters, 7000 meters, and 27,210 meters are not significant. The numbers of significant figures in these values are one, one, and four, respectively. If such zeros were known measured values, however, then they would be significant. For example, if all of the zeros in the measurement 300 meters were significant, writing the value in scientific notation as 3.00×10^2 meters makes it clear that these zeros are significant.

6 There are two situations in which numbers have an unlimited number of significant figures. The first involves counting. If you count 23 people in your classroom, then there are exactly 23 people, and this value has an unlimited number of significant figures. The second situation involves exactly defined quantities such as those found within a system of measurement. When, for example, you write 60 min = 1 hr, or 100 cm = 1 m, each of these numbers has an unlimited number of significant figures. As you shall soon see, exact quantities do not affect the process of rounding an answer to the correct number of significant figures.

Counting Significant Figures in Measurements

How many significant figures are in each measurement?

a. 123 m
b. 40,506 mm
c. 9.8000×10^4 m
d. 22 meter sticks
e. 0.070 80 m
f. 98,000 m

① Analyze *Identify the relevant concepts.*

The location of each zero in the measurement and the location of the decimal point determine which of the rules apply for determining significant figures.

② Solve *Apply the concepts to this problem.*

All nonzero digits are significant (rule 1). Use rules 2 through 6 to determine if the zeros are significant.

a. three (rule 1)
b. five (rule 2)
c. five (rule 4)
d. unlimited (rule 6)
e. four (rules 2, 3, 4)
f. two (rule 5)

Practice Problems

1. Count the significant figures in each length.
   a. 0.057 30 meters
   b. 8765 meters
   c. 0.000 73 meters
   d. 40.007 meters

2. How many significant figures are in each measurement?
   a. 143 grams
   b. 0.074 meter
   c. 8.750×10^{-2} gram
   d. 1.072 meter

Interactive Textbook

Problem-Solving 3.2 Solve Problem 2 with the help of an interactive guided tutorial.

— with **ChemASAP**

Significant Figures in Calculations

Suppose you use a calculator to find the area of a floor that measures 7.7 meters by 5.4 meters. The calculator would give an answer of 41.58 square meters. The calculated area is expressed to four significant figures. However, each of the measurements used in the calculation is expressed to only two significant figures. So the answer must also be reported to two significant figures (42 m²). 🔑 **In general, a calculated answer cannot be more precise than the least precise measurement from which it was calculated.** The calculated value must be rounded to make it consistent with the measurements from which it was calculated.

Rounding To round a number, you must first decide how many significant figures the answer should have. This decision depends on the given measurements and on the mathematical process used to arrive at the answer. Once you know the number of significant figures your answer should have, round to that many digits, counting from the left. If the digit immediately to the right of the last significant digit is less than 5, it is simply dropped and the value of the last significant digit stays the same. If the digit in question is 5 or greater, the value of the digit in the last significant place is increased by 1.

✓**Checkpoint** *Why must a calculated answer generally be rounded?*

SAMPLE PROBLEM 3.1

Rounding Measurements

Round off each measurement to the number of significant figures shown in parentheses. Write the answers in scientific notation.

a. 314.721 meters (four)
b. 0.001 775 meter (two)
c. 8792 meters (two)

1 **Analyze** *Identify the relevant concepts.*

Round off each measurement to the number of significant figures indicated. Then apply the rules for expressing numbers in scientific notation.

2 **Solve** *Apply the concepts to this problem.*

Count from the left and apply the rule to the digit immediately to the right of the digit to which you are rounding. The arrow points to the digit immediately following the last significant digit.

a. 314.721 meters
　　　　↑
　　　2 is less than 5, so you do not round up.
　　　314.7 meters = 3.147×10^2 meters

b. 0.001 775 meter
　　　　　　↑
　　　7 is greater than 5, so round up.
　　　0.0018 meter = 1.8×10^{-3} meter

c. 8792 meters
　　↑
　　9 is greater than 5, so round up
　　8800 meters = 8.8×10^3 meters

3 **Evaluate** *Do the results make sense?*

The rules for rounding and for writing numbers in scientific notation have been correctly applied.

Math **Handbook**

For help with scientific notation, go to page R56.

Practice Problems

3. Round each measurement to three significant figures. Write your answers in scientific notation.
　a. 87.073 meters
　b. 4.3621×10^8 meters
　c. 0.01552 meter
　d. 9009 meters
　e. 1.7777×10^{-3} meter
　f. 629.55 meters

4. Round each measurement in Practice Problem 3 to one significant figure. Write each of your answers in scientific notation.

Problem-Solving 3.3 Solve Problem 3 with the help of an interactive guided tutorial.

————— with **ChemASAP**

Addition and Subtraction The answer to an addition or subtraction calculation should be rounded to the same number of decimal places (not digits) as the measurement with the least number of decimal places. Work through Sample Problem 3.2 below which provides an example of rounding in an addition calculation.

SAMPLE PROBLEM 3.2

Significant Figures in Addition

Calculate the sum of the three measurements. Give the answer to the correct number of significant figures.

$$12.52 \text{ meters} + 349.0 \text{ meters} + 8.24 \text{ meters}$$

❶ Analyze *Identify the relevant concepts.*
Calculate the sum and then analyze each measurement to determine the number of decimal places required in the answer.

❷ Solve *Apply the concepts to this problem.*
Align the decimal points and add the numbers. Round the answer to match the measurement with the least number of decimal places.

$$
\begin{array}{rl}
12.52 & \text{meters} \\
349.0 & \text{meters} \\
+\quad 8.24 & \text{meters} \\
\hline
369.76 & \text{meters}
\end{array}
$$

The second measurement (349.0 meters) has the least number of digits (one) to the right of the decimal point. Thus the answer must be rounded to one digit after the decimal point. The answer is rounded to 369.8 meters, or 3.698×10^2 meters.

❸ Evaluate *Does the result make sense?*
The mathematical operation has been correctly carried out and the resulting answer is reported to the correct number of decimal places.

Practice Problems

5. Perform each operation. Express your answers to the correct number of significant figures.
  a. 61.2 meters + 9.35 meters + 8.6 meters
  b. 9.44 meters − 2.11 meters
  c. 1.36 meters + 10.17 meters
  d. 34.61 meters − 17.3 meters

6. Find the total mass of three diamonds that have masses of 14.2 grams, 8.73 grams, and 0.912 gram.

Math Handbook

For help with significant figures, go to page R59.

ⓘnteractive Textbook

Problem-Solving 3.6 Solve Problem 6 with the help of an interactive guided tutorial.

— with **ChemASAP**

Multiplication and Division In calculations involving multiplication and division, you need to round the answer to the same number of significant figures as the measurement with the least number of significant figures. The position of the decimal point has nothing to do with the rounding process when multiplying and dividing measurements. The position of the decimal point is important only in rounding the answers of addition or subtraction problems.

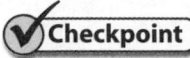 **Checkpoint** *How many significant figures must you round an answer to when performing multiplication or division?*

SAMPLE PROBLEM 3.3

Significant Figures in Multiplication and Division

Perform the following operations. Give the answers to the correct number of significant figures.
a. 7.55 meters $\times$ 0.34 meter
b. 2.10 meters $\times$ 0.70 meter
c. 2.4526 meters $\div$ 8.4

1 Analyze *Identify the relevant concepts.*
Perform the required math operation and then analyze each of the original numbers to determine the correct number of significant figures required in the answer.

2 Solve *Apply the concepts to this problem.*
Round the answers to match the measurement with the least number of significant figures.
a. 7.55 meters $\times$ 0.34 meter = 2.567 (meter)^2 = 2.6 meters^2
(0.34 meter has two significant figures)
b. 2.10 meters $\times$ 0.70 meter = 1.47 (meter)^2 = 1.5 meters^2
(0.70 meter has two significant figures)
c. 2.4526 meters $\div$ 8.4 = 0.291 976 meter = 0.29 meter
(8.4 has two significant figures)

3 Evaluate *Do the results make sense?*
The mathematical operations have been performed correctly, and the resulting answers are reported to the correct number of places.

> **Math** **Handbook**
>
> For help with using a calculator, go to page R62.

Practice Problems

7. Solve each problem. Give your answers to the correct number of significant figures and in scientific notation.
a. 8.3 meters $\times$ 2.22 meters
b. 8432 meters $\div$ 12.5
c. 35.2 seconds $\times \dfrac{1\ \text{minute}}{60\ \text{seconds}}$

8. Calculate the volume of a warehouse that has inside dimensions of 22.4 meters by 11.3 meters by 5.2 meters. (Volume = $l \times w \times h$)

Interactive Textbook

Problem-Solving 3.8 Solve Problem 8 with the help of an interactive guided tutorial.

— with **ChemASAP**

Accuracy and Precision

Purpose
To measure the dimensions of an object as accurately and precisely as possible and to apply rules for rounding answers calculated from the measurements.

Materials
- 3 inch × 5 inch index card
- metric ruler

Procedure
1. Use a metric ruler to measure in centimeters the length and width of an index card as accurately and precisely as you can. The hundredths place in your measurement should be estimated.

2. Calculate the perimeter [2 × (length + width)] and the area (length × width) of the index card. Write both your unrounded answers and your correctly rounded answers on the chalkboard.

Analyze and Conclude
1. How many significant figures are in your measurements of length and of width?

2. How do your measurements compare with those of your classmates?

3. How many significant figures are in your calculated value for the area? In your calculated value for the perimeter? Do your rounded answers have as many significant figures as your classmates' measurements?

4. Assume that the correct (accurate) length and width of the card are 12.70 cm and 7.62 cm, respectively. Calculate the percent error for each of your two measurements.

3.1 Section Assessment

9. **Key Concept** How do measurements relate to experimental science?

10. **Key Concept** How are accuracy and precision evaluated?

11. **Key Concept** Why must a given measurement always be reported to the correct number of significant figures?

12. **Key Concept** How does the precision of a calculated answer compare to the precision of the measurements used to obtain it?

13. A technician experimentally determined the boiling point of octane to be 124.1°C. The actual boiling point of octane is 125.7°C. Calculate the error and the percent error.

14. Determine the number of significant figures in each of the following.
   a. 11 soccer players
   b. 0.070 020 meter
   c. 10,800 meters
   d. 5.00 cubic meters

15. Solve the following and express each answer in scientific notation and to the correct number of significant figures.
   a. $(5.3 \times 10^4) + (1.3 \times 10^4)$
   b. $(7.2 \times 10^{-4}) \div (1.8 \times 10^3)$
   c. $10^4 \times 10^{-3} \times 10^6$
   d. $(9.12 \times 10^{-1}) - (4.7 \times 10^{-2})$
   e. $(5.4 \times 10^4) \times (3.5 \times 10^9)$

Writing Activity

Explanatory Paragraph Explain the differences between the accuracy, precision, and error of a measurement.

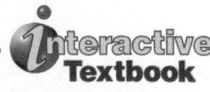

Assessment 3.1 Test yourself on the concepts in Section 3.1.

—— with **ChemASAP**

3.2 The International System of Units

Connecting to Your World

"Are we there yet?" You may have asked this question during a long road trip with family or friends. To find out how much farther you have to go, you can read the roadside signs that list destinations and their distances. In the signs shown here, however, the distances are listed as numbers with no units attached. Is Carrieton 44 kilometers or 44 miles away? Without the units, you can't be sure. When you make a measurement, you must assign the correct units to the numerical value. Without the units, it is impossible to communicate the measurement clearly to others.

Measuring with SI Units

All measurements depend on units that serve as reference standards. The standards of measurement used in science are those of the metric system. The metric system is important because of its simplicity and ease of use. All metric units are based on multiples of 10. As a result, you can convert between units easily. The metric system was originally established in France in 1795. The **International System of Units** (abbreviated **SI,** after the French name, *Le Système International d'Unités*) is a revised version of the metric system. The SI was adopted by international agreement in 1960. There are seven SI base units, which are listed in Table 3.1. From these base units, all other SI units of measurement can be derived. **The five SI base units commonly used by chemists are the meter, the kilogram, the kelvin, the second, and the mole.**

All measured quantities can be reported in SI units. Sometimes, however, non-SI units are preferred for convenience or for practical reasons. In this textbook you will learn about both SI and non-SI units.

Guide for Reading

Key Concepts
- Which five SI base units do chemists commonly use?
- What metric units are commonly used to measure length, volume, mass, temperature, and energy?

Vocabulary

International System of Units (SI)

meter (m)

liter (L)

kilogram (kg)

gram (g)

weight

temperature

Celsius scale

Kelvin scale

absolute zero

energy

joule (J)

calorie (cal)

Reading Strategy

Summarizing As you read about SI units, summarize the main ideas in the text that follows the red and blue headings.

Table 3.1

SI Base Units		
Quantity	**SI base unit**	**Symbol**
Length	meter	m
Mass	kilogram	kg
Temperature	kelvin	K
Time	second	s
Amount of substance	mole	mol
Luminous intensity	candela	cd
Electric current	ampere	A

Table 3.2

Commonly Used Metric Prefixes		
Prefix	**Meaning**	**Factor**
mega (M)	1 million times larger than the unit it precedes	10^6
kilo (k)	1000 times larger than the unit it precedes	10^3
deci (d)	10 times smaller than the unit it precedes	10^{-1}
centi (c)	100 times smaller than the unit it precedes	10^{-2}
milli (m)	1000 times smaller than the unit it precedes	10^{-3}
micro (μ)	1 million times smaller than the unit it precedes	10^{-6}
nano (n)	1000 million times smaller than the unit it precedes	10^{-9}
pico (p)	1 trillion times smaller than the unit it precedes	10^{-12}

Units and Quantities

As you already know, you don't measure length in kilograms or mass in centimeters. Different quantities require different units. Before you make a measurement, you must be familiar with the units corresponding to the quantity that you are trying to measure.

Units of Length Size is an important property of matter. In SI, the basic unit of length, or linear measure, is the **meter (m)**. All measurements of length can be expressed in meters. (The length of a page in this book is about one-fourth of a meter.) For very large and very small lengths, however, it may be more convenient to use a unit of length that has a prefix. Table 3.2 lists the prefixes in common use. For example, the prefix *milli-* means 1/1000 (one-thousandth), so a millimeter (mm) is 1/1000 of a meter, or 0.001 m. A hyphen (-) measures about 1 mm.

For large distances, it is usually most appropriate to express measurements in kilometers (km). The prefix *kilo-* means 1000, so 1 km equals 1000 m. A standard marathon distance race of about 42,000 m is more conveniently expressed as 42 km (42 × 1000 m). **⊙→ Common metric units of length include the centimeter, meter, and kilometer.** Table 3.3 summarizes the relationships among metric units of length.

**Length of
5 city blocks ≈ 1km**

Table 3.3

Metric Units of Length		
Unit	**Relationship**	**Example**
Kilometer (km)	1 km = 10^3 m	length of about five city blocks ≈ 1 km
Meter (m)	base unit	height of doorknob from the floor ≈ 1 m
Decimeter (dm)	10^1 dm = 1 m	diameter of large orange ≈ 1 dm
Centimeter (cm)	10^2 cm = 1 m	width of shirt button ≈ 1 cm
Millimeter (mm)	10^3 mm = 1 m	thickness of dime ≈ 1 mm
Micrometer (μm)	10^6 μm = 1 m	diameter of bacterial cell ≈ 1 μm
Nanometer (nm)	10^9 nm = 1 m	thickness of RNA molecule ≈ 1 nm

Units of Volume The space occupied by any sample of matter is called its volume. You calculate the volume of any cubic or rectangular solid by multiplying its length by its width by its height. The unit for volume is thus derived from units of length. The SI unit of volume is the amount of space occupied by a cube that is 1 m along each edge. This volume is a cubic meter (m^3). An automatic dishwasher has a volume of about 1 m^3.

A more convenient unit of volume for everyday use is the liter, a non-SI unit. A **liter (L)** is the volume of a cube that is 10 centimeters (10 cm) along each edge (10 cm × 10 cm × 10 cm = 1000 cm^3 = 1 L). A decimeter (dm) is equal to 10 cm, so 1 L is also equal to 1 cubic decimeter (dm^3). A smaller non-SI unit of volume is the milliliter (mL); 1 mL is 1/1000 of a liter. Thus there are 1000 mL in 1 L. Because 1 L is defined as 1000 cm^3, 1 mL and 1 cm^3 are the same volume. The units milliliter and cubic centimeter are thus used interchangeably. 🗝 **Common metric units of volume include the liter, milliliter, cubic centimeter, and microliter.** Table 3.4 summarizes the relationships among these units of volume.

There are many devices for measuring liquid volumes, including graduated cylinders, pipets, burets, volumetric flasks, and syringes. Note that the volume of any solid, liquid, or gas will change with temperature (although the change is much more dramatic for gases). Consequently, accurate volume-measuring devices are calibrated at a given temperature—usually 20 degrees Celsius (20°C), which is about normal room temperature.

Figure 3.6 These photographs above give you some idea of the relative sizes of some different units of volume. **ⓐ** The volume of 20 drops of liquid from a medicine dropper is approximately 1 mL. **ⓑ** A sugar cube is 1 cm on each edge and has a volume of 1 cm^3. Note that 1 mL is the same as 1 cm^3. **ⓒ** A gallon of milk has about twice the volume of a 2-L bottle of soda.
Calculating *How many cubic centimeters are in 2 liters?*

✓Checkpoint *What is the SI unit of volume?*

Table 3.4		
Metric Units of Volume		
Unit	**Relationship**	**Example**
Liter (L)	base unit	quart of milk ≈ 1 L
Milliliter (mL)	10^3 mL = 1 L	20 drops of water ≈ 1 mL
Cubic centimeter (cm^3)	1 cm^3 = 1 mL	cube of sugar ≈ 1 cm^3
Microliter (μL)	10^6 μL = 1 L	crystal of table salt ≈ 1 μL

Table 3.5

Metric Units of Mass		
Unit	**Relationship**	**Example**
Kilogram (kg) (base unit)	$1 \text{ kg} = 10^3 \text{ g}$	small textbook $\approx 1 \text{ kg}$
Gram (g)	$1 \text{ g} = 10^{-3} \text{ kg}$	dollar bill $\approx 1 \text{ g}$
Milligram (mg)	$10^3 \text{ mg} = 1 \text{ g}$	ten grains of salt $\approx 1 \text{ mg}$
Microgram (μg)	$10^6 \, \mu\text{g} = 1 \text{ g}$	particle of baking powder $\approx 1 \, \mu\text{g}$

Units of Mass The mass of an object is measured in comparison to a standard mass of 1 **kilogram (kg),** which is the basic SI unit of mass. A kilogram was originally defined as the mass of 1 L of liquid water at 4°C. A cube of water at 4°C measuring 10 cm on each edge would have a volume of 1 L and a mass of 1000 grams (g), or 1 kg. A **gram (g)** is 1/1000 of a kilogram; the mass of 1 cm³ of water at 4°C is 1 g. 🔑 **Common metric units of mass include the kilogram, gram, milligram, and microgram.** The relationships among units of mass are shown in Table 3.5.

You can use a platform balance to measure the mass of an object. The object is placed on one side of the balance, and standard masses are added to the other side until the balance beam is level. The unknown mass is equal to the sum of the standard masses. Laboratory balances range from very sensitive instruments with a maximum capacity of only a few milligrams to devices for measuring quantities in kilograms. An analytical balance is used to measure objects of less than 100 g and can determine mass to the nearest 0.0001 g (0.1 mg).

The astronaut shown on the surface of the moon in Figure 3.7 weighs one sixth of what he weighs on Earth. The reason for this difference is that the force of gravity on Earth is about six times what it is on the moon. **Weight** is a force that measures the pull on a given mass by gravity. Weight, a measure of force, is different from mass, which is a measure of the quantity of matter. Although the weight of an object can change with its location, its mass remains constant regardless of its location. Objects can thus become weightless, but they can never become massless.

✓**Checkpoint** *How does weight differ from mass?*

Figure 3.7 An astronaut's weight on the moon is one sixth as much as it is on Earth. Earth exerts six times the force of gravity as the moon.
Inferring *How does the astronaut's mass on the moon compare to his mass on Earth?*

Units of Temperature When you hold a glass of hot water, the glass feels hot because heat transfers from the glass to your hand. When you hold an ice cube, it feels cold because heat transfers from your hand to the ice cube. **Temperature** is a measure of how hot or cold an object is. An object's temperature determines the direction of heat transfer. When two objects at different temperatures are in contact, heat moves from the object at the higher temperature to the object at the lower temperature.

Almost all substances expand with an increase in temperature and contract as the temperature decreases. (A very important exception is water.) These properties are the basis for the common liquid-in-glass thermometer. The liquid in the thermometer expands and contracts more than the volume of the glass, producing changes in the column height of liquid. Figure 3.8 shows a few different types of thermometers.

Several temperature scales with different units have been devised. 🔑 **Scientists commonly use two equivalent units of temperature, the degree Celsius and the kelvin.** The Celsius scale of the metric system is named after the Swedish astronomer Anders Celsius (1701–1744). It uses two readily determined temperatures as reference temperature values: the freezing point and the boiling point of water. The **Celsius scale** sets the freezing point of water at 0°C and the boiling point of water at 100°C. The distance between these two fixed points is divided into 100 equal intervals, or degrees Celsius (°C).

Another temperature scale used in the physical sciences is the Kelvin, or absolute, scale. This scale is named for Lord Kelvin (1824–1907), a Scottish physicist and mathematician. On the **Kelvin scale,** the freezing point of water is 273.15 kelvins (K), and the boiling point is 373.15 K. Notice that with the Kelvin scale, the degree sign is not used. Figure 3.9 on the next page compares the Celsius and Kelvin scales. A change of one degree on the Celsius scale is equivalent to one kelvin on the Kelvin scale. The zero point on the Kelvin scale, 0 K, or **absolute zero,** is equal to −273.15°C. For problems in this text, you can round −273.15°C to −273°C. Because one degree on the Celsius scale is equivalent to one kelvin on the Kelvin scale, converting from one temperature to another is easy. You simply add or subtract 273, as shown in the following equations.

$$K = {}^\circ C + 273$$

$${}^\circ C = K - 273$$

Figure 3.8 Thermometers are used to measure temperature. ⓐ A liquid-in-glass thermometer contains alcohol or mineral spirits. ⓑ A dial thermometer contains a coiled bimetallic strip. ⓒ A Galileo thermometer contains several glass bulbs that are calibrated to sink or float depending on the temperature. The Galileo thermometer shown uses the Fahrenheit scale, which sets the freezing point of water at 32°F and the boiling point of water at 212°F.

Go Online
NSTA *SciLINKS*
For: Links on Temperature Scales
Visit: www.SciLinks.org
Web Code: cdn-1032

Figure 3.9 These thermometers show a comparison of the Celsius and Kelvin temperature scales. Note that a 1°C change on the Celsius scale is equal to a 1 K change on the Kelvin scale. **Interpreting Diagrams** *What is a change of 10 K equivalent to on the Celsius scale?*

Celsius

100 divisions

0°C
Freezing point of water
273.15 K

100°C
Boiling point of water
373.15 K

100 divisions

Kelvin

SAMPLE PROBLEM 3.4

Converting Between Temperature Scales

Normal human body temperature is 37°C. What is that temperature in kelvins?

1 Analyze *List the known and the unknown.*

Known
• Temperature in °C = 37°C

Unknown
• Temperature in K = ? K

Use the known value and the equation K = °C + 273 to calculate the temperature in kelvins.

Math ▸ Handbook

For help with algebraic equations, go to page R69.

2 Calculate *Solve for the unknown.*

Substitute the known value for the Celsius temperature into the equation and solve.

$$K = °C + 273$$
$$= 37 + 273 = 310 \text{ K}$$

3 Evaluate *Does the result make sense?*

You should expect a temperature in this range, since the freezing point of water is 273 K and the boiling point of water is 373 K; normal body temperature is between these two values.

Practice Problems

16. Liquid nitrogen boils at 77.2 K. What is this temperature in degrees Celsius?

17. The element silver melts at 960.8°C and boils at 2212°C. Express these temperatures in kelvins.

interactive Textbook

Problem-Solving 3.17
Solve Problem 17 with the help of an interactive guided tutorial.

—with ChemASAP

Units of Energy Figure 3.10 shows a house equipped with solar panels. The solar panels convert the radiant energy from the sun into electrical energy that can be used to heat water and power appliances. **Energy** is the capacity to do work or to produce heat.

Like any other quantity, energy can be measured. 🔑 **The joule and the calorie are common units of energy.** The **joule (J)** is the SI unit of energy. It is named after the English physicist James Prescott Joule (1818–1889). One **calorie (cal)** is the quantity of heat that raises the temperature of 1 g of pure water by 1°C. Conversions between joules and calories can be carried out using the following relationships.

$$1 \text{ J} = 0.2390 \text{ cal} \quad 1 \text{ cal} = 4.184 \text{ J}$$

Figure 3.10 Photoelectric panels convert solar energy into electricity.

3.2 Section Assessment

18. 🔑 **Key Concept** Which five SI base units are commonly used in chemistry?

19. 🔑 **Key Concept** Which metric units are commonly used to measure length, volume, mass, temperature, and energy?

20. Name the quantity measured by each of the seven SI base units and give the SI symbol of the unit.

21. What is the symbol and meaning of each prefix?
    a. *milli-*   b. *nano-*
    c. *deci-*   d. *centi-*

22. List the following units in order from largest to smallest: m^3, mL, cL, μL, L, dL.

23. What is the volume of a paperback book 21 cm tall, 12 cm wide, and 3.5 cm thick?

24. State the difference between mass and weight.

25. State the relationship between degrees Celsius and kelvins.

26. Surgical instruments may be sterilized by heating at 170°C for 1.5 hr. Convert 170°C to kelvins.

27. State the relationship between joules and calories.

Elements ➤ **Handbook**

Boiling Points Look up the boiling points of the first four elements in Group 7A on page R32. Convert these temperatures into kelvins.

Interactive Textbook

Assessment 3.2 Test yourself on the concepts in Section 3.2.

with **ChemASAP**

3.3 Conversion Problems

New York Standard: M1.1c

Guide for Reading

 Key Concepts

- What happens when a measurement is multiplied by a conversion factor?
- Why is dimensional analysis useful?
- What types of problems are easily solved by using dimensional analysis?

Vocabulary

conversion factor
dimensional analysis

Reading Strategy

Monitoring Your Understanding
Preview the Key Concepts, the section heads, and boldfaced terms. List three things you expect to learn. After reading, state what you learned about each item listed.

Connecting to Your World

Perhaps you have traveled abroad or are planning to do so. If so, you know—or will soon discover—that different countries have different currencies. As a tourist, exchanging money is essential to the enjoyment of your trip. After all, you must pay for your meals, hotel, transportation, gift purchases, and tickets to exhibits and events. Because each country's currency compares differently with the U.S. dollar, knowing how to convert currency units correctly is very important. Conversion problems are readily solved by a problem-solving approach called dimensional analysis.

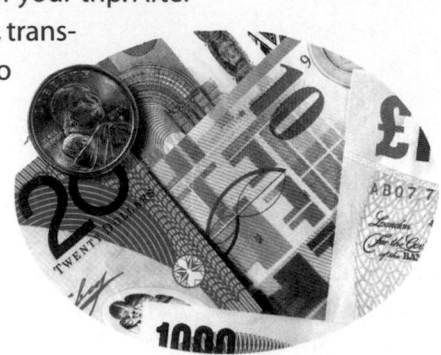

Conversion Factors

If you think about any number of everyday situations, you will realize that a quantity can usually be expressed in several different ways. For example, consider the monetary amount $1.

$$1 \text{ dollar} = 4 \text{ quarters} = 10 \text{ dimes} = 20 \text{ nickels} = 100 \text{ pennies}$$

These are all expressions, or measurements, of the same amount of money. The same thing is true of scientific quantities. For example, consider a distance that measures exactly 1 meter.

$$1 \text{ meter} = 10 \text{ decimeters} = 100 \text{ centimeters} = 1000 \text{ millimeters}$$

These are different ways to express the same length.

Whenever two measurements are equivalent, a ratio of the two measurements will equal 1, or unity. For example, you can divide both sides of the equation 1 m = 100 cm by 1 m or by 100 cm.

$$\frac{1 \text{ m}}{1 \text{ m}} = \frac{100 \text{ cm}}{1 \text{ m}} = 1 \qquad \text{or} \qquad \frac{1 \text{ m}}{100 \text{ cm}} = \frac{100 \text{ cm}}{100 \text{ cm}} = 1$$

conversion factors

A **conversion factor** is a ratio of equivalent measurements. The ratios 100 cm/1 m and 1 m/100 cm are examples of conversion factors. In a conversion factor, the measurement in the numerator (on the top) is equivalent to the measurement in the denominator (on the bottom). The conversion factors above are read "one hundred centimeters per meter" and "one meter per hundred centimeters." Figure 3.11 illustrates another way to look at the relationships in a conversion factor. Notice that the smaller number is part of the measurement with the larger unit. That is, a meter is physically larger than a centimeter. The larger number is part of the measurement with the smaller unit.

Interactive Textbook

Animation 3 Learn how to select the proper conversion factor and how to use it.

with ChemASAP

1 meter   100 centimeters

Smaller number ➡ $\dfrac{1 \; \text{m}}{100 \; \text{cm}}$ ⬅ Larger unit

Larger number ➡ ⬅ Smaller unit

A Conversion Factor

Conversion factors are useful in solving problems in which a given measurement must be expressed in some other unit of measure. ☞ **When a measurement is multiplied by a conversion factor, the numerical value is generally changed, but the actual size of the quantity measured remains the same.** For example, even though the numbers in the measurements 1 g and 10 dg (decigrams) differ, both measurements represent the same mass. In addition, conversion factors within a system of measurement are defined quantities or exact quantities. Therefore, they have an unlimited number of significant figures, and do not affect the rounding of a calculated answer.

Here are some additional examples of pairs of conversion factors written from equivalent measurements. The relationship between grams and kilograms is 1000 g = 1 kg. The conversion factors are:

$$\frac{1000 \text{ g}}{1 \text{ kg}} \quad \text{and} \quad \frac{1 \text{ kg}}{1000 \text{ g}}$$

The scale of the micrograph in Figure 3.12 is in nanometers. Using the relationship 10^9 nm = 1 m, you can write the following conversion factors.

$$\frac{10^9 \text{ nm}}{1 \text{ m}} \quad \text{and} \quad \frac{1 \text{ m}}{10^9 \text{ nm}}$$

Common volumetric units used in chemistry include the liter and the microliter. The relationship 1 L = 10^6 μL yields the following conversion factors.

$$\frac{1 \text{ L}}{10^6 \; \mu\text{L}} \quad \text{and} \quad \frac{10^6 \; \mu\text{L}}{1 \text{ L}}$$

Based on what you know about metric prefixes, you should be able to easily write conversion factors that relate equivalent metric quantities.

 Checkpoint *How many significant figures does a conversion factor within a system of measurement have?*

Figure 3.11 The two parts of a conversion factor, the numerator and the denominator, are equal.

Figure 3.12 In this computer image of atoms, distance is marked off in nanometers (nm). **Inferring** *What conversion factor would you use to convert nanometers to meters?*

Dimensional Analysis

No single method is best for solving every type of problem. Several good approaches are available, and generally one of the best is dimensional analysis. **Dimensional analysis** is a way to analyze and solve problems using the units, or dimensions, of the measurements. The best way to explain this problem-solving technique is to use it to solve an everyday situation.

SAMPLE PROBLEM 3.5

Using Dimensional Analysis

How many seconds are in a workday that lasts exactly eight hours?

1 **Analyze** *List the knowns and the unknown.*

Knowns
- time worked = 8 h
- 1 hour = 60 min
- 1 minute = 60 s

Unknown
- seconds worked = ? s

The first conversion factor must be written with the unit hours in the denominator. The second conversion factor must be written with the unit minutes in the denominator. This will provide the desired unit (seconds) in the answer.

2 **Calculate** *Solve for the unknown.*

Start with the known, 8 hours. Use the first relationship (1 hour = 60 minutes) to write a conversion factor that expresses 8 hours as minutes. The unit hours must be in the denominator so that the known unit will cancel. Then use the second conversion factor to change the unit minutes into the unit seconds. This conversion factor must have the unit minutes in the denominator. The two conversion factors can be used together in a simple overall calculation.

$$8 \text{ h} \times \frac{60 \text{ min}}{1 \text{ h}} \times \frac{60 \text{ s}}{1 \text{ min}} = 28{,}800 \text{ s}$$
$$= 2.8800 \times 10^4 \text{ s}$$

3 **Evaluate** *Does the result make sense?*

The answer has the desired unit (seconds). Since the second is a small unit of time, you should expect a large number of seconds in 8 hours. Before you do the actual arithmetic, it is a good idea to make sure that the units cancel and that the numerator and denominator of each conversion factor are equal to each other. The answer is exact since the given measurement and each of the conversion factors is exact.

Practice Problems

28. How many minutes are there in exactly one week?

29. How many seconds are in exactly a 40-hour work week?

Math **Handbook**

For help with dimensional analysis, go to page R66.

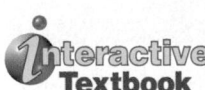
Textbook

Problem-Solving 3.28 Solve Problem 28 with the help of an interactive guided tutorial.
— with **ChemASAP**

There is usually more than one way to solve a problem. When you first read Sample Problem 3.5, you may have thought about different and equally correct ways to approach and solve the problem. Some problems are easily worked with simple algebra. ☞ **Dimensional analysis provides you with an alternative approach to problem solving.** In either case, you should choose the problem-solving method that works best.

SAMPLE PROBLEM 3.6

Using Dimensional Analysis

The directions for an experiment ask each student to measure 1.84 g of copper (Cu) wire. The only copper wire available is a spool with a mass of 50.0 g. How many students can do the experiment before the copper runs out?

1 **Analyze** *List the knowns and the unknown.*

Knowns

• mass of copper available = 50.0 g Cu

• each student needs 1.84 grams of copper, or $\dfrac{1.84 \text{ g Cu}}{\text{student}}$.

Unknown

• number of students = ?

From the known mass of copper, calculate the number of students that can do the experiment by using the appropriate conversion factor. The desired conversion is mass of copper $\longrightarrow$ number of students.

2 **Calculate** *Solve for the unknown.*

Because students is the desired unit for the answer, the conversion factor should be written with students in the numerator. Multiply the mass of copper by the conversion factor.

$$50.0 \text{ g Cu} \times \frac{1 \text{ student}}{1.84 \text{ g Cu}} = 27.174 \text{ students} = 27 \text{ students}$$

Note that because students cannot be fractional, the result is shown rounded down to a whole number.

3 **Evaluate** *Does the result make sense?*

The unit of the answer (students) is the one desired. The number of students (27) seems to be a reasonable answer. You can make an approximate calculation using the following conversion factor.

$$\frac{1 \text{ student}}{2 \text{ g Cu}}$$

Multiplying the above conversion factor by 50 g Cu gives the approximate answer of 25 students, which is close to the calculated answer.

Practice Problems

30. An experiment requires that each student use an 8.5-cm length of magnesium ribbon. How many students can do the experiment if there is a 570-cm length of magnesium ribbon available?

31. A 1.00-degree increase on the Celsius scale is equivalent to a 1.80-degree increase on the Fahrenheit scale. If a temperature increases by 48.0°C, what is the corresponding temperature increase on the Fahrenheit scale?

CHEMath

Conversion Problems

A conversion factor is a ratio of two quantities that are equal to one another. When doing conversions, write the conversion factors so that the unit of a given measurement cancels, leaving the correct unit for your answer. Note that the equalities needed to write a particular conversion may be given in the problem. In other cases, you will need to know or look up the necessary equalities.

Math **Handbook**

For help with conversion problems, go to page R66.

Problem-Solving 3.30 Solve Problem 30 with the help of an interactive guided tutorial.

with ChemASAP

Converting Between Units

In chemistry, as in many other subjects, you often need to express a measurement in a unit different from the one given or measured initially. ☞ **Problems in which a measurement with one unit is converted to an equivalent measurement with another unit are easily solved using dimensional analysis.**

Suppose that a laboratory experiment requires 7.5 dg of magnesium metal, and 100 students will do the experiment. How many grams of magnesium should your teacher have on hand? Multiplying 100 students by 7.5 dg/student gives you 750 dg. But then you must convert dg to grams. Sample Problem 3.7 shows you how to do the conversion.

SAMPLE PROBLEM 3.7

Converting Between Metric Units

Express 750 dg in grams.

1 Analyze *List the knowns and the unknown.*

Knowns
- mass = 750 dg
- 1 g = 10 dg

Unknown
- mass = ? g

The desired conversion is decigrams ⟶ grams. Using the expression relating the units, 10 dg = 1 g, multiply the given mass by the proper conversion factor.

2 Calculate *Solve for the unknown.*

The correct conversion factor is shown below.

$$\frac{1 \text{ g}}{10 \text{ dg}}$$

Note that the known unit is in the denominator and the unknown unit is in the numerator.

$$750 \text{ dg} \times \frac{1 \text{ g}}{10 \text{ dg}} = 75 \text{ g}$$

3 Evaluate *Does the result make sense?*

Because the unit gram represents a larger mass than the unit decigram, it makes sense that the number of grams is less than the given number of decigrams. The unit of the known (dg) cancels, and the answer has the correct unit (g). The answer also has the correct number of significant figures.

Practice Problems

32. Using tables from this chapter, convert the following.
  a. 0.044 km to meters
  b. 4.6 mg to grams
  c. 0.107 g to centigrams

33. Convert the following.
  a. 15 cm³ to liters
  b. 7.38 g to kilograms
  c. 6.7 s to milliseconds
  d. 94.5 g to micrograms

Interactive Textbook

Problem-Solving 3.33 Solve Problem 33 with the help of an interactive guided tutorial.

—with **ChemASAP**

Multistep Problems Many complex tasks in your everyday life are best handled by breaking them down into manageable parts. For example, if you were cleaning a car, you might first vacuum the inside, then wash the exterior, then dry the exterior, and finally put on a fresh coat of wax. Similarly, many complex word problems are more easily solved by breaking the solution down into steps.

When converting between units, it is often necessary to use more than one conversion factor. Sample Problem 3.8 illustrates the use of multiple conversion factors.

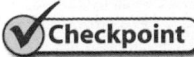 **Checkpoint** *What problem-solving methods can help you solve complex word problems?*

CHEMath

Scientific Notation

A It is often convenient to express very large or very small numbers in scientific notation. The distance between the sun and Earth is 150,000,000 km, which can be written as 1.5×10^8 km. The diameter of a gold atom is 0.000 000 000 274 m, or 2.74×10^{-10} m.

When multiplying numbers written in scientific notation, add the exponents. When dividing numbers written in scientific notation, subtract the exponent in the denominator from the exponent in the numerator.

Math Handbook

For help with scientific notation, go to page R56.

SAMPLE PROBLEM 3.8

Converting Between Metric Units

What is 0.073 cm in micrometers?

1 **Analyze** *List the knowns and the unknown.*

Knowns
- length = 0.073 cm = 7.3×10^{-2} cm
- 10^2 cm = 1 m
- 1 m = $10^6 \mu$m

Unknown
- length = ? μm

The desired conversion is from centimeters to micrometers. The problem can be solved in a two-step conversion.

2 **Calculate** *Solve for the unknown.*

First change centimeters to meters; then change meter to micrometers: centimeters ⟶ meters ⟶ micrometers. Each conversion factor is written so that the unit in the denominator cancels the unit in the numerator of the previous factor.

$$7.3 \times 10^{-2} \text{ cm} \times \frac{1 \text{ m}}{10^2 \text{ cm}} \times \frac{10^6 \mu\text{m}}{1 \text{ m}} = 7.3 \times 10^2 \mu\text{m}$$

3 **Evaluate** *Does the result make sense?*

Because a micrometer is a much smaller unit than a centimeter, the answer should be numerically larger than the given measurement. The units have canceled correctly, and the answer has the correct number of significant figures.

Interactive Textbook

Problem-Solving 3.35 Solve Problem 35 with the help of an interactive guided tutorial.

with **ChemASAP**

Practice Problems

34. The radius of a potassium atom is 0.227 nm. Express this radius in the unit centimeters.

35. The diameter of Earth is 1.3×10^4 km. What is the diameter expressed in decimeters?

Converting Complex Units Many common measurements are expressed as a ratio of two units. For example, the results of international car races often give average lap speeds in kilometers per hour. You measure the densities of solids and liquids in grams per cubic centimeter. You measure the gas mileage in a car in miles per gallon of gasoline. If you use dimensional analysis, converting these complex units is just as easy as converting single units. It will just take multiple steps to arrive at an answer.

SAMPLE PROBLEM 3.9

Converting Ratios of Units

The mass per unit volume of a substance is a property called density. The density of manganese, a metallic element, is 7.21 g/cm^3. What is the density of manganese expressed in units kg/m^3?

1 Analyze *List the knowns and the unknown.*

Knowns
- density of manganese = 7.21 g/cm^3
- 10^3 g = 1 kg
- 10^6 cm^3 = 1 m^3

Unknown
- density manganese = ? kg/m^3

The desired conversion is g/cm^3 ⟶ kg/m^3. The mass unit in the numerator must be changed from grams to kilograms: g ⟶ kg. In the denominator, the volume unit must be changed from cubic centimeters to cubic meters: cm^3 ⟶ m^3. Note that the relationship between cm^3 and m^3 was determined from the relationship between cm and m. Cubing the relationship 10^2 cm = 1 m yields $(10^2 \text{ cm})^3 = (1 \text{ m})^3$, or 10^6 cm^3 = 1 m^3.

2 Calculate *Solve for the unknown.*

$$\frac{7.21 \text{ g}}{1 \text{ cm}^3} \times \frac{1 \text{ kg}}{10^3 \text{ g}} \times \frac{10^6 \text{ cm}^3}{1 \text{ m}^3} = 7.21 \times 10^3 \text{ kg/m}^3$$

3 Evaluate *Does the result make sense?*

Because the physical size of the volume unit m^3 is so much larger than cm^3 (10^6 times), the calculated value of the density should be larger than the given value even though the mass unit is also larger (10^3 times). The units cancel, the conversion factors are correct, and the answer has the correct ratio of units.

Practice Problems

36. Gold has a density of 19.3 g/cm^3. What is the density in kilograms per cubic meter?

37. There are 7.0×10^6 red blood cells (RBC) in 1.0 mm^3 of blood. How many red blood cells are in 1.0 L of blood?

Math ➤ **Handbook**

For help with dimensional analysis, go to page R66.

---

nteractive Textbook

Problem-Solving 3.37 Solve Problem 37 with the help of an interactive guided tutorial.

— with **ChemASAP**

Quick LAB

Dimensional Analysis

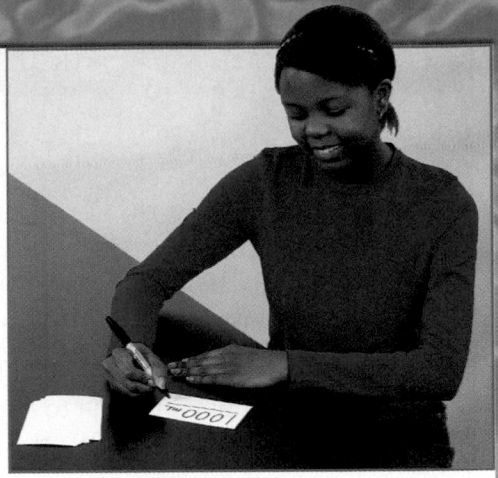

Purpose
To apply the problem-solving technique of dimensional analysis to conversion problems.

Materials
- 3 inch × 5 inch index cards or paper cut to approximately the same size
- pen

Procedure
A conversion factor is a ratio of equivalent measurements. For any relationship, you can write two ratios. On a conversion factor card you can write one ratio on each side of the card.

1. Make a conversion factor card for each metric relationship shown in Tables 3.3, 3.4, and 3.5. Show the inverse of the conversion factor on the back of each card.

2. Use the appropriate conversion factor cards to set up solutions to Sample Problems 3.7 and 3.8. Notice that in each solution, the unit in the denominator of the conversion factor cancels the unit in the numerator of the previous conversion factor.

Analyze and Conclude

1. What is the effect of multiplying a given measurement by one or more conversion factors?

2. Use your conversion factor cards to set up solutions to these problems.
   a. 78.5 cm = ? m
   b. 0.056 L = ? cm^3
   c. 77 kg = ? mg
   d. 0.098 nm = ? dm
   e. 0.96 cm = ? μm
   f. 0.0067 mm = ? nm

3.3 Section Assessment

38. 🔑 **Key Concept** What happens to the numerical value of a measurement that is multiplied by a conversion factor? What happens to the actual size of the quantity?

39. 🔑 **Key Concept** Why is dimensional analysis useful?

40. 🔑 **Key Concept** What types of problems can be solved using dimensional analysis?

41. What conversion factor would you use to convert between these pairs of units?
   a. minutes to hours
   b. grams to milligrams
   c. cubic decimeters to milliliters

42. Make the following conversions. Express your answers in standard exponential form.
   a. 14.8 g to micrograms
   b. 3.72×10^{-3} kg to grams
   c. 66.3 L to cubic centimeters

43. An atom of gold has a mass of 3.271×10^{-22} g. How many atoms of gold are in 5.00 g of gold?

44. Convert the following. Express your answers in scientific notation.
   a. 7.5×10^4 J to kilojoules
   b. 3.9×10^5 mg to decigrams
   c. 2.21×10^{-4} dL to microliters

45. Light travels at a speed of 3.00×10^{10} cm/sec. What is the speed of light in kilometers/hour?

Connecting ▶ **Concepts**

Problem-Solving Skills Reread the passage on solving numeric problems in Section 1.4. Explain how the three-step process might apply to conversion problems that involve dimensional analysis.

Assessment 3.3 Test yourself on the concepts in Section 3.3.

with **ChemASAP**

Scale Models

A scale model is a physical or conceptual representation of an object that is proportional in size to the object it represents. Examples include model trains, model airplanes, and dollhouses. Most model trains are built to a scale of 1:87. This ratio means that the model is $\frac{1}{87}$ the size of an actual train. On the model, 1 cm represents 87 cm on the train.

Scale models aren't just for hobbyists—scientists and engineers use them, too. A simple scientific model in the classroom is a globe, which is a small-scale model of Earth. (A globe with a diameter of 30 cm has a scale of 1:42,500,000.) **Applying Concepts** *How do you use the scale of a model as a conversion factor?*

Scale model
4.5 ft tall, scale 1:192

Architectural drawing
East-west elevation

Computer modeling
By testing a model, engineers can make the product better before it is built. Engineers often design scale models on computers. These automotive engineers are using a computer-aided design (CAD) program to view a digital scale model of a car. Physical models of the car's wheels are on the desk.

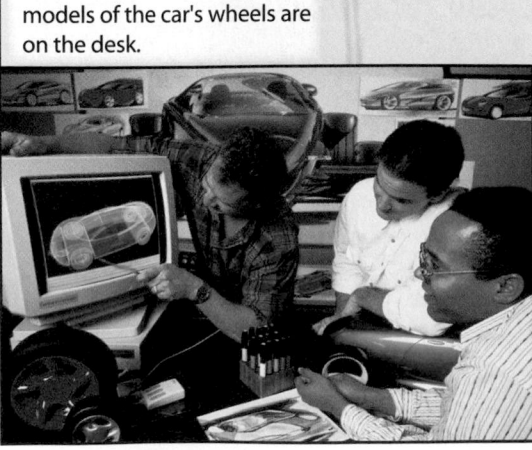

Condé Nast Building
New York City
866 ft (264 m) tall,
48 floors

Model building
Architects use both two-dimensional and three-dimensional scale models to design buildings. A common scale for floor plans is 1: 48.

3.4 Density

New York Standards: M1.1c, S3.3a, S3.3b, 3.1w

Connecting to Your World

Have you ever wondered why some objects float in water, while others sink? If you think that these lily pads float because they are lightweight, you are only partially correct. The ratio of the mass of an object to its volume can be used to determine whether an object floats or sinks in water. For pure water at 4°C, this ratio is 1.000 g/cm³. If an object has a mass-to-volume ratio less than 1.000 g/cm³, it will float in water. If an object has a mass-to-volume ratio greater than this value, it will sink in water.

Determining Density

Perhaps someone has tricked you with this question: "Which is heavier, a pound of lead or a pound of feathers?" Most people would not give the question much thought and would incorrectly answer "lead." Of course, a pound of lead has the same mass as a pound of feathers. What concept, instead of mass, are people really thinking of when they answer this question?

Most people are incorrectly applying a perfectly correct idea: namely, that if a piece of lead and a feather of the same volume are weighed, the lead would have a greater mass than the feather. It would take a much larger volume of feathers to equal the mass of a given volume of lead.

Guide for Reading

 Key Concepts
- What determines the density of a substance?
- How does a change in temperature affect density?

Vocabulary
density

Reading Strategy
Identifying Main Ideas As you read, write the main idea of the text that follows each heading.

Simulation 1 Rank materials according to their densities.
—with **ChemASAP**

	10 g of Lithium	10 g of Water	10 g of Lead
Volume	19 cm³	10 cm³	0.88 cm³
Density	0.53 g/cm³	1.0 g/cm³	11.4 g/cm³

Figure 3.13 A 10-g sample of pure water has less volume than 10 g of lithium, but more volume than 10 g of lead. The faces of the cubes are shown actual size. **Inferring** *Which substance has the highest ratio of mass to volume?*

Table 3.6

Densities of Some Common Materials			
Solids and Liquids		**Gases**	
Material	**Density at 20°C (g/cm³)**	**Material**	**Density at 20°C (g/L)**
Gold	19.3	Chlorine	2.95
Mercury	13.6	Carbon dioxide	1.83
Lead	11.4	Argon	1.66
Aluminum	2.70	Oxygen	1.33
Table sugar	1.59	Air	1.20
Corn syrup	1.35–1.38	Nitrogen	1.17
Water (4°C)	1.000	Neon	0.84
Corn oil	0.922	Ammonia	0.718
Ice (0°C)	0.917	Methane	0.665
Ethanol	0.789	Helium	0.166
Gasoline	0.66–0.69	Hydrogen	0.084

The important relationship in this case is between the object's mass and its volume. This relationship is called density. **Density** is the ratio of the mass of an object to its volume.

$$\text{Density} = \frac{\text{mass}}{\text{volume}}$$

A 10.0-cm³ piece of lead, for example, has a mass of 114 g. What, then, is the density of lead? You can calculate it by substituting the mass and volume into the equation above.

$$\frac{114\ \text{g}}{10.0\ \text{cm}^3} = 11.4\ \text{g/cm}^3$$

Note that when mass is measured in grams, and volume in cubic centimeters, density has units of grams per cubic centimeter (g/cm³).

Figure 3.13 on page 89 compares the density of three substances. Why does each 10-g sample have a different volume? The volumes vary because the substances have different densities. ⊙ **Density is an intensive property that depends only on the composition of a substance, not on the size of the sample.** With a mixture, density can vary because the composition of a mixture can vary.

What do you think will happen if corn oil is poured into a glass containing corn syrup? Using Table 3.6, you can see that the density of corn oil is less than the density of corn syrup. For that reason, the oil floats on top of the syrup, as shown in Figure 3.14.

You have probably seen a helium-filled balloon rapidly rise to the ceiling when it is released. Whether a gas-filled balloon will sink or rise when released depends on how the density of the gas compares with the density of air. Helium is less dense than air, so a helium-filled balloon rises. The densities of various gases are listed in Table 3.6.

Figure 3.14 Because of differences in density, corn oil floats on top of corn syrup.

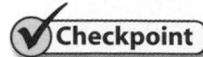 **Checkpoint** *What quantities do you need to measure in order to calculate the density of an object?*

Density and Temperature

Experiments show that the volume of most substances increases as the temperature increases. Meanwhile, the mass remains the same despite the temperature and volume changes. Remember that density is the ratio of an object's mass to its volume. So if the volume changes with temperature (while the mass remains constant), then the density must also change with temperature. ⟾ **The density of a substance generally decreases as its temperature increases.** As you will learn in Chapter 15, water is an important exception. Over a certain range of temperatures, the volume of water increases as its temperature decreases. Ice, or solid water, floats because it is less dense than liquid water.

Go Online

NSTA SciLINKS

For: Links on Density
Visit: www.SciLinks.org
Web Code: cdn-1034

SAMPLE PROBLEM 3.10

Calculating Density

A copper penny has a mass of 3.1 g and a volume of 0.35 cm³. What is the density of copper?

① Analyze *List the knowns and the unknown.*

Knowns
• mass = 3.1 g
• volume = 0.35 cm³

Unknown
• density = ? g/cm³

Use the known values and the following definition of density.

$$\text{Density} = \frac{\text{mass}}{\text{volume}}$$

② Calculate *Solve for the unknown.*

The equation is already set up to solve for the unknown. Substitute the known values for mass and volume, and calculate the density.

$$\text{density} = \frac{\text{mass}}{\text{volume}} = \frac{3.1 \text{ g}}{0.35 \text{ cm}^3} = 8.8571 \text{ g/cm}^3$$

$$= 8.9 \text{ g/cm}^3 \text{ (rounded to two significant figures)}$$

③ Evaluate *Does the result make sense?*

A piece of copper with a volume of about 0.3 cm³ of copper has a mass of about 3 grams. Thus, about three times that volume of copper, 1 cm³, should have a mass three times larger, about 9 grams. This estimate agrees with the calculated result.

Math ▶ **Handbook**

For help with algebraic equations, go to page R69.

Practice Problems

46. A student finds a shiny piece of metal that she thinks is aluminum. In the lab, she determines that the metal has a volume of 245 cm³ and a mass of 612 g. Calculate the density. Is the metal aluminum?

47. A bar of silver has a mass of 68.0 g and a volume 6.48 cm³. What is the density of silver?

Interactive Textbook

Problem-Solving 3.47 Solve Problem 47 with the help of an interactive guided tutorial.

—— with **ChemASAP**

SAMPLE PROBLEM 3.11

Using Density to Calculate Volume

What is the volume of a pure silver coin that has a mass of 14 g? The density of silver (Ag) is 10.5 g/cm³.

1 Analyze *List the knowns and the unknown.*

Knowns
- mass of coin = 14 g
- density of silver = 10.5 g/cm³

Unknown
- volume of coin = ? cm³

You can solve this problem by using density as a conversion factor. You need to convert the mass of the coin into a corresponding volume. The density gives the following relationship between volume and mass.

$$1 \text{ cm}^3 \text{ Ag} = 10.5 \text{ g Ag}$$

Based on this relationship, you can write the following conversion factor.

$$\frac{1 \text{ cm}^3 \text{ Ag}}{10.5 \text{ g Ag}}$$

Notice that the known unit is in the denominator and the unknown unit is in the numerator.

2 Calculate *Solve for the unknown.*

Multiply the mass of the coin by the conversion factor to yield an answer in cm³.

$$14 \text{ g Ag} \times \frac{1 \text{ cm}^3 \text{ Ag}}{10.5 \text{ g Ag}} = 1.3 \text{ cm}^3 \text{ Ag}$$

3 Evaluate *Does the result make sense?*

Because a mass of 10.5 g of silver has a volume of 1 cm³, it makes sense that 14.0 g of silver should have a volume slightly larger than 1 cm³. The answer has two significant figures because the given mass has two significant figures.

Math Handbook

For help with significant figures, go to page R59.

Practice Problems

Interactive Textbook

Problem-Solving 3.48 Solve Problem 48 with the help of an interactive guided tutorial.

— with **ChemASAP**

48. Use dimensional analysis and the given densities to make the following conversions.
   a. 14.8 g of boron to cm³ of boron. The density of boron is 2.34 g/cm³.
   b. 4.62 g of mercury to cm³ of mercury. The density of mercury is 13.5 g/cm³.

49. Rework the preceding problems by applying the following equation.

$$\text{Density} = \frac{\text{mass}}{\text{volume}}$$

Mercury

Analytical Chemist

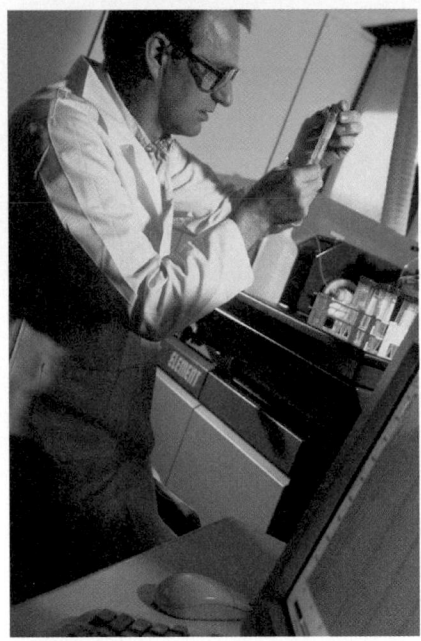

Analytical chemists focus on making quantitative measurements. They must be familiar with many analytical techniques to work successfully on a wide variety of tasks. As an analytical chemist, you would spend your time making measurements and calculations to solve laboratory and math-based research problems. You could, for example, be involved in analyzing the composition of biomolecules. Pharmaceutical companies need people to analyze the composition of medicines and research new combinations of compounds to use as drugs. As an analytical chemist, you must be able to think creatively and develop new means for finding solutions.

Many exciting new fields, such as biomedicine and biochemistry, are now hiring analytical chemists. More traditional areas, including industrial manufacturers, also employ analytical chemists. The educational background you need to enter this field is quite extensive. You would need advanced chemical training, including organic chemistry and quantitative chemistry, as well as some training in molecular biology and computer operation. A master's degree in chemistry may be required, and certain positions require a Ph.D.

For: Careers in Chemistry
Visit: PHSchool.com
Web Code: cdb-1034

3.4 Section Assessment

50. **Key Concept** What determines the density of an object?

51. **Key Concept** How does density vary with temperature?

52. A weather balloon is inflated to a volume of 2.2×10^3 L with 37.4 g of helium. What is the density of helium in grams per liter?

53. A 68-g bar of gold is cut into 3 equal pieces. How does the density of each piece compare to the density of the original gold bar?

54. A plastic ball with a volume of 19.7 cm³ has a mass of 15.8 g. Would this ball sink or float in a container of gasoline?

55. What is the volume, in cubic centimeters, of a sample of cough syrup that has a mass of 50.0 g? The density of cough syrup is 0.950 g/cm³.

56. What is the mass, in kilograms, of 14.0 L of gasoline? (Assume that the density of gasoline is 0.680 g/cm³.)

Elements ▶ **Handbook**

Density Look up the densities of the elements in Group 1A on page R6. Which Group 1A elements are less dense than pure water at 4°C?

Interactive Textbook

Assessment 3.4 Test yourself on the concepts in Section 3.4.

with **ChemASAP**

Now What Do I Do?

Purpose
To solve problems by making accurate measurements and applying mathematics.

Materials
- pencil
- paper
- meter stick
- balance
- pair of dice
- aluminum can
- calculator
- small-scale pipet
- water
- a pre- and post-1982 penny
- 8-well strip
- plastic cup

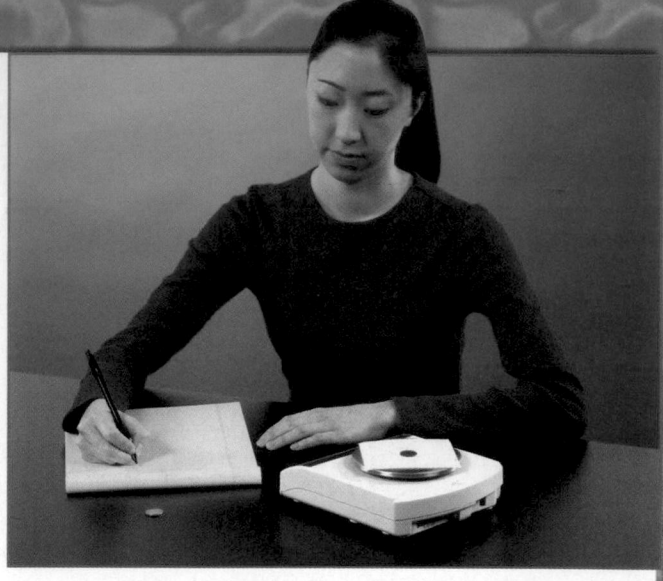

Procedure
1. Determine the mass, in grams, of one drop of water. To do this, measure the mass of an empty cup. Add 50 drops of water from a small-scale pipet to the cup and measure its mass again. Subtract the mass of the empty cup from the mass of the cup with water in it. To determine the average mass in grams of a single drop, divide the mass of the water by the number of drops (50). Repeat this experiment until your results are consistent.

2. Determine the mass of a pre-1982 penny and a post-1982 penny.

Analysis
Using your experimental data, record the answers to the following questions.

1. What is the average mass of a single drop of water in milligrams? (1 g = 1000 mg)

2. The density of water is 1.00 g/cm^3. Calculate the volume of a single drop in cm^3 and mL. (1 mL = 1 cm^3) What is the volume of a drop in microliters (μL)? (1000 μL = 1 mL)

3. What is the density of water in units of mg/cm^3 and mg/mL? (1 g = 1000 mg)

4. Pennies made before 1982 consist of 95.0% copper and 5.0% zinc. Calculate the mass of copper and the mass of zinc in the pre-1982 penny.

5. Pennies made after 1982 are made of zinc with a thin copper coating. They are 97.6% zinc and 2.4% copper. Calculate the mass of copper and the mass of zinc in the newer penny.

6. Why does one penny have less mass than the other?

You're the Chemist
The following small-scale activities allow you to develop your own procedures and analyze the results.

1. **Design It!** Design an experiment to determine if the size of drops varies with the angle at which they are delivered from the pipet. Try vertical (90°), horizontal (0°), and halfway between (45°). Repeat until your results are consistent.

2. **Analyze It!** What is the best angle to hold a pipet for ease of use and consistency of measurement? Explain. Why is it important to expel the air bubbles before you begin the experiment?

3. **Design It!** Make the necessary measurements to determine the volume of aluminum used to make an aluminum soda can. *Hint:* Look up the density of aluminum in your textbook.

4. **Design It!** Design and carry out some experiments to determine the volume of liquid that an aluminum soda can will hold.

5. **Design It!** Measure a room and calculate the volume of air it contains. Estimate the percent error associated with not taking into account the furniture in the room.

6. **Design It!** Make the necessary measurements and do the necessary calculations to determine the volume of a pair of dice. First, ignore the volume of the dots on each face, and then account for the volume of the dots. What is your error and percent error when you ignore the holes?

7. **Design It!** Design an experiment to determine the volume of your body. Write down what measurements you would need to make and what calculations you would do. What additional information might be helpful?

Key Concepts

3.1 Measurements and Their Uncertainty

- Measurements are fundamental to the experimental sciences.
- To evaluate accuracy, the measured value must be compared to the correct value. To evaluate precision, you must compare the values of repeated measurements.
- Calculated answers often depend on the number of significant figures in the values used in the calculation.
- In general, a calculated answer cannot be more precise than the least precise measurement from which it was calculated.

3.2 The International System of Units

- Five commonly used SI base units are the meter, kilogram, kelvin, second, and mole.
- Common metric units of length: cm, m, km.

Common metric units of volume: μL, mL, L, cm^3. Common metric units of mass: mg, g, kg. Common units of temperature: °C and K. Common units of energy: J and cal.

3.3 Conversion Problems

- Multiplying by a conversion factor does not change the actual size of a measurement.
- Dimensional analysis provides an alternative approach to problem solving.
- Conversion problems are easily solved using dimensional analysis.

3.4 Density

- Density is an intensive property that depends only on the composition of a substance.
- The density of a substance generally decreases as its temperature increases.

Vocabulary

- absolute zero (p. 77)
- accepted value (p. 65)
- accuracy (p. 64)
- calorie (cal) (p. 79)
- Celsius scale (p. 77)
- conversion factor (p. 80)
- density (p. 90)
- dimensional analysis (p. 81)
- energy (p. 79)
- error (p. 65)
- experimental value (p. 65)
- gram (g) (p. 76)
- International System of Units (SI) (p. 73)
- joule (J) (p. 79)
- Kelvin scale (p. 77)
- kilogram (kg) (p. 76)
- liter (L) (p. 75)
- measurement (p. 63)
- meter (m) (p. 74)
- percent error (p. 65)
- precision (p. 64)
- scientific notation (p. 63)
- significant figures (p. 66)
- temperature (p. 77)
- weight (p. 76)

Key Equations

- Error = experimental value − accepted value
- Percent error = $\dfrac{|error|}{accepted\ value} \times 100\%$
- K = °C + 273 and °C = K − 273
- 1 J = 0.2390 cal and 1 cal = 4.184 J
- Density = $\dfrac{mass}{volume}$

Organizing Information

Use these terms to construct a concept map that organizes the major ideas of this chapter.

Concept Map 3 Solve the concept map with the help of an interactive guided tutorial.

— with **ChemASAP**

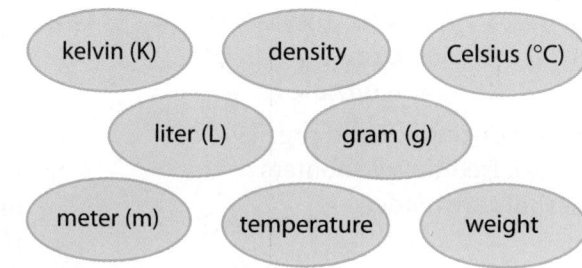

Measurements and their Uncertainty

57. Three students made multiple weighings of a copper cylinder, each using a different balance. Describe the accuracy and precision of each student's measurements if the correct mass of the cylinder is 47.32 g.

Mass of Cylinder (g)			
	Lissa	**Lamont**	**Leigh Anne**
Weighing 1	47.13	47.45	47.95
Weighing 2	47.94	47.39	47.91
Weighing 3	46.83	47.42	47.89
Weighing 4	47.47	47.41	47.93

58. How many significant figures are in each underlined measurement?
   a. <u>60 s</u> = 1 min   **b.** <u>47.70 g</u> of copper
   c. 1 km = <u>1000 m</u>   **d.** <u>25 computers</u>

59. Round off each of these measurements to three significant figures.
   a. 98.473 L   **b.** 0.000 763 21 cg
   c. 57.048 m   **d.** 12.17°C

60. Using the rules for significant figures, round off each of the following answers correctly.
   a. 8.7 g + 15.43 g + 19 g = 43.13 g
   b. 853.2 L − 627.443 L = 225.757 L
   c. 38.742 kg ÷ 0.421 = 92.023 75 kg
   d. 5.40 m × 3.21 m × 1.871 m = 32.431 914 m^3

61. Express each of the rounded-off answers in Questions 59 and 60 in scientific notation.

62. How are the *error* and the *percent error* of a measurement calculated?

63. Explain why precise measurements will not always be accurate measurements.

64. List two possible reasons for reporting precise, but inaccurate, measurements.

65. Rank these masses from smallest to largest.
   a. 5.3×10^4 g   **b.** 57×10^3 g
   c. 4.9×10^{-2} g   **d.** 0.0057 g
   e. 5.1×10^{-3} g   **f.** 0.0072×10^2 g

66. Comment on the accuracy and precision of these basketball free-throw shooters.
   a. 99 of 100 shots are made.

   b. 99 of 100 shots hit the front of the rim and bounce off.
   c. 33 of 100 shots are made; the rest miss.

67. Is it possible for an object to lose weight but at the same time not lose mass? Explain.

68. You are hired to count the number of ducks on three northern lakes during the summer. In the first lake, you estimate 500,000 ducks; in the second, 250,000 ducks; and in the third, 100,000 ducks. You write down that you have counted 850,000 ducks. As you drive away, you see 15 ducks fly in from the south and land on the third lake. Do you change the number of ducks that you report? Justify you answer.

The International System of Units (SI)

69. List the SI base unit of measurement for each of these quantities.
   a. time   **b.** length
   c. temperature   **d.** mass

70. Order these units from smallest to largest: cm, μm, km, mm, m, nm, dm, pm. Then give each measurement in terms of meters.

71. Identify the units that would be appropriate to measure each of the following dimensions.
   a. the height of this letter I
   b. the width of Table 3.3
   c. the height of this page

72. The melting point of silver is 962°C. Express this temperature in kelvins.

73. Fahrenheit is a third temperature scale. Plot the data in the table and use the graph to derive an equation for the relationship between the Fahrenheit and Celsius temperature scales.

Example	°C	°F
Melting point of selenium	221	430
Boiling point of water	100	212
Normal body temperature	37	98.6
Freezing point of water	0	32
Boiling point of chlorine	−34.6	−30.2

74. Which would melt first, germanium with a melting point of 1210K or gold with a melting point of 1064°C?

75. What is the name given to a ratio of two equivalent measurements?

76. What must be true for a ratio of two measurements to be a conversion factor?

77. How do you know which unit of a conversion factor must be in the denominator?

78. Make the following conversions.
   a. 157 cs to seconds
   b. 42.7 L to milliliters
   c. 261 nm to millimeters
   d. 0.065 km to decimeters
   e. 642 cg to kilograms
   f. 8.25×10^2 cg to nanograms

79. Make the following conversions.
   a. 0.44 mL/min to microliters per second
   b. 7.86 g/cm^2 to milligrams per square millimeter
   c. 1.54 kg/L to grams per cubic centimeter

80. How many milliliters are contained in 1 m^3?

81. Complete this table so that all the measurements in each row have the same value.

mg	g	cg	kg
(a)	(b)	28.3	(c)
6.6×10^3	(d)	(e)	(f)
(g)	2.8×10^{-4}	(h)	(i)

82. A watch loses 0.15 s every minute. How many minutes will the watch lose in 1 day?

83. Write six conversion factors involving these units of measure: $1 g = 10^2 cg = 10^3 mg$.

84. How many kilograms of water (at 4°C) are needed to fill an aquarium that measures 40.0 cm by 20.0 cm by 30.0 cm? The density of water is 1.00 g/mL.

85. A cheetah can run 112 km/h over a 100-m distance. What is this speed in meters per second?

86. What equation is used to determine the density of an object?

87. Would the density of a person be the same on the surface of Earth and on the surface of the moon? Explain.

88. A shiny, gold-colored bar of metal weighing 57.3 g has a volume of 4.7 cm^3. Is the bar of metal pure gold?

89. The density of water is 1.0 g/mL. How many deciliters of water will fill a 0.5-L bottle?

90. A piece of wood sinks in ethanol but floats in gasoline. Give a range of possible densities for the wood. Refer to Table 3.6 on page 90.

91. The density of dry air measured at 25°C is 1.19×10^{-3} g/cm^3. What is the volume of 50.0 g of air?

92. A flask that can hold 158 g of water at 4°C can hold only 127 g of ethanol at the same temperature. What is the density of ethanol? The density of water is 1.00 g/mL.

93. What is the mass of a cube of aluminum that is 3.0 cm on each edge? The density of aluminum is 2.7 g/cm^3.

94. Plot these data that show how the mass of sulfur increases with an increase in volume. Determine the density of sulfur from the slope of the line.

Mass of sulfur (g)	Volume of sulfur (cm^3)
23.5	11.4
60.8	29.2
115	55.5
168	81.1

95. The mass of a cube of iron is 355 g. Iron has a density of 7.87 g/cm^3. What is the mass of a cube of lead that has the same dimensions?

Test-Taking Tip

Interpreting Diagrams Diagrams present information in a visual format. Before you answer questions about a diagram, be sure to study the diagram carefully. Ask yourself some questions: *What is the diagram showing? What does the diagram tell me?*

Regents Practice Exam

Part A

For each statement or question write the number of the word or expression that, of those given, best completes the statement or answers the question.

1. A temperature in kelvins is always numerically larger than the same temperature in degrees Celsius because
   (1) the temperature in kelvins equals a temperature in degrees Celsius plus 273
   (2) the temperature in degrees Celsius equals a temperature in kelvins plus 273
   (3) the temperature in kelvins equals a temperature in degrees Celsius minus 273
   (4) the zero point in the Kelvin scale is higher than the zero point in the Celsius scale

2. How many significant figures are in the measurement 0.00450 m?
   (2) 3   (4) 6
   (3) 5

3. The percent error of a measurement is found by
   (1) dividing the accepted value by the amount of error and multiplying by 100%
   (2) dividing the amount of error by the accepted value and multiplying by 100%
   (3) multiplying the accepted value by the amount of error and dividing by 100%
   (4) multiplying the amount of error by the accepted value and dividing by 100%

4. The temperature measured as 0 K equals
   (1) −273°C   (3) 20°C
   (2) 0°C   (4) 273°C

Part B-1

For each statement or question write the number of the word or expression that, of those given, best completes the statement or answers the question.

5. Which of these series of units is ordered from smallest to largest?
   (1) μg, cg, mg, kg
   (2) mm, dm, m, km
   (3) μs, ns, cs, s
   (4) nL, mL, dL, cL

6. Which answer represents the measurement 0.004 28 g rounded off to two significant figures?
   (1) 4.28×10^3 g   (3) 4.3×10^3 g
   (2) 4.3×10^{-3} g   (4) 4.0×10^{-3} g

7. An over-the-counter medicine has 325 mg of its active ingredient per tablet. How many grams does this mass represent?
   (1) 325,000 g   (3) 3.25 g
   (2) 32.5 g   (4) 0.325 g

8. If a substance contracts when it freezes, its density will
   (1) remain the same
   (2) increase
   (3) decrease
   (4) expand

9. If 10^3 mm = 1 m, how many mm³ equal 1 m³?
   (1) 10^3 (3) 10^9
   (2) 10^6 (4) 10^{27}

Use the following information to answer Questions 10–11.

A 2.00-kg sample of bituminous coal is composed of 1.30 kg of carbon, 0.20 kg of ash, 0.15 kg of water, and 0.35 kg of volatile (gas-forming) material.

10. How many kilograms of carbon are in each kilogram of coal?
    (1) 0.65 kg   (3) 1.30 kg
    (2) 0.70 kg   (4) 2.60 kg

11. How many kilograms of carbon are in 125 kg of this coal?
    (1) 81 kg   (3) 160 kg
    (2) 88 kg   (4) 320 kg

12. The average density of Earth is 5.52 g/cm³. Express this density in units of kg/cm³.
    (1) 5.52×10^{-3} kg/cm³   (3) 5.52×10^2 kg/cm³
    (2) 5.52 kg/cm³   (4) 5.52×10^3 kg/cm³

13. The length of a board was found to be 1.42 m. The actual length was 1.45 m. What was the percent error of the measurement?
    (1) 2.07%   (3) 10.2%
    (2) 2.11%   (4) 97.9%

14. A spoon in a pot on the stove is at a higher temperature than a girl's hand. What happens when the girl touches the spoon?
    (1) Heat moves from the hand to the spoon.
    (2) Heat moves from the spoon to the hand.
    (3) No heat transfer occurs.
    (4) The hand and the spoon both move heat to the other object.

Part B-2

Answer each of the following questions.

15. A graduated cylinder contains 44.2 mL of water. A 48.6-g piece of metal is carefully dropped into the cylinder. When the metal is completely covered with water, the water rises to the 51.3-mL mark. What is the density of the metal?

Use the following particle diagrams to answer Questions 16 and 17.

a. **b.** **c.**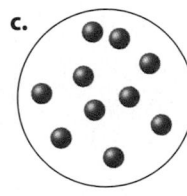

The diagrams represent particles of the same gas occupying the same volume at the same temperature. The systems differ only in the number of gas particles per unit volume.

16. List the diagrams in order of decreasing density.

17. Compare the density of the gas in diagram (a) to the density of the gas in diagram (b).

18. At 20°C, the density of air is 1.20 g/L. Nitrogen's density is 1.17 g/L. Oxygen's density is 1.33 g/L.
   a. Will balloons filled with oxygen and balloons filled with nitrogen rise or sink in air?
   b. Air is mainly a mixture of nitrogen and oxygen. Which gas is the main component? Explain.

19. Earth is approximately 1.5×10^8 km from the sun. The speed of light is 3.0×10^8 m/s.
   a. How far is Earth from the sun in meters?
   b. How many seconds does it take light to travel from the sun to Earth? How many minutes?

20. Alkanes are a class of molecules that have the general formula C_nH_{2n+2}, where n is an integer (whole number). The table below gives the boiling points for the first five alkanes with an odd number of carbon atoms. Using the table, construct a graph with number of carbon atoms on the *x*-axis.

Boiling point (°C)	Number of carbon atoms
−162.0	1
−42.0	3
36.0	5
98.0	7
151.0	9

   a. What are the approximate boiling points for the C_2H_6, C_4H_{10}, C_6H_{14}, and C_8H_{18}?
   b. Which of these nine alkanes are gases at room temperature (20°C)?
   c. How many of these nine alkanes are liquids at 350 K?
   d. Compare the approximate increase in boiling point per additional carbon atom in these alkanes.

21. Equal amounts of mercury, water, and corn oil are added to a beaker. Refer to Table 3.6 to help you answer the following questions.
   a. Describe the arrangement of the layers of liquids in the beaker.
   b. A small sugar cube is added to the beaker. Describe its location.
   c. What change will occur to the sugar cube over time?

Part C

Answer each of the following questions.

22. Different volumes of the same liquid were added to a flask on a balance. After each addition of liquid, the mass of the flask with the liquid was measured. Graph the data using mass as the dependent variable. Use the graph to answer these questions.

Volume (mL)	Mass (g)
14	103.0
27	120.4
41	139.1
55	157.9
82	194.1

   a. What is the mass of the empty flask?
   b. What is the density of the liquid?

23. Three balloons filled with neon, carbon dioxide, and hydrogen are released into the atmosphere. Using the data in Table 3.6, describe the movement of each balloon.

24. One of the first mixtures of metals, called amalgams, used by dentists for tooth fillings consisted of 26.0 g of silver, 10.8 g of tin, 2.4 g of copper, and 0.8 g of zinc. How much silver is in a 25.0-g sample of this amalgam?

Atomic Structure

A scanning tunneling microscope was used to produce this color-enhanced image of iron atoms.

INQUIRY Activity

Electric Charge

Materials
four 25-cm lengths of clear plastic tape and a metric ruler

Procedure
1. Firmly stick two of the 25-cm pieces of tape side-by-side, about 10 cm apart, on your desktop. Leave 2 to 3 cm of tape sticking over the edge of the desk. Grasp the free ends of the tapes and pull sharply upward to peel the tape pieces off of the desk. Slowly bring the pieces, which have similar charges, toward one another. Record your observations.

2. Pull the third and fourth pieces of tape between your thumb and forefinger several times, as if trying to clean each one. Slowly bring these two pieces of tape, which now have similar charges, toward one another. Record your observations.

Think About It
1. Predict what might happen if you brought a piece of tape pulled from your desktop close to a piece of tape pulled between your fingers. Try it, and see what happens. Explain your observations.

2. Do you think the pieces of tape used in Step 1 have the same charge as those used in Step 2? Explain.

New York Standards: S1.1b, S1.3a, 3.1a, 6.2

Connecting to Your World

It often helps to take a closer look. For example, you might walk up to a sign or a poster in order to make out the details. Or you might bring a set of binoculars to a sports stadium so that you can zoom in on the action. The lab technician shown here is using a magnifying lens to examine a bacterial culture in a petri dish. Scientists use many different devices that enhance their ability to see. However, scientists can't always see the details of what they study. In such cases, scientists try to obtain experimental data that helps fill in the picture.

Early Models of the Atom

Have you ever been asked to believe in something you couldn't see? Using your unaided eyes, you cannot see the tiny fundamental particles that make up matter. Yet all matter is composed of such particles, which are called atoms. An **atom** is the smallest particle of an element that retains its identity in a chemical reaction.

The concept of the atom intrigued a number of early scholars. Although these philosophers and scientists could not observe individual atoms, they still were able to propose ideas on the structure of atoms.

Democritus's Atomic Philosophy The Greek philosopher Democritus (460 B.C.–370 B.C.) was among the first to suggest the existence of atoms. **Democritus believed that atoms were indivisible and indestructible.** Although Democritus's ideas agreed with later scientific theory, they did not explain chemical behavior. They also lacked experimental support because Democritus's approach was not based on the scientific method.

Guide for Reading

Key Concepts
- How did Democritus describe atoms?
- How did John Dalton further Democritus's ideas on atoms?
- What instruments are used to observe individual atoms?

Vocabulary

atom

Dalton's atomic theory

Reading Strategy

Summarizing As you read about early atomic models, summarize the main ideas in the text that follow each red and blue heading.

Figure 4.1 Democritus believed that matter consisted of tiny, indivisible, unchangeable particles called atoms. His ideas were later challenged by the Greek philosophers Plato and Aristotle.

Figure 4.2 According to Dalton's atomic theory, an element is composed of only one kind of atom, and a compound is composed of particles that are chemical combinations of different kinds of atoms. **ⓐ** Atoms of element A are identical. **ⓑ** Atoms of element B are identical, but differ from those of element A. **ⓒ** Atoms of elements A and B can physically mix together. **ⓓ** Atoms of elements A and B can chemically combine to form a compound. **Interpreting Diagrams** *How does a mixture of atoms of different elements differ from a compound?*

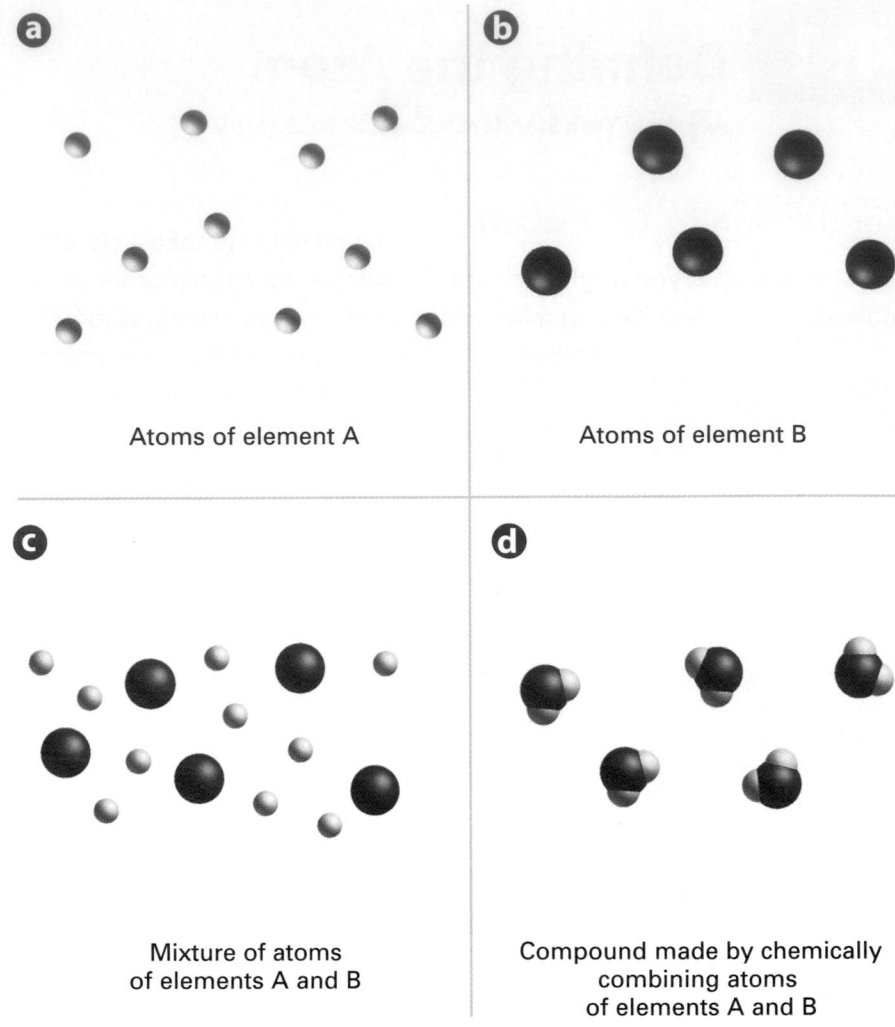

Atoms of element A

Atoms of element B

Mixture of atoms of elements A and B

Compound made by chemically combining atoms of elements A and B

Word *Origins*

Atom comes from the Greek word *atomos,* meaning "indivisible." **If the suffix *-ize* means "to become like," what do you think the word *atomize* means?**

Dalton's Atomic Theory The real nature of atoms and the connection between observable changes and events at the atomic level were not established for more than 2000 years after Democritus. The modern process of discovery regarding atoms began with John Dalton (1766–1844), an English chemist and schoolteacher. **By using experimental methods, Dalton transformed Democritus's ideas on atoms into a scientific theory.** Dalton studied the ratios in which elements combine in chemical reactions. Based on the results of his experiments, Dalton formulated hypotheses and theories to explain his observations. The result was **Dalton's atomic theory,** which includes the ideas illustrated in Figure 4.2 and listed below.

1. All elements are composed of tiny indivisible particles called atoms.
2. Atoms of the same element are identical. The atoms of any one element are different from those of any other element.
3. Atoms of different elements can physically mix together or can chemically combine in simple whole-number ratios to form compounds.
4. Chemical reactions occur when atoms are separated, joined, or rearranged. Atoms of one element, however, are never changed into atoms of another element as a result of a chemical reaction.

✓Checkpoint *What happens to atoms in a chemical reaction according to Dalton's atomic theory?*

Sizing up the Atom

A coin the size of a penny and composed of pure copper (Cu) illustrates Dalton's concept of the atom. Imagine grinding the copper coin into a fine dust. Each speck in the small pile of shiny red dust would still have the properties of copper. If by some means you could continue to make the copper dust particles smaller, you would eventually come upon a particle of copper that could no longer be divided and still have the chemical properties of copper. This final particle is an atom.

Copper atoms are very small. A pure copper coin the size of a penny contains about 2.4×10^{22} atoms. By comparison, Earth's population is only about 6×10^9 people. There are about 4×10^{12} as many atoms in the coin as there are people on Earth. If you could line up 100,000,000 copper atoms side by side, they would produce a line only 1 cm long!

The radii of most atoms fall within the range of 5×10^{-11} m to 2×10^{-10} m. Does seeing individual atoms seem impossible? 🔑 **Despite their small size, individual atoms are observable with instruments such as scanning tunneling microscopes.** Figure 4.3 shows an image of iron atoms generated by a scanning tunneling microscope. Individual atoms can even be moved around and arranged in patterns. The ability to move individual atoms holds future promise for the creation of atomic-sized electronic devices, such as circuits and computer chips. This atomic-scale, or "nanoscale," technology could become essential to future applications in medicine, communications, solar energy, and space exploration.

Figure 4.3 Scientists used a scanning tunneling microscope to generate this image of iron atoms, shown in blue. The radius of this circle of atoms is just 7.13×10^{-9} m.

4.1 Section Assessment

1. 🔑 **Key Concept** How did Democritus characterize atoms?

2. 🔑 **Key Concept** How did Dalton advance the atomic philosophy proposed by Democritus?

3. 🔑 **Key Concept** What instrument can be used to observe individual atoms?

4. In your own words, state the main ideas of Dalton's atomic theory.

5. According to Dalton's theory, is it possible to convert atoms of one element into atoms of another? Explain.

6. Describe the range of the radii of most atoms in nanometers (nm).

7. A sample of copper with a mass of 63.5 g contains 6.02×10^{23} atoms. Calculate the mass of a single copper atom.

Connecting ▶ Concepts

Scientific Methods Reread the description of scientific methods in Section 1.4. Explain why the ideas on atoms proposed by Dalton constitute a theory, while the ideas proposed by Democritus do not.

Interactive Textbook

Assessment 4.1 Test yourself on the concepts in Section 4.1.

— with **ChemASAP**

Structure of the Nuclear Atom

 New York Standards: S1.1a, S1.1c, 3.1a–f

Guide for Reading

 Key Concepts

- What are three kinds of subatomic particles?
- How can you describe the structure of the nuclear atom?

Vocabulary

electrons
cathode ray
protons
neutrons
nucleus

Reading Strategy

Comparing and Contrasting When you compare and contrast things, you examine how they are alike and different. As you read, compare different subatomic particles by listing similarities and differences.

Connecting to Your World

A simple but important device first used by scientists in the late nineteenth century, the cathode-ray tube would achieve its greatest fame as the picture tube of the common television set. Today, cathode-ray tubes are found in TVs, computer monitors, and many other devices with electronic displays. But more than 100 years ago, scientists were the only ones staring into the glow of a cathode-ray tube. Their observations provided important evidence about the structure of atoms.

Subatomic Particles

Much of Dalton's atomic theory is accepted today. One important change, however, is that atoms are now known to be divisible. They can be broken down into even smaller, more fundamental particles, called subatomic particles. **Three kinds of subatomic particles are electrons, protons, and neutrons.**

Electrons In 1897, the English physicist J. J. Thomson (1856–1940) discovered the electron. **Electrons** are negatively charged subatomic particles. Thomson performed experiments that involved passing electric current through gases at low pressure. He sealed the gases in glass tubes fitted at both ends with metal disks called electrodes. The electrodes were connected to a source of electricity, as shown in Figure 4.4. One electrode, the anode, became positively charged. The other electrode, the cathode, became negatively charged. The result was a glowing beam, or **cathode ray,** that traveled from the cathode to the anode.

Figure 4.4 In a cathode-ray tube, electrons travel as a ray from the cathode (−) to the anode (+). A television tube is a specialized type of cathode-ray tube.

High voltage

Gas at very low pressure

Metal disk (cathode)   Vacuum pump

Cathode ray (electrons)

Metal disk (anode)

a

Figure 4.5 Thomson examined
two ways that a cathode ray can
be deflected: **a** by using a
magnet, and **b** by using
electrically charged plates.
Inferring *If a cathode ray is
attracted to a positively
charged plate, what can you
infer about the charge of the
particles that make up the
cathode ray?*

b

High voltage

Slit

Positive
plate

−

+

Cathode

Vacuum pump

Negative
plate

Anode

Figure 4.5a shows how a cathode ray is deflected by a magnet. A cathode ray is also deflected by electrically charged metal plates, as shown in Figure 4.5b. A positively charged plate attracts the cathode ray, while a negatively charged plate repels it. Thomson knew that opposite charges attract and like charges repel, so he hypothesized that a cathode ray is a stream of tiny negatively charged particles moving at high speed. Thomson called these particles corpuscles; later they were named electrons.

To test his hypothesis, Thomson set up an experiment to measure the ratio of the charge of an electron to its mass. He found this ratio to be constant. In addition, the charge-to-mass ratio of electrons did not depend on the kind of gas in the cathode-ray tube or the type of metal used for the electrodes. Thomson concluded that electrons must be parts of the atoms of all elements.

The U.S. physicist Robert A. Millikan (1868–1953) carried out experiments to find the quantity of charge carried by an electron. Using this value and the charge-to-mass ratio of an electron measured by Thomson, Millikan calculated the mass of the electron. Millikan's values for electron charge and mass, reported in 1916, are very similar to those accepted today. An electron carries exactly one unit of negative charge, and its mass is 1/1840 the mass of a hydrogen atom.

Go Online
NSTA SciLINKS

For: Links on J.J. Thomson
Visit: www.SciLinks.org
Web Code: cdn-1042

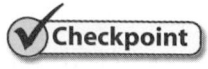 **Checkpoint**) *How do negatively charged plates affect the path of
cathode rays?*

Table 4.1

Properties of Subatomic Particles				
Particle	Symbol	Relative charge	Relative mass (mass of proton = 1)	Actual mass (g)
Electron	e^-	1−	1/1840	9.11×10^{-28}
Proton	p^+	1+	1	1.67×10^{-24}
Neutron	n^0	0	1	1.67×10^{-24}

Protons and Neutrons If cathode rays are electrons given off by atoms, what remains of the atoms that have lost the electrons? For example, after a hydrogen atom (the lightest kind of atom) loses an electron, what is left? You can think through this problem using four simple ideas about matter and electric charges. First, atoms have no net electric charge; they are electrically neutral. (One important piece of evidence for electrical neutrality is that you do not receive an electric shock every time you touch something!) Second, electric charges are carried by particles of matter. Third, electric charges always exist in whole-number multiples of a single basic unit; that is, there are no fractions of charges. Fourth, when a given number of negatively charged particles combines with an equal number of positively charged particles, an electrically neutral particle is formed.

Considering all of this information, it follows that a particle with one unit of positive charge should remain when a typical hydrogen atom loses an electron. Evidence for such a positively charged particle was found in 1886, when Eugen Goldstein (1850–1930) observed a cathode-ray tube and found rays traveling in the direction opposite to that of the cathode rays. He called these rays canal rays and concluded that they were composed of positive particles. Such positively charged subatomic particles are called **protons.** Each proton has a mass about 1840 times that of an electron.

In 1932, the English physicist James Chadwick (1891–1974) confirmed the existence of yet another subatomic particle: the neutron. **Neutrons** are subatomic particles with no charge but with a mass nearly equal to that of a proton. Table 4.1 summarizes the properties of these subatomic particles.

 Checkpoint *What is the charge of a neutron?*

The Atomic Nucleus

When subatomic particles were discovered, scientists wondered how these particles were put together in an atom. This was a difficult question to answer, given how tiny atoms are. Most scientists—including J.J. Thomson, the discoverer of the electron—thought it likely that the electrons were evenly distributed throughout an atom filled uniformly with positively charged material. In Thomson's atomic model, known as the "plum-pudding model," electrons were stuck into a lump of positive charge, similar to raisins stuck in dough. This model of the atom turned out to be short-lived, however, due to the groundbreaking work of Ernest Rutherford (1871–1937), a former student of Thomson.

Figure 4.6 Born in New Zealand, Ernest Rutherford was awarded the Nobel Prize for Chemistry in 1908. His portrait appears on the New Zealand $100 bill.

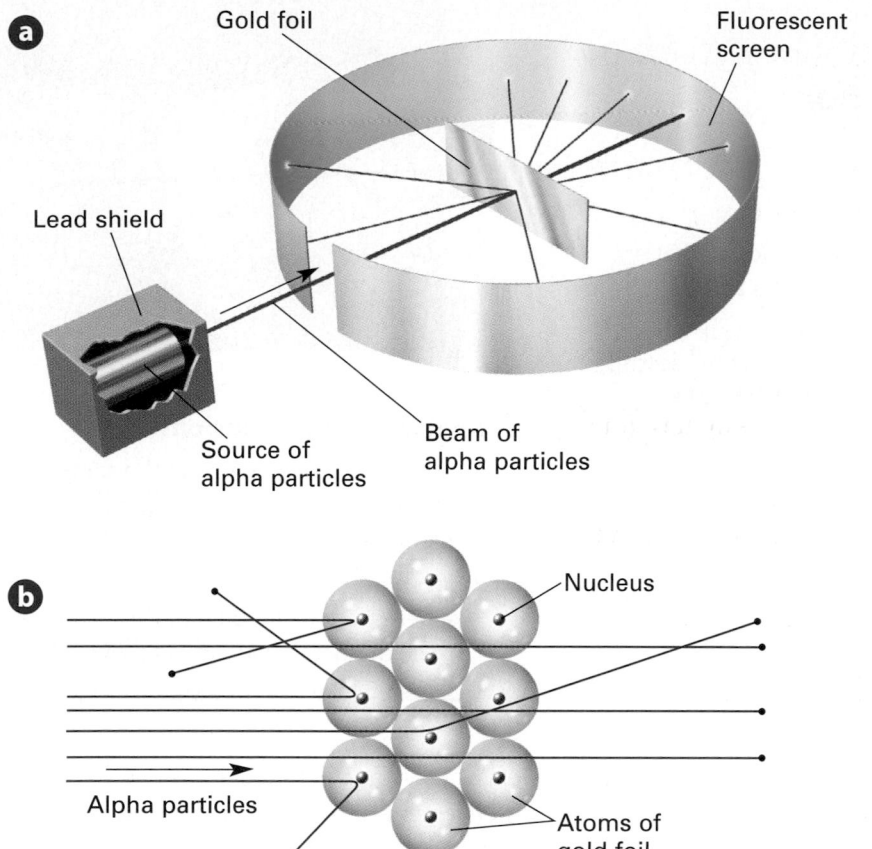

a Gold foil

Fluorescent screen

Lead shield

Source of alpha particles

Beam of alpha particles

b

Nucleus

Alpha particles

Atoms of gold foil

Figure 4.7 Rutherford's gold-foil experiment yielded evidence of the atomic nucleus. **a** Rutherford and his coworkers aimed a beam of alpha particles at a sheet of gold foil surrounded by a fluorescent screen. Most of the particles passed through the foil with no deflection at all. A few particles were greatly deflected. **b** Rutherford concluded that most of the alpha particles pass through the gold foil because the atom is mostly empty space. The mass and positive charge are concentrated in a small region of the atom. Rutherford called this region the nucleus. Particles that approach the nucleus closely are greatly deflected.

Rutherford's Gold-Foil Experiment In 1911, Rutherford and his coworkers at the University of Manchester, England, decided to test what was then the current theory of atomic structure. Their test used relatively massive alpha particles, which are helium atoms that have lost their two electrons and have a double positive charge because of the two remaining protons. In the experiment, illustrated in Figure 4.7, a narrow beam of alpha particles was directed at a very thin sheet of gold foil. According to the prevailing theory, the alpha particles should have passed easily through the gold, with only a slight deflection due to the positive charge thought to be spread out in the gold atoms.

To everyone's surprise, the great majority of alpha particles passed straight through the gold atoms, without deflection. Even more surprisingly, a small fraction of the alpha particles bounced off the gold foil at very large angles. Some even bounced straight back toward the source. Rutherford later recollected, "This is almost as incredible as if you fired a 15-inch shell at a piece of tissue paper and it came back and hit you."

The Rutherford Atomic Model Based on his experimental results, Rutherford suggested a new theory of the atom. He proposed that the atom is mostly empty space, thus explaining the lack of deflection of most of the alpha particles. He concluded that all the positive charge and almost all the mass are concentrated in a small region that has enough positive charge to account for the great deflection of some of the alpha particles. He called this region the nucleus. The **nucleus** is the tiny central core of an atom and is composed of protons and neutrons.

Interactive Textbook

Animation 4 Take a look at Rutherford's gold-foil experiment, its results, and its conclusions.

with ChemASAP

Using Inference: The Black Box

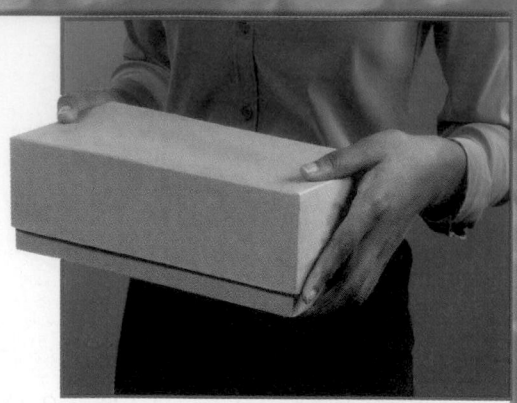

Purpose

To determine the shape of a fixed object inside a sealed box without opening the box.

Materials

- box containing a regularly shaped object fixed in place and a loose marble

Procedure

1. Do not open the box.
2. Manipulate the box so that the marble moves around the fixed object.
3. Gather data (clues) that describe the movement of the marble.
4. Sketch a picture of the object in the box, showing its shape, size, and location within the box.
5. Repeat this activity with a different box containing a different object.

Analysis and Conclusions

1. Find a classmate who had the same lettered box that you had, and compare your findings.
2. What experiment that contributed to a better understanding of the atom does this activity remind you of?

The Rutherford atomic model is known as the nuclear atom. **In the nuclear atom, the protons and neutrons are located in the nucleus. The electrons are distributed around the nucleus and occupy almost all the volume of the atom.** According to this model, the nucleus is tiny compared with the atom as a whole. If an atom were the size of a football stadium, the nucleus would be about the size of a marble.

Although it was an improvement over Thomson's model of the atom, Rutherford's model turned out to be incomplete. In Chapter 5, you will learn how the Rutherford atomic model had to be revised in order to explain the chemical properties of elements.

4.2 Section Assessment

8. **Key Concept** What are three types of subatomic particles?

9. **Key Concept** How does the Rutherford model describe the structure of atoms?

10. What are the charges and relative masses of the three main subatomic particles?

11. Describe Thomson's and Millikan's contributions to atomic theory.

12. Compare Rutherford's expected outcome of the gold-foil experiment with the actual outcome.

13. What experimental evidence led Rutherford to conclude that an atom is mostly empty space?

14. How did Rutherford's model of the atom differ from Thomson's?

Writing ▶ Activity

Explanatory Paragraph Write a paragraph explaining how Rutherford's gold-foil experiment yielded new evidence about atomic structure. *Hint:* First describe the setup of the experiment. Then explain how Rutherford interpreted his experimental data.

Assessment 4.2 Test yourself on the concepts in Section 4.2.

— with **ChemASAP**

Electron Microscopy

Within 30 years of J.J. Thomson's discovery of the electron, scientists were studying how to produce images of objects by using an electron beam. In 1931, German scientists Ernst Ruska and Max Knoll built the first electron microscope. While an ordinary light microscope uses a beam of light and lenses to magnify objects, an electron microscope uses an electron beam and "lenses" consisting of magnetic or electric fields. A typical light microscope is capable of magnifying an object 1000 times. An electron microscope can magnify an object over 100,000 times. **Interpreting Photographs** *What characteristics of the images below provide the viewer with a sense of scale?*

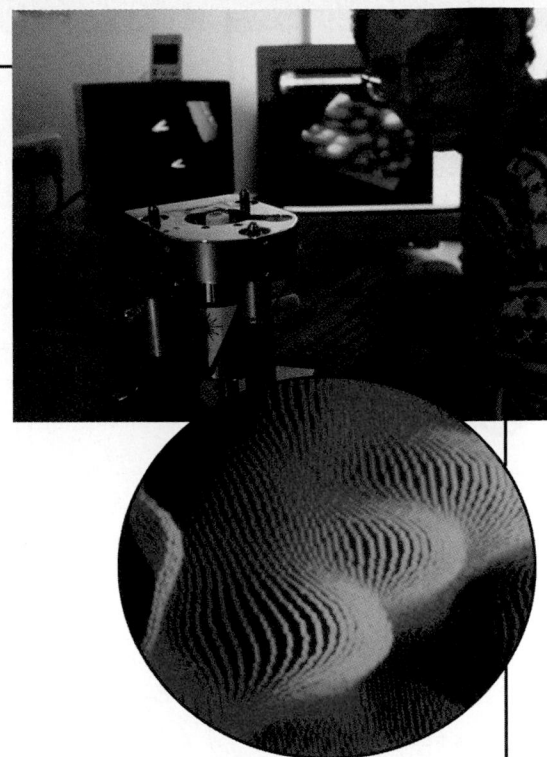

Biochemistry A scientist uses an electron microscope to look at the surface of DNA molecules.

Microelectronics In the colorized electron micrograph below, a wood ant (*Formica fusca*), about 5 mm long, holds a microchip in its jaws. Microelectronics engineers use electron microscopes to measure and analyze the characteristics of microcircuits.

Biology A dust mite (*Dermatophagoides pteronyssinus*), smaller than the period at the end of this sentence, sits on the point of a sewing needle.

Guide for Reading

 Key Concepts

- What makes one element different from another?
- How do you find the number of neutrons in an atom?
- How do isotopes of an element differ?
- How do you calculate the atomic mass of an element?
- Why is a periodic table useful?

Vocabulary

atomic number

mass number

isotopes

atomic mass unit (amu)

atomic mass

periodic table

period

group

Reading Strategy

Building Vocabulary As you read the section, write a definition of each key term in your own words.

Connecting to Your World

Fruits and vegetables come in different varieties. For example, a grocery store might sell three varieties of apples: Granny Smith, Red Delicious, and Golden Delicious. Apple varieties can differ in color, size, texture, aroma, and taste. Just as apples come in different varieties, a chemical element can come in different "varieties" called isotopes. In this section, you will learn how one isotope of an element differs from another.

Atomic Number

Atoms are composed of protons, neutrons, and electrons. Protons and neutrons make up the nucleus. Electrons surround the nucleus. How, then, are atoms of hydrogen, for example, different from atoms of oxygen? Look at Table 4.2. Notice that a hydrogen atom has one proton, but an oxygen atom has eight protons. **Elements are different because they contain different numbers of protons.**

The **atomic number** of an element is the number of protons in the nucleus of an atom of that element. Because all hydrogen atoms have one proton, the atomic number of hydrogen is 1. Similarly, because all oxygen atoms have eight protons, the atomic number of oxygen is 8. The atomic number identifies an element. For each element listed in Table 4.2, the number of protons equals the number of electrons. Remember that atoms are electrically neutral. Thus, the number of electrons (negatively charged particles) must equal the number of protons (positively charged particles).

Table 4.2

Atoms of the First Ten Elements						
Name	Symbol	Atomic number	Protons	Neutrons*	Mass number	Number of electrons
Hydrogen	H	1	1	0	1	1
Helium	He	2	2	2	4	2
Lithium	Li	3	3	4	7	3
Beryllium	Be	4	4	5	9	4
Boron	B	5	5	6	11	5
Carbon	C	6	6	6	12	6
Nitrogen	N	7	7	7	14	7
Oxygen	O	8	8	8	16	8
Fluorine	F	9	9	10	19	9
Neon	Ne	10	10	10	20	10

*Number of neutrons in the most abundant isotope. Isotopes are introduced later in Section 4.3.

CONCEPTUAL PROBLEM 4.1

Understanding Atomic Number

The element nitrogen (N), shown here in liquid form, has an atomic number of 7. How many protons and electrons are in a neutral nitrogen atom?

1 Analyze *Identify the relevant concepts.*

The atomic number gives the number of protons, which in a neutral atom equals the number of electrons.

2 Solve *Apply the concepts to this problem.*

The atomic number of nitrogen is 7, which means that a neutral nitrogen atom has 7 protons and 7 electrons.

Practice Problems

15. Complete the table.

Element	Atomic number	Protons	Electrons
K	19	(a)	19
(b)	(c)	(d)	5
S	16	(e)	(f)
V	(g)	23	(h)

16. How many protons and electrons are in each atom?
  a. fluorine (atomic number = 9)
  b. calcium (atomic number = 20)
  c. aluminum (atomic number = 13)

interactive Textbook

Problem-Solving 4.15 Solve Problem 15 with the help of an interactive guided tutorial.

—with ChemASAP

Mass Number

You know that most of the mass of an atom is concentrated in its nucleus and depends on the number of protons and neutrons. The total number of protons and neutrons in an atom is called the **mass number.** Look again at Table 4.2 and note the mass numbers of helium and carbon. A helium atom has two protons and two neutrons, so its mass number is 4. A carbon atom, which has six protons and six neutrons, has a mass number of 12.

If you know the atomic number and mass number of an atom of any element, you can determine the atom's composition. Table 4.2 shows that an oxygen atom has an atomic number of 8 and a mass number of 16. Because the atomic number equals the number of protons, which equals the number of electrons, an oxygen atom has eight protons and eight electrons. The mass number of oxygen is equal to the number of protons plus the number of neutrons. The oxygen atom, then, has eight neutrons, which is the difference between the mass number and the atomic number $(16 - 8 = 8)$. ✏ **The number of neutrons in an atom is the difference between the mass number and atomic number.**

> Number of neutrons = mass number − atomic number

The composition of any atom can be represented in shorthand notation using atomic number and mass number. Figure 4.8 shows how an atom of gold is represented using this notation. The chemical symbol Au appears with two numbers written to its left. The atomic number is the subscript. The mass number is the superscript.

You can also refer to atoms by using the mass number and the name of the element. For example, $^{197}_{79}\text{Au}$ may be written as gold-197.

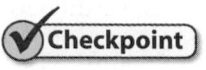**Checkpoint** *How do you calculate mass number?*

Figure 4.8 Au is the chemical symbol for gold. **Applying Concepts** *How many electrons does a gold atom have?*

$^{197}_{79}\text{Au}$

Determining the Composition of an Atom

How many protons, electrons, and neutrons are in each atom?

		Atomic number	Mass number
a.	Beryllium (Be)	4	9
b.	Neon (Ne)	10	20
c.	Sodium (Na)	11	23

1 **Analyze** *List the knowns and the unknowns.*

Knowns	**Unknowns**
• atomic number	• number of protons = ?
• mass number	• number of electrons = ?
	• number of neutrons = ?

Use the definitions of atomic number and mass number to calculate the numbers of protons, electrons, and neutrons.

2 **Calculate** *Solve for the unknowns.*

number of electrons = atomic number

a. 4 **b.** 10 **c.** 11

number of protons = atomic number

a. 4 **b.** 10 **c.** 11

number of neutrons = mass number-atomic number

a. $9 - 4 = 5$ **b.** $20 - 10 = 10$ **c.** $23 - 11 = 12$

3 **Evaluate** *Do the results make sense?*

For each atom, the mass number equals the number of protons plus the number of neutrons. The results make sense.

Practice Problems

17. How many neutrons are in each atom?

a. $^{16}_{8}O$ **b.** $^{32}_{16}S$ **c.** $^{108}_{47}Ag$

d. $^{80}_{35}Br$ **e.** $^{207}_{82}Pb$

18. Use Table 4.2 to express the composition of each atom in shorthand form.

a. carbon-12 **b.** fluorine-19 **c.** beryllium-9

Interactive Textbook

Problem-Solving 4.17
Solve Problem 17 with the help of an interactive guided tutorial.

with ChemASAP

Isotopes

Figure 4.9 shows that there are three different kinds of neon atoms. How do these atoms differ? All have the same number of protons (10) and electrons (10), but they each have different numbers of neutrons. **Isotopes** are atoms that have the same number of protons but different numbers of neutrons. **Because isotopes of an element have different numbers of neutrons, they also have different mass numbers.** Despite these differences, isotopes are chemically alike because they have identical numbers of protons and electrons, which are the subatomic particles responsible for chemical behavior.

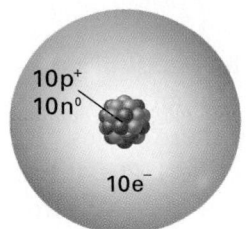
Neon-20
10 protons
10 neutrons
10 electrons

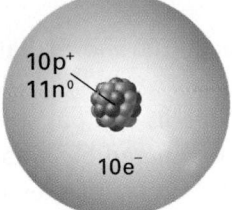
Neon-21
10 protons
11 neutrons
10 electrons

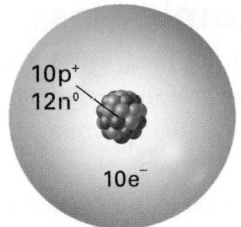
Neon-22
10 protons
12 neutrons
10 electrons

Figure 4.9 Neon-20, neon-21, and neon-22 are three isotopes of neon, a gaseous element used in lighted signs. **Comparing and Contrasting** *How are these isotopes different? How are they similar?*

There are three known isotopes of hydrogen. Each isotope of hydrogen has one proton in its nucleus. The most common hydrogen isotope has no neutrons. It has a mass number of 1 and is called hydrogen-1 ($_1^1H$) or simply hydrogen. The second isotope has one neutron and a mass number of 2. It is called either hydrogen-2 ($_1^2H$) or deuterium. The third isotope has two neutrons and a mass number of 3. This isotope is called hydrogen-3 ($_1^3H$) or tritium.

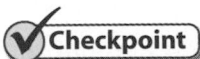 **Checkpoint** *What are three known isotopes of hydrogen?*

CONCEPTUAL PROBLEM 4.2

Writing Chemical Symbols of Isotopes

Diamonds are a naturally occurring form of elemental carbon. Two stable isotopes of carbon are carbon-12 and carbon-13. Write the symbol for each isotope using superscripts and subscripts to represent the mass number and the atomic number.

1 Analyze *Identify the relevant concepts.*

Isotopes are atoms that have the same number of protons but different numbers of neutrons. The composition of an atom can be expressed by writing the chemical symbol, with the atomic number as a subscript and the mass number as a superscript.

2 Solve *Apply the concepts to this problem.*

Based on Table 4.2, the symbol for carbon is C and the atomic number is 6. The mass number for each isotope is given by its name. For carbon-12, the symbol is $_6^{12}C$. For carbon-13, the symbol is $_6^{13}C$.

Practice Problems

19. Three isotopes of oxygen are oxygen-16, oxygen-17, and oxygen-18. Write the symbol for each, including the atomic number and mass number.

20. Three isotopes of chromium are chromium-50, chromium-52, and chromium-53. How many neutrons are in each isotope, given that chromium has an atomic number of 24?

 Textbook

Problem-Solving 4.20
Solve Problem 20 with the help of an interactive guided tutorial.
— with **ChemASAP**

Atomic Mass

A glance back at Table 4.1 on page 106 shows that the actual mass of a proton or a neutron is very small (1.67×10^{-24} g). The mass of an electron is 9.11×10^{-28} g, which is negligible in comparison. Given these values, the mass of even the largest atom is incredibly small. Since the 1920s, it has been possible to determine these tiny masses by using a mass spectrometer. With this instrument, the mass of a fluorine atom was found to be 3.155×10^{-23} g, and the mass of an arsenic atom was found to be 1.244×10^{-22} g. Such data about the actual masses of individual atoms can provide useful information, but, in general, these values are inconveniently small and impractical to work with. Instead, it is more useful to compare the relative masses of atoms using a reference isotope as a standard. The isotope chosen is carbon-12. This isotope of carbon was assigned a mass of exactly 12 atomic mass units. An **atomic mass unit (amu)** is defined as one twelfth of the mass of a carbon-12 atom. Using these units, a helium-4 atom, with a mass of 4.0026 amu, has about one-third the mass of a carbon-12 atom. On the other hand, a nickel-60 atom has about five times the mass of a carbon-12 atom.

A carbon-12 atom has six protons and six neutrons in its nucleus, and its mass is set as 12 amu. The six protons and six neutrons account for nearly all of this mass. Therefore the mass of a single proton or a single

Table 4.3

Natural Percent Abundance of Stable Isotopes of Some Elements

Name	Symbol	Natural percent abundance	Mass (amu)	Average atomic mass
Hydrogen	$^{1}_{1}H$	99.985	1.0078	
	$^{2}_{1}H$	0.015	2.0141	1.0079
	$^{3}_{1}H$	negligible	3.0160	
Helium	$^{3}_{2}He$	0.0001	3.0160	4.0026
	$^{4}_{2}He$	99.9999	4.0026	
Carbon	$^{12}_{6}C$	98.89	12.000	12.011
	$^{13}_{6}C$	1.11	13.003	
Nitrogen	$^{14}_{7}N$	99.63	14.003	14.007
	$^{15}_{7}N$	0.37	15.000	
Oxygen	$^{16}_{8}O$	99.759	15.995	
	$^{17}_{8}O$	0.037	16.995	15.999
	$^{18}_{8}O$	0.204	17.999	
Sulfur	$^{32}_{16}S$	95.002	31.972	
	$^{33}_{16}S$	0.76	32.971	32.06
	$^{34}_{16}S$	4.22	33.967	
	$^{36}_{16}S$	0.014	35.967	
Chlorine	$^{35}_{17}Cl$	75.77	34.969	35.453
	$^{37}_{17}Cl$	24.23	36.966	

Crystalline sulfur

Figure 4.10 Chlorine is a reactive element used to disinfect swimming pools. Chlorine occurs as two isotopes: chlorine-35 and chlorine-37. Because there is more chlorine-35 than chlorine-37, the atomic mass of chlorine, 35.453 amu, is closer to 35 than to 37. **Evaluating** *How does a weighted average differ from an arithmetic mean?*

neutron is about one-twelfth of 12 amu, or about 1 amu. Because the mass of any single atom depends mainly on the number of protons and neutrons in the nucleus of the atom, you might predict that the atomic mass of an element should be a whole number. However, that is not usually the case.

In nature, most elements occur as a mixture of two or more isotopes. Each isotope of an element has a fixed mass and a natural percent abundance. Consider the three isotopes of hydrogen discussed earlier in this section. According to Table 4.3, almost all naturally occurring hydrogen (99.985%) is hydrogen-1. The other two isotopes are present in trace amounts. Notice that the atomic mass of hydrogen listed in Table 4.3 (1.0079 amu) is very close to the mass of hydrogen-1 (1.0078 amu). The slight difference takes into account the larger masses, but smaller amounts, of the other two isotopes of hydrogen.

Now consider the two stable isotopes of chlorine listed in Table 4.3: chlorine-35 and chlorine-37. If you calculate the arithmetic mean of these two masses ((34.969 amu + 36.966 amu)/2), you get an average atomic mass of 35.968 amu. However, this value is higher than the actual value of 35.453. To explain this difference, you need to know the natural percent abundance of the isotopes of chlorine. Chlorine-35 accounts for 75% of the naturally occurring chlorine atoms; chlorine-37 accounts for only 25%. See Figure 4.10. The **atomic mass** of an element is a weighted average mass of the atoms in a naturally occurring sample of the element. A weighted average mass reflects both the mass and the relative abundance of the isotopes as they occur in nature.

Go Online

NSTA SCiLINKS

For: Links on Isotopes
Visit: www.SciLinks.org
Web Code: cdn-1043

Checkpoint *What is the atomic mass of an element?*

CONCEPTUAL PROBLEM 4.3

Using Atomic Mass to Determine the Relative Abundance of Isotopes

The atomic mass of copper is 63.546 amu. Which of copper's two isotopes is more abundant: copper-63 or copper-65?

1 Analyze *Identify the relevant concepts.*

The atomic mass of an element is the weighted average mass of the atoms in a naturally occurring sample of the element. A weighted average mass reflects both the mass and the relative abundance of the isotopes as they occur in nature.

2 Solve *Apply the concepts to this problem.*

The atomic mass of 63.546 amu is closer to 63 than to 65. Because the atomic mass is a weighted average of the isotopes, copper-63 must be more abundant than copper-65.

Practice Problems

21. Boron has two isotopes: boron-10 and boron-11. Which is more abundant, given that the atomic mass of boron is 10.81?

22. There are three isotopes of silicon; they have mass numbers of 28, 29, and 30. The atomic mass of silicon is 28.086 amu. Comment on the relative abundance of these three isotopes.

Problem-Solving 4.21 Solve Problem 21 with the help of an interactive guided tutorial.

with **ChemASAP**

Now that you know that the atomic mass of an element is a weighted average of the masses of its isotopes, you can determine atomic mass based on relative abundance. To do this, you must know three values: the number of stable isotopes of the element, the mass of each isotope, and the natural percent abundance of each isotope. **To calculate the atomic mass of an element, multiply the mass of each isotope by its natural abundance, expressed as a decimal, and then add the products.** The resulting sum is the weighted average mass of the atoms of the element as they occur in nature.

You can calculate the atomic masses listed in Table 4.3 based on the given masses and natural abundances of the isotopes for each element. For example, carbon has two stable isotopes: carbon-12, which has a natural abundance of 98.89%, and carbon-13, which has natural abundance of 1.11%. The mass of carbon-12 is 12.000 amu; the mass of carbon-13 is 13.003 amu. The atomic mass is calculated as follows.

$$\text{Atomic mass of carbon} = (12.000 \text{ amu} \times 0.9889) + (13.003 \text{ amu} \times 0.0111)$$
$$= 12.011 \text{ amu}$$

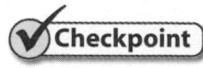 **Checkpoint** *What three values must be known in order to calculate the atomic mass of an element?*

SAMPLE PROBLEM 4.2

Calculating Atomic Mass

Element X has two natural isotopes. The isotope with a mass of 10.012 amu (^{10}X) has a relative abundance of 19.91%. The isotope with a mass of 11.009 amu (^{11}X) has a relative abundance of 80.09%. Calculate the atomic mass of this element.

1 Analyze *List the knowns and the unknown.*

Knowns
- isotope ^{10}X:
  mass = 10.012 amu
  relative abundance = 19.91% = 0.1991
- isotope ^{11}X:
  mass = 11.009 amu
  relative abundance = 80.09% = 0.8009

Unknown
- atomic mass of element X = ?

The mass each isotope contributes to the element's atomic mass can be calculated by multiplying the isotope's mass by its relative abundance. The atomic mass of the element is the sum of these products.

2 Calculate *Solve for the unknown.*

for ^{10}X: $\quad$ 10.012 amu $\times$ 0.1991 = $\quad$ 1.993 amu
for ^{11}X: $\quad$ 11.009 amu $\times$ 0.8009 = $\quad$ <u>8.817 amu</u>
for element X: $\quad\quad$ atomic mass = 10.810 amu

3 Evaluate *Does the result make sense?*

The calculated value is closer to the mass of the more abundant isotope, as would be expected.

Practice Problems

23. The element copper has naturally occurring isotopes with mass numbers of 63 and 65. The relative abundance and atomic masses are 69.2% for mass = 62.93 amu, and 30.8% for mass = 64.93 amu. Calculate the average atomic mass of copper.

24. Calculate the atomic mass of bromine. The two isotopes of bromine have atomic masses and relative abundance of 78.92 amu (50.69%) and 80.92 amu (49.31%).

CHEMath

Percents

A percent is a shorthand way of expressing a fraction whose denominator is 100. For example, 85% is equivalent to 85/100 or 0.85.

When working with percents, it is usually necessary to convert percents to fractions or decimals before using them in a calculation. For instance, if the natural percent abundance of an isotope is 35.6%, then there are 35.6 g of that isotope in 100 g of the element.

Math ▸ **Handbook**

For help with percents, go to page R72.

Interactive Textbook

Problem-Solving 4.24 Solve Problem 24 with the help of an interactive guided tutorial.

— with **ChemASAP**

Bromine

Figure 4.11 Elements are arranged in the modern periodic table in order of atomic number. **Interpreting Diagrams** *How many elements are in Period 2? In Group 2A?*

The Periodic Table—A Preview

Now that you can differentiate between atoms of different elements and also between isotopes of the same element, you need to understand how the elements are organized with respect to each other. A **periodic table** is an arrangement of elements in which the elements are separated into groups based on a set of repeating properties. ⟳ **A periodic table allows you to easily compare the properties of one element (or a group of elements) to another element (or group of elements).**

Figure 4.11 shows the most commonly used form of the modern periodic table, sometimes called the long form. Each element is identified by its symbol placed in a square. The atomic number of the element is shown centered above the symbol. Notice that the elements are listed in order of increasing atomic number, from left to right and top to bottom. Hydrogen (H), the lightest element, is in the top left corner. Helium (He), atomic number 2, is at the top right. Lithium (Li), atomic number 3, is at the left end of the second row.

Each horizontal row of the periodic table is called a **period.** There are seven periods in the modern periodic table. The number of elements per period ranges from 2 (hydrogen and helium) in Period 1, to 32 in Period 6. Within a given period, the properties of the elements vary as you move across it from element to element. This pattern of properties then repeats as you move to the next period.

Each vertical column of the periodic table is called a **group,** or family. Elements within a group have similar chemical and physical properties. Note that each group is identified by a number and the letter A or B. For example, Group 2A contains the elements beryllium (Be), magnesium (Mg), calcium (Ca), strontium (Sr), barium (Ba), and radium (Ra). You will learn more about specific trends in the periodic table in Chapter 6.

Archaeologist

Archaeologists are detectives of the past, sifting for clues that uncover secrets of past civilizations. Archaeologists excavate ancient cities and dwellings looking for artifacts that indicate what kinds of foods ancient people ate, what types of tools they used, and how they interacted with one another as a society. Often, archaeologists must draw conclusions based on indirect evidence.

Knowing when an event occurred or when an artifact was made can provide important information. Archaeologists use techniques such as radiometric-dating, in which a sample is dated by measuring the concentration of certain isotopes, such as carbon-14. This method tells them the age of a sample within a cer-

tain range, and is used with the greatest accuracy for samples no more than 10,000 years old.

Archaeologists also perform chemical tests on artifacts to determine their composition. For example, archaeologists might analyze the glazes used on pottery, or the dyes used in clothing. Archaeologists may also use chemicals to preserve artifacts that have been unearthed, so that the artifacts can be examined without being damaged.

Archaeology requires a background in both history and science. Archaeologists often spend as much time in the laboratory studying their finds as they do out

in the field excavating sites. Archaeologists take courses in archaeological techniques, biology, anatomy, chemistry, math, and history.

Go Online
PHSchool.com

For: Careers in Chemistry
Visit: PHSchool.com
Web Code: cdb-1043

4.3 Section Assessment

25. **Key Concept** What distinguishes the atoms of one element from the atoms of another?

26. **Key Concept** What equation tells you how to calculate the number of neutrons in an atom?

27. **Key Concept** How do the isotopes of a given element differ from one another?

28. **Key Concept** How is atomic mass calculated?

29. **Key Concept** What makes the periodic table such a useful tool?

30. What does the number represent in the isotope platinum-194? Write the symbol for this atom using superscripts and subscripts.

31. The atomic masses of elements are generally not whole numbers. Explain why.

32. List the number of protons, neutrons, and electrons in each pair of isotopes.

    a. $^{6}_{3}\text{Li}$, $^{7}_{3}\text{Li}$ **b.** $^{42}_{20}\text{Ca}$, $^{44}_{20}\text{Ca}$ **c.** $^{78}_{34}\text{Se}$, $^{80}_{34}\text{Se}$

33. Name two elements that have properties similar to those of the element calcium (Ca).

Elements ▸ **Handbook**

Elements Within You Identify the five most abundant elements in the human body, and locate them on the periodic table.

Interactive Textbook

Assessment 4.3 Test yourself on the concepts in Section 4.3.

— with **ChemASAP**

The Atomic Mass of Candium

Purpose
To analyze the isotopes of "candium" and to calculate its atomic mass.

Materials
- sample of candium
- balance
- pencil
- paper

Procedure
Obtain a sample of "candium" that contains three different brands of round, coated candy. Treat each brand of candy as an isotope of candium. Separate the three isotopes into groups labeled A, B, and C, and measure the mass of each isotope. Count the number of atoms in each sample. Make a table similar to the one below to record your measured and calculated data.

	A	B	C	Totals
Total mass (grams)				
Number				
Average mass (grams)				
Relative abundance				
Percent abundance				
Relative mass				

FOR REFERENCE ONLY

Analyze
Using the experimental data, record the answers to the following questions below your data table.

1. Calculate the average mass of each isotope by dividing its total mass by the number of particles of that isotope.

2. Calculate the relative abundance of each isotope by dividing its number of particles by the total number of particles.

3. Calculate the percent abundance of each isotope by multiplying the relative abundance from Step 2 by 100.

4. Calculate the relative mass of each isotope by multiplying its relative abundance from Step 2 by its average mass.

5. Calculate the weighted average mass of all candium particles by adding the relative masses. This weighted average mass is the atomic mass of candium.

6. Explain the difference between percent abundance and relative abundance. What is the result when you total the individual relative abundances? The individual percent abundances?

7. The percent abundance of each kind of candy tells you how many of each kind of candy there are in every 100 particles. What does relative abundance tell you?

8. Compare the total values for rows 3 and 6 in the table. Explain why the totals differ and why the value in row 6 best represents atomic mass.

9. Explain any differences between the atomic mass of your candium sample and that of your neighbor. Explain why the difference would be smaller if larger samples were used.

You're the Chemist
The following small-scale activities allow you to develop your own procedures and analyze the results.

1. **Analyze It!** Determine the atomic mass of a second sample of candium. How does it compare with the first? Suggest reasons for any differences between the samples.

2. **Design It!** Design and test methods to produce identical samples of candium. Try measuring mass or volume as a means of counting. Test these methods by counting each kind of candy in each sample you produce. Which method of sampling gives the most consistent results?

Study Guide

Key Concepts

4.1 Defining the Atom

- Democritus believed that atoms were indivisible and indestructible.
- By using experimental methods, Dalton transformed Democritus's ideas on atoms into a scientific theory.
- Scientists can observe individual atoms by using instruments such as scanning tunneling microscopes.

4.2 Structure of the Nuclear Atom

- Three types of subatomic particles are electrons, protons, and neutrons.
- In the nuclear atom, the protons and neutrons are located in the nucleus. The electrons are distributed around the nucleus and occupy almost all the volume of the atom.

4.3 Distinguishing Among Atoms

- Elements are different because they have different numbers of protons.
- The number of neutrons in an atom is the difference between the mass number and atomic number.
- Because isotopes of an element have different numbers of neutrons, they also have different mass numbers.
- To calculate the atomic mass of an element, multiply the mass of each isotope by its natural percent abundance (expressed as a decimal), and then add the products.
- The periodic table lets you easily compare the properties of one element (or a group of elements) to another element (or group of elements).

Vocabulary

- atom (p. 101)
- atomic mass (p. 115)
- atomic mass unit (amu) (p. 114)
- atomic number (p. 110)
- cathode ray (p. 104)
- Dalton's atomic theory (p. 102)
- electron (p. 104)
- group (p. 118)
- isotopes (p. 112)
- mass number (p. 111)
- neutron (p. 106)
- nucleus (p. 107)
- period (p. 118)
- periodic table (p. 118)
- proton (p. 106)

Key Equation

- number of neutrons = mass number − atomic number

Organizing Information

Use these terms to construct a concept map that organizes the main ideas of this chapter.

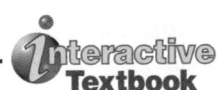

Concept Map 4 Solve the Concept map with the help of an interactive guided tutorial.

— with **ChemASAP**

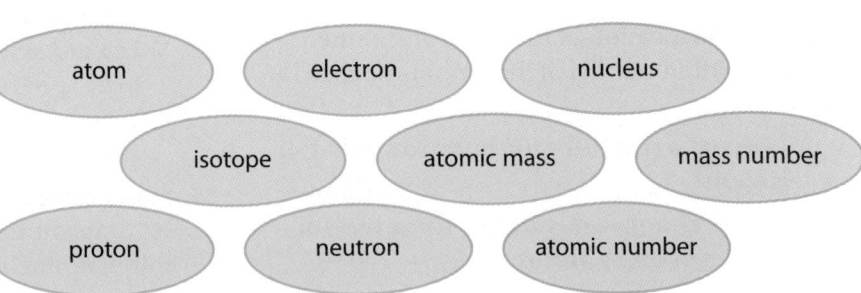

atom   electron   nucleus

isotope   atomic mass   mass number

proton   neutron   atomic number

Defining the Atom

34. What is an atom?

35. What were the limitations of Democritus' ideas about atoms?

36. With which of these statements would John Dalton have agreed in the early 1800s? For each, explain why or why not.
 a. Atoms are the smallest particles of matter.
 b. The mass of an iron atom is different from the mass of a copper atom.
 c. Every atom of silver is identical to every other atom of silver.
 d. A compound is composed of atoms of two or more different elements.

37. Use Dalton's atomic theory to describe how atoms interact during a chemical reaction.

38. Characterize the size of an atom.

39. Dalton's atomic theory was not correct in every detail. Should this be taken as a criticism of Dalton as a scientist? Explain.

40. The law of conservation of mass was introduced in Chapter 2. Use Dalton's atomic theory to explain this law.

Structure of the Nuclear Atom

41. What experimental evidence did Thomson have for each of the following statements?
 a. Electrons have a negative charge.
 b. Atoms of all elements contain electrons.

42. Would you expect two electrons to attract or repel each other?

43. Why does it make sense that if an atom loses electrons, it is left with a positive charge?

44. Describe the location of the electrons in the "plum pudding" model of the atom proposed by Thomson.

45. What were the results of Rutherford's gold foil experiment?

46. What is the charge—positive or negative—of the nucleus of every atom?

47. Which subatomic particles are located in the nucleus?

48. Compare the relative size and relative density of an atom with its nucleus.

49. Describe the numbers and kinds of subatomic particles you would find in the nucleus of a boron-11 atom.

50. What parts of Dalton's atomic theory no longer agree with the current model of the atom?

51. Millikan measured the quantity of charge carried by an electron. How did he then calculate the mass of an electron?

52. Why are atoms considered the basic building blocks of matter even though smaller particles, such as protons and electrons, exist?

53. What characteristics of cathode rays led Thomson to conclude that the rays consisted of negatively charged particles?

54. **The diagram below shows gold atoms being bombarded with fast-moving alpha particles.**

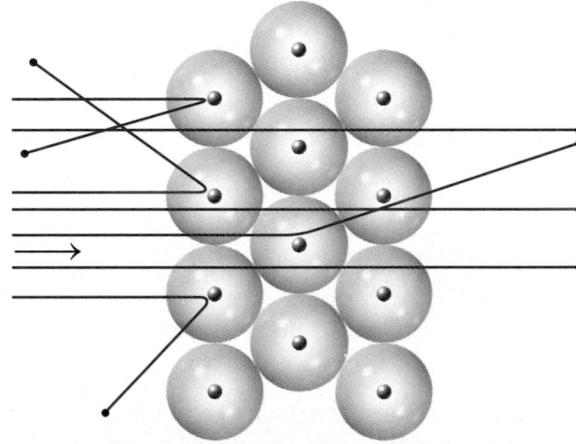

 a. The large yellow spheres represent gold atoms. What do the small gray spheres represent?
 b. List at least two characteristics of the small gray spheres.
 c. Which subatomic particle cannot be found in the area represented by the gray spheres?

55. How could you modify Rutherford's experimental procedure to determine the relative sizes of different nuclei?

56. Rutherford's atomic theory proposed a dense nucleus surrounded by very small electrons. This implies that atoms are composed mainly of empty space. If all matter is mainly empty space, why is it impossible to walk through walls or pass your hand through your desk?

57. When the masses of the particles that make up an atom are added together, the sum is always larger than the actual mass of the atom. The missing mass, called the mass defect, represents the matter converted into energy when the nucleus was formed from its component protons and neutrons. Calculate the mass defect of a chlorine-35 atom by using the data in Table 4.1. The actual mass of a chlorine-35 atom is 5.81×10^{-23} g.

Distinguishing Between Atoms

58. Why is an atom electrically neutral?

59. What does the atomic number of each atom represent?

60. How many protons are in the nuclei of the following atoms?
　　a. phosphorus　　　　d. cadmium
　　b. molybdenum　　　　e. chromium
　　c. aluminum　　　　　f. lead

61. What is the difference between the mass number and the atomic number of an atom?

62. Name two ways that isotopes of an element differ.

63. How can there be more than 1000 different atoms when there are only about 100 different elements?

64. What data must you know about the isotopes of an element to calculate the atomic mass of the element?

65. How is an average mass different than a weighted average mass?

66. What is the atomic mass of an element?

67. How are the elements arranged in the modern periodic table?

68. Look up the word *periodic* in the dictionary. Propose a reason for the naming of the periodic table.

69. How is the number of electrons for a neutral atom of a given element related to the atomic number of that element?

70. How is the atomic mass of an element calculated from isotope data?

71. The four isotopes of lead are shown below, each with its percent by mass abundance and the composition of its nucleus. Using these data, calculate the approximate atomic mass of lead.

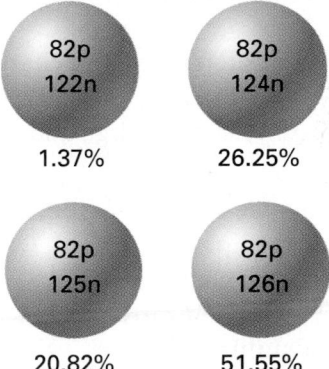

82p 122n	82p 124n
1.37%	26.25%
82p 125n	82p 126n
20.82%	51.55%

72. Using the data for nitrogen listed in Table 4.3, calculate the average atomic mass of nitrogen. Show your work.

73. Do you think there are more elements left to be discovered? Explain your answer.

74. Lithium has two naturally occurring isotopes. Lithium-6 has an atomic mass of 6.015 amu; lithium-7 has an atomic mass of 7.016 amu. The atomic mass of lithium is 6.941 amu. What is the percentage of naturally occurring lithium-7?

Test-Taking Tip

Connectors Sometimes two phrases in a true/false question are connected by a word such as *because* or *therefore*. These words imply a relationship between one part of the sentence and another. Statements that include such words can be false even if both parts of the statement are true by themselves.

Regents Practice Exam

Part A

For each statement or question write the number of the word or expression that, of those given, best completes the statement or answers the question.

1. Which list contains elements that fall within the same group on the periodic table?
   - (1) He, Ar, Xe
   - (2) O, F, Ne
   - (3) K, Rb, Ba
   - (4) H, He, Li

2. Which of the following descriptions is *incorrect?*
   - (1) A proton has a positive charge and is located in the nucleus.
   - (2) A proton has a mass of ≈ 1 atomic mass unit (amu).
   - (3) An electron has a negative charge and a mass of ≈ 1 amu and is found in the nucleus.
   - (4) A neutron has no charge and a mass of ≈ 1 amu.

3. Isotopes of an element have different
   - (1) numbers of protons
   - (2) numbers of electrons
   - (3) numbers of neutrons
   - (4) atomic numbers

4. What is the mass number of an atom that contains 9 electrons, 9 protons, and 10 neutrons?
   - (1) 9
   - (2) 18
   - (3) 19
   - (4) 28

5. The modern model of the atom
   - (1) shows an uncharged nucleus
   - (2) shows protons, neutrons, and electrons evenly distributed throughout the atom
   - (3) shows that all subatomic particles have equal mass
   - (4) has evolved over many years through the work of many scientists

6. Which of the following choices shows particles that have a mass of approximately 1 amu?
   - (1) proton and electron
   - (2) proton and neutron
   - (3) neutron and electron
   - (4) proton, electron, and neutron

7. Copper has an atomic number of 29. This number tells you that copper always has
   - (1) 29 neutrons
   - (2) 29 protons
   - (3) a combined total of 29 protons and neutrons
   - (4) a difference of 29 in its number of protons and neutrons

Part B-1

For each statement or question write the number of the word or expression that, of those given, best completes the statement or answers the question.

8. An atom composed of 16 protons, 16 electrons, and 16 neutrons is
   - (1) $^{48}_{16}S$
   - (2) $^{16}_{32}Ge$
   - (3) $^{32}_{16}S$
   - (4) $^{16}_{32}S$

9. Thallium has two isotopes, thallium-203 and thallium-205. Thallium's atomic number is 81, and its atomic mass is 204.38 amu. Which of the following statements about the thallium isotopes is true?
   - (1) More thallium-203 exists in nature.
   - (2) Atoms of both isotopes have 81 protons.
   - (3) Thallium-205 atoms have fewer neutrons.
   - (4) The most common atom of thallium has a mass of 204.38 amu.

10. Which of the following statements about the periodic table is correct?
    - (1) Elements are arranged in order of increasing atomic mass.
    - (2) A period is a vertical column.
    - (3) The properties of the elements within a period vary from element to element.
    - (4) Elements in a group vary considerably in their chemical properties.

11. Every aluminum-27 atom has
    - (1) 27 protons and 27 electrons
    - (2) an equal number of protons and neutrons
    - (3) 13 protons and 14 neutrons
    - (4) a total of 27 protons and electrons

12. An electron is repelled by a negatively charged particle because
    - (1) an electron has a negative charge
    - (2) an electron has a positive charge
    - (3) an electron has no charge
    - (4) particles with unlike charges repel each other

Part B-2

Answer each of the following questions.

13. Classify each of the following materials as an element, a compound, or a mixture.
    a. sulfur
    c. newspaper
    b. salad oil
    d. orange

14. Oxygen and hydrogen react explosively to form water. In one reaction, 6 g of hydrogen combines with oxygen to form 54 g of water. How much oxygen was used?

15. What is the mass of 4.42 cm³ of platinum? The density of platinum is 22.5 g/cm³.

Use the art to answer Question 16.

16. How many nitrogen-14 atoms would you need to place on the right pan to balance the three calcium-42 atoms on the left pan of the "atomic balance" below? Describe the method you used to determine your answer, including any calculations.

17. If you know the atomic number and mass number of an atom of an element, how can you determine that atom's composition?

18. What makes isotopes of the same element chemically alike?

19. In the periodic table, what happens to the pattern of properties within a period when you move from one period to the next?

20. How do the charge and mass of a neutron compare to those of a proton?

21. Complete the following table by referring to Figure 4.11 on page 118.

Atomic number	Mass number	Number of protons	Number of neutrons	Symbol of element
9	(a)	(b)	10	(c)
(d)	(e)	14	15	(f)
(g)	47	(h)	25	(i)
(j)	55	25	(k)	(l)

Part C

Answer each of the following questions.

22. Diamond and graphite are both composed of carbon atoms. The density of diamond is 3.52 g/cm³. The density of graphite is 2.25 g/cm³. In 1955, scientists successfully made diamond from graphite. Using the relative densities, imagine what happens at the atomic level when this change occurs.

23. This chapter illustrates the scientific method in action. What happens when new experimental results cannot be explained by the existing theory?

24. The following table shows some of the data collected by Rutherford and his colleagues during their gold foil experiment.

Angle of deflection (degrees)	Number of deflections
5	8,289,000
10	502,570
15	120,570
30	7800
45	1435
60	477
75	211
>105	198

a. What percentage of the alpha particle deflections were 5° or less?
b. What percentage of the deflections were 15° or less?
c. What percentage of the deflections were 60° or greater?

A prism separates
white light into
different colors.

INQUIRY Activity

Observing Light Emission From Wintergreen Mints

Materials

3 different brands of wintergreen mints, a pair of
pliers, transparent tape, and a dark room

Procedure

1. Break each mint in half.

2. Wrap the jaws of the pliers with transparent tape.
   Caution *Handle pliers carefully to avoid pinching
   your skin.*

3. Turn off the lights and allow your eyes to adjust to
   the darkness. **Caution** *Never taste any material
   used in the lab, including candy.*

4. Watch the exposed edge of the mint as you carefully crush it between the jaws of the pliers. Note
   the color and brightness of any emitted light.

5. Repeat Step 4 for the other two mints.

Think About It

1. What did you observe when you crushed the
   mints?

2. Did all the mints emit light? Propose an explanation for your observations.

5.1 Models of the Atom

New York Standards: 3.1a–c, 3.1h–k

Connecting to Your World

Aeronautical engineers use wind tunnels and scale models to simulate and test the forces from the moving air on each proposed design. The scale model shown is a physical model. However, not all models are physical. In fact, several theoretical models of the atom have been developed over the last few hundred years. In this section, you will learn about the currently accepted model of how electrons behave in atoms.

The Development of Atomic Models

So far in this textbook, the model for the atom consisted of protons and neutrons making up a nucleus surrounded by electrons. After discovering the atomic nucleus, Rutherford used existing ideas about the atom and proposed an atomic model in which the electrons move around the nucleus, like the planets move around the sun. Rutherford's model explained only a few simple properties of atoms. It could not explain, for example, why metals or compounds of metals give off characteristic colors when heated in a flame, or why objects—when heated to higher and higher temperatures—first glow dull red, then yellow, then white, as shown in Figure 5.1. 🔑 **Rutherford's atomic model could not explain the chemical properties of elements.** Explaining what leads to the chemical properties of elements requires a model that better describes the behavior of electrons within atoms.

Guide for Reading

🔑 **Key Concepts**
- What was inadequate about Rutherford's atomic model?
- What was the new proposal in the Bohr model of the atom?
- What does the quantum mechanical model determine about the electrons in an atom?
- How do sublevels of principal energy levels differ?

Vocabulary

energy levels
quantum
quantum mechanical model
atomic orbital

Reading Strategy

Using Prior Knowledge Before you read, jot down three things you already know about atoms. When you read the section, explain how what you already knew helped you learn something new.

Figure 5.1 Rutherford's model fails to explain why objects change color when heated. As the temperature of this horseshoe is increased, it first appears black, then red, then yellow, and then white. The observed behavior could be explained only if the atoms in the iron gave off light in specific amounts of energy. A better atomic model was needed to explain this observation.

Dalton Model

Tiny, solid sphere

1803 John Dalton pictures atoms as tiny, indestructible particles, with no internal structure.

Thomson Model

Sphere with positive charge throughout

Negatively charged particle (electron)

1897 J.J. Thomson, a British scientist, discovers the electron. The later leads to his "plum-pudding" model. He pictures electrons embedded in a sphere of positive electrical charge.

Path of a moving electron

Nucleus

Rutherford Model

1904 Hantaro Nagaoka, a Japanese physicist, suggests that an atom has a central nucleus. Electrons move in orbits like the rings around Saturn.

1911 New Zealand physicist Ernest Rutherford finds that an atom has a small, dense, positively charged nucleus. Electrons move around the nucleus.

| 1800 | 1805 | 1895 | 1900 | 1905 | 1910 |

Figure 5.2 These illustrations show how the atomic model has changed as scientists learned more about the atom's structure.

The Bohr Model

Niels Bohr (1885–1962), a young Danish physicist and a student of Rutherford, believed Rutherford's model needed improvement. In 1913 Bohr changed Rutherford's model to include newer discoveries about how the energy of an atom changes when it absorbs or emits light. He considered the simplest atom, hydrogen, which has one electron. **Bohr proposed that an electron is found only in specific circular paths, or orbits, around the nucleus.** The timeline in Figure 5.2 shows the development of atomic models from 1800 to 1935.

Each possible electron orbit in Bohr's model has a fixed energy. The fixed energies an electron can have are called **energy levels.** The fixed energy levels of electrons are somewhat like the rungs of the ladder in Figure 5.3a. The lowest rung of the ladder corresponds to the lowest energy level. A person can climb up or down a ladder by going from rung to rung. Similarly, an electron can jump from one energy level to another. A person on a ladder cannot stand between the rungs. Similarly, the electrons in an atom cannot be between energy levels. To move from one rung to another, a person climbing a ladder must move just the right distance. To move from one energy level to another, an electron must gain or lose just the right amount of energy. In general, the higher an electron is on the energy ladder, the farther it is from the nucleus.

A **quantum** of energy is the amount of energy required to move an electron from one energy level to another energy level. The energy of an electron is said to be quantized. You have probably heard the term *quantum leap* used to describe an abrupt change. The term originates from the ideas found in the Bohr model of the atom.

Word *Origins*

Quantum comes from the Latin word *quantus,* meaning "how much." **What other commonly used English word comes from this root?**

An electron *can gain or lose energy by changing its orbit.*

Electron

Nucleus

The nucleus *contains protons and neutrons.*

The electron cloud *is a visual model of the probable locations of electrons in an atom. The probability of finding an electron is higher in the denser regions of the cloud.*

Bohr Model

Electron Cloud Model

1913 In Niels Bohr's model, the electrons move in circular orbits at fixed distances from the nucleus.

1923 French physicist Louis de Broglie proposes that moving particles like electrons have some properties of waves. Within a few years, experimental evidence supports the idea.

1926 Erwin Schrödinger develops mathematical equations to describe the motion of electrons in atoms. His work leads to the electron cloud model.

1932 James Chadwick, an English physicist, confirms the existence of neutrons, which have no charge. Atomic nuclei contain neutrons and positively charged protons.

| 1915 | 1920 | 1925 | 1930 | 1935 |

The amount of energy an electron gains or loses in an atom is not always the same. Like the rungs of the strange ladder in Figure 5.3b, the energy levels in an atom are not equally spaced. The higher energy levels are closer together. It takes less energy to climb from one rung to another near the top of the ladder in Figure 5.3b, where the rungs are closer. Similarly, the higher the energy level occupied by an electron, the less energy it takes to move from that energy level to the next energy level.

The Bohr model gave results in agreement with experiment for the hydrogen atom. However, it still failed in many ways to explain the energies absorbed and emitted by atoms with more than one electron.

Figure 5.3 These ladder steps are somewhat like energy levels. **ⓐ** In an ordinary ladder, the rungs are equally spaced. **ⓑ** The energy levels in atoms are unequally spaced, like the rungs in this ladder. The higher energy levels are closer together.

electron cloud

b

Figure 5.4 The electron cloud of an atom is compared here to photographs of a spinning airplane propeller. **a** The airplane propeller is somewhere in the blurry region it produces in this picture, but the picture does not tell you its exact position at any instant. **b** Similarly, the electron cloud of an atom represents the locations where an electron is likely to be found.

The Quantum Mechanical Model

The Rutherford planetary model and the Bohr model of the atom are based on describing paths of moving electrons as you would describe the path of a large moving object. New theoretical calculations and experimental results were inconsistent with describing electron motion this way. In 1926, the Austrian physicist Erwin Schrödinger (1887–1961) used these new results to devise and solve a mathematical equation describing the behavior of the electron in a hydrogen atom. The modern description of the electrons in atoms, the **quantum mechanical model,** comes from the mathematical solutions to the Schrödinger equation.

Like the Bohr model, the quantum mechanical model of the atom restricts the energy of electrons to certain values. Unlike the Bohr model, however, the quantum mechanical model does not involve an exact path the electron takes around the nucleus. ⟐ **The quantum mechanical model determines the allowed energies an electron can have and how likely it is to find the electron in various locations around the nucleus.**

How likely it is to find the electron in a particular location is described by probability. If you place three red marbles and one green marble into a box and then pick a marble without looking, the probability of picking the green marble is one in four, or 25%. This means that if you put the four marbles in a box and picked one, and repeated this a great many times, you would pick a green marble in 25% of your tries.

The quantum mechanical model description of how the electron moving around the nucleus is similar to the motion of a rotating propeller blade. Figure 5.4a shows that the propeller blade has the same probability of being anywhere in the blurry region it produces in the picture, but you cannot tell its precise location at any instant. Similarly, in the quantum mechanical model of the atom, the probability of finding an electron within a certain volume of space surrounding the nucleus can be represented as a fuzzy cloud. The cloud is more dense where the probability of finding the electron is high. The cloud is less dense where the probability of finding the electron is low. Though it is unclear where the cloud ends, there is at least a slight chance of finding the electron at a considerable distance from the nucleus. Therefore, attempts to show probabilities as a fuzzy cloud are usually limited to the volume in which the electron is found 90% of the time. To visualize an electron probability cloud, imagine that you could mold a sack around the cloud so that the electron was inside the sack 90% of the time. The shape of the sack would then give you a useful picture of the shape of the cloud.

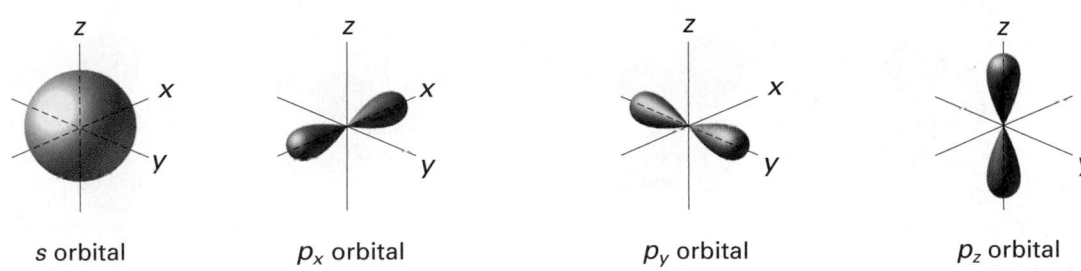

s orbital p_x orbital p_y orbital p_z orbital

Figure 5.5 The electron clouds for the *s* orbital and the *p* orbitals are shown here.

Atomic Orbitals

Solving the Schrödinger equation gives the energies an electron can have. These are its energy levels. For each energy level, the Schrödinger equation also leads to a mathematical expression, called an atomic orbital, describing the probability of finding an electron at various locations around the nucleus. An **atomic orbital** is often thought of as a region of space in which there is a high probability of finding an electron.

The energy levels of electrons in the quantum mechanical model are labeled by principal quantum numbers (*n*). These are assigned the values *n* = 1, 2, 3, 4, and so forth. For each principal energy level, there may be several orbitals with different shapes and at different energy levels. These energy levels within a principal energy level constitute energy sublevels. **Each energy sublevel corresponds to an orbital of different shape describing where the electron is likely to be found.**

Different atomic orbitals are denoted by letters. As Figure 5.5 shows, *s* orbitals are spherical, and *p* orbitals are dumbbell-shaped. Because of the spherical shape of an *s* orbital, the probability of finding an electron at a given distance from the nucleus in an *s* orbital does not depend on direction. The three kinds of *p* orbitals have different orientations in space.

 How do s and p orbitals differ?

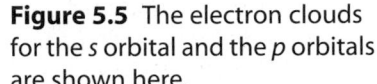
Textbook

Animation 5 Observe the characteristics of atomic orbitals.

Table 5.1

Summary of Principal Energy Levels, Sublevels, and Orbitals		
Principal energy level	**Number of sublevels**	**Type of sublevel**
n = 1	1	1*s* (1 148rbital)
n = 2	2	2*s* (1 orbital), 2*p* (3 orbitals)
n = 3	3	3*s* (1 orbital), 3*p* (3 orbitals), 3*d* (5 orbitals)
n = 4	4	4*s* (1 orbital), 4*p* (3 orbitals), 4*d* (5 orbitals), 4*f* (7 orbitals)

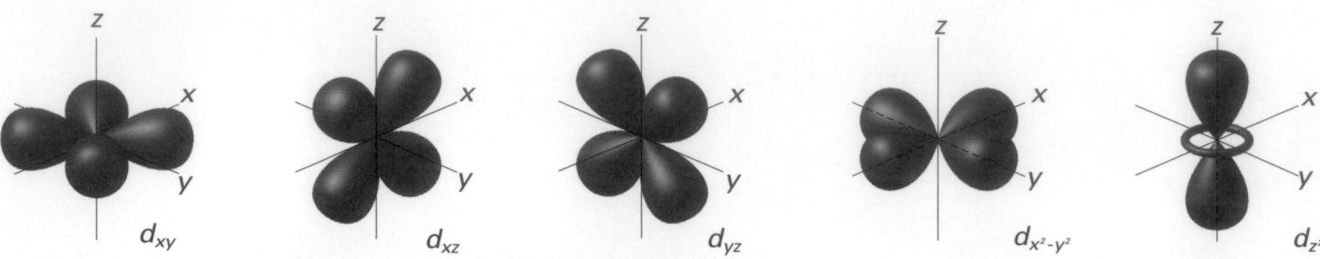

Figure 5.6 The *d* orbitals are illustrated here. Four of the five *d* orbitals have the same shape but different orientations in space. **Interpreting Diagrams** *How are the orientations of the d_{xy} and $d_{x^2-y^2}$ orbitals similar? How are they different?*

Figure 5.6 shows the shapes of *d* orbitals. Four of the five *d* orbitals have clover leaf shapes. The shapes of *f* orbitals are more complicated than for *d* orbitals.

The numbers and kinds of atomic orbitals depend on the energy sublevel. The lowest principal energy level ($n = 1$) has only one sublevel, called 1*s*.

The second principal energy level ($n = 2$) has two sublevels, 2*s* and 2*p*. The 2*p* sublevel is of higher energy than the 2*s* and consists of three *p* orbitals of equal energy. The long axis of each dumbbell-shaped *p* orbital is perpendicular to the other two. It is convenient to label these orbitals $2p_x$, $2p_y$, and $2p_z$. Thus the second principal energy level has four orbitals: 2*s*, $2p_x$, $2p_y$, and $2p_z$.

The third principal energy level ($n = 3$) has three sublevels. These are called 3*s*, 3*p*, and 3*d*. As shown in Figure 5.6, the 3*d* sublevel consists of five *d* orbitals of equal energy. Thus the third principal energy level has nine orbitals (one 3*s*, three 3*p*, and five 3*d* orbitals).

The fourth principal energy level ($n = 4$) has four sublevels, called 4*s*, 4*p*, 4*d*, and 4*f*. The 4*f* sublevel consists of seven *f* orbitals of equal energy. The fourth principal energy level, then, has 16 orbitals (one 4*s*, three 4*p*, five 4*d*, and seven 4*f* orbitals).

As mentioned, the principal quantum number always equals the number of sublevels within that principal energy level. The maximum number of electrons that can occupy a principal energy level is given by the formula $2n^2$, where *n* is the principal quantum number. The number of electrons allowed in each of the first four energy levels is shown in Table 5.2.

Table 5.2

Maximum Numbers of Electrons

Energy level *n*	Maximum number of electrons
1	2
2	8
3	18
4	32

5.1 Section Assessment

1. **Key Concept** Why did Rutherford's atomic model need to be replaced?

2. **Key Concept** What was the basic new proposal in the Bohr model of the atom?

3. **Key Concept** What does the quantum mechanical model determine about electrons in atoms?

4. **Key Concept** How do two sublevels of the same principal energy level differ from each other?

5. How can electrons in an atom move from one energy level to another?

6. The energies of electrons are said to be quantized. Explain what this means.

7. How many orbitals are in the following sublevels?
   a. 3*p* sublevel   **b.** 2*s* sublevel   **c.** 4*p* sublevel
   d. 3*d* sublevel   **e.** 4*f* sublevel

Connecting ▶ **Concepts**

Reread the materials on the quantum mechanical model of the atom. Describe how the quantum mechanical model differs from Dalton's model, from Thomson's model, and from Rutherford's model.

Textbook

Assessment 5.1 Test yourself on the concepts in Section 5.1.

with **ChemASAP**

New York Standards: 3.1a, 3.1h, 3.1i

Connecting to Your World Does this scene look natural to you? Surprisingly, it is. Arrangements like this are rare in nature because they are unstable. Unstable arrangements, whether the grains of sand in a sandcastle or the rock formation shown here, tend to become more stable by losing energy. If this rock were to tumble over, it would end up at a lower height. It would have less energy than before, but its position would be more stable. In this section, you will learn that energy and stability play an important role in determining how electrons are configured in an atom.

Electron Configurations

Try to balance a pencil on its point. Each time you try, the pencil falls over. At the end of its fall, its energy has decreased. In most natural phenomena, change proceeds toward the lowest possible energy. In the atom, electrons and the nucleus interact to make the most stable arrangement possible. The ways in which electrons are arranged into various orbitals around the nuclei of atoms are called **electron configurations.**

🔑 **Three rules—the aufbau principle, the Pauli exclusion principle, and Hund's rule—tell you how to find the electron configurations of atoms.** The three rules are as follows.

Aufbau Principle According to the **aufbau principle,** electrons occupy the orbitals of lowest energy first. Suppose you compare how electrons fill the orbitals in hydrogen with how they fill the orbitals in helium. Continue to examine how each atom's orbitals are filled compared with the atom that has one more proton and one more electron.

Key Concepts
- What are the three rules for writing the electron configurations of elements?
- Why do actual electron configurations for some elements differ from those assigned using the aufbau principle?

Vocabulary
electron configurations
aufbau principle
Pauli exclusion principle
Hund's rule

Reading Strategy
Building Vocabulary As you read the section, write a definition of each key term in your own words.

Figure 5.7 This aufbau diagram shows the energy levels of the various atomic orbitals. Orbitals of greater energy are higher on the diagram. **Using Tables** *Which is of higher energy, a 4d or a 5s orbital?*

Look at Figure 5.7. Each box (□) represents an atomic orbital. The various orbitals for any sublevel of a principal energy level are always of equal energy. Further, within a principal energy level the *s* sublevel is always the lowest-energy sublevel. Yet the range of energy levels within a principal energy level can overlap the energy levels of another principal level. Notice again in Figure 5.7 that the filling of atomic orbitals does not follow a simple pattern beyond the second energy level. For example, the 4*s* orbital is lower in energy than a 3*d* orbital.

Pauli Exclusion Principle According to the **Pauli exclusion principle,** an atomic orbital may describe at most two electrons. For example, either one or two electrons can occupy an *s* orbital or a *p* orbital. To occupy the same orbital, two electrons must have opposite spins; that is, the electron spins must be paired. Spin is a quantum mechanical property of electrons and may be thought of as clockwise or counterclockwise. A vertical arrow indicates an electron and its direction of spin (↑ or ↓). An orbital containing paired electrons is written as ↑↓ .

Hund's Rule When you use the aufbau diagram to decide how electrons occupy orbitals of equal energy, one electron enters each orbital until all the orbitals contain one electron with the same spin direction. **Hund's rule** states that electrons occupy orbitals of the same energy in a way that makes the number of electrons with the same spin direction as large as possible. For example, three electrons would occupy three orbitals of equal energy as follows: ↑ ↑ ↑ . Second electrons then occupy each orbital so that their spins are paired with the first electron in the orbital. Thus each orbital can eventually have two electrons with paired spins.

Table 5.3

Electron Configurations for Some Selected Elements							
	Orbital filling						Electron configuration
Element	1s	2s	2p$_x$	2p$_y$	2p$_z$	3s	
H	↑	□	□	□	□	□	$1s^1$
He	↑↓	□	□	□	□	□	$1s^2$
Li	↑↓	↑	□	□	□	□	$1s^2 2s^1$
C	↑↓	↑↓	↑	↑	□	□	$1s^2 2s^2 2p^2$
N	↑↓	↑↓	↑	↑	↑	□	$1s^2 2s^2 2p^3$
O	↑↓	↑↓	↑↓	↑	↑	□	$1s^2 2s^2 2p^4$
F	↑↓	↑↓	↑↓	↑↓	↑	□	$1s^2 2s^2 2p^5$
Ne	↑↓	↑↓	↑↓	↑↓	↑↓	□	$1s^2 2s^2 2p^6$
Na	↑↓	↑↓	↑↓	↑↓	↑↓	↑	$1s^2 2s^2 2p^6 3s^1$

Interactive Textbook

Simulation 2 Fill atomic orbitals to build the ground state of several atoms.

—— with **ChemASAP**

Look at the orbital filling diagrams of the atoms listed in Table 5.3. An oxygen atom contains eight electrons. The orbital of lowest energy, $1s$, has one electron, then a second electron of opposite spin. The next orbital to fill is $2s$. It also has one electron, then a second electron of opposite spin. One electron then occupies each of the three $2p$ orbitals of equal energy. The remaining electron now pairs with an electron occupying one of the $2p$ orbitals. The other two $2p$ orbitals remain only half filled, with one electron each.

A convenient shorthand method for showing the electron configuration of an atom involves writing the energy level and the symbol for every sublevel occupied by an electron. You indicate the number of electrons occupying that sublevel with a superscript. For hydrogen, with one electron in a $1s$ orbital, the electron configuration is written $1s^1$. For helium, with two electrons in a $1s$ orbital, the configuration is $1s^2$. For oxygen, with two electrons in a $1s$ orbital, two electrons in a $2s$ orbital, and four electrons in $2p$ orbitals, it is $1s^2 2s^2 2p^4$. Note that the sum of the superscripts equals the number of electrons in the atom.

When the configurations are written, the sublevels within the same principal energy level are generally written together. This is not always the same order as given on the aufbau diagram. The $3d$ sublevel, for example, is written before the $4s$ sublevel, even though the aufbau diagram shows the $4s$ sublevel to have lower energy.

Go Online
NSTA SCI_LINKS

For: Links on Electron Configuration
Visit: www.SciLinks.org
Web Code: cdn-1052

CONCEPTUAL PROBLEM 5.1

Writing Electron Configurations

Phosphorus, an element used in matches, has an atomic number of 15. Write the electron configuration of a phosphorus atom.

1 Analyze *Identify the relevant concepts.*
Phosphorus has 15 electrons. There is a maximum of two electrons per orbital. Electrons do not pair up within an energy sublevel (orbitals of equal energy) until each orbital already has one electron.

2 Solve *Apply concepts to this situation.*
Using Figure 5.7 on page 133, place electrons in the orbitals with the lowest energy ($1s$) first, then continue placing electrons in each orbital with the next higher energy.

P $1s^2 2s^2 2p^6 3s^2 3p^3$
The superscripts add up to the number of electrons. When the configurations are written, the sublevels within the same principal energy level are written together. This is not always the same order as given on the aufbau diagram. In this case, the $3d$ sublevel is written before the lower-energy $4s$ sublevel.

Practice Problems

8. Write the electron configuration for each atom.
   a. carbon   **b.** argon   **c.** nickel

9. Write the electron configuration for each atom. How many unpaired electrons does each atom have?
   a. boron   **b.** silicon

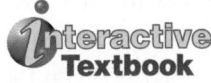
Interactive Textbook

Problem Solving 5.9
Solve Problem 9 with the help of an interactive guided tutorial.
— with **ChemASAP**

Figure 5.8 Copper is a good conductor of electricity and is commonly used in electrical wiring.

Exceptional Electron Configurations

Copper, shown in Figure 5.8, has an electron configuration that is an exception to the aufbau principle. You can obtain correct electron configurations for the elements up to vanadium (atomic number 23) by following the aufbau diagram for orbital filling. If you were to continue in that fashion, however, you would assign chromium and copper the following incorrect configurations:

$$Cr\ 1s^2\ 2s^2\ 2p^6\ 3s^2\ 3p^6\ 3d^4\ 4s^2$$
$$Cu\ 1s^2\ 2s^2\ 2p^6\ 3s^2\ 3p^6\ 3d^9\ 4s^2$$

The correct electron configurations are as follows:

$$Cr\ 1s^2\ 2s^2\ 2p^6\ 3s^2\ 3p^6\ 3d^5\ 4s^1$$
$$Cu\ 1s^2\ 2s^2\ 2p^6\ 3s^2\ 3p^6\ 3d^{10}\ 4s^1$$

These arrangements give chromium a half-filled d sublevel and copper a filled d sublevel. Filled energy sublevels are more stable than partially filled sublevels. 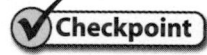 **Some actual electron configurations differ from those assigned using the aufbau principle because half-filled sublevels are not as stable as filled sublevels, but they are more stable than other configurations.** This tendency overcomes the small difference between the energies of the $3d$ and $4s$ sublevels in copper and chromium.

Exceptions to the aufbau principle are due to subtle electron-electron interactions in orbitals with very similar energies. At higher principal quantum numbers, energy differences between some sublevels (such as $5f$ and $6d$, for example) are even smaller than in the chromium and copper examples. As a result, there are other exceptions to the aufbau principle. Although it is worth knowing that exceptions to the aufbau principle occur, it is more important to understand the general rules for determining electron configurations in the many cases where the aufbau rule applies.

✓ Checkpoint *How are energy differences and exceptions to the aufbau principle related?*

5.2 Section Assessment

10. 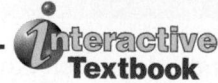 **Key Concept** What are the three rules for writing the electron configuration of elements?

11. **Key Concept** Explain why the actual electron configurations for some elements differ from those assigned using the aufbau principle.

12. Use Figure 5.7 to arrange the following sublevels in order of decreasing energy: $2p$, $4s$, $3s$, $3d$, and $3p$.

13. Why does one electron in a potassium atom go into the fourth energy level instead of squeezing into the third energy level along with the eight already there?

Writing ▶ Activity

Modeling How Orbitals Fill Write a brief description of how trying to place two bar magnets pointing in the same direction alongside each other is like trying to place two electrons into the same orbital.

*i*nteractive **Textbook**

Assessment 5.2 Test yourself on the concepts in Section 5.2.

— with **ChemASAP**

Small-Scale LAB

Atomic Emission Spectra

Purpose

To build a spectroscope and use it to measure the wavelengths, frequencies, and energies of atomic emission lines

Materials

- cereal box
- tape
- pencil
- black construction paper
- diffraction grating
- ruler
- scissors
- white notebook paper

Procedure

Tape together two 2.0 cm × 10 cm strips of black construction paper so that they are parallel and form a narrow slit about 2 mm wide. Remove the top of a cereal box and tape the construction paper slit as shown. Cover the rest of the opening with white notebook paper. Cut a square hole (approximately 2 cm per side) and tape a diffraction grating over the hole as shown. Point the spectroscope toward a fluorescent light. Tape up any light leaks. Your lab partner should mark the exact positions of all the colored emission lines you see on the notebook paper. Measure the distances between the violet line and the other lines you have marked.

Analyze

1. List the number of distinct lines that you see as well as their colors.

2. Each line you see has a property called its wavelength. The prominent violet line has a wavelength of 436 nm and the prominent green line is 546 nm. How many mm apart are these lines on the paper? By how many nm do their wavelengths differ? How many nanometers of wavelength are represented by each millimeter you measured?

Diffraction grating

Black construction paper

Cereal box

Notebook paper

Slit

Spectrum appears here

3. Using the nm/mm value you calculated in Step 2 and the mm distance you measured for each line from the violet reference line, calculate the wavelengths of all the other lines you see.

4. Each wavelength corresponds to another property of light called its frequency. Use the wavelength value of each line to calculate its frequency given that $v = c/\lambda$ where $c = 2.998 \times 10^{17}$ nm/s (2.998×10^8 m/s).

5. The energy (E) of a quantum of light an atom emits is related to its frequency (v) by $E = h \times v$. Use the frequency value for each line and $h = 6.63 \times 10^{-34}$ J·s to calculate its corresponding energy.

You're The Chemist

1. **Design It!** Design and carry out an experiment to measure the longest and shortest wavelengths you can see in daylight. Use your spectroscope to observe light from daylight reflected off a white piece of paper. **Caution:** *Do not look directly at the sun!* Describe the differences in daylight and fluorescent light.

2. **Design It!** Design and carry out and experiment to determine the effect of colored filters on the spectrum of fluorescent light or daylight. For each filter tell which colors are transmitted and which are absorbed.

3. **Analyze It!** Use your spectroscope to observe various atomic emission discharge tubes provided by your teacher. Note and record the lines you see and measure their wavelengths.

New York Standards: 3.1a, 3.1j–k

Guide for Reading

🔑 Key Concepts

- How are the wavelength and frequency of light related?
- What causes atomic emission spectra?
- How are the frequencies of light an atom emits related to changes of electron energies?
- How does quantum mechanics differ from classical mechanics?

Vocabulary

amplitude
wavelength
frequency
hertz
electromagnetic radiation
spectrum
atomic emission spectrum
ground state
photons
Heisenberg uncertainty principle

Reading Strategy

Monitoring Your Understanding
Before you read, preview the Key Concepts, the section heads, the vocabulary terms, and the visuals. List three things you expect to learn. After reading, state what you learned about each item you listed.

Connecting to Your World

If you walk in the evening along a busy street lined with shops and theaters, you are likely to see neon advertising signs. The signs are formed from glass tubes bent in various shapes. An electric current passing through the gas in each glass tube makes the gas glow with its own characteristic color. In this section you will learn why each gas glows with a specific color of light.

Light

The previous sections in this chapter introduced you to some ideas about how electrons in atoms are arranged in orbitals, each with a particular energy level. You also learned how to write electron configurations for atoms. In the remainder of this chapter, you will get a closer look into what led to the development of Schrödinger's equation and the quantum mechanical model of the atom.

Rather curiously, the quantum mechanical model grew out of the study of light. Isaac Newton (1642–1727) tried to explain what was known about the behavior of light by assuming that light consists of particles. By the year 1900, however, there was enough experimental evidence to convince scientists that light consists of waves. Figure 5.9 illustrates some of the properties of waves. As shown, each complete wave cycle starts at zero, increases to its highest value, passes through zero to reach its lowest value, and returns to zero again. The **amplitude** of a wave is the wave's height from zero to the crest, as shown in Figure 5.9. The **wavelength,** represented by λ (the Greek letter lambda), is the distance between the crests. The **frequency,** represented by ν (the Greek letter nu), is the number of wave cycles to pass a given point per unit of time. The units of frequency are usually cycles per second. The SI unit of cycles per second is called a **hertz** (Hz). A hertz can also be expressed as a reciprocal second (s^{-1}).

Figure 5.9 The frequency and wavelength of light waves are inversely related. As the wavelength increases, the frequency decreases.

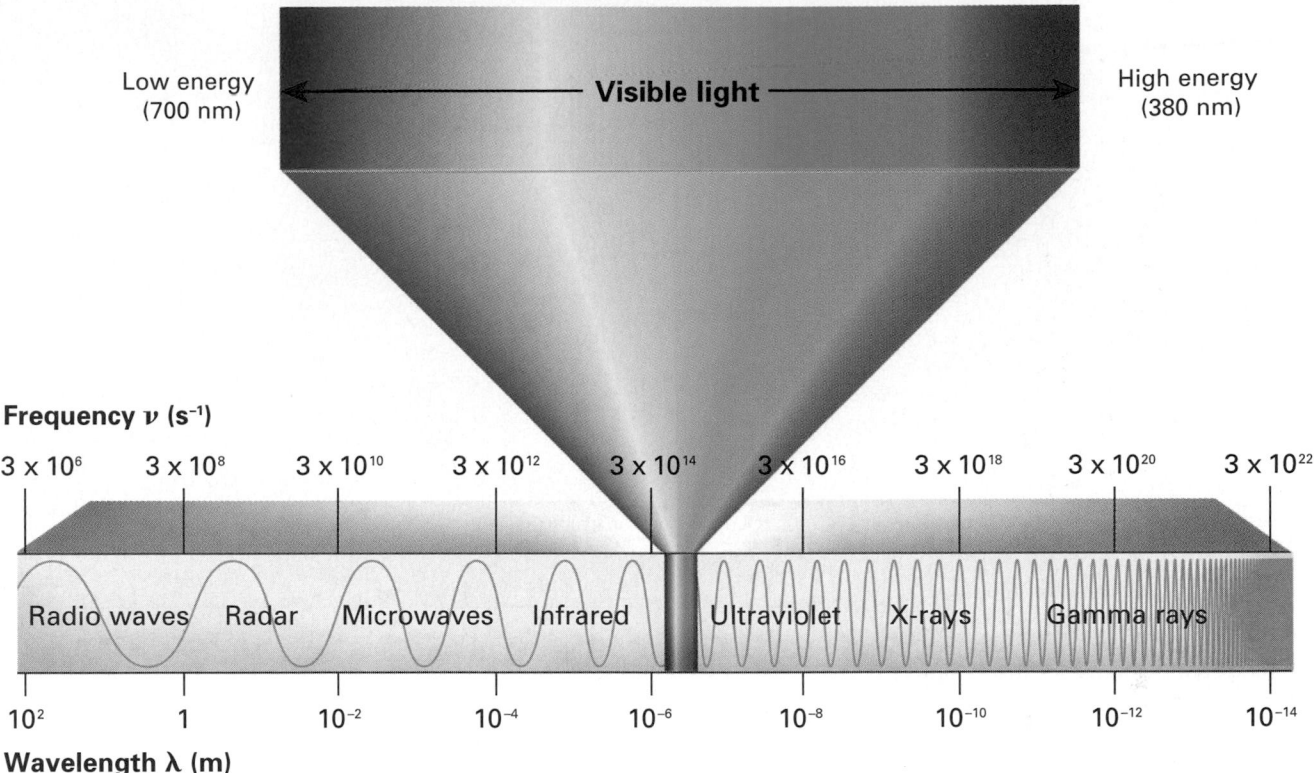

ELECTROMAGNETIC SPECTRUM

The product of frequency and wavelength always equals a constant (*c*), the speed of light:

$$c = \lambda \nu$$

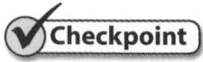 **The wavelength and frequency of light are inversely proportional to each other.** As the wavelength of light increases, for example, the frequency decreases.

According to the wave model, light consists of electromagnetic waves. **Electromagnetic radiation** includes radio waves, microwaves, infrared waves, visible light, ultraviolet waves, X-rays, and gamma rays. All electromagnetic waves travel in a vacuum at a speed of 2.998×10^8 m/s.

Sunlight consists of light with a continuous range of wavelengths and frequencies. As you can see from Figure 5.10, the color of light for each frequency found in sunlight depends on its frequency. When sunlight passes through a prism, the different frequencies separate into a **spectrum** of colors. A rainbow is an example of this phenomenon. Each tiny droplet of water acts as a prism to produce a spectrum. Each color blends into the next in the order red, orange, yellow, green, blue, and violet. In the visible spectrum, as shown in Figure 5.10, red light has the longest wavelength and the lowest frequency.

Checkpoint *What color in the visible spectrum has the longest wavelength?*

Figure 5.10 The electromagnetic spectrum consists of radiation over a broad band of wavelengths. The visible light portion is very small. It is in the 10^{-7}m wavelength range and 10^{15} Hz (s⁻¹) frequency range. **Interpreting Diagrams** *What types of nonvisible radiation have wavelengths close to those of red light? To those of blue light?*

Textbook

Simulation 3 Explore the properties of electromagnetic radiation.

with **ChemASAP**

Figure 5.11 Sodium vapor lamps produce a yellow glow.

CHEMath

Algebraic Equations

An algebraic equation shows the relationship between two or more variables. Often, an equation must be solved for the unknown variable before substituting the known values into the equation and doing the arithmetic.

Most equations can be solved if you remember that you can carry out any mathematical operation, such as addition (+), subtraction (−), multiplication (×), or division (x/y or x ÷ y), without destroying the equality, as long as you do it to both sides of the equation.

Math **Handbook**

For help and practice solving algebraic equations, go to page R69.

*i*nteractive **Textbook**

Problem-Solving 5.15 Solve Problem 15 with the help of an interactive guided tutorial.

— with **ChemASAP**

SAMPLE PROBLEM 5.1

Calculating the Wavelength of Light

Calculate the wavelength of the yellow light emitted by the sodium lamp shown above if the frequency of the radiation is 5.10×10^{14} Hz (5.10×10^{14}/s).

① **Analyze** *List the knowns and the unknown.*

Knowns
- frequency (ν) = 5.10×10^{14}/s
- $c = 2.998 \times 10^8$ m/s

Unknown
- wavelength (λ) = ? m

② **Calculate** *Solve for the unknown.*

Solve the equation $c = \lambda\nu$ for λ.

$$\lambda = \frac{c}{\nu}$$

Substitute the known values and solve.

$$\lambda = \frac{c}{\nu} = \frac{2.998 \times 10^8 \text{ m/s}}{5.10 \times 10^{14}/\text{s}} = 5.88 \times 10^{-7} \text{ m}$$

③ **Evaluate** *Does the result make sense?*

The magnitude of the frequency is much larger than the numerical value of the speed of light, so the answer should be much less than 1. The answer should have three significant figures, because the original known value had three significant figures.

Practice Problems

14. What is the wavelength of radiation with a frequency of 1.50×10^{13} Hz? Does this radiation have a longer or shorter wavelength than red light?

15. What frequency is radiation with a wavelength of 5.00×10^{-8} m? In what region of the electromagnetic spectrum is this radiation?

Light Bulb   Slit   Prism   Screen

Helium Lamp   Slit   Prism   Screen

Atomic Spectra

Passing an electric current through a gas in a neon tube energizes the electrons of the atoms of the gas, and causes them to emit light. 🔑 **When atoms absorb energy, electrons move into higher energy levels, and these electrons lose energy by emitting light when they return to lower energy levels.** Figure 5.12a shows how ordinary light is made up of a mixture of all the wavelengths of light. However, the light emitted by atoms consists of a mixture of only specific frequencies. Each specific frequency of visible light emitted corresponds to a particular color. Therefore, when the light passes through the prism shown in Figure 5.12b, the frequencies of light emitted by an element separate into discrete lines to give the **atomic emission spectrum** of the element.

Each discrete line in an emission spectrum corresponds to one exact frequency of light emitted by the atom. Figure 5.12b shows the visible portion of the emission spectrum of helium.

The emission spectrum of each element is like a person's fingerprint. Just as no two people have the same fingerprints, no two elements have the same emission spectrum. In the same way that fingerprints identify people, atomic emission spectra are useful for identifying elements. Figure 5.13 shows the characteristic colors emitted by mercury and by nitrogen. Much of the knowledge about the composition of the universe comes from studying the atomic spectra of the stars, which are hot glowing bodies of gases.

Figure 5.12 A prism separates light into the colors it contains. **ⓐ** For white light this produces a rainbow of colors. **ⓑ** Light from a helium lamp produces discrete lines. **Identifying** *Which of the bands has the highest frequency?*

Figure 5.13 No two elements have the same emission spectrum. **ⓐ** Mercury vapor lamps produce a blue glow. **ⓑ** Nitrogen gas gives off a yellowish-orange light.

Flame Tests

Purpose
Use the flame test to determine the identity of the cation in an unknown solution based on its characteristic color.

Materials
- Bunsen burner
- small beaker
- 6 small test tubes
- test tube rack
- tongs
- 6 cotton swabs
- 6M HCl
- 0.1M NaCl
- 0.1M CaCl$_2$
- 0.1M LiCl
- 0.1M CuCl$_2$
- 0.1M KCl
- unknown solution

Procedure

1. Make a two-column data table. Label the columns Cation and Flame Color. Enter the cation's name for each salt solution in the first column.

2. Label each of 5 test tubes with the name of a salt solution; label the sixth tube Unknown. Add 1 mL of each salt solution to the appropriately labeled test tube. Add 5 mL HCl to the beaker.

3. Dip one of the cotton ends of a cotton swab into the sodium chloride solution and then hold it briefly in the burner flame. Record the color of the flame. Do not leave the swab in the flame too long or the plastic will melt.

4. Repeat Step 3 for each of the remaining salt solutions using a new cotton swab each time.

5. Perform a flame test with the unknown solution. Note the color of the flame.

Analyze and Conclude

1. Identify the cation in the unknown.

2. Each salt solution produces a unique color. Would you expect this based on the modern view of the atom? Explain.

3. Some commercially available fireplace logs burn with a red and/or green flame. On the basis of your data, what elements could be responsible for these colored flames?

4. Aerial fireworks contain gunpowder and chemicals that produce colors. What elements would you include to produce crimson red? Yellow?

An Explanation of Atomic Spectra

Atomic line spectra were known before Bohr proposed his model of the hydrogen atom. However, Bohr's model not only explained why the emission spectrum of hydrogen consists of specific frequencies of light. It also predicted specific values of these frequencies that agreed with experiment.

In the Bohr model, the lone electron in the hydrogen atom can have only certain specific energies. The lowest possible energy of the electron is its **ground state.** In the ground state, the electron's principal quantum number (n) is 1. Excitation of the electron by absorbing energy raises it from the ground state to an excited state with $n = 2, 3, 4, 5$, or 6, and so forth. A quantum of energy in the form of light is emitted when the electron drops back to a lower energy level. The emission occurs in a single abrupt step, called an electronic transition. Bohr already knew from earlier work that this quantum of energy E is related to the frequency v of the emitted light by the equation $E = h \times v$, where h is equal to 6.626×10^{-34} J·s. ⊙ **The light emitted by an electron moving from a higher to a lower energy level has a frequency directly proportional to the energy change of the electron.** Therefore each transition produces a line of a specific frequency in the spectrum.

Figure 5.14 shows the explanation for the three groups of lines observed in the emission spectrum of hydrogen atoms. The lines at the ultraviolet end of the hydrogen spectrum are the Lyman series. These match expected values for the emission due to the transition of electrons from higher energy levels, called excited states, to $n = 1$. The lines in the visible spectrum are the Balmer series. These lines result from transitions from higher energy levels to $n = 2$. This generally involves a smaller change in electron energy than transitions to $n = 1$. Transitions to $n = 3$ from higher energy levels produce the Paschen series. The energy changes of the electron, and therefore the frequencies of emitted light, are generally smaller still. The lines are in the infrared range. Spectral lines for the transitions from higher energy levels to $n = 4$ and $n = 5$ also exist. Note that the spectral lines in each group become more closely spaced at increased values of n because the energy levels become closer together. There is an upper limit to the frequency of emitted light for each set of lines. The upper limit exists because an electron with enough energy completely escapes the atom.

Bohr's theory of the atom was only partially satisfactory. It explained the emission spectrum of hydrogen but not the emission spectra of atoms with more than one electron. Moreover, it was of no help in understanding how atoms bond to form molecules. Eventually a new and better model, the quantum mechanical model, displaced the Bohr model of the atom. The quantum mechanical model is based on the description of the motion of material objects as waves.

Interactive Textbook

Animation 6 Learn about atomic emission spectra and how neon lights work.

with **ChemASAP**

✓ Checkpoint *What is the name of the series of visible lines in the hydrogen spectrum?*

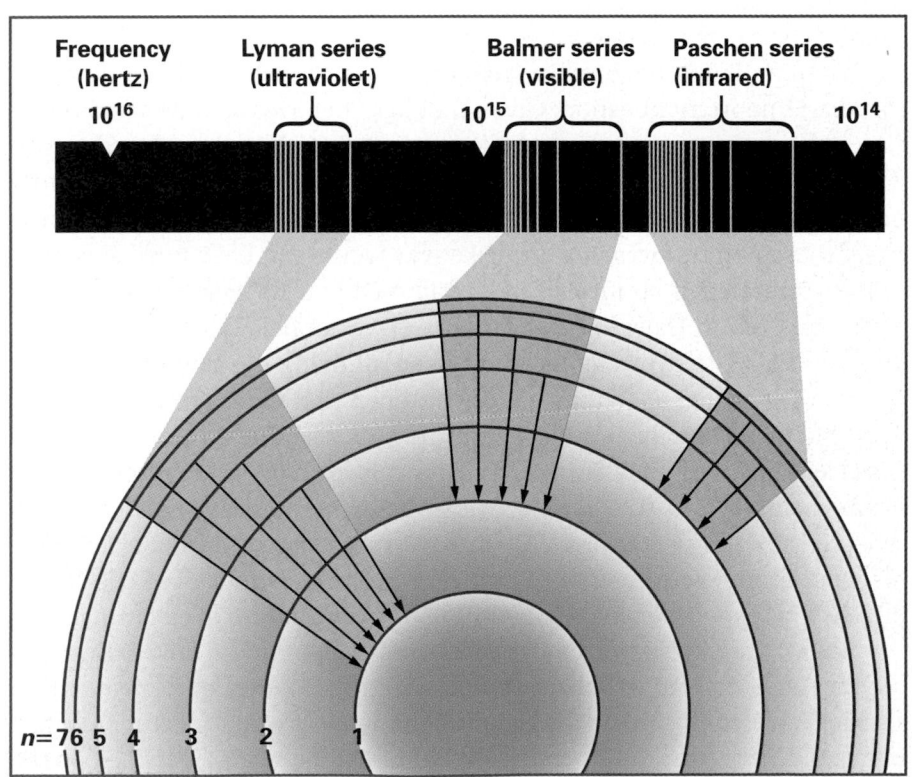

Figure 5.14 The three groups of lines in the hydrogen spectrum correspond to the transition of electrons from higher energy levels to lower energy levels. The Lyman series corresponds to the transition to the $n = 1$ energy level. The Balmer series corresponds to the transition to the $n = 2$ energy level. The Paschen series corresponds to the transition to the $n = 3$ energy level.

Figure 5.15 An electron microscope can produce sharp images of a very small object, such as this mite, because of the small wavelength of a moving electron compared with that of light.

Go Online

NSTA SCiLINKS

For: Links on the Photoelectric Effect
Visit: www.SciLinks.org
Web Code: cdn-1053

Quantum Mechanics

In 1905, Albert Einstein, then a patent examiner in Bern, Switzerland, returned to Newton's idea of particles of light. Einstein successfully explained experimental data by proposing that light could be described as quanta of energy. The quanta behave as if they were particles. Light quanta are called **photons.** Although the wave nature of light was well known, the dual wave-particle behavior of light was difficult for scientists trained in classical physics to accept.

In 1924, Louis de Broglie (1892–1987), a French graduate student, asked an important question: Given that light behaves as waves and particles, can particles of matter behave as waves? De Broglie referred to the wavelike behavior of particles as matter waves. His reasoning led him to a mathematical expression for the wavelength of a moving particle. The proposal that matter moves in a wavelike way would not have been accepted unless experiments confirmed its validity. Only three years later, experiments by Clinton Davisson and Lester Germer at Bell Labs in New Jersey did just that. The two scientists had been studying the bombardment of metals with beams of electrons. They noticed that the electrons reflected from the metal surface produced curious patterns. The patterns were like those obtained when X-rays (which are electromagnetic waves) reflect from metal surfaces. The electrons—believed to be particles—were reflected as if they were waves! De Broglie was awarded the Nobel Prize for his work on the wave nature of matter. Davisson also received the Nobel Prize for his experiments demonstrating the wave nature of electrons.

Today, the wavelike properties of beams of electrons are useful in magnifying objects. The electrons in an electron microscope have much smaller wavelengths than visible light. This allows a much clearer enlarged image of a very small object, such as the mite in Figure 5.15, than is possible with an ordinary microscope.

De Broglie's equation predicts that all moving objects have wavelike behavior. Why are you unable to observe the effects of this wavelike motion for ordinary objects like baseballs and trains? The answer is that the mass of the object must be very small in order for its wavelength to be large enough to observe. For example, a 50-gram golf ball traveling at 40 m/s (about 90 mi/h) has a wavelength of only 3×10^{-34} m, which is much too small to detect experimentally. On the other hand, an electron has a mass of only 9.11×10^{-28} g. If it were moving at a velocity of 40 m/s, it would have a wavelength of 2×10^{-5} m, which is comparable to infrared radiation and is readily measured. The newer theory is called quantum mechanics; the older theory is called classical mechanics. ◐ **Classical mechanics adequately describes the motions of bodies much larger than atoms, while quantum mechanics describes the motions of subatomic particles and atoms as waves.**

German physicist Werner Heisenberg examined another feature of quantum mechanics that is absent in classical mechanics. The **Heisenberg uncertainty principle** states that it is impossible to know exactly both the velocity and the position of a particle at the same time. This limitation is critical in dealing with small particles such as electrons. The Heisenberg uncertainty principle does not matter, however, for ordinary-sized objects such as cars or airplanes.

To understand this principle, consider how you determine the location of an object. To locate a set of keys in a dark room, for example, you can use a flashlight. You see the keys when the light bounces off them and strikes your eyes. Likewise, to locate an electron, you might strike it with a photon of light as shown in Figure 5.16. In contrast to the keys, the electron has such a small mass that striking it with a photon affects its motion in a way that cannot be predicted precisely. So the very act of measuring the position of the electron changes its velocity, and makes its velocity uncertain.

The discovery of matter waves paved the way for Schrödinger's quantum mechanical description of electrons in atoms. Schrödinger's theory leads to the concept of electron orbitals and configurations, and it includes the wavelike motion of matter and the uncertainty principle.

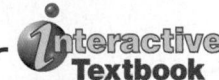
Interactive Textbook

Simulation 4 Simulate the photoelectric effect. Observe the results as a function of radiation frequency and intensity.

—— with **ChemASAP**

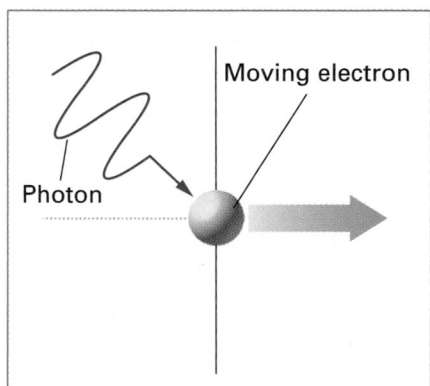

Before collision
A photon strikes an electron during an attempt to observe the electron's position.

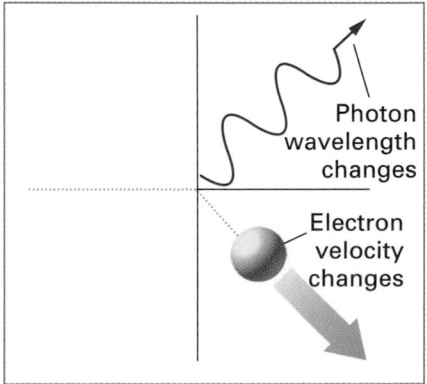

After collision
The impact changes the electron's velocity, making it uncertain.

Figure 5.16 The Heisenberg uncertainty principle states that it is impossible to know exactly both the velocity and the position of a particle at the same time.

Spectroscopist

If you like the idea of finding the chemical content of unknown materials in chemical research, police investigations, and studies of distant stars, you might consider a career as a spectroscopist. Spectroscopy is the recording and analysis of the wavelengths of electromagnetic radiation emitted by samples of materials. Optical emission spectroscopy uses emission lines from atomic transitions in a heated sample of material. Spectroscopists observe various emission lines from the sample, often by recording the spectrum on a photographic plate. They then use a device called a densitometer to measure the density of the photographic images of the spectral lines. This

determines the intensity of each wavelength emitted.

Spectroscopists use spectrometers, densitometers, and other measuring instruments to collect data. They analyze the densitometer or spectrometer readings to find the ratio of various elements in the sample. They calculate the relative concentrations of substances in the sample by comparing with data for known concentrations. They also use their mathematical skills in statistics to calculate a numerical value indicating the reliability of each analysis.

Spectroscopists usually have an advanced degree in chemistry, along with skills in mathematics and in using scientific equipment.

Spectroscopist

For: Careers in Chemistry
Visit: PHSchool.com
Web Code: cdb-1053

5.3 Section Assessment

16. **Key Concept** How are wavelength and frequency of light related?

17. **Key Concept** Describe the cause of atomic emission spectrum of an element.

18. **Key Concept** How is the change in electron energy related to the frequency of light emitted in atomic transitions?

19. **Key Concept** How does quantum mechanics differ from classical mechanics?

20. The lines at the ultraviolet end of the hydrogen spectrum are known as the Lyman series. Which electron transitions within an atom are responsible for these lines?

21. Arrange the following in order of decreasing wavelength.
    a. infrared radiation from a heat lamp
    b. dental X-rays
    c. signal from a shortwave radio station

Elements ▶ Handbook

Color and Transitions Read the article on page R10 of the Elements Handbook. List the colors emitted from strontium compounds and from barium compounds when heated in a flame, and explain how electron transitions account for the specific colors being emitted.

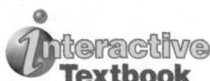
Textbook

Assessment 5.3 Test yourself on the concepts in Section 5.3.

— with **ChemASAP**

Lasers at Work

A laser produces an intense beam of light with the unusual property that the waves contributing to it have crests that coincide. The properties of laser light make it useful for many different purposes, including reading CD-ROMs and DVDs in electronic equipment and scanning bar codes at cash registers. Some industries use high-intensity lasers to cut metal. Other lasers are used in surgery. **Inferring** *Explain how the properties of a laser beam make it useful for the kind of eye surgery shown.*

Flashlight beam vs. laser beam Light from a flashlight travels in different directions, covering a wide area. Light rays from a laser travel parallel to one another, resulting in a narrow beam of intense light in a specific direction.

1 A surgeon prepares for laser eye surgery to reshape the cornea, or clear outermost part of the eye, so that the patient no longer needs eyeglasses to see clearly.

2 The surgeon uses a tool called a microkeratome to make a partial cut in the cornea.

3 The doctor lifts and folds back the cornea.

4 A laser removes some tissue to change the shape of the cornea and correct the patient's vision.

Study Guide

Key Concepts

5.1 Models of the Atom

- Rutherford's planetary model could not explain the chemical properties of elements.
- Bohr proposed that electrons move only in specific circular paths, or orbits, around the nucleus.
- The quantum mechanical model determines the allowed energies an electron can have and how likely it is to be found in various locations around the nucleus.
- Each sublevel of a principal energy level corresponds to an orbital shape describing where the electron is likely to be found.

5.2 Electron Arrangement in Atoms

- Three rules—the aufbau principle, the Pauli exclusion principle, and Hund's rule—tell you how to find the electron configurations of atoms.

- Some actual electron configurations differ from those assigned using the aufbau principle because half-filled levels are not as stable as filled levels, but they are more stable than other configurations.

5.3 Physics and the Quantum Mechanical Model

- The wavelength and frequency of light are inversely proportional to each other.
- When atoms absorb energy, electrons move into higher energy levels, and then lose energy by emitting light when the electrons drop back to lower energy levels.
- The light emitted by an electron moving from a higher to a lower energy level has a frequency directly proportional to the energy change of the electron.
- Classical mechanics adequately describes the motions of bodies much larger than atoms, while quantum mechanics describes the motions of subatomic particles and atoms as waves.

Vocabulary

- amplitude (p. 138)
- atomic emission spectrum (p. 141)
- atomic orbital (p. 131)
- aufbau principle (p. 133)
- electromagnetic radiation (p. 139)
- electron configurations (p. 133)
- energy levels (p. 128)
- frequency (p. 138)
- ground state (p. 142)
- Heisenberg uncertainty principle (p. 145)
- hertz (p. 138)
- Hund's rule (p. 134)
- Pauli exclusion principle (p. 134)
- photons (p. 144)
- quantum (p. 128)
- quantum mechanical model (p. 130)
- spectrum (p. 139)
- wavelength (p. 138)

Key Equation

- $c = \lambda \nu$

Organizing Information

Use these terms to construct a concept map that organizes the major ideas of this chapter.

Concept Map 5 Solve the concept map with the help of an interactive guided tutorial.

with ChemASAP

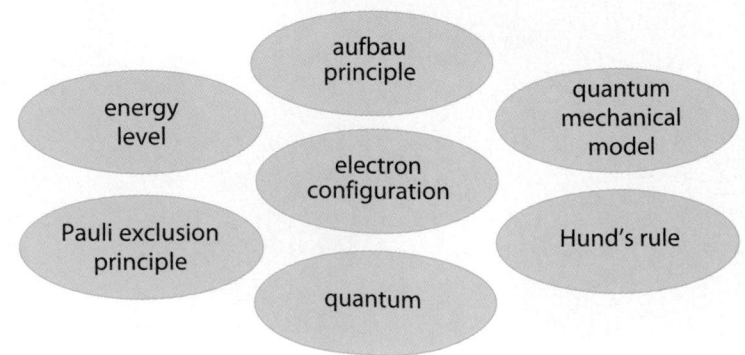

Review and Assessment

Blue questions emphasize Regents Exam content

Models of the Atom

22. What was inadequate about Rutherford's model of the atom? Which subatomic particles did Thomson include in the plum-pudding model of the atom?

23. Describe Rutherford's model of the atom and compare it with the model proposed by his student Niels Bohr.

24. What is the significance of the boundary of an electron cloud?

25. What is an atomic orbital?

26. Sketch $1s$, $2s$, and $2p$ orbitals using the same scale for each.

27. How many sublevels are contained in each of these principal energy levels?
   a. $n = 1$ **b.** $n = 2$ **c.** $n = 3$ **d.** $n = 4$

28. Choose three scientists that were involved in developing atomic theory. Briefly explain how the modern model of the atom has evolved over a long period of time through the work of these scientists.

29. According to modern atomic theory, describe the structure of an atom.

30. How does the energy of one electron in an atom compare to the energy of any other electron in the atom?

31. What happens to an electron in an atom when it gains energy?

32. Explain the difference between an orbit in the Bohr model and an orbital in the quantum mechanical model of the atom.

Electron Arrangement in Atoms

33. How many electrons are in the highest occupied energy level of these atoms?
   a. barium   **b.** sodium
   c. aluminum   **d.** oxygen

34. Name and state the three rules that govern the filling of atomic orbitals by electrons.

35. Write electron configurations for the elements that are identified only by these atomic numbers.
   a. 15   **b.** 12   **c.** 9   **d.** 18

36. What is meant by $3p^3$?

37. Give electron configurations for atoms of these elements.
   a. Na   **b.** S   **c.** Mg   **d.** Ne   **e.** K

38. Which of these orbital designations are invalid?
   a. $4s$ **b.** $3f$ **c.** $2d$ **d.** $3d$

39. What is the maximum number of electrons that can go into each of the following sublevels?
   a. $2s$ **b.** $3p$ **c.** $4s$ **d.** $3d$
   e. $4p$ **f.** $5s$ **g.** $4f$ **h.** $5p$

40. Arrange the following sublevels in order of increasing energy:
   $3d, 2s, 4s, 3p$.

41. How many electrons are in the second energy level of an atom of each of the following elements?
   a. chlorine   **b.** phosphorus   **c.** potassium

42. Write electron configurations for atoms of these elements.
   a. selenium   **b.** vanadium
   c. nickel   **d.** calcium

43. Give the symbol for each atom that corresponds to the number of electrons in consecutive shells as shown below.
   a. 2-8-8
   b. 2-8-18-15-1
   c. 2-8-18-25-9-2

44. Write the electron configuration for an arsenic atom. Calculate the total number of electrons in each energy level and state which energy levels are not full.

45. How many paired electrons are there in an atom of each of the following elements?
   a. helium   **b.** boron
   c. sodium   **d.** oxygen

46. An atom of an element has two electrons in the first energy level and five electrons in the second energy level. Write the electron configuration for this atom and name the element. How many unpaired electrons does an atom of this element have?

47. Give the symbols and names of the elements that correspond to the number of electrons in consecutive shells as shown below.
 a. 2-8-1
 b. 2-5
 c. 2-8-4
 d. 2-6
 e. 2-8-8-1
 f. 2-8-10-2

48. What is the maximum number of electrons that can be found in any orbital of an atom?

49. The lowest sublevel in each principal energy level is represented by the symbol
 a. *f*   **b.** *p*   **c.** *s*   **d.** *d*

50. Select the number of electrons in consecutive shells for a magnesium atom when it is in its ground state. The atomic number of magnesium is 12.
 a. 2-8-2   **b.** 2-8-1
 c. 2-8-1-1   **d.** 2-6-4

51. Identify the elements whose electrically neutral atoms have the following electrons in consecutive shells.
 a. 2-7
 b. 2-8-18-4
 c. 2-8-11-2

52. Why do electrons occupy equal energy orbitals singly before beginning to pair up?

Physics and the Quantum Mechanical Model

53. Wavelength and frequency are two important properties of waves.
 a. What is meant by the frequency of a wave? What are the units of frequency?
 b. Describe the relationship between frequency and wavelength.
 c. Use a diagram to illustrate wavelength, amplitude, and cycle.
 d. List the colors of the visible spectrum in order of increasing wavelength.

54. Explain the difference between the energy lost or gained by an atom according to the laws of classical physics and according to the quantum model of an atom.

55. How are ultraviolet radiation and microwave radiation the same? How are they different?

56. What happens when a hydrogen atom absorbs energy?

57. When white light is viewed through sodium vapor in a spectroscope, the spectrum is continuous except for a dark line at 589 nm. How can you explain this observation?

58. When sodium is placed in a flame, the resulting flame is yellow. Explain how this yellow light is produced in terms of the electrons in the atom.

59. A mercury lamp, such as the one below, emits radiation with a wavelength of 4.36×10^{-7} m.

 a. What is the wavelength of this radiation in centimeters?
 b. In what region of the electromagnetic spectrum is this radiation?
 c. Calculate the frequency of this radiation.

60. Sodium vapor lamps are used to illuminate streets and highways. The very bright light emitted by these lamps is actually due to two closely spaced emission lines in the visible region of the electromagnetic spectrum. One of these lines has a wavelength of 5.890×10^{-7} m, and the other line has a wavelength of 5.896×10^{-7} m. What are the wavelengths of these radiations in centimeters?

61. State the Heisenberg uncertainty principle.

62. Which electron transition results in the emission of energy?
   a. $3p$ to $3s$ **b.** $3p$ to $4p$
   c. $2s$ to $2p$ **d.** $1s$ to $2s$

63. Traditional cooking methods make use of infrared radiation (heat). Microwave radiation cooks food faster. Could radio waves be used for cooking? Explain.

64. Think about the currently accepted models of the atom and of light. In what ways do these models seem strange to you? Why are these models not exact or definite?

65. Orbital diagrams for the ground states of two elements are shown below. Each diagram shows something that is incorrect. Identify the error in each diagram and then draw the correct diagram.
   a. Nitrogen $1s$ $2s$ $2p$

   b. Magnesium $1s$ $2s$ $2p$ $3s$

66. Picture two hydrogen atoms. The electron in the first hydrogen atom is in the first energy level. The electron in the second atom is in the fourth energy level.
   a. Which atom has the ground state electron configuration?
   b. Which atom can emit electromagnetic radiation?
   c. In which atom is the electron in a larger orbital?
   d. Which atom has the lower energy?

67. Which of the following number of electrons in consecutive shells is the ground state of an atom? Which is its excited state? Which is an impossible electron configuration? Identify each element and briefly explain your choices.
   a. 2-8-8-0-1
   b. 2-8-8-1
   c. 1-9-18-2

68. The energy of a photon is related to its wavelength and its frequency. Frequency can be calculated from energy by using the equation $E = h \times v$, where the constant h equals 6.62×10^{-34} J·s and v is the frequency.

Energy of photon (J)	Frequency (s⁻¹)	Wavelength (cm)
3.45×10^{-21}	a.	5.77×10^{-3}
2.92×10^{-20}	b.	6.82×10^{-4}
6.29×10^{-20}	c.	3.16×10^{-4}
1.13×10^{-19}	d.	1.76×10^{-4}
1.46×10^{-19}	e.	1.36×10^{-4}
3.11×10^{-19}	f.	6.38×10^{-5}

   a. Complete the table above.
   b. Plot the energy of the photon (y-axis) versus the frequency (x-axis).
   c. Determine the slope of the line.
   d. What is the significance of this slope?

69. All electromagnetic waves travel in a vacuum at a speed of 3.00×10^8 m/s.
   a. What is this speed in km/s?
   b. The average distance between Earth and Mars is about 2.08×10^8 km. How long does it take in seconds to transmit television pictures from the Mariner spacecraft to Earth from Mars?

70. Bohr's atomic theory can be used to calculate the energy required to remove an electron from an orbit of a hydrogen atom or an ion containing only one electron. This value is the ionization energy for that atom or ion. The formula for determining the ionization energy (E) is

$$E = Z^2 \times \frac{k}{n^2}$$

where Z is the atomic number, k is 2.18×10^{-18} J, and n is the energy level. What is the energy required to eject an electron from a hydrogen atom when the electron is in the ground state ($n = 1$)? In the second energy level? How much energy is required to eject a ground state electron from the species Li^{2+}?

Test-Taking Tip

Eliminate wrong answers If you don't know which response is correct, start by eliminating those you know are wrong. If you can rule out some choices, you'll have fewer left to consider and you'll increase your chances of choosing the correct answer.

Regents Practice Exam

Part A

For each statement or question write the number of the word or expression that, of those given, best completes the statement or answers the question.

1. Which of the following statements is true for the nucleus of every atom?
   (1) It has a negative charge.
   (2) It is very dense.
   (3) It is composed of protons, electrons, and neutrons.
   (4) Its particles form a "cloud."

2. Which of the following choices is a physical change?
   (1) Cider turns to vinegar.
   (2) Bread molds.
   (3) An apple seed sprouts.
   (4) Gold is beaten into a thin sheet.

3. Convert 2.54 mm to meters.
   (1) 2.54×10^{-3} m   (3) 2.54×10^{3} m
   (2) 2.54 m   (4) 254 m

4. An orbital is
   (1) where an electron is most likely to be located
   (2) the probable location of the nucleus
   (3) a definite path that an electron follows
   (4) a positively charged area in an atom

Part B-1

For each statement or question write the number of the word or expression that, of those given, best completes the statement or answers the question.

5. Select the number of electrons in consecutive shells for a silicon atom when it is in its ground state. The atomic number of silicon is 14.
   (1) 2-4-6-2   (3) 2-8
   (2) 2-6-6   (4) 2-8-4

The numbered choices below refer to Questions 6–10. A numbered choice may be used once, more than once, or not at all.

   (1) 2   (2) 4   (3) 6   (4) 8

How many outer-shell electrons are in atoms of each of the following elements?

6. sulfur

7. germanium

8. beryllium

9. krypton

10. strontium

Use the following atomic models to answer Questions 11 and 12.

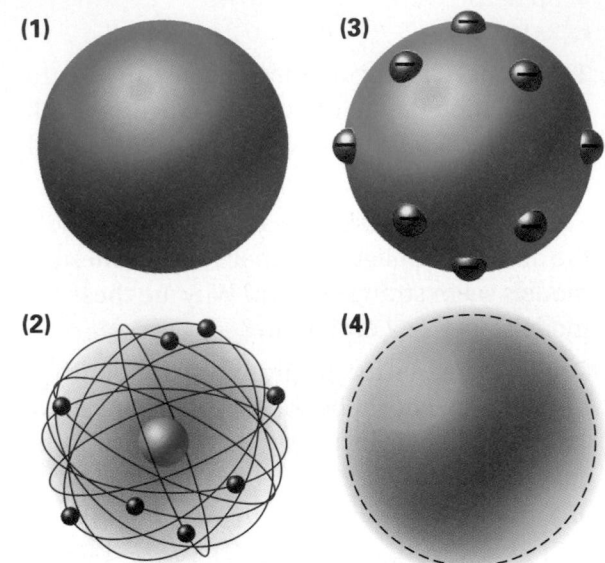

(1)   (3)

(2)   (4)

11. Which model was proposed based on data from Rutherford's gold foil experiment?

12. In which model are electrons in orbitals?

13. How many neutrons are in an atom of phosphorus-31?
    (1) 15   (3) 31
    (2) 16   (4) 46

14. The numbers of electrons in consecutive shells of an atom are 2-8-8-1. The atom is what element?
    (1) Ne   (3) F
    (2) Ar   (4) K

Part B-2

Answer each of the following questions.

15. Classify each of the following as homogeneous or heterogeneous.
    a. a page of this textbook
    b. a banana split
    c. distilled water

16. Homogeneous mixtures and compounds are both composed of two or more elements. How do you distinguish between a homogeneous mixture and a compound?

17. The following photo shows a magnified view of a small piece of granite. Is granite a pure substance, a homogeneous mixture, or a heterogeneous mixture?

18. The diameter of a carbon atom is 77 pm. Express this measurement in μm.

19. A silver bar has a mass of 368 g. What is the volume, in cm^3, of the bar? The density of silver is 19.5 g/cm^3.

20. Which has more mass, a 28.0-cm^3 piece of lead or a 16.0-cm^3 piece of gold? The density of lead is 11.4 g/cm^3. The density of gold is 19.3 g/cm^3.

21. Express the following measurements in scientific notation.
   a. 0.000 039 kg   **c.** 0.0830 g
   b. 784 L   **d.** 9 700 000 ng

22. When a piece of copper with a mass of 36.4 g is placed into a graduated cylinder containing 20.00 mL of water, the water level rose to 24.08 mL. What is the density of copper?

23. The density of gold is 19.3 g/cm^3. What is the mass, in grams, of a cube of gold that is 2.00 cm on each edge? In kilograms?

24. Give the number of protons and electrons in one atom of each of the following elements.
   a. Cs   **b.** Ag   **c.** Cd   **d.** Se

25. How do neon-20 and neon-21 differ from each other?

26. The mass of an atom should be nearly the sum of the masses of its protons and neutrons. The mass of a proton and the mass of a neutron are each close to 1 amu. Why is the atomic mass of chlorine, 35.453 amu, so far from a whole number?

27. The density of corn oil is reported by a student to be 0.922. Why can't this number be an accurate value for the density of corn oil?

28. How many electrons are contained in the highest occupied energy level of each of the following atoms in its ground state?
   a. boron   **c.** bromine
   b. sulfur   **d.** krypton

Part C

Answer each of the following questions.

29. Hamburger undergoes a chemical change when cooked on a grill. All chemical changes are subject to the law of conservation of mass. Yet a cooked hamburger will invariably weigh less than the uncooked meat patty. Explain.

30. A balloon filled with helium will rise upward when released. What does this result show about the relative densities of helium and air? Explain.

31. Iodine-131 is used to diagnose and treat thyroid disease. How many protons, neutrons, and electrons are in an atom of iodine-131?

32. Many colored electric signs contain gases whose atoms give off a certain color of light when electricity is passed through the gas. In terms of excited atoms, explain why you can look at such a sign and tell what type of atom it contains.

The Periodic Table

INTERNATIONAL SIZE CONVERSION
MEN'S BOTTOMS

U.S.	28	30	32	34	36	38	40
U.K.	28	30	32	34	36	38	40
France	38	40	42	44	46	48	50
Italy	44	46	48	50	52	54	56
Germany	38	40	42	44	46	48	50
Japan	71cm	76cm	81cm	86cm	91cm	96cm	101cm

These jeans are organized by color and size. In a periodic table, elements with similar properties are in the same group.

INQUIRY Activity

Trends in Physical Properties

Procedure

1. Make a table with five columns. In the first column, list the metal elements lithium (Li), sodium (Na), potassium (K), rubidium (Rb), and cesium (Cs) in order. Title the other four columns Atomic number, Melting point, Boiling point, and Density.

2. Make a similar table for the nonmetal elements fluorine (F), chlorine (Cl), bromine (Br), and iodine (I).

3. Use Table B3 in Appendix B to complete each table. Include the appropriate units for each property.

Think About It

1. For the metals, what are the trends for the melting points and boiling points as the atomic number increases?

2. Are the trends for melting and boiling points the same for the nonmetals? Explain.

3. What is the general trend in densities of the metals with increasing atomic number?

4. Why is the range of densities much greater among the nonmetals than among the metals? (*Hint:* The densities listed are for elements at 0°C.)

6.1 Organizing the Elements

 New York Standards: 3.1v, 3.1y, 3.1aa

Connecting to Your World

In 1916, a self-service grocery store opened in Memphis, Tennessee. Shoppers could select items from shelves instead of waiting for a clerk to gather the items for them. In a self-service store, the customers must know how to find the products. From your experience, you know that products are grouped according to similar characteristics. You don't expect to find fresh fruit with canned fruit, or bottled juice with frozen juice. With a logical classification system, finding and comparing products is easy. In this section, you will learn how elements are arranged in the periodic table and what that arrangement reveals about the elements.

Guide for Reading

Key Concepts
- How did chemists begin to organize the known elements?
- How did Mendeleev organize his periodic table?
- How is the modern periodic table organized?
- What are three broad classes of elements?

Vocabulary
periodic law
metals
nonmetals
metalloid

Reading Strategy
Comparing and Contrasting As you read, compare and contrast Figures 6.4 and 6.5. How are these two versions of the periodic table similar? How are they different?

Searching For an Organizing Principle

A few elements have been known for thousands of years, including copper, silver, and gold. Yet only 13 elements had been identified by the year 1700. Chemists suspected that other elements existed. They had even assigned names to some of these elements, but they were unable to isolate the elements from their compounds. As chemists began to use scientific methods to search for elements, the rate of discovery increased. In one decade (1765–1775), chemists identified five new elements, including three colorless gases—hydrogen, nitrogen, and oxygen. Was there a limit to the number of elements? How would chemists know when they had discovered all the elements? To begin to answer these questions, chemists needed to find a logical way to organize the elements.

 Chemists used the properties of elements to sort them into groups. In 1829, a German chemist, J. W. Dobereiner (1780–1849), published a classification system. In his system, elements were grouped into triads. A triad is a set of three elements with similar properties. The elements in Figure 6.1 formed one triad. Chlorine, bromine, and iodine may look different. But they have very similar chemical properties. For example, they react easily with metals. Dobereiner noted a pattern in his triads. One element in each triad tended to have properties with values that fell midway between those of the other two elements. For example, the average of the atomic masses of chlorine and iodine is [(35.453 + 126.90)/2] or 81.177 amu. This value is close to the atomic mass of bromine, which is 79.904 amu. Unfortunately, all the known elements could not be grouped into triads.

Figure 6.1 Chlorine, bromine, and iodine have very similar chemical properties. The numbers shown are the average atomic masses for these elements.

Chlorine	Bromine	Iodine
35.453 amu	79.904 amu	126.90 amu

Figure 6.2 Dimitri Mendeleev proposed a periodic table that could be used to predict the properties of undiscovered elements.

Mendeleev's Periodic Table

From 1829 to 1869, different systems were proposed, but none of them gained wide acceptance. In 1869, a Russian chemist and teacher, Dmitri Mendeleev, published a table of the elements. Later that year, a German chemist, Lothar Meyer, published a nearly identical table. Mendeleev was given more credit than Meyer because he published his table first and because he was better able to explain its usefulness. The stamp in Figure 6.2 is one of many ways that Mendeleev's work has been honored.

Mendeleev developed his table while working on a textbook for his students. He needed a way to show the relationships among more than 60 elements. He wrote the properties of each element on a separate note card. This approach allowed him to move the cards around until he found an organization that worked. The organization he chose was a periodic table. Elements in a periodic table are arranged into groups based on a set of repeating properties. ☞ **Mendeleev arranged the elements in his periodic table in order of increasing atomic mass.**

Figure 6.3 is an early version of Mendeleev's periodic table. Look at the column that starts with Ti = 50. Notice the two question marks between the entries for zinc (Zn) and arsenic (As). Mendeleev left these spaces in his table because he knew that bromine belonged with chlorine and iodine. He predicted that elements would be discovered to fill those spaces, and he predicted what their properties would be based on their locations in the table. The elements between zinc and arsenic were gallium and germanium, which were discovered in 1875 and 1886, respectively. There was a close match between the predicted properties and the actual properties of these elements. This match helped convince scientists that Mendeleev's periodic table was a powerful tool.

Figure 6.3 In this early version of Mendeleev's periodic table, the rows contain elements with similar properties.
Observing *A fourth element is grouped with chlorine (Cl), bromine (Br), and (I) iodine. What is this element's symbol?*

но въ ней, мнѣ кажется, уже ясно выражается примѣнимость выставляемаго мною начала ко всей совокупности элементовъ, пай которыхъ извѣстенъ съ достовѣрностію. На этотъ разъ я и желалъ преимущественно найдти общую систему элементовъ. Вотъ этотъ опытъ:

				Ti=50	Zr=90	?=180.
				V=51	Nb=94	Ta=182.
				Cr=52	Mo=96	W=186.
				Mn=55	Rh=104,4	Pt=197,4
				Fe=56	Ru=104,4	Ir=198.
			Ni=Co=59		Pl=106₆,	Os=199.
H=1				Cu=63,4	Ag=108	Hg=200.
	Be=9,4	Mg=24	Zn=65,2	Cd=112		
	B=11	Al=27,4	?=68	Ur=116	Au=197?	
	C=12	Si=28	?=70	Sn=118		
	N=14	P=31	As=75	Sb=122	Bi=210	
	O=16	S=32	Se=79,4	Te=128?		
	F=19	Cl=35,5	Br=80	I=127		
Li=7	Na=23	K=39	Rb=85,4	Cs=133	Tl=204	
		Ca=40	Sr=57,6	Ba=137	Pb=207.	
		?=45	Ce=92			
		?Er=56	La=94			
		?Yt=60	Di=95			
		?In=75,6	Th=118?			

1 1 H																		2 He
2 3 Li	4 Be												5 B	6 C	7 N	8 O	9 F	10 Ne
3 11 Na	12 Mg												13 Al	14 Si	15 P	16 S	17 Cl	18 Ar

The Periodic Law

The atomic mass of iodine (I) is 126.90. The atomic mass of tellurium (Te) is 127.60. Based on its chemical properties, iodine belongs in a group with bromine and chlorine. So Mendeleev broke his rule and placed tellurium before iodine in his periodic table. He assumed that the atomic masses for iodine and tellurium were incorrect, but they were not. Iodine has a smaller atomic mass than tellurium does. A similar problem occurred with other pairs of elements. The problem wasn't with the atomic masses but with using atomic mass to organize the periodic table.

Mendeleev developed his table before scientists knew about the structure of atoms. He didn't know that the atoms of each element contain a unique number of protons. Remember that the number of protons is the atomic number. In 1913, a British physicist, Henry Moseley, determined an atomic number for each known element. Tellurium's atomic number is 52 and iodine's is 53. So it makes sense for iodine to come after tellurium in the periodic table. **In the modern periodic table, elements are arranged in order of increasing atomic number.**

The elements in Figure 6.4 are arranged in order of atomic number, starting with hydrogen, which has atomic number 1. There are seven rows, or periods, in the table. Period 1 has 2 elements, Period 2 has 8 elements, Period 4 has 18 elements, and Period 6 has 32 elements. Each period corresponds to a principal energy level. There are more elements in higher numbered periods because there are more orbitals in higher energy levels. (Recall the rules you studied in Chapter 5 for how electrons fill orbitals.)

The elements within a column, or group, in the periodic table have similar properties. The properties of the elements within a period change as you move across a period from left to right. However, the pattern of properties within a period repeats as you move from one period to the next. This pattern gives rise to the **periodic law:** When elements are arranged in order of increasing atomic number, there is a periodic repetition of their physical and chemical properties.

 Checkpoint *How many periods are there in a periodic table?*

Figure 6.4 In the modern periodic table, the elements are arranged in order of increasing atomic number. **Interpreting Diagrams** *How many elements are there in the second period?*

Word *Origins*

Periodic comes from the Greek roots *peri* meaning "around" and *hodos,* meaning "path." In a periodic table, properties repeat from left to right across each period. The Greek word *metron* means "measure." **What does *perimeter* mean?**

Periodic Table (Figure 6.5)

1 IA 1A																	18 VIIB 8A
1 **H**	2 IIA 2A		Metals		Metalloids		Nonmetals					13 IIIB 3A	14 IVB 4A	15 VB 5A	16 IVB 6A	17 VIB 7A	2 **He**
3 **Li**	4 **Be**											5 **B**	6 **C**	7 **N**	8 **O**	9 **F**	10 **Ne**
11 **Na**	12 **Mg**	3 IIIA 3B	4 IVA 4B	5 VA 5B	6 VIA 6B	7 VIIA 7B	8	9 VIIIA 8B	10	11 IB 1B	12 IIB 2B	13 **Al**	14 **Si**	15 **P**	16 **S**	17 **Cl**	18 **Ar**
19 **K**	20 **Ca**	21 **Sc**	22 **Ti**	23 **V**	24 **Cr**	25 **Mn**	26 **Fe**	27 **Co**	28 **Ni**	29 **Cu**	30 **Zn**	31 **Ga**	32 **Ge**	33 **As**	34 **Se**	35 **Br**	36 **Kr**
37 **Rb**	38 **Sr**	39 **Y**	40 **Zr**	41 **Nb**	42 **Mo**	43 **Tc**	44 **Ru**	45 **Rh**	46 **Pd**	47 **Ag**	48 **Cd**	49 **In**	50 **Sn**	51 **Sb**	52 **Te**	53 **I**	54 **Xe**
55 **Cs**	56 **Ba**	71 **Lu**	72 **Hf**	73 **Ta**	74 **W**	75 **Re**	76 **Os**	77 **Ir**	78 **Pt**	79 **Au**	80 **Hg**	81 **Tl**	82 **Pb**	83 **Bi**	84 **Po**	85 **At**	86 **Rn**
87 **Fr**	88 **Ra**	103 **Lr**	104 **Rf**	105 **Db**	106 **Sg**	107 **Bh**	108 **Hs**	109 **Mt**	110 **Ds**	111 **Uuu**	112 **Uub**		114 **Uuq**				

57 **La**	58 **Ce**	59 **Pr**	60 **Nd**	61 **Pm**	62 **Sm**	63 **Eu**	64 **Gd**	65 **Tb**	66 **Dy**	67 **Ho**	68 **Er**	69 **Tm**	70 **Yb**
89 **Ac**	90 **Th**	91 **Pa**	92 **U**	93 **Np**	94 **Pu**	95 **Am**	96 **Cm**	97 **Bk**	98 **Cf**	99 **Es**	100 **Fm**	101 **Md**	102 **No**

Figure 6.5 One way to classify elements in the periodic table is as metals, nonmetals, and metalloids. **Inferring** *What is the purpose for the black stair-step line?*

Metals, Nonmetals, and Metalloids

Most periodic tables are laid out like the one in Figure 6.5. Some elements from Periods 6 and 7 are placed beneath the table. This arrangement makes the periodic table more compact. It also reflects an underlying structure of the periodic table, which you will study in Section 6.2. Each group in the table in Figure 6.5 has three labels. Scientists in the United States used the labels shown in red. Scientists in Europe used the labels shown in blue. There is some overlap between the systems, but in many cases two different groups have the same letter and number combination.

For scientists to communicate clearly, they need to agree on the standards they will use. The International Union of Pure and Applied Chemistry (IUPAC) is an organization that sets standards for chemistry. In 1985, IUPAC proposed a new system for labeling groups in the periodic table. They numbered the groups from left to right 1 through 18 (the black labels in Figure 6.5). The large periodic table in Figure 6.9 includes the IUPAC system and the system used in the United States. The latter system will be most useful when you study how compounds form in Chapters 7 and 8.

Dividing the elements into groups is not the only way to classify them based on their properties. The elements can be grouped into three broad classes based on their general properties. ☛ **Three classes of elements are metals, nonmetals, and metalloids.** Across a period, the properties of elements become less metallic and more nonmetallic.

Metals The number of yellow squares in Figure 6.5 shows that most elements are metals—about 80 percent. **Metals** are good conductors of heat and electric current. A freshly cleaned or cut surface of a metal will have a high luster, or sheen. The sheen is caused by the metal's ability to reflect light. All metals are solids at room temperature, except for mercury (Hg). Many metals are ductile, meaning that they can be drawn into wires. Most metals are malleable, meaning that they can be hammered into thin sheets without breaking. Figure 6.6 shows how the properties of metals can determine how metals are used.

Nonmetals In Figure 6.5, blue is used to identify the nonmetals. These elements are in the upper-right corner of the periodic table. There is a greater variation in physical properties among nonmetals than among metals. Most nonmetals are gases at room temperature, including the main components of air—nitrogen and oxygen. A few are solids, such as sulfur and phosphorus. One nonmetal, bromine, is a dark-red liquid.

The variation among nonmetals makes it difficult to describe one set of general properties that will apply to all nonmetals. However, nonmetals are not metals, as their name implies. So they tend to have properties that are opposite to those of metals. In general, **nonmetals** are poor conductors of heat and electric current. Carbon is an exception to this rule. Solid nonmetals tend to be brittle, meaning that they will shatter if hit with a hammer.

✓Checkpoint *Which type of elements tend to be good conductors of heat and electric current?*

Iron (Fe)
The Gateway Arch in St. Louis, Missouri, is covered in stainless steel containing iron and two other metals, chromium (Cr) and nickel (Ni). The steel is shiny, malleable, and strong. It also resists rusting.

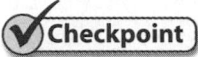

Figure 6.6 The metals iron, copper, and aluminum have many important uses. How each metal is used is determined by its properties.

Copper (Cu)
Copper is ductile and second to only silver as a conductor of electric current. The copper used in electrical cables must be 99.99% pure.

Aluminum (Al)
Aluminum is one of the metals that can be shaped into a thin sheet, or foil. To qualify as a foil, a metal must be no thicker than about 0.15 mm.

Figure 6.7 Pancake-sized circular slices of silicon, called wafers, are used to make computer chips. Because a tiny speck of dust can ruin a wafer, the people who handle the wafers must wear "bunny" suits. The suits prevent skin, hair, or lint from clothing from entering the room's atmosphere.

Metalloids There is a heavy stair-step line in Figure 6.5 that separates the metals from the nonmetals. Most of the elements that border this line are shaded green. These elements are metalloids. A **metalloid** generally has properties that are similar to those of metals and nonmetals. Under some conditions, a metalloid may behave like a metal. Under other conditions, it may behave like a nonmetal. The behavior often can be controlled by changing the conditions. For example, pure silicon is a poor conductor of electric current, like most nonmetals. But if a small amount of boron is mixed with silicon, the mixture is a good conductor of electric current, like most metals. Silicon can be cut into wafers, like those being inspected in Figure 6.7, and used to make computer chips.

6.1 Section Assessment

1. **Key Concept** How did chemists begin the process of organizing elements?

2. **Key Concept** What property did Mendeleev use to organize his periodic table?

3. **Key Concept** How are elements arranged in the modern periodic table?

4. **Key Concept** Name the three broad classes of elements.

5. Which of these sets of elements have similar physical and chemical properties?
   a. oxygen, nitrogen, carbon, boron
   b. strontium, magnesium, calcium, beryllium
   c. nitrogen, neon, nickel, niobium

6. Identify each element as a metal, metalloid, or nonmetal.
   a. gold   b. silicon
   c. sulfur   d. barium

7. Name two elements that have properties similar to those of the element sodium.

Connecting Concepts

Atomic Number What does an atomic number tell you about the atoms of an element? Why is atomic number better than atomic mass for organizing the elements in a periodic table? Use what you learned in Section 4.2 to answer this question.

*i***nteractive Textbook**

Assessment 6.1 Test yourself on the concepts in Section 6.1.
with ChemASAP

Connecting to Your World

The sculptor Augustus Saint-Gaudens designed this gold coin at the request of Theodore Roosevelt. President Roosevelt wanted coins minted in the United States to be as beautiful as ancient Greek coins, which he admired. The coin is an example of a double eagle. The name derives from the fact that the coin was worth twice as much as $10 coins called eagles. A coin may contain a lot of information in a small space—its value, the year it was minted, and its country of origin. Each square in a periodic table also contains a lot of information. In this section, you will learn what types of information are usually listed in a periodic table.

Squares in the Periodic Table

🔑 **The periodic table displays the symbols and names of the elements, along with information about the structure of their atoms.** Figure 6.8 shows one square from the detailed periodic table of the elements in Figure 6.9 on page 162. In the center of the square is the symbol for sodium (Na). The atomic number for sodium (11) is above the symbol. The element name and average atomic mass are below the symbol. There is also a vertical column with the numbers 2, 8, and 1, which are the number of electrons in each occupied energy level of a sodium atom.

The symbol for sodium is printed in black because sodium is a solid at room temperature. In Figure 6.9, the symbols for gases are in red. The symbols for the two elements that are liquids at room temperature, mercury and bromine, are in blue. The symbols for some elements in Figure 6.9 are printed in green. These elements are not found in nature. In Chapter 25, you will learn how scientists produce these elements.

The background colors in the squares are used to distinguish groups of elements. For example, two shades of gold are used for the metals in Groups 1A and 2A. The Group 1A elements are called **alkali metals,** and the Group 2A elements are called **alkaline earth metals.** The name alkali comes from the Arabic *al aqali,* meaning "the ashes." Wood ashes are rich in compounds of the alkali metals sodium and potassium. Some groups of nonmetals also have special names. The nonmetals of Group 7A are called **halogens.** The name halogen comes from the combination of the Greek word *hals,* meaning salt, and the Latin word *genesis,* meaning "to be born." There is a general class of compounds called salts, which include the compound called table salt. Chlorine, bromine and iodine, the most common halogens, can be prepared from their salts.

Guide for Reading

🔑 **Key Concepts**
- What type of information can be displayed in a periodic table?
- How can elements be classified based on their electron configurations?

Vocabulary
alkali metals
alkaline earth metals
halogens
noble gases
representative elements
transition metal
inner transition metal

Reading Strategy
Relating Text and Visuals
As you read, look carefully at Figure 6.9. After you read the section, explain what you can tell about an element from the color assigned to its square and the color assigned to its symbol.

Figure 6.8 This is the element square for sodium from the periodic table in Figure 6.9. **Interpreting Diagrams** *What does the data in the square tell you about the structure of sodium atoms?*

Periodic Table of the Elements

Figure 6.9 In this periodic table, the colors of the boxes are used to classify representative elements and transition elements.

Atomic number
Electrons in each energy level
Element symbol
Element name
Average atomic mass

14	2 8 4
Si	
Silicon	
28.086	

									18 8A
									2 **He** Helium 4.0026

	13 3A	14 4A	15 5A	16 6A	17 7A	

5 2 3 **B** Boron 10.81	6 2 4 **C** Carbon 12.011	7 2 5 **N** Nitrogen 14.007	8 2 6 **O** Oxygen 15.999	9 2 7 **F** Fluorine 18.998	10 2 8 **Ne** Neon 20.179

13 2 8 3 **Al** Aluminum 26.982	14 2 8 4 **Si** Silicon 28.086	15 2 8 5 **P** Phosphorus 30.974	16 2 8 6 **S** Sulfur 32.06	17 2 8 7 **Cl** Chlorine 35.453	18 2 8 8 **Ar** Argon 39.948

10	11 1B	12 2B

28 2 8 16 2 **Ni** Nickel 58.71	29 2 8 18 1 **Cu** Copper 63.546	30 2 8 18 2 **Zn** Zinc 65.38	31 2 8 18 3 **Ga** Gallium 69.72	32 2 8 18 4 **Ge** Germanium 72.59	33 2 8 18 5 **As** Arsenic 74.922	34 2 8 18 6 **Se** Selenium 78.96	35 2 8 18 7 **Br** Bromine 79.904	36 2 8 18 8 **Kr** Krypton 83.80

46 2 8 18 18 **Pd** Palladium 106.4	47 2 8 18 18 1 **Ag** Silver 107.87	48 2 8 18 18 2 **Cd** Cadmium 112.41	49 2 8 18 18 3 **In** Indium 114.82	50 2 8 18 18 4 **Sn** Tin 118.69	51 2 8 18 18 5 **Sb** Antimony 121.75	52 2 8 18 18 6 **Te** Tellurium 127.60	53 2 8 18 18 7 **I** Iodine 126.90	54 2 8 18 18 8 **Xe** Xenon 131.30

78 2 8 18 32 17 1 **Pt** Platinum 195.09	79 2 8 18 32 18 1 **Au** Gold 196.97	80 2 8 18 32 18 2 **Hg** Mercury 200.59	81 2 8 18 32 18 3 **Tl** Thallium 204.37	82 2 8 18 32 18 4 **Pb** Lead 207.2	83 2 8 18 32 18 5 **Bi** Bismuth 208.98	84 2 8 18 32 18 6 **Po** Polonium (209)	85 2 8 18 32 18 7 **At** Astatine (210)	86 2 8 18 32 18 8 **Rn** Radon (222)

110 2 8 18 32 32 17 1 **Ds** Darmstadtium (269)	111 2 8 18 32 32 18 1 * **Uuu** Unununium (272)	112 2 8 18 32 32 18 2 * **Uub** Ununbium (277)		114 * **Uuq** Ununquadium

*Name not officially assigned.

63 2 8 18 25 8 2 **Eu** Europium 151.96	64 2 8 18 25 9 2 **Gd** Gadolinium 157.25	65 2 8 18 27 8 2 **Tb** Terbium 158.93	66 2 8 18 28 8 2 **Dy** Dysprosium 162.50	67 2 8 18 29 8 2 **Ho** Holmium 164.93	68 2 8 18 30 8 2 **Er** Erbium 167.26	69 2 8 18 31 8 2 **Tm** Thulium 168.93	70 2 8 18 32 8 2 **Yb** Ytterbium 173.04

95 2 8 18 32 25 8 2 **Am** Americium (243)	96 2 8 18 32 25 9 2 **Cm** Curium (247)	97 2 8 18 32 27 8 2 **Bk** Berkelium (247)	98 2 8 18 32 28 8 2 **Cf** Californium (251)	99 2 8 18 32 29 8 2 **Es** Einsteinium (252)	100 2 8 18 32 30 8 2 **Fm** Fermium (257)	101 2 8 18 32 31 8 2 **Md** Mendelevium (258)	102 2 8 18 32 32 8 2 **No** Nobelium (259)

Electron Configurations in Groups

Electrons play a key role in determining the properties of elements. So there should be a connection between an element's electron configuration and its location in the periodic table. ⬤ **Elements can be sorted into noble gases, representative elements, transition metals, or inner transition metals based on their electron configurations.** You may want to refer to Figure 6.9 as you read about these classes of elements.

The Noble Gases The blimp in Figure 6.10 is filled with helium. Helium is an example of a noble gas. The **noble gases** are the elements in Group 8A of the periodic table. These nonmetals are sometimes called the inert gases because they rarely take part in a reaction. The electron configurations for the first four noble gases in Group 8A are listed below.

Helium (He)	$1s^2$
Neon (Ne)	$1s^2 2s^2 2p^6$
Argon (Ar)	$1s^2 2s^2 2p^6 3s^2 3p^6$
Krypton (Kr)	$1s^2 2s^2 2p^6 3s^2 3p^6 3d^{10} 4s^2 4p^6$

Figure 6.10 This blimp contains helium, one of the noble gases. **Applying Concepts** *What does the ability of a helium-filled blimp to rise in air tell you about the density of helium?*

Look at the description of the highest occupied energy level for each element, which is highlighted in yellow. The s and p sublevels are completely filled with electrons. Chapter 7 will explain how this arrangement of electrons is related to the relative inactivity of the noble gases.

The Representative Elements Figure 6.11 shows the portion of the periodic table containing Groups 1A through 7A. Elements in these groups are often referred to as **representative elements** because they display a wide range of physical and chemical properties. Some are metals, some are nonmetals, and some are metalloids. Most of them are solids, but a few are gases at room temperature, and one, bromine, is a liquid.

In atoms of representative elements, the s and p sublevels of the highest occupied energy level are not filled. Look at the electron configurations for lithium, sodium, and potassium. In atoms of these Group 1A elements, there is only one electron in the highest occupied energy level. The electron is in an s sublevel.

Lithium (Li)	$1s^2 2s^1$
Sodium (Na)	$1s^2 2s^2 2p^6 3s^1$
Potassium (K)	$1s^2 2s^2 2p^6 3s^2 3p^6 4s^1$

In atoms of carbon, silicon, and germanium, in Group 4A, there are four electrons in the highest occupied energy level.

Carbon (C)	$1s^2 2s^2 2p^2$
Silicon (Si)	$1s^2 2s^2 2p^6 3s^2 3p^2$
Germanium (Ge)	$1s^2 2s^2 2p^6 3s^2 3p^6 3d^{10} 4s^2 4p^2$

For any representative element, its group number equals the number of electrons in the highest occupied energy level.

Go Online
NSTA *SciLINKS*
For: Links on Chemical Families
Visit: www.SciLinks.org
Web Code: cdn-1062

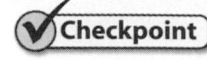 **Checkpoint** *Why are noble gases sometimes referred to as inert gases?*

Magnesium This magnified view of a leaf shows the green structures where light energy is changed into chemical energy. The compound chlorophyll, which contains magnesium, absorbs the light.

Sodium When salt lakes evaporate, they form salt pans like this one in Death Valley, California. The main salt in a salt pan is sodium chloride.

Figure 6.11 Some of the representative elements exist in nature as elements. Others are found only in compounds.

1A							
1 **H** Hydrogen 1.0079							
2A		3A	4A	5A	6A	7A	
3 **Li** Lithium 6.941	4 **Be** Beryllium 9.0122	5 **B** Boron 10.81	6 **C** Carbon 12.011	7 **N** Nitrogen 14.007	8 **O** Oxygen 15.999	9 **F** Fluorine 18.998	
11 **Na** Sodium 22.990	12 **Mg** Magnesium 24.305	13 **Al** Aluminum 26.982	14 **Si** Silicon 28.086	15 **P** Phosphorus 30.974	16 **S** Sulfur 32.06	17 **Cl** Chlorine 35.453	
19 **K** Potassium 39.098	20 **Ca** Calcium 40.08	31 **Ga** Gallium 69.72	32 **Ge** Germanium 72.59	33 **As** Arsenic 74.922	34 **Se** Selenium 78.96	35 **Br** Bromine 79.904	
37 **Rb** Rubidium 85.468	38 **Sr** Strontium 87.62	49 **In** Indium 114.82	50 **Sn** Tin 118.69	51 **Sb** Antimony 121.75	52 **Te** Tellurium 127.60	53 **I** Iodine 126.90	
55 **Cs** Cesium 132.91	56 **Ba** Barium 137.33	81 **Tl** Thallium 204.37	82 **Pb** Lead 207.2	83 **Bi** Bismuth 208.98	84 **Po** Polonium (209)	85 **At** Astatine (210)	
87 **Fr** Francium (223)	88 **Ra** Radium (226)						

Sulfur These scientists are sampling gases being released from a volcano through a vent called a fumarole. The yellow substance is sulfur.

Arsenic This bright red ore is a major source of arsenic in Earth's crust. It contains a compound of arsenic and sulfur.

Transition Elements

In the periodic table, the B groups separate the A groups on the left side of the table from the A groups on the right side. Elements in the B groups, which provide a connection between the two sets of representative elements, are referred to as transition elements. There are two types of transition elements—transition metals and inner transition metals. They are classified based on their electron configurations.

The transition metals are the Group B elements that are usually displayed in the main body of a periodic table. Copper, silver, gold, and iron are transition metals. In atoms of a **transition metal,** the highest occupied s sublevel and a nearby d sublevel contain electrons. These elements are characterized by the presence of electrons in d orbitals.

The inner transition metals appear below the main body of the periodic table. In atoms of an **inner transition metal,** the highest occupied s sublevel and a nearby f sublevel generally contain electrons. The inner transition metals are characterized by f orbitals that contain electrons. Before scientists knew much about inner transition metals, people began to refer to them as rare-earth elements. This name is misleading because some inner transition metals are more abundant than other elements.

Blocks of Elements If you consider both the electron configurations and the positions of the elements in the periodic table, another pattern emerges. In Figure 6.12, the periodic table is divided into sections, or blocks, that correspond to the highest occupied sublevels. The s block contains the elements in Groups 1A and 2A and the noble gas helium. The p block contains the elements in Groups 3A, 4A, 5A, 6A, 7A, and 8A, with the exception of helium. The transition metals belong to the d block, and the inner transition metals belong to the f block.

You can use Figure 6.12 to help determine electron configurations of elements. Each period on the periodic table corresponds to a principal energy level. Say an element is located in period 3. You know that the s and p sublevels in energy levels 1 and 2 are filled with electrons. You read across period 3 from left to right to complete the configuration. For transition elements, electrons are added to a d sublevel with a principal energy level that is one less than the period number. For the inner transition metals, the principal energy level of the f sublevel is two less than the period number. This procedure gives the correct electron configurations for most atoms.

Figure 6.12 This diagram classifies elements into blocks according to sublevels that are filled or filling with electrons. **Interpreting Diagrams** *In the highest occupied energy level of a halogen atom, how many electrons are in the p sublevel?*

CONCEPTUAL PROBLEM 6.1

Using Energy Sublevels to Write Electron Configurations

Nitrogen is an element that organisms need to remain healthy. However, most organisms cannot obtain nitrogen directly from air. A few organisms can convert elemental nitrogen into a form that can be absorbed by plant and animal cells. These include bacteria that live in lumps called *nodules* on the roots of legumes. The photograph shows the nodules on a bean plant. Use Figure 6.12 to write the electron configuration for nitrogen (N), which has atomic number 7.

1 Analyze *Identify the relevant concepts.*

For all elements, the atomic number is equal to the total number of electrons. For a representative element, the highest occupied energy level is the same as the number of the period in which the element is located. From the group in which the element is located, you can tell how many electrons are in this energy level.

2 Solve *Apply concepts to this situation.*

Nitrogen is located in the second period of the periodic table and in the third group of the *p* block. Nitrogen has seven electrons. Based on Figure 6.12, the configuration for the two electrons in the first energy level is $1s^2$. The configuration for the five electrons in the second energy level is $2s^22p^3$.

Practice Problems

8. Use Figure 6.9 and Figure 6.12 to write the electron configurations of the following elements.
a. carbon   **b.** strontium   **c.** vanadium

(*Hint:* Remember that the principal energy level number for elements in the *d* block is always one less than the period number.)

9. List the symbols for all the elements whose electron configurations end as follows. Each *n* represents an energy level.
a. ns^2np^1
b. ns^2np^5
c. ns^2nd^2

6.2 Section Assessment

10. 🔑 **Key Concept** What information can be included in a periodic table?

11. 🔑 **Key Concept** Into what four classes can elements be sorted based on their electron configurations?

12. Why do the elements potassium and sodium have similar chemical properties?

13. Classify each element as a representative element, transition metal, or noble gas.
a. $1s^22s^22p^63s^23p^63d^{10}4s^24p^6$
b. $1s^22s^22p^63s^23p^63d^64s^2$
c. $1s^22s^22p^63s^23p^2$

14. Which of the following elements are transition metals: Cu, Sr, Cd, Au, Al, Ge, Co?

15. How many electrons are in the highest occupied energy level of a Group 5A element?

Elements ▶ **Handbook**

Noble Gases Look at the atomic properties of noble gases on page R36. In a gas discharge tube, what color light is produced by each noble gas? Use what you know about the structure of atoms to explain why the color is different for each gas.

Interactive Textbook

Assessment 6.2 Test yourself on the concepts in Section 6.2.

—— with **ChemASAP**

True Colors

Paint consists essentially of a pigment, a binder, and a liquid in which the other components are dissolved or dispersed. The liquid keeps the mixture thin enough to flow. The binder attaches the paint to the surface being painted, and the pigment determines the color. Pigments may be natural or manufactured. They may be inorganic or organic. The same pigment can be used in a water-based or oil-based paint. **Comparing and Contrasting** *Describe at least three differences between the cave painting and the painting by Jacob Lawrence.*

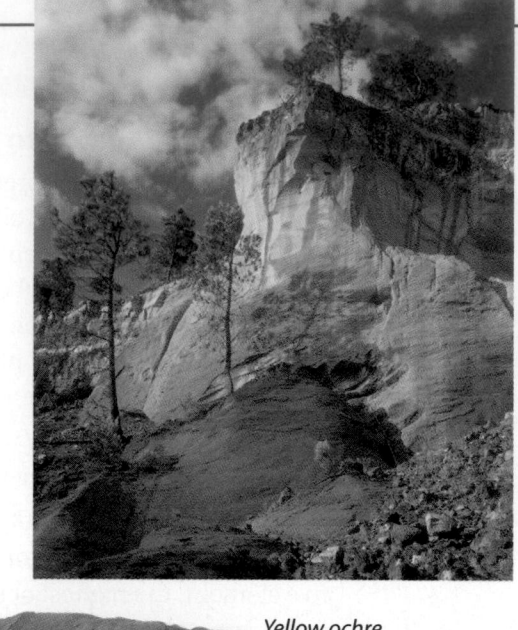

Natural pigments A prehistoric artist had a limited choice of colors— black from charcoal and red, brown, and yellow from oxides of iron in Earth's crust. These oxides (or ochre) pigments are often referred to as earth tones.

Yellow ochre

Red ochre

Charred wood is a source of charcoal.

Prehistoric art Around 14,000 years ago, an artist painted this bison on the ceiling of a cave in Spain. It is about two meters long.

Red Iron Oxide

Cadmium Orange

Cobalt Yellow

Zinc White

Chromium Oxide Green

Manganese Violet

Cobalt Blue

Manufactured pigments

Alchemists (and the Chemists) made pigments that don't exist in nature. They also made purer versions of natural pigments. Many of these pigments contain transition metals.

From pigments to paint

Artists mixed manufactured pigments with binders and solvents to make paint. Although premixed paints became available around 1800, some artists, including Jacob Lawrence, continued to mix their own paints.

The Builders, 1974, by Jacob Lawrence

6.3 Periodic Trends

New York Standards: 3.1aa–bb, 5.2c, 5.2j

Guide for Reading

 Key Concepts

- What are the trends among the elements for atomic size?
- How do ions form?
- What are the trends among the elements for first ionization energy, ionic size, and electronegativity?
- What is the underlying cause of periodic trends?

Vocabulary

atomic radius

ion

cation

anion

ionization energy

electronegativity

Reading Strategy

Building Vocabulary After you read this section, explain the difference between a cation and an anion.

Connecting to Your World

An atom doesn't have a sharply defined boundary. So the radius of an atom cannot be measured directly. There are ways to estimate the sizes of atoms. In one method, a solid is bombarded with X rays, and the paths of the X rays are recorded on film. Sodium chloride (table salt) produced the geometric pattern in the photograph. Such a pattern can be used to calculate the position of nuclei in a solid. The distances between nuclei in a solid are an indication of the size of the particles in the solid. In this section, you will learn how properties such as atomic size are related to the location of elements in the periodic table.

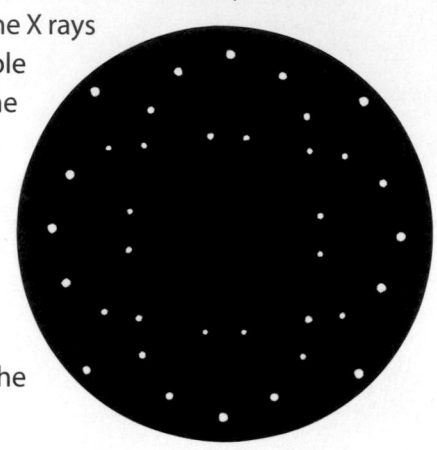

Trends in Atomic Size

Another way to think about atomic size is to look at the units that form when atoms of the same element are attached to one another. These units are called molecules. Figure 6.13 shows models of molecules (molecular models) for seven nonmetals. Because the atoms in each molecule are identical, the distance between the nuclei of these atoms can be used to estimate the size of the atoms. This size is expressed as an atomic radius. The **atomic radius** is one half of the distance between the nuclei of two atoms of the same element when the atoms are joined.

The distances between atoms in a molecule are extremely small. So the atomic radius is often measured in picometers. Recall that there are one trillion, or 10^{12}, picometers in a meter. Look at the diagram of an iodine molecule in Figure 6.13. The distance between the nuclei in the molecule is 280 pm. Because the atomic radius is one half the distance between the nuclei, a value of 140 pm (280/2) is assigned as the radius of the iodine atom. **In general, atomic size increases from top to bottom within a group and decreases from left to right across a period.**

Figure 6.13 This diagram lists the atomic radii of seven nonmetals. An atomic radius is half the distance between the nuclei of two atoms of the same element when the atoms are joined.

Atomic Radius Versus Atomic Number

Figure 6.14 This graph plots atomic radius versus atomic number for 55 elements.

INTERPRETING GRAPHS

a. Analyzing Data Which alkali metal has an atomic radius of 238 pm?

b. Drawing Conclusions Based on the data for alkali metals and noble gases, how does atomic size change within a group?

c. Predicting Is an atom of barium, atomic number 56, smaller or larger than an atom of cesium (Cs)?

Group Trends in Atomic Size In the Figure 6.14 graph, atomic radius is plotted versus atomic number. Look at the data for the alkali metals and noble gases. The atomic radius within these groups increases as the atomic number increases. This increase is an example of a trend.

As the atomic number increases within a group, the charge on the nucleus increases and the number of occupied energy levels increases. These variables affect atomic size in opposite ways. The increase in positive charge draws electrons closer to the nucleus. The increase in the number of occupied orbitals shields electrons in the highest occupied energy level from the attraction of protons in the nucleus. The shielding effect is greater than the effect of the increase in nuclear charge. So the atomic size increases.

Periodic Trends in Atomic Size Look again at Figure 6.14. In general, atomic size decreases across a period from left to right. Each element has one more proton and one more electron than the preceding element. Across a period, the electrons are added to the same principal energy level. The shielding effect is constant for all the elements in a period. The increasing nuclear charge pulls the electrons in the highest occupied energy level closer to the nucleus and the atomic size decreases. Figure 6.15 summarizes the group and period trends in atomic size.

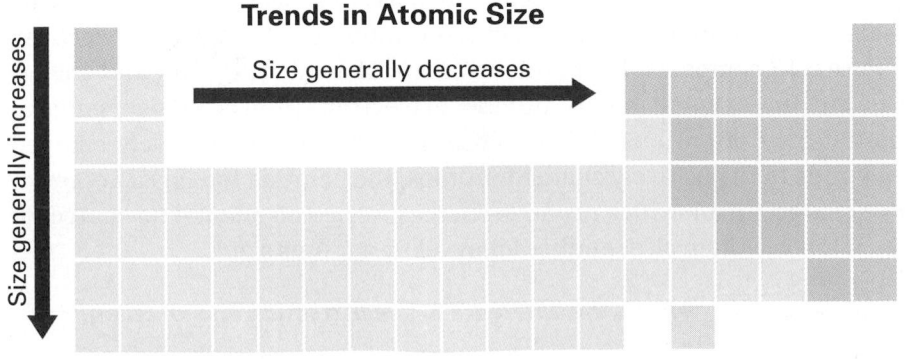

Trends in Atomic Size

Size generally increases

Size generally decreases

Figure 6.15 The size of atoms tends to decrease from left to right across a period and increase from top to bottom within a group. **Predicting** *If a halogen and an alkali metal are in the same period, which one will have the larger radius?*

Figure 6.16 When a sodium atom loses an electron, it becomes a positively charged ion. When a chlorine atom gains an electron, it becomes a negatively charged ion. **Interpreting Diagrams** *What happens to the protons and neutrons during this change?*

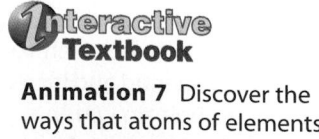

Animation 7 Discover the ways that atoms of elements combine to form compounds.

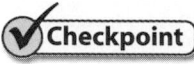

Ions

Some compounds are composed of particles called ions. An **ion** is an atom or group of atoms that has a positive or negative charge. An atom is electrically neutral because it has equal numbers of protons and electrons. For example, an atom of sodium (Na) has 11 positively charged protons and 11 negatively charged electrons. The net charge on a sodium atom is zero [(11+) + (−11) = 0].

⬤ **Positive and negative ions form when electrons are transferred between atoms.** Atoms of metallic elements, such as sodium, tend to form ions by losing one or more electrons from their highest occupied energy levels. A sodium atom tends to lose one electron. Figure 6.16 compares the atomic structure of a sodium atom and a sodium ion. In the sodium ion, the number of electrons (10) is no longer equal to the number of protons (11). Because there are more positively charged protons than negatively charged electrons, the sodium ion has a net positive charge. An ion with a positive charge is called a **cation.** The charge for a cation is written as a number followed by a plus sign. If the charge is 1+, the number 1 is usually omitted from the complete symbol for the ion. So Na^+ is equivalent to Na^{1+}.

Atoms of nonmetallic elements, such as chlorine, tend to form ions by gaining one or more electrons. A chlorine atom tends to gain one electron. Figure 6.16 compares the atomic structure of a chlorine atom and a chloride ion. In a chloride ion, the number of electrons (18) is no longer equal to the number of protons (17). Because there are more negatively charged electrons than positively charged protons, the chloride ion has a net negative charge. An ion with a negative charge is called an **anion.** The charge for an anion is written as a number followed by a minus sign.

✓ **Checkpoint** *What is the difference between a cation and an anion?*

Trends in Ionization Energy

Recall that electrons can move to higher energy levels when atoms absorb energy. Sometimes there is enough energy to overcome the attraction of the protons in the nucleus. The energy required to remove an electron from an atom is called **ionization energy.** This energy is measured when an element is in its gaseous state. The energy required to remove the first electron from an atom is called the first ionization energy. The cation produced has a 1+ charge. **First ionization energy tends to decrease from top to bottom within a group and increase from left to right across a period.**

Table 6.1 lists the first, second, and third ionization energies for the first 20 elements. The second ionization energy is the energy required to remove an electron from an ion with a 1+ charge. The ion produced has a 2+ charge. The third ionization energy is the energy required to remove an electron from an ion with a 2+ charge. The ion produced has a 3+ charge.

Ionization energy can help you predict what ions elements will form. Look at the data in Table 6.1 for lithium (Li), sodium (Na), and potassium (K). The increase in energy between the first and second ionization energies is large. It is relatively easy to remove one electron from a Group 1A metal atom, but it is difficult to remove a second electron. So Group 1A metals tend to form ions with a 1+ charge.

Table 6.1

Ionization Energies of First 20 Elements (kJ/mol*)			
Symbol	First	Second	Third
H	1312		
He (noble gas)	2372	5247	
Li	520	7297	11,810
Be	899	1757	14,840
B	801	2430	3659
C	1086	2352	4619
N	1402	2857	4577
O	1314	3391	5301
F	1681	3375	6045
Ne (noble gas)	2080	3963	6276
Na	496	4565	6912
Mg	738	1450	7732
Al	578	1816	2744
Si	786	1577	3229
P	1012	1896	2910
S	999	2260	3380
Cl	1256	2297	3850
Ar (noble gas)	1520	2665	3947
K	419	3069	4600
Ca	590	1146	4941

*An amount of matter equal to the atomic mass in grams.

Figure 6.17 This graph reveals group and period trends for ionization energy.

First Ionization Energy Versus Atomic Number

INTERPRETING GRAPHS

a. Analyzing Data Which element in period 2 has the lowest first ionization energy? In period 3?

b. Drawing Conclusions What is the group trend for first ionization energy for noble gases and alkali metals?

c. Predicting If you drew a graph for second ionization energy, which element would you have to omit? Explain.

Group Trends in Ionization Energy Figure 6.17 is a graph of first ionization energy versus atomic number. Each red dot represents the data for one element. Look at the data for the noble gases and the alkali metals. In general, first ionization energy decreases from top to bottom within a group. Recall that the atomic size increases as the atomic number increases within a group. As the size of the atom increases, nuclear charge has a smaller effect on the electrons in the highest occupied energy level. So less energy is required to remove an electron from this energy level and the first ionization energy is lower.

Periodic Trends in Ionization Energy In general, the first ionization energy of representative elements tends to increase from left to right across a period. This trend can be explained by the nuclear charge, which increases, and the shielding effect, which remains constant. The nuclear charge increases across the period, but the shielding effect remains constant. So there is an increase in the attraction of the nucleus for an electron. Thus, it takes more energy to remove an electron from an atom. Figure 6.18 summarizes the group and period trends for first ionization energy.

Trends in First Ionization Energy

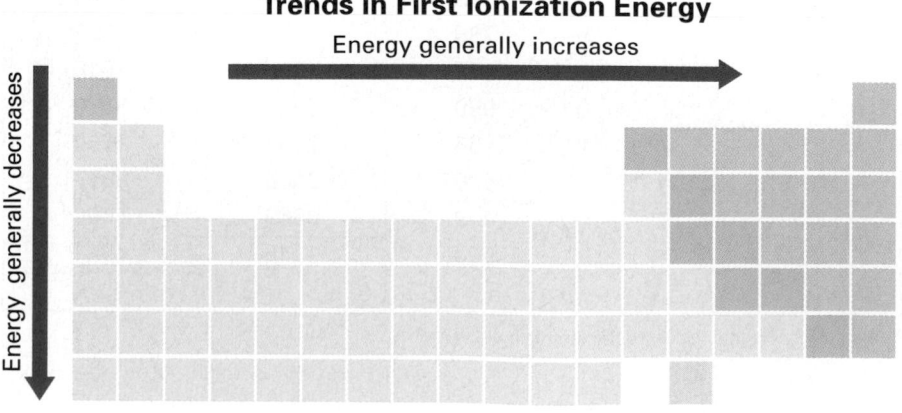

Figure 6.18 First ionization energy tends to increase from left to right across a period and decrease from top to bottom within a group.
Predicting *Which element would have the larger first ionization energy—an alkali metal in period 2 or an alkali metal in period 4?*

Quick LAB

Periodic Trends in Ionic Radii

Purpose
Make a graph of ionic radius versus atomic number and use the graph to identify periodic and group trends.

Materials
• graph paper

Procedure
Use the data presented in Figure 6.19 to plot ionic radius versus atomic number.

Analyze and Conclude
1. Describe how the size changes when an atom forms a cation and when an atom forms an anion.

2. How do the ionic radii vary within a group of metals? How do they vary within a group of nonmetals?

3. Describe the shape of a portion of the graph that corresponds to one period.

4. Is the trend across a period similar or different for periods 2, 3, 4, and 5?

5. Propose explanations for the trends you have described for ionic radii within groups and across periods.

Ionic Radii vs. Atomic Number

Figure 6.19 Atomic and ionic radii are an indication of the relative size of atoms and ions. The data listed in Figure 6.19 is reported in picometers (pm).

1A							8A
30 **H**							50 **He**

	2A	3A	4A	5A	6A	7A	
156 **Li** 60 1+	113 **Be** 44 2+	83 **B** 23 3+	77 **C** 15 4+	70 **N** 146 3−	66 **O** 140 2−	62 **F** 133 1−	70 **Ne**
191 **Na** 95 1+	160 **Mg** 66 2+	143 **Al** 51 3+	109 **Si** 41 4+	109 **P** 212 3−	105 **S** 184 2−	102 **Cl** 181 1−	94 **Ar**
238 **K** 133 1+	197 **Ca** 99 2+	141 **Ga** 62 3+	122 **Ge** 53 4+	122 **As** 222 3−	120 **Se** 198 2−	120 **Br** 196 1−	111 **Kr**
255 **Rb** 148 1+	215 **Sr** 112 2+	166 **In** 81 3+	139 **Sn** 71 4+	137 **Sb** 62 5+	139 **Te** 221 2−	140 **I** 220 1−	130 **Xe**
273 **Cs** 169 1+	224 **Ba** 134 2+	172 **Tl** 95 3+	175 **Pb** 84 4+	170 **Bi** 74 5+	168 **Po**	140 **At**	140 **Rn**

156 — Atomic radius

Li

60 —— Ionic radius

⬤ Metal

⬤ Metalloid

⬤ Nonmetal

⬤ Cation

⬤ Anion

Figure 6.20 This diagram compares the relative sizes of atoms and ions for selected alkali metals and halogens. The data are given in picometers.
Comparing and Contrasting
What happens to the radius when an atom forms a cation? When an atom forms an anion?

Group 1A

Li 156 → e⁻ → Li⁺ 60

Na 191 → e⁻ → Na⁺ 95

K 238 → e⁻ → K⁺ 133

Group 7A

e⁻ → F 62 → F⁻ 133

e⁻ → Cl 102 → Cl⁻ 181

e⁻ → Br 120 → Br⁻ 196

Trends in Ionic Size

During reactions between metals and nonmetals, metal atoms tend to lose electrons and nonmetal atoms tend to gain electrons. The transfer has a predictable affect on the size of the ions that form. **Cations are always smaller than the atoms from which they form. Anions are always larger than the atoms from which they form.**

Figure 6.20 compares the relative sizes of the atoms and ions for three metals in Group 1A. For each of these elements, the ion is much smaller than the atom. For example, the radius of a sodium ion (95 pm) is about half the radius of a sodium atom (191 pm). When a sodium atom loses an electron, the attraction between the remaining electrons and the nucleus is increased. The electrons are drawn closer to the nucleus. Also, metals that are representative elements tend to lose all their outermost electrons during ionization. So the ion has one fewer occupied energy level.

The trend is the opposite for nonmetals like the halogens in Group 7A. For each of these elements, the ion is much larger than the atom. For example, the radius of a fluoride ion (133 pm) is more than twice the radius of a fluorine atom (62 pm). As the number of electrons increases, the attraction of the nucleus for any one electron decreases.

Look back at Figure 6.19. From left to right across a period, two trends are visible—a gradual decrease in the size of the positive ions followed by a gradual decrease in the size of the negative ions. Figure 6.21 summarizes the group and periodic trends in ionic size.

Figure 6.21 The ionic radii for cations and anions decrease from left to right across periods and increase from top to bottom within groups.

Trends in Ionic Size

Size of cations decreases

Size of anions decreases

Size generally increases

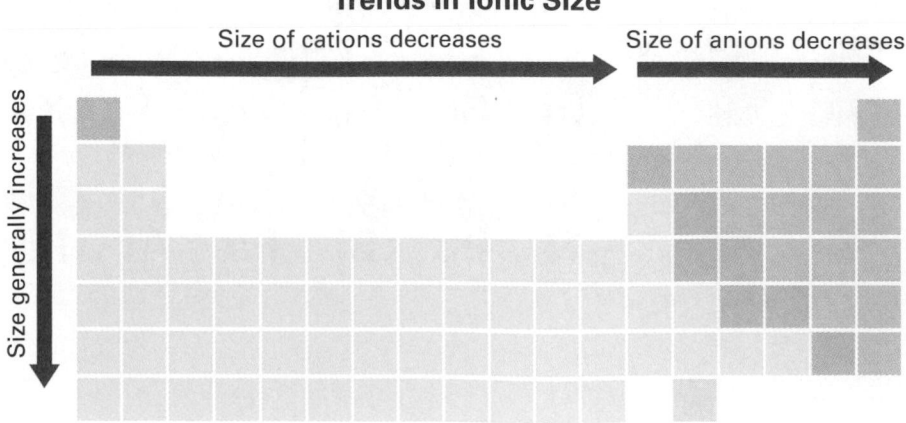

Trends in Electronegativity

In Chapters 7 and 8, you will study two types of bonds that can exist in compounds. Electrons are involved in both types of bonds. There is a property that can be used to predict the type of bond that will form during a reaction. This property is called electronegativity. **Electronegativity** is the ability of an atom of an element to attract electrons when the atom is in a compound. Scientists use factors such as ionization energy to calculate values for electronegativity.

Table 6.2 lists electronegativity values for representative elements in Groups 1A through 7A. The elements are arranged in the same order as in a periodic table. The noble gases are omitted because they do not form many compounds. The data in Table 6.2 is expressed in units called Paulings. Linus Pauling won a Nobel Prize in Chemistry for his work on chemical bonds. He was the first to define electronegativity.

In general, electronegativity values decrease from top to bottom within a group. For representative elements, the values tend to increase from left to right across a period. Metals at the far left of the periodic table have low values. By contrast, nonmetals at the far right (excluding noble gases) have high values. The electronegativity values among the transition metals are not as regular.

The least electronegative element is cesium, with an electronegativity value of 0.7. It has the least tendency to attract electrons. When it reacts, it tends to lose electrons and form positive ions. The most electronegative element is fluorine, with a value of 4.0. Because fluorine has such a strong tendency to attract electrons, when it is bonded to any other element it either attracts the shared electrons or forms a negative ion.

✓ Checkpoint *Why are values for noble gases omitted from Table 6.2?*

Go Online
NSTA SciLINKS

For: Links on Electronegativity
Visit: www.SciLinks.org
Web Code: cdn-1063

Table 6.2

Electronegativity Values for Selected Elements						
H 2.1						
Li 1.0	**Be** 1.5	**B** 2.0	**C** 2.5	**N** 3.0	**O** 3.5	**F** 4.0
Na 0.9	**Mg** 1.2	**Al** 1.5	**Si** 1.8	**P** 2.1	**S** 2.5	**Cl** 3.0
K 0.8	**Ca** 1.0	**Ga** 1.6	**Ge** 1.8	**As** 2.0	**Se** 2.4	**Br** 2.8
Rb 0.8	**Sr** 1.0	**In** 1.7	**Sn** 1.8	**Sb** 1.9	**Te** 2.1	**I** 2.5
Cs 0.7	**Ba** 0.9	**Tl** 1.8	**Pb** 1.9	**Bi** 1.9		

Figure 6.22 Properties that vary within groups and across periods include atomic size, ionic size, ionization energy, electronegativity, nuclear charge, and shielding effect.
Interpreting Diagrams
Which properties tend to decrease across a period?

Atomic size decreases
Ionization energy increases
Electronegativity increases
Nuclear charge increases
Shielding is constant

Atomic size increases
Ionic size increases
Ionization energy decreases
Electronegativity decreases
Nuclear charge increases
Shielding increases

Size of cations decreases   Size of anions decreases

Summary of Trends

Figure 6.22 shows the trends for atomic size, ionization energy, ionic size, and electronegativity in Groups 1A through 8A. These properties vary within groups and across periods.  **The trends that exist among these properties can be explained by variations in atomic structure.** The increase in nuclear charge within groups and across periods explains many trends. Within groups an increase in shielding has a significant effect.

6.3 Section Assessment

16. 🔑 **Key Concept** How does atomic size change within groups and across periods?

17. 🔑 **Key Concept** When do ions form?

18. 🔑 **Key Concept** What happens to first ionization energy within groups and across periods?

19. 🔑 **Key Concept** Compare the size of ions to the size of the atoms from which they form.

20. 🔑 **Key Concept** How does electronegativity vary within groups and across periods?

21. 🔑 **Key Concept** In general, how can the periodic trends displayed by elements be explained?

22. Arrange these elements in order of decreasing atomic size: sulfur, chlorine, aluminum, and sodium. Does your arrangement demonstrate a periodic trend or a group trend?

23. Which element in each pair has the larger first ionization energy?
    a. sodium, potassium
    b. magnesium, phosphorus

Writing ▶ **Activity**

Explaining Trends in Atomic Size Explain why the size of an atom tends to increase from top to bottom within a group. Explain why the size of an atom tends to decrease from left to right across a period.

ℹ️**nteractive Textbook**

Assessment 6.3 Test yourself on the concepts in Section 6.3.

——with **ChemASAP**

Periodicity in Three Dimensions

Purpose
To build three-dimensional models for periodic trends.

Materials
- 96-well spot plate
- straws
- scissors
- metric ruler
- permanent fine-line marker

Procedure

1. Measure the depth of a well in the spot plate by inserting a straw into a well and holding the straw upright as shown in the photograph. Make a mark on the straw at the point where the straw meets the surface of the plate. Measure the distance from the end of the straw to the mark in centimeters. Record this distance as well depth.

2. Cut the straw to a length that is 4.0 cm plus well depth. The straw will extend exactly 4.0 cm above the surface of the plate.

3. Fluorine has an electronegativity value of 4.0. On a scale of one cm equals one unit of electronegativity, the portion of the straw that extends above the surface of the plate represents the electronegativity value for fluorine. Using the same scale, cut straws to represent the electronegativity values for all the elements listed in Table 6.2. Remember to add the well depth to the electronegativity value before cutting a straw. As you cut the straws, mark each straw with the chemical symbol of the element that the straw represents.

4. Arrange the straws in the spot plate in rows and columns to match the locations of the elements in the periodic table.

5. Make a rough sketch of your completed model.

Analyze and Conclude
Observe your model and record the answers to the following questions below your sketch.

1. Which element represented in your model is the most electronegative?

2. Based on your model, what is the general trend in electronegativity from left to right across a period?

3. Relate the trend in electronegativity across a period to the location of metals and nonmetals in the periodic table.

4. What is the general trend in electronegativity within a group? Are there any notable exceptions?

5. Why do you think that the electronegativity value for hydrogen is so high given its location in the table?

You're the Chemist
The following small-scale activities allow you to develop your own procedures and analyze the results.

1. **Design It!** Construct a similar 3-D model for first ionization energies. Use the data in Table 6.1. Use a scale of one cm equals 300 kJ/mol.

2. **Design It!** Design and construct a 3-D model that shows trends in atomic and ionic radii for the elements in Groups 1A and 7A. Devise a way to display both ionic and atomic radii in the same model.

3. **Analyze it!** Xenon has an electronegativity value of 2.6. Cut and place a straw in your first model to represent xenon. Does xenon support the trend for electronegativity across a period? Is xenon likely to form compounds? Explain your answers.

Key Concepts

6.1 Organizing the Elements

- Chemists used the properties of elements to sort them into groups.

- Mendeleev arranged the elements in his periodic table in order of increasing atomic mass.

- In the modern periodic table, elements are arranged in order of increasing atomic number. The elements within a group in the table have similar properties.

- Three classes of elements are metals, non-metals, and metalloids.

6.2 Classifying the Elements

- The periodic table displays the symbols and names of elements, along with information on the structure of their atoms.

- Elements can be sorted into noble gases, representative elements, transition metals, or inner transition metals based on their electron configurations.

- The periodic table can be divided into *s, p, d,* and *f* blocks that correspond to the highest occupied sublevels in atoms of elements.

6.3 Periodic Trends

- In general, atomic size increases from top to bottom within a group and decreases from left to right across a period.

- Positive and negative ions form when electrons are transferred between atoms.

- First ionization energy tends to decrease from top to bottom within a group and increase from left to right across a period.

- Cations are always smaller than the atoms from which they form. Anions are always larger than the atoms from which they form.

- In general, electronegativity values decrease from top to bottom within a group. For representative elements, the values tend to increase from left to right across a period.

- Trends in atomic size, ionization energy, ionic size, and electronegativity can be explained by variations in atomic structure. The increase in nuclear charge within groups and across periods explains many trends. Within groups an increase in shielding has a significant effect.

Vocabulary

- alkali metals (p. 161)
- alkaline earth metals (p. 161)
- anion (p. 172)
- atomic radius (p. 170)
- cation (p. 172)
- electronegativity (p. 177)
- halogens (p. 161)
- inner transition metal (p. 166)
- ion (p. 172)
- ionization energy (p. 173)
- metalloids (p. 160)
- metals (p. 158)
- noble gases (p. 164)
- nonmetals (p. 159)
- periodic law (p. 157)
- representative elements (p. 164)
- transition metal (p. 166)

Organizing Information

Use these terms to construct a concept map that organizes the major ideas of this chapter.

Concept Map 6 Solve the Concept Map with the help of an interactive guided tutorial.

—— with **ChemASAP**

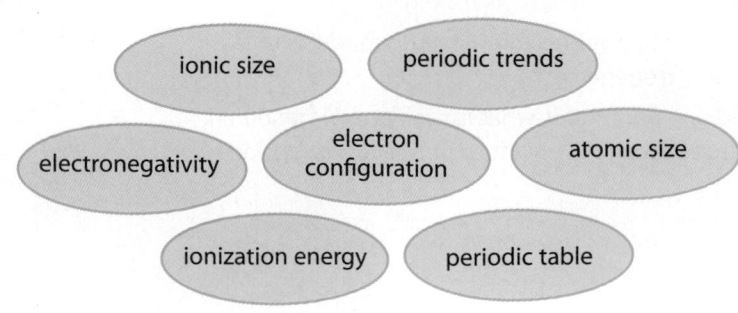

ionic size   periodic trends

electronegativity   electron configuration   atomic size

ionization energy   periodic table

Review and Assessment

Blue questions emphasize Regents Exam content

Organizing the Elements

24. Why did Mendeleev leave spaces in his periodic table?

25. What effect did the discovery of gallium have on the acceptance of Mendeleev's table?

26. What pattern is revealed when the elements are arranged in a periodic table in order of increasing atomic number?

27. Based on their locations in the periodic table, would you expect carbon and silicon to have similar properties? Explain your answer.

28. Identify each property below as more characteristic of a metal or a nonmetal.
   a. a gas at room temperature
   b. brittle
   c. malleable
   d. poor conductor of electric current
   e. shiny

29. How are the properties of metalloids different from those of metals and nonmetals?

30. The bar graph below shows how many elements were discovered before 1750 and in each 50-year period between 1750 and 2000.
   a. In which 50-year period were the most elements discovered?
   b. How did Mendeleev's work contribute to the discovery of so many elements?
   c. What percent of the elements were discovered by 1900?

Discovery of Elements

31. Write the symbol of the element or elements that fit each description.
   a. a nonmetal in Group 4A (14)
   b. the inner transition metal with the lowest atomic number
   c. all of the nonmetals for which the atomic number is a multiple of five
   d. a metal in Group 5A (15)

32. In which pair of elements are the chemical properties of the elements most similar? Explain your reasoning.
   a. sodium and chlorine
   b. nitrogen and phosphorus
   c. boron and oxygen

33. Do you think there are more elements left to discover? If so, what is the lowest atomic number a new element could have? Explain your answers.

34. Make a graph of average atomic mass versus atomic number. Choose 11 points (atomic number 1, 10, 20, and so forth up to atomic number 100) to make your graph. Use the graph to describe the relationship between average atomic mass and atomic number. Is there a 1:1 correspondence between average atomic mass and atomic number? Explain how you reached your conclusion.

Classifying the Elements

35. Where are the noble gases located in the periodic table?

36. Which of the following are symbols for representative elements: Na, Mg, Fe, Ni, Cl?

37. Which noble gas does not have eight electrons in its highest occupied energy level?

38. Which of these metals is *not* a transition metal?
   a. aluminum   **b.** silver
   c. iron   **d.** zirconium

39. Write the electron configurations of the following elements.
   a. boron   **d.** zinc
   b. arsenic   **e.** aluminum
   c. fluorine

CHAPTER
6
Review and Assessment *continued*
Blue questions emphasize Regents Exam content

40. Identify and write the electron configuration of these elements.
    a. the noble gas in period 3
    b. the metalloid in period 3
    c. the metal in the second group and the third period

41. List the symbols for all the elements with electron configurations that end as follows. Each n represents an energy level.
    a. ns^1
    b. ns^2np^4
    c. ns^2nd^{10}

42. Explain why there should be a connection between an element's electron configuration and its location on the periodic table.

43. Atoms and ions with the same number of electrons are called isoelectronic.
    a. Write the symbol for a positive ion and a negative ion that are isoelectronic with krypton.
    b. Is it possible for a positive ion to be isoelectronic with a negative ion from the same period? Explain.

Periodic Trends

44. Which element in each pair has atoms with a larger atomic radius?
    a. sodium, lithium
    b. strontium, magnesium
    c. carbon, germanium
    d. selenium, oxygen

45. Explain the difference between the first and second ionization energy of an element.

46. Which element in each pair has a greater first ionization energy?
    a. lithium, boron
    b. magnesium, strontium
    c. cesium, aluminum

47. Arrange the following groups of elements in order of increasing ionization energy.
    a. Be, Mg, Sr
    b. Bi, Cs, Ba
    c. Na, Al, S

48. Why is there a large increase between the first and second ionization energies of the alkali metals?

49. How does the ionic radius of a typical metallic atom compare with its atomic radius?

50. Which particle has the larger radius in each atom/ion pair?
    a. Na, Na^+
    b. S, S^{2-}
    c. I, I^-
    d. Al, Al^{3+}

51. Which element in each pair has a higher electronegativity value?
    a. Cl, F   b. C, N   c. Mg, Ne   d. As, Ca

52. Why are noble gases not included in Table 6.2?

53. When the elements in each pair are chemically combined, which element in each pair has a greater attraction for electrons?
    a. Ca or O
    b. O or F
    c. H or O
    d. K or S

54. Explain why fluorine has a smaller atomic radius than both oxygen and chlorine.

55. Would you expect metals or nonmetals in the same period to have higher ionization energies? Give a reason for your answer.

56. In each pair, which ion is larger?
    a. Ca^{2+}, Mg^{2+} b. Cl^-, P^{3-} c. Cu^+, Cu^{2+}

57. Use the graph in Figure 6.14 to estimate the atomic radius of the indium atom.

58. What trend is demonstrated by the following series of equations?
    $$Li + 520\ kJ/mol \longrightarrow Li^+ + e^-$$
    $$O + 1314\ kJ/mol \longrightarrow O^+ + e^-$$
    $$F + 1681\ kJ/mol \longrightarrow F^+ + e^-$$
    $$Ne + 2080\ kJ/mol \longrightarrow Ne^+ + e^-$$

59. There is a large jump between the second and third ionization energies of magnesium. There is a large jump between the third and fourth ionization energies of aluminum. Explain this observed difference.

60. The bar graph shows the relationship between atomic and ionic radii for Group 1A (1) elements.
    a. Describe and explain the trend in atomic radius within the group.

b. Explain the difference between the size of the atoms and the size of the ions.

Comparing Radii of Alkali Metals

61. The graphs below show the relationship between the electronegativities and first ionization energies for Period 2 and Period 3 elements.
a. Based on data for these two periods, what is the general trend between these two values?
b. Use nuclear charge and shielding effect to explain this trend.

Period 2

Period 3

62. Explain why it takes more energy to remove a valence electron from zinc than from calcium.

63. Explain each of the following comparisons.
a. Calcium has a smaller second ionization energy than does potassium.
b. Magnesium has a larger third ionization energy than does aluminum.

64. Explain why lithium has a larger first ionization energy than does cesium.

65. The Mg^{2+} and Na^+ ions each have ten electrons. Which ion would you expect to have the smaller radius? Explain your choice.

66. The ions S^{2-}, Cl^-, K^+, Ca^{2+}, and Sc^{3+} have the same total number of electrons as the noble gas argon. How would you expect the radii of these ions to vary? Would you expect to see the same variation in the series O^{2-}, F^-, Na^+, Mg^{2+}, and Al^{3+}, in which each ion has the same total number of electrons as the noble gas neon? Explain your answer.

67. The ionization energies for the removal of the first six electrons in carbon are, starting with the first electron, 1086 kJ/mol, 2352 kJ/mol, 4619 kJ/mol, 6220 kJ/mol, 37,820 kJ/mol, and 47,260 kJ/mol.
a. Make a graph of ionization energy versus ionization number. The ionization number indicates which electron is lost.
b. Between which two ionization numbers does the ionization energy have the largest increase? Explain why this behavior is predictable.

Test-Taking Tip

Interpreting Data Tables Tables present a large amount of data in a small space. Before you try to answer questions based on a table, look at the table. Read the title, if there is one, and the column headings. Then read the questions. As you read each question, decide which data you will need to use to answer the question. You may need to focus on a single entry or column or to find a relationship using data from multiple columns.

Regents Practice Exam

Part A

For each statement or question write the number of the word or expression that, of those given, best completes the statement or answers the question.

1. Electronegativity values are higher for
   (1) metals than for nonmetals
   (2) nonmetals than for metals
   (3) noble gases than for metals
   (4) noble gases than for nonmetals

2. A calcium atom is larger than a calcium ion because
   (1) ions are always larger than the atoms from which they were formed
   (2) ions are always smaller than the atoms from which they were formed
   (3) negative ions are always smaller than positive ions
   (4) positive ions are always smaller than negative ions

3. In any period on the periodic table, the noble gas always has the
   (1) smallest ionization energy
   (2) greatest ionization energy
   (3) ion with the largest charge
   (4) same properties as other elements in the period

4. Which of the following properties decreases as you move across a period from left to right?
   (1) electronegativity
   (2) ionization energy
   (3) atomic radius
   (4) nuclear charge

5. A measurement of 9.37 mm equals
   (1) 9.37 m   (3) 9.37×10^{-3} m
   (2) 9.37×10^3 m   (4) 937 m

Part B-1

For each statement or question write the number of the word or expression that, of those given, best completes the statement or answers the question.

6. How many neutrons are present in an atom of $^{185}_{75}Re$?
   (1) 75   (3) 185
   (2) 110   (4) 260

7. How many electrons are present in an atom of $^{96}_{42}Mo$?
   (1) 42   (3) 96
   (2) 54   (4) 138

8. How many electrons are present in an atom of $^{45}_{21}Sc$?
   (1) 21   (3) 45
   (2) 24   (4) 66

9. Which of the following choices shows the symbols for sodium, sulfur, and cesium in order of increasing atomic radii?
   (1) Na, S, Cs   (3) S, Na, Cs
   (2) Cs, Na, S   (4) Cs, S, Na

Use the data table and information to answer Questions 10 and 11. The numbered choices below refer to these questions. A numbered choice may be used once, more than once, or not at all

Alkali metal	Atomic radius (pm)	First ionization energy (kJ/mol)	Electronegativity value
Li	152	520	1.0
Na	186	495.8	0.9
K	227	418.8	0.8
Rb	244	250	0.8
Cs	262	210	0.7

In each of the following questions, if you plotted the two variables, what type of relationship would be shown on the graph?
   (1) direct   (3) varying
   (2) indirect   (4) no relationship

10. atomic radius versus electronegativity

11. first ionization energy versus electronegativity

12. The number of valence electrons in a Group 7A (17) element is
   (1) 1   (3) 7
   (2) 2   (4) 8

13. Which equation represents the first ionization energy of a metal atom from the first group on the periodic table?
   (1) $Cl \longrightarrow Cl^+ + e^-$ (3) $K \longrightarrow K^+ + e^-$
   (2) $Ca \longrightarrow Ca^+ + e^-$ (4) $H \longrightarrow H^+ + e^-$

14. For which of these properties does lithium have a larger value than potassium?
   (1) first ionization energy   (3) electronegativity
   (2) atomic radius   (4) ionic radius

Part B-2

Answer each of the following questions.

15. Describe at least two methods to separate a mixture of small copper and iron beads.

16. The volume of the liquid in the following graduated cylinder is reported as 31.8 mL.
   a. How many significant figures are in this measurement?
   b. Which digit is uncertain?

17. Convert the following measurements to meters. Express your answers in scientific notation.
   a. 2.24 nm   **b.** 8.13 cm   **c.** 7.4 pm

18. Make a graph of mass versus volume for sulfur. Determine the density of sulfur from the best-fit line.

Mass of Sulfur Versus Volume of Sulfur	
Mass of sulfur (g)	Volume of sulfur (cm³)
23.5	11.4
60.8	29.2
115	55.5
168	81.1

19. Calculate the volume of acetone with the same mass as 15.0 mL of mercury. The density of mercury is 13.59 g/mL. The density of acetone is 0.792 g/mL.

20. How many neutrons does an atom of each of the following isotopes contain?
   a. $^{84}_{36}$Kr   **b.** $^{79}_{35}$Br   **c.** $^{190}_{76}$Os

21. Name the element and calculate the number of requested subatomic particles in each isotope.
   a. neutrons in $^{109}_{47}$Ag   **b.** protons in $^{118}_{50}$Sn

Use the spheres to answer Questions 22 and 23.

a.   **b.**

22. If the spheres above represent K and K^+, which sphere would most likely represent a potassium atom? Which sphere would most likely represent a potassium ion?

23. If the spheres represent an atom and a negative ion of the same element, which sphere represents the atom, and which represents the ion?

Part C

Answer each of the following questions.

24. Identify each of the following processes as a chemical or a physical change.
   a. melting of iron
   b. lighting a match
   c. grinding corn
   d. souring of milk

25. In the United States, a typical soft-drink can holds 355 mL. How many 2.00-L bottles could be filled from a 24-can case of soft drinks?

26. An apprentice jeweler determines the density of a sample of pure gold to be 20.3 g/cm³. The accepted value is 19.3 g/cm³. What is the percent error of the jeweler's density measurement?

27. A black olive containing its seed has a mass of 4.5 g and a volume of 4.3 mL. Will the olive sink or float in water? The density of water is 1.00 g/mL.

28. A rectangular container has inside dimensions of 15.2 cm by 22.9 cm and is about 1 meter tall. Water is poured into the container to a height of 55.0 cm. When a jagged rock with a mass of 5.21 kg is placed in the container, it sinks to the bottom. The water level rises to 58.4 cm. What is the density of the rock?

Ionic and Metallic Bonding

Sodium chloride crystallizes in cubic-shaped formations.

 INQUIRY **Activity**

Shapes of Crystalline Materials

Materials

4 small disposable cups, distilled water, a ruler, a spoon, sodium chloride (table salt), sucrose (table sugar), sodium hydrogen carbonate (baking soda), magnesium sulfate, a small clean mirror, a magnifying glass

Procedure

1. Label each cup with the name of one of the solids. Pour water into each cup to a depth of 1 cm.

2. Add a spoonful of each solid to its corresponding cup. Swirl each cup for 30 seconds and then let it stand for a few minutes.

3. Swirl the cups at least two more times. Each time, note whether any of the solids completely

dissolves. If so, add more of that solid and repeat the swirling. Continue this process until there is some undissolved solid at the bottom of each cup.

4. Set the mirror on a flat surface and place 2 or 3 drops of each liquid onto separate areas of the mirror.

5. Use a magnifying glass to examine each drop of liquid after 15 minutes, and then again after 24 hours.

Think About It

1. For each material, did the solids crystallize?

2. Did the crystals form at the same time?

3. Describe the crystals that formed.

7.1 Ions

 New York Standards: 3.1l, 5.2b–d

Connecting to Your World

Pyrite (FeS$_2$), a common mineral that emits sparks when struck against steel, is often mistaken for gold—hence its nickname, "fool's gold." Although certainly not worth its weight in gold, pyrite can be used as a source of sulfur in the production of sulfuric acid, a common industrial chemical. Pyrite is an example of a crystalline solid. In crystalline solids, the component particles of the substance are arranged in an orderly, repeating fashion. In this chapter, you will learn about crystalline solids composed of ions that are bonded together. But first you need to understand how ions form from neutral atoms.

Valence Electrons

Mendeleev used similarities in the properties of elements to organize his periodic table. Scientists later learned that all of the elements within each group of the periodic table behave similarly because they have the same number of valence electrons. **Valence electrons** are the electrons in the highest occupied energy level of an element's atoms. The number of valence electrons largely determines the chemical properties of an element.

The number of valence electrons is related to the group numbers in the periodic table. **To find the number of valence electrons in an atom of a representative element, simply look at its group number.** For example, the elements of Group 1A (hydrogen, lithium, sodium, potassium, and so forth) all have one valence electron, corresponding to the 1 in 1A. Carbon and silicon, in Group 4A, have four valence electrons. Nitrogen and phosphorus, in Group 5A, have five valence electrons; and oxygen and sulfur, in Group 6A, have six. The noble gases (Group 8A) are the only exceptions to the group-number rule: Helium has two valence electrons, and all of the other noble gases have eight. Figure 7.1 shows some applications of Group 4A elements.

Guide for Reading

Key Concepts
- How do you find the number of valence electrons in an atom of a representative element?
- Atoms of which elements tend to gain electrons? Atoms of which elements tend to lose electrons?
- How are cations formed?
- How are anions formed?

Vocabulary
valence electrons
electron dot structures
octet rule
halide ions

Reading Strategy
Summarizing Write a one-paragraph summary of how the octet rule applies to the formation of ions.

Figure 7.1 Group 4A elements include carbon, silicon, and germanium. ⓐ This saw blade contains carbon in the form of diamond. ⓑ Silicon is used in the manufacture of microchips. ⓒ Germanium is one of the materials used to make thermoscanning goggles.

Table 7.1

Electron Dot Structure of Some Group A Elements

Period	Group							
	1A	2A	3A	4A	5A	6A	7A	8A
1	H·							He:
2	Li·	·Be·	·B·	·C·	·N·	·O·	·F·	·Ne:
3	Na·	·Mg·	·Al·	·Si·	·P·	·S·	·Cl·	·Ar:
4	K·	·Ca·	·Ga·	·Ge·	·As·	·Se·	·Br·	·Kr:

Valence electrons are usually the only electrons used in chemical bonds. Therefore, as a general rule, only the valence electrons are shown in electron dot structures. **Electron dot structures** are diagrams that show valence electrons as dots. Table 7.1 shows electron dot structures for atoms of some Group A elements. Notice that all of the elements within a given group (with the exception of helium) have the same number of electron dots in their structures.

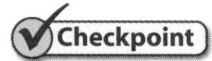 **Checkpoint** *What is an electron dot structure?*

The Octet Rule

You learned in Chapter 6 that noble gases, such as neon and argon, are unreactive in chemical reactions. That is, they are stable. In 1916, chemist Gilbert Lewis used this fact to explain why atoms form certain kinds of ions and molecules. He called his explanation the **octet rule:** In forming compounds, atoms tend to achieve the electron configuration of a noble gas. An octet is a set of eight. Recall that each noble gas (except helium) has eight electrons in its highest energy level and a general electron configuration of ns^2np^6. Thus the octet rule takes its name from this fact about noble gases. **Atoms of the metallic elements tend to lose their valence electrons, leaving a complete octet in the next-lowest energy level. Atoms of some nonmetallic elements tend to gain electrons or to share electrons with another nonmetallic element to achieve a complete octet.** Although there are exceptions, the octet rule applies to atoms in most compounds.

Formation of Cations

An atom is electrically neutral because it has equal numbers of protons and electrons; an ion forms when an atom or group of atoms loses or gains electrons. **An atom's loss of valence electrons produces a cation, or a positively charged ion.** Note that for metallic elements, the name of a cation is the same as the name of the element. For example, a sodium atom (Na) forms a sodium cation (Na^+). Likewise, a calcium atom (Ca) forms a calcium cation (Ca^{2+}). Although their names are the same, there are many important chemical differences between metals and their cations. Sodium metal, for example, reacts explosively with water. By contrast, sodium cations are quite unreactive. As you may know, they are a component of table salt, a compound that is very stable in water.

The most common cations are those produced by the loss of valence electrons from metal atoms. Most of these atoms have one to three valence electrons, which are easily removed. Sodium, in Group 1A of the periodic table, is typical. Sodium atoms have a total of eleven electrons, including one valence electron. A sodium atom can lose an electron to become a positively charged sodium ion. The sodium ion has an electron configuration that is identical to the noble gas neon. When forming a compound, a sodium atom loses its one valence electron and is left with an octet (eight electrons) in what is now its highest energy level. Because the number of protons in the sodium nucleus is still eleven, the loss of one unit of negative charge (an electron) produces a cation with a charge of $1+$. You can represent the electron loss, or ionization, of the sodium atom by drawing the complete electron configuration of the atom and of the ion formed.

$$\text{Na} \; 1s^2 2s^2 2p^6 3s^1 \xrightarrow{\;-e^-\;} \text{Na}^+ \; 1s^2 \underbrace{2s^2\, 2p^6}_{\text{octet}}$$

Notice that the electron configuration of the sodium ion ($1s^2 2s^2 2p^6$) is the same as that of a neon atom. The diagrams below help illustrate this point.

Both the sodium ion and the neon atom have eight electrons in their valence shells. Using electron dot structures, you can show the ionization more simply.

$$\text{Na·} \xrightarrow[\text{ionization}]{\substack{\text{loss of valence} \\ \text{electron}}} \text{Na}^+ \;+\; e^-$$

Sodium atom (electrically neutral, charge = 0) Sodium ion (plus sign indicates one unit of positive charge) electron (minus sign indicates one unit of negative charge)

Figure 7.2 The sodium atoms in a sodium-vapor lamp ionize to form sodium cations (Na^+). **Applying Concepts** *How many electrons are in the highest energy level of Na^+?*

Figure 7.3 Walnuts are a good dietary source of magnesium. Magnesium ions (Mg^{2+}) aid in digestive processes.

Figure 7.4 Cations of Group 1A elements have a charge of 1+. Cations of Group 2A elements have a charge of 2+.

Magnesium (atomic number 12) belongs to Group 2A of the periodic table, so it has two valence electrons. A magnesium atom attains the electron configuration of neon by losing both valence electrons. The loss of the valence electrons produces a magnesium cation with a charge of 2+.

$$\cdot Mg \cdot \longrightarrow Mg^{2+} + 2e^-$$

| Magnesium atom (electrically neutral, charge = 0) | Magnesium ion (2+ indicates two units of positive charge) | (2 in front of e⁻ indicates two units of negative charge) |

Figure 7.4 lists the symbols of cations formed by metals in Groups 1A and 2A. Cations of Group 1A elements always have a charge of 1+. Similarly, the cations of Group 2A elements always have a charge of 2+. This consistency can be explained in terms of the loss of valence electrons by metal atoms: The atoms lose enough electrons to attain the electron configuration of a noble gas. For example, all Group 2A elements have two valence electrons. In losing these two electrons, they form 2+ cations.

For transition metals, the charges of cations may vary. An atom of iron, for example, may lose two or three electrons. In the first case, it forms the Fe^{2+} ion. In the second case, it forms the Fe^{3+} ion.

Some ions formed by transition metals do not have noble-gas electron configurations (ns^2np^6) and are therefore exceptions to the octet rule. Silver, with the electron configuration of $1s^22s^22p^63s^23p^63d^{10}4s^24p^64d^{10}5s^1$, is an example. To achieve the structure of krypton, which is the preceding noble gas, a silver atom would have to lose eleven electrons. To acquire the electron configuration of xenon, which is the following noble gas, silver would have to gain seven electrons. Ions with charges of three or greater are uncommon, and these possibilities are extremely unlikely. Thus silver does not achieve a noble-gas configuration. But if it loses its $5s^1$ electron, the configuration that results ($4s^24p^64d^{10}$), with 18 electrons in the outer energy level and all of the orbitals filled, is relatively favorable in compounds. Such a configuration is known as a pseudo noble-gas electron configuration. Silver forms a positive ion (Ag^+) in this way. Other elements that behave similarly to silver are found at the right of the transition metal block. For example, a copper atom can ionize to form a 1+ cation (Cu^+), as illustrated below.

By losing its lone $4s$ electron, copper attains a pseudo noble-gas electron configuration. Likewise, cations of gold (Au^+), cadmium (Cd^{2+}), and mercury (Hg^{2+}) also have pseudo noble-gas configurations.

Formation of Anions

An anion is an atom or a group of atoms with a negative charge. 🔑 **The gain of negatively charged electrons by a neutral atom produces an anion.** Note that the name of an anion of a nonmetallic element is not the same as the element name. The name of the anion typically ends in *-ide*. Thus a chlorine atom (Cl) forms a chloride ion (Cl⁻), and an oxygen atom (O) forms an oxide ion (O²⁻). Figure 7.5 shows the symbols of anions formed by some elements in Groups 5A, 6A, and 7A.

Because they have relatively full valance shells, atoms of nonmetallic elements attain noble-gas electron configurations more easily by gaining electrons than by losing them. For example, chlorine belongs to Group 7A (the halogen family) and has seven valence electrons. A gain of one electron gives chlorine an octet and converts a chlorine atom into a chloride ion.

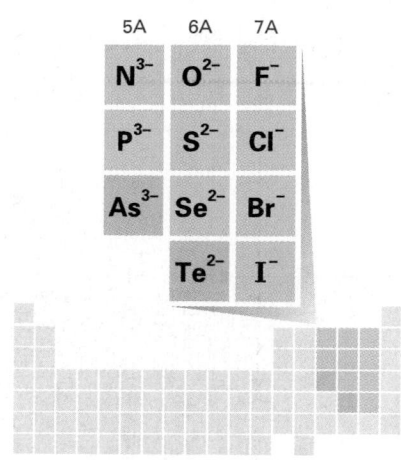

Figure 7.5 Atoms of nonmetallic elements form anions by gaining enough valence electrons so as to attain the electron configuration of the nearest noble gas. **Interpreting Diagrams** *In which group of the periodic table do the elements bromine and iodine belong?*

$$Cl \quad 1s^2 2s^2 2p^6 3s^2 3p^5 \xrightarrow{+e^-} Cl^- \quad 1s^2 2s^2 2p^6 \underbrace{3s^2 3p^6}_{octet}$$

The chloride ion is an anion with a single negative charge. Notice that it has the same electron configuration as the noble gas argon.

$$Ar \quad 1s^2 2s^2 2p^6 \underbrace{3s^2 3p^6}_{octet}$$

Chlorine atoms, therefore, need one more valence electron to achieve the electron configuration of the nearest noble gas. The diagrams below illustrate how both the chloride ion and the argon atom have an octet of electrons in their highest energy levels.

Based on the diagrams above, you use electron dot structures to write an equation showing the formation of a chloride ion from a chlorine atom.

In this equation, each dot in the electron dot structure represents an electron in the valence shell in the electron configuration diagram.

✓ **Checkpoint** *Which noble gas has the same electron configuration as a chloride ion?*

The ions that are produced when atoms of chlorine and other halogens gain electrons are called **halide ions.** All halogen atoms have seven valence electrons and need to gain only one electron to achieve the electron configuration of a noble gas. Thus all halide ions (F^-, Cl^-, Br^-, and I^-) have a charge of $1-$. The seawater in Figure 7.6 contains many different ions, but the negatively charged ions—the anions—are mostly chloride ions.

Look at another example. Oxygen is in Group 6A, and oxygen atoms each have six valence electrons. Oxygen atoms attain the electron configuration of neon by gaining two electrons, as shown in the diagrams below.

Figure 7.6 The six most abundant ions in seawater are chloride (Cl^-), sulfate (SO_4^{2-}), sodium (Na^+), magnesium (Mg^{2+}), calcium (Ca^{2+}), and potassium (K^+).

The resulting oxide ions have charges of $2-$ and are written as O^{2-}. Using electron dot structures, you can write the equation for the formation of oxide ions as follows.

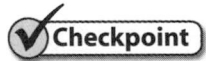

Table 7.2 lists some common anions that you will be learning about in this book. Note that not all of the anions listed end with the suffix -*ide*.

✓ Checkpoint *How many electrons do halogen atoms need to gain in order to achieve the electron configuration of a noble gas?*

Table 7.2

Some Common Anions					
1−		**2−**		**3−**	
F^-	fluoride	O^{2-}	oxide	N^{3-}	nitride
Cl^-	chloride	S^{2-}	sulfide	P^{3-}	phosphide
Br^-	bromide	SO_4^{2-}	sulfate	PO_4^{3-}	phosphate
I^-	iodide	CO_3^{2-}	carbonate		
OH^-	hydroxide				
ClO^-	hypochlorite				
NO_3^-	nitrate				
$C_2H_3O_2^-$	acetate				
HCO_3^-	hydrogen carbonate				

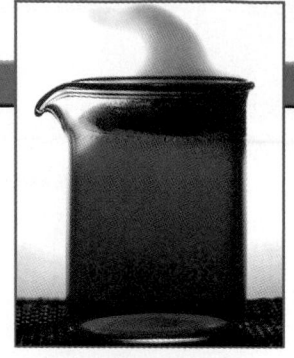

Writing the Symbols and Names of Ions

The beaker shown on the right contains iodine vapor. Write the symbol and name of the ion formed when
a. an iodine atom gains one electron.
b. a strontium atom loses two electrons.

1 **Analyze** *Identify the relevant concepts.*

a. An atom that gains electrons forms a negatively charged ion (anion). The name of an anion of a nonmetallic element ends in -*ide*.

b. An atom that loses electrons forms a positively charged ion (cation). The name of a cation of a metallic element is the same as the name of the element.

2 **Solve** *Apply concepts to this situation.*

a. I^-, iodide ion (an anion)
b. Sr^{2+}, strontium ion (a cation)

Practice Problems

1. Write the name and symbol of the ion formed when
  a. a sulfur atom gains two electrons.
  b. an aluminum atom loses three electrons.

2. How many electrons are lost or gained in forming each ion?
  a. Ba^{2+} **b.** As^{3-} **c.** Cu^{2+}

Interactive Textbook

Problem-Solving 7.1 Solve Problem 1 with the help of an interactive guided tutorial.

— with **ChemASAP**

7.1 Section Assessment

3. 🔑 **Key Concept** How can you determine the number of valence electrons in an atom of a representative element?

4. 🔑 **Key Concept** Atoms of which elements tend to gain electrons? Atoms of which elements tend to lose electrons?

5. 🔑 **Key Concept** How do cations form?

6. 🔑 **Key Concept** How do anions form?

7. How many valence electrons are in each atom?
  a. potassium   **b.** carbon
  c. magnesium   **d.** oxygen

8. Write the electron dot structure for each element in Question 7.

9. How many electrons will each element gain or lose in forming an ion?
  a. calcium (Ca)   **b.** fluorine (F)
  c. aluminum (Al)   **d.** oxygen (O)

10. Write the name and symbol of the ion formed when
  a. a potassium atom loses one electron.
  b. a zinc atom loses two electrons.
  c. a fluorine atom gains one electron.

11. Write the electron configuration of Cd^{2+}.

Connecting Concepts

Ionization Energy Reread Section 6.3. How does the octet rule explain the large increase in energy between the first and second ionization energies of Group 1A metals?

Interactive Textbook

Assessment 7.1 Test yourself on the concepts in Section 7.1.

— with **ChemASAP**

New York Standards: 3.1rr, 5.2a, 5.2h, 5.2n

Guide for Reading

Key Concepts
- What is the electrical charge of an ionic compound?
- What are three properties of ionic compounds?

Vocabulary
ionic compounds
ionic bonds
chemical formula
formula unit
coordination number

Reading Strategy
Previewing Before you read this section, rewrite the headings as *how*, *why*, and *what* questions about ionic compounds. As you read, write answers to the questions.

Connecting to Your World
You have heard of harvesting crops such as wheat or rice—but salt? In many coastal countries that have warm, relatively dry climates, salt is produced by the evaporation of seawater. The salty water is channeled into a series of shallow ponds, where it becomes more concentrated as the water evaporates by exposure to the sun. When the saltwater is concentrated enough, it is diverted into a pan, on which the sodium chloride crystals deposit. Salt farmers then drain the pans and collect the salt into piles to dry. In this section, you will learn how cations and anions combine to form stable compounds such as sodium chloride.

Formation of Ionic Compounds

Compounds composed of cations and anions are called **ionic compounds.** Ionic compounds are usually composed of metal cations and nonmetal anions. For example, sodium chloride, or table salt, is composed of sodium cations and chloride anions. **Although they are composed of ions, ionic compounds are electrically neutral.** The total positive charge of the cations equals the total negative charge of the anions.

Ionic Bonds Anions and cations have opposite charges and attract one another by means of electrostatic forces. The electrostatic forces that hold ions together in ionic compounds are called **ionic bonds.**

Sodium chloride provides a simple example of how ionic bonds are formed. Consider the reaction between a sodium atom and a chlorine atom. Sodium has a single valence electron that it can easily lose. (If the sodium atom loses its valence electron, it achieves the stable electron configuration of neon.) Chlorine has seven valence electrons and can easily gain one. (If the chlorine atom gains a valence electron, it achieves the stable electron configuration of argon.) When sodium and chlorine react to form a compound, the sodium atom gives its one valence electron to a chlorine atom. Thus sodium and chlorine atoms combine in a one-to-one ratio and both ions have stable octets.

Interactive Textbook

Animation 8 Take an atomic-level look at the formation of KCl.

—— with **ChemASAP**

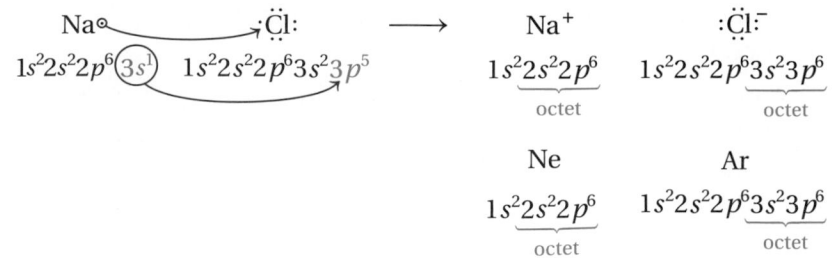

Figure 7.7 shows aluminum and bromine reacting to form the compound aluminum bromide. Each aluminum atom has three valence electrons to lose. Each bromine atom has seven valence electrons and readily gains one additional electron. Therefore, when aluminum and bromine react, three bromine atoms combine with each aluminum atom.

Formula Units The ionic compound sodium chloride is composed of equal numbers of sodium cations (Na^+) and chloride anions (Cl^-). As you can see in Figure 7.8, the ions in solid sodium chloride are arranged in an orderly pattern. There are no single discrete units, only a continuous array of ions.

Chemists represent the composition of substances by writing chemical formulas. A **chemical formula** shows the kinds and numbers of atoms in the smallest representative unit of a substance. NaCl, for example, is the chemical formula for sodium chloride. Note, however, that the formula NaCl does not represent a single discrete unit. Because an ionic compound exists as a collection of positively and negatively charged ions arranged in repeating patterns, its chemical formula refers to a ratio known as a formula unit. A **formula unit** is the lowest whole-number ratio of ions in an ionic compound. For sodium chloride, the lowest whole-number ratio of the ions is 1:1 (one Na^+ to each Cl^-). Thus the formula unit for sodium chloride is NaCl. Although ionic charges are used to derive the correct formula, they are not shown when you write the formula unit of the compound.

The ionic compound magnesium chloride contains magnesium cations (Mg^{2+}) and chloride anions (Cl^-). In magnesium chloride, the ratio of magnesium cations to chloride anions is 1:2 (one Mg^{2+} to two Cl^-). So its formula unit is $MgCl_2$. Because there are twice as many chloride anions (each with a 1+ charge) as magnesium cations (each with a 2+ charge), the compound is electrically neutral. In aluminum bromide, described earlier, the ratio of aluminum cations to bromide ions is 1:3 (one Al^{3+} to three Br^- ions), so the formula unit is $AlBr_3$.

Checkpoint *What is the formula unit for magnesium chloride?*

Bromine (Br_2)   Aluminum (Al)

Aluminum bromide ($AlBr_3$)

Figure 7.7 Aluminum metal and the nonmetal bromine react to form an ionic solid, aluminum bromide.

Figure 7.8 Sodium cations and chloride anions form a repeating three-dimensional array in sodium chloride (NaCl).
Inferring *How does the arrangement of ions in a sodium chloride crystal help explain why the compound is so stable?*

Chloride ion (Cl^-)
$18e^-$

$17p^+$
$18n^0$

Sodium ion (Na^+)
$10e^-$

$11p^+$
$12n^0$

Structure of sodium ion and chloride ion

Arrangement of Na^+ ions and Cl^- ions in a crystal of sodium chloride

Crystals of sodium chloride

Predicting Formulas of Ionic Compounds

The ionic compound formed from potassium and oxygen is used in ceramic glazes. Use electron dot structures to predict the formulas of the ionic compounds formed from the following elements.

a. potassium and oxygen   **b.** magnesium and nitrogen

1 **Analyze** *Identify the relevant concepts.*

Atoms of metals lose their valence electrons when forming an ionic compound. Atoms of nonmetals gain electrons. Enough atoms of each element must be used in the formula so that electrons lost equals electrons gained.

2 **Solve** *Apply concepts to this situation.*

a. Start with the atoms.

$$K\cdot \quad \text{and} \quad \cdot \ddot{O}:$$

In order to have a completely filled valence shell, oxygen must gain two electrons. These electrons come from two potassium atoms, each of which loses one electron.

$$\begin{matrix} K\cdot \\ K\cdot \end{matrix} + \cdot\ddot{O}: \longrightarrow \begin{matrix} K^+ \\ K^+ \end{matrix} \quad :\ddot{O}:^{2-}$$

Electrons lost now equals electrons gained. The formula of the compound formed (potassium oxide) is K_2O.

b. Start with the atoms.

$$\dot{M}g \quad \text{and} \quad \cdot\dot{N}:$$

Each nitrogen needs three electrons to have an octet, but each magnesium can lose only two electrons. Thus three magnesium atoms are needed for every two nitrogen atoms.

$$\begin{matrix} Mg \\ Mg \\ Mg \end{matrix} + \begin{matrix} \cdot\dot{N}: \\ \cdot\dot{N}: \end{matrix} \longrightarrow \begin{matrix} Mg^{2+} \\ Mg^{2+} \\ Mg^{2+} \end{matrix} \begin{matrix} :\ddot{N}:^{3-} \\ :\ddot{N}:^{3-} \end{matrix}$$

The formula of the compound formed (magnesium nitride) is Mg_3N_2.

Practice Problems

12. Use electron dot structures to determine formulas of the ionic compounds formed when
  a. potassium reacts with iodine.
  b. aluminum reacts with oxygen.

13. What is the formula of the ionic compound composed of calcium cations and chloride anions?

Interactive Textbook

Problem-Solving 7.12 Solve Problem 12 with the help of an interactive guided tutorial.

with ChemASAP

Properties of Ionic Compounds

For: Links on Ionic Compounds
Visit: www.SciLinks.org
Web Code: cdn-1072

Figure 7.9 shows the striking beauty of the crystals of some ionic compounds. ⚷ **Most ionic compounds are crystalline solids at room temperature.** The component ions in such crystals are arranged in repeating three-dimensional patterns. The composition of a crystal of sodium chloride is typical. In solid NaCl, each sodium ion is surrounded by six chloride ions, and each chloride ion is surrounded by six sodium ions. In this arrangement, each ion is attracted strongly to each of its neighbors and repulsions are minimized. The large attractive forces result in a very stable structure. This is reflected in the fact that NaCl has a melting point of about 800°C. ⚷ **Ionic compounds generally have high melting points.**

Figure 7.9 The beauty of crystalline solids, such as these, comes from the orderly arrangement of their component ions.

Simulation 5 Simulate the formation of ionic compounds at the atomic level.

—with **ChemASAP**

Fluorite (CaF_2)

Grossularite ($Ca_3Al_2(SiO_4)_3$)

Aragonite ($CaCO_3$)

Barite ($BaSO_4$) and calcite ($CaCO_3$)

Wulfenite ($PbMoO_4$)

Beryl ($BeAl_2(SiO_3)_6$)

Franklinite ((Zn, Mn^{2+}, Fe^{2+})(Fe^{3+}, Mn^{3+}))

Pyrite (FeS_2)

Hematite (Fe_2O_3)

Rutile (TiO_2)

Cinnabar (HgS)

ⓐ Sodium chloride (NaCl)

◯ Cl⁻
● Na⁺

ⓑ Cesium chloride (CsCl)

◯ Cl⁻
● Cs⁺

ⓒ Rutile (TiO₂)

● O²⁻
● Ti⁴⁺

Figure 7.10 Sodium chloride and cesium chloride form cubic crystals. **ⓐ** In NaCl, each ion has a coordination number of 6. **ⓑ** In CsCl, each ion has a coordination number of 8. **ⓒ** Titanium dioxide forms tetragonal crystals. In TiO₂, each Ti⁴⁺ ion has a coordination number of 6, while each O²⁻ ion has a coordination number of 3.

The **coordination number** of an ion is the number of ions of opposite charge that surround the ion in a crystal. Figure 7.10a shows the three-dimensional arrangement of ions in NaCl. Because each Na⁺ ion is surrounded by six Cl⁻ ions, Na⁺ has a coordination number of 6. Each Cl⁻ ion is surrounded by six Na⁺ ions and also has a coordination number of 6. Cesium chloride (CsCl) has a formula unit that is similar to that of NaCl. As Figure 7.10b illustrates, both compounds have cubic crystals, but their internal crystal structures are different. Each Cs⁺ ion is surrounded by eight Cl⁻ ions, and each Cl⁻ ion is surrounded by eight Cs⁺ ions. The anion and cation in cesium chloride each have a coordination number of 8.

Figure 7.10c shows the crystalline form of titanium dioxide (TiO_2), also known as rutile. In this compound, the coordination number for the cation (Ti^{4+}) is 6. Each Ti^{4+} ion is surrounded by six O^{2-} ions. The coordination number of the anion (O^{2-}) is 3. Each O^{2-} ion is surrounded by three Ti^{4+} ions.

Another characteristic property of ionic compounds has to do with conductivity. **☞ Ionic compounds can conduct an electric current when melted or dissolved in water.** As Figure 7.11 shows, when sodium chloride is melted, the orderly crystal structure breaks down. If a voltage is applied across this molten mass, cations migrate freely to one electrode and anions migrate to the other. This ion movement allows electricity to flow between the electrodes through an external wire. For a similar reason, ionic compounds also conduct electricity if they are dissolved in water. When dissolved, the ions are free to move about in the aqueous solution.

✓ Checkpoint *What is the coordination number of Ti⁴⁺ in TiO₂?*

Figure 7.11 When sodium chloride melts, the sodium and chloride ions are free to move throughout the molten salt. If a voltage is applied, positive sodium ions move to the negative electrode (the cathode), and negative chloride ions move to the positive electrode (the anode). **Predicting** *What would happen if the voltage was applied across a solution of NaCl dissolved in water?*

Solutions Containing Ions

Purpose
To show that ions in solution conduct an electric current.

Materials
- 3 D-cell batteries
- masking tape
- 2 30-cm lengths of bell wire with ends scraped bare
- clear plastic cup
- distilled water
- tap water
- vinegar
- sucrose
- sodium chloride
- baking soda
- conductivity probe (optional)

Procedure

 Probe version available in the Probeware Lab Manual.

1. Tape the batteries together so the positive end of one touches the negative end of another. Tape the bare end of one wire to the positive terminal of the battery assembly and the bare end of the other wire to the negative terminal. **CAUTION** *Bare wire ends can be sharp and scratch skin. Handle with care.*

2. Half fill the cup with distilled water. Hold the bare ends of the wires close together in the water. Look for the production of bubbles. They are a sign that the solution conducts electricity.

3. Repeat Step 2 with tap water, vinegar, and concentrated solutions of sucrose, sodium chloride, and baking soda (sodium hydrogen carbonate).

Analyze and Conclude

1. Which solutions produced bubbles of gas? Explain.

2. Which samples did not produce bubbles of gas? Explain.

3. Would you expect the same results if you used only one battery? If you used six batteries? Explain your answer.

7.2 Section Assessment

14. **Key Concept** How can you describe the electrical charge of an ionic compound?

15. **Key Concept** What properties characterize ionic compounds?

16. Define an ionic bond.

17. How can you represent the composition of an ionic compound?

18. Write the correct chemical formula for the compounds formed from each pair of ions.
    a. K^+, S^{2-}
    b. Ca^{2+}, O^{2-}
    c. Na^+, O^{2-}
    d. Al^{3+}, N^{3-}

19. Write formulas for each compound.
    a. barium chloride
    b. magnesium oxide
    c. lithium oxide
    d. calcium fluoride

20. Which pairs of elements are likely to form ionic compounds?
    a. Cl, Br
    b. Li, Cl
    c. K, He
    d. I, Na

21. Describe the arrangement of sodium ions and chloride ions in a crystal of sodium chloride.

22. Why do ionic compounds conduct electricity when they are melted or dissolved in water?

Elements ▸ Handbook

Restoring Electrolytes Read the feature on electrolytes on page R8. Write electron configurations for the two principal ions found in body fluids.

Assessment 7.2 Test yourself on the concepts in Section 7.2.
── with **ChemASAP**

Analysis of Anions and Cations

Purpose
To develop tests for various ions and use the tests to analyze unknown substances.

Materials
- pencil
- ruler
- medicine droppers
- chemicals shown in Figures A and B
- paper
- reaction surface
- pipet

Figure A
Anion Analysis

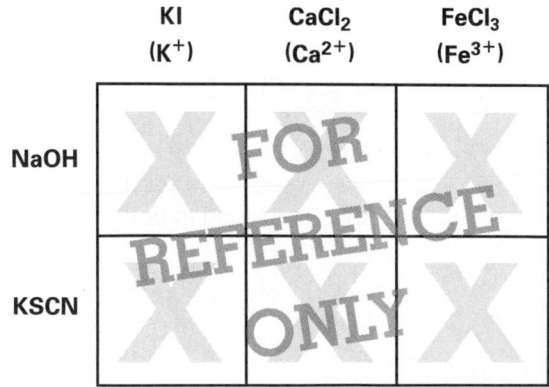

Figure B
Cation Analysis

Procedure
On one sheet of paper, draw grids similar to Figure A and Figure B. Draw similar grids on a second sheet of paper. Make each square 2 cm on each side. Place a reaction surface over the grids on one of the sheets of paper and add one drop of each solution or one piece of each solid as shown in Figures A and B. Stir each solution by blowing air through an empty pipet. Use the grids on the second sheet of paper as a data table to record your observations for each solution.

Analyze
Using your experimental data, record the answers to the following questions below your data table.

1. Carefully examine the reaction of Fe(s) and HCl in the presence of HNO_3. What is unique about this reaction? How can you use it to identify nitrate ion?

2. Which solutions from Figure A are the best for identifying each anion? Which solutions from Figure B are the best for identifying each cation? Explain.

3. Can your experiments identify K^+ ions? Explain.

You're the Chemist
The following small-scale activities allow you to develop your own procedures and analyze the results.

1. **Design It!** Obtain a set of unknown anion solutions from your teacher and design and carry out a series of tests that will identify each anion.

2. **Design It!** Obtain a set of unknown cation solutions from your teacher and design and carry out a series of tests that will identify each cation.

3. **Design It!** Obtain a set of unknown solid ionic compounds from your teacher. Design and carry out a series of tests that will identify each ion present.

7.3 Bonding in Metals

New York Standards: M1.1d, 3.1s–t, 5.2a

Connecting to Your World

You have probably seen decorative fences, railings, or weathervanes made of a metal called wrought iron. Wrought iron is a very pure form of iron that contains trace amounts of carbon. It is a tough, malleable, ductile, and corrosion-resistant material that melts at a very high temperature. As you already know, metals often have distinctive, useful properties. In this section, you will learn how metallic properties derive from the way that metal ions form bonds with one another.

Metallic Bonds and Metallic Properties

Metals are made up of closely packed cations rather than neutral atoms. **The valence electrons of metal atoms can be modeled as a sea of electrons.** That is, the valence electrons are mobile and can drift freely from one part of the metal to another. **Metallic bonds** consist of the attraction of the free-floating valence electrons for the positively charged metal ions. These bonds are the forces of attraction that hold metals together.

The sea-of-electrons model explains many physical properties of metals. For example, metals are good conductors of electrical current because electrons can flow freely in them. As electrons enter one end of a bar of metal, an equal number leave the other end. Metals are ductile—that is, they can be drawn into wires, as shown in Figure 7.12. Metals are also malleable, which means that they can be hammered or forced into shapes.

Guide for Reading

Key Concepts
- How can you model the valence electrons of metal atoms?
- How are metal atoms arranged?
- Why are alloys important?

Vocabulary
metallic bonds
alloys

Reading Strategy
Using Prior Knowledge Before you read, jot down three things you know about metals. When you have read the section, explain how what you already knew helped you learn something new.

Animation 9 See how metallic bonding explains some physical properties of metals.

—with ChemASAP

ⓐ Metal   **ⓑ Ionic crystal**

Figure 7.12 A metal rod can be forced through a narrow opening in a die to produce wire. ⓐ As this occurs, the metal changes shape but remains in one piece. ⓑ If an ionic crystal were forced through the die, it would shatter. **Interpreting Diagrams** *What causes the ionic crystal to break apart?*

Both the ductility and malleability of metals can be explained in terms of the mobility of valence electrons. A sea of drifting valence electrons insulates the metal cations from one another. When a metal is subjected to pressure, the metal cations easily slide past one another like ball bearings immersed in oil. In contrast, if an ionic crystal is struck with a hammer, the blow tends to push ions of like charge into contact. They repel, and the crystal shatters.

Crystalline Structure of Metals

The next time you visit a grocery store, take a look at how the apples or oranges are stacked. More than likely, they will have a close-packed arrangement, as shown in Figure 7.13. This arrangement helps save space while allowing as many oranges to be stacked as possible.

Similar arrangements can be found in the crystalline structures of metals. You may be surprised to learn that metals are crystalline. In fact, metals that contain just one kind of atom are among the simplest forms of all crystalline solids. **Metal atoms are arranged in very compact and orderly patterns.** For spheres of identical size, such as metal atoms, there are several closely packed arrangements that are possible. Figure 7.14 shows three such arrangements: body-centered cubic, face-centered cubic, and hexagonal close-packed arrangements.

In a body-centered cubic structure, every atom (except those on the surface) has eight neighbors. The metallic elements sodium, potassium, iron, chromium, and tungsten crystallize in a body-centered cubic pattern. In a face-centered cubic arrangement, every atom has twelve neighbors. Among the metals that form a face-centered cubic lattice are copper, silver, gold, aluminum, and lead. In a hexagonal close-packed arrangement, every atom also has twelve neighbors. Because of its hexagonal shape, however, the pattern is different from the face-centered cubic arrangement. Metals that have the hexagonal close-packed crystal structure include magnesium, zinc, and cadmium.

Figure 7.13 These oranges illustrate a pattern called a hexagonal close-packed arrangement.

Figure 7.14 Metal atoms crystallize in characteristic patterns. **a** Chromium atoms have a body-centered cubic arrangement. **b** Gold atoms have a face-centered cubic arrangement. **c** Zinc atoms have a hexagonal close-packed arrangement. **Inferring Which of these arrangements is the most closely packed?**

✔Checkpoint) *What metals crystallize in a face-centered cubic pattern?*

Chromium

Body-centered cubic

Gold

Face-centered cubic

Zinc

Hexagonal close-packed

Figure 7.15 Bicycle frames are often made of titanium alloys that contain aluminum and vanadium.

Alloys

Although every day you use metallic items, such as spoons, very few of these objects are pure metals. Instead, most of the metals you encounter are alloys. **Alloys** are mixtures composed of two or more elements, at least one of which is a metal. Brass, for example, is an alloy of copper and zinc.

🔑 **Alloys are important because their properties are often superior to those of their component elements.** Sterling silver (92.5% silver and 7.5% copper) is harder and more durable than pure silver but still soft enough to be made into jewelry and tableware. Bronze is an alloy generally containing seven parts of copper to one part of tin. Bronze is harder than copper and more easily cast. Nonferrous (non-iron) alloys, such as bronze, copper-nickel, and aluminum alloys, are commonly used to make coins.

The most important alloys today are steels. The principal elements in most steel, in addition to iron and carbon, are boron, chromium, manganese, molybdenum, nickel, tungsten, and vanadium. Steels have a wide range of useful properties, such as corrosion resistance, ductility, hardness, and toughness. Table 7.3 lists the composition of some common alloys.

Alloys can form from their component atoms in different ways. If the atoms of the components in an alloy are about the same size, they can replace each other in the crystal. This type of alloy is called a substitutional alloy. If the atomic sizes are quite different, the smaller atoms can fit into the interstices (spaces) between the larger atoms. Such an alloy is called an interstitial alloy. In the various types of steel, for example, carbon atoms occupy the spaces between the iron atoms. Thus, steels are interstitial alloys.

Table 7.3

Composition of Some Common Alloys

Name	Composition (by mass)	
Sterling silver	Ag	92.5%
	Cu	7.5%
Cast iron	Fe	96%
	C	4%
Stainless steel	Fe	80.6%
	Cr	18.0%
	C	0.4%
	Ni	1.0%
Spring steel	Fe	98.6%
	Cr	1.0%
	C	0.4%
Surgical steel	Fe	67%
	Cr	18%
	Ni	12%
	Mo	3%

7.3 Section Assessment

23. 🔑 **Key Concept** How do chemists model the valence electrons in metal atoms?

24. 🔑 **Key Concept** How can you describe the arrangement of atoms in metals?

25. 🔑 **Key Concept** Why are alloys more useful than pure metals?

26. Describe what is meant by ductile and malleable.

27. Why is it possible to bend metals but not ionic crystals?

28. What are three different packing arrangements found in metallic crystals?

29. Describe two widely used alloys.

Writing ▶ Activity

Explanatory Paragraph Write a paragraph describing how the sea-of-electrons model is used to explain the physical properties of metals. *Hint:* First write a sentence that summarizes the model. Then discuss how the model applies to specific properties of metals.

Textbook

Assessment 7.3 Test yourself on the concepts in Section 7.3.

with ChemASAP

Building with Alloys

Modern architecture would be a lot shorter if it weren't for steel. Since the late 1800s, using steel columns and girders in construction has allowed architects to design taller, stronger, and lighter buildings. Unlike buildings made of wood, brick, or stone, steel structures are strong enough to accommodate large, open interior spaces that do not require supporting walls. Usually, you can't see the steel used to construct a building; either it's hidden by the floors and walls, or—in the case of a building made of reinforced concrete—it's actually embedded in the floors and walls. The exteriors of buildings often feature lighter alloys, such as alloys of aluminum or titanium that resist corrosion.

Comparing and Contrasting *How does steel-frame construction differ from reinforced-concrete construction?*

Jewish Museum Berlin
Berlin, Germany
This angular building is covered in thin sheets of zinc-titanium alloy. The untreated alloy will slowly oxidize and change color from exposure to the air and weather.

The Atomium
Brussels, Belgium
Designed to resemble a crystal of iron magnified 165 billion times, the Atomium consists of nine spheres made of aluminum-alloy panels and connected by steel tubes. The top sphere contains an observation deck 92 meters above ground.

Chrysler Building
New York City
Completed in 1930, this steel-frame high-rise stands 319 m tall and features a distinctive spire sheathed in shiny stainless steel.

Steel-frame construction
The most common method to build a high-rise is to use a steel framework. Steel frames can be assembled quickly and allow for flexible interior spaces.

Reinforced-concrete construction
Another method for building high-rises is to use reinforced concrete. Concrete is more rigid than steel and holds up better structurally in fires. In addition, a concrete frame takes up less vertical space than a steel frame, meaning that a concrete-frame building can contain more floors than a steel-frame building of the same height.

Study Guide

🔑 7.1 Ions

- To find the number of valence electrons in an atom of a representative element, simply look at its group number.

- Atoms of the metallic elements tend to lose their valence electrons, leaving a complete octet in the next-lowest energy level. Atoms of some nonmetallic elements tend to gain electrons to achieve a complete octet.

- An atom's loss of valence electrons produces a positively charged cation.

- The gain of electrons by a neutral atom produces negatively charged anion.

🔑 7.2 Ionic Bonds and Ionic Compounds

- Although they are composed of ions, ionic compounds are electrically neutral.

- Most ionic compounds are crystalline solids at room temperature, and they generally have high melting points. Ionic compounds can conduct an electric current when melted or dissolved in water.

🔑 7.3 Bonding in Metals

- The valence electrons of metal atoms can be modeled as a sea of electrons.

- Metal atoms are arranged in very compact and orderly patterns.

- Alloys are important because their properties are often superior to those of their component elements.

Vocabulary

- alloys (p. 203)
- chemical formula (p. 195)
- coordination number (p. 198)
- electron dot structure (p. 188)
- formula unit (p. 195)
- halide ion (p. 192)

- ionic bonds (p. 194)
- ionic compounds (p. 194)
- metallic bonds (p. 201)
- octet rule (p. 188)
- valence electron (p. 187)

Organizing Information

Use these terms to construct a concept map that organizes the major ideas of this chapter.

ionic bond

valence electron

stable electron configuration

properties of ionic compounds

octet rule

metallic bond

ionic compound

Textbook

Concept Map 7 Solve the Concept Map with the help of an interactive guided tutorial.

— with **ChemASAP**

7.1 Ions

30. Describe two ways that an ion forms from an atom.

31. State the number of electrons either lost or gained in forming each ion.
a. Br^- b. Na^+
c. As^{3-} d. Ca^{2+}
e. Cu^+ f. H^-

32. Name each ion in Problem 31.

33. Define valence electrons.

34. How many electrons does each of the following atoms have? What group is each in?
a. nitrogen   b. lithium
c. phosphorus   d. barium
e. bromine   f. carbon

35. Write electron dot structures for each of the following elements.
a. Cl   b. S
c. Al   d. Li

36. How many electrons must each atom lose to attain a noble-gas electron configuration?
a. Ca   b. Al
c. Li   d. Ba

37. Write the formula for the ion formed when each of the following elements loses its valence electrons.
a. aluminum   b. lithium
c. barium   d. potassium
e. calcium   f. strontium

38. Why do nonmetals tend to form negative ions when they react to form compounds?

39. What is the formula of the ion formed when the following elements gain or lose valence electrons and attain noble-gas configurations?
a. sulfur   b. sodium
c. fluorine   d. phosphorus

40. How many electrons must be gained by each of the following atoms to achieve a stable electron configuration?
a. N   b. S
c. Cl   d. P

41. Which of the following electron configurations represents a nitride ion?
a. $1s^2 2s^2 3s^2 4s^2$ b. $1s^2 2s^2 2p^3$
c. $1s^2 2s^2 2p^6$ d. $1s^2$

42. Construct a table that shows the relationship among the group number, valence electrons lost or gained, and the formula of the ion produced for the following metallic and nonmetallic elements: Na, Ca, Al, N, S, Br.

43. Write electron dot formulas for the following atoms.
a. C   b. Be
c. O   d. F
e. Na   f. P

44. Show the relationship between the electron dot structure of a representative element and the location of the element in the periodic table.

45. In terms of electrons, why do metal ions have a positive charge?

46. Why does a nonmetallic ion have a negative charge?

47. The spheres below represent the relative diameters of atoms or ions. Rearrange the sequences in a. and b. so the relative sizes of the particles correspond to the increasing size of the particles in the illustration.

a. oxygen atom, oxide ion, sulfur atom, sulfide ion
b. sodium atom, sodium ion, potassium atom, potassium ion

48. Write electron configurations for the dipositive ions (2+) of these elements.
a. Fe   b. Co
c. Ni

49. Write electron configurations for the tripositive ions (3+) of these elements.
a. chromium   b. manganese
c. iron

50. The atoms of the noble gas elements are stable. Explain.

51. Write the formula for the ion formed when each element gains electrons and attains a noble-gas configuration.
    a. Br
    b. H
    c. As
    d. Se

52. Write electron configurations for these atoms and ions, and comment on the result.
    a. Ar
    b. Cl^-
    c. S^{2-}
    d. P^{3-}

53. Write electron configurations for the following and comment on the result.
    a. N^{3-}
    b. O^{2-}
    c. F^-
    d. Ne

54. Name the first four halogens. What group are they in, and how many valence electrons does each have?

55. Write complete electron configurations for the following atoms and ions. For each group, comment on the result.
    a. Ar, K^+, Ca^{2+}
    b. Ne, Na^+, Mg^{2+}, Al^{3+}

56. What is the relationship between the number of electrons in the valence shells in an electron configuration diagram and the number of dots in the corresponding electron dot structure?

57. Why are many elements more stable as ions than they are as atoms?

58. Describe the formation of a cation that is an exception to the octet rule. In your description, compare the electron configuration of the cation to the electron configurations of the nearest noble gases.

59. Classify each atom in the following list. Will each atom form a positive ion or a negative ion? Or is it chemically unreactive? For the atoms that do form ions during a chemical reaction, write the number of electrons the atom will gain or lose.
    a. lithium
    b. sodium
    c. neon
    d. chlorine
    e. magnesium

60. Write the IUPAC name and the formula of the positive ion in each transition metal compound.
    a. $FeCl_2$
    b. Fe_2O_3
    c. CuO
    d. Cu_2O
    e. $CoCl_3$

7.2 Ionic Bonds and Ionic Compounds

61. Which of the following pairs of atoms would you expect to combine chemically to form an ionic compound?
    a. Al and O
    b. I and K

62. Identify the ions that form each of the following ionic compounds.
    a. calcium fluoride, CaF_2
    b. aluminum bromide, $AlBr_3$
    c. lithium oxide, Li_2O
    d. aluminum sulfide, Al_2S_3
    e. potassium nitride, K_3N

63. Explain why ionic compounds are electrically neutral.

64. Which of the following pairs of elements will *not* form ionic compounds?
    a. sulfur and oxygen
    b. sodium and calcium
    c. sodium and sulfur
    d. oxygen and chlorine

65. Write the formulas for the ions in the following compounds.
    a. KCl
    b. $BaSO_4$
    c. $MgBr_2$
    d. Li_2CO_3

66. Most ionic substances are brittle. Why?

67. Explain why molten $MgCl_2$ does conduct an electric current although crystalline $MgCl_2$ does not.

68. If ionic compounds are composed of charged particles (ions), why isn't every ionic compound either positively or negatively charged?

69. Which of the following substances are most likely *not* ionic?
    a. H_2O
    b. Na_2O
    c. CO_2
    d. CaS
    e. SO_2
    f. NH_3

70. Can you predict the coordination number of an ion from the formula of an ionic compound? Explain.

71. Explain how hexagonal close-packed, face-centered cubic, and body-centered cubic unit cells are different from one another.

72. Is it accurate to describe sodium chloride (NaCl) as consisting of individual particles, each made up of one Na^+ ion and one Cl^- ion? Explain your answer.

73. How do the motions of sodium ions and chloride ions in molten sodium chloride differ from those of these ions in sodium chloride crystals?

74. How atoms and ions are arranged in crystals is not just dependent on size. The spheres in each atomic window below are identical in size. The windows have exactly the same area. In which window are the spheres more closely packed? Explain your reasoning.

a.   **b.**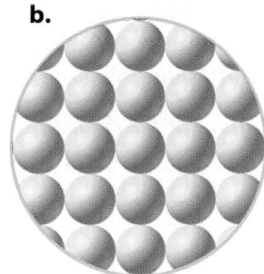

75. The chemically similar alkali metal chlorides NaCl and CsCl have different crystal structures, whereas the chemically different NaCl and MnS have the same crystal structures. Why?

<u>**7.3** Bonding in Metals</u>

76. Explain briefly why metals are good conductors of electricity.

77. Name the three crystal arrangements of closely packed metal atoms. Give an example of a metal that crystallizes in each arrangement.

78. Name some alloys that you have used or seen today.

79. Why aren't the properties of all steels identical? Explain.

80. Metallic cobalt crystallizes in a hexagonal close-packed structure. How many neighbors will a cobalt atom have?

81. The properties of all samples of brass are not identical. Explain.

82. Compare and contrast the physical and chemical characteristics of metals and ionic compounds.

83. Silver crystallizes in a face-centered cubic arrangement. A silver atom is at the edge of each lattice point. The length of the edge of the unit cell is 0.4086 nm. What is the atomic radius of silver?

84. List the elements that are used to make each alloy.
  a. brass   **b.** sterling silver
  c. bronze   **d.** stainless steel
  e. surgical steel   **f.** spring steel

Regents Practice Exam

Part A

For each statement or question write the number of the word or expression that, of those given, best completes the statement or answers the question.

1. Which subatomic particle plays the most important role in determining the chemical properties of an atom?
   (1) proton
   (2) neutron
   (3) electron
   (4) nucleus

2. When a bromine atom gains an electron
   (1) a bromide ion forms
   (2) the ion formed has a 1– charge
   (3) the ion formed has a negative charge
   (4) all the above are correct

3. How many valence electrons does an arsenic atom have?
   (1) 2
   (2) 3
   (3) 4
   (4) 5

4. An alloy is a mixture of atoms of a metal and at least one other element on the atomic level. Which of the following statements is *not* true about an alloy?
   (1) The elements in an alloy can vary in proportion from sample to sample.
   (2) The alloy can conduct an electric current.
   (3) An alloy is a heterogeneous mixture.
   (4) Each component of the alloy keeps its original properties.

Part B-1

For each statement or question write the number of the word or expression that, of those given, best completes the statement or answers the question.

5. Which of the following choices is a heterogeneous mixture?
   (1) spaghetti sauce
   (2) cane sugar
   (3) a gold ring
   (4) saltwater

6. Which of the following linear measurements is the longest?
   (1) 6×10^4 cm
   (2) 6×10^6 mm
   (3) 0.06 km
   (4) 6×10^9 nm

7. Which of the following compounds is *not* ionic?
   (1) KF
   (2) Na_2SO_4
   (3) SiO_2
   (4) Na_2O

8. Which of the following statements is correct when barium and oxygen react to form an ionic compound?
   (1) Barium atoms each lose two electrons and form negative ions.
   (2) Oxygen atoms form oxide ions.
   (3) In the compound, the ratio of barium to oxygen atoms is 2 to 1.
   (4) The formula of the compound is BaO_2.

9. For which compound name is the *incorrect* formula given?
   (1) magnesium iodide, MgI_2
   (2) potassium selenide, K_2Se
   (3) calcium oxide, Ca_2O_2
   (4) aluminum sulfide, Al_2S_3

The numbered choices below refer to Questions 10–13. A numbered choice may be used once, more than once, or not at all.

   (1) gains one electron
   (2) loses one electron
   (3) loses two electrons
   (4) gains three electrons

Which choice describes what happens as each of the following elements forms its ion?

10. iodine

11. magnesium

12. cesium

13. phosphorus

14. Which of the following pairs of atoms would you expect to combine chemically to form an ionic compound?
    (1) Li and S
    (2) O and S
    (3) F and Cl
    (4) H and N

Part B-2

Answer each of the following questions.

15. Classify the following examples as chemical changes or physical changes.
   a. Cookies are baked.
   b. A firefly emits light.
   c. A figure is carved from wood.
   d. Caramel is made from sugar.

16. What physical state(s) can each of the following substances become as you raise its temperature above 20°C?
   a. silver   **c.** ice
   b. gasoline   **d.** wax

17. Round each measurement to the number of significant figures indicated in parentheses.
   a. 56.55 g (3)   **c.** 1.8072 L (3)
   b. 0.004 849 m (2)   **d.** 4.007×10^3 mg (2)

18. The density of silicon is 2.33 g/cm³. What is the volume of a piece of silicon that has a mass of 62.9 g?

19. The three isotopes of oxygen are O-16, O-17, and O-18. Determine the number of protons, electrons, and neutrons in each of these isotopes.

20. For each of the following elements, give the symbol and write its electron configuration.
   a. nitrogen   **c.** phosphorus
   b. beryllium   **d.** potassium

21. An atom of an element has 17 electrons. Give the name and symbol of the element and write the complete electron configuration.

22. Give the symbol and the complete electron configuration of the element found at each location in the periodic table.
   a. Group 1A (1), period 4
   b. Group 3A (13), period 3
   c. Group 6A (16), period 3
   d. Group 2A (2), period 6

23. Give the name and symbol of two elements that have properties similar to those of potassium.

Use the description and the graph to answer Questions 24–26.

Lattice energy is the energy required to change one mole of a crystalline, ionic solid to gaseous ions. The following graph shows the lattice energy for ionic compounds formed between selected Group 1A (1) metals and halogens, which are Group 7A (17).

Lattice Energy for Selected Ionic Compounds

24. For a given alkali metal, what is the trend in lattice energy as the atomic radius of the halogens increases?

25. For a given halogen, what is the trend in lattice energy as the atomic radius of the alkali metals increases?

26. Complete this sentence. "As the atomic radius of either the halogen or the alkali metal increases, the lattice energy _____."

27. Express the composition of each of the following atoms.
   a. zinc-64   **c.** hydrogen-3
   b. chlorine-37   **d.** calcium-40

Part C

Answer each of the following questions.

28. A physical property of metals is ductility. The wires in your electrical cords and household wiring are made from metals because metals conduct electricity and are ductile. Explain ductility based on what you know about the valence electrons of metal atoms.

29. Helium is used in balloons because it is lighter than air and does not react with other elements. It has a boiling point of 4 K, which is the lowest boiling point of any liquid. Express this temperature in degrees Celsius.

Water droplets result from bonds between oxygen and hydrogen atoms.

INQUIRY Activity

Shapes of Molecules

Materials

nine spherical balloons, several short pieces of string

Procedure

1. Inflate the nine balloons to approximately the same size and tie them off.

2. Use short pieces of string to tie the ends of two balloons together to form a cluster. Tie the ends of three other balloons together to form a second cluster, and then tie the remaining four balloons to form a third cluster.

3. Hold the four balloons from the tied ends and observe how they tend to arrange themselves.

4. Sketch the three-dimensional shape of each balloon cluster.

Think About It

1. What are some geometric terms that you can use to describe the shapes?

2. Some of the terms used by chemists to describe these shapes are trigonal planar, tetrahedral, and linear. Match each term with one of the shapes you made.

8.1 Molecular Compounds

Connecting to Your World

These toy models are made of the same basic pieces, joined together by sticks in units in different ways. Even when the toy models are made of the same kind of pieces, the units they form can be different because of the different numbers and arrangements of the wooden bars joining them. Atoms can join in ways that are like these models, with different possible ways of joining the atoms. In this section, you will learn how atoms can share electrons to form a bond, called a covalent bond, and how the atoms join to form units called molecules.

Guide for Reading

 Key Concepts
- How are the melting points and boiling points of molecular compounds different from ionic compounds?
- What information does a molecular formula provide?

Vocabulary
covalent bond
molecule
diatomic molecule
molecular compound
molecular formula

Reading Strategy
Building Vocabulary As you read the section, write a definition of each key term in your own words.

Molecules and Molecular Compounds

In nature, matter takes many forms. The noble gas elements, such as helium and neon shown in Figure 8.1, exist as atoms. They are monatomic; that is, they consist of single atoms. You learned in the previous chapter that atoms of some elements combine to form salts. Salts, such as sodium chloride (NaCl), are crystalline solids with high melting points.

Other compounds, however, can have very different properties. Hydrogen chloride (HCl), for example, is a gas at room temperature. Water (H_2O) is a liquid at room temperature. These two compounds are so different from salts that you might correctly suspect that electrostatic attraction between ions fails to explain their bonding. Such compounds are not ionic. Their combining atoms do not give up electrons or accept electrons as readily as sodium does in combining with chlorine.

Instead, a "tug of war" for the electrons takes place between the atoms, bonding the atoms together. The atoms held together by sharing electrons are joined by a **covalent bond.**

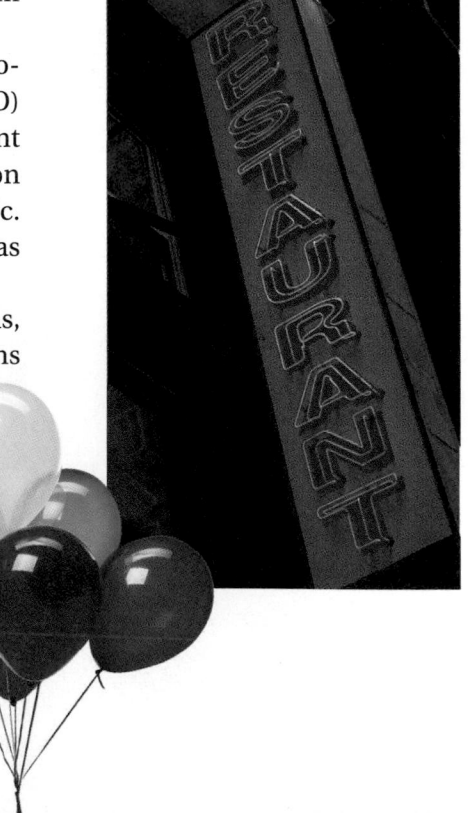

Figure 8.1 The noble gases, including helium and neon, are monatomic. That means they exist as single atoms. Helium, being less dense than air, is often used to inflate balloons. The colors produced in what we commonly call neon lights are a result of passing an electric current through one or more noble gases.

Water (H$_2$O)

Carbon monoxide (CO)

Figure 8.2 Water is a molecular compound with molecules composed of two hydrogen atoms and one oxygen atom. Carbon monoxide is a molecular compound with molecules composed of one carbon atom and one oxygen atom.

Many elements found in nature are in the form of molecules. A **molecule** is a neutral group of atoms joined together by covalent bonds. For example, air contains oxygen molecules. Each oxygen molecule consists of two oxygen atoms joined by covalent bonds. A **diatomic molecule** is a molecule consisting of two atoms. An oxygen molecule is a diatomic molecule.

Atoms of different elements can combine chemically to form compounds. In many compounds, atoms are bonded to each other to form molecules. Examples include water and carbon monoxide shown in Figure 8.2. A compound composed of molecules is called a **molecular compound.** The molecules of a given molecular compound are all the same. Remember, there is no such thing as a molecule of sodium chloride or magnesium chloride. Instead, these ionic compounds exist as collections of positively and negatively charged ions arranged in repeating three-dimensional patterns. Recall from Chapter 7 that the composition of ionic compounds is expressed as formula units.

🔑 **Molecular compounds tend to have relatively lower melting and boiling points than ionic compounds.** Many molecular compounds are gases or liquids at room temperature. In contrast to ionic compounds, which are formed from a metal combined with a non-metal, most molecular compounds are composed of atoms of two or more nonmetals. For example, one atom of carbon can combine with one atom of oxygen to produce one molecule of a compound known as carbon monoxide. Carbon monoxide is a poisonous gas produced by burning gasoline in internal combustion engines. Figure 8.3 illustrates some differences between ionic and covalent compounds, using sodium chloride and water as examples.

Go Online
NSTA SC*LINKS*

For: Links on Covalent Bonds
Web Code: cdn-1081

Figure 8.3 Sodium chloride, which is an ionic compound, and water, which is a molecular compound, are compared here. **Interpreting Diagrams** *How do molecular compounds differ from ionic compounds?*

Ionic compound – Salt

Array of sodium ions and chloride ions

Formula unit of sodium chloride:

Na$^+$ Cl$^-$

Chemical formula: NaCl

Molecular compound – Water

Collection of water molecules

Molecule of water:

H   O   H

Chemical formula: H$_2$O

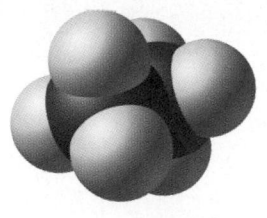

Ethane (C_2H_6)

Figure 8.4 Ethane is a component of natural gas. **Inferring** *What information about the ethane molecule given by its molecular formula C_2H_6 is also given by the drawing shown here?*

Molecular Formulas

A **molecular formula** is the chemical formula of a molecular compound. 🔑 **A molecular formula shows how many atoms of each element a molecule contains.** A water molecule consists of two hydrogen atoms and one oxygen atom. The molecular formula of water is H_2O. Notice that a subscript written after the symbol indicates the number of atoms of each element in the molecule. If there is only one atom, the subscript 1 is omitted. The molecular formula of carbon dioxide is CO_2. This formula represents a molecule containing one carbon atom and two oxygen atoms. As shown in Figure 8.4, ethane, a component of natural gas, is also a molecular compound. The molecular formula for ethane is C_2H_6. According to this formula, one molecule of ethane contains two carbon atoms and six hydrogen atoms. A molecular formula reflects the actual number of atoms in each molecule. The subscripts are not necessarily lowest whole-number ratios.

Molecular formulas also describe molecules consisting of one element. Because the oxygen molecule consists of two oxygen atoms bonded together, its molecular formula is O_2.

A molecular formula does not tell you about a molecule's structure. In other words, it does not show either the arrangement of the various atoms in space or which atoms are covalently bonded to one another. A variety of diagrams and molecular models, some of them illustrated in Figure 8.5, can be used to show the arrangement of atoms in a molecule. Diagrams and models like these will be used throughout the textbook.

✔Checkpoint *What is the molecular formula for ethane?*

Ammonia

$NH_3(g)$

Molecular formula

H———N———H
      |
      H

Structural formula

Space-filling molecular model

Perspective drawing

Ball-and-stick molecular model

Figure 8.5 Ammonia (NH_3) is used in solution as a cleaning agent. You can represent the ammonia molecule by its molecular formula, its structural formula, a space-filling molecular model, a perspective drawing, or by a ball-and stick molecular model.

Figure 8.6 The formula of a molecular compound indicates the numbers and kinds of atoms. The arrangement of the atoms within a molecule is called its molecular structure. **Using Models** *Which of these molecules has the greatest number of oxygen atoms?*

Hydrogen atom (H) Carbon atom (C) Oxygen atom (O)

Water (H_2O)
1 molecule of H_2O contains
2 hydrogen atoms
1 oxygen atom

Carbon dioxide (CO_2)
1 molecule of CO_2 contains
2 oxygen atoms
1 carbon atom

Ethanol (C_2H_6O)
1 molecule of C_2H_6O contains
6 hydrogen atoms
2 carbon atoms
1 oxygen atom

Figure 8.6 shows the chemical formulas and structures of some other molecular compounds. Carbon dioxide, for example, is a gas produced by the complete burning of carbon. It occurs in our atmosphere and dissolves in seawater. It is also used to carbonate many beverages. The molecular structure of carbon dioxide in Figure 8.6 shows how the carbon atom in each molecule has two oxygen atoms on opposite sides of it. It shows how the three atoms are arranged in a row. The molecular structure of water shows how the hydrogen atoms, in contrast, are mainly on one side of the water molecule. The molecular structure of ethanol is more complicated, but the molecular structure illustrated in Figure 8.6 also shows how many of each kind of atom are in each molecule, and how the atoms are arranged with respect to one another.

8.1 Section Assessment

1. 🔑 **Key Concept** How are the melting points and boiling points of molecular compounds usually different from ionic compounds?

2. 🔑 **Key Concept** What information does a molecular formula provide?

3. What are the only elements that exist in nature as uncombined atoms? What term is used to describe such elements?

4. Describe how the molecule whose formula is NO is different from the molecule whose formula is N_2O.

5. Give an example of a diatomic molecule found in Earth's atmosphere.

6. What information does a molecule's molecular structure give?

Writing ▶ Activity

Elements and Compounds Explain how the terms *atoms, molecules,* and *ions* apply to *elements* and *compounds.* Your explanation should focus on whether elements are found in nature as individual atoms or only as molecules, with an example of each possibility, and whether compounds are found in nature to consist of ions or of molecules, with an example of each possibility.

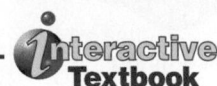
Interactive Textbook

Assessment 8.1 Test yourself on the important concepts of Section 8.1.

——with **ChemASAP**

8.2 The Nature of Covalent Bonding

 New York Standards: 5.2b, 5.2d–e, 5.2i

Connecting to Your World

You know that without oxygen to breathe, you could not live. But did you know that oxygen plays another important role in your life? High in the atmosphere, a different form of oxygen, called ozone, forms a layer that filters out harmful radiation from the sun. The colors in this map indicate the concentrations of atmospheric ozone in various parts of Earth. In this section, you will learn how oxygen atoms can join in pairs to form the oxygen you breathe and can also join in groups of three oxygen atoms to form ozone high in the atmosphere.

The Octet Rule in Covalent Bonding

Recall that in forming ionic compounds, electrons tend to be transferred so that each ion acquires a noble gas configuration. A similar rule applies for covalent bonds. **In forming covalent bonds, electron sharing usually occurs so that atoms attain the electron configurations of noble gases.** For example, each hydrogen atom has one electron. But a pair of hydrogen atoms share these two electrons when they form a covalent bond in the hydrogen molecule. Each hydrogen atom thus attains the electron configuration of helium, a noble gas with two electrons. Combinations of atoms of the nonmetallic elements in Groups 4A, 5A, 6A, and 7A of the periodic table are likely to form covalent bonds. In this case the atoms usually acquire a total of eight electrons, or an octet, by sharing electrons, so that the octet rule applies.

Single Covalent Bonds

The hydrogen atoms in a hydrogen molecule are held together mainly by the attraction of the shared electrons to the positive nuclei. Two atoms held together by sharing a pair of electrons are joined by a **single covalent bond.** Hydrogen gas consists of pairs of diatomic molecules whose atoms share only one pair of electrons, forming a single covalent bond.

Guide for Reading

Key Concepts

- How does electron sharing occur in forming covalent bonds?
- How do electron dot structures represent shared electrons?
- How do atoms form double or triple covalent bonds?
- How are coordinate covalent bonds different from other covalent bonds?
- How is the strength of a covalent bond related to its bond dissociation energy?
- How are oxygen atoms bonded in ozone?
- What are some exceptions to the octet rule?

Vocabulary

single covalent bond
structural formula
unshared pair
double covalent bond
triple covalent bond
coordinate covalent bond
polyatomic ion
bond dissociation energy
resonance structure

Reading Strategy

Identifying Main Idea/Details
List the main idea involved in the paragraph following the heading *The Octet Rule in Covalent Bonding.* As you read, list examples of how this rule is followed by forming a single covalent bond, a double covalent bond, and a triple covalent bond.

An electron dot structure such as H:H represents the shared pair of electrons of the covalent bond by two dots. The pair of shared electrons forming the covalent bond is also often represented as a dash, as in H—H for hydrogen. A **structural formula** represents the covalent bonds by dashes and shows the arrangement of covalently bonded atoms. In contrast, the molecular formula of hydrogen, H_2, indicates only the number of hydrogen atoms in each molecule.

The halogens also form single covalent bonds in their diatomic molecules. Fluorine is one example. Because a fluorine atom has seven valence electrons, it needs one more to attain the electron configuration of a noble gas. By sharing electrons and forming a single covalent bond, two fluorine atoms each achieve the electron configuration of neon.

$$:\ddot{\text{F}}\cdot \quad + \quad \cdot\ddot{\text{F}}: \quad \longrightarrow \quad :\ddot{\text{F}}:\ddot{\text{F}}: \;\; or \;\; :\ddot{\text{F}}\!-\!\ddot{\text{F}}:$$

Fluorine Fluorine   Fluorine
atom   atom   molecule

	1s	2s	2p		
F	↑↓	↑↓	↑↓ ↑↓ ↑		
F	↑↓	↑↓	↑↓ ↑↓ ↓		

1s   2s   2p

Fluorine
molecule

In the F_2 molecule, each fluorine atom contributes one electron to complete the octet. Notice that the two fluorine atoms share only one pair of valence electrons. A pair of valence electrons that is not shared between atoms is called an **unshared pair,** also known as a lone pair or a nonbonding pair.

You can draw electron dot structures for molecules of compounds in much the same way that you draw them for molecules of diatomic elements. Water (H_2O) is a molecule containing three atoms with two single covalent bonds. Two hydrogen atoms share electrons with one oxygen atom. The hydrogen and oxygen atoms attain noble-gas configurations by sharing electrons. As you can see in the electron dot structures below, the oxygen atom in water has two unshared pairs of valence electrons.

$$2\text{H}\cdot \quad + \quad :\ddot{\text{O}}\cdot \quad \longrightarrow \quad \begin{matrix}:\ddot{\text{O}}:\text{H}\\ \overset{\shortmid}{\text{H}}\end{matrix} \;\; or \;\; \begin{matrix}:\ddot{\text{O}}\!-\!\text{H}\\ \shortmid\\ \text{H}\end{matrix}$$

Hydrogen   Oxygen   Water molecule
atoms   atom

Water molecule

✓ Checkpoint *What does a structural formula represent?*

You can draw the electron dot structure for ammonia (NH_3), a suffocating gas, in a similar way. The ammonia molecule has one unshared pair of electrons.

$$3H\cdot \quad + \quad :\overset{\cdot}{N}\cdot \quad \longrightarrow \quad \overset{\displaystyle H}{\underset{\displaystyle \overset{\cdot\cdot}{H}}{:N:H}} \quad or \quad :\overset{\displaystyle H}{\underset{\displaystyle H}{N-H}}$$

Hydrogen atoms   Nitrogen atom   Ammonia molecule

Ammonia molecule

Methane (CH_4) contains four single covalent bonds. The carbon atom has four valence electrons and needs four more valence electrons to attain a noble-gas configuration. Each of the four hydrogen atoms contributes one electron to share with the carbon atom, forming four identical carbon-hydrogen bonds. As you can see in the electron dot structure below, methane has no unshared pairs of electrons.

$$4H\cdot \quad + \quad \cdot\overset{\cdot}{C}\cdot \quad \longrightarrow \quad \overset{\displaystyle H}{\underset{\displaystyle \overset{\cdot\cdot}{H}}{H:C:H}} \quad or \quad H-\overset{\displaystyle H}{\underset{\displaystyle H}{C}}-H$$

Hydrogen atoms   Carbon atom   Methane molecule

Methane molecule

When carbon forms bonds with other atoms, it usually forms four bonds. You would not predict this based on carbon's electron configuration, shown below.

$$1s^2 \quad 2s^2 \quad 2p^2$$

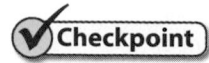 **Checkpoint** *What is the electron dot structure of a methane molecule?*

If you tried to form covalent C—H bonds for methane by combining the two $2p$ electrons of the carbon with two $1s$ electrons of hydrogen atoms, you would incorrectly predict a molecule with the formula CH_2 (instead of CH_4). The formation of four bonds by carbon can be simply explained. One of carbon's $2s$ electrons is promoted to the vacant $2p$ orbital to form the following electron configuration.

$$\underset{1s^2}{\uparrow\downarrow} \quad \underset{2s \text{ and } 2p}{\boxed{\uparrow \quad \uparrow \quad \uparrow \quad \uparrow}}$$

This electron promotion requires only a small amount of energy. The promotion provides four electrons of carbon that are capable of forming covalent bonds with four hydrogen atoms. Methane, the carbon compound formed by electron sharing of carbon with four hydrogen atoms, is much more stable than CH_2. The stability of the resulting methane more than compensates for the small energy cost of the electron promotion. Therefore, formation of methane (CH_4) is more energetically favored than the formation of CH_2.

CONCEPTUAL PROBLEM 8.1

Drawing an Electron Dot Structure

Hydrochloric acid (HCl (*aq*)) is prepared by dissolving gaseous hydrogen chloride (HCl (*g*)) in water. Hydrogen chloride is a diatomic molecule with a single covalent bond. Draw the electron dot structure for HCl.

1 **Analyze** *Identify the relevant concepts.*

In a single covalent bond, a hydrogen and a chlorine atom must share a pair of electrons. Each must contribute one electron to the bond. First, draw the electron dot structures for the two atoms. Then show the electron sharing in the compound they produce.

2 **Solve** *Apply concepts to the situation.*

$$\text{H·} \quad + \quad \text{·}\ddot{\text{C}}\text{l:} \quad \longrightarrow \quad \text{H:}\ddot{\text{C}}\text{l:}$$

| Hydrogen atom | Chlorine atom | Hydrogen chloride molecule |

In the electron dot structures, the hydrogen atom and the chlorine atom are each correctly shown to have an unpaired electron. Through electron sharing, the hydrogen and chlorine atoms are shown to attain the electron configurations of the noble gases helium and argon, respectively.

Practice Problems

7. Draw electron dot structures for each molecule.
   a. chlorine   **b.** bromine   **c.** iodine

8. The following molecules have single covalent bonds. Draw an electron dot structure for each.
   a. H_2O_2 **b.** PCl_3

Problem Solving 8.8 Solve Problem 8 with the help of an interactive guided tutorial.

— with **ChemASAP**

Double and Triple Covalent Bonds

Sometimes atoms bond by sharing more than one pair of electrons. **Atoms form double or triple covalent bonds if they can attain a noble gas structure by sharing two pairs or three pairs of electrons.** A bond that involves two shared pairs of electrons is a **double covalent bond.** A bond formed by sharing three pairs of electrons is a **triple covalent bond.**

You might think that an oxygen atom, with six valence electrons, would form a double bond by sharing two of its electrons with another oxygen atom.

interactive Textbook

Simulation 6 Simulate the covalent bonding between molecules.

—— with **ChemASAP**

In such an arrangement, all the electrons within the molecule would be paired. Experimental evidence, however, indicates that two of the electrons in O_2 are still unpaired. Thus, the bonding in the oxygen molecule (O_2) does not obey the octet rule. You cannot draw an electron dot structure that adequately describes the bonding in the oxygen molecule.

An element whose molecules contain triple bonds is nitrogen (N_2), a major component of Earth's atmosphere illustrated in Figure 8.7. In the nitrogen molecule, each nitrogen atom has one unshared pair of electrons. A single nitrogen atom has five valence electrons. Each nitrogen atom in the nitrogen molecule must gain three electrons to have the electron configuration of neon.

Figure 8.7 Oxygen and nitrogen are the main components of Earth's atmosphere. The oxygen molecule is an exception to the octet rule. It has two unpaired electrons. Three pairs of electrons are shared in a nitrogen molecule.

Table 8.1

			The Diatomic Elements
Name	**Chemical formula**	**Electron dot structure**	**Properties and uses**
Fluorine	F_2	:F̈—F̈:	Greenish-yellow reactive toxic gas. Compounds of fluorine, a halogen, are added to drinking water and toothpaste to promote healthy teeth.
Chlorine	Cl_2	:C̈l—C̈l:	Greenish-yellow reactive toxic gas. Chlorine is a halogen used in household bleaching agents.
Bromine	Br_2	:B̈r—B̈r:	Dense red-brown liquid with pungent odor. Compounds of bromine, a halogen, are used in the preparation of photographic emulsions.
Iodine	I_2	:Ï—Ï:	Dense gray-black solid that produces purple vapors; a halogen. A solution of iodine in alcohol (tincture of iodine) is used as an antiseptic.
Hydrogen	H_2	H—H	Colorless, odorless, tasteless gas. Hydrogen is the lightest known element.
Nitrogen	N_2	:N≡N:	Colorless, odorless, tasteless gas. Air is almost 80% nitrogen by volume.
Oxygen	O_2	Inadequate	Colorless, odorless, tasteless gas that is vital for life. Air is about 20% oxygen by volume.

Figure 8.8 Carbon dioxide gas is soluble in water and is used to carbonate many beverages. A carbon dioxide molecule has two carbon–oxygen double bonds.

Up to this point in your textbook, the examples of single and triple covalent bonds have involved diatomic molecules. Table 8.1 lists the properties and uses of the elements that exist as diatomic molecules. Single, double, and triple covalent bonds can also exist between unlike atoms. For example, consider carbon dioxide (CO_2), which is present in the atmosphere and is used to carbonate many soft drinks as shown in Figure 8.8. The carbon dioxide molecule contains two oxygens, each of which shares two electrons with carbon to form a total of two carbon–oxygen double bonds.

The two double bonds in the carbon dioxide molecule are identical to each other. Carbon dioxide is an example of a triatomic molecule, which is a molecule consisting of three atoms.

Coordinate Covalent Bonds

Carbon monoxide (CO) is an example of a type of covalent bonding different from that seen in water, ammonia, methane, and carbon dioxide. A carbon atom needs to gain four electrons to attain the electron configuration of neon. An oxygen atom needs two electrons. Yet it is possible for both atoms to achieve noble-gas electron configurations by a type of bonding called coordinate covalent bonding. To see how, begin by looking at the double covalent bond between carbon and oxygen.

With the double bond in place, the oxygen has a stable configuration but the carbon does not. As shown above, the dilemma is solved if the oxygen also donates one of its unshared pairs of electrons for bonding.

$$:C::\overset{\frown}{O.} \longrightarrow :C::O:$$

Carbon monoxide
molecule

A **coordinate covalent bond** is a covalent bond in which one atom contributes both bonding electrons. In a structural formula, you can show coordinate covalent bonds as arrows that point from the atom donating the pair of electrons to the atom receiving them. The structural formula of carbon monoxide, with two covalent bonds and one coordinate covalent bond, is $C\equiv O$. **In a coordinate covalent bond, the shared electron pair comes from one of the bonding atoms.** Once formed, a coordinate covalent bond is like any other covalent bond.

The ammonium ion (NH_4^+) consists of atoms joined by covalent bonds, including a coordinate covalent bond. A **polyatomic ion,** such as NH_4^+, is a tightly bound group of atoms that has a positive or negative charge and behaves as a unit. The ammonium ion forms when a positively charged hydrogen ion (H^+) attaches to the unshared electron pair of an ammonia molecule (NH_3). Because most common plants need nitrogen already in chemical compounds rather than in the air to grow, the ammonium ion is useful in the chemical fertilizer shown in Figure 8.9.

Figure 8.9 The polyatomic ammonium ion (NH_4^+), present in ammonium sulfate, is an important component of fertilizer for field crops, home gardens, and potted plants.

unshared electron pair

$$H^+ \ + \ :\overset{H}{\underset{H}{N}}:H \ \longrightarrow \ \left[H:\overset{H}{\underset{H}{N}}:H \right]^+ \ or \ H\leftarrow\overset{H}{\underset{H}{N}^\pm}\rightarrow H$$

Hydrogen   Ammonia   Ammonium
ion   molecule   ion
(proton)   (NH_3)   (NH_4^+)

 Checkpoint *What is a polyatomic ion?*

Most polyatomic cations and anions contain both covalent and coordinate covalent bonds. Therefore, compounds containing polyatomic ions include both ionic and covalent bonding.

As another example, draw the electronic structure of polyatomic ion SO_3^{2-}. Start by drawing the dot structures for the oxygen and sulfur atoms, their valence electrons, and the two extra electrons indicated by the charge. Then join two of the oxygens to sulfur by single covalent bonds.

$$:\ddot{O}\cdot \ \cdot\ddot{S}\cdot \ \cdot\ddot{O}: \ + \ \cdot\cdot \ \longrightarrow \ :\ddot{O}:\ddot{S}:\ \cdot\ddot{O}:$$
$$\cdot\ddot{O}: \qquad\qquad\qquad \cdot\ddot{O}:$$

Then join the remaining oxygen by a coordinate covalent bond, with sulfur donating one of its unshaved pairs to oxygen, and add the two extra electrons. Put brackets about the structure and indicate the 2− charge, giving the result shown.

$$:\ddot{O}:\ddot{S}:\ddot{O}: \ + \ \cdot\cdot \ \longrightarrow \ \left[:\ddot{O}:\ddot{S}:\ddot{O}:\right]^{2-}$$
$$\cdot\ddot{O}: \qquad\qquad\qquad :\ddot{O}:$$

Each of the atoms of the completed structure has eight valence electrons, satisfying the octet rule. Without the two extra electrons, two of the oxygens would be electron-deficient.

Table 8.2 lists electron dot structures of some common compounds with covalent bonds.

Table 8.2

Some Common Molecular Compounds

Name	Chemical formula	Structure	Properties and uses
Hydrogen peroxide	H_2O_2	H—:Ö—Ö:—H	Colorless, unstable liquid when pure. It is used as rocket fuel. A 3% solution is used as a bleach and antiseptic.
Sulfur dioxide	SO_2	:Ö=S—Ö:	Oxides of sulfur are produced in combustion of petroleum products and coal. They are major air pollutants in industrial areas. Oxides of sulfur can lead to respiratory problems.
Sulfur trioxide	SO_3	:Ö=S—Ö: (with Ö:)	
Nitric oxide	NO	:Ö=Ṅ·	Oxides of nitrogen are major air pollutants produced by the combustion of fossil fuels in automobile engines. They irritate the eyes, throat, and lungs.
Nitrogen dioxide	NO_2	:Ö=N—Ö:	
Nitrous oxide	N_2O	:Ö←N≡N:	Colorless, sweet-smelling gas. It is used as an anesthetic commonly called laughing gas.
Hydrogen cyanide	HCN	H—C≡N:	Colorless, toxic gas with the smell of almonds.
Hydrogen fluoride	HF	H—F̈:	Two hydrogen halides, all extremely soluble in water. Hydrogen chloride, a colorless gas with pungent odor, readily dissolves in water to give a solution called hydrochloric acid.
Hydrogen chloride	HCl	H—C̈l:	

Remember, the electron dot structure for a neutral molecule contains the same number of electrons as the total number of valence electrons in the combining atoms. The negative charge of a polyatomic ion shows the number of electrons in addition to the valence electrons of the atoms present. Because a negatively charged polyatomic ion is part of an ionic compound, the positive charge of the cation of the compound balances these additional electrons.

CONCEPTUAL PROBLEM 8.2

Drawing the Electron Dot Formula of a Polyatomic Ion

The polyatomic hydronium ion (H_3O^+), which is found in acidic systems such as lemon juice, contains a coordinate covalent bond. The H_3O^+ ion forms when a hydrogen ion is attracted to an unshared electron pair in a water molecule. Draw the electron dot structure of the hydronium ion.

1 Analyze *Identify the relevant concepts.*

H_3O^+ forms by the addition of a hydrogen ion to a water molecule. Draw the electron dot structure of the water molecule. Then, add the hydrogen ion. Oxygen must share a pair of electrons with the added hydrogen ion to form a coordinate covalent bond.

2 Solve *Apply the concepts to this situation.*

$$H^+ \ + \ :\overset{H}{\underset{}{\ddot{O}}}:H \longrightarrow \left[H:\overset{H}{\underset{}{\ddot{O}}}:H \right]^+ \ or \ \left[H \leftarrow \overset{H}{\underset{}{O}} - H \right]^+$$

Hydrogen ion (proton)   Water molecule (H_2O)   Hydronium ion (H_3O^+)

The oxygen in the hydronium ion has eight valence electrons, and each hydrogen shares two valence electrons. This satisfies the needs of both hydrogen and oxygen for valence electrons. The water molecule is electrically neutral, and the hydrogen ion has a positive charge. The combination of these two species must have a charge of 1+, as is found in the hydronium ion.

Practice Problems

9. Draw the electron dot structure of the hydroxide ion (OH^-).

10. Draw the electron dot structure of the polyatomic boron tetrafluoride anion (BF_4^-).

11. Draw the electron dot structures for sulfate (SO_4^{2-}) and carbonate (CO_3^{2-}). Sulfur and carbon are the central atoms, respectively.

12. Draw the electron dot structure for the hydrogen carbonate ion (HCO_3^-). Carbon is the central atom, and hydrogen is attached to oxygen in this polyatomic anion.

Problem-Solving 8.10 Solve Problem 10 with the help of an interactive guided tutorial.

— with **ChemASAP**

Quick LAB

Strengths of Covalent Bonds

Purpose

To compare and contrast the stretching of rubber bands and the dissociation energy of covalent bonds.

Materials

- 1 170-g (6-oz) can of food
- 2 454-g (16-oz) cans of food
- 3 No. 25 rubber bands
- metric ruler
- coat hanger
- plastic grocery bag
- paper clip
- graph paper
- pencil
- motion detector (optional)

Procedure

 Sensor version available in the Probeware Lab Manual.

1. Bend the coat hanger to fit over the top of a door. The hook should hang down on one side of the door. Measure the length of the rubber bands (in cm). Hang a rubber band on the hook created by the coat hanger.

2. Place the 170-g can in the plastic bag. Use the paper clip to fasten the bag to the end of the rubber band. Lower the bag gently until it is suspended from the end of the rubber band. Measure and record the length of the stretched rubber band. Using different combinations of food cans, repeat this process three times with the following masses: 454 g, 624 g, and 908 g.

3. Repeat Step 2, first using two rubber bands to connect the hanger and the paper clip, and then using three.

4. Graph the length difference: (stretched rubber band) − (unstretched rubber band) on the y-axis versus mass (kg) on the x-axis for one, two, and three rubber bands. Draw the straight line that

you estimate best fits the points for each set of data. (Your graph should have three separate lines.) The x-axis and y-axis intercepts of the lines should pass through zero, and the lines should extend past 1 kg on the x-axis. Determine the slope of each line in cm/kg.

Analyze and Conclude

1. Assuming the rubber bands are models for covalent bonds, what can you conclude about the relative strengths of single, double, and triple bonds?

2. How does the behavior of the rubber bands differ from that of covalent bonds?

Bond Dissociation Energies

A large quantity of heat is liberated when hydrogen atoms combine to form hydrogen molecules. This suggests that the product is more stable than the reactants. The covalent bond in the hydrogen molecule (H_2) is so strong that it would take 435 kJ of energy to break apart all of the bonds in 1 mole (about 2 grams) of H_2. (The important chemical quantity, the mole, abbreviated mol, here always represents 6.03×10^{23} bonds; you will study the mole further in Chapter 12.) The energy required to break the bond between two covalently bonded atoms is known as the **bond dissociation energy.** This is usually expressed as the energy needed to break one mole of bonds. The bond dissociation energy for the H_2 molecule is 435 kJ/mol.

🔑 **A large bond dissociation energy corresponds to a strong covalent bond.** A typical carbon–carbon single bond has a bond dissociation energy of about 347 kJ/mol. Strong carbon–carbon bonds help explain the stability of carbon compounds. Compounds with only C—C and C—H single covalent bonds, such as methane, tend to be quite unreactive chemically. They are unreactive partly because the dissociation energy for each of these bonds is high.

Resonance

Ozone in the upper atmosphere blocks harmful ultraviolet radiation from the sun. At the lower elevations shown in Figure 8.10, it contributes to smog. The ozone molecule has two possible electron dot structures.

$$:\ddot{O}:\ddot{O}::\ddot{O}: \longleftrightarrow :\ddot{O}::\ddot{O}:\ddot{O}:$$

Notice that the structure on the left can be converted to the one on the right by shifting electron pairs without changing the positions of the oxygen atoms.

As drawn, these electron dot structures suggest that the bonding in ozone consists of one single coordinate covalent bond and one double covalent bond. Because earlier chemists imagined that the electron pairs rapidly flip back and forth, or resonate, between the different electron dot structures, they used double-headed arrows to indicate that two or more structures are in resonance.

Double covalent bonds are usually shorter than single bonds, so it was believed that the bond lengths in ozone were unequal. Experimental measurements show, however, that this is not the case. The two bonds in ozone are the same length. This result can be explained if you assume that the actual bonding in the ozone molecule is the average of the two electron dot structures. The electron pairs do not actually resonate back and forth. **The actual bonding of oxygen atoms in ozone is a hybrid, or mixture, of the extremes represented by the resonance forms.**

The two electron dot formulas for ozone are examples of what are still referred to as resonance structures. A **resonance structure** is a structure that occurs when it is possible to write two or more valid electron dot formulas that have the same number of electron pairs for a molecule or ion. Resonance structures are simply a way to envision the bonding in certain molecules. Although no back-and-forth changes occur, double-headed arrows are used to connect resonance structures.

✓ Checkpoint *What shows that the two covalent bonds in O$_3$ are the same?*

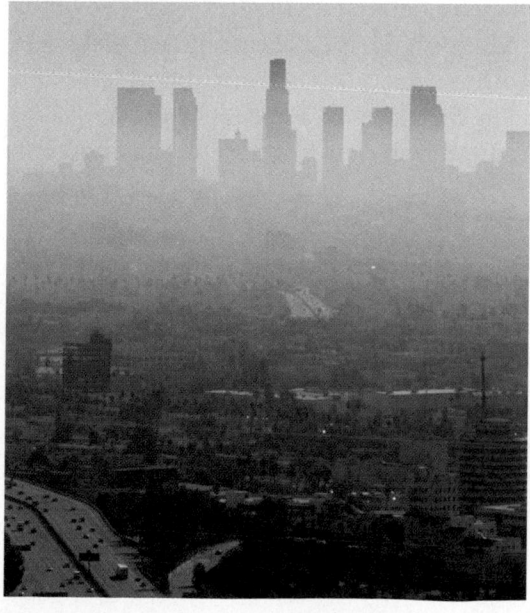

Figure 8.10 Although ozone high above the ground forms a protective layer that absorbs ultraviolet radiation from the sun, at lower elevations ozone is a pollutant that contributes to smog.

Exceptions to the Octet Rule

The octet rule provides guidance for drawing electron dot structures. For some molecules or ions, however, it is impossible to draw structures that satisfy the octet rule. ⬤ **The octet rule cannot be satisfied in molecules whose total number of valence electrons is an odd number. There are also molecules in which an atom has fewer, or more, than a complete octet of valence electrons.** The nitrogen dioxide (NO_2) molecule, for example, contains a total of seventeen, an odd number, of valence electrons. Each oxygen contributes six electrons and the nitrogen contributes five. Two plausible resonance structures can be written for the NO_2 molecule.

$$:\ddot{O}\!=\!\dot{N}\!-\!\ddot{O}:$$

$$:\ddot{O}\!-\!\dot{N}\!=\!\ddot{O}:$$

	1s	2s	2p		
O	↑↓	↑↓	↑↓	↑	↑
N	↑↓	↑↓	↓	↓	↓
O	↑↓	↑↓	↑	↑	↑↓
	1s	2s	2p		

Nitrogen dioxide molecule

An unpaired electron is present in each of these structures, both of which fail to follow the octet rule. It is impossible to draw an electron dot structure for NO_2 that satisfies the octet rule for all atoms. Yet, NO_2 does exist as a stable molecule. In fact, it is produced naturally by lightning strikes of the sort shown in Figure 8.11.

A number of other molecules also have an odd number of electrons. In these molecules, as in NO_2, complete pairing of electrons is not possible. It is not possible to draw an electron dot structure that satisfies the octet rule. Examples of such molecules include chlorine dioxide (ClO_2) and nitric oxide (NO).

Several molecules with an even number of electrons, such as some compounds of boron, also fail to follow the octet rule. This may happen because an atom acquires less than an octet of eight electrons. The boron atom in boron trifluoride (BF_3), for example, is deficient by two electrons, and therefore is an exception to the octet rule. Boron trifluoride readily reacts with ammonia to make the compound $BF_3 \cdot NH_3$. In doing so, the boron atom accepts the unshared electron pair from ammonia and completes the octet.

Figure 8.11 Lightning is one means by which nitrogen and oxygen in the atmosphere produce nitrogen oxide.

$$\underset{:\ddot{F}:}{\overset{:\ddot{F}:}{:\ddot{F}\!-\!B}} \ + \ \underset{H}{\overset{H}{:N\!-\!H}} \ \longrightarrow \ \underset{:\ddot{F}:\ H}{\overset{:\ddot{F}:\ H}{:\ddot{F}\!-\!B\!\leftarrow\!N\!-\!H}}$$

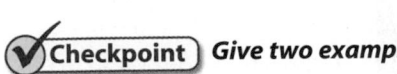 **✓Checkpoint** *Give two examples of exceptions to the octet rule.*

Figure 8.12 Phosphorus pentachloride, used as a chlorinating and dehydrating agent, and sulfur hexafluoride, used as an insulator for electrical equipment, are exceptions to the octet rule. **Interpreting Diagrams** *How many valence electrons does the sulfur in sulfur hexafluoride (SF₆) have for the structure shown in the figure?*

Phosphorus pentachloride

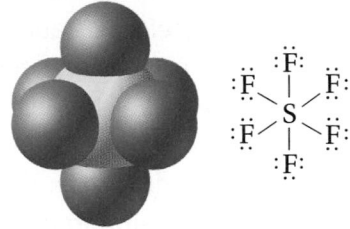

Sulfur hexafluoride

A few atoms, especially phosphorus and sulfur, sometimes expand the octet to include ten or twelve electrons. Consider phosphorus trichloride (PCl_3) and phosphorus pentachloride (PCl_5). Both are stable compounds in which all of the chlorines are bonded to a single phosphorus atom. Covalent bonding in PCl_3 follows the octet rule because all the atoms have eight valence electrons. However, as shown in Figure 8.12, the electron dot structure for PCl_5 can be written so that phosphorus has ten valence electrons.

8.2 Section Assessment

13. 🔑 **Key Concept** What electron configurations do atoms usually achieve by sharing electrons to form covalent bonds?

14. 🔑 **Key Concept** How is an electron dot structure used to represent a covalent bond?

15. 🔑 **Key Concept** When are two atoms likely to form a double bond between them? A triple bond?

16. 🔑 **Key Concept** How is a coordinate covalent bond different from other covalent bonds?

17. 🔑 **Key Concept** How is the strength of a covalent bond related to its bond dissociation energy?

18. 🔑 **Key Concept** Draw the electron dot resonance structures for ozone and explain how they describe its bonding.

19. 🔑 **Key Concept** List three ways in which the octet rule can sometimes fail to be obeyed.

20. What kinds of information does a structural formula reveal about the compound it represents?

21. Draw electron dot structures for the following molecules, which have only single covalent bonds.
   a. H_2S **b.** PH_3 **c.** ClF

22. Use the bond dissociation energies of H_2 (435 kJ/mol) and of a typical carbon–carbon bond (347 kJ/mol) to decide which bond is stronger. Explain your reasoning.

Elements ▶ Handbook

Ozone Read the feature on ozone on page R31 of the Elements Handbook. Describe the effect of CFCs on the ozone layer. Explain why the United States has banned the use of CFCs in aerosols.

Interactive Textbook

Assessment 8.2 Test yourself on the important concepts of Section 8.2.

— with **ChemASAP**

8.3 Bonding Theories

New York Standards: M1.1d, 5.2e

Guide for Reading

🔑 Key Concepts

- How are atomic and molecular orbitals related?
- How does VSEPR theory help predict the shapes of molecules?
- In what ways is orbital hybridization useful in describing molecules?

Vocabulary

molecular orbitals
bonding orbital
sigma bond
pi bond
tetrahedral angle
VSEPR theory
hybridization

Reading Strategy

Summarizing When you summarize, you review and state, in the correct order, the main points you have read. As you read about bonding theories, write a brief summary of the text following each heading. Your summary should include only the most important information.

Connecting to Your World

This car is being painted by a process called electrostatic spray painting. A custom-designed spray nozzle wired up to an electric power supply imparts a negative charge to the paint droplets as they exit the spray gun. The negatively charged droplets are attracted to the auto body. Painting with attractive forces is very efficient, because almost all the paint is applied to the car body and very little is wasted. In this section, you will learn how attractive and repulsive forces influence the shapes of molecules.

Molecular Orbitals

The model for covalent bonding you have been using assumes that the orbitals are those of the individual atoms. There is a quantum mechanical model of bonding, however, that describes the electrons in molecules using orbitals that exist only for groupings of atoms. When two atoms combine, this model assumes that their atomic orbitals overlap to produce **molecular orbitals,** or orbitals that apply to the entire molecule.

In some ways, atomic orbitals and molecular orbitals are similar. 🔑 **Just as an atomic orbital belongs to a particular atom, a molecular orbital belongs to a molecule as a whole.** Each atomic orbital is filled if it contains two electrons. Similarly, two electrons are required to fill a molecular orbital. A molecular orbital that can be occupied by two electrons of a covalent bond is called a **bonding orbital.**

Sigma Bonds When two atomic orbitals combine to form a molecular orbital that is symmetrical around the axis connecting two atomic nuclei, a **sigma bond** is formed, as illustrated in Figure 8.13. The symbol for this bond is the Greek letter sigma (σ).

Figure 8.13 Two *s* atomic orbitals can combine to form a molecular orbital, as in the case of hydrogen (H_2). In a bonding molecular orbital, the electron density between the nuclei is high.

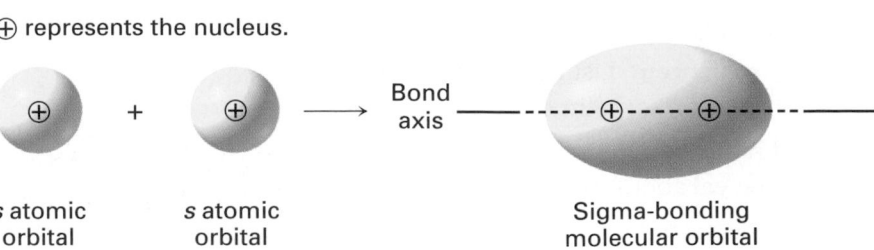

⊕ represents the nucleus.

s atomic orbital   +   *s* atomic orbital   →   Sigma-bonding molecular orbital

Bond axis

⊕ represents the nucleus.

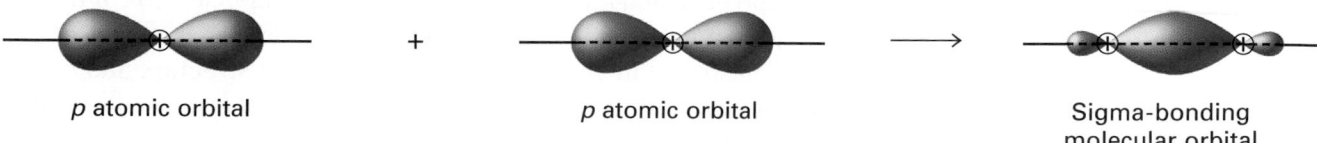

p atomic orbital   +   p atomic orbital   ⟶   Sigma-bonding
molecular orbital

In general, covalent bonding results from an imbalance between the attractions and repulsions of the nuclei and electrons involved. Because their charges have opposite signs, the nuclei and electrons attract each other. Because their charges have the same sign, nuclei repel other nuclei and electrons repel other electrons. In a hydrogen molecule, the nuclei repel each other, as do the electrons. In a bonding molecular orbital of hydrogen, however, the attractions between the hydrogen nuclei and the electrons are stronger than the repulsions. The balance of all the interactions between the hydrogen atoms is thus tipped in favor of holding the atoms together. The result is a stable diatomic molecule of H_2.

Atomic p orbitals can also overlap to form molecular orbitals. A fluorine atom, for example, has a half-filled $2p$ orbital. When two fluorine atoms combine, as shown in Figure 8.14, the p orbitals overlap to produce a bonding molecular orbital. There is a high probability of finding a pair of electrons between the positively charged nuclei of the two fluorines. The fluorine nuclei are attracted to this region of high electron density. This attraction holds the atoms together in the fluorine molecule (F_2). The overlap of the $2p$ orbitals produces a bonding molecular orbital that is symmetrical when viewed around the F—F bond axis connecting the nuclei. Therefore, the F—F bond is a sigma bond.

Pi Bonds In the sigma bond of the fluorine molecule, the p atomic orbitals overlap end-to-end. In some molecules, however, orbitals can overlap side-by-side. As shown in Figure 8.15, the side-by-side overlap of atomic p orbitals produces what are called pi molecular orbitals. When a pi molecular orbital is filled with two electrons, a pi bond results. In a **pi bond** (symbolized by the Greek letter π), the bonding electrons are most likely to be found in sausage-shaped regions above and below the bond axis of the bonded atoms. It is not symmetrical around the F—F bond axis. Atomic orbitals in pi bonding overlap less than in sigma bonding. Therefore, pi bonds tend to be weaker than sigma bonds.

Figure 8.14 Two p atomic orbitals can combine to form a sigma-bonding molecular orbital, as in the case of fluorine (F_2). Notice that the sigma bond is symmetrical around the bond axis connecting the nuclei.

⊕ represents the nucleus.

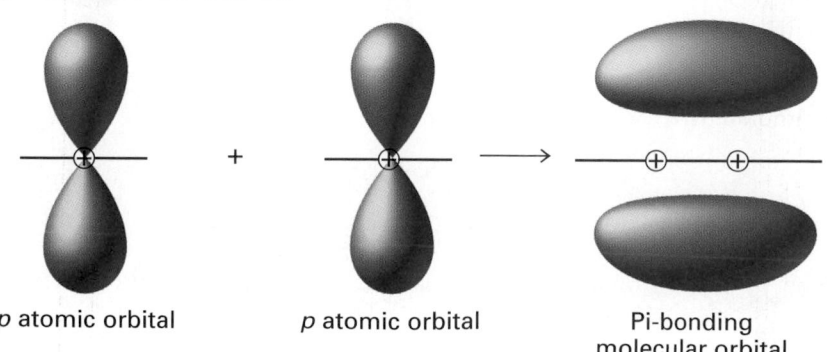

p atomic orbital   +   p atomic orbital   ⟶   Pi-bonding
molecular orbital

Figure 8.15 The side-by-side overlap of two p atomic orbitals produces a pi-bonding molecular orbital. Together, the two sausage-shaped regions in which the bonding electron pair is most likely to be found constitute one pi-bonding molecular orbital.

VSEPR Theory

A photograph or sketch may fail to do justice to your appearance. Similarly, electron dot structures fail to reflect the three-dimensional shapes of the molecules illustrated in Figure 8.16. The electron dot structure and structural formula of methane (CH_4), for example, show the molecule as if it were flat and merely two-dimensional.

$$H\overset{\displaystyle H}{\underset{\displaystyle H}{:\overset{..}{\underset{..}{C}}:}}H$$

Methane
(electron dot structure)

$$H-\overset{\displaystyle H}{\underset{\displaystyle H}{\overset{|}{\underset{|}{C}}}}-H$$

Methane
(structural formula)

In reality, methane molecules are three-dimensional. As Figure 8.16a shows, the hydrogens in a methane molecule are at the four corners of a geometric solid called a regular tetrahedron. In this arrangement, all of the H—C—H angles are 109.5°, the **tetrahedral angle.**

The valence-shell electron-pair repulsion theory, or **VSEPR theory,** explains the three-dimensional shape of methane. ⊂⊃ **According to VSEPR theory, the repulsion between electron pairs causes molecular shapes to adjust so that the valence-electron pairs stay as far apart as possible.** The methane molecule has four bonding electron pairs and no unshared pairs. The bonding pairs are farthest apart when the angle between the central carbon and its attached hydrogens is 109.5°. This is the H—C—H bond angle found experimentally.

Unshared pairs of electrons are also important in predicting the shapes of molecules. The nitrogen in ammonia (NH_3) is surrounded by four pairs of valence electrons, so you might predict the tetrahedral angle of 109.5° for the H—N—H bond angle. However, one of the valence-electron pairs shown in Figure 8.16b is an unshared pair. No bonding atom is vying for these unshared electrons. Thus they are held closer to the nitrogen than are the bonding pairs. The unshared pair strongly repels the bonding pairs, pushing them together. The measured H—N—H bond angle is only 107°.

Word *Origins*

Tetrahedral comes from the Greek *tetra-*, meaning "four," and *hedra*, meaning "face." The Greek *pod* means "foot." **What do you think *tetrapod* means?**

Figure 8.16 Methane and ammonia, represented here, are three-dimensional molecules. **ⓐ** Methane is a tetrahedral molecule. The hydrogens in methane are at the four corners of a regular tetrahedron, and the bond angles are all 109.5°. **ⓑ** An ammonia molecule is pyramidal. The unshared pair of electrons repels the bonding pairs. **Interpreting Diagrams** *How do the resulting H—N—H bond angles compare to the tetrahedral angle?*

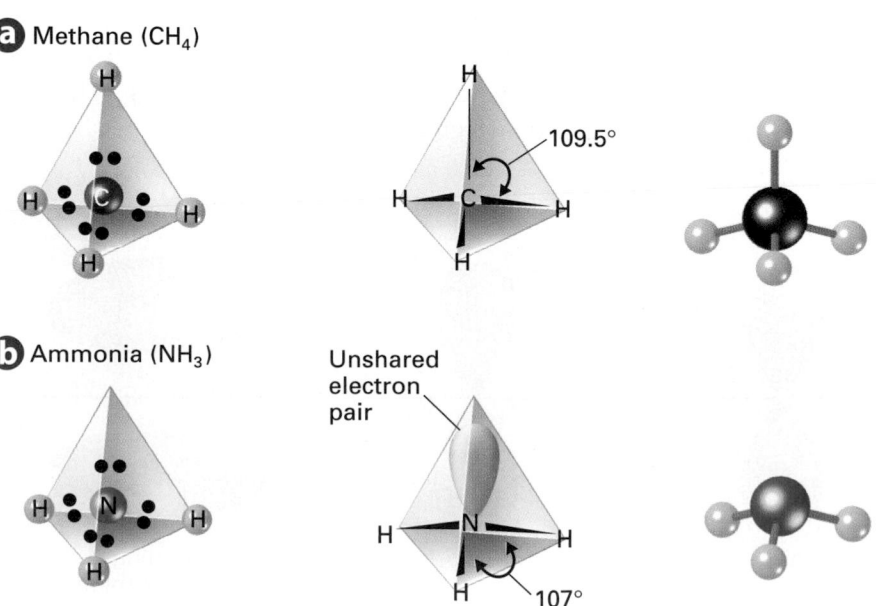

ⓐ Methane (CH_4)

109.5°

ⓑ Ammonia (NH_3)

Unshared electron pair

107°

232   Chapter 8

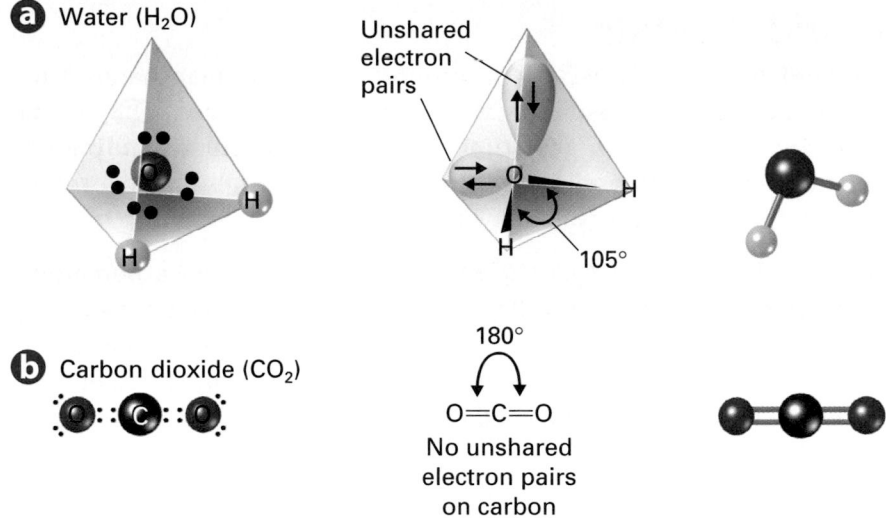

(a) Water (H₂O)

Unshared electron pairs

105°

(b) Carbon dioxide (CO₂)

180°

O=C=O

No unshared electron pairs on carbon

Figure 8.17 This comparison of water and carbon dioxide illustrates how unpaired electrons can affect the shape of a molecule made of three atoms. **ⓐ** The water molecule is bent because the two unshared pairs of electrons on oxygen repel the bonding electrons. **ⓑ** In contrast, the carbon dioxide molecule is linear. The carbon atom has no unshared electron pairs.

In a water molecule, oxygen forms single covalent bonds with two hydrogen atoms. The two bonding pairs and the two unshared pairs of electrons form a tetrahedral arrangement around the central oxygen. Thus the water molecule is planar (flat) but bent. With two unshared pairs repelling the bonding pairs, the H—O—H bond angle is compressed in comparison with the H—C—H bond angle in methane. The experimentally measured bond angle in water is about 105°, as shown in Figure 8.17a.

In contrast, the carbon in a carbon dioxide molecule has no unshared electron pairs. The double bonds joining the oxygens to the carbon are farthest apart when the O=C=O bond angle is 180° as illustrated in Figure 8.17b. Thus CO₂ is a linear molecule. Nine of the possible molecular shapes are shown in Figure 8.18.

Go Online

SCI*LINKS*

For: Links on VSEPR Theory
Visit: www.SciLinks.org
Web Code: cdn-1083

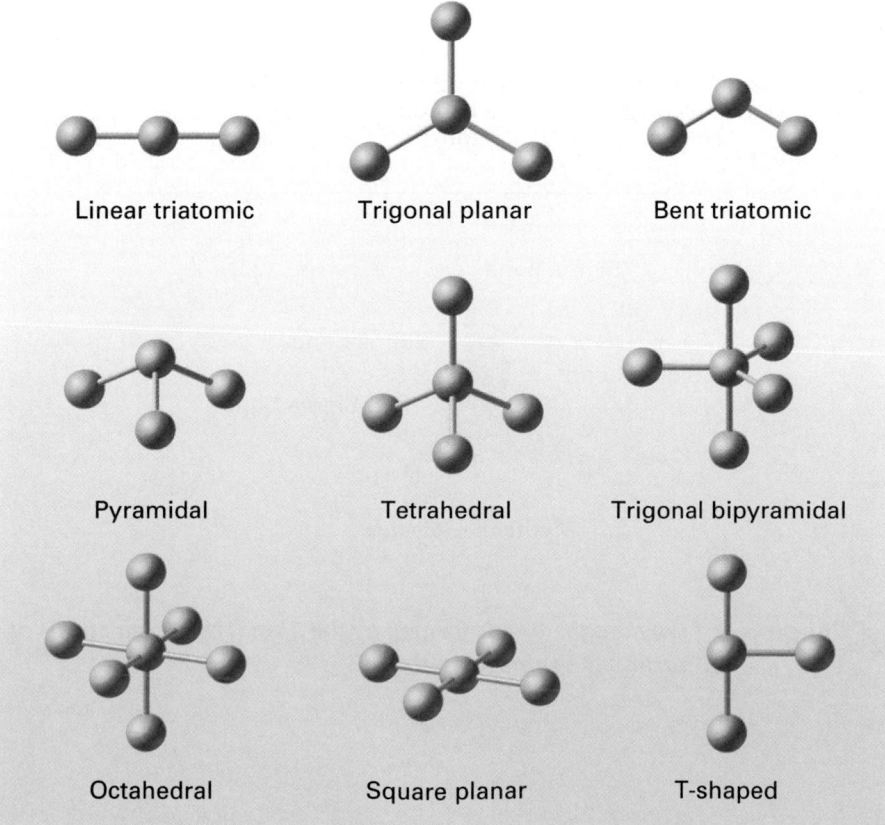

Linear triatomic   Trigonal planar   Bent triatomic

Pyramidal   Tetrahedral   Trigonal bipyramidal

Octahedral   Square planar   T-shaped

Figure 8.18 Shown here are common molecular shapes.

Hybrid Orbitals

The VSEPR theory works well when accounting for molecular shapes, but it does not help much in describing the types of bonds formed. ⚷ **Orbital hybridization provides information about both molecular bonding and molecular shape.** In **hybridization,** several atomic orbitals mix to form the same total number of equivalent hybrid orbitals.

Hybridization Involving Single Bonds Recall that the carbon atom's outer electron configuration is $2s^2\,2p^2$, but one of the $2s$ electrons is promoted to a $2p$ orbital to give one $2s$ electron and three $2p$ electrons, allowing it to bond to four hydrogen atoms in methane. You might suspect that one bond would be different from the other three. In fact, all the bonds are identical. This is explained by orbital hybridization.

The one $2s$ orbital and three $2p$ orbitals of a carbon atom mix to form four sp^3 hybrid orbitals. These are at the tetrahedral angle of 109.5°. As you can see in Figure 8.19, the four sp^3 orbitals of carbon overlap with the $1s$ orbitals of the four hydrogen atoms. The sp^3 orbitals extend farther into space than either s or p orbitals, allowing a great deal of overlap with the hydrogen $1s$ orbitals. The eight available valence electrons fill the molecular orbitals to form four C—H sigma bonds. The extent of overlap results in unusually strong covalent bonds.

Figure 8.19 In methane, each of the four sp^3 hybrid orbitals of carbon overlaps with a $1s$ orbital of hydrogen.

Atomic orbitals of two hydrogen atoms   Hybrid orbitals of a carbon atom   Atomic orbitals of two hydrogen atoms

Methane molecule

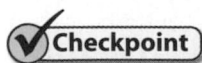 **Checkpoint** *Why are the bonds formed by the 2s and the 2p electrons of carbon the same in methane?*

Ethene molecule

Hybridization Involving Double Bonds

Hybridization is also useful in describing double covalent bonds. Ethene is a relatively simple molecule that has one carbon–carbon double bond and four carbon–hydrogen single bonds.

$$H_2C{=}CH_2 \quad \text{Ethene}$$

Experimental evidence indicates that the H—C—H bond angles in ethene are about 120°. In ethene, sp^2 hybrid orbitals form from the combination of one $2s$ and two $2p$ atomic orbitals of carbon. As you can see in Figure 8.20, each hybrid orbital is separated from the other two by 120°. Two sp^2 hybrid orbitals of each carbon form sigma-bonding molecular orbitals with the four available hydrogen $1s$ orbitals. The third sp^2 orbitals of each of the two carbons overlap to form a carbon–carbon sigma-bonding orbital. The nonhybridized $2p$ carbon orbitals overlap side-by-side to form a pi-bonding orbital. A total of twelve electrons fill six bonding molecular orbitals. Thus five sigma bonds and one pi bond hold the ethene molecule together. The sigma bonds and the pi bond are two-electron covalent bonds. Although they are drawn alike in structural formulas, pi bonds are weaker than sigma bonds. In chemical reactions that involve breaking one bond of a carbon–carbon double bond, the pi bond is more likely to break than the sigma bond.

Hybridization Involving Triple Bonds

A third type of covalent bond is a triple bond, such as is found in ethyne (C_2H_2), also called acetylene.

$$H{-}C{\equiv}C{-}H$$

As with other molecules, the hybrid orbital description of ethyne is guided by an understanding of the properties of the molecule. Ethyne is a linear molecule. The best hybrid orbital description is obtained if a $2s$ atomic orbital of carbon mixes with only one of the three $2p$ atomic orbitals. The result is two sp hybrid orbitals for each carbon.

Figure 8.21 In an ethyne molecule, one *sp* hybrid orbital from each carbon overlaps with a 1*s* orbital of hydrogen to form a sigma bond. The other *sp* hybrid orbital of each carbon overlaps to form a carbon–carbon sigma bond. The two *p* atomic orbitals from each carbon also overlap. **Interpreting Diagrams** *How many pi bonds are formed in an ethyne molecule?*

| Atomic orbital of a hydrogen atom | Atomic orbitals and hybrid orbitals of a carbon atom | Atomic orbitals and hybrid orbitals of a carbon atom | Atomic orbital of a hydrogen atom |

Ethyne molecule

The carbon–carbon sigma-bonding molecular orbital of the ethyne molecule in Figure 8.21 forms from the overlap of one *sp* orbital from each carbon. The other *sp* orbital of each carbon overlaps with the 1*s* orbital of each hydrogen, also forming sigma-bonding molecular orbitals. The remaining pair of *p* atomic orbitals on each carbon overlap side-by-side. They form two pi-bonding molecular orbitals that surround the central carbons. The ten available electrons completely fill five bonding molecular orbitals. The bonding of ethyne consists of three sigma bonds and two pi bonds.

Interactive Textbook

Simulation 7 Compare *sp*, *sp²*, and *sp³* hybrid orbitals.

with ChemASAP

8.3 Section Assessment

23. 🔑 **Key Concept** How are atomic and molecular orbitals related?

24. 🔑 **Key Concept** Explain how the VSEPR theory can be used to predict the shapes of molecules.

25. 🔑 **Key Concept** How is orbital hybrization useful in describing molecules?

26. What shape would you expect a simple carbon-containing compound to have if the carbon atom has the following hybridizations?
    a. sp^2 **b.** sp^3 **c.** sp

27. What is a sigma bond? Describe, with the aid of a diagram, how the overlap of two half-filled 1*s* orbitals produces a sigma bond?

28. How many sigma and how many pi bonds are in an ethyne molecule (C_2H_2)?

29. The BF_3 molecule is planar. The attachment of a fluoride ion to the boron in BF_3, through a coordinate covalent bond, creates the BF_4^- ion. What is the geometric shape of this ion?

Writing ▶ Activity

Molecular Bonding in Oxygen Research how chemists know that an oxygen molecule has unpaired electrons. Write a brief report on what you find.

Interactive Textbook

Assessment 8.3 Test yourself on the important concepts of Section 8.3.

with ChemASAP

Connecting to Your World   Snow covers approximately 23 percent of Earth's surface. Each individual snowflake is formed from as many as 100 snow crystals. The size and shape of each crystal depends mainly on the air temperature and amount of water vapor in the air at the time the snow crystal forms. In this section, you will see that the polar bonds in water molecules influence the distinctive geometry of snowflakes.

Bond Polarity

Covalent bonds involve electron sharing between atoms. However, covalent bonds differ in terms of how the bonded atoms share the electrons. The character of the bonds in a given molecule depends on the kind and number of atoms joined together. These features, in turn, determine the molecular properties.

The bonding pairs of electrons in covalent bonds are pulled, as in the tug-of-war in Figure 8.22, between the nuclei of the atoms sharing the electrons. When the atoms in the bond pull equally (as occurs when identical atoms are bonded), the bonding electrons are shared equally, and the bond is a **nonpolar covalent bond.** Molecules of hydrogen (H_2), oxygen (O_2), and nitrogen (N_2) have nonpolar covalent bonds. Diatomic halogen molecules, such as Cl_2, are also nonpolar.

Guide for Reading

Key Concepts
- How do electronegativity values determine the charge distribution in a polar bond?
- What happens to polar molecules between a pair of oppositely charged metal plates.
- How do intermolecular attractions compare with ionic and covalent bonds?
- Why do network solids have high melting points?

Vocabulary
nonpolar covalent bond
polar covalent bond
polar bond
polar molecule
dipole
van der Waals forces
dipole interactions
dispersion forces
hydrogen bonds
network solids

Reading Strategy

Relating Text and Visuals As you read, look closely at Figures 8.22 and 8.23. Explain how these illustrations help you understand how molecules attract each other.

Shared pair of electrons

Nucleus +   + Nucleus

Figure 8.22 The nuclei of atoms pull on the shared electrons, much as the knot in the rope is pulled toward opposing sides in a tug-of-war.

Figure 8.23 This electron-cloud picture of hydrogen chloride shows that the chlorine atom attracts the electron cloud more than the hydrogen atom does. **Inferring** *Which atom is more electronegative, a chlorine atom or a hydrogen atom?*

A **polar covalent bond,** known also as a **polar bond,** is a covalent bond between atoms in which the electrons are shared unequally. 🔑 **The more electronegative atom attracts electrons more strongly and gains a slightly negative charge. The less electronegative atom has a slightly positive charge.** Refer back to Table 6.2 in Chapter 6 to see the electronegativities of some common elements. The higher the electronegativity value, the greater the ability of an atom to attract electrons to itself.

Consider the hydrogen chloride molecule (HCl) shown in Figure 8.23. Hydrogen has an electronegativity of 2.1, and chlorine has an electronegativity of 3.0. These values are significantly different, so the covalent bond in hydrogen chloride is polar. The chlorine atom acquires a slightly negative charge. The hydrogen atom acquires a slightly positive charge. The lowercase Greek letter delta (δ) denotes that atoms involved in the covalent bond acquire only partial charges, less than 1+ or 1−.

$$\overset{\delta+}{H} — \overset{\delta-}{Cl}$$

The minus sign in this notation shows that chlorine has acquired a slightly negative charge. The plus sign shows that hydrogen has acquired a slightly positive charge. These partial charges are shown as clouds of electron density. The polar nature of the bond may also be represented by an arrow pointing to the more electronegative atom, as shown here.

$$\overset{+\!\longrightarrow}{H — Cl}$$

The O—H bonds in the water molecule are also polar. The highly electronegative oxygen partially pulls the bonding electrons away from hydrogen. The oxygen acquires a slightly negative charge. The hydrogen is left with a slightly positive charge.

$$\underset{\delta+H \qquad H\delta+}{\overset{\delta- \; \delta-}{O}} \quad or \quad \underset{H \qquad H}{\overset{O}{}}$$

As shown in Table 8.3, the electronegativity difference between two atoms tells you what kind of bond is likely to form. Remember when you use the table that there is no sharp boundary between ionic and covalent bonds. As the electronegativity difference between two atoms increases, the polarity of the bond increases. If the electronegativity difference is greater than 2.0, it is very likely that electrons will be pulled away completely by one of the atoms. In that case, an ionic bond will form.

Table 8.3		
Electronegativity Differences and Bond Types		
Electronegativity difference range	**Most probable type of bond**	**Example**
0.0–0.4	Nonpolar covalent	H—H (0.0)
0.4–1.0	Moderately polar covalent	$\overset{\delta+}{H} — \overset{\delta-}{Cl}$ (0.9)
1.0–2.0	Very polar covalent	$\overset{\delta+}{H} — \overset{\delta-}{F}$ (1.9)
≥ 2.0	Ionic	Na^+Cl^- (2.1)

CONCEPTUAL PROBLEM 8.3

Identifying Bond Type

Which type of bond (nonpolar covalent, moderately-polar covalent, or ionic) will form between each of the following pairs of atoms?

a. N and H   **b.** F and F   **c.** Ca and Cl   **d.** Al and Cl

① Analyze *Identify the relevant concepts.*

In each case, the pairs of atoms involved in the bonding pair are given. The types of bonds depend on the electronegativity differences between the bonding elements. Use Table 6.2 to find the electronegativity difference, then use Table 8.3 to determine the bond type.

② Solve *Apply concepts to this situation.*

From Tables 6.2 and 8.3, the electronegativities,

their differences, and the corresponding bond types are as follows.

a. N (3.0), H (2.1); 0.9 moderately polar covalent
b. F (4.0), F (4.0); 0.0; nonpolar covalent
c. Ca (1.0), Cl (3.0); 2.0; ionic
d. Al (1.5), Cl (3.0); 1.5; very polar covalent

Practice Problems

30. Identify the bonds between atoms of each pair of elements as nonpolar covalent, moderately polar covalent, very covalent, or ionic.

a. H and Br   **b.** K and Cl   **c.** C and O
d. Cl and F   **e.** Li and O   **f.** Br and Br

31. Place the following covalent bonds in order from least to most polar.

a. H — Cl   **b.** H — Br
c. H — S   **d.** H — C

Polar Molecules

The presence of a polar bond in a molecule often makes the entire molecule polar. In a **polar molecule,** one end of the molecule is slightly negative and the other end is slightly positive. In the hydrogen chloride molecule, for example, the partial charges on the hydrogen and chlorine atoms are electrically charged regions or poles. A molecule that has two poles is called a dipolar molecule, or **dipole.** The hydrogen chloride molecule is a dipole. Look at Figure 8.24. 🔑 **When polar molecules are placed between oppositely charged plates, they tend to become oriented with respect to the positive and negative plates.**

Interactive Textbook

Animation 10 Learn to distinguish between polar and nonpolar molecules.

— with **ChemASAP**

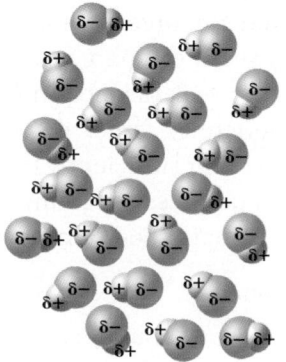

Electric field absent.
Polar molecules orient randomly.

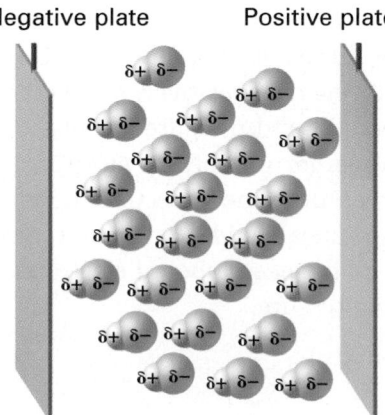

Negative plate   Positive plate

Electric field on.
Polar molecules line up.

Figure 8.24 When polar molecules, such as HCl, are placed in an electric field, the slightly negative ends of the molecules become oriented toward the positively charged plate and the slightly positive ends of the molecules become oriented toward the negatively charged plate. **Predicting** *What would happen if, instead, carbon dioxide molecules were placed between the plates? Why?*

The effect of polar bonds on the polarity of an entire molecule depends on the shape of the molecule and the orientation of the polar bonds. A carbon dioxide molecule, for example, has two polar bonds and is linear.

$$\overset{\longleftarrow}{O} = \overset{+}{C} = \overset{\longrightarrow}{O}$$

Note that the carbon and oxygens lie along the same axis. Therefore, the bond polarities cancel because they are in opposite directions. Carbon dioxide is thus a nonpolar molecule, despite the presence of two polar bonds.

The water molecule also has two polar bonds. However, the water molecule is bent rather than linear. Therefore, the bond polarities do not cancel and a water molecule is polar.

Attractions Between Molecules

Molecules can attract each other by a variety of forces. ⚷ **Intermolecular attractions are weaker than either ionic or covalent bonds.** Nevertheless, you should not underestimate the importance of these forces. Among other things, these attractions are responsible for determining whether a molecular compound is a gas, a liquid, or a solid at a given temperature.

Van der Waals Forces The two weakest attractions between molecules are collectively called **van der Waals forces,** named after the Dutch chemist Johannes van der Waals (1837–1923). Van der Waals forces consist of dipole interactions and dispersion forces.

Dipole interactions occur when polar molecules are attracted to one another. The electrical attraction involved occurs between the oppositely charged regions of polar molecules, as shown in Figure 8.25. The slightly negative region of a polar molecule is weakly attracted to the slightly positive region of another polar molecule. Dipole interactions are similar to but much weaker than ionic bonds.

Dispersion forces, the weakest of all molecular interactions, are caused by the motion of electrons. They occur even between non-polar molecules. When the moving electrons happen to be momentarily more on the side of a molecule closest to a neighboring molecule, their electric force influences the neighboring molecule's electrons to be momentarily more on the opposite side. This causes an attraction between the two molecules similar to, but much weaker than, the force between permanently polar molecules. The strength of dispersion forces generally increases as the number of electrons in a molecule increases. The halogen diatomic molecules, for example, attract each other mainly by means of dispersion forces. Fluorine and chlorine have relatively few electrons and are gases at ordinary room temperature and pressure because of their especially weak dispersion forces. The larger number of electrons in bromine generates larger dispersion forces. Bromine molecules therefore attract each other sufficiently to make bromine a liquid at ordinary room temperature and pressure. Iodine, with a still larger number of electrons, is a solid at ordinary room temperature and pressure.

Figure 8.25 Polar molecules are attracted to one another by dipole interactions, a type of van der Waals force.

hydrogen bonds

Figure 8.26 The strong hydrogen bonding between water molecules accounts for many properties of water, such as the fact that water is a liquid rather than a gas at ordinary temperatures.

Hydrogen Bonds The dipole interactions in water produce an attraction between water molecules. Each O—H bond in the water molecule is highly polar, and the oxygen acquires a slightly negative charge because of its greater electronegativity. The hydrogens in water molecules acquire a slightly positive charge. The positive region of one water molecule attracts the negative region of another water molecule, as illustrated in Figure 8.26. This attraction between the hydrogen of one water molecule and the oxygen of another water molecule is strong compared to other dipole interactions. This relatively strong attraction, which is also found in hydrogen-containing molecules other than water, is given the special name hydrogen bond. Figure 8.26 illustrates hydrogen bonding in water.

Hydrogen bonds are attractive forces in which a hydrogen covalently bonded to a very electronegative atom is also weakly bonded to an unshared electron pair of another electronegative atom. This other atom may be in the same molecule or in a nearby molecule. Hydrogen bonding always involves hydrogen. It is the only chemically reactive element with valence electrons that are not shielded from the nucleus by a layer of underlying electrons.

Remember that a hydrogen bond is an attraction to a hydrogen atom already bonded to a strongly electronegative atom. The covalent bond between hydrogen and a very electronegative atom such as oxygen, nitrogen, or fluorine is strongly polar. This leaves the hydrogen nucleus very electron-deficient. The sharing of a nonbonding electron pair on another nearby electronegative atom compensates for the deficiency. The resulting hydrogen bond has about 5% of the strength of an average covalent bond. Hydrogen bonds are the strongest of the intermolecular forces. They are extremely important in determining the properties of water and biological molecules such as proteins. Figure 8.27 shows how the relatively strong attractive forces between water molecules causes the water to form small drops on a waxy surface.

Figure 8.27 The strong attractions between water molecules compared with their attraction to molecules in the surface of this flower cause the water to pull together into small drops rather than spread over the surface.

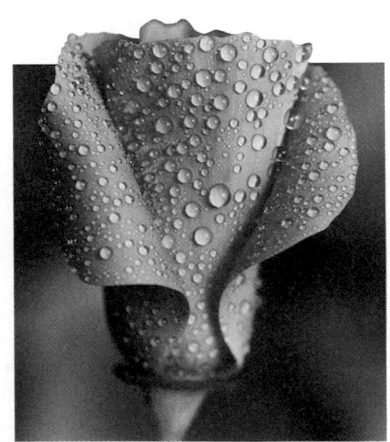

✓ Checkpoint **What are hydrogen bonds?**

The Chemistry of Adhesives

Most common adhesives are sticky substances that you can use to bind two surfaces together. The diagram shows how some adhesives work. The adhesive is a liquid until the surfaces are in position. Then the adhesive sets into a solid. Adhesion can work in three ways: Molecules of the polymer and the surface may become physically connected, the molecules may also become attracted by intermolecular forces, or they may react by forming covalent bonds.

Interpreting Diagrams *Explain the purpose of a stabilizer in an adhesive.*

It also sticks handles to teapots.

Permanent adhesion An epoxy resin attached this automobile to the billboard. Epoxy resins are often stored in two parts that are mixed just before the epoxy is used. Strong binding forces in these adhesives make them heat- and water-resistant.

1 **Liquid adhesive** In a typical adhesive, monomer molecules and a stabilizer are in a solvent. The stabilizer stops the monomers from forming a solid polymers

Tube

Monomer molecule

Stabilizer

Temporary adhesion The sticky strip on a reusable note is a microsphere adhesive. The microspheres limit the amount of surface area contact, so the paper sticks lightly and repositions easily.

Solvent

2 **Applying the adhesive** Squeezing the tube releases the liquid onto one of the surfaces to be joined.

3 **Setting the adhesive** Contact with water in the air and on the surfaces being joined makes the stabilizer inactive. The monomers then begin to join together to form polymers. As the chain lengthens, the adhesive changes from a liquid to a solid.

Monomers join together.

Intermolecular Attractions and Molecular Properties

At room temperature, some compounds are gases, some are liquids, and some are solids. The physical properties of a compound depend on the type of bonding it displays—in particular, on whether it is ionic or covalent. A great range of physical properties occurs among covalent compounds. This is mainly because of widely varying intermolecular attractions.

The melting and boiling points of most compounds composed of molecules are low compared with those of ionic compounds. In most solids formed from molecules, only the weak attractions between molecules need to be broken. However, a few solids that consist of molecules do not melt until the temperature reaches 1000°C or higher, or they decompose without melting at all. Most of these very stable substances are **network solids** (or network crystals), solids in which all of the atoms are covalently bonded to each other. ⟱ **Melting a network solid would require breaking covalent bonds throughout the solid.**

Diamond is an example of a network solid. As shown in Figure 8.28, each carbon atom in a diamond is covalently bonded to four other carbons, interconnecting carbon atoms throughout the diamond. Cutting a diamond requires breaking a multitude of these bonds. Diamond does not melt; rather, it vaporizes to a gas at 3500°C and above.

Silicon carbide, with the formula SiC and a melting point of about 2700°C, is also a network solid. Silicon carbide is so hard that it is used in grindstones and as an abrasive as illustrated in Figure 8.29. The molecular structures of silicon carbide and diamond are similar to each other. You can think of samples of diamond, silicon carbide, and other network solids as single molecules.

✔Checkpoint *What substance is an example of a network solid?*

Figure 8.28 Diamond is a network-solid form of carbon. Diamond has a three-dimensional structure, with each carbon at the center of a tetrahedron.

For: Links on Diamond
Visit: www.SciLinks.org
Web Code: cdn-1085

Figure 8.29 Silicon carbide, a network solid, is so hard that it is used in this grindstone to wear down the end of a hardened steel cutting tool to form a sharp edge.

Simulation 8 Relate melting and boiling points to the strength of intermolecular forces.

with **ChemASAP**

Table 8.4 summarizes some of the characteristic differences between ionic and covalent (molecular) substances. Note that ionic compounds have higher melting points than molecular compounds. Ionic compounds also tend to be soluble in water.

Table 8.4

Characteristics of Ionic and Covalent Compounds

Characteristic	Ionic compound	Covalent compound
Representative unit	Formula unit	Molecule
Bond formation	Transfer of one or more electrons between atoms	Sharing of electron pairs between atoms
Type of elements	Metallic and nonmetallic	Nonmetallic
Physical state	Solid	Solid, liquid, or gas
Melting point	High (usually above 300°C)	Low (usually below 300°C)
Solubility in water	Usually high	High to low
Electrical conductivity of aqueous solution	Good conductor	Poor to nonconducting

8.4 Section Assessment

32. 🔑 **Key Concept** How do electronegativity values determine the charge distribution in a polar covalent bond?

33. 🔑 **Key Concept** What happens when polar molecules are between metal plates with oppositely charged metal plates?

34. 🔑 **Key Concept** Compare the strengths of intermolecular forces to the strengths of ionic bonds and covalent bonds.

35. 🔑 **Key Concept** Explain why network solids have high melting points.

36. Not every molecule with polar bonds is polar. Explain this statement. Use CCl_4 as an example.

37. Draw the electron dot structure for each molecule. Identify polar covalent bonds by assigning slightly positive ($\delta+$) and slightly negative ($\delta-$) symbols to the appropriate atoms.
  a. HOOH   **b.** BrCl   **c.** HBr   **d.** H_2O

38. How does a network solid differ from most other covalent compounds?

Connecting ▶ **Concepts**

Dipole Forces and Dispersion Forces Explain how dipole and dispersion forces are related. First, explain what produces the forces between polar molecules. Then explain what produces dispersion forces between molecules. Identify what is similar and what is different in the two mechanisms of molecular attraction.

Interactive Textbook

Assessment 8.4 Test yourself on the important concepts of Section 8.4.

── **with ChemASAP**

Paper Chromatography of Food Dyes

Purpose
To use paper chromatography to separate and identify food dyes in various samples.

Materials
- pencil
- paper
- ruler
- scissors
- toothpicks
- 4 different colors of food coloring
- plastic cup
- 0.1% NaCl solution
- chromatography paper

Procedure

Cut a 5 cm × 10 cm strip of chromatography paper and label it with a pencil, as shown below. Use a different toothpick to place a spot of each of the four food colors on the Xs on your chromatography paper. Allow the spots to dry for a few minutes. Fill the plastic cup so its bottom is just covered with the solvent (0.1% NaCl solution). Wrap the chromatography paper around a pencil. Remove the pencil and place the chromatography paper, color-spot side down, in the solvent. When the solvent reaches the top of the chromatography paper, remove the paper and allow it to dry.

Analysis
Using your experimental data, record the answers to the following questions below your data table.

1. If a food color sample yields a single streak or spot, it is usually a pure compound. Which food colors consist of pure compounds?

2. Which food colors are mixtures of compounds?

3. Food colors often consist of a mixture of three colored dyes: Red No. 40, Yellow No. 5, and Blue No. 1. Read the label on the food color package. Which dyes do your food color samples contain?

4. Identify each spot or streak on your chromatogram as Red No. 40, Yellow No. 5, or Blue No. 1.

5. Paper chromatography separates polar covalent compounds on the basis of their relative polarities. The most polar dyes migrate the fastest and appear at the top of the paper. Which dye is the most polar? The least polar?

You're The Chemist
The following small-scale activities allow you to develop your own procedures and analyze the results.

1. **Design It!** Design and carry out an experiment to identify the dyes in various colored candies.

2. **Design It!** Design and carry out an experiment to identify the dyes in various colored markers using the paper chromatography method.

3. **Design It!** Design and carry out an experiment to identify the dyes in various colored powdered drinks using the paper chromatography method.

4. **Analyze It!** Use different solvents, such as 2-propanol (rubbing alcohol), vinegar, and ammonia, to separate food colors. Does the choice of solvent affect the results?

5. **Analyze It!** Explore the effect of different papers on your results. Try paper towels, notebook paper, and coffee filters. Report your results. Examine the relative positions of Blue No. 1 and Yellow No. 5. What do you observe?

Study Guide

Key Concepts

8.1 Molecules and Molecular Compounds
- Molecular compounds tend to have relatively low melting and boiling points.
- A molecular formula shows how many atoms of each element a molecule contains.

8.2 The Nature of Covalent Bonding
- Electron sharing occurs so that atoms attain the configurations of noble gases.
- An electron dot structure shows the shared electrons of a covalent bond by a pair of dots.
- Atoms form double or triple bonds by sharing two or three pairs of electrons.
- In a coordinate covalent bond, the shared electron pair comes from a single atom.
- A large bond dissociation energy corresponds to a strong covalent bond.
- In ozone, the bonding of oxygen atoms is a hybrid of the extremes represented by the resonance forms.
- The octet rule is not satisfied in molecules with an odd number of electrons, and in molecules where an atom has less, or more, than a complete octet of valence electrons.

8.3 Bonding Theories
- Just as an atomic orbital belongs to a particular atom, a molecular orbital belongs to a molecule as a whole.
- According to VSEPR theory, the repulsion between electron pairs causes molecular shapes to adjust so that the valence-electron pairs stay as far apart as possible.
- Orbital hybridization provides information about both molecular bonding and molecular shape.

8.4 Polar Bonds and Molecules
- When different atoms bond, the more electronegative atom attracts electrons more strongly and acquires a slight negative charge.
- Polar molecules between oppositely charged metal plates tend to become oriented with respect to the positive and negative plates.
- Intermolecular attractions are weaker than either an ionic or covalent bond.
- Melting a network solid requires breaking covalent bonds throughout the solid.
- bond dissociation energy (p. 226)

Vocabulary

- bonding orbital (p. 230)
- covalent bond (p. 213)
- coordinate covalent bond (p. 223)
- diatomic molecule (p. 214)
- dipole (p. 239)
- dipole interactions (p. 240)
- dispersion forces (p. 240)
- double covalent bond (p. 221)
- hybridization (p. 234)
- hydrogen bonds (p. 241)
- molecular compound (p. 214)
- molecular formula (p. 215)
- molecular orbital (p. 230)
- molecule (p. 214)
- network solids (p. 243)
- nonpolar covalent bond (p. 237)
- pi bond (p. 231)
- polar bond (p. 238)
- polar covalent bond (p. 238)
- polar molecule (p. 239)
- polyatomic ion (p. 223)
- resonance structure (p. 227)
- sigma bond (p. 230)
- single covalent bond (p. 217)
- structural formula (p. 218)
- tetrahedral angle (p. 232)
- triple covalent bond (p. 221)
- unshared pair (p. 218)
- van der Waals forces (p. 240)
- VSEPR theory (p. 232)

Organizing Information

Construct a concept map that organizes the major ideas of this chapter.

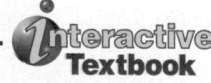

Concept Map 8 Solve the Concept Map with the help of an interactive guided tutorial.

— with **ChemASAP**

molecular orbital

covalent bond

polar bond

intermolecular attraction

coordinate covalent bond

resonance structure

hybrid orbital

VSEPR theory

covalent compound

8.1 Molecular Compounds

39. The melting point of a compound is 1240°C. Is this compound most likely an ionic or a molecular compound?

40. Identify the number and kinds of atoms present in a molecule of each compound.
 a. ascorbic acid (vitamin C), $C_6H_8O_6$
 b. sucrose (table sugar), $C_{12}H_{22}O_{11}$
 c. trinotrotolunene (TNT), $C_7H_5N_3O_6$

8.2 The Nature of Covalent Bonding

41. Explain why neon is monatomic, but chlorine is diatomic.

42. Classify the following compounds as ionic or covalent.
 a. $MgCl_2$ **b.** Na_2S **c.** H_2O **d.** H_2S

43. Describe the difference between an ionic and a covalent bond.

44. How many electrons do two atoms in a double covalent bond share? How many in a triple covalent bond?

45. Write plausible electron dot structures for the following substances. Each substance contains only single covalent bonds.
 a. I_2 **b.** OF_2 **c.** H_2S **d.** NI_3

46. Characterize a coordinate covalent bond and give an example.

47. Explain why compounds containing C—N and C—O single bonds can form coordinate covalent bonds with H^+ but compounds containing only C—H and C—C single bonds cannot.

48. Using electron dot structures, draw at least two resonance structures for the nitrite ion (NO_2^-). The oxygen atoms in NO_2^- are attached to the nitrogen.

49. Which of these compounds would you expect to contain elements that do not follow the octet rule? Explain.
 a. NF_3 **b.** PCl_2F_3 **c.** SF_4 **d.** SCl_2

50. Explain what is meant by bond dissociation energy.

51. What is the relationship between the magnitude of a molecule's bond dissociation energy and its expected chemical reactivity?

52. The chlorine and oxygen atoms in thionyl chloride ($SOCl_2$) are bonded directly to the sulfur. Write an acceptable electron dot structure for thionyl chloride.

53. Explain why each electron dot structure is incorrect. Replace each structure with one that is more acceptable.
 a. $[:C::N:]^-$ **b.** $:\ddot{F}:P::\ddot{F}:$
  $:\ddot{F}:$

54. Which of the following molecules contains a central atom that does not obey the octet rule?
 a. PBr_5 **b.** AlI_3 **c.** PF_3 **d.** $SiCl_4$

55. Make a list of the elements found in Table 8.2 on page 224. What do the elements that form covalent bonds have in common?

56. Although the relative positions of the atoms are correct in each of these molecules, there are one or more incorrect bonds in each of the electron dot structures. Identify the incorrect bonds.
 a. H=C=C=H **b.** :F—O—H
 c. :I:::Cl: **d.** H—N:::N—H

57. There are some compounds in which one atom has more electrons than the corresponding noble gas. Examples are PCl_5, SF_6, and IF_7. Write the electron dot structures of P, S, and I atoms and of these compounds. Considering the outer shell configuration of P, S, and I, develop an orbital hybridization scheme to explain the existence of these compounds.

58. Draw the electron dot structure of formic acid, H_2CO_2. The carbon is the central atom, and all the atoms are attached to the carbon except for a hydrogen bonded to an oxygen.

59. Draw as many resonance structures as you can for HN_3. *Hint:* the three nitrogen atoms are bonded in a row and the hydrogen atom is bonded to a nitrogen atom at the end of the row of nitrogen atoms.

8.3 Bonding Theories

60. What is a pi bond? Describe, with the aid of a diagram, how the overlap of two half-filled p atomic orbitals produce a pi bond.

61. Use electron dot structures to predict the shapes of the following species.
 a. CO_2 b. $SiCl_4$ c. SO_3
 d. SCl_2 e. CO f. H_2Se

62. The molecule CO_2 has two carbon–oxygen double bonds. Describe the bonding in the CO_2 molecule, which involves hybridized orbitals for carbon and oxygen.

63. What types of hybrid orbitals are involved in the bonding of the carbon atoms in the following molecules?
 a. CH_4 b. $H_2C{=}CH_2$
 c. $HC{\equiv}CH$ d. $N{\equiv}C-C{\equiv}N$

64. Devise a hybridization scheme for PCl_3, and predict the molecular shape based on this scheme.

65. Use electron dot formulas to predict the shape of each of the following molecules.
 a. $SiCl_4$ b. CCl_4 c. SCl_2

66. Give the angles between the orbitals of each hybrid.
 a. sp^3 hybrids   b. sp^2 hybrids   c. sp hybrids

67. What is the shape of each of these simple molecules?

a.   b.

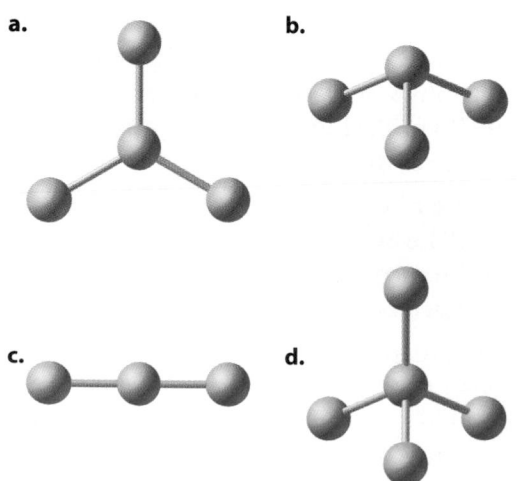

c.   d.

68. Ethyl alcohol and dimethyl ether each have the same molecular formula, C_2H_6O. Ethyl alcohol has a much higher boiling point (78°C) than dimethyl ether (−25°C). Propose an explanation for this difference.

69. What shape do you expect for a molecule with a central atom and the following?
 a. two bonding pairs of electrons and two nonbonding pairs of electrons
 b. four bonding pairs and zero nonbonding pairs
 c. three bonding pairs and one nonbonding pair

70. The electron structure and geometry of the methane molecule (CH_4) can be described by a variety of models, including electron dot structure, simple overlap of atomic orbitals, and orbital hybridization of carbon. Write the electron dot structure of CH_4. Sketch two molecular orbital pictures of the CH_4 molecule. For your first sketch, assume that one of the paired $2s^2$ electrons of carbon has been promoted to the empty $2p$ orbital. Overlap each half-filled atomic orbital of carbon to a half-filled $2s$ orbital of hydrogen. What is the predicted geometry of the CH_4 molecule, using this simple overlap method? In your second sketch, assume hybridization of the $2s$ and $2p$ orbitals of carbon. Now what geometry would you predict for CH_4? Which picture is preferable based on the facts that all H—C—H bond angles in CH_4 are 109.5° and all C—H bond distances are identical?

8.4 Polar Bonds and Molecules

71. How must the electronegativies of two atoms compare if a covalent bond between them is to be polar?

72. The bonds between the following pairs of elements are covalent. Arrange them according to polarity, naming the most polar bond first.
 a. H—Cl   b. H—C   c. H—F
 d. H—O   e. H—H   f. S—Cl

73. What is a hydrogen bond?

74. Depict the hydrogen bonding between two ammonia molecules and between one ammonia molecule and one water molecule.

75. Why do compounds with strong intermolecular attractive forces have higher boiling points than compounds with weak intermolecular attractive forces?

The following graph shows how the percent ionic character of a single bond varies according to the difference in electronegativity between the two elements forming the bond. Answer Questions 76–78 using this graph and Table 6.1.

Single Bond Ionic Character

76. What is the relationship between the percent ionic character of single bonds and the electronegativity difference of their elements?

77. What electronegativity difference will result in a bond with a 50% ionic character?

78. Estimate the percent ionic character of the bonds formed between the following pairs of elements.
a. lithium and oxygen
b. nitrogen and oxygen
c. magnesium and chlorine
d. nitrogen and fluorine

79. Is there a clear difference between a very polar covalent bond and an ionic bond? Explain.

For Questions 80 and 81, identify the type of intermolecular bonding represented by the dotted lines in the drawings.

80. BrCl (bromine chloride)

81. CH_3OH (methanol)

Regents Practice Exam

Part A

For each statement or question write the number of the word or expression that, of those given, best completes the statement or answers the question.

1. In a neutral atom, the number of which sub-atomic particles must always be equal?
   (1) electrons and neutrons
   (2) protons and neutrons
   (3) electrons and protons
   (4) electrons, protons, and neutrons

2. In the periodic table, atoms are arranged in order of
   (1) increasing atomic mass
   (2) decreasing atomic mass
   (3) increasing atomic number
   (4) decreasing atomic number

3. What element is likely to form an ionic compound with chlorine?
   (1) iodine   (3) helium
   (2) cesium   (4) oxygen

4. Which of the following statements about the periodic table is *not* true?
   (1) A period is a horizontal row.
   (2) A group is a vertical column.
   (3) Most of the elements in the table are metals.
   (4) Nonmetals are located on the left side of the periodic table.

5. A bond in which two atoms share two electrons is
   (1) a single covalent bond
   (2) a double covalent bond
   (3) a triple covalent bond
   (4) an ionic bond

6. Which of the following substances contains both covalent and ionic bonds?
   (1) NH_4NO_3 (3) LiF
   (2) CH_3OCH_3 (4) $CaCl_2$

Part B-1

For each statement or question write the number of the word or expression that, of those given, best completes the statement or answers the question.

7. Which of the following ions has the same number of electrons as a noble gas?
   (1) Cu^+ (3) H^+
   (2) N^{5-} (4) Al^{3+}

8. How many valence electrons are in a molecule of phosphoric acid, H_3PO_4?
   (1) 7   (2) 16   (3) 24   (4) 32

9. Which of the following bonds is most polar?
   (1) H—Cl   (3) H—F
   (2) H—Br   (4) H—I

10. Which of the following molecules can form a hydrogen bond with a water molecule?
    (1) N_2 (3) O_2
    (2) NH_3 (4) CH_4

11. What type of bonding is shown in the following diagram?

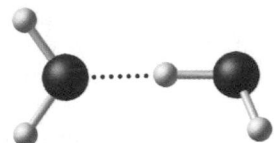

    (1) ionic   (3) covalent
    (2) metallic   (4) hydrogen

12. A carbon monoxide molecule contains a triple covalent bond because
    (1) a shared pair of electrons forms a covalent bond
    (2) the atoms both attain a noble gas configuration by sharing three pairs of electrons
    (3) carbon is stable when it shares electrons with two oxygen atoms
    (4) both carbon and oxygen are diatomic

13. Xenon has a higher boiling point than neon because intermolecular forces
    (1) between xenon atoms are stronger than those between neon atoms
    (2) between neon atoms are stronger than those between xenon atoms
    (3) include hydrogen bonds for xenon
    (4) include hydrogen bonds for neon

Part B-2

Answer each of the following questions.

14. Make the following conversions.
    a. 66.5 mm to micrometers
    b. 4×10^{-2} g to centigrams
    c. 5.62 mg/mL to decigrams per liter
    d. 85 km/h to meters per second

15. How many significant figures are in each of the following measurements?
    a. 0.00052 m   **c.** 5.050 mg
    b. 9.8×10^4 g **d.** 8.700 mL

16. How many neutrons are in each of the following atoms?
    a. silicon-30   **c.** nitrogen-15
    b. magnesium-24   **d.** chromium-50

17. How do isotopes of an atom differ?

18. Write correct electron configurations for atoms of the following elements.
    a. sodium   **c.** phosphorus
    b. sulfur   **d.** nitrogen

19. How does the ionic radius of a typical negative ion compare with the radius for the corresponding neutral atom?

20. Give the electron configuration of the element found at each location in the periodic table.
    a. Group 1A (1), period 3
    b. Group 3A (13), period 4
    c. Group 5A (15), period 5
    d. Group 2A (2), period 3

21. Identify the larger atom of each pair.
    a. calcium and barium
    b. silicon and sulfur
    c. sodium and nitrogen

22. How many valence electrons does each of the following atoms have?
    a. argon   **c.** selenium
    b. aluminum   **d.** beryllium

23. Write the electron configuration of each of the following ions.
    a. oxide ion   **c.** nitride ion
    b. magnesium ion   **d.** potassium ion

Use the following description and data table to answer Questions 24 and 25.

The table relates molecular shape to the number of bonding and nonbonding electron pairs in molecules.

Bonding pairs	Non-bonding pairs	Arrangement of electron pairs	Molecular shape	Example
4	0	tetrahedral	tetrahedral	CH_4
3	1	tetrahedral	pyramidal	NCl_3
2	2	tetrahedral	bent	H_2S
1	3	tetrahedral	linear	HF

24. Draw the electron dot structure for each example molecule.

25. H_2S has two hydrogen atoms bonded to a sulfur atom. Why isn't the molecule linear?

Part C

Answer each of the following questions.

26. Which of the following gases in Earth's atmosphere would you expect to find as molecules and which as individual atoms? Explain.
    a. nitrogen   **b.** oxygen   **c.** argon

27. Oxalic acid, $C_2H_2O_4$, is used in polishes and rust removers. Draw the electron dot structure for oxalic acid given that the two carbon atoms are bonded together but neither of the hydrogen atoms is bonded to a carbon atom.

28. Vinegar contains the compound ethanoic acid, whose molecular formula is CH_3COOH.
    a. Draw the electron dot structure of ethanoic acid.
    b. Is the bonding between each of the oxygen atoms and the carbon the same?
    c. Is the bonding between the carbon atom and each oxygen atom a polar or nonpolar bond?
    d. Is ethanoic acid a polar molecule?

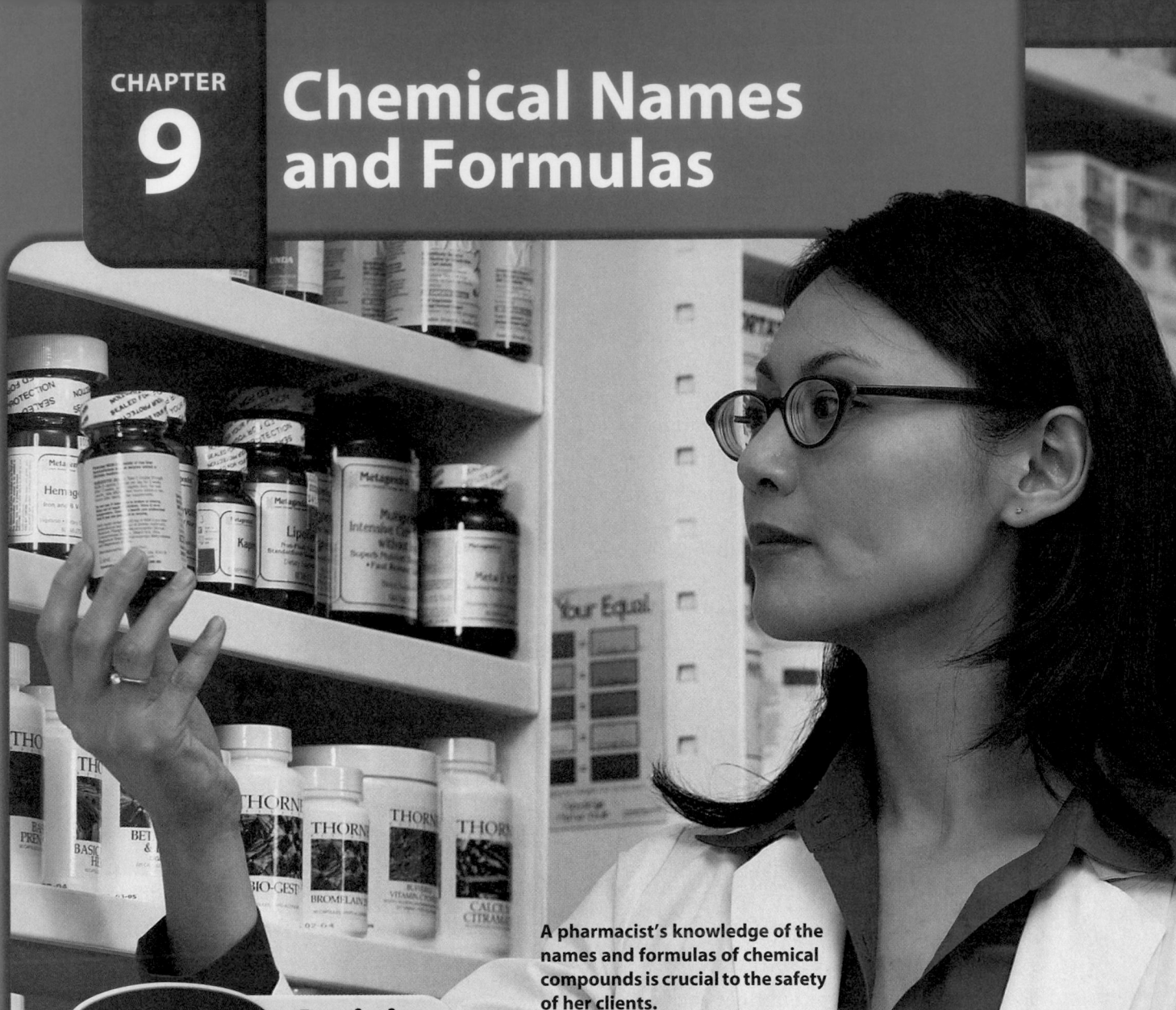

Chemical Names and Formulas

A pharmacist's knowledge of the names and formulas of chemical compounds is crucial to the safety of her clients.

INQUIRY Activity

Element Name Search

Materials

Ingredient labels from items such as bread, cake mixes, baking soda, cereal, soap, shampoo, conditioner, toothpaste, and antacids

Procedure

1. Select a variety of ingredient labels from the suggested items or from similar ones.

2. List all the ingredients that you recognize. Don't be discouraged by the many unfamiliar names. Thousands upon thousands of substances are used in everyday products.

3. With the help of a periodic table, make another list of all the ingredient names that contain or are derived from the name of an element.

Think About It

1. How often did you find the same element name in more than one product?

2. What element names are on both lists?

3. Did all the ingredients have complex chemical-sounding names?

4. How do the names of element-containing compounds compare with the other names on your list?

9.1 Naming Ions

New York Standards: 3.1z, 5.2c

Connecting to Your World

In the play *Romeo and Juliet*, William Shakespeare wrote, "What's in a name? That which we call a rose/By any other name would smell as sweet." A rose is *rosa* in Spanish, *warda* in Arabic, and *julab* in Hindi. To truly understand another culture, you must first learn the language used in that culture. Similarly, to understand chemistry, you must learn its language. Part of learning the language of chemistry involves understanding how to name ionic compounds. For this you need to know how to name ions.

Monatomic Ions

Ionic compounds consist of a positive metal ion and a negative nonmetal ion combined in a proportion such that their charges add up to a net charge of zero. For example, the ionic compound sodium chloride (NaCl) consists of one sodium ion (Na^+) and one chloride ion (Cl^-). Probably you are already familiar with the name and formula of sodium chloride, which is common table salt. But it is important, in learning the language of chemistry, to be able to name and write the chemical formulas for all ionic compounds. The first step is to learn about the ions that form ionic compounds. Some ions, called **monatomic ions,** consist of a single atom with a positive or negative charge resulting from the loss or gain of one or more valence electrons, respectively.

Cations Recall that metallic elements tend to lose valence electrons. Lithium, sodium, and potassium in Group 1A lose one electron to form cations. All the Group 1A ions have a 1+ charge (Li^+, Na^+, K^+, Rb^+, and Cs^+). Magnesium and calcium are Group 2A metals. They tend to lose two electrons to form cations with a 2+ charge (Mg^{2+} and Ca^{2+}), as do all the other Group 2A metals. Aluminum is the only common Group 3A metal. As you might expect, it tends to lose three electrons to form a 3+ cation (Al^{3+}). **When the metals in Groups 1A, 2A, and 3A lose electrons, they form cations with positive charges equal to their group number.** Figure 9.1 shows some of the elements whose ionic charges can be obtained from their positions in the periodic table. The names of the cations of the Group 1A, Group 2A, and Group 3A metals are the same as the name of the metal, followed by the word *ion* or *cation*. Thus Na^+ is the sodium ion (or cation), Ca^{2+} is the calcium ion (or cation), and Al^{3+} is the aluminum ion (or cation).

Guide for Reading

Key Concepts
- How are the charges of Group A metal and nonmetal ions related to their positions in the periodic table?
- How are the charges of some transition metal ions determined?
- What are the two endings of the names of most polyatomic ions?

Vocabulary
monatomic ion
polyatomic ion

Reading Strategy
Outlining As you read, make an outline of the most important ideas in this section. Use the red headings as the main topics and the blue headings as subtopics. Add a sentence or a note after each heading to provide key information about the topic.

Figure 9.1 The representative elements shown form positive ions with charges equal to their group numbers. **Applying Concepts** *Are the ions anions or cations?*

Figure 9.2 Note the positions of the nonmetals and the metalloid, arsenic. These elements form anions. Common transition elements that form more than one ion are also shown. **Applying Concepts** *Do the transition metals form anions or cations?*

Figure 9.3 The ions of these transition metals produce an array of colors when dissolved in water. From left to right, the ions are Co^{3+}, Cr^{3+}, Fe^{3+}, Ni^{2+}, and Mn^{2+}.

Table 9.1							
Ionic Charges of Representative Elements							
1A	**2A**	**3A**	**4A**	**5A**	**6A**	**7A**	**8A**
Li^+	Be^{2+}			N^{3-}	O^{2-}	F^-	
Na^+	Mg^{2+}	Al^{3+}		P^{3-}	S^{2-}	Cl^-	
K^+	Ca^{2+}			As^{3-}	Se^{2-}	Br^-	
Rb^+	Sr^{2+}					I^-	
Cs^+	Ba^{2+}						

Anions Nonmetals tend to gain electrons to form anions, so the charge of a nonmetallic ion is negative. 🔑 **The charge of any ion of a Group A nonmetal is determined by subtracting 8 from the group number.** The elements in Group 7A form anions with a 1− charge ($7 - 8 = -1$). The name of an anion is not the same as the element's name. Anion names start with the stem of the element name and end in -*ide*. For example, two elements in Group 7A are fluorine and chlorine. The anions for these nonmetals are the fluor*ide* ion (F^-) and chlor*ide* ion (Cl^-). Anions of nonmetals in Group 6A have a 2− charge ($6 - 8 = -2$). Group 6A elements, oxygen and sulfur, form the ox*ide* anion (O^{2-}) and the sulf*ide* anion (S^{2-}), respectively. The three nonmetals in Group 5A—nitrogen, phosphorus, and arsenic—can form anions with a 3− charge ($5 - 8 = -3$). These have the symbols N^{3-}, P^{3-}, and As^{3-} and are called, respectively, nitride ion, phosphide ion, and arsenide ion. Figure 9.2 shows the Group A elements that form anions. Table 9.1 summarizes the ionic charges of representative elements that can be obtained from the periodic table.

The majority of the elements in the two remaining representative groups, 4A and 8A, usually do not form ions.

 What is the name of the anion N^{3-}?

Ions of Transition Metals The metals of Groups 1A, 2A, and 3A consistently form cations with charges of 1+, 2+, and 3+, respectively. Many of the transition metals (Groups 1B–8B) form more than one cation with different ionic charges. Some of these are shown in Figure 9.2. 🔑 **The charges of the cations of many transition metal ions must be determined from the number of electrons lost.** For example, the transition metal iron forms two common cations, Fe^{2+} (two electrons lost) and Fe^{3+} (three electrons lost). Cations of tin and lead, the two metals in Group 4A, can also have more than one charge. Table 9.2 lists symbols for common ions of many of the metals that form more than one ion. Two methods are used to name these ions. The preferred method is called the Stock system. In the Stock system, a Roman numeral in parentheses is placed after the name of the element to indicate the numerical value of the charge. Table 9.2 shows that the cation Fe^{2+} is named iron(II) ion. Note that no space is left between the element name and the Roman numeral in parentheses. The name for Fe^{2+} is read "iron two ion." The Fe^{3+} ion is named iron(III) ion and is read "iron three ion." Colorful solutions of the transition metal ions Co^{3+}, Cr^{3+}, Fe^{3+}, Ni^{2+}, and Mn^{2+} are shown in Figure 9.3.

An older, less useful method for naming these cations uses a root word with different suffixes at the end of the word. The older, or classical, name of the element is used to form the root name for the element. For example, *ferrum* is Latin for iron, so *ferr-* is the root name for iron. The suffix *-ous* is used to name the cation with the lower of the two ionic charges. The suffix *-ic* is used with the higher of the two ionic charges. Using this system, Fe^{2+} is the ferrous ion, and Fe^{3+} is the ferric ion, as shown in Table 9.2. Notice that you can usually identify an element from what may be an unfamiliar classical name by looking for the element's symbol in the name. Thus *fer*-rous (Fe) is iron; *cu*prous (Cu) is copper; and *sta*nnous (Sn) is tin. A major disadvantage of using classical names for ions is that they do not tell you the actual charge of the ion. A classical name tells you only that the cation has either the smaller (*-ous*) or the larger (*-ic*) charge of the pair of possible ions for that element.

A few transition metals have only one ionic charge. The names of these cations do not have a Roman numeral. These exceptions include silver, with cations that have a 1+ charge (Ag^+), as well as cadmium and zinc, with cations that have a 2+ charge (Cd^{2+} and Zn^{2+}). As Figure 9.4 shows, many transition metal compounds are colored and can be used as pigments. Pigments are compounds having intense colors that can be used to color other materials. For example, compounds of chromium are pigments used to make yellow, orange, red, or green paints. Various cadmium compounds range in color from yellow to red and maroon. Prussian blue is an important pigment composed of the transition element iron combined with carbon, hydrogen, and nitrogen.

Figure 9.4 Many transition metals form brightly colored compounds that are used in making artists' paints.

Table 9.2

Symbols and Names of Common Metal Ions with More than One Ionic Charge

Symbol	Stock name	Classical name
Cu^+	Copper(I) ion	Cuprous ion
Cu^{2+}	Copper(II) ion	Cupric ion
Fe^{2+}	Iron(II) ion	Ferrous ion
Fe^{3+}	Iron(III) ion	Ferric ion
*Hg_2^{2+}	Mercury(I) ion	Mercurous ion
Hg^{2+}	Mercury(II) ion	Mercuric ion
Pb^{2+}	Lead(II) ion	Plumbous ion
Pb^{4+}	Lead(IV) ion	Plumbic ion
Sn^{2+}	Tin(II) ion	Stannous ion
Sn^{4+}	Tin(IV) ion	Stannic ion
Cr^{2+}	Chromium(II) ion	Chromous ion
Cr^{3+}	Chromium(III) ion	Chromic ion
Mn^{2+}	Manganese(II) ion	Manganous ion
Mn^{3+}	Manganese(III) ion	Manganic ion
Co^{2+}	Cobalt(II) ion	Cobaltous ion
Co^{3+}	Cobalt(III) ion	Cobaltic ion

*A diatomic elemental ion.

Careers *in* Chemistry

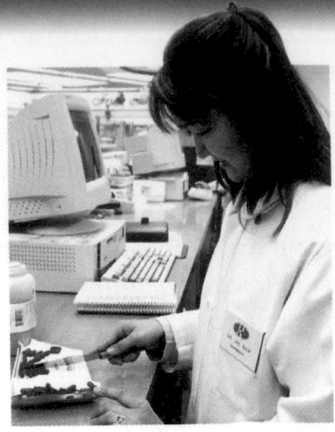

Pharmacist

Doctors provide written instructions to pharmacists about medicines they wish to have dispensed to their patients. It is the responsibility of the pharmacist to prepare the medicine and to advise the patient about possible side effects. Pharmacists also make sure that physicians have not prescribed a medicine or dosage that could harm the patient.

A person with some knowledge of chemistry and biology could become a pharmacist's assistant with on-the-job training. Advancement to the position of pharmacist requires a college degree in pharmacy. This degree includes the study of chemistry, biology, mathematics, and statistics. Pharmacists must also learn about the biological effects of drugs and drug interactions (pharmacology). To obtain a license to dispense drugs, pharmacists are required to pass a state test and must work for a specified period of time under the supervision of another pharmacist.

Go Online
—PHSchool.com

For: Careers in Chemistry
Visit: PHSchool.com
Web Code: cdb-1091

CONCEPTUAL PROBLEM 9.1

Classifying and Naming Cations and Anions

Write the symbol for the ion formed by each element. Classify the ions as cations or anions and name the ion. Potassium and iodine combine to form potassium iodide, an additive to table salt that protects the thyroid gland.

  a. potassium   **b.** iodine   **c.** sulfur   **d.** lead, 4 electrons lost

1 **Analyze** *Identify the relevant concepts.*

  a.–d. Use the periodic table or the electrons lost to write the symbol for the ion. Ions with positive charges are cations; ions with negative charges are anions. Apply the rules for naming cations and anions. The names of nonmetallic anions end in *-ide*. Metallic cations take the name of the metal. If the metal ion can have more than one ionic charge, use a Roman numeral in the Stock name or use the classical name with a suffix.

2 **Solve** *Apply concepts to this situation.*

  a. K^+: cation, potassium ion
  b. I^-: anion, iodide ion
  c. S^{2-}: anion, sulfide ion
  d. Pb^{4+}: cation, lead(IV) or plumbic ion

The ions formed by metals are cations and the ions formed by nonmetals are anions. The rules for naming have been correctly applied.

Practice Problems

1. Name the ions formed by these elements and classify them as anions or cations.
  a. selenium   **b.** barium   **c.** phosphorus

2. How many electrons were lost or gained to form these ions?
  a. Fe^{3+} **b.** O^{2-} **c.** Cu^+

Textbook

Problem-Solving 9.1 Solve Problem 1 with the help of an interactive guided tutorial.

— with **ChemASAP**

Ammonium ion
(NH_4^+)

Nitrate ion
(NO_3^-)

Sulfate ion
(SO_4^{2-})

Phosphate ion
(PO_4^{3-})

Figure 9.5 These molecular models show the arrangement of atoms in four common polyatomic ions. **Interpreting Diagrams** *How does the ammonium ion differ from the other three?*

Polyatomic Ions

Some ions, called **polyatomic ions,** are composed of more than one atom. The sulfate anion consists of one sulfur atom and four oxygen atoms. These five atoms together comprise a single anion with an overall 2− charge. The formula is written SO_4^{2-}. Polyatomic ions, such as the sulfate ion, are tightly bound groups of atoms that behave as a unit and carry a charge. You can see the structures of four common polyatomic ions in Figure 9.5.

The names and formulas of some common polyatomic ions are shown in Table 9.3 grouped according to their charges. 🔑 **The names of most polyatomic anions end in *-ite* or *-ate.*** For example, notice the endings of the names of the hypochlor*ite* ion (ClO^-) and the hydrogen carbon*ate* ion (HCO_3^-). Also notice that three important ions have different endings. The positively charged ammonium cation (NH_4^+) ends in *-ium*, and the cyanide ion (CN^-) and the hydroxide ion (OH^-) end in *-ide*. Use Table 9.3 as a reference until you have memorized its contents.

Sometimes the same two or three elements combine in different ratios to form different polyatomic ions. You can see examples in Table 9.3. Look for pairs of ions for which there is both an *-ite* and an *-ate* ending, for example, sulfite and sulfate. In the list below, examine the charge on each ion in the pair. Note the number of oxygen atoms and the endings on each name. You should be able to discern a pattern in the naming convention.

-ite	*-ate*
SO_3^{2-}, sulfite	SO_4^{2-}, sulfate
NO_2^-, nitrite	NO_3^-, nitrate
ClO_2^-, chlorite	ClO_3^-, chlorate

The charge on each polyatomic ion in a given pair is the same. The *-ite* ending indicates one less oxygen atom than the *-ate* ending. However, the ending does not tell you the actual number of oxygen atoms in the ion. For example, the nitrite ion has two oxygen atoms and the sulfite ion has three oxygen atoms. All anions with names ending in *-ite* or *-ate* contain oxygen.

✅**Checkpoint** *What is the formula for the hydrogen sulfite polyatomic ion?*

Table 9.3	
Common Polyatomic Ions	
Formula	**Name**
Charge = 1−	
$H_2PO_4^-$	Dihydrogen phosphate
$C_2H_3O_2^-$	Acetate
HSO_3^-	Hydrogen sulfite
HSO_4^-	Hydrogen sulfate
HCO_3^-	Hydrogen carbonate
NO_2^-	Nitrite
NO_3^-	Nitrate
CN^-	Cyanide
OH^-	Hydroxide
MnO_4^-	Permanganate
ClO^-	Hypochlorite
ClO_2^-	Chlorite
ClO_3^-	Chlorate
ClO_4^-	Perchlorate
Charge = 2−	
HPO_4^{2-}	Hydrogen phosphate
$C_2O_4^{2-}$	Oxalate
SO_3^{2-}	Sulfite
SO_4^{2-}	Sulfate
CO_3^{2-}	Carbonate
CrO_4^{2-}	Chromate
$Cr_2O_7^{2-}$	Dichromate
SiO_3^{2-}	Silicate
Charge = 3−	
PO_3^{3-}	Phosphite
PO_4^{3-}	Phosphate
Charge = 1+	
NH_4^+	Ammonium

a   b   c

Figure 9.6 Hydrogen-containing polyatomic ions are part of many compounds that affect your daily life. ⓐ Sodium hydrogen carbonate, which contains the HCO_3^- ion, can relieve an upset stomach. ⓑ The presence of dissolved HCO_3^-, HPO_4^{2-}, and $H_2PO_4^-$ ions in your blood is critical for your health. ⓒ Crop dusters spread fertilizers containing HPO_4^{2-} and $H_2PO_4^-$ ions.

When the formula for a polyatomic ion begins with H (hydrogen), you can think of the H as representing a hydrogen ion (H^+) combined with another polyatomic ion. For example, HCO_3^- is a combination of H^+ and CO_3^{2-}. Note that the charge on the new ion is the algebraic sum of the ionic charges.

$$H^+ + CO_3^{2-} \longrightarrow HCO_3^-$$
carbonate   hydrogen carbonate

$$H^+ + PO_4^{3-} \longrightarrow HPO_4^{2-}$$
phosphate   hydrogen phosphate

$$H^+ + HPO_4^{2-} \longrightarrow H_2PO_4^-$$
hydrogen phosphate   dihydrogen phosphate

The hydrogen carbonate anion (HCO_3^-), the hydrogen phosphate anion (HPO_4^{2-}), and the dihydrogen phosphate anion ($H_2PO_4^-$) are essential components of living systems. In contrast, the cyanide ion (CN^-) is extremely poisonous to living systems because it blocks a cell's means of producing energy. Figure 9.6 shows some uses for compounds with hydrogen-containing polyatomic ions.

9.1 Section Assessment

3. 🔑 **Key Concept** Explain how the charges of Group A metal and nonmetal ions are related to their positions in the periodic table.

4. 🔑 **Key Concept** How are the charges of some transition metal ions determined?

5. 🔑 **Key Concept** What are the usual endings for the names of polyatomic ions?

6. What are the charges on ions of Group 1A, Group 3A (aluminum), and Group 5A?

7. How does a polyatomic anion differ from a monatomic anion?

8. Write the symbol for the ion of each element. Classify the ion as an anion or a cation, and name the ion.
   a. potassium   **b.** oxygen
   c. tin (2 electrons lost)   **d.** bromine
   e. beryllium   **f.** cobalt (3 electrons lost)

9. Write the symbol or formula (including charge) for each of the following ions.
   a. ammonium ion   **b.** tin(II) ion
   c. chromate ion   **d.** nitrate ion

Writing ▸ Activity

Essay Sodium ions (Na^+) and potassium ions (K^+) are needed for the human body to function. Research where these ions are most likely to be found in the body and the roles they play. Write a brief essay describing your findings.

Assessment 9.1 Test yourself on the concepts in Section 9.1.

with **ChemASAP**

Plasma TV

Today, a TV can be mounted on the wall just as if it were a picture in a frame. The cathode ray tube (CRT), which bulges from the back of a conventional TV, has been replaced by plasma. Plasma is a gaseous mixture of high-energy electrons and ions that activates tiny fluorescent tubes in chambers called pixels. A TV picture is created by hundreds of thousands of pixels, each contributing a single point of colored light. **Inferring *Explain why you don't see the points of light.***

How it works A computer controls the output of each pixel individually. Varying the electrical current flowing through the cells changes the intensity of the phosphor color in any cell to create millions of colors.

5 in.

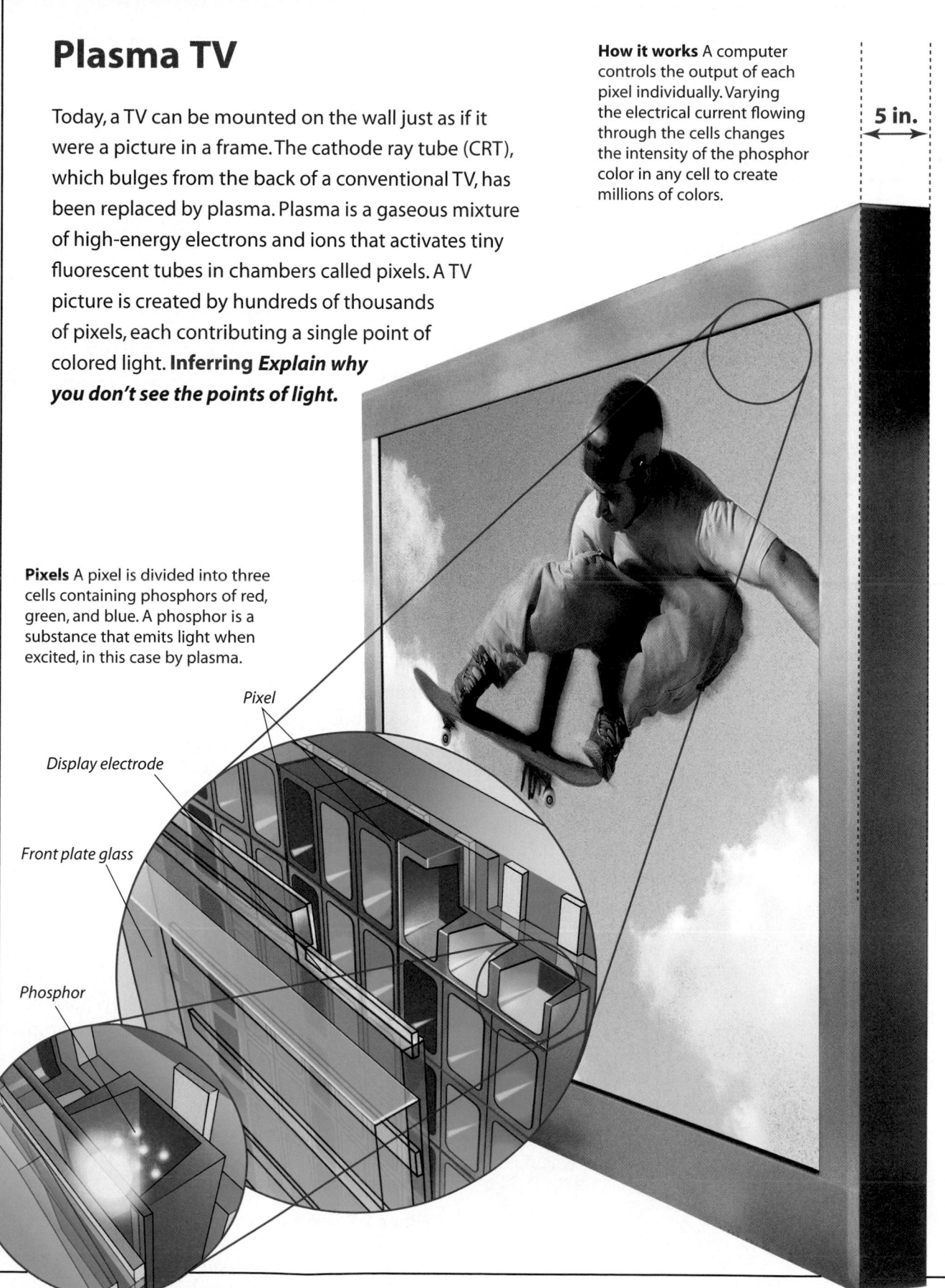

Pixels A pixel is divided into three cells containing phosphors of red, green, and blue. A phosphor is a substance that emits light when excited, in this case by plasma.

Pixel

Display electrode

Front plate glass

Phosphor

New York Standards: 3.1cc

Guide for Reading

 Key Concepts

- How are the names of binary ionic compounds determined?
- How do you write the formulas for binary ionic compounds?
- How do you write the formulas and names of compounds containing polyatomic ions?

Vocabulary

binary compound

Reading Strategy

Predicting Before you read, preview the section by reading the Key Concepts, the headings, and the boldfaced sentences. Predict how you would write the formulas for binary ionic compounds. After you have read the section, check the accuracy of your prediction.

Connecting to Your World At festivals throughout the summer, contestants compete for blue ribbons for the best barbecue. Some cooks say the recipe for their barbecue sauce is the key to winning and they may hint at a secret ingredient. The recipe is the formula for the sauce—a complete list of ingredients and their proportions. With the recipe, anyone could reproduce a sauce, so a cook is likely to keep a prize-winning recipe a closely guarded secret. Chemistry also uses formulas, but without any secrets. Once you know the rules, you can write the formula for any chemical compound. In this section, you will learn how to write the formulas for ionic compounds.

Binary Ionic Compounds

In the days before the science of chemistry developed, the person who discovered a new compound often named it anything he or she wished. It was not uncommon for the name to describe some property of the substance or its source. For example, a common name for potassium carbonate (K_2CO_3) is *potash*. The name evolved because the compound was obtained by boiling wood ashes in iron pots. Baking soda ($NaHCO_3$) is added to batter to make cakes rise. Plaster of paris ($CaSO_4 \cdot 2H_2O$) is the name for a substance used in wallboard and to make face masks like those shown in Figure 9.7. Gypsum and lye are other common names of chemical compounds. Unfortunately, such names do not tell you anything about the chemical composition of a compound or give you any indication about how it is related to other compounds.

The French chemist Antoine-Laurent Lavoisier (1743–1794) determined the composition of many compounds in his experiments to show how chemical compounds form. As more and more compounds were identified, Lavoisier recognized that it was becoming impossible to memorize all the unrelated names of the compounds. He worked with other chemists to develop a systematic method for naming chemical compounds. Their work is the basis for naming compounds today.

Figure 9.7 These masks are made of an ionic compound with the common name *plaster of paris* ($CaSO_4 \cdot 2H_2O$). Plaster of paris is also used in wallboard.

Naming Binary Ionic Compounds A **binary compound** is composed of two elements and can be either ionic or molecular. If you know the formula for a binary ionic compound, you can write its name. First you must verify that the compound is composed of a monatomic metallic cation and a monatomic nonmetallic anion. The compound Cs_2O is composed of the metal cesium and the nonmetal oxygen. Both cesium and oxygen are Group A elements, so each ion has only one charge. 🔑 **To name any binary ionic compound, place the cation name first, followed by the anion name.** The name of Cs_2O, then, is cesium oxide. The name of NaBr is sodium bromide and the name of SrF_2 is strontium fluoride. But suppose you want to name the binary ionic compound CuO. Following the rule above, you would name this compound copper oxide. However, the name *copper oxide* is incomplete. Recall that copper commonly forms two cations: Cu^+ and Cu^{2+}. The names of these ions are copper(I) ion and copper(II) ion, respectively. How can you tell which of these cations forms the compound CuO? Working backward will help. The formula indicates that the copper cation and the oxide anion combine in a 1:1 ratio. You know that the oxide anion always has a 2− charge. Therefore, the charge of the copper cation must be 2+ in order to balance the 2− charge. The compound CuO must be copper(II) oxide. The formula for copper(I) oxide is Cu_2O.

Table 9.2 lists the symbols and names of the common metal ions that form more than one ion. Recall that the charges of monatomic anions can be determined from the periodic table; those of polyatomic anions are shown in Table 9.3. Using these sources, you can write the names of SnF_2 and SnS_2. Tin (Sn) forms cations with 2+ and 4+ charges. Fluorine is a Group 7A element, so the charge of the fluoride ion is 1−. In SnF_2, the ratio of cation to anion is 1:2. Therefore, the charge of the tin cation must be 2+ to balance the combined 2− charge of two fluoride ions. The name of SnF_2 is tin(II) fluoride or stannous fluoride. However, the name of SnS_2 is not tin(II) sulfide. Sulfur is a Group 6A element, so its charge is 2−. The charge of the tin cation must be 4+ to balance the combined charges of two sulfur anions. Thus the name of SnS_2 is tin(IV) sulfide or stannic sulfide. Figure 9.8 shows examples of uses of stannous fluoride and stannic sulfide.

✓ **Checkpoint**) *What are the charges of the two ions of tin?*

Word *Origins*
Binary comes from the Latin word *bini* meaning "two by two" or "twofold." Binary compounds consist of two elements. **Predict what a binary star might be and then check your prediction in the dictionary.**

Figure 9.8 Tin(II) fluoride and tin(IV) sulfide have different compositions and uses. ⓐ Tin(II) fluoride is added to toothpastes to prevent cavities. ⓑ Tin(IV) sulfide is used in glazes for porcelain fixtures and dishes. **Inferring** *What are the charges on the tin ions in the two compounds?*

Figure 9.9 In the process for making steel, iron is extracted from hematite, an ore containing iron(III) oxide. **Applying Concepts** *What is the formula for iron(III) oxide?*

For: Links on Ionic Compounds
Visit: www.SciLinks.org
Web Code: cdn-1092

Writing Formulas for Binary Ionic Compounds If you know the name of a binary ionic compound, you can write its formula. ◉ **Write the symbol of the cation and then the anion. Add whatever subscripts are needed to balance the charges.** The positive charge of the cation must balance the negative charge of the anion so that the net ionic charge of the formula is zero. The ionic compound potassium chloride is composed of potassium cations (K^+) and chloride anions (Cl^-), so potassium chloride is a binary ionic compound. The charge of each K^+ cation is balanced by the charge of each Cl^- anion, so in potassium chloride, the potassium and chloride ions combine in a 1:1 ratio. Thus the formula for potassium chloride is KCl. The net ionic charge of the formula unit is zero.

The binary ionic compound calcium bromide is composed of calcium cations (Ca^{2+}) and bromide anions (Br^-). The two ions do not have equal numerical charges. Thus each calcium ion with its 2+ charge must combine with (or be balanced by) two bromide ions, each with a 1− charge. That means that the ions must combine in a 1:2 ratio, so the formula for calcium bromide is $CaBr_2$. The net ionic charge of the formula unit is zero.

Figure 9.9 shows one step in the process of making steel from iron ore. Hematite, a common ore of iron, contains iron(III) oxide. What is the formula for this compound? Recall that a Roman numeral in the name of an ion shows the charge of the metal ion. Thus iron(III) oxide contains Fe^{3+} cations combined with oxide anions (O^{2-}). How can you balance a 3+ charge and a 2− charge? You must find the least common multiple of the charges, which is 6. Iron's three charges taken two times equals six ($3 \times 2 = 6$). Oxygen's two charges taken three times also equals six. Thus two Fe^{3+} cations (a 6+ charge) will balance three O^{2-} anions (a 6− charge). The balanced formula, then, is Fe_2O_3.

Another approach to writing a balanced formula for a compound is to use the crisscross method. In this method, the numerical value of the charge of each ion is crossed over and becomes the subscript for the other ion. Notice that the signs of the charges are dropped.

$$\text{Fe}_2\text{O}_3$$
$$2(3+) + 3(2-) = 0$$

The formula is correct because the overall charge of the formula is zero and the subscripts are in the lowest whole number ratio.

Textbook

Simulation 9 Simulate combining ions and deriving the chemical formulas for several ionic compounds.

— with **ChemASAP**

If you use the crisscross method to write the formula for some compounds such as calcium sulfide (Ca^{2+} and S^{2-}), you will obtain the result Ca_2S_2. The 2:2 ratio of calcium and sulfide ions is not the lowest whole number ratio. The formula for calcium sulfide is CaS.

Ca_2S_2 reduces to CaS

$$1(2+) + 1(2-) = 0$$

Of course, if the magnitudes of the charges of the cation and anion are the same, as they are in this case, the ions combine in a 1:1 ratio and the charges are balanced.

✓ Checkpoint   *Explain why the formula CaS is correct.*

CONCEPTUAL PROBLEM 9.2

Writing Formulas for Binary Ionic Compounds

Write formulas for these binary ionic compounds.
a. copper(II) sulfide, shown in the photo
b. potassium nitride

1 **Analyze** *Identify the relevant concepts.*
Binary ionic compounds are composed of a monatomic cation and a monatomic anion. The ionic charges in an ionic compound must balance (add up to zero), and the ions must be in the lowest whole number ratio. The symbol for the cation appears first in the formula for the compound.

2 **Solve** *Apply concepts to this situation.*
Write the symbol and charge for each ion in each compound.
a. Cu^{2+} and S^{2-} **b.** K^+ and N^{3-}

Balance the formula using appropriate subscripts.
a.

CuS

b.

K_3N

The ions are in the lowest whole number ratio, and the net ionic charge is zero:
$$1(2+) + 1(2-) = 0 \text{ and } 3(1+) + 1(3-) = 0.$$

Practice Problems

10. Write formulas for compounds formed from these pairs of ions.
   a. Ba^{2+}, S^{2-} **b.** Li^+, O^{2-}
   c. Ca^{2+}, N^{3-} **d.** Cu^{2+}, I^-

11. Write formulas for these compounds.
   a. sodium iodide   **b.** stannous chloride
   c. potassium sulfide   **d.** calcium iodide

Interactive Textbook

Problem-Solving 9.11 Solve Problem 11 with the help of an interactive guided tutorial.

— with **ChemASAP**

Compounds with Polyatomic Ions

The pearl and the oyster shell shown in Figure 9.10 are both made of calcium carbonate ($CaCO_3$). Calcium carbonate is obviously not a binary compound because it contains more than two elements. Remember that an *-ate* or *-ite* ending on the name of a compound indicates that the compound contains a polyatomic anion that includes oxygen. This compound contains one monatomic ion (Ca^{2+}) and one polyatomic ion (CO_3^{2-}). Figure 9.10 also shows a typical automobile battery called a lead storage battery. The energy-producing reaction inside the battery uses the ionic compound lead(II) sulfate ($PbSO_4$), which consists of the monatomic ion Pb^{2+} and the polyatomic ion SO_4^{2-}. The fertilizer mixture also shown in the illustration could have been produced from such compounds as potassium hydrogen phosphate (K_2HPO_4), potassium sulfate (K_2SO_4), or sodium nitrate ($NaNO_3$). Each contains a polyatomic anion. How would you write the formula for an ionic compound with a polyatomic ion? You would do what you did for binary ionic compounds. **Write the symbol for the cation followed by the formula for the polyatomic ion and balance the charges.** For example, calcium nitrate is composed of a calcium cation (Ca^{2+}) and a polyatomic nitrate anion (NO_3^-). In calcium nitrate, two nitrate anions, each with a 1− charge, are needed to balance the 2+ charge of each calcium cation.

$$Ca(NO_3)_2$$
$$1(2+) + 2(1-) = 0$$

The charge is balanced and the ions are in the lowest whole number ratio, so the formula is correct. Parentheses are used around the nitrate ion in the formula because more than one nitrate anion is needed. The subscript 2 that follows the parentheses shows that the compound contains two nitrate anions. Use parentheses to set off the polyatomic ion in a formula only when the compound contains more than one polyatomic ion. The formula for strontium sulfate, $SrSO_4$, has no parentheses because one polyatomic sulfate anion balances the charge of the strontium cation.

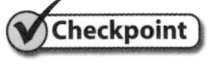 **Checkpoint** *When are parentheses used in a formula containing a polyatomic ion?*

Figure 9.10 Some examples of ionic compounds containing polyatomic ions are shown. **ⓐ** Oysters produce calcium carbonate to form their shells and sometimes pearls. **ⓑ** Lead(II) sulfate is an important component of an automobile battery. **ⓒ** Compounds such as ammonium sulfate or ammonium phosphate are common fertilizers.

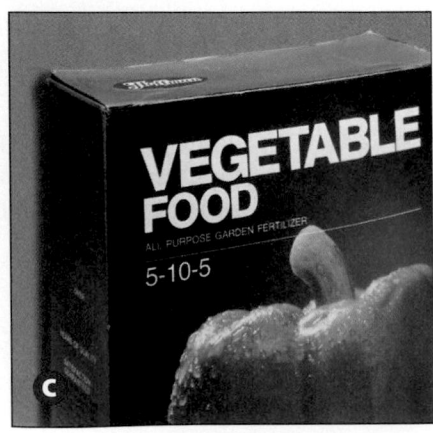

Lithium carbonate is a compound composed of lithium cations (Li^+) and polyatomic carbonate anions (CO_3^{2-}).

$$Li_2CO_3$$

In lithium carbonate, two lithium cations, each with a 1+ charge, are needed to balance the 2– charge of one carbonate anion. Parentheses are not needed to set off the polyatomic carbonate anion. Lithium carbonate can be prescribed for patients who have mood disorders, such as manic-depressive or bipolar disorder. A person with bipolar disorder experiences distressing mood swings, from elation to depression and back again. The exact mechanism is not known, but lithium ions may exert a mood-stabilizing effect on neurotransmission. Neurotransmission is the process by which "messages" are sent and received between nerve cells, including those in the brain.

CONCEPTUAL PROBLEM 9.3

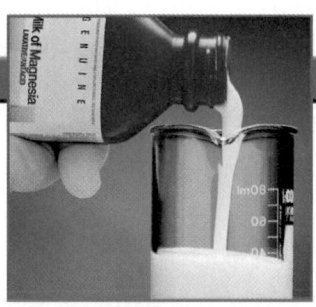

Writing Formulas for Compounds with Polyatomic Ions

What are the formulas for these ionic compounds?
a. magnesium hydroxide, shown in the photo as milk of magnesia
b. potassium sulfate

1 **Analyze** *Identify the relevant concepts.*
Write the formula for each ion in the order listed in the name. Use subscripts to balance the charges. If more than one polyatomic ion is needed to balance a formula, place the polyatomic ion formula in parentheses, followed by a subscript showing the number needed.

2 **Solve** *Apply concepts to this situation.*
a.

$$Mg(OH)_2$$

Two hydroxide anions with 1– charges are needed to balance the 2+ charge on one magnesium cation. The formula for magnesium hydroxide must make use of parentheses.

b.

$$K_2SO_4$$

Two potassium cations with 1+ charges are needed to balance the 2– charge on one sulfate anion. The formula for potassium sulfate is K_2SO_4.

Practice Problems

12. Write formulas for compounds formed from these pairs of ions.
   a. NH_4^+, SO_3^{2-}
   b. calcium ion, phosphate ion

13. Write formulas for these compounds.
   a. lithium hydrogen sulfate
   b. chromium(III) nitrite

interactive
Textbook
Problem-Solving 9.12 Solve Problem 12 with the help of an interactive guided tutorial.
—— with **ChemASAP**

Naming Compounds with Polyatomic Ions You have learned to write formulas for compounds containing polyatomic ions when you were given their names. Now, if you were given the formulas for these compounds, could you name them? When naming compounds containing polyatomic ions, follow these guidelines. First, recognize that the compound contains a polyatomic ion. If the ion is unfamiliar, find its name in Table 9.3. How would you name the compound LiCN? You could easily think that this compound is composed of individual atoms of lithium, carbon, and nitrogen. But you know that lithium is a Group 1A element and that this group forms 1+ ions. In addition, carbon is a Group 4A element that does not form a monatomic ion. From this you might suspect that the carbon and nitrogen atoms are part of a polyatomic ion with a 1− charge. Table 9.3 confirms your conclusion and tells you that the ion's name is cyanide ion. ⚷ **To name a compound containing a polyatomic ion, state the cation first and then the anion just as you did in naming binary ionic compounds.** The name of LiCN is lithium cyanide.

The compound NaClO is used as a bleach and a disinfectant for swimming pools, as shown in Figure 9.11. The metallic cation in this compound is sodium (Na^+), a Group IA element that forms 1+ cations. The polyatomic ion must be ClO^-. This ion is called hypochlorite ion, so the name for NaClO is sodium hypochlorite.

Some ionic compounds containing polyatomic ions do not include a metal cation. Instead, the cation may be the polyatomic ammonium ion (NH_4^+). What is the name of $(NH_4)_2C_2O_4$? The ammonium cation has a charge of 1+. The anion must have a charge of 2− to balance the combined 2+ charge of two ammonium ions. Table 9.3 shows that the name of the anion $C_2O_4^{2-}$ is oxalate ion, so $(NH_4)_2C_2O_4$ is named ammonium oxalate.

Figure 9.11 Sodium hypochlorite (NaClO) is often added to the water in swimming pools to keep bacteria at a safe level.

9.2 Section Assessment

14. ⚷ **Key Concept** Describe how to determine the names of binary ionic compounds.

15. ⚷ **Key Concept** Describe how to write the formulas for binary ionic compounds.

16. ⚷ **Key Concept** How do you write the formulas and the names of compounds with polyatomic ions?

17. Write the formula for these binary compounds.
   a. beryllium chloride
   b. cesium sulfide
   c. sodium iodide
   d. strontium oxide

18. Write the formula for these compounds containing polyatomic ions.
   a. chromium(III) nitrite
   b. sodium perchlorate
   c. magnesium hydrogen carbonate
   d. calcium acetate

19. Identify any incorrect formulas. Explain your answer.
   a. $Mg_2(SO_4)_3$ **b.** Rb_3As
   c. $BeCl_3$ **d.** NaF

Elements ▶ **Handbook**

Successful treatment of bipolar disorder often involves the use of lithium carbonate. Refer to page R9 to read more about this disorder. Write a short report summarizing what you learn.

ℹ️ **interactive Textbook**

Assessment 9.2 Test yourself on the concepts in Section 9.2.

—— with **ChemASAP**

Small-Scale LAB

Names and Formulas for Ionic Compounds

Purpose
To observe the formation of compounds, and to write their names and formulas.

Materials
- pencil
- paper
- ruler
- reaction surface
- spatula
- chemicals shown in Figure A

Procedure
On separate sheets of paper, draw two grids similar to Figure A. Make each square 2 cm on each side. Draw black Xs on one of the grids. Use the other grid as a data table to record your observations. Place a reaction surface over the grid with black Xs and add the chemicals as shown in Figure A.

Analyze
Using your experimental data, record the answers to the following questions below your data table.

1. Describe each precipitate (solid product) that forms. Use terms such as milky, grainy, cloudy, or gelatinous. Which mixture(s) did not form a precipitate?

2. Write the formulas and names of the chemical compounds produced in the mixings.

You're The Chemist
The following small-scale activities allow you to develop your own procedures and analyze the results.

1. **Analyze It!** Repeat the experiment, using the chemicals in Figure B. Identify the precipitates, write their formulas, and name them.

2. **Explain It!** In ionic equations, the precipitate is written to the right of an arrow, and the ions that produced it are written to the left. Write ionic equations for the precipitates formed from the reactions related to Figure B. For example:

$$2Ag^+ + CO_3^{2-} \longrightarrow Ag_2CO_3$$

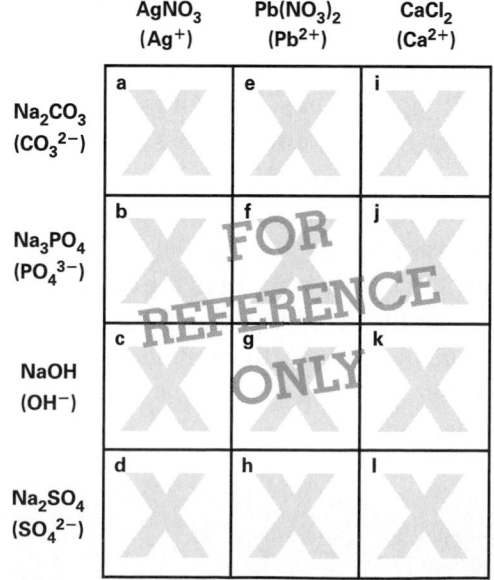

	$AgNO_3$ (Ag^+)	$Pb(NO_3)_2$ (Pb^{2+})	$CaCl_2$ (Ca^{2+})
Na_2CO_3 (CO_3^{2-})	a	e	i
Na_3PO_4 (PO_4^{3-})	b	f	j
NaOH (OH^-)	c	g	k
Na_2SO_4 (SO_4^{2-})	d	h	l

Figure A

	$FeCl_3$ (Fe^{3+})	$MgSO_4$ (Mg^{2+})	$CuSO_4$ (Cu^{2+})
Na_2CO_3 (CO_3^{2-})	a	e	i
Na_3PO_4 (PO_4^{3-})	b	f	j
NaOH (OH^-)	c	g	k
Na_2SO_4 (SO_4^{2-})	d	h	l

Figure B

Naming and Writing Formulas for Molecular Compounds

 New York Standards: 3.1cc

Guide for Reading

 Key Concepts

- What does a prefix in the name of a binary molecular compound tell you about the compound's composition?
- How do you write the formula for a binary molecular compound?

Reading Strategy

Monitoring Your Understanding
Before you read, preview the Key Concepts, the headings, the bold-faced sentences, and the visuals. List two things you expect to learn. After reading, state what you learned about each item you listed.

Connecting to Your World

Gold was one of the first metals to attract human attention. When gold was discovered in California in the late 1840s, people from all over the world came to find it and make their fortune. Today, gold is still greatly prized and valued. Whereas one milligram of gold is worth only about one cent, one kilogram of gold is worth approximately \$12,500. In this case, using the correct prefix (*milli-* or *kilo-*) makes quite a difference! Prefixes are important in chemistry, too. In this section, you will learn how prefixes in the name of a binary molecular compound tell you its composition.

Naming Binary Molecular Compounds

Recall that binary ionic compounds are composed of the ions of two elements, a metal and a nonmetal. Binary molecular compounds are also composed of two elements, but both elements are nonmetals and they are not ions. These differences affect the naming of these compounds and their formulas. Binary molecular compounds are composed of molecules, not ions, so ionic charges cannot be used to write formulas or to name them. In addition, when two nonmetallic elements combine, they often do so in more than one way. For example, the elements carbon and oxygen combine to form two invisible gaseous compounds, CO and CO_2, which are illustrated in Figure 9.12. How would you name a binary compound formed by the combination of carbon and oxygen atoms? It might seem satisfactory to call it carbon oxide. However, the two carbon oxides, CO and CO_2, are very different compounds. Sitting in a room with small amounts of the carbon oxide CO_2 in the air would not present any problems. You exhale CO_2 as a product of your body chemistry. Thus it is normally present in the air you breathe. On the other hand, if the same amount of the other carbon oxide, CO, were in the room, you could die of asphyxiation. The binary compound CO is a poisonous gas that interferes with your blood's ability to carry oxygen to body cells. Obviously, a naming system that distinguishes between these two compounds is needed.

a

b

Table 9.4

Prefixes Used in Naming Binary Molecular Compounds									
Prefix	Mono-	Di-	Tri-	Tetra-	Penta-	Hexa-	Hepta-	Octa-	Nona-	Deca-
Number	1	2	3	4	5	6	7	8	9	10

Just as prefixes in the masses of gold samples distinguish between large and small samples, so prefixes in the names of binary molecular compounds help distinguish compounds containing different amounts of the same two elements. **The prefix in the name of a binary molecular compound tells how many atoms of each element are present in each molecule of the compound.** Table 9.4 lists the prefixes used to name binary molecular compounds. According to the table, the prefix *mono-* indicates the presence of one oxygen atom in CO. The prefix *di-* indicates the presence of the two oxygen atoms in CO_2. The two compounds of carbon and oxygen, CO and CO_2, are thus named carbon monoxide and carbon dioxide, respectively. *Laughing gas* is the common name for the gaseous compound dinitrogen monoxide (N_2O), which is used as an anesthetic. When inhaled, N_2O tends to make people laugh. Notice that the second element in the name ends with -*ide*. The names of all binary molecular compounds end in -*ide*. Also note that the vowel at the end of a prefix often is dropped when the name of the element begins with a vowel. For CO, you would write carbon *mon*oxide, not carbon *mono*oxide. If just one atom of the first element is in the formula, omit the prefix *mono-*.

Here are some guidelines for naming binary molecular compounds. First, confirm that the compound is a binary molecular compound—that is, a compound composed of two nonmetals. The name must identify the elements in the molecule and indicate the number of each atom of each element. Name the elements in the order listed in the formula. Use prefixes to indicate the number of each kind of atom. Omit the prefix *mono-* when the formula contains only one atom of the first element in the name. The suffix of the name of the second element is -*ide*. Now, apply these guidelines to naming N_2O. The formula shows that the compound consists of two nonmetals, so it is a binary molecular compound. Two atoms of nitrogen are combined with one atom of oxygen. Thus the prefix of nitrogen is *di-* and the prefix of oxygen is *mono-*. The name of the compound is dinitrogen monoxide. Using the same guidelines, the name of SF_6 is sulfur hexafluoride. Notice that it is not necessary to use the prefix *mono-* before sulfur. What about the compound Cl_2O_8? This binary molecular compound consists of two chlorine atoms (prefix *di-*) and eight oxygen atoms (prefix *octa-*). The name is dichlorine octoxide.

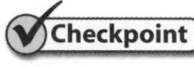 **Checkpoint** *What suffix ends the names of all binary molecular compounds?*

Go Online
NSTA SC*i*LINKS
For: Links on Carbon Monoxide
Visit: www.SciLinks.org
Web Code: cdn-1093

Figure 9.12 Carbon monoxide and carbon dioxide are two invisible, gaseous compounds of carbon and oxygen. ⓐ Carbon dioxide is a product of respiration. ⓑ Carbon monoxide is a toxic product of incomplete burning, such as occurs in automobile engines and faulty furnaces.

Figure 9.13 A grinding wheel made of silicon carbide (SiC) can shape even the toughest materials. **Inferring** *What causes the sparks?*

Writing Formulas for Binary Molecular Compounds

Suppose you know the name of a molecular compound and want to write the formula. **Use the prefixes in the name to tell you the subscript of each element in the formula. Then write the correct symbols for the two elements with the appropriate subscripts.** A simple example is silicon carbide. Silicon carbide is a hard material like diamond. It is used as an abrasive and for cutting and grinding, as shown in Figure 9.13. The name *silicon carbide* has no prefixes, so the subscripts of silicon and carbon must be one. Thus the formula for silicon carbide is SiC. The name of another binary molecular compound is dinitrogen tetroxide. The prefix *di-* before nitrogen tells you that the compound contains two nitrogen atoms; the prefix *tetra-* tells you that the molecule also contains four oxygen atoms. Thus the formula for dinitrogen tetroxide is N_2O_4.

9.3 Section Assessment

20. **Key Concept** What information do prefixes in the name of a binary molecular compound tell you about the composition of the compound?

21. **Key Concept** Describe how to write the formula of a binary molecular compound.

22. Write the names for these molecular compounds.
   a. NCl_3 **b.** BCl_3 **c.** NI_3
   d. SO_3 **e.** N_2H_4 **f.** N_2O_3

23. Write the formulas or names for these molecular compounds.
   a. CS_2 **b.** carbon tetrabromide
   c. Cl_2O_7 **d.** diphosphorus trioxide

24. Write the formulas for these binary molecular compounds.
   a. phosphorus pentachloride
   b. iodine heptafluoride
   c. chlorine trifluoride
   d. iodine dioxide

25. The name a student gives for the molecular compound $SiCl_4$ is monosilicon trichloride. Is this name correct? Explain.

Connecting **Concepts**

Covalent Bonds In Section 8.1, you learned about covalent bonds. Are the bonds between silicon and chlorine in silicon tetrachloride ($SiCl_4$) single bonds? Justify your answer by drawing an electron dot structure of silicon tetrachloride.

*i*nteractive **Textbook**

Assessment 9.3 Test yourself on the concepts in Section 9.3.
— with **ChemASAP**

Naming and Writing Formulas for Acids and Bases

 New York Standards: 3.1cc, 3.1vv–ww

Some ants can give painful stings when threatened or disturbed. Certain ant species called formicines have poison glands that produce venom containing formic acid. Formicines protect themselves by spraying this venom on their predators. Formic acid can stun or even kill the ants' most common enemies. A formicine attack on a human, however, is much less severe. The contact of formic acid with the skin usually results only in blistering. In this section, you will learn the names and formulas of some important acids such as formic acid.

Guide for Reading

Key Concepts
- What are the three rules for naming acids?
- How are the formulas of acids determined?
- How are bases named?

Vocabulary
acid
base

Reading Strategy
Comparing and Contrasting When you compare and contrast things, you examine how they are alike and how they are different. After you have read this section, list similarities and differences between acids and bases and how they are named.

Naming Acids

Acids are a group of ionic compounds with unique properties. As you will see in Chapter 19, acids can be defined in several ways. For now, it is enough to know that an **acid** is a compound that contains one or more hydrogen atoms and produces hydrogen ions (H^+) when dissolved in water. Acids have various uses, one of which is shown in Figure 9.14. When naming an acid, you can consider the acid to consist of an anion combined with as many hydrogen ions as are needed to make the molecule electrically neutral. Therefore, the chemical formulas of acids are in the general form H_nX where X is a monatomic or polyatomic anion and n is a subscript indicating the number of hydrogen ions that are combined with the anion.

Figure 9.14 To create designs such as this on glass, the glass is first coated with wax and the design is drawn through the wax. When the glass is dipped into hydrofluoric acid (HF), the acid etches (eats away) the glass wherever the wax has been removed.

Table 9.5

Naming Common Acids			
Anion ending	**Example**	**Acid name**	**Example**
-ide	chlor*ide*, Cl^-	*hydro*-(stem)-*ic acid*	*hydro*chlor*ic acid*
-ite	sulf*ite*, SO_3^{2-}	(stem)-*ous acid*	sulfur*ous acid*
-ate	nitr*ate*, NO_3^-	(stem)-*ic acid*	nitr*ic acid*

Go Online

NSTA *SciLinks*

For: Links on Acids
Visit: www.SciLinks.org
Web Code: cdn-1094

Three rules can help you name an acid with the general formula H_nX. Read the rules and the examples carefully. Notice that the naming system depends on the name of the anion. Each of the rules deals with an anion with a different suffix: *-ide*, *-ite*, and *-ic*.

1. ⚷ **When the name of the anion (X) ends in *-ide*, the acid name begins with the prefix *hydro-*. The stem of the anion has the suffix *-ic* and is followed by the word *acid*.** Therefore, HCl(aq) (X = chloride) is named *hydro*chlor*ic acid*. $H_2S(aq)$ (X = sulfide) is named *hydro*sulfur*ic acid*.

2. ⚷ **When the anion name ends in *-ite*, the acid name is the stem of the anion with the suffix *-ous*, followed by the word *acid*.** Thus H_2SO_3 (*aq*) (X = sulfite) is named sulfur*ous acid*.

3. ⚷ **When the anion name ends in *-ate*, the acid name is the stem of the anion with the suffix *-ic* followed by the word *acid*.** Thus $HNO_3(aq)$ (X = nitrate) is named nitr*ic acid*.

The three rules are summarized in Table 9.5. Use the table to help you write acid names until you become an expert.

Writing Formulas for Acids

If you know the name of an acid, you can write its formula. ⚷ **Use the rules for writing the names of acids in reverse to write the formulas for acids.** For example, what is the formula of hydrobromic acid? Following Rule 1, hydrobromic acid (*hydro-* prefix and *-ic* suffix) must be a combination of hydrogen ion (H^+) and bromide ion (Br^-). The formula of hydrobromic acid is HBr. How do you write the formula for phosphorous acid? Using Rule 2, hydrogen ion and phosphite ion (PO_3^{3-}) must be the components of phosphorous acid. The formula of phosphorous acid is H_3PO_3. (*Note:* Do not confuse *phosphorous* with *phosphorus*, the element name.) Finally, what is the formula for formic acid, the defensive weapon of the ants you read about in Connecting to Your World? According to Rule 3, formic acid (*-ic* ending) must be a combination of hydrogen ion (H^+) and form*ate* ion ($HCOO^-$). The formula for formic acid is HCOOH.

Many industrial processes, including steel and fertilizer manufacturing, use acids. In the laboratory, you will regularly use a few common acids such as those listed in Table 9.6. You should become familiar with their names and formulas.

Table 9.6

Common Acids	
Name	**Formula**
Hydrochloric acid	HCl
Sulfuric acid	H_2SO_4
Nitric acid	HNO_3
Acetic acid	CH_3COOH
Phosphoric acid	H_3PO_4
Carbonic acid	H_2CO_3

✓**Checkpoint** *When does an acid name begin with the prefix* **hydro-**?

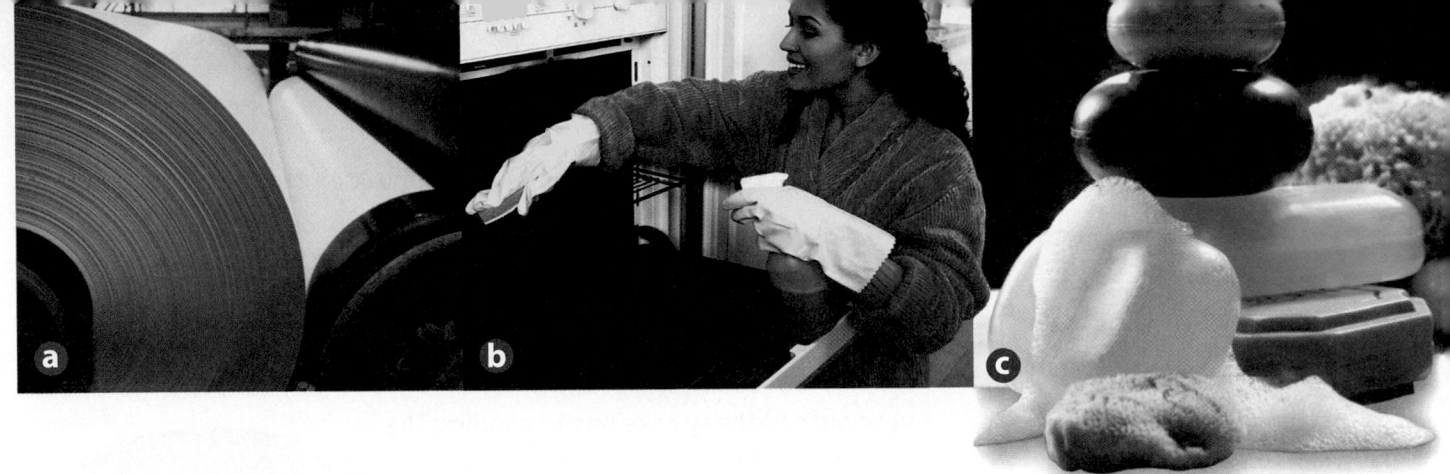

Names and Formulas for Bases

Another group of ionic compounds is the bases. A **base** is an ionic compound that produces hydroxide ions when dissolved in water. 🔑 **Bases are named in the same way as other ionic compounds—the name of the cation is followed by the name of the anion.** For example, sodium hydroxide (NaOH) is a base used in making paper, cleaners, and soap, as shown in Figure 9.15. To write the formulas for bases, write the symbol for the metal cation followed by the formula for the hydroxide ion. Balance the ionic charges just as you do for any ionic compound. For example, aluminum hydroxide consists of the aluminum cation (Al^{3+}) and the hydroxide anion (OH^-). You need three hydroxide ions to balance the 3+ charge of the aluminum cation. Thus the formula for aluminum hydroxide is $Al(OH)_3$. In some bases, the cation is not a metal ion but a polyatomic ion. For example, in ammonium hydroxide (NH_4OH), the cation is NH_4^+.

Figure 9.15 Sodium hydroxide is an important industrial and consumer product. ❶ Recycled paper and wood are digested with NaOH to make pulp in the first step in making paper. ❷ Cleaners containing NaOH cut through heavy grease. ❸ An important use of sodium hydroxide is in making soap. **Inferring** *Why is the woman in the second photo wearing gloves?*

9.4 Section Assessment

26. 🔑 **Key Concept** List the rules for naming acids.

27. 🔑 **Key Concept** How are the formulas for acids determined?

28. 🔑 **Key Concept** How are bases named?

29. Give the names of these acids.
   a. HNO_2 **b.** $HMnO_4$
   c. HCN   **d.** H_2S

30. Write the names of these bases.
   a. LiOH   **b.** $Pb(OH)_2$
   c. $Mg(OH)_2$ **d.** $Al(OH)_3$

31. Identify each compound as an acid or a base.
   a. $Ba(OH)_2$ **b.** $HClO_4$
   c. $Fe(OH)_3$ **d.** KOH

32. Write the formulas for these compounds.
   a. carbonic acid
   b. sulfurous acid
   c. iron(III) hydroxide
   d. strontium hydroxide

33. What element generally appears in the formula of an acid? What ion generally appears in the formula of a base?

> **Writing** ▶ **Activity**
>
> **Report** Investigate the importance of sulfuric acid in the economy. Write a brief report that includes information on the manufacturing process, the annual output, and the variety of ways in which H_2SO_4 is used.

Textbook

Assessment 9.4 Test yourself on the concepts in Section 9.4.

——with **ChemASAP**

New York Standards: 3.1cc, 5.2g

Guide for Reading

🔑 Key Concepts

- What are the two laws that describe how compounds form?
- How do you use a flowchart to write the name of a chemical compound?
- What four guidelines should you follow to write the formula of a chemical compound?

Vocabulary

law of definite proportions
law of multiple proportions

Reading Strategy

Relating Text and Visuals As you read, use Figure 9.20 and Figure 9.22 to help you become thoroughly familiar with writing the names and formulas for chemical compounds.

Water

ⓐ

Hydrogen peroxide

ⓑ

Figure 9.16 Water and hydrogen peroxide contain the same two elements, but they have different properties. ⓐ Water does not bleach dyes. ⓑ Hydrogen peroxide is a bleach.

Connecting to Your World

A birthday cake for a four-year-old has four candles. The ratio of candles to birthday cake is 4:1. A sixteen-year-old's birthday cake has 16 candles. The ratio of candles to cake is also a whole number ratio, 16:1. Is there a whole number ratio between the numbers of candles on one cake at two different birthdays? For the sixteenth and fourth birthdays, the ratio is 16:4 or 4:1. In chemistry, similar relationships exist among the masses of elements as they combine in compounds.

The Laws of Definite and Multiple Proportions

The rules for naming and writing formulas for compounds are possible only because compounds form from the elements in predictable ways. 🔑 **These ways are summed up in two laws: the law of definite proportions and the law of multiple proportions.**

The Law of Definite Proportions A chemical formula tells you, by means of subscripts, the ratio of atoms of each element in the compound. Ratios of atoms can also be expressed as ratios of masses. Magnesium sulfide (MgS) is composed of magnesium cations and sulfide anions. If you could take 100.00 g of magnesium sulfide and break it down into its elements, you will obtain 43.13 g of magnesium and 56.87 g of sulfur. The Mg:S ratio of these masses is 43.13/56.87 or 0.758:1. This mass ratio does not change no matter how the magnesium sulfide is formed or the size of the sample. Magnesium sulfide illustrates the **law of definite proportions,** which states that in samples of any chemical compound, the masses of the elements are always in the same proportions. Because atoms combine in simple whole-number ratios, it follows that their proportions by mass must always be the same.

The Law of Multiple Proportions Figure 9.16 shows two compounds, water (H_2O) and hydrogen peroxide (H_2O_2). Although these compounds are formed by the same two elements, they have different physical and chemical properties. Each compound obeys the law of definite proportions. In every sample of hydrogen peroxide, 16.0 g of oxygen are present for each 1.0 g of hydrogen. The mass ratio of oxygen to hydrogen is always 16:1. In every sample of water, the mass ratio of oxygen to hydrogen is always 8:1. If a sample of hydrogen peroxide has the same mass of hydrogen as a sample of water, the ratio of the mass of oxygen in the two compounds is exactly 2:1.

$$\frac{16 \text{ g O (in } H_2O_2 \text{ sample that has 1 g H)}}{8 \text{ g O (in } H_2O \text{ sample that has 1 g H)}} = \frac{16}{8} = \frac{2}{1} = 2:1$$

Using the results from studies of this kind, John Dalton stated the **law of multiple proportions:** Whenever the same two elements form more than one compound, the different masses of one element that combine with the same mass of the other element are in the ratio of small whole numbers. Figure 9.17 illustrates the law of multiple proportions.

SAMPLE PROBLEM 9.1

Calculating Mass Ratios

Carbon reacts with oxygen to form two compounds. Compound A contains 2.41 g of carbon for each 3.22 g of oxygen. Compound B contains 6.71 g of carbon for each 17.9 g of oxygen. What is the lowest whole number mass ratio of carbon that combines with a given mass of oxygen?

1 Analyze *List the knowns and the unknown.*

Knowns
• Compound A = 2.41 g C and 3.22 g O
• Compound B = 6.71 g C and 17.9 g O

Unknown
• Lowest whole number ratio of carbon per gram of oxygen in the two compounds = ?

Apply the law of multiple proportions to the two compounds. For each compound, find the grams of carbon that combine with 1.00 g of oxygen by dividing the mass of carbon by the mass of oxygen. Then find the ratio of the masses of carbon in the two compounds by dividing the larger value by the smaller. Confirm that the ratio is the lowest whole number ratio.

2 Calculate *Solve for the unknown.*

• Compound A $\quad \dfrac{2.41 \text{ g C}}{3.22 \text{ g O}} = \dfrac{0.748 \text{ g C}}{1.00 \text{ g O}}$

• Compound B $\quad \dfrac{6.71 \text{ g C}}{17.9 \text{ g O}} = \dfrac{0.375 \text{ g C}}{1.00 \text{ g O}}$

Compare the masses of carbon per gram of oxygen in the compounds.

$$\frac{0.748 \text{ g C (in compound A)}}{0.375 \text{ g C (in compound B)}} = \frac{1.99}{1} = \text{roughly } \frac{2}{1} = 2:1$$

The mass ratio of carbon per gram of oxygen in the two compounds is 2:1.

3 Evaluate *Does the result make sense?*

The ratio is a low whole number ratio, as expected. For a given mass of oxygen, compound A contains twice the mass of carbon as compound B.

Practice Problems

34. Lead forms two compounds with oxygen. One contains 2.98 g of lead and 0.461 g of oxygen. The other contains 9.89 g of lead and 0.763 g of oxygen. For a given mass of oxygen, what is the lowest whole number mass ratio of lead in the two compounds?

Compound X

A + **B** = **X**
5g   2g   7g

Compound Y

A + **B** = **Y**
10g   2g   12g

Figure 9.17 The diagram illustrates the law of multiple proportions. Two compounds, X and Y, contain equal masses of element B. The ratio of the masses of A in these compounds is 5:10 or 1:2 (a small whole number ratio). **Applying Concepts** *Would the ratio be different if samples of X and Y contained 3 g of B?*

Math / Handbook

For help with using a calculator go to page R62.

interactive Textbook

Problem-Solving 9.34 Solve Problem 34 with the help of an interactive guided tutorial.

— with **ChemASAP**

Figure 9.18 If someone ingests a poison, the poison control center can provide information about what immediate action to take. **Inferring** *What information about the poison would be most helpful to the center?*

Figure 9.19 A variety of compounds create a colorful display in the clay cliffs at Gay Head, Massachusetts on the island of Martha's Vineyard. Each colored compound can be named by the methods you are learning if you know the compound's formula.

Practicing Skills: Naming Chemical Compounds

In the average home, you can probably find hundreds of chemicals, including cleaning products, drugs, and pesticides. Figure 9.18 shows a typical warning label on a product that tells about its possible dangers. Most people would not know what to do if some of these chemicals accidentally mixed together and began to react or if a small child ingested one. A phone call to a poison control center can provide lifesaving information to victims of such poisonings. But a poison control center can be much more effective if the caller can supply some information about the name or formula of the substance.

In this chapter, you learned two basic skills that could help you to deal with an emergency involving chemicals: writing chemical formulas and naming chemical compounds. If this is the first time you have tried to master these skills, you may feel a little overwhelmed. For example, you may find it difficult to know when you should or should not use prefixes and Roman numerals in a name. Or you may have trouble determining if a compound's name should end in -*ate*, -*ide*, or -*ite*. The flowchart in Figure 9.20 provides you with a sequence of questions for naming a compound when you know its formula. ☚ **Follow the arrows and answer the questions on the flowchart to write the correct name for a compound.** The sequence of questions can help you name chemicals you may have in your home as well as the colorful compounds that create the picturesque landscape of Gay Head, Massachusetts shown in Figure 9.19.

The flowchart shows the routes to the names of several compounds: HNO_3, N_2O_3, BaS, Li_2CO_3, $CuSO_4$, and $FeCl_2$. Apply the general formula Q_xR_y to each compound. Q and R can be atoms, monatomic ions, or polyatomic ions. For example, to name HNO_3, let H = Q and NO_3 = R. Follow the first arrow down to the question Q = H? The answer is yes, so the arrow to the right tells you that the compound is an acid. You can then follow the rules for naming acids. HNO_3 is nitric acid.

To name N_2O_3, let Q = N and R = O. The answer to the question Q = H? is no, so follow the arrow down. Does the compound have more than two elements? The answer is no, so follow the arrow to the left. The compound is binary and its name ends in -*ide*. Is Q a metal? The answer is no, so you must use prefixes in the name, which is *di*nitrogen *tri*oxide.

Figure 9.20 This flowchart will help you name chemical compounds. Begin with the letters Q and R in the general formula Q_xR_y. Q and R can be atoms, monatomic ions, or polyatomic ions.

$$Q_xR_y$$

Q = H? — yes → Compound is an acid. (HNO_3, nitric acid)

no ↓

Compound is binary; name ends in *-ide*. ← no — **> 2 Elements?** — yes → Compound contains a polyatomic ion; name generally ends in *-ite* or *-ate*.

Q = Metal?

no → Compound is binary molecular; use prefixes in the name. (N_2O_3, dinitrogen trioxide)

yes ↓

Q = Group A?

yes → Name the ions. (BaS, barium sulfide)

no → Name the ions; use a Roman numeral with the cation. ($FeCl_2$, iron(II) chloride)

Q = Group A?

yes → Name the ions. (Li_2CO_3, lithium carbonate)

no → Name the ions; use a Roman numeral with the cation. ($CuSO_4$, copper(II) sulfate)

Another example shown on the flowchart is $CuSO_4$. In this case, Q = Cu and R = SO_4. Q does not equal H. The compound does have more than two elements, so it contains a polyatomic ion. Thus you should expect that the name will end in *-ite* or *-ate*. The answer to the next question, Q = Group A? is no, so you must name the ions and use a Roman numeral to identify the charge of the transition metal. The name is copper(II) sulfate. A sample of copper(II) sulfate is shown in Figure 9.21. Practice with the other compounds listed above, and then use the flowchart when doing naming exercises. Soon you won't need it anymore.

 Checkpoint *Identify Q and R in the compound MgSO₄.*

Figure 9.21 Dry copper sulfate is a white solid, as shown on the right. When water is added, the white solid absorbs water into its crystal structure and turns blue.

Practicing Skills: Writing Chemical Formulas

In writing a chemical formula from a chemical name, it is helpful to remember the following guidelines.

1. An *-ide* ending generally indicates a binary compound.

2. An *-ite* or *-ate* ending means a polyatomic ion that includes oxygen is in the formula.

3. Prefixes in a name generally indicate that the compound is molecular.

4. A Roman numeral after the name of a cation shows the ionic charge of the cation.

These guidelines and the questions in the flowchart in Figure 9.22 will help you write the formula for a compound when you know its name. For example, use the flowchart to write the formula for sodium chromate. The name does not contain prefixes, so it is ionic. The ions are sodium ion and chromate ion. Follow the arrows to the right and left. Sodium is a Group A element, so use the periodic table or Table 9.1 to obtain its ionic charge (1+). Chromate ion is a polyatomic ion, so use Table 9.3 to obtain its charge (2−). Balance the charges to obtain the formula Na_2CrO_4. Practice formula writing using the flowchart until you don't need it anymore.

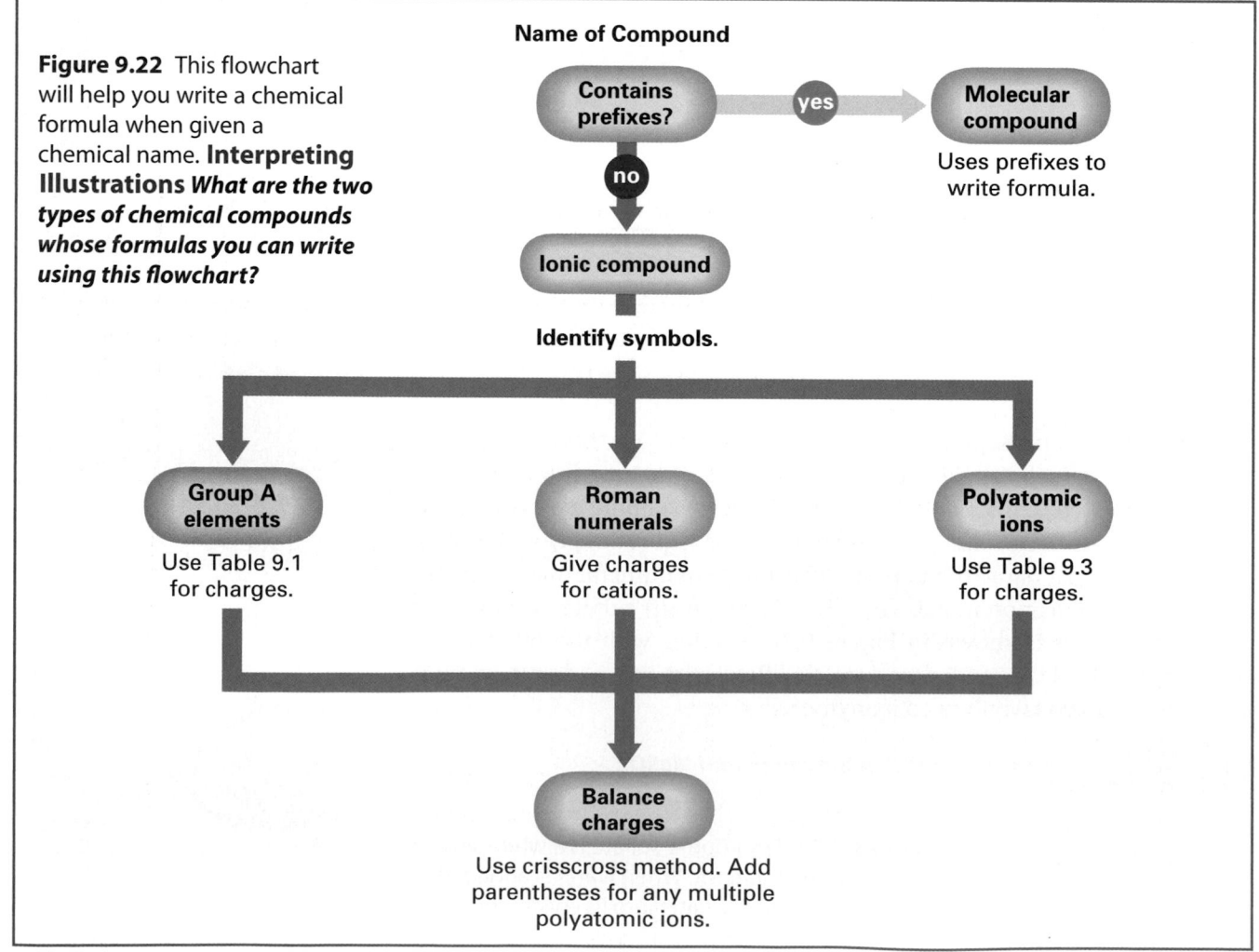

Figure 9.22 This flowchart will help you write a chemical formula when given a chemical name. **Interpreting Illustrations** *What are the two types of chemical compounds whose formulas you can write using this flowchart?*

Quick LAB

Making Ionic Compounds

Purpose
To mix solutions containing cations and anions to make ionic compounds.

Materials
- 9 small test tubes
- test tube rack
- paper, pencil, ruler
- 6 solutions in plastic dropper bottles containing the following ions:

  Solution A (Fe^{3+} ion) Solution X (CO_3^{2-} ion)
  Solution B (Ag^+ ion) Solution Y (OH^- ion)
  Solution C (Pb^{2+} ion) Solution Z (PO_4^{3-} ion)

Procedure

1. Label three test tubes A, three test tubes B, and three test tubes C.
2. Add 10 drops (approximately 0.5 mL) of solutions A, B, and C to appropriately labeled test tubes.
3. Add 10 drops of solution X to one test tube of A, 10 drops to one test tube of B, and 10 drops to one test tube of C. Observe each for the formation of a solid.

4. Make a 3-by-3 inch grid in which to record your observations. Label the rows A, B, and C. Label the columns X, Y, and Z. Describe any solid material you observe.
5. Repeat Step 3, adding 10 drops of solution Y to test tubes A, B, and C. Record your observations.
6. Repeat Step 3, adding 10 drops of solution Z to test tubes A, B, and C. Record your observations.

Analyze and Conclude

1. Some ionic compounds are insoluble (do not dissolve in water). Explain what you observed.
2. Write the formula for each ionic compound formed.
3. Name each ionic compound formed.
4. Will mixing any cation with any anion always lead to the formation of an insoluble ionic compound? Explain.

9.5 Section Assessment

35. **Key Concept** What two laws describe how chemical compounds form?
36. **Key Concept** How should you use a flowchart to name a chemical compound?
37. **Key Concept** What are four guidelines for writing the formulas of chemical compounds?
38. Two compounds containing copper and oxygen were found to contain the following masses:
    Compound A: 32.10 g Cu and 17.90 g Cl
    Compound B: 23.64 g Cu and 26.37 g Cl

    Are the compounds the same? If not, what is the lowest whole number mass ratio of copper that combines with a given mass of chlorine?
39. Name these compounds.
    a. $CaCO_3$ **b.** $PbCrO_4$ **c.** $SnCr_2O_7$
40. Write formulas for these compounds.
    a. tin(II) hydroxide   **b.** barium fluoride

41. Identify the incorrect names or formulas.
    a. calcium(II) oxide   **b.** aluminum oxide
    c. $Na_2C_2O_4$ **d.** $Mg(NH_4)_2$

Connecting ▶ **Concepts**

Ionic Bonds Review ionic bonds in Section 7.2 and show by means of electron dot structures why an ionic compound always has a charge of zero. Use magnesium bromide as an example.

Textbook

Assessment 9.5 Test yourself on the concepts in Section 9.5.

— with **ChemASAP**

Study Guide

Key Concepts

🔑 9.1 Naming Ions

- When the metals in Groups 1A, 2A, and 3A lose electrons, they form cations with positive charges equal to their group number.
- The charge of any ion of a Group A nonmetal is determined by subtracting 8 from the group number.
- The charges of cations of many transition metal ions must be determined from the number of electrons lost. When a cation can have more than one ionic charge, a Roman numeral is used in the name to indicate the charge.
- The names of most polyatomic anions end in *-ite* or *-ate*.

🔑 9.2 Naming and Writing Formulas for Ionic Compounds

- The name of a binary ionic compound is the cation name followed by the anion name.
- To write the formula for a binary ionic compound, write the symbol for the cation and then the anion. Then balance the charges.
- To write formulas for compounds containing polyatomic ions, write the symbol for the metal ion followed by the formula for the polyatomic ion and balance the charges.
- To name a compound containing a polyatomic ion, state the cation first and then the anion.

🔑 9.3 Naming and Writing Formulas for Molecular Compounds

- Prefixes show how many atoms of each element are present in a molecule of a binary compound.
- To write the formula for a binary molecular compound, write the symbols for the elements and use the prefixes to determine the subscripts. Omit *mono-* for a single atom.

🔑 9.4 Naming and Writing Formulas for Acids and Bases

- An acid is a combination of a monatomic or polyatomic anion with sufficient hydrogen atoms to make the compound electrically neutral. Acids are named as shown in Table 9.5.
- A base is a combination of a cation with as many hydroxide ions as are needed to make the compound electrically neutral. Bases are named in the same way as other ionic compounds.

🔑 9.5 The Laws Governing Formulas and Names

- The ways that compounds form are summed up in two laws: the law of definite proportions and the law of multiple proportions.
- To name a compound or write its formula, follow the flowcharts in Figures 9.20 and 9.22 to the correct name or formula.

Vocabulary

- acid (p. 271)
- base (p. 273)
- binary compound (p. 261)
- law of definite proportions (p. 274)
- law of multiple proportions (p. 275)
- monatomic ion (p. 253)
- polyatomic ion (p. 257)

Organizing Information

Use these terms to construct a concept map that organizes the major ideas of this chapter.

Textbook

Concept Map 9 Solve the Concept Map with the help of an interactive guided tutorial.

— with **ChemASAP**

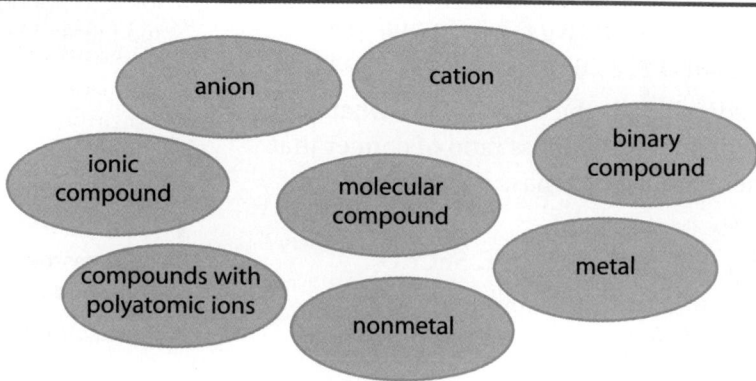

Review and Assessment

Blue questions emphasize Regents Exam content

9.1 Naming Ions

42. Give the expected charges on the ions of elements of these groups of the periodic table.
 a. Group 6A (16) **b.** Group 1A (1)
 c. Group 7A (17) **d.** Group 3A (13)

43. Give the expected charge of the positive ions of these elements.
 a. Sr **b.** Ca **c.** Al **d.** Cs

44. Name the following ions. Use Table 9.2 if necessary.
 a. Ba^{2+} **b.** I^- **c.** Ag^+ **d.** Hg^{2+}

45. Write the names and formulas of the two negative polyatomic ions in Table 9.3 with names that do not end in *-ite* or *-ate*.

46. Name the following ions.
 a. OH^- **b.** Pb^{4+} **c.** SO_4^{2-} **d.** O^{2-}

47. How can you determine the ionic charge of any metal from the position of the element in the periodic table?

9.2 Naming and Writing Formulas for Ionic Compounds

48. What is the net ionic charge of every ionic compound? Explain.

49. How are formulas written for binary ionic compounds, given their names? How is the reverse done?

50. How do you determine the charge of a transition metal cation from the formula of an ionic compound?

51. How are formulas written for ionic compounds with polyatomic ions, given their names? How is the reverse done?

52. Binary compounds contain only two different elements. Which of the following compounds are binary?
 a. KBr **b.** ammonium chloride
 c. K_3PO_4 **d.** calcium sulfate

53. When must parentheses be used in a formula?

54. Complete the following table by writing correct formulas for the compounds formed by combining positive and negative ions. Then name each compound.

	NO_3^-	CO_3^{2-}	CN^-	PO_4^{3-}
NH_4^+	a. ____	b. ____	c. ____	d. ____
Sn^{4+}	e. ____	f. ____	g. ____	h. ____
Fe^{3+}	i. ____	j. ____	k. ____	l. ____
Mg^{2+}	m. ____	n. ____	o. ____	p. ____

55. Write formulas for these compounds.
 a. potassium permanganate
 b. calcium hydrogen carbonate
 c. dichlorine heptoxide
 d. trisilicon tetranitride
 e. sodium dihydrogen phosphate
 f. phosphorous pentabromide
 g. carbon tetrachloride

56. Write formulas for these compounds.
 a. magnesium sulfide **b.** sodium phosphite
 c. barium hydroxide **d.** copper(II) nitrite
 e. potassium sulfite **f.** calcium carbonate
 g. sodium bromide **h.** iron(III) sulfate

57. Name these compounds.
 a. $NaClO_3$ **b.** Hg_2Br_2 **c.** K_2CrO_4
 d. $HClO_4$ **e.** SnO_2 **f.** $Fe(C_2H_3O_2)_3$
 g. $KHSO_4$ **h.** $Ca(OH)_2$ **i.** BaS

58. A compound of general formula Q_xR_y contains no hydrogen, Q is the metal of lowest atomic mass, and R contains the elements oxygen and carbon in a 3:1 ratio. Write the name and the formula of the compound.

59. Two compounds contain only tin and chlorine. The ratio of the masses of chlorine combined with 1.00 g of tin in the two compounds is 2. If one compound has the formula $SnCl_2$, what is the formula for the other compound?

60. Analysis of two compounds shows that they contain only lead and iodine in the following amounts:
 Compound I: 22.48 g Pb and 27.52 g I
 Compound II: 5.798 g Pb and 14.20 g I
 a. Determine the ratio of lead contained in the two compounds for every 1 g of iodine.
 b. Use your ratio and your knowledge of ionic charges to write the formulas and the names of the two compounds.

61. Summarize the rules that chemists use for naming ionic compounds. What is the purpose for each rule?

62. Examine the following names for ionic compounds. Show, by writing all possible formulas for the compounds, that the names are incomplete. Then, write the complete names.
    a. copper sulfide   b. iron sulfate   c. lead oxide

63. Explain what is wrong with each formula.
    a. $CsCl_2$ b. ZnO_2 c. $LiNe$ d. Ba_2S_2

64. *The Handbook of Chemistry and Physics* is a reference book that contains a wealth of information about elements and compounds. Two sections of this book you might use are "Physical Constants of Inorganic Compounds" and "Physical Constants of Organic Compounds." To familiarize yourself with this work, make a table with these headings: Name, Formula, Crystalline Form or Color, Density, Melting Point (°C), Boiling Point (°C), and Solubility in Water. Enter these substances in the body of the table: ammonium chloride, barium, barium sulfate, bromine, calcium carbonate, chlorine, copper(II) sulfate pentahydrate, iodine, iron(II) sulfate pentahydrate, mercury, potassium carbonate, and sulfur. Use the handbook to complete the table.

65. Use the table you prepared for Problem 64 to answer the following questions.
    a. You have two unlabeled bottles, each containing a white powder. One of the substances is calcium carbonate, and the other is potassium carbonate. Describe a simple physical test you could carry out to distinguish between these two compounds.
    b. How would you distinguish between samples of copper(II) sulfate pentahydrate and iron(II) sulfate pentahydrate?
    c. A bottle contains a mixture of ammonium chloride and barium sulfate. How could you separate these two compounds?
    d. List the elements in the table in order of increasing density. Identify the elements as metals or nonmetals.

    e. List the compounds in the table in order of decreasing density.
    f. Calculate the mass of 47.0 cm³ of mercury.
    g. Calculate the volume of 16.6 g of sulfur.
    h. How would you distinguish among the Group 7A (17) elements (halogens) listed in the table?

9.3 Naming and Writing Formulas for Molecular Compounds

66. What are the components of a binary molecular compound?

67. Which prefix indicates each of the following numbers of atoms in a molecular compound formula?
    a. 3   b. 1   c. 2   d. 6   e. 5   f. 4

68. How are formulas for molecular compounds containing only two different elements written, given their names? How is the reverse done?

69. Write the formula or name for each of these compounds.
    a. boron trichloride   b. N_2O_5
    c. dinitrogen tetrahydride   d. CCl_4

70. Name each substance.
    a. $LiClO_4$ b. Cl_2O c. HgF_2
    d. CaO e. $Ba_3(PO_4)_2$ f. I_2
    g. $SrSO_4$ h. $CuC_2H_3O_2$ i. $SiCl_4$

71. Name each compound.
    a. $Mg(MnO_4)_2$ b. $Be(NO_3)_2$ c. K_2CO_3
    d. N_2H_4 e. $LiOH$ f. BaF_2
    g. PI_3 h. ZnO i. H_3PO_3

72. Write formulas for these compounds.
    a. calcium bromide   b. silver chloride
    c. aluminum carbide   d. nitrogen dioxide
    e. tin(IV) cyanide   f. lithium hydride
    g. strontium acetate   h. sodium silicate

73. Compare and contrast the information conveyed by a molecular formula with that given by a formula unit of a compound.

74. With the exception of hydrogen, where on the periodic table will you find the elements in a molecular compound?

75. Nitrogen and oxygen form a number of stable chemical compounds. In the models below, nitrogen is blue; oxygen is red. Write the chemical formula and name of each.

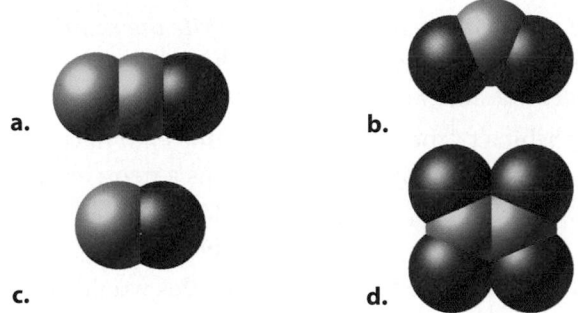

a.

b.

c.

d.

9.4 Naming and Writing Formulas for Acids and Bases

76. Give the name or the formula for these acids.
   a. HCl
   b. sulfuric acid
   c. HNO_3
   d. acetic acid

77. Is every molecular compound that contains hydrogen an acid? Explain.

78. Write formulas for these compounds.
   a. strontium hydroxide
   b. aluminum hydroxide
   c. phosphoric acid

79. Write names or formulas for these compounds.
   a. iron(II) hydroxide
   b. $Pb(OH)_2$
   c. copper(II) hydroxide
   d. $Co(OH)_2$

80. Separate the following compounds into five categories: binary ionic compounds, binary molecular compounds, compounds with polyatomic ions, acids, and bases. Some compounds may fit in more than one category.
   a. CBr_4 b. HCN   c. NH_4OH
   d. MgS   e. H_2SiO_3 f. ClBr
   g. Al_2O_3 h. Na_2HPO_4 i. $KMnO_4$

9.5 The Laws Governing Formulas and Names

81. What is the law of definite proportions?

82. Describe the law of multiple proportions.

83. Nitrous oxide is known as laughing gas and is used as an anesthetic in dentistry. The mass ratio of nitrogen to oxygen is 7:4. A 68-g sample of a compound composed of nitrogen and oxygen contains 42 g of nitrogen. Is the sample nitrous oxide? Explain.

84. A compound of general formula Q_xR_y contains no hydrogen, and the elements Q and R are different. Neither Q nor R is a metal. Is Q_xR_y an acid, a binary ionic compound, an ionic compound containing a polyatomic anion, or a binary molecular compound?

85. Why is it important for chemists to have a system of writing chemical names and formulas?

86. The United States produces thousands of different kinds of inorganic chemicals. The table shows the amounts (in billions of kg) of the top ten inorganic chemicals produced in a recent year.

Chemical	Amount produced (billions of kg)
Sulfuric acid	39.4
Nitrogen	26.9
Oxygen	17.7
Ammonia	16.5
Lime	16.3
Phosphoric acid	11.2
Sodium hydroxide	11.0
Chlorine	10.3
Sodium carbonate	9.3
Nitric acid	6.8

   a. What percentage of the total production of the top ten is lime (calcium oxide)?
   b. Three diatomic gases are on the list. What are their names? What was the combined production of these gases in billions of kilograms?
   c. What percentage of the total production of the top ten is the three acids?
   d. Write formulas for the top ten inorganic chemicals.

Test-Taking Tip

Eliminate Wrong Answers If you don't know which response is correct, start by eliminating those you know are wrong. If you can rule out some choices, you'll have fewer left to consider and you'll increase your chances of choosing the correct answer.

Regents Practice Exam

Part A

For each statement or question write the number of the word or expression that, of those given, best completes the statement or answers the question.

Use the following explanation and diagrams to answer Questions 1–4.

The following diagrams show two early models of the atom.

a.   b.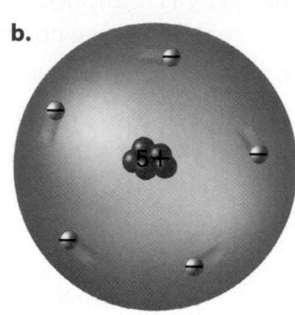

1. The model that is more accurate is the one on the
   (1) left because charge is evenly distributed
   (2) left because the particles have no motion
   (3) right because some particles are in motion and there is a nucleus
   (4) right because the particles are all attracted to each other

2. The blue particles are negatively charged. What do these particles represent?
   (1) protons   (3) electrons
   (2) neutrons   (4) nuclei

3. The red particles are positively charged. What do these particles represent?
   (1) protons   (3) electrons
   (2) neutrons   (4) nuclei

4. What major subatomic particle is missing in both of these models?
   (1) protons   (3) electrons
   (2) neutrons   (4) nuclei

5. The Roman numeral in manganese(IV) sulfide indicates the
   (1) group number on the periodic table
   (2) positive charge on the manganese ion
   (3) number of manganese ions in the formula
   (4) number of sulfide ions needed in the formula

6. What is the name of $AlCl_3$?
   (1) aluminum trichloride
   (2) aluminum(III) chloride
   (3) aluminum chlorate
   (4) aluminum chloride

Part B-1

For each statement or question write the number of the word or expression that, of those given, best completes the statement or answers the question.

7. Which of the following ions does *not* have the same electron configuration as a neon atom?
   (1) F^- (3) Li^+
   (2) O^{2-} (4) Na^+

8. Which of the following molecules would you expect to be polar?
   (1) Cl_2 (3) CCl_4
   (2) NH_3 (4) CH_4

9. Identify the pair in which the formula does not match the name.
   (1) sulfite, SO_3^{2-}
   (2) hydroxide, OH^-
   (3) nitrite, NO_3^-
   (4) dichromate, $Cr_2O_7^{2-}$

10. Which of these compounds is *not* ionic?
    (1) $CaSO_4$ (3) NH_4NO_3
    (2) N_2O_4 (4) CaS

11. What is the formula of ammonium carbonate?
    (1) $(NH_4)_2CO_3$ (3) NH_4NO_3
    (2) NH_4C (4) $(NH_3)_2CO_3$

The numbered choices below refer to Questions 12–16. A numbered choice may be used once, more than once, or not at all.

   (1) QR   (2) QR_2 (3) Q_2R (4) Q_2R_3

Which formula shows the correct ratio of ions in the compound formed by each pair of elements?

	Element Q	**Element R**
12.	aluminum	sulfur
13.	potassium	oxygen
14.	lithium	chlorine
15.	strontium	bromine
16.	sodium	sulfur

Part B-2

Answer each of the following questions.

17. List five properties of the chair you are sitting on. Classify each property as physical or chemical.

18. How many significant figures are in each of the following measurements?
   a. 15.05 g   **c.** 890 mL   **e.** 3.0×10^5 kg
   b. 0.31 cm   **d.** 300.0 cm³   **f.** 0.001 mm

19. Determine the sum of the following measurements to the correct number of significant figures.

   1.55 cm + 0.235 cm + 3.4 cm

20. Make the following conversions.
   a. 775 mL to microliters (μL)
   b. −65°C to K
   c. 8.32 mg Ag to centigrams of silver (cg Ag)

21. A student finds that 6.62 g of a substance occupies a volume of 12.3 cm³. What is the density of the substance?

22. Compare and contrast neutrons and protons with respect to their charge, mass, and position in the atom.

23. How many valence electrons do atoms of each of the following elements have?
   a. lithium   **c.** phosphorus   **e.** bromine
   b. sulfur   **d.** calcium   **f.** neon

24. Where are metalloids found on the periodic table? Compare the properties of the metalloids to those of metals and nonmetals.

25. Arrange the following groups of elements in order of increasing ionization energy.
   a. potassium, cesium, lithium, sodium
   b. fluorine, boron, beryllium, carbon, neon

26. From the positions of the elements in the periodic table, choose the element in each pair with the higher electronegativity.
   a. Cs and Li   **c.** S and Mg   **e.** Te and N
   b. Sr and I   **d.** O and Se   **f.** C and F

27. The ions of the elements of Groups 1A (1) and 2A (2) have smaller radii than their neutral atoms, whereas the ions of Group 7A (17) have larger radii than their neutral atoms. Explain.

28. How many protons and electrons are in each of the following ions?
   a. magnesium ion   **c.** strontium ion
   b. bromide ion   **d.** sulfide ion

29. Which of these compounds would you expect to contain covalent bonds? Why?
   a. KCl   **b.** PBr₃   **c.** ClBr   **d.** NaI

30. Draw electron dot structures for the following molecules.
   a. Cl₂   **b.** CCl₄   **c.** CH₄

31. Explain what a hydrogen bond is and what kinds of compounds form hydrogen bonds.

32. Explain the difference between an ionic bond and a covalent bond. Use electron dot structures to illustrate your explanation.

Use the particle diagrams to answer Questions 33 and 34.

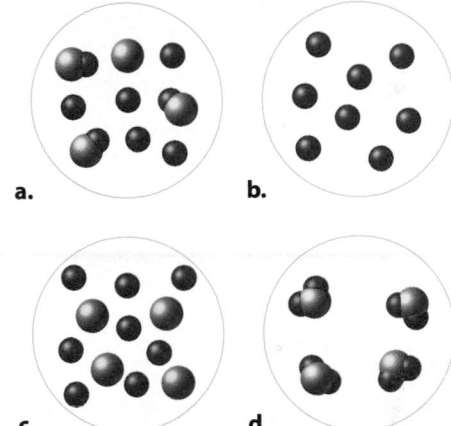

33. Identify the contents of each particle diagram as a substance or a mixture.

34. Classify the contents of each diagram as compounds only, elements only, or elements and compounds.

Part C

Answer each of the following questions.

Use the data table to answer Questions 35–36. The table gives formulas for some of the ionic compounds formed when positive metal ions (M, N, P) combine with negative nonmetal ions (A, B, C, D).

35. Use the given formulas to determine the ionic charge for each positive and negative ion.

36. Write the formulas for compounds 1–6.

Cation	Anion			
	A	B	C	D
M	MA₂	(1)	(2)	MD
N	(3)	N₂B	(4)	(5)
P	PA₃	(6)	PC	P₂(D)₃

Chemists measure matter in a unit called the mole just as florists sell roses by the dozen.

INQUIRY Activity

Counting by Measuring Mass

Materials

100 paper clips of the same size, centigram balance

Procedure

1. Find the mass of 25 paper clips. Divide the total mass by 25 to find the average mass of a paper clip. Repeat this step using 25 different paper clips until your average masses agree.

2. Select about 75 percent of your paper clips and find their mass. Without counting, calculate the number of paper clips in your sample.

3. Count the number of paper clips in your sample.

4. Repeat Steps 2 and 3 with a different sample size.

Think About It

1. Did the number of paper clips you counted in the sample (Step 3) equal the number you calculated by mass (Step 2)?

2. Explain how you would use the balance to count out 185 paper clips.

3. What is the advantage of using a larger sample size in Step 1? What is a disadvantage?

10.1 The Mole: A Measurement of Matter

 New York Standard: 3.3e

Connecting to Your World

Every year, contestants from all over the world travel to Harrison Hot Springs in British Columbia, Canada, to compete in the world championship sand sculpture contest. Each contestant creates a beautiful work of art out of millions of tiny grains of sand. You could measure the amount of sand in a sculpture by counting the grains of sand. But wouldn't it be much easier to weigh the sand? In this section, you'll discover how chemists measure the amount of a substance using a unit called a mole.

Measuring Matter

You live in a quantitative world. The grade you got on your last exam, the number of times you heard your favorite song on the radio yesterday, and the cost of a bicycle you would like to own are all important quantities to you. These are quantities that answer questions such as "How much?" or "How many?" Scientists answer similar questions. How many kilograms of iron can be obtained from one hundred kilograms of iron ore? How many grams of hydrogen and nitrogen must be combined to make 200 grams of the fertilizer ammonia (NH_3)? Questions like these illustrate that chemistry is a quantitative science. In your study of chemistry, you will analyze the composition of samples of matter and perform chemical calculations that relate quantities of reactants in a chemical reaction to quantities of products. To solve these and other problems, you will have to be able to measure the amount of matter you have.

How do you measure matter? One way is to count how many of something you have. For example, you can count the CDs in your collection or the number of pins you knock down when bowling. Another way to measure matter is to determine its mass. You can buy potatoes by the kilogram or pound and gold by the gram or ounce. You can also measure matter by volume. For instance, people buy gasoline by the liter or the gallon and take cough medicine by the milliliter or the teaspoon. **You often measure the amount of something by one of three different methods—by count, by mass, and by volume.** For example, you can buy soda by the six-pack or by the liter. Figure 10.1 shows how you might measure the amount of grapes you want to buy.

Guide for Reading

Key Concepts
- What are three methods for measuring the amount of something?
- How is Avogadro's number related to a mole of any substance?
- How is the atomic mass of an element related to the molar mass of an element?
- How is the mass of a mole of a compound calculated?

Vocabulary
mole
Avogadro's number
representative particle
molar mass

Reading Strategy
Relating Text and Visuals As you read, look closely at Table 10.2. Explain how the information in the table helps you understand the basis for the molar masses of the elements.

Figure 10.1 A grocer's scale measures the weight of the grapes you want to buy.

Some of the units used for measuring indicate a specific number of items. For example, a pair always means two. A pair of shoes is two shoes, and a pair of aces is two aces. Similarly, a dozen always means 12. A dozen eggs is 12 eggs and a dozen pens is 12 pens.

Apples are measured in three different ways. At a fruit stand, they are often sold by the count (3 for $2.40). In a supermarket, you usually buy apples by weight ($1.29/pound) or mass ($2.79/kg). At an orchard, you can buy apples by volume ($12.00/bushel). Each of these different ways to measure apples can be equated to a dozen apples.

By count: 1 dozen apples = 12 apples

For average-sized apples the following approximations can be used.

By mass: 1 dozen apples = 2.0 kg apples

By volume: 1 dozen apples = 0.20 bushel apples

Figure 10.2 shows other items sold by count, weight, and volume.

Knowing how the count, mass, and volume of apples relate to a dozen apples allows you to convert among these units. For example, based on the unit relationships given above, you could calculate the mass of a bushel of apples or the mass of 90 average-sized apples using conversion factors such as the following.

$$\frac{1 \text{ dozen apples}}{12 \text{ apples}} \qquad \frac{2.0 \text{ kg apples}}{1 \text{ dozen apples}} \qquad \frac{1 \text{ dozen apples}}{0.20 \text{ bushel apples}}$$

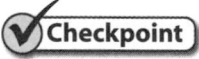 **Checkpoint** *What are three ways of measuring the amount of a substance?*

Figure 10.2 You can buy items by different types of measurements, such as a count, a weight or mass, or a volume. **Classifying** *Which of these common items are being sold by weight? By volume? By count?*

SAMPLE PROBLEM 10.1

Finding Mass from a Count

What is the mass of 90 average-sized apples if 1 dozen of the apples has a mass of 2.0 kg?

1 **Analyze** *List the knowns and the unknown.*

Knowns
- number of apples = 90 apples
- 12 apples = 1 dozen apples
- 1 dozen apples = 2.0 kg apples

Unknown
- mass of 90 apples = ? kg

You can use dimensional analysis to convert the number of apples to the mass of apples. Carry out this conversion by performing the following sequence of conversions:

Number of apples $\longrightarrow$ dozens of apples $\longrightarrow$ mass of apples.

2 **Calculate** *Solve for the unknown.*

The first conversion factor is $\dfrac{1 \text{ dozen apples}}{12 \text{ apples}}$.

The second conversion factor is $\dfrac{2.0 \text{ kg apples}}{1 \text{ dozen apples}}$.

Multiplying the original number of apples by these two conversion factors gives the answer in kilograms.

$$\text{mass of apples} = 90 \text{ apples} \times \frac{1 \text{ dozen apples}}{12 \text{ apples}} \times \frac{2.0 \text{ kg apples}}{1 \text{ dozen apples}}$$

$$= 15 \text{ kg apples}$$

The mass of 90 average-sized apples is 15 kg.

3 **Evaluate** *Does the result make sense?*

Because a dozen apples has a mass of 2.0 kg, and 90 apples is less than 10 dozen apples, the mass should be less than 20 kg of apples (10 dozen × 2.0 kg/dozen).

Practice Problems

1. If 0.20 bushel is 1 dozen apples and a dozen apples has a mass of 2.0 kg, what is the mass of 0.50 bushel of apples?

2. Assume 2.0 kg of apples is 1 dozen and that each apple has 8 seeds. How many apple seeds are in 14 kg of apples?

Interactive Textbook

Problem-Solving 10.1
Solve Problem 1 with the help of an interactive guided tutorial.

—with **ChemASAP**

Figure 10.3 Words other than *mole* are used to describe a number of something—for example, a *ream* of paper (500 sheets), a *gross* of pencils (144), and a *dozen* eggs (12).

What Is a Mole?

Counting objects as big as apples is a reasonable way to measure the amount of apples. But imagine trying to count the grains of sand in a sand sculpture. That would be an endless job. Recall that matter is composed of atoms, molecules, and ions. These particles are much smaller than grains of sand and an extremely large number of them are in even a small sample of a substance. Obviously, counting particles one by one is not practical. However, think about counting eggs. It's easier when the eggs are grouped into dozens. A dozen is a specified number, 12, of things. Other common groupings of items are shown in Figure 10.3. Chemists also use a unit that is a specified number of particles. The unit is called a mole. Just as a dozen eggs is 12 eggs, a **mole** (mol) of a substance is 6.02×10^{23} representative particles of that substance and is the SI unit for measuring the amount of a substance. The number of representative particles in a mole, 6.02×10^{23}, is called **Avogadro's number.** It was named in honor of the Italian scientist Amedeo Avogadro di Quaregna (1776–1856) who helped clarify the difference between atoms and molecules.

The term **representative particle** refers to the species present in a substance: usually atoms, molecules, or formula units. The representative particle of most elements is the atom. Iron is composed of iron atoms. Helium is composed of helium atoms. Seven elements, however, normally exist as diatomic molecules (H_2, N_2, O_2, F_2, Cl_2, Br_2, and I_2). The representative particle of these elements and of all molecular compounds is the molecule. The molecular compounds water (H_2O) and sulfur dioxide (SO_2) are composed of H_2O and SO_2 molecules, respectively. For ionic compounds, such as calcium chloride, the representative particle is the formula unit $CaCl_2$.

🔑 **A mole of any substance contains Avogadro's number of representative particles, or 6.02×10^{23} representative particles.** Table 10.1 summarizes the relationship between representative particles and moles of substances.

Converting Number of Particles to Moles The relationship, 1 mol = 6.02×10^{23} representative particles, is the basis for a conversion factor that you can use to convert numbers of representative particles to moles.

$$\text{moles} = \text{representative particles} \times \frac{1 \text{ mole}}{6.02 \times 10^{23} \text{ representative particles}}$$

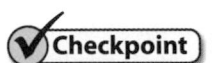 *How many representative particles are in one mole?*

For: Links on the Mole
Visit: www.SciLinks.org
Web Code: cdn-1101

Table 10.1

Representative Particles and Moles			
Substance	**Representative particle**	**Chemical formula**	**Representative particles in 1.00 mole**
Atomic nitrogen	Atom	N	6.02×10^{23}
Nitrogen gas	Molecule	N_2	6.02×10^{23}
Water	Molecule	H_2O	6.02×10^{23}
Calcium ion	Ion	Ca^{2+}	6.02×10^{23}
Calcium fluoride	Formula unit	CaF_2	6.02×10^{23}
Sucrose	Molecule	$C_{12}H_{22}O_{11}$	6.02×10^{23}

SAMPLE PROBLEM 10.2

Converting Number of Atoms to Moles

Magnesium is a light metal used in the manufacture of aircraft, automobile wheels, tools, and garden furniture. How many moles of magnesium is 1.25×10^{23} atoms of magnesium?

1 **Analyze** *List the knowns and the unknown.*

Knowns
- number of atoms = 1.25×10^{23} atoms Mg
- 1 mol Mg = 6.02×10^{23} atoms Mg
- The desired conversion is: atoms $\longrightarrow$ moles

Unknown
- moles = ? mol Mg

2 **Calculate** *Solve for the unknown.*

The conversion factor is $\dfrac{1 \text{ mol Mg}}{6.02 \times 10^{23} \text{ atoms Mg}}$.

Multiplying atoms of Mg by the conversion factor gives the answer.

$$\text{moles} = 1.25 \times 10^{23} \text{ atoms Mg} \times \frac{1 \text{ mol Mg}}{6.02 \times 10^{23} \text{ atoms Mg}}$$

$$\text{moles} = 2.08 \times 10^{-1} \text{ mol Mg} = 0.208 \text{ mol Mg}$$

3 **Evaluate** *Does the result make sense?*

Because the given number of atoms is less than one-fourth of Avogadro's number, the answer should be less than one-fourth mole of atoms. The answer should have three significant figures.

Practice Problems

3. How many moles is 2.80×10^{24} atoms of silicon?

4. How many moles is 2.17×10^{23} representative particles of bromine?

Math ▶ **Handbook**

For help with dimensional analysis, go to page R68.

*i*nteractive **Textbook**

Problem-Solving 10.4
Solve Problem 4 with the help of an interactive guided tutorial.

with **ChemASAP**

Converting Moles to Number of Particles Now suppose you want to determine how many atoms are in a mole of a compound. To do this, you must know how many atoms are in a representative particle of the compound. This number is determined from the chemical formula. Figure 10.4 illustrates this idea with marbles (atoms) in cups (molecules). The number of marbles in a dozen cups is (6×12), or 72 marbles. In the formula of a molecule of carbon dioxide (CO_2), the subscripts show that carbon dioxide is composed of three atoms: one carbon atom and two oxygen atoms. A mole of carbon dioxide contains Avogadro's number of CO_2 molecules. But each molecule contains three atoms. Thus a mole of carbon dioxide contains three times Avogadro's number of atoms. A molecule of carbon monoxide (CO) consists of two atoms, so a mole of carbon monoxide contains two times Avogadro's number of atoms.

Figure 10.4 A dozen cups of marbles contain more than a dozen marbles. Similarly, a mole of molecules contains more than a mole of atoms. **Calculating** *How many atoms are in one mole of molecules if each molecule consists of six atoms?*

To find the number of atoms in a mole of a compound, you must first determine the number of representative particles. You can use the following conversion factor to convert a number of moles of a compound to the number of representative particles (molecules or formula units).

$$\text{representative particles} = \text{moles} \times \frac{6.02 \times 10^{23} \text{ representative particles}}{1 \text{ mole}}$$

The next step is to multiply the number of representative particles by the number of atoms in each molecule or formula unit.

SAMPLE PROBLEM 10.3

Converting Moles to Number of Atoms

Propane is a gas used for cooking and heating. How many atoms are in 2.12 mol of propane (C_3H_8)?

1 **Analyze** *List the knowns and the unknown.*

Knowns
- number of moles = 2.12 mol C_3H_8
- 1 mol C_3H_8 = 6.02×10^{23} molecules C_3H_8
- 1 molecule C_3H_8 = 11 atoms
  (3 carbon atoms and 8 hydrogen atoms)
- The desired conversion is: moles $\longrightarrow$ molecules $\longrightarrow$ atoms.

  Use the relationships among units given above to write the desired conversion factors.

Unknown
- number of atoms = ? atoms

2 **Calculate** *Solve for the unknown.*

The first conversion factor is $\dfrac{6.02 \times 10^{23} \text{ molecules } C_3H_8}{1 \text{ mol } C_3H_8}$.

The second conversion factor is $\dfrac{11 \text{ atoms}}{1 \text{ molecule } C_3H_8}$.

Multiply the moles of C_3H_8 by the proper conversion factors:

$$2.12 \text{ mol } C_3H_8 \times \frac{6.02 \times 10^{23} \text{ molecules } C_3H_8}{1 \text{ mol } C_3H_8} \times \frac{11 \text{ atoms}}{1 \text{ molecule } C_3H_8}$$
$$= 1.4039 \times 10^{25} \text{ atoms} = 1.40 \times 10^{25} \text{ atoms}$$

3 **Evaluate** *Does the result make sense?*

Because there are 11 atoms in each molecule of propane and more than 2 mol of propane, the answer should be more than 20 times Avogadro's number of propane molecules. The answer has three significant figures based on the three significant figures in the given measurement.

Practice Problems

5. How many atoms are in 1.14 mol SO_3?

6. How many moles are in 4.65×10^{24} molecules of NO_2?

Math Handbook

For help with dimensional analysis, go to page R68.

interactive Textbook

Problem-Solving 10.5
Solve Problem 5 with the help of an interactive guided tutorial.

—with **ChemASAP**

Perhaps you are wondering just how large a mole is. The SI unit, the mole, is not related to the small burrowing animal of the same name shown in Figure 10.5. But this little animal can help you appreciate the size of the number 6.02×10^{23}. Assume that an average animal-mole is 15 cm long, 5 cm tall, and has a mass of 150 g. Based on this information, the mass of 6.02×10^{23} animal-moles is 9.03×10^{22} kg. That means that the mass of Avogadro's number of animal-moles is equal to more than 60 times the combined mass of Earth's oceans. If spread over the entire surface of Earth, Avogadro's number of animal-moles would form a layer more than 8 million animal-moles thick. What about the length of 6.02×10^{23} animal-moles? If lined up end-to-end, 6.02×10^{23} animal-moles would stretch from Earth to the nearest star, Alpha Centauri, more than two million times. Are you beginning to understand how enormous Avogadro's number is?

The Mass of a Mole of an Element

Remember that the atomic mass of an element (the mass of a single atom) is expressed in atomic mass units (amu). The atomic masses are relative values based on the mass of the most common isotope of carbon (carbon-12). Table 10.2 shows that an average carbon atom (C) with an atomic mass of 12.0 amu is 12 times heavier than an average hydrogen atom (H) with an atomic mass of 1.0 amu. Therefore, 100 carbon atoms are 12 times heavier than 100 hydrogen atoms. In fact, any number of carbon atoms is 12 times heavier than the same number of hydrogen atoms. The mass ratio of 12 carbon atoms to 1 hydrogen atom remains the same no matter what unit is used to express the masses. So 12.0 g of carbon atoms and 1.0 g of hydrogen atoms must contain the same number of atoms.

Figure 10.5 An average animal-mole has a mass of 150 g. The mass of 6.02×10^{23} animal-moles is 9.03×10^{22} kg.

Interactive Textbook

Animation 11 Find out how Avogadro's number is based on the relationship between the amu and the gram.

— with **ChemASAP**

Table 10.2

CARBON ATOMS		HYDROGEN ATOMS		MASS RATIO
Number	Mass (amu)	Number	Mass (amu)	$\dfrac{\text{Mass carbon}}{\text{Mass hydrogen}}$
●	12	●	1	$\dfrac{12 \text{ amu}}{1 \text{ amu}} = \dfrac{12}{1}$
●●	24 [2 × 12]	● ●	2 [2 × 1]	$\dfrac{24 \text{ amu}}{2 \text{ amu}} = \dfrac{12}{1}$
●●●●● ●●●●●	120 [10 × 12]	●●●●● ●●●●●	10 [10 × 1]	$\dfrac{120 \text{ amu}}{10 \text{ amu}} = \dfrac{12}{1}$
●●●●●●●●●● (50 atoms)	600 [50 × 12]	●●●●●●●●●● (50 atoms)	50 [50 × 1]	$\dfrac{600 \text{ amu}}{50 \text{ amu}} = \dfrac{12}{1}$
Avogadro's number	$(6.02 \times 10^{23}) \times (12)$	Avogadro's number	$(6.02 \times 10^{23}) \times (1)$	$\dfrac{(6.02 \times 10^{23}) \times (12)}{(6.02 \times 10^{23}) \times (1)} = \dfrac{12}{1}$

If you look at the atomic masses of the elements in the periodic table, you will notice that they are not whole numbers. For example, the atomic mass of carbon is not exactly 12 times the mass of hydrogen. Recall from Chapter 4 that this is because atomic masses are weighted average masses of the isotopes of each element.

Quantities measured in grams are convenient for working in the laboratory, so chemists have converted the relative scale of masses of the elements in amu to a relative scale of masses in grams. **The atomic mass of an element expressed in grams is the mass of a mole of the element.** The mass of a mole of an element is its **molar mass**. For carbon, the molar mass is 12.0 g. For atomic hydrogen, the molar mass is 1.0 g. Figure 10.6 shows one molar mass of mercury, carbon, iron, and sulfur. Compare the molar masses in the figure to the atomic masses in your periodic table. Notice that the molar masses were rounded off to one place after the decimal point. All the examples and problems in this text use molar masses that are rounded off in this way. If your teacher uses a different rounding rule for molar masses, your answers to problems may differ slightly from the answers given in the text.

If you were to compare 12.0 g of carbon atoms with 16.0 g of oxygen atoms, you would find they contain the same number of atoms. The molar masses of any two elements must contain the same number of atoms. How many atoms are contained in the molar mass of an element? You already know. The molar mass of any element contains 1 mol or 6.02×10^{23} atoms of that element.

The mole can now be further defined as the amount of substance that contains as many representative particles as the number of atoms in 12.0 g of carbon-12. You know that 12.0 g is the molar mass of carbon-12, so 12.0 g is 1 mol of carbon. The same relationship applies to hydrogen: 1.0 g of hydrogen is 1 mol of hydrogen atoms. Similarly, because 24.3 g is the molar mass of magnesium, 1 mol of magnesium (or 6.02×10^{23} atoms of magnesium) has a mass of 24.3 g. Molar mass is the mass of 1 mol of atoms of any element.

✓Checkpoint *How many atoms are in one mole of magnesium?*

1 mol of mercury atoms
200.6 g = 1 molar mass Hg

1 mol of carbon atoms
12.0 g C = 1 molar mass C

Figure 10.6 One molar mass of mercury, carbon, iron and sulfur are shown. Each of the quantities contains one mole of the element. **Applying Concepts** *How many atoms of each element are shown?*

1 mol of iron atoms
55.8 g Fe = 1 molar mass Fe

1 mol of sulfur atoms
32.1 g = 1 molar mass S

1 mol of glucose molecules (blood sugar)
180.0 g $C_6H_{12}O_6$ = 1 molar mass $C_6H_{12}O_6$

1 mol of paradichlorobenzene
molecules (moth crystals)
147.0 g $C_6H_4Cl_2$ = 1 molar mass $C_6H_4Cl_2$

glucose

paradichlorobenzene

water

1 mol of water molecules
18.0 g H_2O = 1 molar mass H_2O

Figure 10.7 One molar mass is shown for each of three molecular compounds. **Inferring** *How can you know they each contain Avogadro's number of molecules?*

The Mass of a Mole of a Compound

To find the mass of a mole of a compound, you must know the formula of the compound. The formula of sulfur trioxide is SO_3. A molecule of SO_3 is composed of one atom of sulfur and three atoms of oxygen.

SO_3 = 1 S atom + 3 O atoms

You can calculate the mass of a molecule of SO_3 by adding the atomic masses of the atoms making up the molecule. From the periodic table, the atomic mass of sulfur (S) is 32.1 amu. The mass of three atoms of oxygen is three times the atomic mass of a single oxygen atom (O): 3×16.0 amu = 48.0 amu. So, the molecular mass of SO_3 is 32.1 amu + 48.0 amu = 80.1 amu.

1 S atom   3 O atoms
32.1 amu + 16.0 amu + 16.0 amu + 16.0 amu = 80.1 amu

Now substitute the unit grams for atomic mass units to find the molar mass of SO_3. The molar mass (g/mol) of any compound is the mass in grams of 1 mol of that compound. Thus 1 mol of SO_3 has a mass of 80.1 g. This is the mass of 6.02×10^{23} molecules of SO_3.

To calculate the molar mass of a compound, find the number of grams of each element in one mole of the compound. Then add the masses of the elements in the compound. This method for calculating molar mass applies to any compound, molecular or ionic. The molar masses of glucose ($C_6H_{12}O_6$, 180.0 g), water (H_2O, 18.0 g), and paradichlorobenzene ($C_6H_4Cl_2$, 147.0 g) in Figure 10.7 were obtained in this way.

SAMPLE PROBLEM 10.4

Finding the Molar Mass of a Compound

The decomposition of hydrogen peroxide (H_2O_2) provides sufficient energy to launch a rocket. What is the molar mass of hydrogen peroxide?

1 Analyze *List the knowns and the unknown.*

Knowns
- molecular formula = H_2O_2
- 1 molar mass H = 1 mol H = 1.0 g H
- 1 molar mass O = 1 mol O = 16.0 g O

Unknown
- molar mass = ? g

One mol of hydrogen peroxide has 2 mol of hydrogen atoms and 2 mol of oxygen atoms. Convert moles of atoms to grams by using conversion factors (g/mol) based on the molar mass of each element. The sum of the masses of the elements is the molar mass.

Math **Handbook**

For help with significant figures, go to page R61.

2 Calculate *Solve for the unknown.*

Convert moles of hydrogen and oxygen to grams of hydrogen and oxygen. Then add the results.

$$2 \text{ mol H} \times \frac{1.0 \text{ g H}}{1 \text{ mol H}} = 2.0 \text{ g H}$$

$$2 \text{ mol O} \times \frac{16.0 \text{ g O}}{1 \text{ mol O}} = 32.0 \text{ g O}$$

$$\text{molar mass of } H_2O_2 = 34.0 \text{ g}$$

3 Evaluate *Does the result make sense?*

The answer is the sum of two times the molar mass of hydrogen and oxygen. The answer is expressed to the tenth's place because the numbers being added are expressed to the tenth's place.

interactive
Textbook

Problem-Solving 10.7
Solve Problem 7 with the help of an interactive guided tutorial.

— with **ChemASAP**

Practice Problems

7. Find the molar mass of PCl_3.

8. What is the mass of 1.00 mol of sodium hydrogen carbonate?

10.1 Section Assessment

9. 🔑 **Key Concept** What are three ways to measure the amount of something?

10. 🔑 **Key Concept** Describe the relationship between Avogadro's number and one mole of any substance.

11. 🔑 **Key Concept** How is the atomic mass of an element related to the molar mass of the element?

12. 🔑 **Key Concept** How can you calculate the mass of a mole of a compound?

13. How many moles is 1.50×10^{23} molecules NH_3?

14. How many atoms are in 1.75 mol $CHCl_3$?

15. What is the molar mass of $CaSO_4$?

Writing **Activity**

Report Research the history of Avogadro's number. What elements other than carbon have been used to define a mole? Write a report that summarizes your findings.

interactive
Textbook

Assessment 10.1 Test yourself on the concepts in Section 10.1.

— with **ChemASAP**

10.2 Mole–Mass and Mole–Volume Relationships

 New York Standards: 3.3e, 3.4e

Connecting to Your World

Guess how many jelly beans are in the container and win a prize! You decide to enter the contest and you win. Was it just a lucky guess? Not exactly. You estimated the length and diameter of a jelly bean to find its approximate volume. Then you estimated the dimensions of the container to obtain its volume. You did the arithmetic and made your guess. In a similar way, chemists use the relationships between the mole and quantities such as mass, volume, and number of particles to solve chemistry problems. In this section you will find out how the mole and mass are related.

The Mole–Mass Relationship

In the previous section, you learned that the molar mass of any substance is the mass in grams of one mole of that substance. This definition applies to all substances—elements, molecular compounds, and ionic compounds. In some situations, however, the term molar mass may be unclear. For example, suppose you were asked what the molar mass of oxygen is? How you answer this question depends on what you assume to be the representative particle. If you assume the oxygen in the question is molecular oxygen (O_2), then the molar mass is 32.0 g (2 × 16.0 g). If you assume that the question is asking for the mass of a mole of oxygen atoms (O), then the answer is 16.0 g. You can avoid confusion such as this by using the formula of the substance, in this case, O_2 or O.

Suppose you need 3.00 mol of sodium chloride (NaCl) for a laboratory experiment. How can you measure this amount? It would be convenient to use a balance to measure the mass. But what mass in grams is 3.00 mol of NaCl? **Use the molar mass of an element or compound to convert between the mass of a substance and the moles of a substance.** The conversion factor for the calculation is based on the relationship: molar mass = 1 mol. Use the following equation to calculate the mass in grams of a given number of moles.

$$\text{mass (grams)} = \text{number of moles} \times \frac{\text{mass (grams)}}{1 \text{ mole}}$$

The molar mass of NaCl is 58.5 g/mol, so the mass of 3.00 mol NaCl is calculated in this way.

$$\text{mass of NaCl} = 3.00 \text{ mol} \times \frac{58.5 \text{ g}}{1 \text{ mol}} = 176 \text{ g}$$

When you measure 176 g of NaCl on a balance, you are measuring 3.00 moles of NaCl.

Guide for Reading

Key Concepts
- How do you convert the mass of a substance to the number of moles of the substance?
- What is the volume of a gas at STP?

Vocabulary

Avogadro's hypothesis

standard temperature and pressure (STP)

molar volume

Reading Strategy

Monitoring Your Understanding Before you read, preview the key concepts, the section heads, the boldfaced terms, and the visuals. List three things you expect to learn. After reading, state what you learned about each item you listed.

SAMPLE PROBLEM 10.5

Converting Moles to Mass

The aluminum satellite dishes in Figure 10.8 are resistant to corrosion because the aluminum reacts with oxygen in the air to form a coating of aluminum oxide (Al_2O_3). This tough, resistant coating prevents any further corrosion. What is the mass of 9.45 mol of aluminum oxide?

1 **Analyze** *List the known and the unknown.*

Known
• number of moles = 9.45 mol Al_2O_3

Unknown
• mass = ? g Al_2O_3

The mass of the compound is calculated from the known number of moles of the compound. The desired conversion is moles $\longrightarrow$ mass.

2 **Calculate** *Solve for the unknown.*

Determine the molar mass of Al_2O_3: 1 mol Al_2O_3 = 102.0 g Al_2O_3
Multiply the given number of moles by the conversion factor relating moles of Al_2O_3 to grams of Al_2O_3.

$$\text{mass} = 9.45 \, \cancel{\text{mol } Al_2O_3} \times \frac{102.0 \text{ g } Al_2O_3}{1 \, \cancel{\text{mol } Al_2O_3}}$$

$$= 964 \text{g } Al_2O_3$$

3 **Evaluate** *Does the result make sense?*

The number of moles of Al_2O_3 is approximately 10, and each has a mass of approximately 100 g. The answer should be about 1000 g. The answer has been rounded to the correct number of significant figures.

Practice Problems

16. Find the mass, in grams, of 4.52×10^{-3} mol $C_{20}H_{42}$.

17. Calculate the mass, in grams, of 2.50 mol of iron(II) hydroxide.

Math **Handbook**

For help with significant figures go to page R61.

interactive **Textbook**

Problem-Solving 10.16
Solve Problem 16 with the help of an interactive guided tutorial.

—— with **ChemASAP**

Figure 10.8 These aluminum satellite dishes at the National Radio Astronomy Observatory near Soccoro, New Mexico are naturally protected from corrosion by the formation of a thin film of aluminum oxide (Al_2O_3).

In Sample Problem 10.5, you used a conversion factor based on the molar mass to convert moles to mass. Now suppose that in a laboratory experiment you obtain 10.0 g of sodium sulfate (Na_2SO_4). How many moles is this? You can calculate the number of moles using the same relationship you used in Sample Problem 10.5, 1 mol = molar mass, but this time the conversion factor is inverted. Use the following equation to convert your 10.0 g of Na_2SO_4 into moles.

$$\text{moles} = \text{mass (grams)} \times \frac{1 \text{ mole}}{\text{mass (grams)}}$$

The molar mass of Na_2SO_4 is 142.1 g/mol, so the number of moles of Na_2SO_4 is calculated this way.

$$\text{moles of } Na_2SO_4 = 10.0 \text{ g} \times \frac{1 \text{ mol}}{142.1 \text{ g}} = 7.04 \times 10^{-2} \text{ mol}$$

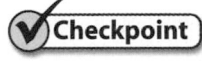 **Checkpoint** *What conversion factor should you use to convert mass to moles?*

SAMPLE PROBLEM 10.6

Converting Mass to Moles

When iron is exposed to air, it corrodes to form red-brown rust. Rust is iron(III) oxide (Fe_2O_3). How many moles of iron(III) oxide are contained in 92.2 g of pure Fe_2O_3?

1 **Analyze** *List the known and the unknown.*

Known
• mass = 92.2 g Fe_2O_3

Unknown
• number of moles = ? mol Fe_2O_3

The unknown number of moles of the compound is calculated from a known mass of a compound. The conversion is mass $\longrightarrow$ moles.

2 **Calculate** *Solve for the unknown.*
Determine the molar mass of Fe_2O_3: 1 mol = 159.6 g Fe_2O_3
Multiply the given mass by the conversion factor relating mass of Fe_2O_3 to moles of Fe_2O_3.

$$\text{moles} = 92.2 \text{ g } Fe_2O_3 \times \frac{1 \text{ mol } Fe_2O_3}{159.6 \text{ g } Fe_2O_3}$$

$$= 0.578 \text{ mol } Fe_2O_3$$

3 **Evaluate** *Does the result make sense?*
Because the given mass (about 90 g) is slightly larger than the mass of one-half mole of Fe_2O_3 (about 160 g), the answer should be slightly larger than one-half (0.5) mol.

Practice Problems

18. Find the number of moles in 3.70×10^{-1} g of boron.

19. Calculate the number of moles in 75.0 g of dinitrogen trioxide.

Rust weakens an iron chain.

Math **Handbook**

For help with using a calculator, go to page R62.

interactive Textbook

Problem-Solving 10.18
Solve Problem 18 with the help of an interactive guided tutorial.

— with **ChemASAP**

The Mole–Volume Relationship

Look back at Figure 10.7. Notice that the volumes of one mole of different solid and liquid substances are not the same. For example, the volumes of one mole of glucose (blood sugar) and one mole of paradichlorobenzene (moth crystals) are much larger than the volume of one mole of water. What about the volumes of gases? Unlike liquids and solids, the volumes of moles of gases, measured under the same physical conditions, are much more predictable. Why should this be?

In 1811, Amedeo Avogadro proposed a groundbreaking explanation. **Avogadro's hypothesis** states that equal volumes of gases at the same temperature and pressure contain equal numbers of particles. The particles that make up different gases are not the same size. But the particles in all gases are so far apart that a collection of relatively large particles does not require much more space than the same number of relatively small particles. Whether the particles are large or small, large expanses of space exist between individual particles of gas, as shown in Figure 10.9.

If you buy a party balloon filled with helium and take it home on a cold day, you might notice that the balloon shrinks while it is outside. The volume of a gas varies with a change in temperature. The volume of a gas also varies with a change in pressure. In Figure 10.10, notice the changes in an empty water bottle when it is in the cabin of an airplane while in flight and after the plane has landed. The trapped air occupies the full volume of the bottle in the cabin where the air pressure is lower than it is on the ground. The increase in pressure when the plane lands causes the volume of the air in the bottle to decrease. Because of these variations due to temperature and pressure, the volume of a gas is usually measured at a standard temperature and pressure. **Standard temperature and pressure (STP)** means a temperature of 0°C and a pressure of 101.3 kPa, or 1 atmosphere (atm). **At STP, 1 mol or 6.02×10^{23} representative particles, of any gas occupies a volume of 22.4 L.** Figure 10.11 gives you an idea of the size of 22.4 L. The quantity, 22.4 L, is called the **molar volume** of a gas.

Checkpoint *What is meant by standard temperature and pressure?*

Figure 10.9 In each container, the volume occupied by the gas molecules is small compared with the container's volume, so the molecules are not tightly packed. **a** The molecules in this container are small. **b** This container can accommodate the same number of larger molecules.

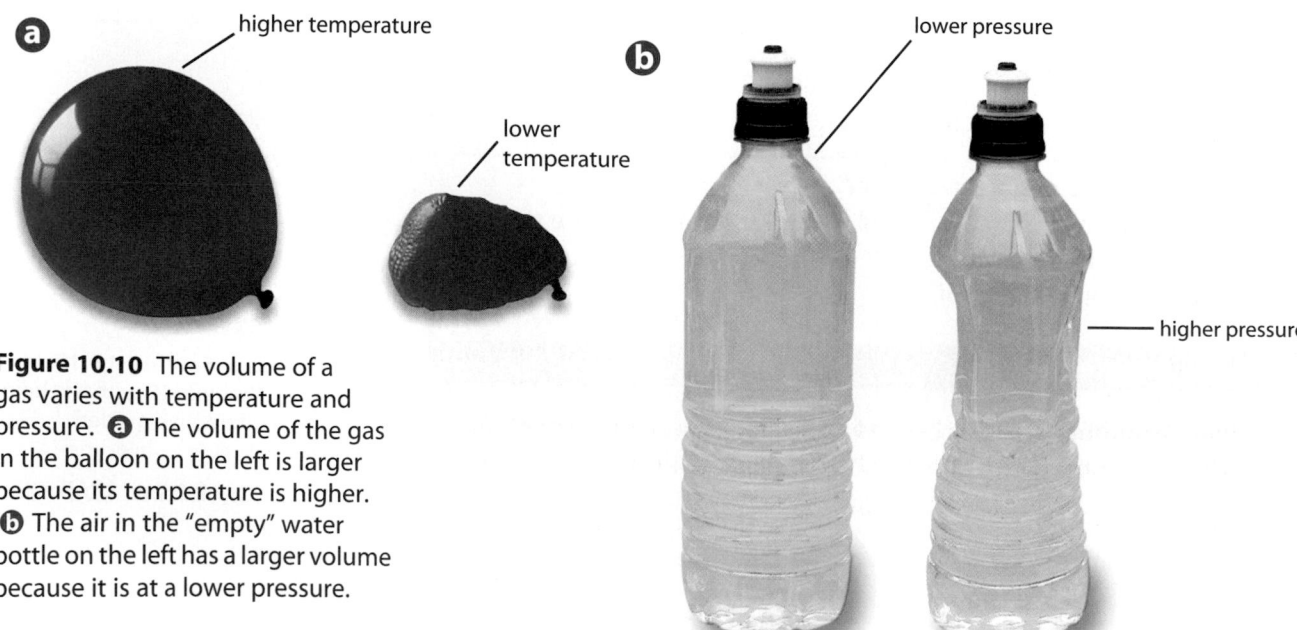

Figure 10.10 The volume of a gas varies with temperature and pressure. **a** The volume of the gas in the balloon on the left is larger because its temperature is higher. **b** The air in the "empty" water bottle on the left has a larger volume because it is at a lower pressure.

higher temperature

lower temperature

lower pressure

higher pressure

Calculating Volume at STP The molar volume is used to convert a known number of moles of gas to the volume of the gas at STP. The relationship 22.4 L = 1 mol at STP provides the conversion factor.

$$\text{volume of gas} = \text{moles of gas} \times \frac{22.4 \text{ L}}{1 \text{ mol}}$$

Suppose you have 0.375 mol of oxygen gas and want to know what volume the gas will occupy at STP.

$$\text{volume of O}_2 = 0.375 \text{ mol} \times \frac{22.4 \text{ L}}{1 \text{ mol}} = 8.40 \text{ L}$$

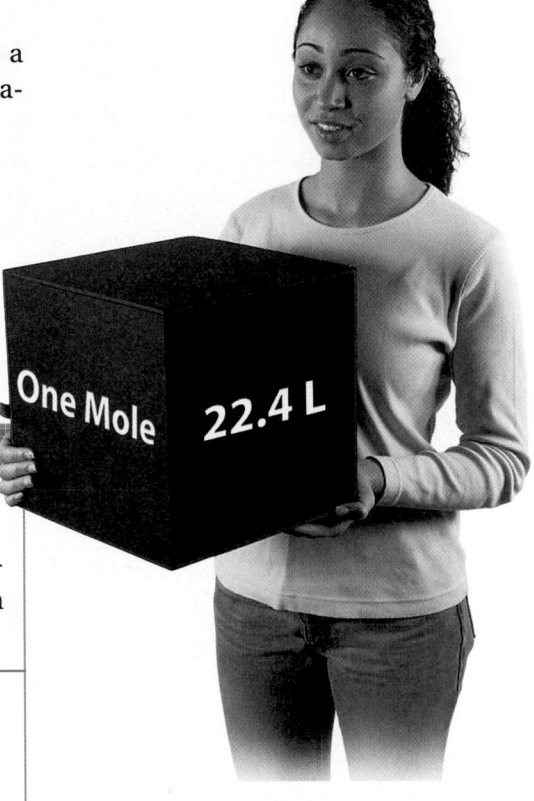

SAMPLE PROBLEM 10.7

Calculating the Volume of a Gas at STP

Sulfur dioxide (SO_2) is a gas produced by burning coal. It is an air pollutant and one of the causes of acid rain. Determine the volume, in liters, of 0.60 mol SO_2 gas at STP.

① Analyze *List the knowns and the unknown.*

Knowns
- moles = 0.60 mol SO_2
- 1 mol SO_2 = 22.4 L SO_2

Unknown
- volume = ? L SO_2

Figure 10.11 This box, with a volume of 22.4 L, holds one mole of gas at STP.

Use the relationship 1 mol SO_2 = 22.4 L SO_2 (at STP) to write the conversion factor needed to convert moles to volume.

The conversion factor is $\dfrac{22.4 \text{ L SO}_2}{1 \text{ mol SO}_2}$.

② Calculate *Solve for the unknown.*

$$\text{volume} = 0.60 \text{ mol SO}_2 \times \frac{22.4 \text{ L SO}_2}{1 \text{ mol SO}_2} = 13 \text{ L SO}_2$$

Math Handbook

For help with dimensional analysis, go to page R68.

③ Evaluate *Does the result make sense?*

Because 1 mol of any gas at STP has a volume of 22.4 L, 0.60 mol should have a volume slightly larger than one half of a mole or 11.2 L. The answer should have two significant figures.

Practice Problems

20. What is the volume of these gases at STP?
  a. 3.20×10^{-3} mol CO_2
  b. 3.70 mol N_2

21. At STP, what volume do these gases occupy?
  a. 1.25 mol He
  b. 0.335 mol C_2H_6

Interactive Textbook

Problem-Solving 10.20
Solve Problem 20 with the help of an interactive guided tutorial.

_____ with **ChemASAP**

The opposite conversion, from the volume of a gas at STP to the number of moles of gas, uses the same relationship: 22.4 L = 1 mol at STP. Suppose, in an experiment, you collect 0.200 liter of hydrogen gas at STP. You can calculate the number of moles of hydrogen in this way.

$$\text{moles} = 0.200 \text{ L H}_2 \times \frac{1 \text{ mol H}_2}{22.4 \text{ L H}_2} = 8.93 \times 10^{-3} \text{ mol H}_2$$

Calculating Molar Mass from Density A gas-filled balloon will either sink or float in the air depending on whether the density of the balloon's gas is greater or less than the density of the surrounding air. Different gases have different densities. Usually the density of a gas is measured in grams per liter (g/L) and at a specific temperature. The density of a gas at STP and the molar volume at STP (22.4 L/mol) can be used to calculate the molar mass of the gas.

$$\text{molar mass} = \text{density at STP} \times \text{molar volume at STP}$$

$$\frac{\text{grams}}{\text{mole}} = \frac{\text{grams}}{\text{L}} \times \frac{22.4 \text{ L}}{1 \text{ mole}}$$

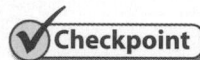 **Checkpoint** *How is the density of a gas usually measured?*

SAMPLE PROBLEM 10.8

Calculating the Molar Mass of a Gas at STP

The density of a gaseous compound containing carbon and oxygen is found to be 1.964 g/L at STP. What is the molar mass of the compound?

1 Analyze *List the knowns and the unknown.*

Knowns
- density = 1.964 g/L
- 1 mol (gas at STP) = 22.4 L

Unknown
- molar mass = ? g/mol

The conversion factor needed to convert density to molar mass is $\frac{22.4 \text{ L}}{1 \text{ mol}}$.

$$\text{molar mass} = \frac{\text{grams}}{\text{L}} \times \frac{22.4 \text{ L}}{1 \text{ mol}}$$

2 Calculate *Solve for the unknown.*

$$\text{molar mass} = \frac{1.964 \text{ g}}{1 \text{ L}} \times \frac{22.4 \text{ L}}{1 \text{ mol}}$$
$$= 44.0 \text{ g/mol}$$

3 Evaluate *Does the result make sense?*

The ratio of the calculated mass (44.0 g) to the volume (22.4 L) is about 2, which is close to the known density. The answer should have three significant figures.

Practice Problems

22. A gaseous compound composed of sulfur and oxygen, which is linked to the formation of acid rain, has a density of 3.58 g/L at STP. What is the molar mass of this gas?

23. What is the density of krypton gas at STP?

Math **Handbook**

For help with significant figures, go to page R61.

Interactive Textbook

Problem-Solving 10.22
Solve Problem 22 with the help of an interactive guided tutorial.

——with **ChemASAP**

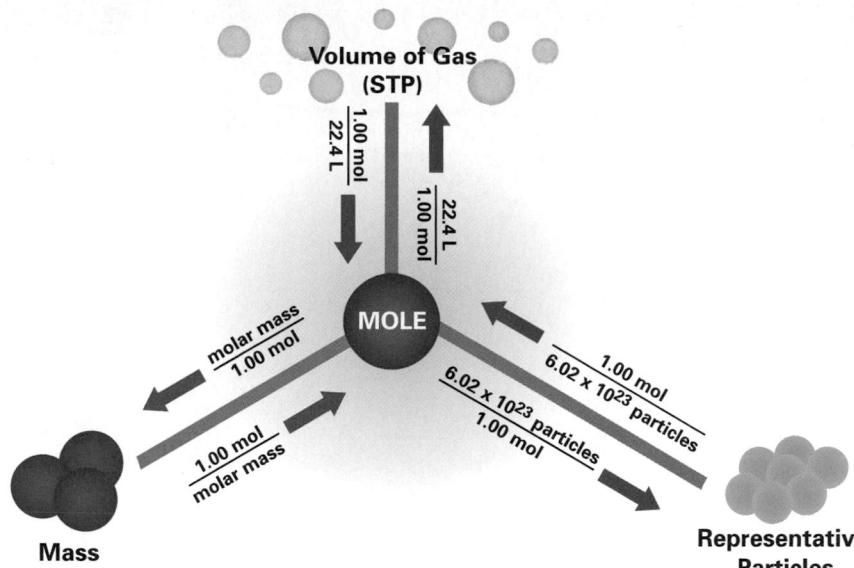

Volume of Gas (STP)

$\dfrac{1.00 \text{ mol}}{22.4 \text{ L}}$ $\dfrac{22.4 \text{ L}}{1.00 \text{ mol}}$

MOLE

$\dfrac{\text{molar mass}}{1.00 \text{ mol}}$ $\dfrac{1.00 \text{ mol}}{6.02 \times 10^{23} \text{ particles}}$ $\dfrac{6.02 \times 10^{23} \text{ particles}}{1.00 \text{ mol}}$

$\dfrac{1.00 \text{ mol}}{\text{molar mass}}$

Mass

Representative Particles

Figure 10.12 The map shows the conversion factors needed to convert among volume, mass, and number of particles. **Interpreting Diagrams** *How many conversion factors are needed to convert from the mass of a gas to the volume of a gas at STP?*

The Mole Road Map

You have now examined a mole in terms of particles, mass, and volume of gases at STP. Figure 10.12 summarizes these relationships and illustrates the importance of the mole. The mole is at the center of your chemical calculations. To convert from one unit to another, you must use the mole as an intermediate step. The form of the conversion factor depends on what you know and what you want to calculate.

Interactive Textbook

Simulation 10 Use the mole road map to convert among mass, volume, and number of representative particles.

with ChemASAP

10.2 Section Assessment

24. 🔑 **Key Concept** Describe how to convert between the mass and the number of moles of a substance.

25. 🔑 **Key Concept** What is the volume of one mole of any gas at STP?

26. How many grams are in 5.66 mol of $CaCO_3$?

27. Find the number of moles in 508 g of ethanol (C_2H_6O).

28. Calculate the volume, in liters, of 1.50 mol Cl_2 at STP.

29. The density of an elemental gas is 1.7824 g/L at STP. What is the molar mass of the element?

30. The densities of gases A, B, and C at STP are 1.25 g/L, 2.86 g/L, and 0.714 g/L, respectively. Calculate the molar mass of each substance. Identify each substance as ammonia (NH_3), sulfur dioxide (SO_2), chlorine (Cl_2), nitrogen (N_2), or methane (CH_4).

31. Three balloons filled with three different gaseous compounds each have a volume of 22.4 L at STP. Would these balloons have the same mass or contain the same number of molecules? Explain.

Connecting ▶ Concepts

Density In Chapter 3 you learned that the densities of solids and liquids are measured in g/cm³ but the densities of gases are measured in g/L. Draw atomic diagrams of a solid and a gas that show why the two different units are practical.

Interactive Textbook

Assessment 10.2 Test yourself on the concepts in Section 10.2.

with ChemASAP

Counting by Measuring Mass

Purpose

To determine the mass of several samples of chemical compounds and use the data to count atoms.

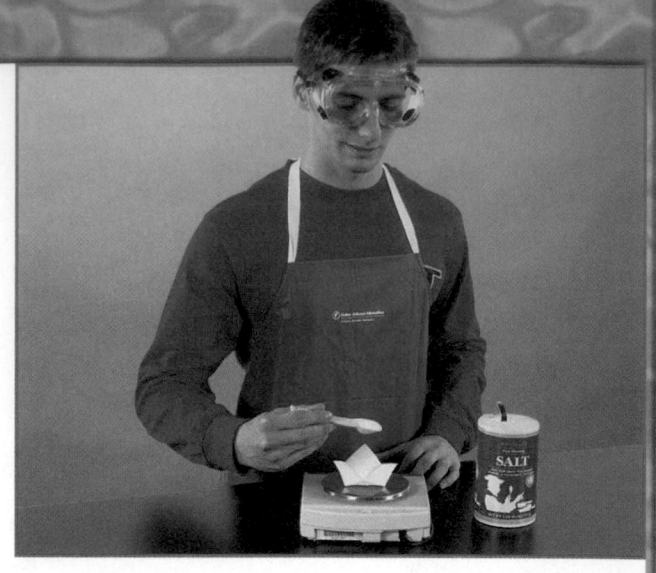

Materials

- chemicals shown in the table
- plastic spoon
- weighing paper
- watchglass or small beaker
- balance
- paper
- pencil
- ruler

Procedure

Measure the mass of one level teaspoon of sodium chloride (NaCl), water (H_2O), and calcium carbonate ($CaCO_3$). Make a table similar to the one below.

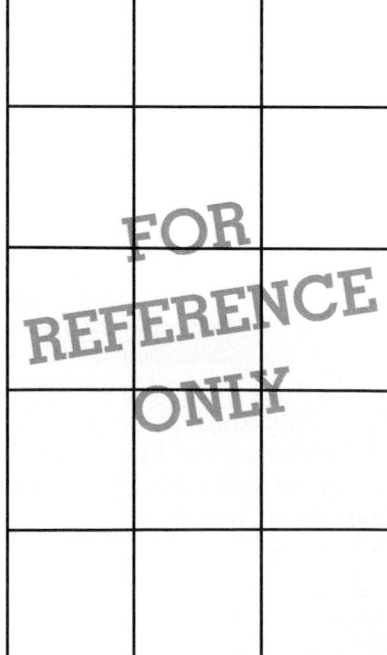

	$H_2O(l)$	$NaCl(s)$	$CaCO_3(s)$
Mass (grams)			
Molar Mass (g/mol)			
Moles of each compound			
Moles of each element			
Atoms of each element			

Analyze

Use your data to complete the following steps. Record your answers in or below your data table.

1. Calculate the moles of NaCl contained in one level teaspoon.

$$\text{moles of NaCl} = \text{g NaCl} \times \frac{1 \text{ mol NaCl}}{58.5 \text{ g}}$$

2. Repeat Step 1 for the remaining compounds. Use the periodic table to calculate the molar mass of water and calcium carbonate.

3. Calculate the number of moles of each element present in the teaspoon-sized sample of H_2O.

$$\text{moles of H} = \text{mol } H_2O \times \frac{2 \text{ mol H}}{1 \text{ mol } H_2O}$$

Repeat for the other compounds in your table.

4. Calculate the number of atoms of each element present in the teaspoon-sized sample of H_2O.

$$\text{atoms of H} = \text{mol H} \times \frac{6.02 \times 10^{23} \text{ atoms H}}{1 \text{ mol } H_2O}$$

Repeat for the other compounds in your table.

5. Which of the three teaspoon-sized samples contains the greatest number of moles?

6. Which of the three compounds contains the most atoms?

You're the Chemist!

The following small-scale activities allow you to develop your own procedures and analyze the results.

1. **Design It!** Can you count by measuring volume? Design and carry out an experiment to do it!

2. **Design It!** Design an experiment that will determine the number of atoms of calcium, carbon, and oxygen it takes to write your name on the chalkboard with a piece of chalk. Assume chalk is 100 percent calcium carbonate, $CaCO_3$.

10.3 Percent Composition and Chemical Formulas

 New York Standards: 3.1r, 3.1ee, 3.3e, 3.3f

Connecting to Your World

Is your shirt made of 100 percent cotton or wool, or is the fabric a combination of two or more fibers? A tag sewed into the seam of the shirt usually tells you what fibers were used to make the cloth and the percent of each. It helps to know the percents of the components in the shirt because they affect how warm it is, whether it will need to be ironed, and how it should be cleaned. In this section you will learn how the percents of the elements in a compound are important in chemistry.

The Percent Composition of a Compound

If you have had experience with lawn care, you know that the relative amount, or the percent, of each nutrient in fertilizer is important. In spring, you may use a fertilizer that has a relatively high percent of nitrogen to "green" the grass. In fall, you may want to use a fertilizer with a higher percent of potassium to strengthen the root system. Knowing the relative amounts of the components of a mixture or compound is often useful.

The relative amounts of the elements in a compound are expressed as the **percent composition** or the percent by mass of each element in the compound. The percent composition of a compound consists of a percent value for each different element in the compound. As you can see in Figure 10.13, the percent composition of K_2CrO_4 is K = 40.3%, Cr = 26.8%, and O = 32.9%. These percents must total 100% (40.3% + 26.8% + 32.9% = 100%). ⚷ **The percent by mass of an element in a compound is the number of grams of the element divided by the mass in grams of the compound, multiplied by 100%.**

$$\% \text{ mass of element} = \frac{\text{mass of element}}{\text{mass of compound}} \times 100\%$$

Percent Composition from Mass Data Imagine you are a chemist who has just finished the synthesis of a new compound. You have purified your product and stored the crystalline solid in a vial. Now you must verify the composition of your new compound and determine its molecular formula. You use analytical procedures to determine the relative masses of each element in the compound and calculate the percent composition.

Figure 10.13 Potassium chromate (K_2CrO_4) is composed of 40.3% potassium, 26.8% chromium, and 32.9% oxygen. **Interpreting Diagrams** *How does this percent composition differ from the percent composition of potassium dichromate ($K_2Cr_2O_7$), a compound composed of the same three elements?*

K_2CrO_4

26.8% Cr   32.9% O   40.3% K

Potassium chromate, K_2CrO_4

$K_2Cr_2O_7$

35.4% Cr   38.1% O   26.5% K

Potassium dichromate, $K_2Cr_2O_7$

Guide for Reading

⚷ **Key Concepts**
- How do you calculate the percent by mass of an element in a compound?
- What does the empirical formula of a compound show?
- How does the molecular formula of a compound compare with the empirical formula?

Vocabulary
percent composition
empirical formula

Reading Strategy
Comparing and Contrasting
When you compare and contrast things, you examine how they are alike and different. As you read, list the similarities and differences between empirical and molecular formulas.

Calculating Percent Composition from Mass Data

When a 13.60-g sample of a compound containing only magnesium and oxygen is decomposed, 5.40 g of oxygen is obtained. What is the percent composition of this compound?

1 Analyze *List the knowns and the unknowns.*

Knowns
- mass of compound = 13.60 g
- mass of oxygen = 5.40 g O
- mass of magnesium =
  13.60 g − 5.40 g = 8.20 g Mg

Unknowns
- percent Mg = ? % Mg
- percent O = ? % O

The percent by mass of an element in a compound is the mass of that element divided by the mass of the compound multiplied by 100%.

2 Calculate *Solve for the unknown.*

$$\% \text{ Mg} = \frac{\text{mass of Mg}}{\text{mass of compound}} \times 100\% = \frac{8.20 \text{ g}}{13.60 \text{ g}} \times 100\%$$

$$= 60.3\%$$

$$\% \text{ O} = \frac{\text{mass of O}}{\text{mass of compound}} \times 100\% = \frac{5.40 \text{ g}}{13.60 \text{ g}} \times 100\%$$

$$= 39.7\%$$

3 Evaluate *Does the result make sense?*

The percents of the elements add up to 100%:

$$60.3\% + 39.7\% = 100\%.$$

Practice Problems

32. A compound is formed when 9.03 g Mg combines completely with 3.48 g N. What is the percent composition of this compound?

33. When a 14.2-g sample of mercury(II) oxide is decomposed into its elements by heating, 13.2 g Hg is obtained. What is the percent composition of the compound?

Math Handbook

For help with percents go to page R72.

interactive Textbook

Problem-Solving 10.33
Solve Problem 33 with the help of an interactive guided tutorial.

with **ChemASAP**

Figure 10.14 The percent composition of water is always the same regardless of the volume of the water sample. A sample of water is always 11.1% H and 88.9% O by mass.

Percent Composition from the Chemical Formula You can also calculate the percent composition of a compound if you know only its chemical formula. The subscripts in the formula of the compound are used to calculate the mass of each element in a mole of that compound. The sum of these masses is the molar mass. Using the individual masses of the elements and the molar mass you can calculate the percent by mass of each element in one mole of the compound. Divide the mass of each element by the molar mass and multiply the result by 100%.

$$\% \text{ mass} = \frac{\text{mass of element in 1 mol compound}}{\text{molar mass of compound}} \times 100\%$$

The percent composition of a compound is always the same, as Figure 10.14 on the preceding page indicates.

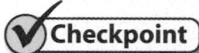 **Checkpoint** *How can you determine the percent by mass of an element in a compound if you know only the compound's formula?*

Go Online
NSTA *SciLINKS*
For: Links on Percent Composition
Visit: www.SciLinks.org
Web Code: cdn-1103

SAMPLE PROBLEM 10.10

Calculating the Percent Composition from a Formula

Propane (C_3H_8), the fuel commonly used in gas grills, is one of the lighter compounds obtained from petroleum. Calculate the percent composition of propane.

1 Analyze *List the knowns and the unknowns.*

Knowns
- mass of C in 1 mol C_3H_8 = 36.0 g
- mass of H in 1 mol C_3H_8 = 8.0 g
- molar mass of C_3H_8 = 44.0 g/mol

Unknowns
- percent C = ? % C
- percent H = ? % H

Calculate the percent by mass of each element by dividing the mass of that element in one mole of the compound by the molar mass of the compound and multiplying by 100%.

2 Calculate *Solve for the unknowns.*

$$\% \text{ C} = \frac{\text{mass of C}}{\text{mass of propane}} \times 100\% = \frac{36.0 \text{ g}}{44.0 \text{ g}} \times 100\% = 81.8\%$$

$$\% \text{ H} = \frac{\text{mass of H}}{\text{mass of propane}} \times 100\% = \frac{8.0 \text{ g}}{44.0 \text{ g}} \times 100\% = 18\%$$

3 Evaluate *Does the result make sense?*

The percents of the elements add up to 100% when the answers are expressed to two significant figures.

Math Handbook

For help with significant figures go to page R61.

Practice Problems

34. Calculate the percent composition of these compounds.
  a. ethane (C_2H_6)
  b. sodium bisulfate ($NaHSO_4$)

35. Calculate the percent nitrogen in these common fertilizers.
  a. NH_3
  b. NH_4NO_3

interactive Textbook

Problem-Solving 10.34
Solve Problem 34 with the help of an interactive guided tutorial.

— with **ChemASAP**

Percent Composition

Purpose
To measure the percent of water in a series of crystalline compounds called hydrates.

Materials
- centigram balance
- Bunsen burner
- 3 medium-sized test tubes
- test tube holder
- test tube rack
- spatula
- hydrated salts of copper(II) sulfate, calcium chloride, and sodium sulfate

Procedure

1. Label each test tube with the name of a salt. Measure and record the masses.
2. Add 2–3 g of salt (a good-sized spatula full) to the appropriately labeled test tube. Measure and record the mass of each test tube and salt.
3. Hold one of the tubes at a 45° angle and gently heat its contents over the burner, slowly passing it in and out of the flame. Note any change in the appearance of the solid salt.
4. As moisture begins to condense in the upper part of the test tube, gently heat the entire length of the tube. Continue heating until all of the moisture is driven from the tube. This may take 2–3 minutes. Repeat Steps 3 and 4 for the other two tubes.
5. Allow each tube to cool. Then measure and record the mass of each test tube and the heated salt.

Think About It!

1. Set up a data table so that you can subtract the mass of the empty tube from the mass of the salt and the test tube, both before and after heating.
2. Calculate the difference between the mass of each salt before and after heating. This difference represents the amount of water lost by the hydrate on heating.
3. Calculate the percent by mass of water lost by each compound.
4. Which compound lost the greatest percent by mass of water? The smallest?

Percent Composition as a Conversion Factor You can use percent composition to calculate the number of grams of any element in a specific mass of a compound. To do this, multiply the mass of the compound by a conversion factor based on the percent composition of the element in the compound. Suppose you want to know how much carbon and hydrogen are contained in 82.0 g of propane. In Sample Problem 10.10, you found that propane is 81.8% carbon and 18% hydrogen. That means that in a 100-g sample of propane, you would have 81.8 g of carbon and 18 g of hydrogen. You can use the ratio 81.8 g C/100 g C_3H_8 to calculate the mass of carbon contained in 82.0 g of propane (C_3H_8).

$$82.0 \text{ g } C_3H_8 \times \frac{81.8 \text{ g C}}{100 \text{ g } C_3H_8} = 67.1 \text{ g C}$$

Using the ratio 18 g H/100 g C_3H_8, you can calculate the mass of hydrogen.

$$82.0 \text{ g } C_3H_8 \times \frac{18 \text{ g H}}{100 \text{ g } C_3H_8} = 15 \text{ g H}$$

The sum of the two masses equals 82 g, the sample size, to two significant figures (67.1 g C + 15 g H = 82 g C_3H_8).

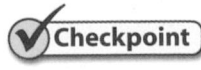 **Checkpoint** *How many grams of hydrogen are contained in a 100-g sample of propane?*

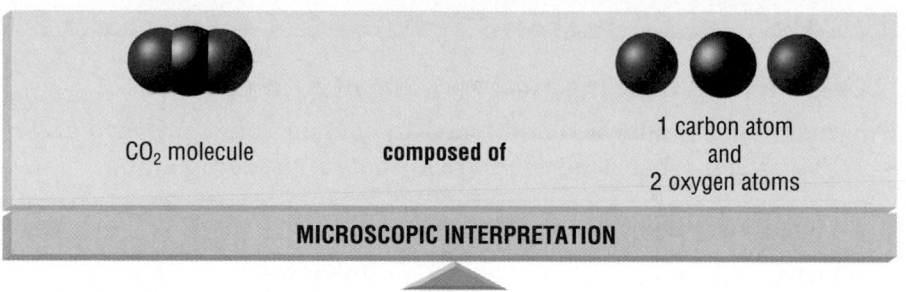

CO₂ molecule — composed of — 1 carbon atom and 2 oxygen atoms

MICROSCOPIC INTERPRETATION

CO_2

MACROSCOPIC INTERPRETATION

1 mol CO_2 — composed of — 6.02×10^{23} carbon atoms (1 mol C atoms) and $2 \times (6.02 \times 10^{23})$ oxygen atoms (2 mol O atoms)

Word *Origins*

Empirical comes from the Latin word *empiricus* meaning a doctor relying on experience alone. An empirical formula must be obtained from experimental data. Thus, an empirical formula relies on experience. **Is a molecular formula also based on experimental data?**

Empirical Formulas

A useful formula for cooking rice is to use one cup of rice and two cups of water. If a larger amount of rice is needed, you could double or triple the amounts, for example, two cups of rice and four cups of water. The formulas for some compounds also show a basic ratio of elements. Multiplying that ratio by any factor can produce the formulas for other compounds.

The percent composition of your newly synthesized compound is the data you need to calculate the basic ratio of the elements contained in the compound. The basic ratio, called the **empirical formula,** gives the lowest whole-number ratio of the atoms of the elements in a compound. For example, a compound may have the empirical formula CO_2. The empirical formula shows the kinds and lowest relative count of atoms or moles of atoms in molecules or formula units of a compound. Figure 10.15 shows that empirical formulas may be interpreted at the microscopic (atomic) or macroscopic (molar) level.

An empirical formula may or may not be the same as a molecular formula. For example, the lowest ratio of hydrogen to oxygen in hydrogen peroxide is 1:1. Thus the empirical formula of hydrogen peroxide is HO. The actual molecular formula of hydrogen peroxide has twice the number of atoms as the empirical formula. The molecular formula is (HO) $\times$ 2, or H_2O_2. But notice that the ratio of hydrogen to oxygen is still the same, 1:1.
⚷ **The empirical formula of a compound shows the smallest whole-number ratio of the atoms in the compound.** The molecular formula tells the actual number of each kind of atom present in a molecule of the compound. For carbon dioxide, the empirical and molecular formulas are the same—CO_2. Figure 10.16 shows two compounds of carbon having the same empirical formula (CH) but different molecular formulas.

Figure 10.16 Ethyne (C_2H_2), also called acetylene, is a gas used in welder's torches. Styrene (C_8H_8) is used in making polystyrene. These two compounds have the same empirical formula.
Calculating *What is the empirical formula of ethyne and styrene?*

Determining the Empirical Formula of a Compound

A compound is analyzed and found to contain 25.9% nitrogen and 74.1% oxygen. What is the empirical formula of the compound?

1 Analyze *List the knowns and the unknown.*

Knowns
- percent of nitrogen = 25.9% N
- percent of oxygen = 74.1% O

Unknown
- Empirical formula = $N_?O_?$

The percent composition tells the ratio of the mass of nitrogen atoms to the mass of oxygen atoms in the compound. Change the ratio of masses to a ratio of moles by using conversion factors based on the molar mass of each element. Then reduce this ratio to the lowest whole-number ratio.

2 Calculate *Solve for the unknown.*

Because percent means parts per 100, you can assume that 100.0 g of the compound contains 25.9 g N and 74.1 g O. Use these values to convert to moles.

$$25.9 \ \cancel{g \ N} \times \frac{1 \ mol \ N}{14.0 \ \cancel{g \ N}} = 1.85 \ mol \ N$$

$$74.1 \ \cancel{g \ O} \times \frac{1 \ mol \ O}{16.0 \ \cancel{g \ O}} = 4.63 \ mol \ O$$

The mole ratio of nitrogen to oxygen is $N_{1.85}O_{4.63}$. But formulas must have whole-number subscripts. Divide each molar quantity by the smaller number of moles. This gives 1 mol for the element with the smaller number of moles.

$$\frac{1.85 \ mol \ N}{1.85} = 1 \ mol \ N; \quad \frac{4.63 \ mol \ O}{1.85} = 2.50 \ mol \ O$$

The result, $N_1O_{2.5}$, still has a subscript that is not a whole number. To obtain the lowest whole number ratio, multiply each part of the ratio by the smallest whole number (in this case 2) that will convert both subscripts to whole numbers.

$$1 \ mol \ N \times 2 = 2 \ mol \ N$$
$$2.5 \ mol \ O \times 2 = 5 \ mol \ O$$

The empirical formula is N_2O_5.

3 Evaluate *Does the result make sense?*

The subscripts are whole numbers, and the percent composition of this empirical formula equals the percents given in the original problem.

Practice Problems

36. Calculate the empirical formula of each compound.
   a. 94.1% O, 5.9% H
   b. 67.6% Hg, 10.8% S, 21.6% O

37. 1,6-diaminohexane is used to make nylon. What is the empirical formula of this compound if it is 62.1% C, 13.8% H, and 24.1% N?

Math ▶ **Handbook**

For help with dimensional analysis go to page R68.

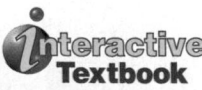
Textbook

Problem-Solving 10.36
Solve Problem 36 with the help of an interactive guided tutorial.

with ChemASAP

Table 10.3

Comparison of Empirical and Molecular Formulas

Formula (name)	Classification of formula	Molar mass
CH	Empirical	13
C_2H_2 (ethyne)	Molecular	26 (2 × 13)
C_6H_6 (benzene)	Molecular	78 (6 × 13)
CH_2O (methanal)	Empirical and Molecular	30
$C_2H_4O_2$ (ethanoic acid)	Molecular	60 (2 × 30)
$C_6H_{12}O_6$ (glucose)	Molecular	180 (6 × 30)

Molecular Formulas

Look at the compounds listed in Table 10.3. Ethyne and benzene have the same empirical formula—CH. Methanal, ethanoic acid, and glucose, shown in Figure 10.17 have the same empirical formula—CH_2O. But the compounds in these two groups have different molar masses. Their molar masses are simple whole-number multiples of the molar masses of the empirical formulas, CH and CH_2O. **The molecular formula of a compound is either the same as its experimentally determined empirical formula, or it is a simple whole-number multiple of its empirical formula.**

Once you have determined the empirical formula of your newly synthesized compound, you can determine its molecular formula, but you must know the compound's molar mass. A chemist often uses an instrument called a mass spectrometer to determine molar mass. The compound is broken into charged fragments (ions) that travel through a magnetic field. The magnetic field deflects the particles from their straight-line paths. The mass of the compound is determined from the amount of deflection experienced by the particles.

From the empirical formula, you can calculate the empirical formula mass (efm). This is simply the molar mass represented by the empirical formula. Then you can divide the experimentally determined molar mass by the empirical formula mass. This gives the number of empirical formula units in a molecule of the compound and is the multiplier to convert the empirical formula to the molecular formula. For example, recall that the empirical formula of hydrogen peroxide is HO. Its empirical formula mass is 17.0 g/mol. The molar mass of H_2O_2 is 34.0 g/mol.

$$\frac{34.0 \text{ g/mol}}{17.0 \text{ g/mol}} = 2$$

To obtain the molecular formula of hydrogen peroxide from its empirical formula, multiply the subscripts in the empirical formula by 2. (HO) × 2 = H_2O_2.

 **Checkpoint** *How does the molecular formula for a compound relate to its empirical formula?*

Figure 10.17 Methanal (formaldehyde), ethanoic acid (acetic acid), and glucose have the same empirical formula. **Applying Concepts** *How could you easily obtain the molar mass of glucose using the molar mass of methanal?*

SAMPLE PROBLEM 10.12

Finding the Molecular Formula of a Compound

Calculate the molecular formula of a compound whose molar mass is 60.0 g/mol and empirical formula is CH_4N.

1 **Analyze** *List the knowns and the unknown.*

Knowns
- empirical formula = CH_4N
- molar mass = 60.0 g/mol

Unknown
- molecular formula = ?

2 **Calculate** *Solve for the unknown.*

First calculate the empirical formula mass. Then divide the molar mass by the empirical formula mass to obtain a whole number. To get the molecular formula, multiply the formula subscripts by this value.

Empirical formula	efm	Molar mass/efm	Molecular formula
CH_4N	30.0	60.0/30.0 = 2	$C_2H_8N_2$

3 **Evaluate** *Does the result make sense?*

The molecular formula has the molar mass of the compound.

Practice Problems

Problem-Solving 10.38 Solve Problem 38 with the help of an interactive guided tutorial.

— with **ChemASAP**

38. Find the molecular formula of ethylene glycol, which is used as antifreeze. The molar mass is 62 g/mol and the empirical formula is CH_3O.

39. Which pair of molecules has the same empirical formula?
  a. $C_2H_4O_2$, $C_6H_{12}O_6$
  b. $NaCrO_4$, $Na_2Cr_2O_7$

10.3 Section Assessment

40. 🔑 **Key Concept** How do you calculate the percent by mass of an element in a compound?

41. 🔑 **Key Concept** What information can you obtain from an empirical formula?

42. 🔑 **Key Concept** How is the molecular formula of a compound related to its empirical formula?

43. Calculate the percent composition of the compound that forms when 222.6 g N combines completely with 77.4 g O.

44. Calculate the percent composition of calcium acetate ($Ca(C_2H_3O_2)_2$).

45. The compound methyl butanoate smells like apples. Its percent composition is 58.8% C, 9.8% H, and 31.4% O and its molar mass is 102 g/mol. What is its empirical formula? What is its molecular formula?

46. What is an empirical formula? Which of the following molecular formulas are also empirical formulas?
  a. ribose ($C_5H_{10}O_5$)
  b. ethyl butyrate ($C_6H_{12}O_2$)
  c. chlorophyll ($C_{55}H_{72}MgN_4O_5$)
  d. DEET ($C_{12}H_{17}ON$)

Elements ▶ **Handbook**

Calcium Select three important compounds that contain calcium from among those discussed on page R11 of the Elements Handbook. Determine the percent of calcium in each.

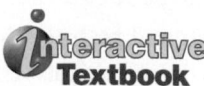

Assessment 10.3 Test yourself on the concepts in Section 10.3.

— with **ChemASAP**

Drug Testing

A test to identify an abused substance in the body must be extremely accurate. A false-positive result could ruin a career. A false-negative result could endanger lives. The best method currently available to test for drug abuse is the gas chromatography/mass spectrometer system, or GC/MS. Gas chromatography separates a chemical mixture and identifies its components. Mass spectrometry uses masses to verify the identification. Used together, the GC/MS testing is nearly 100% reliable.

Interpreting Diagrams *What is the purpose of the separation column?*

Testing athletes The results of a drug test could keep an athlete out of an upcoming event, and possibly off the team permanently.

2 The separation column is packed with a material that interacts physically with the vaporized sample. Components of the mixture move at different rates along the column and then pass through a detector.

3 Each peak on a gas chromatogram shows the retention time for a component. Retention time is used to identify compounds.

Detector

Heated metal block

1 The sample to be tested, such as urine or blood serum, is vaporized and mixed with an unreactive carrier gas such as helium. The resulting gas mixture is forced through a separation column.

HELIUM

4 The separated component enters a mass spectrometer where its identity is confirmed.

Key Concepts

 10.1 The Mole: A Measurement of Matter

- Three methods for measuring the amount of a substance are by count, by mass, and by volume.
- A mole of any substance always contains Avogadro's number of representative particles, or 6.02×10^{23} representative particles.
- The atomic mass of an element expressed in grams is the mass of a mole of the element.
- To calculate the molar mass of a compound, find the number of grams of each element contained in one mole of the compound. Then add the masses of the elements in the compound.

 10.2 Mole–Mass and Mole–Volume Relationships

- The molar mass of an element or compound is the conversion factor for converting between the mass and the number of moles of a substance.

- One mole of any gas occupies a volume of 22.4 L at standard temperature and pressure. One mole of any substance contains Avogadro's number of particles, so 22.4 L of any gas at STP contains 6.02×10^{23} representative particles of that gas.

 10.3 Percent Composition and Chemical Formulas

- To determine the percent by mass of any element in a given compound, divide the element's mass by the mass of the compound and multiply by 100%.
- An empirical formula of a compound is the simplest whole-number ratio of atoms of the elements in the compound.
- The molecular formula of a compound is either the same as its experimentally determined empirical formula, or it is a simple whole-number multiple of it.

Vocabulary

- Avogadro's hypothesis (p. 300)
- Avogadro's number (p. 290)
- empirical formula (p. 309)
- molar mass (p. 294)
- molar volume (p. 300)
- mole (mol) (p. 290)
- percent composition (p. 305)
- representative particle (p. 290)
- standard temperature and pressure (STP) (p. 300)

Key Equations

- $\text{moles} = \text{representative particles} \times \dfrac{1 \text{ mole}}{6.02 \times 10^{23} \text{ representative particles}}$

- $\text{representative particles} = \text{moles} \times \dfrac{6.02 \times 10^{23} \text{ representative particles}}{1 \text{ mole}}$

- $\text{mass (grams)} = \text{number of moles} \times \dfrac{\text{mass (grams)}}{1 \text{ mole}}$

- $\text{moles} = \text{mass (grams)} \times \dfrac{1 \text{ mole}}{\text{mass (grams)}}$

- $\dfrac{\text{grams}}{\text{mole}} = \dfrac{\text{grams}}{\text{L}} \times \dfrac{22.4 \text{ L}}{1 \text{ mole}}$

- $\text{volume of gas} = \text{moles of gas} \times \dfrac{22.4 \text{ L}}{1 \text{ mol}}$

- $\% \text{ mass of element} = \dfrac{\text{mass of element}}{\text{mass of compound}} \times 100\%$

Organizing Information

Organize the major ideas of the chapter.

Concept Map 10 Solve the Concept Map with the help of an interactive tutorial.

──with ChemASAP

Avogadro's number

Empirical formula

Molar volume

Molar mass

Mole (mol)

Percent composition

Representative particle

Standard temperature and pressure (STP)

10.1 The Mole: A Measurement of Matter

47. List three common ways that matter is measured. Give examples of each.

48. Name the representative particle (atom, molecule, or ion) of each substance.
   a. oxygen gas   **b.** sodium sulfide
   c. sulfur dioxide   **d.** potassium

49. How many hydrogen atoms are in a representative particle of each substance?
   a. $Al(OH)_3$ **b.** $H_2C_2O_4$
   c. $(NH_4)_2HPO_4$ **d.** $C_4H_{10}O$

50. Which contains more molecules: 1.00 mol H_2O_2, 1.00 mol C_2H_6, or 1.00 mol CO?

51. Which contains more atoms: 1.00 mol H_2O_2, 1.00 mol C_2H_6, or 1.00 mol CO?

52. Find the number of representative particles in each substance.
   a. 3.00 mol Sn   **b.** 0.400 mol KCl
   c. 7.50 mol SO_2 **d.** 4.80×10^{-3} mol NaI

53. Calculate the molar mass of each substance.
   a. H_3PO_4 **b.** N_2O_3 **c.** $CaCO_3$
   d. $(NH_4)_2SO_4$ **e.** $C_4H_9O_2$ **f.** Br_2

54. Calculate the mass of 1.00 mol of each of these substances.
   a. silicon dioxide (SiO_2)
   b. diatomic nitrogen (N_2)
   c. iron(III) hydroxide ($Fe(OH)_3$)
   d. copper (Cu)

55. List the steps you would take to calculate the molar mass of any compound.

56. What is the molar mass of chlorine gas?

57. Construct a numerical problem to illustrate the size of Avogadro's number. Exchange problems with a classmate and then compare your answers.

58. Explain what is wrong with each statement.
   a. One mole of any substance contains the same number of atoms.
   b. A mole and a molecule of a substance are identical in amount.
   c. One molar mass of CO_2 contains Avogadro's number of atoms.

59. A typical virus is 5×10^{-6} cm in diameter. If Avogadro's number of these virus particles were laid in a row, how many kilometers long would the line be?

60. How many water molecules are in a 1-L bottle of water? The density of water is 1.00 g/mL.

61. Why does one mole of carbon have a smaller mass than one mole of sulfur? How are the atomic structures of these elements different?

62. The density of nickel is 8.91 g/cm³. How large a cube, in cm³, would contain 2.00×10^{24} atoms of nickel?

63. Dry air is about 20.95% oxygen by volume. Assuming STP, how many oxygen molecules are in a 75.0-g sample of air? The density of air is 1.19 g/L.

64. The table below gives the molar mass and density of seven gases at STP.

Substance	Molar mass (g)	Density (g/L)
Oxygen	32.0	1.43
Carbon dioxide	44.0	1.96
Ethane	30.0	1.34
Hydrogen	2.0	0.089
Sulfur dioxide	64.1	2.86
Ammonia	17.0	0.759
Fluorine	38.0	1.70

   a. Plot these data, with density on the x-axis.
   b. What is the slope of the straight-line plot?
   c. What is the molar mass of a gas at STP that has a density of 1.10 g/L?
   d. A mole of a gas at STP has a mass of 56.0 g. Use the graph to determine its density.

65. A cubic meter of ocean water contains 6×10^{-6} g gold. If the total mass of the water in Earth's oceans is 4×10^{20} kg, how many kilograms of gold are distributed throughout the oceans? (Assume that the density of seawater is 1 g/cm³.) How many liters of seawater would have to be processed to recover 1 kg of gold (which has a value of about $8850 at 2001 prices)? Do you think this recovery operation is feasible?

66. Avogadro's number has been determined by about 20 different methods. In one approach, the spacing between ions in an ionic substance

CHAPTER
10
Review and Assessment *continued*
Blue questions emphasize Regents Exam content

NEW YORK

is determined by using a technique called X-ray diffraction. X-ray diffraction studies of sodium chloride have shown that the distance between adjacent Na^+ and Cl^- ions is 2.819×10^{-28} cm. The density of solid sodium chloride is 2.165 g/cm^3. By calculating the molar mass to four significant figures, you can determine Avogadro's number. What value do you obtain?

10.2 Mole-Mass and Mole-Volume Relationships

67. How many moles is in each of the following?
 a. 15.5 g SiO_2 b. 0.0688 g AgCl
 c. 79.3 g Cl_2 d. 5.96 g KOH
 e. 937 g $Ca(C_2H_3O_2)_2$ f. 0.800 g Ca

68. Find the mass of each substance.
 a. 1.50 mol C_5H_{12} b. 14.4 mol F_2
 c. 0.780 mol $Ca(CN)_2$ d. 7.00 mol H_2O_2
 e. 5.60 mol NaOH f. 3.21×10^{-2} mol Ni

Use the following information to answer Questions 69 and 70.

Equal volumes of gases at the same temperature and pressure contain an equal number of particles. At STP, 22.4 L of a gas contains one mole of the gas.

69. Calculate the volume of each of the following gases at STP.
 a. 7.6 mol Ar b. 0.44 mol C_2H_6

70. What is the density of each of the following gases at STP?
 a. C_3H_8 b. Ne c. NO_2

71. Find each of the following quantities.
 a. the volume, in liters, of 835 g SO_3 at STP
 b. the mass, in grams, of a molecule of aspirin ($C_9H_8O_4$)
 c. the number of atoms in 5.78 mol NH_4NO_3

72. How can you determine the molar mass of a gaseous compound if you do not know its molecular formula?

73. Which of the following choices contains the largest number of moles?
 a. 82.0 g Kr b. 0.842 mol C_2H_4
 c. 36.0 g N_2

74. What is the total mass of a mixture of 3.50×10^{22} formula units Na_2SO_4, 0.500 mol H_2O, and 7.23 g AgCl?

75. What mass of helium is needed to inflate a balloon to a volume of 5.50 L at STP?

76. One mole of any gas at STP equals 22.4 L of that gas. It is also true that different elements have different atomic volumes, or diameters. How can you reconcile these two statements?

10.3 Percent Composition and Chemical Formulas

77. Calculate the percent composition of each compound.
 a. H_2S b. $(NH_4)_2C_2O_4$
 c. $Mg(OH)_2$ d. Na_3PO_4

78. Using your answers from Problem 77, calculate the number of grams of these elements.
 a. sulfur in 3.54 g H_2S
 b. nitrogen in 25.0 g $(NH_4)_2C_2O_4$
 c. magnesium in 97.4 g $Mg(OH)_2$
 d. phosphorus in 804 g Na_3PO_4

79. Which of the following compounds has the highest iron content?
 a. $FeCl_2$ b. $Fe(C_2H_3O_2)_3$
 c. $Fe(OH)_2$ d. FeO

80. You find that 7.36 g of a compound has decomposed to give 6.93 g of oxygen. The only other element in the compound is hydrogen. If the molar mass of the compound is 34.0 g/mol, what is the molecular formula?

81. Classify each formula as an empirical or a molecular formula.
 a. S_2Cl_2 b. $C_6H_{10}O_4$ c. Na_2SO_3

82. What is the molecular formula for each compound? Each compound's empirical formula and molar mass is given.
 a. CH_2O, 90 g/mol b. HgCl, 472.2 g/mol

83. Determine the molecular formula for each compound.
 a. 94.1% O and 5.9% H; molar mass = 34 g
 b. 50.7% C, 4.2% H, and 45.1% O; molar mass = 142 g

84. A series of compounds has the empirical formula CH_2O. The graph that follows shows the relationship between the molar mass of the compounds and the mass of carbon in each compound.

Molar mass vs. mass of carbon

a. What are the molecular formulas for the compounds represented by data points A, D, and E?

b. Find the slope of the line. Is this value consistent with the empirical formula? Explain.

c. Two other valid data points fall on the line between points A and D. What are the (x, y) values for these data points?

85. Determine the empirical formulas of compounds with the following percent compositions.
a. 42.9% C and 57.1% O
b. 32.00% C, 42.66% O, 18.67% N, and 6.67% H
c. 71.72% Cl, 16.16% O, and 12.12% C

86. An imaginary "atomic balance" is shown below. Fifteen atoms of boron on the left side of the balance are balanced by six atoms of an unknown element E on the right side.

a. What is the atomic mass of element E?
b. What is the identity of element E?

87. Calculate the empirical formula for each compound.
a. compound consisting of 0.40 mol Cu and 0.80 mol Br

b. compound with 4 atoms of carbon for every 12 atoms of hydrogen

88. The molecular formula of the antibacterial drug Cipro is $C_{17}H_{18}FN_3O_3$. How many fluorine atoms are in a 150-mg tablet of Cipro?

89. What is the empirical formula of a compound that has three times as many hydrogen atoms as carbon atoms, but only half as many oxygen atoms as carbon atoms?

90. How are the empirical and molecular formulas of a compound related?

91. The graph shows the percent composition of phenylalanine.

Percent Composition of Phenylalanine

a. What is the empirical formula for phenylalanine?
b. If the molar mass of phenylalanine is 165.2 g/mol, what is its molecular formula?

92. Nitroglycerine contains 60% as many carbon atoms as hydrogen atoms, three times as many oxygen atoms as nitrogen atoms, and the same number of carbon and nitrogen atoms. The number of moles of nitroglycerine in 1.00 g is 0.00441. What is the molecular formula of nitroglycerine?

Test-Taking Tip

Wear a Watch. Be aware of how many questions you have to answer and how much time you have to answer them. Look at your watch or a clock frequently to keep track of your progress.

Regents Practice Exam

Part A

For each statement or question write the number of the word or expression that, of those given, best completes the statement or answers the question.

1. The sum of the atomic masses of the atoms in a compound is the
   (1) mass number
   (3) formula mass
   (2) molar mass
   (4) atomic number

2. The formula $C_6H_{12}O_6$ is an example of a(n)
   (1) empirical formula
   (2) molecular formula
   (3) structural formula
   (4) percent composition

3. A unit used for molar mass is
   (1) g/L
   (3) g
   (2) g/mL
   (4) amu

4. Percent composition can be calculated by
   (1) dividing the mass of each element by the total mass and multiplying by 100%
   (2) dividing the total mass by the mass of each element and multiplying by 100%
   (3) multiplying the mass of each element by the total mass and dividing by 100%
   (4) multiplying the total mass by the mass of each element and dividing by 100%

Part B-1

For each statement or question write the number of the word or expression that, of those given, best completes the statement or answers the question.

5. One balloon contains 1.00 L of nitrogen gas, and another balloon contains 1.00 L of carbon dioxide gas. The balloons are at the same temperature and pressure. Which of the following statements is true?
   (1) The balloons contain the same mass of gas.
   (2) The balloons contain the same number of gas particles.
   (3) One balloon contains more gas particles than the other balloon contains.
   (4) The balloons will have the same volume only at that temperature and pressure.

6. A red rose turning brown is an example of a
   (1) chemical change
   (3) physical change
   (2) chemical property
   (4) physical property

7. Which of the following statements is *not* true about every solution?
   (1) Solutions are liquid.
   (2) Solutions are homogeneous.
   (3) Solutions are mixtures.
   (4) Solutions are composed of at least two substances.

8. Which of the following chemical formulas is correct?
   (1) HO_2
   (3) SrO
   (2) CaS_2
   (4) $BaOH$

9. The molar mass of ammonium phosphate is
   (1) 149.0 g
   (3) 242.0 g
   (2) 113.0 g
   (4) 121.0 g

10. The structural formula for tartaric acid, a compound found in grape juice, is shown below. What is the empirical formula for tartaric acid?

$$HO - CH - COOH$$
$$| $$
$$HO - CH - COOH$$

   (1) $C_2H_3O_3$
   (3) CHO
   (2) $C_4H_6O_6$
   (4) $C_1H_{1.5}O_{1.5}$

11. How many hydrogen atoms are in six molecules of ethylene glycol, $HOCH_2CH_2OH$?
   (1) 6 H atoms
   (3) 3.6×10^{24} H atoms
   (2) 36 H atoms
   (4) 2.2×10^{25} H atoms

12. Which of the following compounds has the largest percent by mass of nitrogen?
   (1) NO
   (3) NO_2
   (2) N_2O_3
   (4) N_2O

Part B-2

Answer each of the following questions.

13. Identify at least one chemical change and one physical change that are occurring in the photo.

14. How does a molecule differ from an atom?

15. A student writes down the density of table sugar as 1.59 and the density of carbon dioxide as 1.83. Can these values be correct? Explain.

16. Convert each of the following measurements.
   a. 4.72 g to mg
   b. 2.7×10^3 cm to km
   c. 4.4 mm to dm

17. How many protons, electrons, and neutrons are in each of the following isotopes?
   a. zirconium-90   **c.** bromine-81
   b. palladium-108   **d.** antimony-123

18. Write the complete electron configuration for each of the following atoms.
   a. fluorine   **b.** lithium   **c.** rubidium

19. Why do the elements magnesium and barium have similar chemical and physical properties?

20. How can the periodic table be used to infer the number of valence electrons in an atom?

21. Draw electron dot structures for each of the following molecules. Use the structures to predict whether the molecules are polar or not.
   a. PH_3 **b.** CO   **c.** CS_2 **d.** CF_4

22. How are single, double, and triple bonds indicated in electron dot structures?

23. Explain how you can use electronegativity values to classify a bond as nonpolar covalent, polar covalent, or ionic.

24. Name each of the following compounds.
   a. $Fe(OH)_3$ **c.** Na_2CO_3
   b. NH_4I **d.** CCl_4

25. Write formulas for each of the following compounds.
   a. potassium nitrate   **c.** magnesium nitride
   b. copper(II) oxide   **d.** silver fluoride

26. What is the empirical formula for each of the following compounds?
   a. C_8H_{12} **c.** $C_{12}H_{24}$ **e.** C_4H_{10}
   b. C_6H_6 **d.** C_2H_6

Use the following ball-and-stick models to answer Questions 27–29. In the models, carbon is black, hydrogen is light blue, oxygen is red, and nitrogen is dark blue. Write the molecular formula for each compound. Then calculate its molar mass.

27.

28.

29.

Part C

Answer each of the following questions.

30. A block of wood measuring 2.75 cm × 4.80 cm × 7.50 cm has a mass of 84.0 g. Will the block of wood sink in water, or will it float? The density of water is 1.00 g/mL.

31. Classify each of the following events as either a physical change or a chemical change.
   a. An aspirin tablet is crushed to a powder.
   b. Grape juice turns to wine.
   c. Fingernail polish remover evaporates.
   d. A bean seed sprouts.
   e. A piece of copper is beaten into a thin sheet.

32. Allicin, $C_6H_{10}S_2O$, is the compound that gives garlic its odor. A sample of allicin contains 3.0×10^{21} atoms of carbon. How many atoms of hydrogen does this sample contain?
   (1) 1.8×10^{21} atoms   **(3)** 5.0×10^{21} atoms
   (2) 10 atoms   **(4)** 1.0×10^{21} atoms

33. Muscle fatigue can result from the buildup of lactic acid resulting from over-exercising. The empirical formula of lactic acid is CH_2O.
   a. What is the percent composition of lactic acid?
   b. What is the molecular formula of lactic acid if its molar mass is 90.0 g/mol?

The brilliant colors of Autumn are evidence that chemical reactions have occurred.

INQUIRY Activity

Modeling Chemical Reactions

Materials
36 colored paper clips (12 each of 3 different colors)

Procedure
1. Each paper clip represents a single atom. Designate a different color of paper clip to represent atoms of oxygen (O), hydrogen (H), and carbon (C). Make two molecules each of hydrogen (H_2) and methane (CH_4) and six molecules of oxygen (O_2).

2. "React" one H_2 with one O_2 by splitting the molecules and joining one oxygen atom to two hydrogen atoms. Because there is an unreacted oxygen atom, you must react it with another hydrogen molecule to form a second water molecule.

3. Summarize what happened in this reaction by placing the number of each molecule reacted or formed in front of its formula.

$$\_\_\_H_2 + \_\_\_O_2 \longrightarrow \_\_\_H_2O$$

4. Now "react" methane (CH_4) with oxygen (O_2) to produce carbon dioxide (CO_2) and water (H_2O). Start with one molecule of methane and one molecule of oxygen. Continue reacting molecules of CH_4 and O_2 until all the reactant atoms have been used to form products.

5. Summarize what happened in this reaction.

$$\_\_\_CH_4 + \_\_\_O_2 \longrightarrow \_\_\_CO_2 + \_\_\_H_2O$$

Think About It

1. Summarize Dalton's atomic theory.

2. How might the numbers and kinds of atoms to the left and right of the arrow ($\longrightarrow$) in the model reactions you performed support this theory?

320

11.1 Describing Chemical Reactions

New York Standards: 3.3a, 3.3c, 3.4f

Connecting to Your World

On May 6, 1937, the huge airship Hindenburg was heading for its landing site in Lakehurst, New Jersey, after an uneventful trans-Atlantic crossing. Suddenly, to the horror of observers on the ground, the airship erupted into a fireball. Within a short time, 210,000 cubic meters of the airship's lifting gas, hydrogen, had burned and the airship was destroyed. The chemical reaction that occurred can be described as "hydrogen combines with oxygen to produce water." In this section, you will learn to represent this chemical reaction by a chemical equation.

Guide for Reading

Key Concepts
- How do you write a word equation?
- How do you write a skeleton equation?
- What are the steps in writing a balanced chemical equation?

Vocabulary
chemical equation
skeleton equation
catalyst
coefficients
balanced equation

Reading Strategy

Relating Text and Visuals As you read this lesson, look carefully at the illustrations of equations. In your notebook, explain how the illustrations demonstrate the difference between a balanced and unbalanced chemical equation.

Writing Chemical Equations

Every minute of the day chemical reactions take place—both inside you and around you. Not all are as dramatic as the explosion of the Hindenburg, but many are more complex. After a meal, a series of chemical reactions take place as your body digests food. Similarly, plants use sunlight to drive the photosynthetic processes needed to produce plant growth. Although the chemical reactions involved in photosynthesis and digestion are different, both chemical reactions are necessary to sustain life.

In a chemical reaction, one or more substances (the reactants) change into one or more new substances (the products). Figure 11.1a shows the ingredients for making leavened bread—flour, salt, yeast, and water. These are the reactants in a chemical reaction that takes place when the ingredients are mixed together and heated in the oven. Figure 11.1b shows the product—a loaf of bread. The four ingredients (reactants) were changed to bread (the product). Like all chemical reactions, baking bread involves changing substances. Chemists use a chemical equation—a quick, shorthand notation—to convey as much information as possible about what happens in a chemical reaction.

Figure 11.1 Chemical changes occur when bread is baked. **ⓐ** Flour, salt, yeast, and water are the ingredients for making leavened bread. **ⓑ** The reactants (ingredients) undergo chemical changes to form the product (baked bread).
Observing *What evidence shows that chemical changes have occurred?*

Figure 11.2 Three common chemical reactions are shown. **ⓐ** When methane gas burns, it combines with oxygen to form carbon dioxide and water. **ⓑ** Iron turns to red-brown rust (iron(III) oxide) in the presence of oxygen in the air. **ⓒ** Hydrogen peroxide decomposes to water and oxygen when used as an antiseptic.

Word Equations How do you describe what happens in a chemical reaction? Recall from Chapter 2 the shorthand method for writing a description of a chemical reaction. In this method, the reactants were written on the left and the products on the right. An arrow separated them. You read the arrow as *yields*, *gives*, or *reacts to produce*.

$$\text{Reactants} \longrightarrow \text{products}$$

How could you describe the rusting of iron shown in Figure 11.2b? You could say: "Iron reacts with oxygen to produce iron(III) oxide (rust)." That's a perfectly good description, but it might be quicker and easier to identify the reactants and product by means of a word equation.

$$\text{Iron} + \text{oxygen} \longrightarrow \text{iron(III) oxide}$$

🔑 **To write a word equation, write the names of the reactants to the left of the arrow separated by plus signs; write the names of the products to the right of the arrow, also separated by plus signs.** Notice that no plus sign is needed on the product side of this equation because iron(III) oxide is the only product.

Have you ever poured the antiseptic hydrogen peroxide on an open cut? Bubbles of oxygen gas form rapidly, as shown in Figure 11.2c. The production of a new substance, a gas, is evidence of a chemical change. Two new substances are produced in this reaction, oxygen gas and liquid water. You could describe this reaction by saying, "Hydrogen peroxide decomposes to form water and oxygen gas." You could also write a word equation.

$$\text{Hydrogen peroxide} \longrightarrow \text{water} + \text{oxygen}$$

When you light a burner on your stove, methane gas bursts into flames and produces the energy needed to heat your soup. Methane is the major component of natural gas, a common fuel for heating homes and cooking food. The burning of methane, as shown in Figure 11.2a, is a chemical reaction. How would you write the word equation for this reaction? Burning a substance typically requires oxygen, so methane and oxygen are the reactants. The products are water and carbon dioxide. Thus the word equation is this:

$$\text{Methane} + \text{oxygen} \longrightarrow \text{carbon dioxide} + \text{water}$$

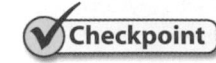 **Checkpoint** *What does the arrow (——→) in a word equation mean?*

Chemical Equations Word equations adequately describe chemical reactions, but they are cumbersome. It's easier to use the formulas for the reactants and products to write chemical equations. A **chemical equation** is a representation of a chemical reaction; the formulas of the reactants (on the left) are connected by an arrow with the formulas of the products (on the right). Here is a chemical equation for rusting:

$$Fe + O_2 \longrightarrow Fe_2O_3$$

Equations that show just the formulas of the reactants and products are called skeleton equations. A **skeleton equation** is a chemical equation that does not indicate the relative amounts of the reactants and products. The first step in writing a complete chemical equation is to write the skeleton equation. ⊙ **Write the formulas of the reactants to the left of the yields sign (arrow) and the formulas of the products to the right.**

To add more information to the equation, you can indicate the physical states of substances by putting a symbol after each formula. Use (*s*) for a solid, (*l*) for a liquid, (*g*) for a gas, and (*aq*) for a substance in aqueous solution (a substance dissolved in water). Here is the equation for rusting with symbols for the physical states added:

$$Fe(s) + O_2(g) \longrightarrow Fe_2O_3(s)$$

In many chemical reactions, a catalyst is added to the reaction mixture. A **catalyst** is a substance that speeds up the reaction but is not used up in the reaction. A catalyst is neither a reactant nor a product, so its formula is written above the arrow in a chemical equation. For example, Figure 11.3 shows that the compound manganese(IV) oxide ($MnO_2(s)$) catalyzes the decomposition of an aqueous solution of hydrogen peroxide ($H_2O_2(aq)$) to produce water and oxygen.

$$H_2O_2(aq) \xrightarrow{MnO_2} H_2O(l) + O_2(g)$$

Many of the symbols commonly used in writing chemical equations are listed in Table 11.1.

a

b

Figure 11.3 Hydrogen peroxide decomposes to form water and oxygen gas. **a** Bubbles of oxygen appear slowly as decomposition proceeds. **b** With the addition of the catalyst manganese(IV) oxide (MnO_2), decomposition speeds up. The white "smoke" is condensed water vapor.

Table 11.1	
Symbols Used in Chemical Equations	

Symbol	Explanation
+	Used to separate two reactants or two products
$\longrightarrow$	"Yields," separates reactants from products
$\rightleftharpoons$	Used in place of $\longrightarrow$ for reversible reactions
(*s*)	Designates a reactant or product in the solid state; placed after the formula
(*l*)	Designates a reactant or product in the liquid state; placed after the formula
(*g*)	Designates a reactant or product in the gaseous state; placed after the formula
(*aq*)	Designates an aqueous solution; the substance is dissolved in water; placed after the formula
$\xrightarrow{\Delta} \xrightarrow{heat}$	Indicates that heat is supplied to the reaction
$\xrightarrow{Pt}$	A formula written above or below the yield sign indicates its use as a catalyst (in this example, platinum).

***i*nteractive Textbook**

Animation 12 Relate chemical symbols and formulas to the information they communicate.

— with **ChemASAP**

Writing a Skeleton Equation

Hydrochloric acid and solid sodium hydrogen carbonate are shown before being placed in the beaker to react. The products formed are aqueous sodium chloride, water, and carbon dioxide gas. Write a skeleton equation for this chemical reaction.

1 **Analyze** *Identify the relevant concepts.*

Write the correct formula for each substance in the reaction. Separate the reactants from the products by means of an arrow. Indicate the state of each substance.

2 **Solve** *Apply concepts to this situation.*

solid sodium hydrogen carbonate: $NaHCO_3(s)$
hydrochloric acid: $HCl(aq)$
aqueous sodium chloride: $NaCl(aq)$
water: $H_2O(l)$
carbon dioxide gas: $CO_2(g)$
$NaHCO_3(s) + HCl(aq) \longrightarrow NaCl(aq) + H_2O(l) + CO_2(g)$

Practice Problems

1. Write a sentence that describes this chemical reaction.
$Na(s) + H_2O(l) \longrightarrow NaOH(aq) + H_2(g)$

2. Sulfur burns in oxygen to form sulfur dioxide. Write a skeleton equation for this chemical reaction. Include appropriate symbols from Table 11.1.

Textbook

Problem-Solving 11.2
Solve Problem 2 with the help of an interactive guided tutorial.

with ChemASAP

Balancing Chemical Equations

How would you write a word equation for the manufacture of bicycles? Simplify your task by limiting yourself to four major components: frames, wheels, handlebars, and pedals. Your word equation for making a bicycle could read like this.

$$\text{Frame} + \text{wheel} + \text{handlebar} + \text{pedal} \longrightarrow \text{bicycle}$$
$$\text{(reactants)} \qquad\qquad\qquad\qquad \text{(product)}$$

Your word equation shows the reactants (the kinds of parts) and the product (a bicycle). But if you were responsible for ordering parts to make a bicycle, this word equation would be inadequate because it does not indicate the quantity of each part needed to make one bicycle.

A standard bicycle is composed of one frame (F), two wheels (W), one handlebar (H), and two pedals (P). Using these symbols, the formula for a bicycle would be FW_2HP_2. The skeleton equation for bicycle assembly would be this:

$$F + W + H + P \longrightarrow FW_2HP_2$$

This is an unbalanced equation. An unbalanced equation does not indicate the quantity of the reactants needed to make the product. A complete description of the reaction must include not only the kinds of parts involved but also the quantities of parts required.

$$\text{F} \qquad + \qquad \text{2W} \qquad + \quad \text{H} \quad + \quad \text{2P} \longrightarrow \text{FW}_2\text{HP}_2$$

This is a balanced equation for making a bicycle. It tells you that one frame, two wheels, one handlebar, and two pedals produce one bicycle. To balance the equation, the number 2 was placed before wheels and pedals. The number 1 is understood to be in front of frame, handlebar, and bicycle. These numbers are called **coefficients**—small whole numbers that are placed in front of the formulas in an equation in order to balance it. In this balanced equation, the number of each bicycle part on the reactant side is the same as the number of those parts on the product side. A chemical reaction is also described by a **balanced equation** in which each side of the equation has the same number of atoms of each element and mass is conserved. Real bicycles are being assembled in Figure 11.4.

Recall that John Dalton's atomic theory states that as reactants are converted to products, the bonds holding the atoms together are broken and new bonds are formed. The atoms themselves are neither created nor destroyed; they are merely rearranged. This part of Dalton's theory explains the law of conservation of mass: In any chemical change, mass is conserved. The atoms in the products are the same atoms that were in the reactants—they are just rearranged.

Representing a chemical reaction by a balanced chemical equation is a two-step process. ☞ **To write a balanced chemical equation, first write the skeleton equation. Then use coefficients to balance the equation so that it obeys the law of conservation of mass.** In every balanced equation, each side of the equation has the same number of atoms of each element.

Sometimes a skeleton equation may already be balanced. For example, carbon burns in the presence of oxygen to produce carbon dioxide.

C(s)	+	O$_2$(g) $\longrightarrow$ CO$_2$(g)
Reactants		**Product**
1 carbon atom, 2 oxygen atoms		1 carbon atom, 2 oxygen atoms

This equation is balanced. One carbon atom and two oxygen atoms are on each side of the equation. You do not need to change the coefficients; they are all understood to be 1.

✓ Checkpoint *What is the law of conservation of mass?*

Figure 11.4 If a bicycle factory runs out of any part needed for a bicycle, production must stop.

Removing Silver Tarnish

Materials

- aluminum foil, 20 cm × 20 cm
- large beaker or glass pan
- tarnished silver fork or spoon
- sodium hydrogen carbonate
- plastic tablespoon
- hot water

Procedure

1. Fill the beaker about three-quarters full of hot water and add 2 tablespoons of sodium hydrogen carbonate ($NaHCO_3$).

2. Crush the aluminum foil into a loose ball and place it in the beaker.

3. Write a brief description of the tarnished silver fork, then place it in the beaker so that it is touching the aluminum ball.

4. Allow the beaker to stand undisturbed for 30 minutes.

5. Remove the fork and aluminum ball and rinse them with water.

Analyze and Conclude

1. Compare the silver fork with your observations before placing the fork in the water. What changes do you observe?

2. Did a chemical reaction occur? How do you know?

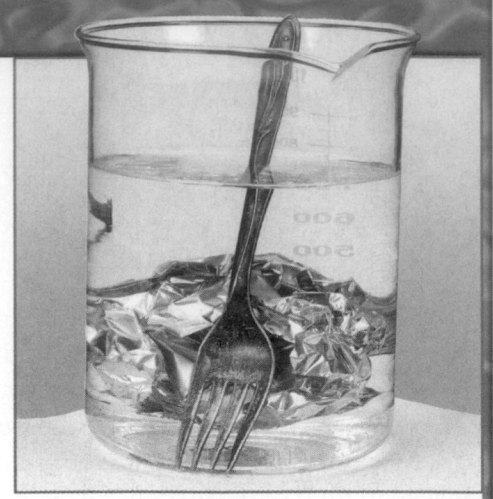

3. The tarnish on the silver fork is silver sulfide (Ag_2S). Silver becomes tarnished when it is exposed to air, egg yolk, or rubber bands. Each of these substances contains sulfur. Look carefully for a pale yellow precipitate of aluminum sulfide on the bottom of the beaker. Write the formula for aluminum sulfide.

4. The unbalanced equation for the reaction is

$$Ag_2S(s) + Al(s) \longrightarrow Al_2S_3(s) + Ag(s)$$

Balance the equation.

What about the equation for the reaction of hydrogen gas and oxygen gas? This is the reaction that occurred in the Hindenburg disaster, which you read about in *Connecting to Your World*. When hydrogen and oxygen are mixed, a spark will initiate a rapid reaction. The product of the reaction is water. This is the equation for the burning of hydrogen:

$H_2(g)$	+	$O_2(g)$	$\longrightarrow$	$H_2O(l)$
Hydrogen		Oxygen		Water
Reactants				**Product**
2 hydrogen atoms				2 hydrogen atoms
2 oxygen atoms				1 oxygen atom

Textbook

Simulation 11 Sharpen your skills by balancing chemical equations.

with ChemASAP

The formulas for all the reactants and product are correct, but this equation is not balanced. Count the atoms on both sides of the equation. Two oxygen atoms are on the reactant (left) side of the equation and only one oxygen atom is on the product (right) side. As written, the equation does not obey the law of conservation of mass and so it does not describe what really happens. What can you do to balance it? A few guidelines for writing and balancing equations will help.

Rules for Writing and Balancing Equations

1. Determine the correct formulas for all the reactants and products.

2. Write the skeleton equation by placing the formulas for the reactants on the left and the formulas for the products on the right with a yields sign (⟶) in between. If two or more reactants or products are involved, separate their formulas with plus signs.

3. Determine the number of atoms of each element in the reactants and products. Count a polyatomic ion as a single unit if it appears unchanged on both sides of the equation.

4. Balance the elements one at a time by using coefficients. When no coefficient is written, it is assumed to be 1. Begin by balancing elements that appear only once on each side of the equation. Never balance an equation by changing the subscripts in a chemical formula. Each substance has only one correct formula.

5. Check each atom or polyatomic ion to be sure they are equal on both sides of the equation.

6. Make sure all the coefficients are in the lowest possible ratio.

CONCEPTUAL PROBLEM 11.2

Writing a Balanced Chemical Equation

Hydrogen and oxygen react to form water. The reaction releases enough energy to launch a rocket. Write a balanced equation for the reaction.

① Analyze *Identify the relevant concepts.*
Apply the rules for balancing equations to the skeleton equation describing the reaction.

② Solve *Apply concepts to this situation.*
Write correct formulas to give the skeleton equation.

$$H_2(g) + O_2(g) \longrightarrow H_2O(l)$$

Count the number of each kind of atom. Hydrogen is balanced but oxygen is not. If you put the coefficient 2 in front of H_2O, the oxygen will be balanced.

$$H_2(g) + O_2(g) \longrightarrow 2H_2O(l)$$

Now twice as many hydrogen atoms are in the product as are in the reactants. To correct this, put the coefficient 2 in front of H_2. Four hydrogen atoms and two oxygen atoms are on each side of the chemical equation. The equation is now balanced.

$2H_2(g)$	+	$O_2(g)$	⟶	$2H_2O(l)$
Hydrogen		Oxygen		Water

Reactants
4 hydrogen atoms
2 oxygen atoms

Products
4 hydrogen atoms
2 oxygen atoms

Practice Problems

3. Balance each equation.
   a. $AgNO_3 + H_2S \longrightarrow Ag_2S + HNO_3$
   b. $Zn(OH)_2 + H_3PO_4 \longrightarrow Zn_3(PO_4)_2 + H_2O$

4. Rewrite these word equations as balanced chemical equations.
   a. hydrogen + sulfur ⟶ hydrogen sulfide
   b. iron(III) chloride + calcium hydroxide ⟶ iron(III) hydroxide + calcium chloride

Problem-Solving 11.4 Solve Problem 4 with the help of an interactive guided tutorial.

with ChemASAP

The reaction of copper metal with an aqueous solution of silver nitrate is described by this skeleton equation. How can it be balanced?

$$Cu(s) + AgNO_3(aq) \longrightarrow Cu(NO_3)_2(aq) + Ag(s)$$

The nitrate ion appears unchanged on both sides of the equation, so this ion can be balanced as a unit. Do this by placing a 2 in front of $AgNO_3$.

$$Cu(s) + 2AgNO_3(aq) \longrightarrow Cu(NO_3)_2(aq) + Ag(s)$$

But now the atoms of silver are not balanced. You must add a 2 in front of Ag on the product side to balance the atoms of silver.

$$Cu(s) + 2AgNO_3(aq) \longrightarrow Cu(NO_3)_2(aq) + 2Ag(s)$$

The equation is now balanced because the same number of each kind of atom are on both sides of the equation.

CONCEPTUAL PROBLEM 11.3

Balancing a Chemical Equation

Aluminum is a good choice for outdoor furniture because it reacts with oxygen in the air to form a thin protective coat of aluminum oxide. Balance the equation for this reaction.

$$Al(s) + O_2(g) \longrightarrow Al_2O_3(s)$$

1 **Analyze** *Identify the relevant concepts.*
Apply the rules for balancing equations.

2 **Solve** *Apply concepts to this situation.*
First balance the aluminum by placing the coefficient 2 in front of $Al(s)$.

$$2Al(s) + O_2(g) \longrightarrow Al_2O_3(s)$$

How can the odd number of oxygen atoms in the product (right side) balance the even number of oxygen atoms on the left? Any whole-number coefficient placed in front of the O_2 will give an even number of oxygen atoms on the left. This is because the coefficient is always being multiplied by the subscript 2. The solution is to multiply the formula with the odd number of oxygen atoms by 2.

$$2Al(s) + O_2(g) \longrightarrow 2Al_2O_3(s)$$

Now six oxygen atoms are on the right. Balance the oxygens on the left by placing a 3 in front of O_2. Then rebalance the aluminum by changing the coefficient of $Al(s)$ from 2 to 4.

$$4Al(s) + 3O_2(g) \longrightarrow 2Al_2O_3(s)$$

Suppose the equation for the formation of aluminum oxide was written this way.

$$8Al(s) + 6O_2(g) \longrightarrow 4Al_2O_3(s)$$

Because this equation obeys the law of conservation of mass, it is correct. However, equations are normally written with coefficients in their lowest possible ratio. Each of the coefficients can be divided by 2 to give the previous equation, which has the lowest whole-number ratio of coefficients.

Practice Problems

5. Balance each equation.
  a. $FeCl_3 + NaOH \longrightarrow Fe(OH)_3 + NaCl$
  b. $CS_2 + Cl_2 \longrightarrow CCl_4 + S_2Cl_2$

6. Write and balance this equation.
  calcium hydroxide + sulfuric acid $\longrightarrow$
     calcium sulfate + water

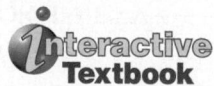
Textbook

Problem-Solving 11.6
Solve Problem 6 with the help of an interactive guided tutorial.

with **ChemASAP**

Careers *in* Chemistry

Hazardous Materials Specialist

Hazardous materials specialists do the vital work of keeping the environment safe from harmful substances. Backed by regulations devised primarily by the Environmental Protection Agency (EPA), these specialists are responsible for the safe handling, treatment,

storage, and transportation of hazardous materials. They work at all levels of government and are employed by industries and universities where dangerous materials are generated or used. Part of their jobs may be to educate those who need to know, including the public, about the rules and regulations applied to hazardous materials.

Hazardous materials specialists often work in the field inspecting, testing, overseeing cleanup work, and determining whether storage facilities are in compliance with regulations. First on the scene when a chemical spill occurs, these specialists must be able to identify the spilled chemical substance and know how to take

emergency action to neutralize its effect and thus protect the public. Then they must devise a cleanup procedure and oversee its implementation.

Entry into the field usually requires a degree from a four-year college with a major in chemistry or other physical science. Other areas of concentration might be industrial hygiene, environmental health, or engineering.

Go Online
PHSchool.com

For: Careers in Chemistry
Visit: PHSchool.com
Web Code: cdb-1111

11.1 Section Assessment

7. **Key Concept** How do you write a word equation?

8. **Key Concept** How do you write a skeleton equation?

9. **Key Concept** Describe the steps in writing a balanced chemical equation.

10. Write skeleton equations for these reactions.
    a. Heating copper(II) sulfide in the presence of diatomic oxygen produces pure copper and sulfur dioxide gas.
    b. When heated, baking soda (sodium hydrogen carbonate) decomposes to form the products sodium carbonate, carbon dioxide, and water.

11. Write and balance equations for the following reactions.
    a. Iron metal and chlorine gas react to form solid iron(III) chloride.
    b. Solid aluminum carbonate decomposes to form solid aluminum oxide and carbon dioxide gas.

c. Solid magnesium reacts with aqueous silver nitrate to form solid silver and aqueous magnesium nitrate.

12. Balance the following equations.
    a. $SO_2 + O_2 \longrightarrow SO_3$
    b. $Fe_2O_3 + H_2 \longrightarrow Fe + H_2O$
    c. $P + O_2 \longrightarrow P_4O_{10}$
    d. $Al + N_2 \longrightarrow AlN$

Writing ▶ **Activity**

Paragraph Some products are marketed as biodegradable. What does *biodegradable* mean? Identify three biodegradable products. How do these products benefit the environment?

Assessment 11.1 Test yourself on the concepts in Section 11.1.

with ChemASAP

Guide for Reading

 Key Concepts
- What are the five general types of reactions?
- How can you predict the products of the five general types of reactions?

Vocabulary

combination reaction
decomposition reaction
single-replacement reaction
activity series
double-replacement reaction
combustion reaction

Reading Strategy

Outlining As you read, make an outline of the most important ideas in this section. Use the red headings as the main topics and the blue headings as subtopics. Add a sentence or a note after each heading to provide key information about each topic.

For: Links on Reaction Types
Visit: www.SciLinks.org
Web Code: cdn-1112

Connecting to Your World

Often charcoal briquettes provide the heat for barbeque grills through the burning of carbon. Have you ever felt the heat and smelled the smoke coming from a burning charcoal grill? The heat and smoke are the products of a combustion reaction. Combustion is one of the five general types of chemical reactions. In this chapter, you will learn that if you can recognize a reaction as being a particular type, you may be able to predict the products of the reaction.

Classifying Reactions

 The five general types of reaction are combination, decomposition, single-replacement, double-replacement, and combustion. Not all chemical reactions fit uniquely into only one category. Occasionally, a reaction may fit equally well into two categories. Nevertheless, recognizing a reaction as a particular type is useful. Patterns of chemical behavior will become apparent and allow you to predict the products of reactions.

Combination Reactions The first type of reaction is the combination, or synthesis, reaction. A **combination reaction** is a chemical change in which two or more substances react to form a single new substance. As shown in Figure 11.5, magnesium metal and oxygen gas combine to form the compound magnesium oxide.

$$2Mg(s) + O_2(g) \longrightarrow 2MgO(s)$$

Notice that in this reaction, as in all combination reactions, the product is a single substance (MgO), which is a compound. The reactants in this combination reaction (Mg and O_2) are two elements. This is often the case, but two compounds may also combine to form a single substance.

When a Group A metal and a nonmetal react, the product is a compound consisting of the metal cation and the nonmetal anion.

$$2K(s) + Cl_2(g) \longrightarrow 2KCl(s)$$

When two nonmetals react in a combination reaction, more than one product is often possible.

$$S(s) + O_2(g) \longrightarrow SO_2(g) \text{ sulfur dioxide}$$
$$2S(s) + 3O_2(g) \longrightarrow 2SO_3(g) \text{ sulfur trioxide}$$

More than one product may also result from the combination reaction of a transition metal and a nonmetal.

$$Fe(s) + S(s) \longrightarrow FeS(s) \text{ iron(II) sulfide}$$
$$2Fe(s) + 3S(s) \longrightarrow Fe_2S_3(s) \text{ iron(III) sulfide}$$

Figure 11.5 When ignited, magnesium ribbon reacts with oxygen in the surrounding air to form magnesium oxide, a white solid. This is a combination reaction. **Observing** *Why do you think this reaction was once used in flashbulbs for photography?*

$$2Mg(s) + O_2(g) \longrightarrow 2MgO(s)$$
Magnesium + Oxygen → Magnesium oxide

CONCEPTUAL PROBLEM 11.4

Writing Equations for Combination Reactions

Copper and sulfur, shown in the photo, are the reactants in a combination reaction. Complete the equation for the reaction.

$$Cu(s) + S(s) \longrightarrow \text{(two reactions possible)}$$

1 **Analyze** *Identify the relevant concepts.*
Two reactions are possible because copper is a transition metal and has more than one common ionic charge (Cu^+ and Cu^{2+}). Determine the formulas for the two products. Balance the two possible equations.

2 **Solve** *Apply concepts to this situation.*
Write the skeleton equation first, then apply the rules for balancing equations.
For copper(II):
$$Cu(s) + S(s) \longrightarrow CuS(s) \text{ (balanced)}$$
For copper(I):
$$Cu(s) + S(s) \longrightarrow Cu_2S(s)$$
$$2Cu(s) + S(s) \longrightarrow Cu_2S(s) \text{ (balanced)}$$

Practice Problems

13. Complete and balance this equation for a combination reaction.
$$Be + O_2 \longrightarrow$$

14. Write and balance the equation for the formation of magnesium nitride(Mg_3N_2) from its elements.

Textbook

Problem-Solving 11.14 Solve Problem 14 with the help of an interactive guided tutorial.

── with **ChemASAP**

Figure 11.6 When orange-colored mercury(II) oxide is heated, it decomposes into its constituent elements: liquid mercury and gaseous oxygen. **Comparing and Contrasting** *How are the reactions pictured in Figures 11.5 and 11.6 similar? How are they different?*

Hg^{2+} O^{2-} Hg   O$_2$

2HgO(s) $\xrightarrow{\text{heat}}$ 2Hg(l)   +   O$_2$(g)
Mercury(II) oxide   Mercury   Oxygen

Decomposition Reactions When mercury(II) oxide is heated, it decomposes or breaks down into two simpler compounds, as shown in Figure 11.6.

$$2HgO(s) \longrightarrow 2Hg(l) + O_2(g)$$

A **decomposition reaction** is a chemical change in which a single compound breaks down into two or more simpler products. Decomposition reactions involve only one reactant and two or more products. The products can be any combination of elements and compounds. It is usually difficult to predict the products of decomposition reactions. However, when a simple binary compound such as HgO breaks down, you know that the products must be the constituent elements Hg and O$_2$. Most decomposition reactions require energy in the form of heat, light, or electricity.

CONCEPTUAL PROBLEM 11.5

Writing the Equation for a Decomposition Reaction

Decomposition reactions that produce gases and heat are sometimes explosive, as the photo shows. Write a balanced equation for the following decomposition reaction.

$$H_2O(l) \xrightarrow{\text{electricity}}$$

1 **Analyze** *Identify the relevant concepts.*
Water, a binary compound, breaks down into its elements. Balance the equation, remembering that hydrogen and oxygen are both diatomic molecules.

2 **Solve** *Apply concepts to this situation.*
Write the skeleton equation, then apply the rules for balancing equations.

$$H_2O(l) \xrightarrow{\text{electricity}} H_2(g) + O_2(g)$$
$$2H_2O(l) \xrightarrow{\text{electricity}} 2H_2(g) + O_2(g) \text{ (balanced)}$$

Practice Problems

15. Complete and balance this decomposition reaction.

$$HI \longrightarrow$$

16. Write the formula for the binary compound that decomposes to the products H$_2$ and Br$_2$.

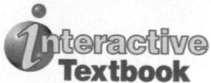
interactive Textbook

Problem-Solving 11.15
Solve Problem 15 with the help of an interactive guided tutorial.

—— with **ChemASAP**

Single-Replacement Reactions Dropping a small piece of potassium into a beaker of water creates the vigorous reaction shown in Figure 11.7. The reaction produces hydrogen gas and a large quantity of heat. The released hydrogen gas can ignite explosively.

$$2K(s) + 2H_2O(l) \longrightarrow 2KOH(aq) + H_2(g)$$

Similar but less spectacular reactions can occur. For example, if you drop a piece of zinc into a solution of copper nitrate, this reaction occurs:

$$Zn(s) + Cu(NO_3)_2(aq) \longrightarrow Cu(s) + Zn(NO_3)_2(aq)$$

These equations describe two examples of single-replacement reactions. A **single-replacement reaction** is a chemical change in which one element replaces a second element in a compound. You can identify a single-replacement reaction by noting that both the reactants and the products consist of an element and a compound. In the equation above, zinc and copper change places. The reacting element Zn replaces copper in the reactant compound $Cu(NO_3)_2$. The products are the element Cu and the compound $Zn(NO_3)_2$.

Whether one metal will displace another metal from a compound depends upon the relative reactivities of the two metals. The **activity series** of metals, given in Table 11.2, lists metals in order of decreasing reactivity. A reactive metal will replace any metal listed below it in the activity series. Thus iron will displace copper from a copper compound in solution, but iron does not similarly displace zinc or calcium.

A halogen can also replace another halogen from a compound. The activity of the halogens decreases as you go down Group 7A of the periodic table—fluorine, chlorine, bromine, and iodine. Bromine is more active than iodine, so this reaction occurs:

$$Br_2(aq) + NaI(aq) \longrightarrow NaBr(aq) + I_2(aq)$$

But bromine is less active than chlorine, so this reaction does not occur:

$$Br_2(aq) + NaCl(aq) \longrightarrow \text{No reaction}$$

Table 11.2

Activity Series of Metals

	Name	Symbol
Decreasing reactivity →	Lithium	Li
	Potassium	K
	Calcium	Ca
	Sodium	Na
	Magnesium	Mg
	Aluminum	Al
	Zinc	Zn
	Iron	Fe
	Lead	Pb
	(Hydrogen)	(H)*
	Copper	Cu
	Mercury	Hg
	Silver	Ag

*Metals from Li to Na will replace H from acids and water; from Mg to Pb they will replace H from acids only.

Figure 11.7 The alkali metal potassium displaces hydrogen from water and forms a solution of potassium hydroxide in a single-replacement reaction. The heat of the reaction is often sufficient to ignite the hydrogen. **Inferring** *Why are alkali metals stored under mineral oil or kerosene?*

2K(s)	+	2H₂O(l)	⟶	2KOH(aq)	+	H₂(g)
Potassium		Water		Potassium hydroxide		Hydrogen

Writing Equations for Single-Replacement Reactions

The photo shows the reaction between $Zn(s)$ and $H_2SO_4(aq)$. Write a balanced chemical equation for each single-replacement reaction. The reactions take place in aqueous solution.

a. $Zn(s) + H_2SO_4(aq) \longrightarrow$

b. $Cl_2(aq) + NaBr(aq) \longrightarrow$

1 Analyze *Identify the relevant concepts.*

a. According to the activity series of metals, zinc displaces hydrogen from an acid and takes its place. Balance the equation, remembering that elemental hydrogen is diatomic.

b. Chlorine is more reactive than bromine and displaces bromine from its compounds. Balance the equation. Bromine is diatomic.

2 Solve *Apply concepts to this situation.*

Write the skeleton equation first, then apply the rules for balancing equations.

a. $Zn(s) + H_2SO_4(aq) \longrightarrow ZnSO_4(aq) + H_2(g)$ (balanced)

b. $Cl_2(aq) + NaBr(aq) \longrightarrow NaCl(aq) + Br_2(aq)$
$Cl_2(aq) + 2NaBr(aq) \longrightarrow 2NaCl(aq) +$
$Br_2(aq)$ (balanced)

Practice Problem

17. Complete the equations for these single-replacement reactions in aqueous solution. Balance each equation. Write "no reaction" if a reaction does not occur. Use the activity series.

a. $Fe(s) + Pb(NO_3)_2(aq) \longrightarrow$

b. $Cl_2(aq) + NaI(aq) \longrightarrow$

c. $Ca(s) + H_2O(l) \longrightarrow$

Textbook

Problem-Solving 11.17 Solve Problem 17 with the help of an interactive guided tutorial.

— with **ChemASAP**

Double-Replacement Reactions Sometimes, when two solutions of ionic compounds are mixed, nothing happens. At other times, the ions in the two solutions react. Figure 11.8 shows that mixing aqueous solutions of potassium carbonate and barium chloride results in a chemical reaction. A white precipitate of solid barium carbonate is formed. Potassium chloride, the other product of the reaction, remains in solution. This is an example of a **double-replacement reaction,** which is a chemical change involving an exchange of positive ions between two compounds. Double-replacement reactions are also referred to as double-displacement reactions. They generally take place in aqueous solution and often produce a precipitate, a gas, or a molecular compound such as water. For a double-replacement reaction to occur, one of the following is usually true.

1. One of the products is only slightly soluble and precipitates from solution. For example, the reaction of aqueous solutions of sodium sulfide and cadmium nitrate produces a yellow precipitate of cadmium sulfide.

$$Na_2S(aq) + Cd(NO_3)_2(aq) \longrightarrow CdS(s) + 2NaNO_3(aq)$$

2. One of the products is a gas. Poisonous hydrogen cyanide gas is produced when aqueous sodium cyanide is mixed with sulfuric acid.

$$2NaCN(aq) + H_2SO_4(aq) \longrightarrow 2HCN(g) + Na_2SO_4(aq)$$

3. One product is a molecular compound such as water. Combining solutions of calcium hydroxide and hydrochloric acid produces water.

$$Ca(OH)_2(aq) + 2HCl(aq) \longrightarrow CaCl_2(aq) + 2H_2O(l)$$

Figure 11.8 Aqueous solutions of potassium carbonate and barium chloride react in a double-replacement reaction to form the white precipitate barium carbonate. Potassium chloride, the other product of the reaction, remains in solution.

K^+ CO_3^{2-} Ba^{2+} Cl^- K^+ Cl^- Ba^{2+} CO_3^2

$K_2CO_3(aq)$ + $BaCl_2(aq)$ ⟶ $2KCl(aq)$ + $BaCO_3(s)$
Potassium carbonate   Barium chloride   Potassium chloride   Barium carbonate

CONCEPTUAL PROBLEM 11.7

Writing Equations for Double-Replacement Reactions

Write a balanced chemical equation for each double-replacement reaction.
a. $CaBr_2(aq) + AgNO_3(aq) \longrightarrow$ (A precipitate of silver bromide is formed.)
b. $FeS(s) + HCl(aq) \longrightarrow$ (Hydrogen sulfide gas (H_2S) is formed.)

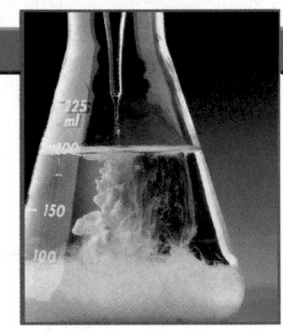

① Analyze *Identify the relevant concepts.*
   a. The driving force behind the reaction is the formation of a precipitate, which is shown in the photo. Write correct formulas of the products using ionic charges. Then balance the equation.
   b. A gas is formed. Use ionic charges to write the correct formula of the other product. Then balance the equation.

② Solve *Apply concepts to this situation.*
   For each reaction, write the skeleton equation first, then apply the rules for balancing equations.
   a. $CaBr_2(aq) + AgNO_3(aq) \longrightarrow$
$$AgBr(s) + Ca(NO_3)_2(aq)$$
$$CaBr_2(aq) + 2AgNO_3(aq) \longrightarrow$$
$$2AgBr(s) + Ca(NO_3)_2(aq) \text{ (balanced)}$$
   b. $FeS(s) + HCl(aq) \longrightarrow H_2S(g) + FeCl_2(aq)$
$$FeS(s) + 2HCl(aq) \longrightarrow$$
$$H_2S(g) + FeCl_2(aq) \text{ (balanced)}$$

Practice Problems

18. Write the products of these double-replacement reactions. Then balance each equation.
   a. $NaOH(aq) + Fe(NO_3)_3(aq) \longrightarrow$
(Iron(III) hydroxide is a precipitate.)
   b. $Ba(NO_3)_2(aq) + H_3PO_4(aq) \longrightarrow$
(Barium phosphate is a precipitate.)

19. Write a balanced equation for each reaction.
   a. $KOH(aq) + H_3PO_4(aq) \longrightarrow$
   b. $H_2SO_4(aq) + Al(OH)_3(aq) \longrightarrow$

Textbook

Problem-Solving 11.18 Solve Problem 18 with the help of an interactive guided tutorial.

with **ChemASAP**

Go Online

NSTA SC*LINKS*

For: Links on Combustion
Visit: www.SciLinks.org
Web Code: cdn-1114

Combustion Reactions The flames of a campfire or a gas grill are evidence that a combustion reaction is taking place. A **combustion reaction** is a chemical change in which an element or a compound reacts with oxygen, often producing energy in the form of heat and light. A combustion reaction always involves oxygen as a reactant. Often the other reactant is a hydrocarbon, which is a compound composed of hydrogen and carbon. The complete combustion of a hydrocarbon produces carbon dioxide and water. But if the supply of oxygen is limited during a reaction, the combustion will not be complete. Elemental carbon (soot) and toxic carbon monoxide gas may be additional products. The complete combustion of a hydrocarbon releases a large amount of energy as heat. That's why hydrocarbons such as methane (CH_4), propane (C_3H_8), and butane (C_4H_{10}) are important fuels. The combustion reaction for methane is shown in Figure 11.9. Gasoline is a mixture of hydrocarbons that can be approximately represented by the formula C_8H_{18}. The complete combustion of gasoline in a car engine is shown by this equation.

$$2C_8H_{18}(l) + 25O_2(g) \longrightarrow 16CO_2(g) + 18H_2O(l)$$

The reactions between oxygen and some elements other than carbon are also examples of combustion reactions. For example, both magnesium and sulfur will burn in the presence of oxygen. As you look at these combustion equations, notice that the reactions could also be classified as combination reactions.

$$2Mg(s) + O_2(g) \longrightarrow 2MgO(s)$$

$$S(s) + O_2(g) \longrightarrow SO_2(g)$$

✓**Checkpoint** *What are the products of the combustion of a hydrocarbon?*

$CH_4(g)$ + $2O_2(g)$ $\longrightarrow$ $CO_2(g)$ + $2H_2O(g)$
Methane   Oxygen   Carbon dioxide   Water

Figure 11.9 Methane gas reacts with oxygen from the surrounding air in a combustion reaction to produce carbon dioxide and water.
Inferring *What else is produced in this reaction?*

CONCEPTUAL PROBLEM 11.8

Writing Equations for Combustion Reactions

An alcohol lamp often uses ethanol as its fuel. Write balanced equations for the complete combustion of these compounds.

a. benzene $(C_6H_6(l))$ **b.** ethanol $(CH_3CH_2OH(l))$

1 Analyze *Identify the relevant concepts.*

Oxygen is the other reactant in these combustion reactions. The products are CO_2 and H_2O. Write the skeleton equation for each reaction, then balance the equation.

2 Solve *Apply concepts to this situation.*

For each reaction, write the skeleton equation, then apply the rules for balancing equations.

a. $C_6H_6(l) + O_2(g) \longrightarrow CO_2(g) + H_2O(g)$
$2C_6H_6(l) + 15O_2(g) \longrightarrow 12CO_2(g) + 6H_2O(g)$
(balanced)

b. $CH_3CH_2OH(l) + O_2(g) \longrightarrow CO_2(g) + H_2O(g)$
$CH_3CH_2OH(l) + 3O_2(g) \longrightarrow 2CO_2(g) +$
$3H_2O(g)$ (balanced)

Practice Problems

20. Write a balanced equation for the complete combustion of each compound.
    a. formic acid (HCOOH)
    b. heptane (C_7H_{16})

21. Write a balanced equation for the complete combustion of glucose $(C_6H_{12}O_6)$.

Problem-Solving 11.21
Solve Problem 21 with the help of an interactive guided tutorial.
— with **ChemASAP**

Predicting the Products of a Chemical Reaction

Now that you have learned about some of the basic reaction types, you can predict the products of many reactions. 🔑 **The number of elements and/ or compounds reacting is a good indicator of possible reaction type and thus possible products.** For example, in a combination reaction, two or more reactants (elements or compounds) combine to form a single product. In a decomposition reaction, a single compound is the reactant; two or more substances are the products. An element and a compound are the reactants in a single-replacement reaction. A different element and a new compound are the products. In a double-replacement reaction, two ionic compounds are the reactants; two new compounds are the products. The reactants in a combustion reaction are oxygen and usually a hydrocarbon. The products of most combustion reactions are carbon dioxide and water.

Simulation 12 Practice classifying reactions according to reaction type.
— with **ChemASAP**

Figure 11.10 The five types of chemical reactions discussed in this chapter are summarized here.

1 Combination Reaction

General Equation: R + S $\longrightarrow$ RS

Reactants: Generally two elements, or two compounds (where at least one compound is a molecular compound)
Probable Products: A single compound
Example: Burning magnesium in air

$$2Mg(s) + O_2(g) \longrightarrow 2MgO(s)$$

2 Decomposition Reaction

General Equation: RS $\longrightarrow$ R + S

Reactants: Generally a single binary compound or a compound with a polyatomic ion
Probable Products: Two elements (for a binary compound), or two or more elements and/or compounds (for a compound with a polyatomic ion)
Example: Heating mercury(II) oxide

$$2HgO(s) \longrightarrow 2Hg(l) + O_2(g)$$

3 Single-Replacement Reaction

General Equation: T + RS $\longrightarrow$ TS + R

Reactants: An element and a compound
In a single-replacement reaction, an element replaces another element from a compound in aqueous solution. For a single-replacement reaction to occur, the element that is displaced must be less active than the element that is doing the displacing.
Probable Products: A different element and a new compound
Example: Potassium in water

$$2K(s) + 2H_2O(l) \longrightarrow 2KOH(aq) + H_2(g)$$

4 Double-Replacement Reaction

General Equation: $R^+S^- + T^+U^- \longrightarrow R + U^- + T^+S^-$

Reactants: Two ionic compounds
In a double-replacement reaction, two ionic compounds react by exchanging cations to form two different compounds.
Probable Products: Two new compounds
Double-replacement reactions are driven by the formation of a precipitate, a gaseous product, or water.
Example: Reaction of aqueous solutions of barium chloride and potassium carbonate

$$K_2CO_3(aq) + BaCl_2(aq) \longrightarrow 2KCl(aq) + BaCO_3(s)$$

5 Combustion Reaction

General Equation: $C_xH_y + (x + y/4)\, O_2 \longrightarrow xCO_2 + (y/2)H_2O$

Reactants: Oxygen and a compound of C, H, (O)
When oxygen reacts with an element or compound, combustion may occur.
Probable Products: CO_2 and H_2O
With incomplete combustion, C and CO may also be products.
Example: The combustion of methane gas in air

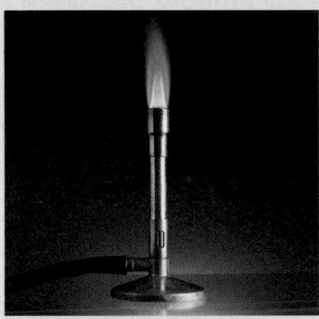

$$CH_4(g) + 2O_2(g) \longrightarrow CO_2(g) + 2H_2O(g)$$

11.2 Section Assessment

22. 🔑 **Key Concept** What are the five types of chemical reactions?

23. 🔑 **Key Concept** What are the keys to predicting the products of the five general types of reactions?

24. Classify each reaction and balance the equations.
a. $C_3H_6 + O_2 \longrightarrow CO_2 + H_2O$
b. $Al(OH)_3 \longrightarrow Al_2O_3 + H_2O$
c. $Li + O_2 \longrightarrow Li_2O$
d. $Zn + AgNO_3 \longrightarrow Ag + Zn(NO_3)_2$

25. Which of the five general types of reaction would most likely occur, given each set of reactants? What are the probable products?
a. an aqueous solution of two ionic compounds
b. a single compound
c. two elements
d. oxygen and a compound of carbon and hydrogen

26. Complete and balance an equation for each reaction.
a. $CaI_2 + Hg(NO_3)_2 \longrightarrow$ (HgI_2 precipitates.)

b. $Al + Cl_2 \longrightarrow$
c. $Ag + HCl \longrightarrow$
d. $C_2H_2 + O_2 \longrightarrow$
e. $MgCl_2 \longrightarrow$

27. What are the three types of products that result from double-replacement reactions?

Connecting ▸ Concepts

Molecular Compounds Hydrogen peroxide is an antiseptic that undergoes a decomposition reaction in the presence of living cells. Refer to Section 8.1 and write a paragraph giving evidence that hydrogen peroxide is a molecular compound.

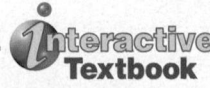
Interactive Textbook

Assessment 11.2 Test yourself on the concepts in Section 11.2.

—— with **ChemASAP**

Combating Combustion

A fire has three requirements: oxygen, fuel, and a temperature high enough to initiate and sustain combustion. Firefighters put out fires by eliminating one or more of these requirements. When water is sprayed on a typical building fire, it stops the fire by lowering the temperature of the burning material and soaking it with noncombustible water. Steam from the vaporizing water also tends to displace air from around the flames and deny them oxygen. To improve the ability of water to saturate the fuel, for example, upholstered furniture and rugs, a substance called a surfactant is added to the water to form a penetrating foam. **Inferring** *How can it help to roll on the ground if your clothes are on fire?*

Water Water is the most important tool for firefighters. Water-based foams are more effective and environmentally friendly, but they are also more expensive.

Forest fires Firefighters combat forest fires from the air by spreading substances that coat the surfaces of the trees to prevent burning. They can also cut the fire off from its fuel by using bulldozers to cut a clear path through the trees or by setting a controlled blaze.

Grease fires Water sprayed on a grease fire can spread the flames. A carbon-dioxide fire extinguisher produces a cloud of heavier-than-air CO_2 that blankets the fire and cuts off the oxygen supply.

Electrical fires Chemicals such as sodium hydrogen carbonate and ammonium dihydrogen phosphate, blown from a dry-chemical extinguisher, cover an electrical fire and cut off oxygen. This type of extinguisher also works on burning metals such as magnesium and sodium.

11.3 Reactions in Aqueous Solution

New York Standards: S1.1b, 3.3c

Guide for Reading

 Key Concepts

- What does a net ionic equation show?
- How can you predict the formation of a precipitate in a double-replacement reaction?

Vocabulary

complete ionic equation
spectator ion
net ionic equation

Reading Strategy

Comparing and Contrasting
When you compare and contrast things, you examine how they are alike and different. As you read, list the ways that complete ionic equations and net ionic equations are the same and how they are different.

Figure 11.11 A precipitate of silver chloride forms when aqueous solutions of silver nitrate and sodium chloride are mixed. **Inferring** *Which ions do not participate in the reaction?*

Connecting to Your World The beauty of a limestone cavern is the result of chemical reactions involving water. Limestone caverns form as calcium carbonate reacts with carbon dioxide dissolved in water and forms soluble calcium hydrogen carbonate. Additional carbon dioxide then converts the calcium hydrogen carbonate back into calcium carbonate. The calcium carbonate precipitates and forms dramatic stalactites and stalagmites. In this section, you will learn to predict the formation of precipitates and write equations to describe the reactions that produce them.

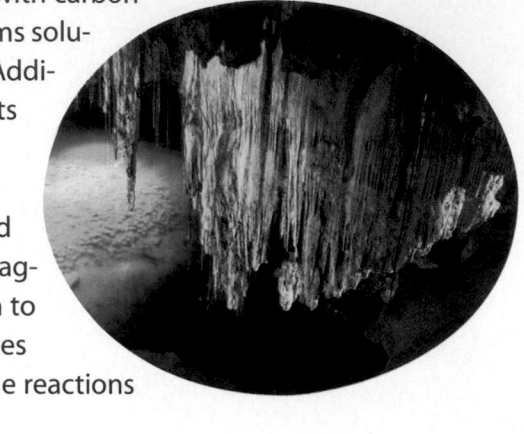

Net Ionic Equations

Your world is water-based. More than 70% of Earth's surface is covered by water, and about 66% of the adult human body is water. It is not surprising, then, that many important chemical reactions take place in water—that is, in aqueous solution.

The reaction of aqueous solutions of silver nitrate with sodium chloride to form solid silver chloride and aqueous sodium nitrate is a double-replacement reaction. The reaction is shown in Figure 11.11.

$$AgNO_3(aq) + NaCl(aq) \longrightarrow AgCl(s) + NaNO_3(aq)$$

This is the way you have been writing equations involving aqueous solutions of ionic compounds. However, the equation does not show that like most ionic compounds, the reactants and one of the products dissociate, or separate, into cations and anions when they dissolve in water. For example, when sodium chloride dissolves in water, it separates into sodium ions ($Na^+(aq)$) and chloride ions ($Cl^-(aq)$). Similarly, silver nitrate dissociates into silver ions ($Ag^+(aq)$) and nitrate ions ($NO_3^-(aq)$). You can use these ions to write a **complete ionic equation,** an equation that shows dissolved ionic compounds as dissociated free ions.

$$Ag^+(aq) + NO_3^-(aq) + Na^+(aq) + Cl^-(aq) \longrightarrow$$
$$AgCl(s) + Na^+(aq) + NO_3^-(aq)$$

Notice that the nitrate ion and the sodium ion appear unchanged on both sides of the equation. The equation can be simplified by eliminating these ions because they don't participate in the reaction.

$$Ag^+(aq) + \cancel{NO_3^-(aq)} + \cancel{Na^+(aq)} + Cl^-(aq) \longrightarrow$$
$$AgCl(s) + \cancel{Na^+(aq)} + \cancel{NO_3^-(aq)}$$

An ion that appears on both sides of an equation and is not directly involved in the reaction is called a **spectator ion.** When you rewrite an equation leaving out the spectator ions, you have the net ionic equation. The **net ionic equation** is an equation for a reaction in solution that shows only those particles that are directly involved in the chemical change.

$$Ag^+(aq) + Cl^-(aq) \longrightarrow AgCl(s)$$

In writing balanced net ionic equations, you must make sure that the ionic charge is balanced. For the previous reaction, the net ionic charge on each side of the equation is zero and is therefore balanced. But consider the skeleton equation for the reaction of lead with silver nitrate.

$$Pb(s) + AgNO_3(aq) \longrightarrow Ag(s) + Pb(NO_3)_2(aq)$$

The nitrate ion is the spectator ion in this reaction. The net ionic equation is this.

$$Pb(s) + Ag^+(aq) \longrightarrow Ag(s) + Pb^{2+}(aq) \text{ (unbalanced)}$$

Why is this equation unbalanced? Notice that a single unit of positive charge is on the reactant side of the equation. Two units of positive charge are on the product side. Placing the coefficient 2 in front of $Ag^+(aq)$ balances the charge. A coefficient of 2 in front of $Ag(s)$ rebalances the atoms.

$$Pb(s) + 2Ag^+(aq) \longrightarrow 2Ag(s) + Pb^{2+}(aq) \text{ (balanced)}$$

 A net ionic equation shows only those particles involved in the reaction and is balanced with respect to both mass and charge.

Word *Origins*

Spectator comes from the Latin verb *spectare*, meaning "to watch." Thus a spectator ion can be thought of as only watching a reaction, not participating. **During a football game, what analogy can you draw to the people in the seats and the football players on the field?**

CONCEPTUAL PROBLEM 11.9

Writing and Balancing Net Ionic Equations

In the photograph, aqueous solutions of iron(III) chloride and potassium hydroxide are mixed. A precipitate of iron(III) hydroxide forms. Identify the spectator ions and write a balanced net ionic equation for the reaction.

1 Analyze *Identify the relevant concepts.*
Write the complete ionic equation for the reaction, showing any soluble ionic compounds as individual ions. Eliminate aqueous ions that appear as both reactants and products. Balance the net ionic equation.

2 Solve *Apply concepts to this situation.*
$$Fe^{3+}(aq) + 3Cl^-(aq) + 3K^+(aq) + 3OH^-(aq)$$
$$\longrightarrow Fe(OH)_3(s) + 3K^+(aq) + 3Cl^-(aq)$$
The spectator ions are K^+ and Cl^-. The balanced net ionic equation is
$$Fe^{3+}(aq) + 3OH^-(aq) \longrightarrow Fe(OH)_3(s)$$

Practice Problems

28. Write the balanced net ionic equation for this reaction.
$$Ca^{2+}(aq) + OH^-(aq) + H^+(aq) + PO_4{}^{3-}(aq) \longrightarrow$$
$$Ca^{2+}(aq) + PO_4{}^{3-}(aq) + H_2O(l)$$

29. Write the complete ionic equation and net ionic equation for the reaction of aqueous calcium hydroxide with phosphoric acid. The products are calcium phosphate and water.

Problem-Solving 11.28 Solve Problem 28 with the help of an interactive guided tutorial.

with ChemASAP

Table 11.3

Solubility Rules for Ionic Compounds

Compounds	Solubility
Salts of alkali metals and ammonia	Soluble
Nitrate salts and chlorate salts	Soluble
Sulfate salts, except compounds with Pb^{2+}, Ag^+, Hg_2^{2+}, Ba^{2+}, Sr^{2+}, and Ca^{2+}	Soluble
Chloride salts, except compound with Ag^+, Pb^{2+}, and Hg_2^{2+}	Soluble
Carbonates, phosphates, chromates, sulfides, and hydroxides	Most are insoluble

Predicting the Formation of a Precipitate

You have seen that mixing solutions of two ionic compounds can sometimes result in the formation of an insoluble salt called a precipitate. Some combinations of solutions produce precipitates, while others do not. Whether or not a precipitate forms depends upon the solubility of the new compounds that form. ☞ **You can predict the formation of a precipitate by using the general rules for solubility of ionic compounds.** These rules are shown in Table 11.3. Will a precipitate form when aqueous solutions of $Na_2CO_3(aq)$ and $Ba(NO_3)_2(aq)$ are mixed?

$$2Na^+(aq) + CO_3^{2-}(aq) + Ba^{2+}(aq) + 2NO_3^-(aq) \longrightarrow ?$$

When these four ions are mixed, the cations could change partners. If they did, the two new compounds that would form are $NaNO_3$ and $BaCO_3$. These are the only new combinations of cation and anion possible. To find out if an exchange will occur, refer to Table 11.3, which gives guidelines for determining whether ion combinations are soluble. Recall that sodium is an alkali metal. Rows 1 and 2 tell you that sodium nitrate will not form a precipitate because alkali metal salts and nitrate salts are soluble. Row 5 indicates that carbonates in general are insoluble. Barium carbonate will precipitate. In this reaction Na^+ and NO_3^- are spectator ions. The net ionic equation for this reaction is as follows.

$$Ba^{2+}(aq) + CO_3^{2-}(aq) \longrightarrow BaCO_3(s)$$

11.3 Section Assessment

30. ☞ **Key Concept** What is a net ionic equation?

31. ☞ **Key Concept** How can you predict the formation of a precipitate in a double-replacement reaction?

32. Write a balanced net ionic equation for each reaction.
  a. $Pb(NO_3)_2(aq) + H_2SO_4(aq) \longrightarrow PbSO_4(s) + HNO_3(aq)$
  b. $Pb(C_2H_3O_2)_2(aq) + HCl(aq) \longrightarrow PbCl_2(s) + HC_2H_3O_2(aq)$
  c. $Na_3PO_4(aq) + FeCl_3(aq) \longrightarrow NaCl(aq) + FePO_4(s)$
  d. $(NH_4)_2S(aq) + Co(NO_3)_2(aq) \longrightarrow CoS(s) + NH_4NO_3(aq)$

33. Write a balanced net ionic equation for each reaction. Identify the spectator ions in each reaction.
  a. $HCl(aq) + AgNO_3(aq) \longrightarrow$
  b. $Pb(C_2H_3O_2)_2(aq) + LiCl(aq) \longrightarrow$
  c. $Na_3PO_4(aq) + CrCl_3(aq) \longrightarrow$

34. Identify the precipitate formed when solutions of these ionic compounds are mixed.
  a. $H_2SO_4 + BaCl_2 \longrightarrow$
  b. $Al_2(SO_4)_3 + NH_4OH \longrightarrow$
  c. $AgNO_3 + H_2S \longrightarrow$

  d. $CaCl_2 + Pb(NO_3)_2 \longrightarrow$
  e. $Ca(NO_3)_2 + Na_2CO_3 \longrightarrow$

35. Will a precipitate form when the following aqueous solutions of ionic compounds are mixed?
  a. $AgNO_3$ and Na_2SO_4
  b. NH_4Cl and $Ba(NO_3)_2$
  c. $CaCl_2$ and K_2SO_4
  d. $Pb(NO_3)_2$ and HCl

> **Elements ▶ Handbook**
>
> **Limestone Caves** Refer to page R13 in the Elements Handbook to learn more about the formation of limestone caves. What part does acid (hydrogen ion) play in the dissolving process? What is the reaction that deposits stalactites and stalagmites?

Interactive Textbook

Assessment 11.3 Test yourself on the concepts in Section 11.3.
— with **ChemASAP**

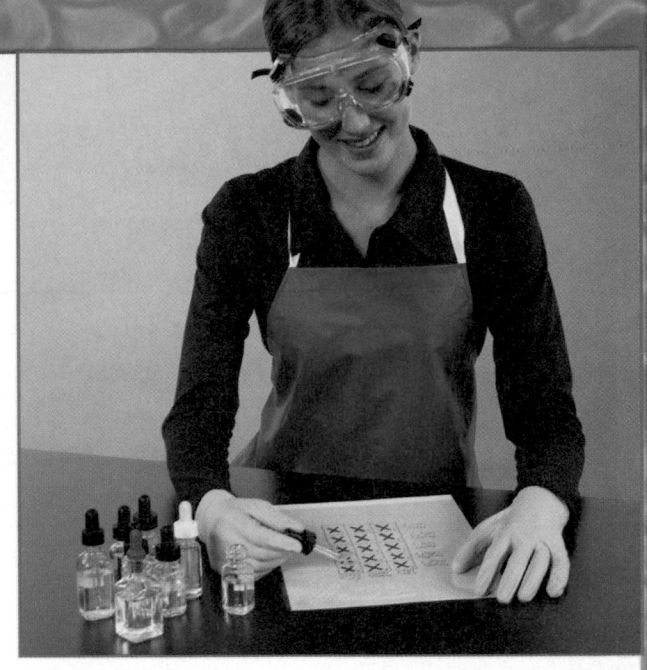

Precipitation Reactions: Formation of Solids

Purpose

To observe, identify, and write balanced equations for precipitation reactions.

Materials

- pencil
- paper
- ruler
- reaction surface
- chemicals shown in the grid below

	AgNO₃ (Ag⁺)	Pb(NO₃)₂ (Pb²⁺)	CaCl₂ (Ca²⁺)
Na₂CO₃ (CO₃²⁻)	a	f	k
Na₃PO₄ (PO₄³⁻)	b	g	l
NaOH (OH⁻)	c	h	m
Na₂SO₄ (SO₄²⁻)	d	i	n
NaCl (Cl⁻)	e	j	o

Procedure

Copy the grid on two sheets of paper. Make each square 2 cm on each side. Draw large black Xs on one of the grids. Place a reaction surface over the grid with black Xs and add the chemicals as shown. Use the other grid as a data table to record your observations for each solution.

Analyze

Using your experimental data, record your answers to the following in the space below your data table.

1. Translate the following word equations into balanced chemical equations and explain how the equations represent what happens in grid spaces *a* and *g*.

   a. In grid space *a*, sodium carbonate reacts with silver nitrate to produce sodium nitrate and solid silver carbonate.

   b. In grid space *g*, sodium phosphate reacts with lead(II) nitrate to produce sodium nitrate and solid lead(II) phosphate.

2. Write a word equation to represent what happens in grid space *m*.

3. What happens in grid space *d*? Which other mixings gave similar results? Is it necessary to write an equation when no reaction occurs? Explain.

4. Write balanced equations for the other precipitation reactions you observed.

5. Write balanced net ionic equations for the other precipitation reactions you observed.

You're The Chemist

The following small-scale activities allow you to develop your own procedures and analyze the results.

1. **Explain It!** Mix a solution of potassium iodide (KI) with silver nitrate. Then mix potassium iodide solution with lead(II) nitrate. Describe your results. Write balanced equations and net ionic equations for each reaction.

2. **Design It!** Table salt is mostly sodium chloride. Design and carry out an experiment to find out if table salt will form a precipitate with either lead(II) nitrate or silver nitrate. Interpret your results.

3. **Design It!** Design and carry out an experiment to show that iodized table salt contains potassium iodide.

Key Concepts

 11.1 Describing Chemical Reactions

- To write a word equation, write the names of the reactants to the left of the arrow separated by plus signs; write the names of the products to the right of the arrow, also separated by plus signs.

- To write a skeleton equation, write the formulas for the reactants to the left of the yields sign and the formulas for the products to the right.

- After writing the skeleton equation, use coefficients to balance the equation so that it obeys the law of conservation of mass.

11.2 Types of Chemical Reactions

- The five general types of reactions are combination, decomposition, single-replacement, double-replacement, and combustion.

- The number of elements and/or compounds reacting is a good indicator of possible reaction type and thus possible products.

- In a combination reaction, there is always a single product.

- A decomposition reaction involves the breakdown of a single compound into two or more simpler substances.

- In a single-replacement reaction, both the reactants and the products are an element and a compound.

- A double-replacement reaction generally takes place between two ionic compounds in aqueous solution.

- A combustion reaction always involves oxygen as a reactant.

11.3 Reactions in Aqueous Solution

- A net ionic equation shows only those particles involved in the reaction and is balanced with respect to mass and charge.

- You can predict the formation of a precipitate by using the general rules for solubility of ionic compounds.

Vocabulary

- activity series (p. 333)
- balanced equation (p. 325)
- catalyst (p. 323)
- chemical equation (p. 323)
- coefficients (p. 325)
- combination reaction (p. 330)
- combustion reaction (p. 336)
- complete ionic equation (p. 342)
- decomposition reaction (p. 332)
- double-replacement reaction (p. 334)
- net ionic equation (p. 343)
- single-replacement reaction (p. 333)
- skeleton equation (p. 323)
- spectator ion (p. 343)

Organizing Information

Use these terms to construct a concept map that organizes the major ideas of this chapter.

Concept Map 11 Solve the Concept Map with the help of an interactive tutorial.

— with **ChemASAP**

36. Identify the reactants and products in each chemical reaction.
    a. Hydrogen gas and sodium hydroxide are formed when sodium is dropped into water.
    b. In photosynthesis, carbon dioxide and water react to form oxygen gas and glucose.

37. How did John Dalton explain a chemical reaction using his atomic theory?

38. What is the function of an arrow ($\longrightarrow$) in a chemical equation? A plus sign ($+$)?

39. Write sentences that completely describe each of the chemical reactions shown in these skeleton equations.
    a. $NH_3(g) + O_2(g) \xrightarrow{Pt} NO(g) + H_2O(g)$
    b. $H_2SO_4(aq) + BaCl_2(aq) \longrightarrow$
       $BaSO_4(s) + HCl(aq)$
    c. $N_2O_3(g) + H_2O(l) \longrightarrow HNO_2(aq)$

40. What is the purpose of a catalyst?

41. Balance the equations for each item. The formula for each product (object) is given.
    a. a basketball team
       center + forward + guard $\longrightarrow$ team
       $C + F + G \longrightarrow CF_2G_2$
    b. a tricycle
       frame + wheel + seat + pedal $\longrightarrow$ tricycle
       $F + W + S + P \longrightarrow FW_3SP_2$

42. The equation for the formation of water from its elements, $H_2(g) + O_2(g) \longrightarrow H_2O(l)$, can be "balanced" by changing the formula of the product to H_2O_2. Explain why this method is incorrect.

43. Balance the following equations.
    a. $PbO_2 \longrightarrow PbO + O_2$
    b. $Fe(OH)_3 \longrightarrow Fe_2O_3 + H_2O$
    c. $(NH_4)_2CO_3 \longrightarrow NH_3 + H_2O + CO_2$
    d. $NaCl + H_2SO_4 \longrightarrow Na_2SO_4 + HCl$

44. Each equation is incorrect. Find the errors, then rewrite and balance each equation.
    a. $Cl_2 + NaI \longrightarrow NaCl_2 + I$
    b. $NH_3 \longrightarrow N + H_3$
    c. $Na + O_2 \longrightarrow NaO_2$

45. Write a balanced chemical equation for each reaction. Use the necessary symbols from Table 11.1 to describe the reaction completely.

a. Bubbling chlorine gas through a solution of potassium iodide gives elemental iodine and a solution of potassium chloride.
b. Bubbles of hydrogen gas and aqueous iron(III) chloride are produced when metallic iron is dropped into hydrochloric acid.
c. Solid tetraphosphorus decoxide reacts with water to produce phosphoric acid.

46. Write a balanced equation for each reaction. The product that is not in solution is given.
    a. $H_2C_2O_4 + KOH \longrightarrow H_2O + ?$
    b. $CdBr_2 + Na_2S \longrightarrow CdS + ?$
    c. $NaOH + Fe(NO_3)_3 \longrightarrow Fe(OH)_3 + ?$

47. Fill in the missing reactant and then balance each equation.
    a. $K(s) + \underline{\quad} \longrightarrow KOH(aq) + H_2(g)$
    b. $C_2H_5OH(l) + \underline{\quad} \longrightarrow CO_2(g) + H_2O(g)$
    c. $Bi(NO_3)_3(aq) + \underline{\quad} \longrightarrow Bi_2S_3(s) + HNO_3(aq)$
    d. $Al(s) + \underline{\quad} \longrightarrow AlBr_3(s)$
    e. $HNO_3(aq) + \underline{\quad} \longrightarrow Ba(NO_3)_2(aq) + H_2O(l)$

48. What is a characteristic of every combination (synthesis) reaction?

49. Write balanced chemical equations for the following combination (synthesis) reactions.
    a. $Mg + O_2 \longrightarrow$
    b. $P + O_2 \longrightarrow$ diphosphorus pentoxide
    c. $Ca + S \longrightarrow$

50. What is a distinguishing feature of every decomposition reaction?

51. Write a balanced chemical equation for each of the following decomposition reactions.

    a. $Ag_2O(s) \xrightarrow{\Delta} ?$

    b. ammonium nitrate $\xrightarrow{\Delta}$
       dinitrogen monoxide + water

52. Use the activity series of metals to write a balanced chemical equation for each single-replacement reaction that occurs. If no reaction occurs, write "no reaction."
    a. $Au(s) + KNO_3(aq) \longrightarrow$
    b. $Zn(s) + AgNO_3(aq) \longrightarrow$
    c. $Al(s) + H_2SO_4(aq) \longrightarrow$

53. Write a balanced equation for each of the following double-replacement reactions.
  a. $H_2C_2O_4(aq) + KOH(aq) \longrightarrow$
  b. $CdBr_2(aq) + Na_2S(aq) \longrightarrow$
      (Cadmium sulfide is a precipitate.)

54. What substance is common to all combustion reactions?

55. Write a balanced equation for the complete combustion of each compound.
  a. butane (C_4H_8)
  b. acetone (C_3H_6O)

56. Balance each equation and identify its type.
  a. $Hf + N_2 \longrightarrow Hf_3N_4$
  b. $Mg + H_2SO_4 \longrightarrow MgSO_4 + H_2$
  c. $C_2H_6 + O_2 \longrightarrow CO_2 + H_2O$
  d. $Pb(NO_3)_2 + NaI \longrightarrow PbI_2 + NaNO_3$
  e. $Fe + O_2 \longrightarrow Fe_3O_4$

57. Write a balanced chemical equation for each combination (synthesis) reaction.
  a. sodium oxide + water $\longrightarrow$
  b. hydrogen + bromine $\longrightarrow$

58. Write a balanced chemical equation for each single-replacement reaction that takes place in aqueous solution. Write "no reaction" if a reaction does not occur.
  a. A piece of steel wool (iron) is placed in sulfuric acid.
  b. Aluminum is placed into an aqueous solution of zinc nitrate.
  c. Bromine reacts with aqueous barium iodide.

59. Pieces of sodium and magnesium are dropped into separate water-filled test tubes (A and B). Tube A bubbles vigorously; Tube B does not.
  a. Which tube contains the sodium metal?
  b. Write an equation for the reaction in the tube containing the sodium metal. What type of reaction is occurring in this tube?

60. Write a balanced equation for the complete combustion of each compound. Assume that the products are carbon dioxide and water.
  a. octane (C_8H_{18})
  b. glucose ($C_6H_{12}O_6$)
  c. acetic acid ($HC_2H_3O_2$)

61. Write balanced chemical equations for these decomposition reactions.
  a. Aluminum is obtained from aluminum oxide with the addition of a large amount of electrical energy.
  b. Heating tin(IV) hydroxide gives tin(IV) oxide and water.
  c. Silver carbonate decomposes into silver oxide and carbon dioxide when it is heated.

62. Each of these equations has water as either a reactant or a product. Balance each equation and identify the type.
  a. $K_2O(s) + H_2O(l) \longrightarrow KOH(aq)$
  b. $C_{19}H_{40}(s) + O_2(g) \longrightarrow CO_2(g) + H_2O(l)$
  c. $Rb(s) + H_2O(l) \longrightarrow H_2(g) + RbOH(aq)$

63. Why is smoking not permitted near an oxygen source? What would happen if a match were struck in a room filled with oxygen?

64. Alkanes are hydrocarbon molecules that have the general formula C_nH_{2n+2}. The graph shows the number of oxygen, carbon dioxide, and water molecules needed to balance the equations for the complete combustion of every alkane having from one to ten carbon atoms.
  $C_nH_{2n+2} + \underline{\quad} O_2 \longrightarrow \underline{\quad} CO_2 + \underline{\quad} H_2O$

Coefficients in Combustion Equations

Equation Coefficients

● ● ● Carbon dioxide
▲ ▲ ▲ Oxygen
■ ■ ■ Water

  a. Use the graph to write balanced equations for the combustion of C_5H_{12} and C_9H_{20}.

b. Extrapolate the graph and write balanced equations for the combustion of $C_{12}H_{26}$ and $C_{17}H_{36}$.

c. The coefficient for O_2 in the general equation is as follows.

$$n + \left(\frac{n+1}{2} \right)$$

What are the coefficients for CO_2 and H_2O?

65. Write a balanced chemical equation for each reaction. Classify each as to type.
   a. Sodium iodide reacts with phosphoric acid.
   b. Potassium oxide reacts with water.
   c. Heating sulfuric acid produces water, oxygen, and sulfur dioxide.
   d. Aluminum reacts with sulfuric acid.
   e. Pentane (C_5H_{12}) reacts with oxygen.

66. The photos (from top left, clockwise) show various types of reactions.

(1) **(2)**

(3) **(4)**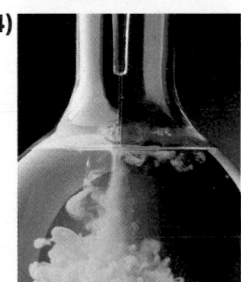

(1) Aluminum reacting with bromine
(2) The reaction of copper with aqueous silver nitrate
(3) Propane (C_3H_8) reacting with oxygen
(4) The reaction of lead(II) nitrate with potassium iodide
a. Identify each type of reaction.
b. Write the equation for each reaction.

67. When pale yellow chlorine gas is bubbled through a clear, colorless solution of sodium iodide, the solution turns brown.
   a. What type of reaction is taking place?
   b. Write the net ionic equation.

11.3 Reactions in Aqueous Solution

68. What is a spectator ion?

69. Write a balanced equation for the following reactions.
   a. $HCl(aq) + Ca(OH)_2(aq) \longrightarrow$
   b. $AgNO_3(aq) + AlCl_3(aq) \longrightarrow$
   (Silver chloride is a precipitate.)

70. Complete and balance each of the following equations. If no reaction occurs, write "no reaction."
   a. $Al(s) + H_2SO_4(aq) \longrightarrow$
   b. $HCl(aq) + Ba(OH)_2(aq) \longrightarrow$
   c. $Au(s) + HCl(aq) \longrightarrow$

71. Write balanced chemical equations for these double-replacement reactions that occur in aqueous solution.
   a. Zinc sulfide is added to sulfuric acid.
   b. Sodium hydroxide reacts with nitric acid.
   c. Solutions of potassium fluoride and calcium nitrate are mixed.

72. Aqueous solutions of sodium sulfide and cadmium nitrate were mixed in a beaker. A yellow precipitate forms.
   a. Write the formula of the yellow precipitate.
   b. Identify the ions that remain in solution above the precipitate.
   c. Write a balanced equation for the reaction.

Test-Taking Tip

Before you answer questions about a diagram, study the diagram carefully. Read all captions and labels. Look at all the information in the diagram and think about how it all relates together. Ask yourself some questions. *What is this diagram showing? What does this diagram tell me?*

Regents Practice Exam

For each statement or question write the number of the word or expression that, of those given, best completes the statement or answers the question.

The lettered choices below refer to Questions 1–6. A lettered choice may be used once, more than once, or not at all.

(1) combination (synthesis)
(2) decomposition
(3) single-replacement
(4) double-replacement

Match each of the following to the correct type of reaction.

1. one compound ⟶ two compounds

2. one element + one compound ⟶ one element + one compound

3. two elements ⟶ one compound

4. one compound ⟶ two elements

5. two compounds ⟶ two compounds

6. two compounds ⟶ one compound

7. Which of the following numbers is used to balance chemical equations?
(1) superscript

(2) charge   **(4)** coefficient
(3) subscript

8. A combustion reaction always involves the element
(1) hydrogen   **(3)** carbon
(2) oxygen   **(4)** nitrogen

9. The coefficients in a balanced chemical equation can be used to determine
(1) mole ratios
(2) the ratio of elements in a compound
(3) the charges on ions
(4) relative masses of reactants and products

Part B-1

For each statement or question write the number of the word or expression that, of those given, best completes the statement or answers the question.

10. Which of the following formulas for ionic compounds is incorrect?
(1) KBr   **(3)** CaN_2
(2) Na_2S **(4)** Al_2O_3

11. When the equation $Fe_2O_3 + H_2 \longrightarrow Fe + H_2O$ is balanced using whole-number coefficients, what is the coefficient of H_2?
(1) 1   **(3)** 3
(2) 2   **(4)** 6

12. Magnesium ribbon reacts with an aqueous solution of copper(II) chloride in a single-replacement reaction. If all reactants are used up in the reaction, what metal ion is present in the final solution?
(1) Mg^{2+} **(3)** Cl^-
(2) Cu^+ **(4)** Cu^{2+}

13. What are the expected products of the decomposition reaction of potassium oxide, K_2O?
(1) $K^+(s)$ and $O^{2-}(g)$
(2) $K^+(s)$ and $O_2(g)$
(3) $K(s)$ and $O_2{}^{2-}(g)$
(4) $K(s)$ and $O_2(g)$

Use the particle diagrams to answer Questions 14 and 15. In the diagrams, oxygen atoms are red, and nitrogen atoms are blue. The reaction taking place is represented by the balanced chemical equation $2NO(g) + O_2(g) \longrightarrow 2NO_2(g)$.

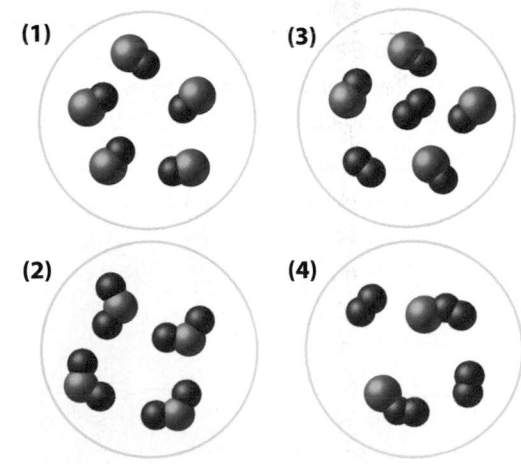

14. Which diagram represents the reactants in the reaction?

15. Which diagram represents the product in the reaction?

Part B-2

Answer each of the following questions.

16. A block of ice measures 25.0 cm × 42.0 cm × 38.0 cm. What is the mass of the ice in kilograms? The density of ice is 0.917 g/cm³.

17. List the number of protons, neutrons, and electrons in this isotope of titanium: $_{22}^{50}$Ti.

18. Write electron configurations for the following ions:
a. Sr^{2+} **b.** S^{2-} **c.** Ga^{3+} **d.** Cu^+

19. Explain what is meant by electronegativity. How do electronegativity values change across period 3?

20. Give the name or formula for the following compounds.
a. potassium chromate
b. sodium sulfite
c. $HMnO_4$
d. $K_2C_2O_4$

21. Calculate the number of moles in each sample of substance.
a. 1.68 g of magnesium ions
b. 69.6 g of sodium hypochlorite

22. What is the percent composition of $MnSO_4$?

23. Many coffees and colas contain the stimulant caffeine. The empirical formula of caffeine is $C_4H_5N_2O$. What is the molecular formula of caffeine if the molar mass is 194.1 g/mol?

24. Calcium chloride, $CaCl_2$, is a white solid used as a drying agent. The maximum amount of water absorbed by different quantities of $CaCl_2$ is given in the table below.

CaCl₂ (g)	CaCl₂ (mol)	H₂O (g)	H₂O (mol)
17.3	a. ____	5.62	b. ____
48.8	c. ____	15.8	d. ____
124	e. ____	40.3	f. ____
337	g. ____	109	h. ____

a. Complete the table.
b. Plot the moles of water absorbed (*y*-axis) versus the moles of $CaCl_2$.
c. Based on your graph, how many moles of water does each mole of $CaCl_2$ absorb?

25. Two compounds formed from iron, sulfur, and oxygen have the formulas $FeSO_4$ and $Fe_2(SO_4)_3$.
a. What is the percent composition of each of these compounds?
b. Name each of the compounds.

Use the following diagram to answer Questions 26–28.

26. When ammonium carbonate is heated, water, ammonia, and carbon dioxide are produced. What type of chemical reaction is occurring?

27. Write formulas for the reaction products.

28. Write a balanced equation for the reaction. Include states for reactants and products.

Part C

Answer each of the following questions.

29. When you take a glass of cold liquid outside on a warm, humid day, drops of liquid soon form on the outside of the glass.
a. What is the liquid?
b. Where did the liquid come from?
c. Did a chemical change or a physical change produce the liquid?

30. Hamburger undergoes a chemical change when cooked on a grill. All chemical changes are subject to the law of conservation of mass. Yet the mass of a cooked hamburger is always less than the mass of the uncooked patty meat. Explain.

Like a chemical equation, a recipe tells you the amount of ingredients (your reactants) needed to make a pie (your product).

INQUIRY Activity

How Many Can You Make?

Materials

20 metal paper clips (symbol M), 20 identically colored vinyl-coated paper clips (symbol C), plastic sandwich bag.

Procedure

1. Join together pairs of paper clips of the same color to form models representing 10 diatomic molecules of each reactant. Place these molecules in the plastic bag.

2. Without looking, remove 15 molecules from the plastic bag.

3. Line up the M_2 and C_2 molecules in two adjacent vertical rows.

4. Pair up reactant molecules in the 1:3 M_2-to-C_2 ratio as shown in the equation $M_2 + 3C_2 \longrightarrow 2MC_3$.

5. Make the molecules "react" by taking them apart and forming two molecules of the product.

6. Continue making M_2 and C_2 react in a 1:3 ratio until you run out of one of the reactants.

Think About It

1. List the number of each type of reactant molecule that you removed from the bag.

2. How many molecules of the product did you form?

3. Which reactant molecule did you run out of first?

4. How many molecules of each reactant remained at the completion of the reaction?

5. Repeat the experiment and compare the results.

Connecting to Your World

Silk is one of the most beautiful and luxurious of all fabrics. It is spun from the cocoons of silkworms. Silk manufacturers know from experience that to produce enough silk to make just one elegant Japanese kimono they will need over 3000 cocoons. In a similar fashion, chemists need to know how much reactant is needed to make a certain amount of product. The answer lies in chemical equations. From a balanced chemical equation, you can determine the quantities of reactants and products in a reaction.

Using Everyday Equations

When you bake cookies, you probably use a recipe. A cookie recipe tells you the precise amounts of ingredients to mix to make a certain number of cookies, as shown in Figure 12.1. If you need a larger number of cookies than the recipe provides, you can double or triple the amounts of ingredients. **A balanced chemical equation provides the same kind of quantitative information that a recipe does.** In a cookie recipe, you can think of the ingredients as the reactants, and the cookies as the products.

Here is another example. Imagine you are in charge of manufacturing for the Tiny Tyke Tricycle Company. The business plan for Tiny Tyke requires the production of 640 custom-made tricycles each week. One of your responsibilities is to be sure that there are enough parts available at the start of each workweek to make these tricycles. How can you determine the number of parts you need per week?

Guide for Reading

Key Concepts
- How is a balanced equation like a recipe?
- How do chemists use balanced chemical equations?
- In terms of what quantities can you interpret a balanced chemical equation?
- What quantities are conserved in every chemical reaction?

Vocabulary

stoichiometry

Reading Strategy

Using Prior Knowledge Before you read, jot down three things you know about balanced chemical equations. When you have read the section, explain how what you already knew helped you learn something new.

Figure 12.1 A cookie recipe tells you the number of cookies that you can expect to make from the listed amounts of ingredients. **Using Models** *How can you express a cookie recipe as a balanced equation?*

To simplify this discussion, assume that the major components of the tricycle are the frame (F), the seat (S), the wheels (W), the handlebars (H), and the pedals (P), in other words, your reactants. The figure below illustrates how an equation can represent the manufacturing of a single tricycle.

$$F \quad + \quad S \quad + \quad 3W \quad + \quad H \quad + \quad 2P \longrightarrow FSW_3HP_2$$

The finished tricycle, your product, has a "formula" of FSW_3HP_2. The balanced equation for making a single tricycle is

$$F + S + 3W + H + 2P \longrightarrow FSW_3HP_2$$

This balanced equation is a "recipe" to make a single tricycle: Making a tricycle requires assembling one frame, one seat, three wheels, one handlebar, and two pedals. Now look at Sample Problem 12.1. It shows you how to use the balanced equation to calculate the number of parts needed to manufacture a given number of tricycles.

Using Balanced Chemical Equations

Nearly everything you use is manufactured from chemicals—soaps, shampoos and conditioners, CDs, cosmetics, medicines, and clothes. In manufacturing such items, the cost of making them cannot be greater than the price they are sold at. Otherwise, the manufacturer will not make a profit. Therefore, the chemical processes used in manufacturing must be carried out economically. This is where balanced equations help.

A balanced chemical equation tells you what amounts of reactants to mix and what amounts of product to expect. **Chemists use balanced chemical equations as a basis to calculate how much reactant is needed or product is formed in a reaction.** When you know the quantity of one substance in a reaction, you can calculate the quantity of any other substance consumed or created in the reaction. Quantity usually means the amount of a substance expressed in grams or moles. However, quantity could just as well be in liters, tons, or molecules.

The calculation of quantities in chemical reactions is a subject of chemistry called **stoichiometry.** Calculations using balanced equations are called stoichiometric calculations. For chemists, stoichiometry is a form of bookkeeping. For example, accountants can track income, expenditures, and profits for a small business by tallying each in dollars and cents. Chemists can track reactants and products in a reaction by stoichiometry. It allows chemists to tally the amounts of reactants and products using ratios of moles or representative particles.

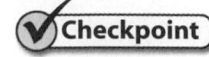 *How is stoichiometry similar to bookkeeping?*

SAMPLE PROBLEM 12.1

Using a Balanced Equation as a Recipe

In a five-day workweek, Tiny Tyke is scheduled to make 640 tricycles. How many wheels should be in the plant on Monday morning to make these tricycles?

1 **Analyze** *List the knowns and the unknown.*

Knowns
• number of tricycles = 640 tricycles = 640 FSW_3HP_2
• $F + S + 3W + H + 2P \longrightarrow FSW_3HP_2$

Unknown
• number of wheels = ? wheels

The desired conversion is tricycles (FSW_3HP_2) $\longrightarrow$ wheels (W). The balanced equation tells you that each tricycle has three wheels, or 1 FSW_3HP_2 = 3 W. The problem can be solved by using the proper conversion factor derived from this expression.

2 **Calculate** *Solve for the unknown.*

You can write two conversion factors relating wheels to tricycles.

$$\frac{3\ W}{1\ FSW_3HP_2} \quad \text{and} \quad \frac{1\ FSW_3HP_2}{3\ W}$$

The desired unit is W, so use the conversion factor on the left—the one that has W in the numerator. Multiply the number of tricycles by the conversion factor.

$$640\ \cancel{FSW_3HP_2} \times \frac{3W}{1\ \cancel{FSW_3HP_2}} = 1920\ W$$

3 **Evaluate** *Does the result make sense?*

If three wheels are required for each tricycle, and a total of more than 600 tricycles are being made, then a number of wheels in excess of 1800 is a logical answer. The unit of the known cancels with the unit in the denominator of the conversion factor, and the answer is in the unit of the unknown.

Practice Problems

1. Tiny Tike has decided to make 288 tricycles each day. How many tricycle seats, wheels, and pedals are needed?

2. Write an equation that gives your own "recipe" for making a skateboard.

Math ▶ **Handbook**

For help with dimensional analysis, go to page R66.

Problem Solving 12.1 Solve Problem 1 with the help of an interactive guided tutorial.

—— with **ChemASAP**

Interpreting Chemical Equations

In gardens such as the one shown in Figure 12.2, fertilizers are often used to improve the growth of flowers. As you may recall from Chapter 10, ammonia is widely used as a fertilizer. Ammonia is produced industrially by the reaction of nitrogen with hydrogen.

$$N_2(g) + 3H_2(g) \longrightarrow 2\,NH_3(g)$$

The balanced chemical equation tells you the relative amounts of reactants and product in the reaction. However, your interpretation of the equation depends on how you quantify the reactants and products. **A balanced chemical equation can be interpreted in terms of different quantities, including numbers of atoms, molecules, or moles; mass; and volume.** As you study stoichiometry, you will learn how to read a chemical equation in terms of any of these quantities.

Number of Atoms At the atomic level, a balanced equation indicates that the number and type of each atom that makes up each reactant also makes up each product. Thus, both the number and types of atoms are not changed in a reaction. In the synthesis of ammonia, the reactants are composed of two atoms of nitrogen and six atoms of hydrogen. These eight atoms are recombined in the product.

Number of Molecules The balanced equation indicates that one molecule of nitrogen reacts with three molecules of hydrogen. Nitrogen and hydrogen will always react to form ammonia in a 1:3:2 ratio of molecules. If you could make 10 molecules of nitrogen react with 30 molecules of hydrogen, you would expect to get 20 molecules of ammonia. Of course, it is not practical to count such small numbers of molecules and allow them to react. You could, however, take Avogadro's number of nitrogen molecules and make them react with three times Avogadro's number of hydrogen molecules. This would be the same 1:3 ratio of molecules of reactants. The reaction would form two times Avogadro's number of ammonia molecules.

Moles A balanced chemical equation also tells you the number of moles of reactants and products. The coefficients of a balanced chemical equation indicate the relative numbers of moles of reactants and products in a chemical reaction. This is the most important information that a balanced chemical equation provides. Using this information, you can calculate the amounts of reactants and products. In the synthesis of ammonia, one mole of nitrogen molecules reacts with three moles of hydrogen molecules to form two moles of ammonia molecules. As you can see from this reaction, the total number of moles of reactants does not equal the total number of moles of product.

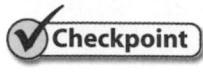 **What do the coefficients of a balanced chemical equation indicate?**

Mass A balanced chemical equation obeys the law of conservation of mass. This law states that mass can be neither created nor destroyed in an ordinary chemical or physical process. As you recall, the number and type of atoms does not change in a chemical reaction. Therefore, the total mass of the atoms in the reaction does not change. Using the mole relationship, you can relate mass to the number of atoms in the chemical equation. The mass of 1 mol of N_2 (28.0 g) plus the mass of 3 mol of H_2 (6.0 g) equals the mass of 2 mol of NH_3 (34 g). Although the number of moles of reactants does not equal the number of moles of product, the total number of grams of reactants does equal the total number of grams of product.

Volume If you assume standard temperature and pressure, the equation also tells you about the volumes of gases. Recall that 1 mol of any gas at STP occupies a volume of 22.4 L. The equation indicates that 22.4 L of N_2 reacts with 67.2 L (3 × 22.4 L) of H_2. This reaction forms 44.8 L (2 × 22.4 L) of NH_3.

Go Online
SciLINKS

For: Links on Conservation of Mass
Visit: www.SciLinks.org
Web Code: cdn-1121

Mass Conservation in Chemical Reactions

Figure 12.3 summarizes the information derived from the balanced chemical equation for the formation of ammonia. As you can see, the mass of the reactants equals the mass of the products. In addition, the number of atoms of each type in the reactants equals the number atoms of each type in the product. **Mass and atoms are conserved in every chemical reaction.** However, molecules, formula units, moles, and volumes are not necessarily conserved—although they may be. Consider, for example, the formation of hydrogen iodide,

$$H_2(g) + I_2(g) \longrightarrow 2HI(g)$$

In this reaction, molecules, moles, and volume are all conserved. But in the majority of chemical reactions, they are not.

$N_2(g)$	+	$3H_2(g)$	→	$2NH_3(g)$
2 atoms N	+	6 atoms H	→	2 atoms N and 6 atoms H
1 molecule N_2	+	3 molecules H_2	→	2 molecules NH_3
10 molecules N_2	+	30 molecules H_2	→	20 molecules NH_3
$1 \times \left(\dfrac{6.02 \times 10^{23}}{\text{molecules } N_2} \right)$	+	$3 \times \left(\dfrac{6.02 \times 10^{23}}{\text{molecules } H_2} \right)$	→	$2 \times \left(\dfrac{6.02 \times 10^{23}}{\text{molecules } NH_3} \right)$
1 mol N_2	+	3 mol H_2	→	2 mol NH_3
28 g N_2	+	3 × 2 g H_2	→	2 × 17 g NH_3
		34 g reactants	→	34 g products
Assume STP 22.4 L	+	22.4 L 22.4 L 22.4 L	→	22.4 L 22.4 L
22.4 L N_2		67.2 L H_2		44.8 L NH_3

Figure 12.3 The balanced chemical equation for the formation of ammonia can be interpreted in several ways. **Predicting** *How many molecules of NH_3 could be made from 5 molecules of N_2 and 15 molecules of H_2?*

Interpreting a Balanced Chemical Equation

Hydrogen sulfide, which smells like rotten eggs, is found in volcanic gases. The balanced equation for the burning of hydrogen sulfide is:

$$2H_2S(g) + 3O_2(g) \longrightarrow 2SO_2(g) + 2H_2O(g)$$

Interpret this equation in terms of
a. numbers of representative particles and moles.
b. masses of reactants and products.

1 **Analyze** *Identify the relevant concepts.*

a. The coefficients in the balanced equation give the relative number of molecules or moles of reactants and products.

b. A balanced chemical equation obeys the law of conservation of mass.

2 **Solve** *Apply concepts to this situation.*

a. 2 molecules H_2S + 3 molecules $O_2 \longrightarrow$
2 molecules SO_2 + 2 molecules H_2O
2 mol H_2S + 3 mol $O_2 \longrightarrow$
2 mol SO_2 + 2 mol H_2O

b. Multiply the number of moles of each reactant and product by its molar mass:

2 mol H_2S + 3 mol $O_2 \longrightarrow$ 2 mol SO_2 + 2 mol H_2O.

$$\left(2 \text{ mol} \times 34.1\frac{g}{mol}\right) + \left(3 \text{ mol} \times 32.0\frac{g}{mol}\right) \longrightarrow$$

$$\left(2 \text{ mol} \times 64.1\frac{g}{mol}\right) + \left(2 \text{ mol} \times 18.0\frac{g}{mol}\right)$$

68.2 g H_2S + 96.0 g $O_2 \longrightarrow$ 128.2 g SO_2 + 36.0 g H_2O

164.2 g = 164.2 g

Practice Problems

3. Interpret the equation for the formation of water from its elements in terms of numbers of molecules and moles, and volumes of gases at STP.

$$2H_2(g) + O_2(g) \longrightarrow 2H_2O(g)$$

4. Balance the following equation.

$$C_2H_2(g) + O_2(g) \longrightarrow CO_2(g) + H_2O(g)$$

Interpret the balanced equation in terms of

relative numbers of moles, volumes of gas at STP, and masses of reactants and products.

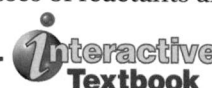
Interactive Textbook

Problem-Solving 12.4 Solve Problem 4 with the help of an interactive guided tutorial.

— with **ChemASAP**

12.1 Section Assessment

5. 🔑 **Key Concept** How is a balanced equation similar to a recipe?

6. 🔑 **Key Concept** How do chemists use balanced equations?

7. 🔑 **Key Concept** Chemical reactions can be described in terms of what quantities?

8. 🔑 **Key Concept** What quantities are always conserved in chemical reactions?

9. Interpret the given equation in terms of relative numbers of representative particles, numbers of moles, and masses of reactants and products.

$$2K(s) + 2H_2O(l) \longrightarrow 2KOH(aq) + H_2(g)$$

10. Balance this equation: $C_2H_5OH(l) + O_2(g) \longrightarrow CO_2(g) + H_2O(g)$. Show that the balanced equation obeys the law of conservation of mass.

Writing ▶ Activity

Explanatory Paragraph Explain this statement: "Mass and atoms are conserved in every chemical reaction, but moles are not necessarily conserved."

Interactive Textbook

Assessment 12.1 Test yourself on the concepts in Section 12.1.

— with **ChemASAP**

12.2 Chemical Calculations

New York Standards: 3.3a, 3.3c, 3.3e, 3.4e

Connecting to Your World

Air bags inflate almost instanta-neously upon a car's impact. The effectiveness of air bags is based on the rapid conversion of a small mass of sodium azide into a large volume of

gas. The gas fills an air bag, preventing the driver from hitting the steering wheel or dashboard. The entire reaction occurs in less than a second. In this section you will learn how to use a balanced chemical equation to calculate the amount of product formed in a chemical reaction.

Guide for Reading

 Key Concepts
- How are mole ratios used in chemical calculations?
- What is the general procedure for solving a stoichiometric problem?

Vocabulary

mole ratio

Reading Strategy

Relating Text and Visuals As you read, look closely at Figure 12.9. Explain how this illustration helps you understand the relationship between known and unknown quantities in a stoichiometric problem.

Writing and Using Mole Ratios

As you just learned, a balanced chemical equation provides a great deal of quantitative information. It relates particles (atoms, molecules, formula units), moles of substances, and masses. A balanced chemical equation also is essential for all calculations involving amounts of reactants and products. For example, suppose you know the number of moles of one substance. The balanced chemical equation allows you to determine the number of moles of all other substances in the reaction.

Look again at the balanced equation for the production of ammonia from nitrogen and hydrogen:

$$N_2(g) + 3H_2(g) \longrightarrow 2NH_3(g)$$

The most important interpretation of this equation is that 1 mol of nitrogen reacts with 3 mol of hydrogen to form 2 mol of ammonia. Based on this interpretation, you can write ratios that relate moles of reactants to moles of product. A **mole ratio** is a conversion factor derived from the coefficients of a balanced chemical equation interpreted in terms of moles. **In chemical calculations, mole ratios are used to convert between moles of reactant and moles of product, between moles of reactants, or between moles of products.** Three mole ratios derived from the balanced equation above are:

$$\frac{1 \text{ mol } N_2}{3 \text{ mol } H_2} \qquad \frac{2 \text{ mol } NH_3}{1 \text{ mol } N_2} \qquad \frac{3 \text{ mol } H_2}{2 \text{ mol } NH_3}$$

Mole-Mole Calculations In the mole ratio below, W is the unknown quantity. The values of a and b are the coefficients from the balanced equation. Thus a general solution for a mole-mole problem, such as Sample Problem 12.2, is given by

$$x \text{ mol } G \times \frac{b \text{ mol } W}{a \text{ mol } G} = \frac{xb}{a} \text{ mol } W$$

Given   Mole ratio   Calculated

Figure 12.4 Manufacturing plants produce ammonia by combining nitrogen with hydrogen. Ammonia is used in cleaning products, fertilizers, and in the manufacture of other chemicals.

Figure 12.5 To determine the number of moles in a sample of a compound, first measure the mass of the sample. Then use the molar mass to calculate the number of moles in that mass.

For help with dimensional analysis, go to page R66.

Interactive Textbook

Problem-Solving 12.12 Solve Problem 12 with the help of an interactive guided tutorial.

with ChemASAP

SAMPLE PROBLEM 12.2

Calculating Moles of a Product

How many moles of ammonia are produced when 0.60 mol of nitrogen reacts with hydrogen?

1 Analyze *List the known and the unknown.*

Known
- moles of nitrogen = 0.60 mol N_2

Unknown
- moles of ammonia = ? mol NH_3

The conversion is mol $N_2 \longrightarrow$ mol NH_3. According to the balanced equation, 1 mol N_2 combines with 3 mol H_2 to produce 2 mol NH_3. To determine the number of moles of NH_3, the given quantity of N_2 is multiplied by the form of the mole ratio from the balanced equation that allows the given unit to cancel. This mole ratio is 2 mol NH_3/1 mol N_2.

2 Calculate *Solve for the unknown.*

$$0.60 \ \cancel{\text{mol } N_2} \times \frac{2 \text{ mol } NH_3}{1 \ \cancel{\text{mol } N_2}} = 1.2 \text{ mol } NH_3$$

3 Evaluate *Does the result make sense?*

The ratio of 1.2 mol NH_3 to 0.60 mol N_2 is 2:1, as predicted by the balanced equation.

Practice Problems

11. This equation shows the formation of aluminum oxide, which is found on the surface of aluminum objects exposed to the air.

$$4Al(s) + 3O_2(g) \longrightarrow 2Al_2O_3(s)$$

a. Write the six mole ratios that can be derived from this equation.

b. How many moles of aluminum are needed to form 3.7 mol Al_2O_3?

12. According to the equation in Problem 11:

a. How many moles of oxygen are required to react completely with 14.8 mol Al?

b. How many moles of Al_2O_3 are formed when 0.78 mol O_2 reacts with aluminum?

Mass-Mass Calculations No laboratory balance can measure substances directly in moles. Instead, the amount of a substance is usually determined by measuring its mass in grams, as shown in Figure 12.5. From the mass of a reactant or product, the mass of any other reactant or product in a given chemical equation can be calculated. The mole interpretation of a balanced equation is the basis for this conversion. If the given sample is measured in grams, the mass can be converted to moles by using the molar mass. Then the mole ratio from the balanced equation can be used to calculate the number of moles of the unknown. If it is the mass of the unknown that needs to be determined, the number of moles of the unknown can be multiplied by the molar mass. As in mole-mole calculations, the unknown can be either a reactant or a product.

SAMPLE PROBLEM 12.3

Calculating the Mass of a Product

Calculate the number of grams of NH_3 produced by the reaction of 5.40 g of hydrogen with an excess of nitrogen. The balanced equation is

$$N_2(g) + 3H_2(g) \longrightarrow 2NH_3(g)$$

1 **Analyze** *List the knowns and the unknown.*

Knowns
- mass of hydrogen = 5.40 g H_2
- 3 mol H_2 = 2 mol NH_3 (from balanced equation)
- 1 mol H_2 = 2.0 g H_2 (molar mass)
- 1 mol NH_3 = 17.0 g NH_3 (molar mass)

Unknown
- mass of ammonia = ? g NH_3

The mass in grams of hydrogen will be used to find the mass in grams of ammonia:

$$g\ H_2 \longrightarrow g\ NH_3$$

The following steps are necessary to determine the mass of ammonia:

$$g\ H_2 \longrightarrow mol\ H_2 \longrightarrow mol\ NH_3 \longrightarrow g\ NH_3$$

The coefficients of the balanced equation show that 3 mol H_2 reacts with 1 mol N_2 to produce 2 mol NH_3. The mole ratio relating mol NH_3 to mol H_2 is 2 mol NH_3/3 mol H_2.

2 **Calculate** *Solve for the unknown.*

This following series of calculations can be combined:

$$g\ H_2 \longrightarrow mol\ H_2 \longrightarrow mol\ NH_3 \longrightarrow g\ NH_3$$

$$5.40\ \text{g}\ \cancel{H_2} \times \frac{1\ \text{mol}\ \cancel{H_2}}{2.0\ \text{g}\ \cancel{H_2}} \times \frac{2\ \text{mol}\ \cancel{NH_3}}{3\ \text{mol}\ \cancel{H_2}} \times \frac{17.0\ \text{g}\ NH_3}{1\ \text{mol}\ \cancel{NH_3}} = 31\ \text{g}\ NH_3$$

| Given quantity | Change given unit to moles | Mole ratio | Change moles to grams |

3 **Evaluate** *Does the result make sense?*

Because there are three conversion factors involved in this solution, it is more difficult to estimate an answer. However, because the molar mass of NH_3 is substantially greater than the molar mass of H_2, the answer should have a larger mass than the given mass. The answer should have two significant figures.

Practice Problems

13. Acetylene gas (C_2H_2) is produced by adding water to calcium carbide (CaC_2).

$$CaC_2(s) + 2H_2O(l) \longrightarrow$$
$$C_2H_2(g) + Ca(OH)_2(aq)$$

How many grams of acetylene are produced by adding water to 5.00 g CaC_2?

14. Using the same equation, determine how many moles of CaC_2 are needed to react completely with 49.0 g H_2O.

CHEMath

Significant Figures

The significant figures in a measurement are all the digits known with certainty plus one estimated digit. The number of significant figures in the measurements used in a calculation determines how you round the answer.

When multiplying and dividing measurements, the rounded answer can have no more significant figures than the least number of significant figures in any measurement in the calculation.

The product of 3.6 m × 2.48 m = 8.928 m² is rounded to 8.9 m² (2 significant figures).

When adding and subtracting measurements, the answer can have no more decimal places than the least number of decimal places in any measurement in the problem. The difference of 8.78 cm − 2.2 cm = 6.58 cm is rounded to 6.6 cm (one decimal place).

Math **Handbook**

For help with significant figures, go to page R59.

interactive **Textbook**

Problem-Solving 12.13 Solve Problem 13 with the help of an interactive guided tutorial.

with **ChemASAP**

Figure 12.6 In this Hubble Space Telescope image, clouds of condensed ammonia are visible covering the surface of Saturn.

If the law of conservation of mass is true, how is it possible to make 31 g NH_3 from only 5.40 g H_2? Looking back at the equation for the reaction, you will see that hydrogen is not the only reactant. Another reactant, nitrogen, is also involved. If you were to calculate the number of grams of nitrogen needed to produce 31 g NH_3 and then compare the total masses of reactants and products, you would have an answer to this question. Go ahead and try it!

Mass-mass problems are solved in basically the same way as mole-mole problems. Figure 12.7 reviews the steps for the mass-mass conversion of any given mass (G) and any wanted mass (W).

Steps in Solving a Mass-Mass Problem

1. Change the mass of G to moles of G (mass $G \longrightarrow$ mol G) by using the molar mass of G.

$$\text{mass } G \times \frac{1 \text{ mol } G}{\text{molar mass } G} = \text{mol } G$$

2. Change the moles of G to moles of W (mol $G \longrightarrow$ mol W) by using the mole ratio from the balanced equation.

$$\text{mol } G \times \frac{b \text{ mol } W}{a \text{ mol } G} = \text{mol } W$$

3. Change the moles of W to grams of W (mol $W \longrightarrow$ mass W) by using the molar mass of W.

$$\text{mol } W \times \frac{\text{molar mass } W}{1 \text{ mol } W} = \text{mass } W$$

Figure 12.7 also shows the steps for doing mole-mass and mass-mole stoichiometric calculations. For a mole-mass problem, the first conversion (from mass to moles) is skipped. For a mass-mole problem, the last conversion (from moles to mass) is skipped. You can use parts of the three-step process shown in Figure 12.7 as they are appropriate to the problem you are solving.

Figure 12.7 This general solution diagram indicates the steps necessary to solve a mass-mass stoichiometry problem: convert mass to moles, use the mole ratio, and then convert moles to mass. **Inferring** *Is the given always a reactant?*

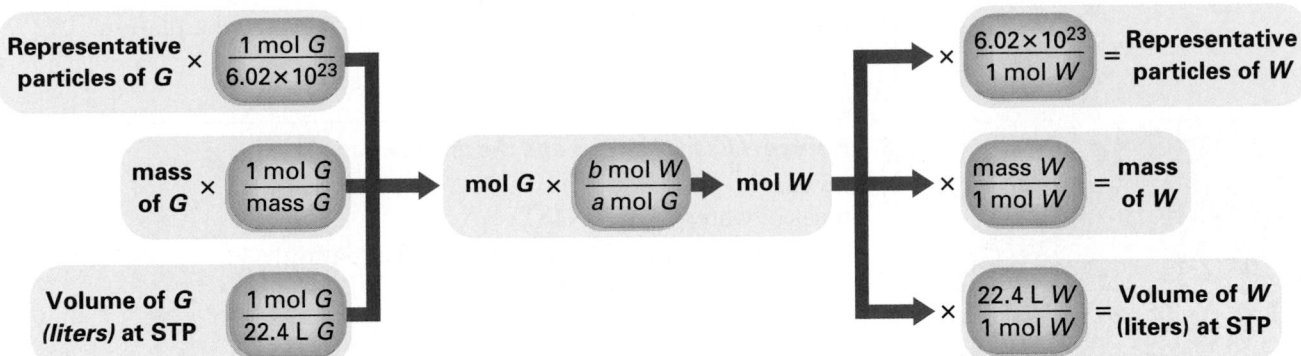

Other Stoichiometric Calculations

As you already know, you can obtain mole ratios from a balanced chemical equation. From the mole ratios, you can calculate any measurement unit that is related to the mole. The given quantity can be expressed in numbers of representative particles, units of mass, or volumes of gases at STP. The problems can include mass-volume, particle-mass and volume-volume calculations. For example, you can use stoichiometry to relate volumes of reactants and products in the reaction shown in Figure 12.8. 🗝 **In a typical stoichiometric problem, the given quantity is first converted to moles. Then the mole ratio from the balanced equation is used to calculate the number of moles of the wanted substance. Finally, the moles are converted to any other unit of measurement related to the unit mole, as the problem requires.**

Thus far, you have learned how to use the relationship between moles and mass (1 mol = molar mass) in solving mass-mass, mass-mole, and mole-mass stoichiometric problems. The mole-mass relationship gives you two conversion factors.

$$\frac{1\ mol}{molar\ mass} \quad and \quad \frac{molar\ mass}{1\ mol}$$

Recall from Chapter 10 that the mole can be related to other quantities as well. For example, 1 mol = 6.02×10^{23} representative particles, and 1 mol of a gas = 22.4 L at STP. These two relationships provide four more conversion factors that you can use in stoichiometric calculations.

$$\frac{1\ mol}{6.02\ \times\ 10^{23}\ particles} \quad and \quad \frac{6.02\ \times\ 10^{23}\ particles}{1\ mol}$$

$$\frac{1\ mol}{22.4\ L} \quad and \quad \frac{22.4\ L}{1\ mol}$$

Figure 12.8 summarizes the steps for a typical stoichiometric problem. Notice that the units of the given quantity will not necessarily be the same as the units of the wanted quantity. For example, given the mass of *G*, you might be asked to calculate the volume of *W* at STP.

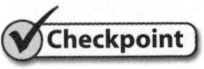 **Checkpoint** *What conversion factors can you write based on the mole-mass and mole-volume relationships?*

Figure 12.8 With your knowledge of conversion factors and this problem-solving approach, you can solve a variety of stoichiometric problems. **Identifying** *What conversion factor is used to convert moles to representative particles?*

Hydrogen (H_2)   Oxygen (O_2)

The electrolysis of water causes it to decompose into hydrogen and oxygen.

Math ▸ **Handbook**

For help with dimensional analysis, go to page R66.

interactive
Textbook

Problem-Solving 12.15 Solve Problem 15 with the help of an interactive guided tutorial.

—with **ChemASAP**

Calculating Molecules of a Product

How many molecules of oxygen are produced when 29.2 g of water is decomposed by electrolysis according to this balanced equation?

$$2H_2O(l) \xrightarrow{\text{electricity}} 2H_2(g) + O_2(g)$$

1 **Analyze** *List the knowns and the unknown.*

Knowns
- mass of water = 29.2 g H_2O
- 2 mol H_2O = 1 mol O_2 (from balanced equation)
- 1 mol H_2O = 18.0 g H_2O (molar mass)
- 1 mol O_2 = 6.02×10^{23} molecules O_2

Unknown
- molecules of oxygen = ? molecules O_2

The following calculations need to be done:

$$\text{g } H_2O \longrightarrow \text{mol } H_2O \longrightarrow \text{mol } O_2 \longrightarrow \text{molecules } O_2$$

The appropriate mole ratio relating mol O_2 to mol H_2O from the balanced equation is 1 mole O_2/2 mol H_2O.

2 **Calculate** *Solve for the unknown.*

$$29.2 \text{ g } H_2O \times \frac{1 \text{ mol } H_2O}{18.0 \text{ g } H_2O} \times \frac{1 \text{ mol } O_2}{2 \text{ mol } H_2O} \times \frac{6.02 \times 10^{23} \text{ molecules } O_2}{1 \text{ mol } O_2}$$

Given quantity   Change to moles   Mole ratio   Change to molecules

$$= 4.88 \times 10^{23} \text{ molecules } O_2$$

3 **Evaluate** *Does the result make sense?*

The given mass of water should produce a little less than 1 mol of oxygen, or a little less than Avogadro's number of molecules. The answer should have three significant figures.

Practice Problems

15. How many molecules of oxygen are produced by the decomposition of 6.54 g of potassium chlorate ($KClO_3$)?

$$2KClO_3(s) \longrightarrow$$
$$2KCl(s) + 3O_2(g)$$

16. The last step in the production of nitric acid is the reaction of nitrogen dioxide with water.

$$3NO_2(g) + H_2O(l) \longrightarrow$$
$$2HNO_3(aq) + NO(g)$$

How many grams of nitrogen dioxide must react with water to produce 5.00×10^{22} molecules of nitrogen monoxide?

The coefficients in a chemical equation indicate the relative number of particles and the relative number of moles of reactants and products. For a reaction involving gaseous reactants or products, the coefficients also indicate relative amounts of each gas. As a result, you can use volume ratios in the same way you have used mole ratios.

SAMPLE PROBLEM 12.5

Volume-Volume Stoichiometric Calculations

Nitrogen monoxide and oxygen gas combine to form the brown gas nitrogen dioxide, which contributes to photochemical smog. How many liters of nitrogen dioxide are produced when 34 L of oxygen reacts with an excess of nitrogen monoxide? Assume conditions of STP.

$$2NO(g) + O_2(g) \longrightarrow 2NO_2(g)$$

1 **Analyze** *List the knowns and the unknown.*

Knowns
- volume of oxygen = 34 L O_2
- 2 mol NO_2/1 mol O_2 (mole ratio from balanced equation)
- 1 mol O_2 = 22.4 L O_2 (at STP)
- 1 mol NO_2 = 22.4 L NO_2 (at STP)

Unknown
- volume of nitrogen dioxide = ? L NO_2

2 **Calculate** *Solve for the unknown.*

$$34 \text{ L } O_2 \times \frac{1 \text{ mol } O_2}{22.4 \text{ L } O_2} \times \frac{2 \text{ mol } NO_2}{1 \text{ mol } O_2} \times \frac{22.4 \text{ L } NO_2}{1 \text{ mol } NO_2} = 68 \text{ L } NO_2$$

| Given quantity | Change to moles | Mole ratio | Change to liters |

3 **Evaluate** *Does the result make sense?*

Because 2 mol NO_2 is produced for each 1 mol O_2 that reacts, the volume of NO_2 should be twice the given volume of O_2. The answer should have two significant figures.

Practice Problems

17. The equation for the combustion of carbon monoxide is

$$2CO(g) + O_2(g) \longrightarrow 2CO_2(g)$$

How many liters of oxygen are required to burn 3.86 L of carbon monoxide?

18. Phosphorus and hydrogen can be combined to form phosphine (PH_3).

$$P_4(s) + 6H_2(g) \longrightarrow 4PH_3(g)$$

How many liters of phosphine are formed when 0.42 L of hydrogen reacts with phosphorus?

 Interactive Textbook

Problem-Solving 12.18 Solve Problem 18 with the help of an interactive guided tutorial.

with **ChemASAP**

Did you notice that in Sample Problem 12.5 the 22.4 L/mol factors canceled out? This will always be true in a volume-volume problem. Remember that coefficients in a balanced chemical equation indicate the relative numbers of moles. The coefficients also indicate the relative volumes of interacting gases.

SAMPLE PROBLEM 12.6

Finding the Volume of a Gas Needed for a Reaction

Assuming STP, how many milliliters of oxygen are needed to produce 20.4 mL SO_3 according to this balanced equation?

$$2SO_2(g) + O_2(g) \longrightarrow 2SO_3(g)$$

1 **Analyze** *List the knowns and the unknown.*

Knowns
• volume of sulfur trioxide = 20.4 mL
• 2 mL SO_3/1 mL O_2 (volume ratio from balanced equation)

Unknown
• volume of oxygen = ? mL O_2

Math **Handbook**

For help with dimensional analysis, go to page R66.

2 **Calculate** *Solve for the unknown.*

$$20.4 \ \text{mL } SO_3 \times \frac{1 \ \text{mL } O_2}{2 \ \text{mL } SO_3} = 10.2 \ \text{mL } O_2$$

3 **Evaluate** *Does the result make sense?*

Because the volume ratio is 2 volumes SO_3 to 1 volume O_2, the volume of O_2 should be half the volume of SO_3. The answer should have three significant figures.

Practice Problems

Consider this equation:

$$CS_2(l) + 3O_2(g) \longrightarrow CO_2(g) + 2SO_2(g)$$

19. Calculate the volume of sulfur dioxide produced when 27.9 mL O_2 reacts with carbon disulfide.

20. How many deciliters of carbon dioxide are produced when 0.38 L SO_2 is formed?

*i*nteractive
Textbook

Problem-Solving 12.19 Solve Problem 19 with the help of an interactive guided tutorial.

with ChemASAP

12.2 Section Assessment

21. 🔑 **Key Concept** How are mole ratios used in chemical calculations?

22. 🔑 **Key Concept** Outline the sequence of steps needed to solve a typical stoichiometric problem.

23. Write the 12 mole ratios that can be derived from the equation for the combustion of isopropyl alcohol.

$$2C_3H_7OH(l) + 9O_2(g) \longrightarrow 6CO_2(g) + 8H_2O(g)$$

24. The combustion of acetylene gas is represented by this equation:

$$2C_2H_2(g) + 5O_2(g) \longrightarrow 4CO_2(g) + 2H_2O(g)$$

How many grams of CO_2 and grams of H_2O are produced when 52.0 g C_2H_2 burns in oxygen?

Connecting **Concepts**

Chemical Quantities Review the "mole road map" at the end of Section 10.2. Explain how this road map ties into the summary of steps for stoichiometric problems shown in Figure 12.8.

*i*nteractive
Textbook

Assessment 12.2 Test yourself on the concepts in Section 12.2.

with ChemASAP

Small-Scale LAB

Analysis of Baking Soda

Purpose
To determine the mass of sodium hydrogen carbonate in a sample of baking soda using stoichiometry.

Materials
- baking soda
- 3 plastic cups
- soda straw
- balance
- pipets of HCl, NaOH, and thymol blue
- pH sensor (optional)

Procedure

 Probeware version available in the Probeware Lab Manual.

A. Measure the mass of a clean, dry plastic cup.

B. Using the straw as a scoop, fill one end with baking soda to a depth of about 1 cm. Add the sample to the cup and measure its mass again.

C. Place two HCl pipets that are about 3/4 full into a clean cup and measure the mass of the system.

D. Transfer the contents of both HCl pipets to the cup containing baking soda. Swirl until the fizzing stops. Wait 5–10 minutes to be sure the reaction is complete. Measure the mass of the two empty HCl pipets in their cup again.

E. Add 5 drops of thymol blue to the plastic cup.

F. Place two full NaOH pipets in a clean cup and measure the mass of the system.

G. Add NaOH slowly to the baking soda/HCl mixture until the pink color just disappears. Measure the mass of the NaOH pipets in their cup again.

Analyze
Using your experimental data, record the answers to the following questions below your data table.

1. Write a balanced equation for the reaction between baking soda ($NaHCO_3$) and HCl.

2. Calculate the mass in grams of the baking soda.

$$(Step\ B - Step\ A)$$

3. Calculate the total mmol of 1M HCl.
Note: Every gram of HCl contains 1 mmol.

$$(Step\ C - Step\ D) \times 1.00\ mmol/g$$

4. Calculate the total mmol of 0.5M NaOH.
Note: Every gram of NaOH contains 0.5 mmol.

$$(Step\ F - Step\ G) \times 0.500\ mmol/g$$

5. Calculate the mmol of HCl that reacted with the baking soda. *Note:* The NaOH measures the amount of HCl that did not react.

$$(Step\ 3 - Step\ 4)$$

6. Calculate the mass of the baking soda from the reaction data.

$$(0.084\ g/mmol \times Step\ 5)$$

7. Calculate the percent error of the experiment.

$$\frac{(Step\ 2 - Step\ 6)}{Step\ 2} \times 100\%$$

You're the Chemist
The following small-scale activities allow you to develop your own procedures and analyze the results.

1. Analyze It! For each calculation you did, substitute each quantity (number and unit) into the equation and cancel the units to explain why each step gives the quantity desired.

2. Design It! Baking powder consists of a mixture of baking soda, sodium hydrogen carbonate, and a solid acid, usually calcium dihydrogen phosphate ($Ca(H_2PO_4)_2$). Design and carry out an experiment to determine the percentage of baking soda in baking powder.

New York Standards: 3.3c, 3.3e

Guide for Reading

🔑 **Key Concepts**

• How is the amount of product in a reaction affected by an insufficient quantity of any of the reactants?

• What does the percent yield of a reaction measure?

Vocabulary

limiting reagent
excess reagent
theoretical yield
actual yield
percent yield

Reading Strategy

Building Vocabulary After you have read the section, explain the differences among *theoretical yield, actual yield,* and *percent yield.*

Connecting to Your World If a carpenter had two table-tops and seven table legs, he would have difficulty building more than one functional four-legged table. The first table would require four of the legs, leaving just three legs for the second table. In this case, the number of table legs is the limiting factor in the construction of four-legged tables. A similar concept applies in chemistry. The amount of product made in a chemical reaction may be limited by the amount of one or more of the reactants.

Limiting and Excess Reagents

Many cooks follow a recipe when making a new dish. They know that sufficient quantities of all the ingredients must be available. Suppose, for example, that you are preparing to make lasagna and you have more than enough meat, tomato sauce, ricotta cheese, eggs, mozzarella cheese, spinach, and seasoning on hand. However, you have only half a box of lasagna noodles. The amount of lasagna you can make will be limited by the quantity of noodles you have. Thus, the noodles are the limiting ingredient in this baking venture. Figure 12.9 illustrates another example of a limiting ingredient in the kitchen. A chemist often faces a similar situation. 🔑 **In a chemical reaction, an insufficient quantity of any of the reactants will limit the amount of product that forms.**

Figure 12.9 The amount of product is determined by the quantity of the limiting reagent. In this example, the rolls are the limiting reagent. No matter how much of the other ingredients you have, with two rolls you can make only two sandwiches.

Chemical Equations

	N₂(g)	+	3H₂(g)	→	2NH₃(g)
"Microscopic recipe"	1 molecule N₂	+	3 molecules H₂	→	2 molecules NH₃
"Macroscopic recipe"	1 mol N₂	+	3 mol H₂	→	2 mol NH₃

Experimental Conditions

	Reactants		Products
Before reaction	2 molecules N₂	3 molecules H₂	0 molecules NH₃
After reaction	1 molecule N₂	0 molecules H₂	2 molecules NH₃

Figure 12.10 The "recipe" calls for 3 molecules of H₂ for every 1 molecule of N₂. In this particular experiment, H₂ is the limiting reagent and N₂ is in excess. **Inferring** *How would the amount of products formed change if you started with four molecules of N₂ and three molecules of H₂?*

As you know, a balanced chemical equation is a chemist's recipe. You can interpret the recipe on a microscopic scale (interacting particles) or on a macroscopic scale (interacting moles). The coefficients used to write the balanced equation give both the ratio of representative particles and the mole ratio. Recall the equation for the preparation of ammonia:

$$N_2(g) + 3H_2(g) \longrightarrow 2NH_3(g)$$

When one molecule (mole) of N_2 reacts with three molecules (moles) of H_2, two molecules (moles) of NH_3 are produced. What would happen if two molecules (moles) of N_2 reacted with three molecules (moles) of H_2? Would more than two molecules (moles) of NH_3 be formed? Figure 12.10 shows both the particle and the mole interpretations of this problem.

Before the reaction takes place, nitrogen and hydrogen are present in a 2:3 molecule (mole) ratio. The reaction takes place according to the balanced equation. One molecule (mole) of N_2 reacts with three molecules (moles) of H_2 to produce two molecules (moles) of NH_3. At this point, all the hydrogen has been used up, and the reaction stops. One molecule (mole) of unreacted nitrogen is left in addition to the two molecules (moles) of NH_3 that have been produced by the reaction.

In this reaction, only the hydrogen is completely used up. It is the **limiting reagent,** or the reagent that determines the amount of product that can be formed by a reaction. The reaction occurs only until the limiting reagent is used up. By contrast, the reactant that is not completely used up in a reaction is called the **excess reagent.** In this example, nitrogen is the excess reagent because some nitrogen will remain unreacted.

Sometimes in stoichiometric problems, the given quantities of reactants are expressed in units other than moles. In such cases, the first step in the solution is to convert each reactant to moles. Then the limiting reagent can be identified. The amount of product formed in a reaction can be determined from the given amount of limiting reagent.

Go Online

SC*LINKS*

For: Links on Hydrogen
Visit: www.SciLinks.org
Web Code: cdn-1123

*i*nteractive
Textbook

Animation 13 Apply the limiting reagent concept to the production of iron from iron ore.

with **ChemASAP**

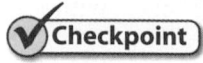 **Checkpoint** *How do limiting and excess reagents differ?*

Sulfur (S)   Copper (Cu)

Copper(I) sulfide (Cu₂S)

Math Handbook

For help with dimensional analysis, go to page R66.

ℹnteractive
Textbook

Problem-Solving 12.25 Solve Problem 25 with the help of an interactive guided tutorial.

—with **ChemASAP**

SAMPLE PROBLEM 12.7

Determining the Limiting Reagent in a Reaction

Copper reacts with sulfur to form copper(I) sulfide according to the following balanced equation.

$$2Cu(s) + S(s) \longrightarrow Cu_2S(s)$$

What is the limiting reagent when 80.0 g Cu reacts with 25.0 g S?

① Analyze *List the knowns and the unknown.*

Knowns
- mass of copper = 80.0 g Cu
- mass of sulfur = 25.0 g S

Unknown
- limiting reagent = ?

The number of moles of each reactant must first be found:

$$g\ Cu \longrightarrow mol\ Cu$$

$$g\ S \longrightarrow mol\ S$$

The balanced equation is used to calculate the number of moles of one reactant needed to react with the given amount of the other reactant:

$$mol\ Cu \longrightarrow mol\ S$$

The mole ratio relating mol S to mol Cu from the balanced chemical equation is 1 mol S/2 mol Cu.

② Calculate *Solve for the unknown.*

$$80.0\ g\ \cancel{Cu} \times \frac{1\ mol\ Cu}{63.5\ g\ \cancel{Cu}} = 1.26\ mol\ Cu$$

$$25.0\ g\ \cancel{S} \times \frac{1\ mol\ S}{32.1\ g\ \cancel{S}} = 0.779\ mol\ S$$

$$1.26\ \cancel{mol\ Cu} \times \frac{1\ mol\ S}{2\ \cancel{mol\ Cu}} = 0.630\ mol\ S$$

| Given quantity | Mole ratio | Needed amount |

Comparing the amount of sulfur needed (0.630 mol S) with the given amount (0.779 mol S) indicates that sulfur is in excess. Thus copper is the limiting reagent.

③ Evaluate *Do the results make sense?*

Since the ratio of the given mol Cu to mol S was less than the ratio (2:1) from the balanced equation, copper should be the limiting reagent.

Practice Problems

25. The equation for the complete combustion of ethene (C₂H₄) is

$$C_2H_4(g) + 3O_2(g) \longrightarrow$$
$$2CO_2(g) + 2H_2O(g)$$

If 2.70 mol C₂H₄ is reacted with 6.30 mol O₂, identify the limiting reagent.

26. Hydrogen gas can be produced by the reaction of magnesium metal with hydrochloric acid.

$$Mg(s) + 2HCl(aq) \longrightarrow$$
$$MgCl_2(aq) + H_2(g)$$

Identify the limiting reagent when 6.00 g HCl reacts with 5.00 g Mg.

In Sample Problem 12.7, you may have noticed that even though the mass of copper used in the reaction is greater than the mass of sulfur, copper is the limiting reagent. The reactant that is present in the smaller amount by mass or volume is not necessarily the limiting reagent.

SAMPLE PROBLEM 12.8

Using a Limiting Reagent to Find the Quantity of a Product

What is the maximum number of grams of Cu_2S that can be formed when 80.0 g Cu reacts with 25.0 g S?

$$2Cu(s) + S(s) \longrightarrow Cu_2S(s)$$

1 Analyze *List the knowns and the unknown.*

Knowns
- limiting reagent = 1.26 mol Cu (from Sample Problem 12.7)
- 1 mol Cu_2S = 159.1 g Cu_2S (molar mass)

Unknown
- mass copper(I) sulfide = ? g Cu_2S

The limiting reagent, which was determined in the previous sample problem, is used to calculate the maximum amount of Cu_2S formed:

$$mol\ Cu \longrightarrow mol\ Cu_2S \longrightarrow g\ Cu_2S$$

2 The equation yields the appropriate mole ratio: 1 mol Cu_2S/2 mol Cu.

Calculate *Solve for the unknown.*

$$1.26\ \cancel{mol\ Cu} \times \frac{1\ \cancel{mol\ Cu_2S}}{2\ \cancel{mol\ Cu}} \times \frac{159.1\ g\ Cu_2S}{1\ \cancel{mol\ Cu_2S}} = 1.00 \times 10^2\ g\ Cu_2S$$

The given quantity of copper, 80.0 g, could have been used for this step instead of the moles of copper, which were calculated in Sample Problem 12.7.

Problem-Solving 12.28 Solve Problem 28 with the help of an interactive guided tutorial.

with ChemASAP

3 Evaluate *Do the results make sense?*

Copper is the limiting reagent in this reaction. The maximum number of grams of Cu_2S produced should be more than the amount of copper that initially reacted because copper is combining with sulfur. However, the mass of Cu_2S produced should be less than the total mass of the reactants (105.0 g) because sulfur was in excess.

Practice Problems

27. The equation below shows the incomplete combustion of ethene.

$$C_2H_4(g) + 2O_2(g) \longrightarrow$$
$$2CO(g) + 2H_2O(g)$$

If 2.70 mol C_2H_4 is reacted with 6.30 mol O_2,
a. identify the limiting reagent.
b. calculate the moles of water produced.

28. The heat from an acetylene torch is produced by burning acetylene (C_2H_2) in oxygen.

$$2C_2H_2(g) + 5O_2(g) \longrightarrow$$
$$4CO_2(g) + 2H_2O(g)$$

How many grams of water can be produced by the reaction of 2.40 mol C_2H_2 with 7.4 mol O_2?

Limiting Reagents

Purpose
To illustrate the concept of a limiting reagent in a chemical reaction.

Materials
- graduated cylinder
- balance
- 3 250-mL Erlenmeyer flasks
- 3 rubber balloons
- 4.2 g magnesium ribbon
- 300 mL 1.0*M* hydrochloric acid

Procedure
1. Add 100 mL of the hydrochloric acid solution to each flask.
2. Weigh out 0.6 g, 1.2 g, and 2.4 g of magnesium ribbon, and place each sample into its own balloon.
3. Stretch the end of each balloon over the mouth of each flask. Do not allow the magnesium ribbon in the balloon to fall into the flask.
4. Magnesium reacts with hydrochloric acid to form hydrogen gas. When you mix the magnesium with the hydrochloric acid in the next step, you will generate a certain volume of hydrogen gas. How do you think the volume of hydrogen produced in each flask will compare?
5. Lift up on each balloon and shake the magnesium into each flask. Observe the volume of gas produced until the reaction in each flask is completed.

Analysis and Conclusions
1. How did the volumes of hydrogen gas produced, as measured by the size of the balloons, compare? Did the results agree with your prediction?
2. Write a balanced equation for the reaction you observed.
3. The 100 mL of hydrochloric acid contained 0.10 mol HCl. Show by calculation why the balloon with 1.2 g Mg inflated to about twice the size of the balloon with 0.60 g Mg.
4. Show by calculation why the balloons with 1.2 g and 2.4 g Mg inflated to approximately the same volume. What was the limiting reagent when 2.4 g Mg was added to the acid?

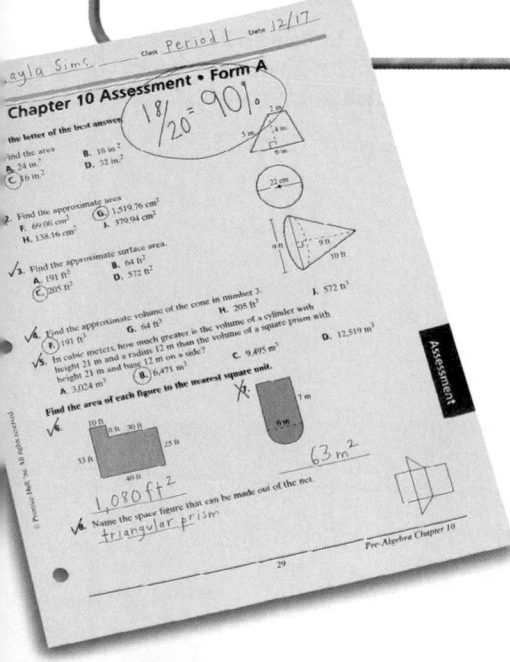

Figure 12.11 Calculating the ratio of the number of correct answers to the number of questions on the exam is a measure of how well the student performed on the exam.

Percent Yield

In theory, when a teacher gives an exam to the class, every student should get a grade of 100%. This generally does not occur, as shown in Figure 12.11. Instead, the performance of the class is usually spread over a range of grades. Your exam grade, expressed as a percentage, is a ratio of two items. The first item is the number of questions you answered correctly. The second is the total number of questions. The grade compares how well you performed with how well you could have performed if you had answered all the questions correctly. Chemists perform similar calculations in the laboratory when the product from a chemical reaction is less than expected, based on the balanced chemical equation.

When an equation is used to calculate the amount of product that will form during a reaction, the calculated value represents the theoretical yield. The **theoretical yield** is the maximum amount of product that could be formed from given amounts of reactants. In contrast, the amount of product that actually forms when the reaction is carried out in the laboratory is called the **actual yield.** The **percent yield** is the ratio of the actual yield to the theoretical yield expressed as a percent.

$$\text{Percent yield} = \frac{\text{actual yield}}{\text{theoretical yield}} \times 100\%$$

Figure 12.12 A batting average is actually a percent yield.

Because the actual yield of a chemical reaction is often less than the theoretical yield, the percent yield is often less than 100%. 🔑 **The percent yield is a measure of the efficiency of a reaction carried out in the laboratory.** This is similar to an exam score measuring your efficiency of learning, or a batting average measuring your efficiency of hitting a baseball.

A percent yield should not normally be larger than 100%. Many factors cause percent yields to be less than 100%. Reactions do not always go to completion; when this occurs, less than the calculated amount of product is formed. Impure reactants and competing side reactions may cause unwanted products to form. Actual yield can also be lower than the theoretical yield due to a loss of product during filtration or in transferring between containers. Moreover, if reactants or products have not been carefully measured, a percent yield of 100% is unlikely.

An actual yield is an experimental value. Figure 12.13 shows a typical laboratory procedure for determining the actual yield of a product of a decomposition reaction. For reactions in which percent yields have been determined, you can calculate and therefore predict an actual yield if the reaction conditions remain the same.

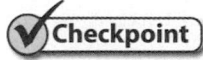 *What factors can cause the actual yield to be less than the theoretical yield?*

Figure 12.13 Sodium hydrogen carbonate ($NaHCO_3$) will decompose when heated. **a** The mass of $NaHCO_3$, the reactant, is measured. **b** The reactant is heated. **c** The mass of one of the products, sodium carbonate (Na_2CO_3), the actual yield, is measured. The percent yield is calculated once the actual yield is determined. **Predicting What are the other products of this reaction?**

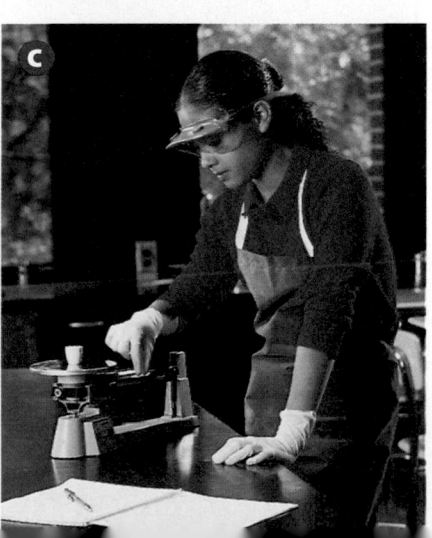

Calculating the Theoretical Yield of a Reaction

Calcium carbonate, which is found in seashells, is decomposed by heating. The balanced equation for this reaction is:

$$CaCO_3(s) \xrightarrow{\Delta} CaO(s) + CO_2(g)$$

What is the theoretical yield of CaO if 24.8 g $CaCO_3$ is heated?

1 **Analyze** *List the knowns and the unknown.*

Knowns
- mass of calcium carbonate = 24.8 g $CaCO_3$
- 1 mol $CaCO_3$ = 100.1 g $CaCO_3$ (molar mass)
- 1 mol CaO = 56.1 g CaO (molar mass)

Unknown
- theoretical yield of calcium oxide = ? g CaO

Calculate the theoretical yield using the mass of the reactant:

$$g\ CaCO_3 \longrightarrow mol\ CaCO_3 \longrightarrow mol\ CaO \longrightarrow g\ CaO$$

The appropriate mole ratio is 1 mol CaO/1 mol $CaCO_3$.

2 **Calculate** *Solve for the unknown.*

$$24.8\ \cancel{g\ CaCO_3} \times \frac{1\ \cancel{mol\ CaCO_3}}{100.1\ \cancel{g\ CaCO_3}} \times \frac{1\ \cancel{mol\ CaO}}{1\ \cancel{mol\ CaCO_3}} \times \frac{56.1\ g\ CaO}{1\ \cancel{mol\ CaO}}$$

$$= 13.9\ g\ CaO$$

3 **Evaluate** *Does the result make sense?*

The mole ratio of CaO to $CaCO_3$ is 1:1. The ratio of their masses in the reaction should be the same as the ratio of their molar masses, which is slightly greater than 1:2. The result of the calculations shows that the mass of CaO is slightly greater than half the mass of $CaCO_3$.

Practice Problems

29. When 84.8 g of iron(III) oxide reacts with an excess of carbon monoxide, iron is produced

$$Fe_2O_3(s) + 3CO(g) \longrightarrow$$
$$2Fe(s) + 3CO_2(g)$$

What is the theoretical yield of this reaction?

30. When 5.00 g of copper reacts with excess silver nitrate, silver metal and copper (II) nitrate are produced. What is the theoretical yield of silver in this reaction?

Recall that the percent yield is calculated by multiplying the ratio of the actual yield to theoretical yield by 100%. Therefore, you must have values of both the theoretical yield and the actual yield to calculate the percent yield.

Math **Handbook**

For help with dimensional analysis, go to page R66.

Interactive Textbook

Problem-Solving 12.29 Solve Problem 29 with the help of an interactive guided tutorial.

— with **ChemASAP**

SAMPLE PROBLEM 12.10

Calculating the Percent Yield of a Reaction

What is the percent yield if 13.1 g CaO is actually produced when 24.8 g $CaCO_3$ is heated?

$$CaCO_3(s) \xrightarrow{\Delta} CaO(s) + CO_2(g)$$

1 **Analyze** *List the knowns and the unknown.*

Knowns
- actual yield = 13.1 g CaO
- theoretical yield = 13.9 g CaO (from Sample Problem 12.9)
- percent yield = $\dfrac{\text{actual yield}}{\text{theoretical yield}} \times 100\%$

Unknown
- percent yield = ? %

2 **Calculate** *Solve for the unknown.*

$$\text{percent yield} = \frac{13.1 \text{ g } CaO}{13.9 \text{ g } CaO} \times 100\% = 94.2\%$$

Math ▸ **Handbook**

For help with percents, go to page R72.

3 **Evaluate** *Does the result make sense?*

In this example, the actual yield is slightly less than theoretical yield. Therefore, the percent yield should be slightly less than 100%. The answer should have three significant figures.

Practice Problems

31. If 50.0 g of silicon dioxide is heated with an excess of carbon, 27.9 g of silicon carbide is produced.
$$SiO_2(s) + 3C(s) \longrightarrow$$
$$SiC(s) + 2CO(g)$$
What is the percent yield of this reaction?

32. If 15.0 g of nitrogen reacts with 15.0 g of hydrogen, 10.5 g of ammonia is produced. What is the percent yield of this reaction?

Interactive Textbook

Problem-Solving 12.31 Solve Problem 31 with the help of an interactive guided tutorial.

— with **ChemASAP**

12.3 Section Assessment

33. 🔑 **Key Concept** In a chemical reaction, how does an insufficient quantity of a reactant affect the amount of product formed?

34. 🔑 **Key Concept** How can you gauge the efficiency of a reaction carried out in the laboratory?

35. What is the percent yield if 4.65 g of copper is produced when 1.87 g of aluminum reacts with an excess of copper(II) sulfate?

$$2Al(s) + 3CuSO_4(aq) \longrightarrow Al_2(SO_4)_3(aq) + 3Cu(s)$$

Elements ▸ **Handbook**

Haber Process Read the feature on ammonia on page R26. Examine the flow chart summarizing the Haber process. What experimental data would you need to determine the percent yield of the Haber process?

Interactive Textbook

Assessment 12.3 Test yourself on the concepts in Section 12.3.

— with **ChemASAP**

Just the Right Volume of Gas

In a front-end collision, proper inflation of an air bag may save your life. Engineers use stoichiometry to determine the exact quantity of each reactant in the air bag's inflation system. **Interpreting Diagrams** *What is the source of the gas that fills an air bag?*

Car Facts

17.1 million cars and light trucks were sold in 2002 in the United States.

In the United States, the Cadillac Escalade SUV has the most frequent theft claims among 2000–02 model passenger vehicles.

Monaco has the highest number of vehicles in relation to its road network. In 1996 (most recent figures), it had 480 vehicles for each kilometer of road. If they were required to park behind one another on the streets, half would have nowhere to park!

At night, headlights illuminate 160 ft in front of your car. If you are driving 40 mi/h at night, your reaction distance is 88 ft and your braking distance is 101 ft. Is your stopping distance less than or greater than 160 ft?

$$\text{Reaction distance} + \text{Braking distance} = \text{Stopping distance}$$

Air bag folded into steering wheel

Ignition unit

Igniter

Steering wheel

Sodium azide pellets

1 A collision triggers crash sensors, which send a signal to an igniter.

2 The igniter triggers a series of chemical reactions that release a large volume of nitrogen gas, which fills the air bag. Within 0.05 seconds of the collision the air bag is fully inflated.

Sodium azide pellets decomposing
$$2NaN_3 \longrightarrow 2Na + 3N_2$$

Nitrogen gas

Igniter

Electrical signal from crash sensor

Steering wheel

Steering wheel

Deflated air bag

Nontoxic residue of secondary reactions

3 Small holes in the bag allow nitrogen gas to escape, causing the bag to deflate.

CHAPTER 12 Study Guide

Key Concepts

12.1 The Arithmetic of Equations

- A balanced chemical equation provides the same kind of quantitative information that a recipe does.
- Chemists use balanced chemical equations as a basis to calculate how much reactant is needed or product is formed in a reaction.
- A balanced chemical equation can be interpreted in terms of different quantities, including numbers of atoms, molecules, or moles; mass; and volume.
- Mass and atoms are conserved in every chemical reaction.

12.2 Chemical Calculations

- In chemical calculations, mole ratios are used to convert between moles of reactant and moles of product, between moles of reactants, or between moles of products.

- In a typical stoichiometric problem, the given quantity is first converted to moles. Then the mole ratio from the balanced equation is used to calculate the moles of the wanted substance. Finally, the moles are converted to any other unit of measurement related to the unit mole.

12.3 Limiting Reagent and Percent Yield

- In a chemical reaction, an insufficient quantity of any of the reactants will limit the amount of product that forms.
- The percent yield is a measure of the efficiency of a reaction performed in the laboratory.

Vocabulary

- actual yield (p. 372)
- excess reagent (p. 369)
- limiting reagent (p. 369)
- mole ratio (p. 359)
- percent yield (p. 372)
- stoichiometry (p. 354)
- theoretical yield (p. 372)

Key Equations

- mole-mole relationship for $aG \longrightarrow bW$:

$$x \text{ mol } G \times \frac{b \text{ mol } W}{a \text{ mol } G} = \frac{xb}{a} \text{ mol } W$$

- $\text{percent yield} = \dfrac{\text{actual yield}}{\text{theoretical yield}} \times 100\%$

Organizing Information

Use these terms to construct a concept map that organizes the major ideas of this chapter.

Concept Map 12 Create your Concept Map using the computer.

with ChemASAP

mole ratio percent yield chemical equation

actual yield theoretical yield

excess reagent stoichiometry limiting reagent

12.1 The Arithmetic of Equations

34. In terms of the types of basic particles involved, write word equations for each of the following chemical equations.
   a. $2KClO_3(s) \longrightarrow 2KCl(s) + 3O_2(g)$
   b. $4NH_3(g) + 6NO(g) \longrightarrow 5N_2(g) + 6H_2O(g)$
   c. $4K(s) + O_2(g) \longrightarrow 2K_2O(s)$

35. Rewrite the word equations you wrote in Problem 34 in terms of interacting numbers of moles of reactants and products.

36. Calculate and compare the mass of the reactants with the mass of the products for each equation in Problem 34. Show that each balanced equation obeys the law of conservation of mass.

37. Would the law of conservation of mass hold in a net ionic equation? Explain.

38. A bicycle-built-for-three has a frame, two wheels, six pedals, and three seats. The balanced equation for this bicycle is

   $$F + 2W + 6P + 3S \longrightarrow FW_2P_6S_3$$

   How many of each part are needed to make 29 bicycles-built-for-three?
   a. frames   b. wheels
   c. pedals   d. seats

12.2 Chemical Calculations

39. Explain the term *mole ratio* in your own words. When would you use this term?

40. The reaction of fluorine with ammonia produces dinitrogen tetrafluoride and hydrogen fluoride.

   $$5F_2(g) + 2NH_3(g) \longrightarrow N_2F_4(g) + 6HF(g)$$

   In this particular reaction, 66.6 g NH_3 reacts completely with fluorine.
   a. How many moles of ammonia react?
   b. How many moles of fluorine also react?
   c. How many grams of fluorine are involved in the reaction?

41. What information about a chemical reaction is derived from the coefficients in a balanced equation?

42. Lithium nitride reacts with water to form ammonia and aqueous lithium hydroxide.

   $$Li_3N(s) + 3H_2O(l) \longrightarrow NH_3(g) + 3LiOH(aq)$$

   In this particular reaction, 32.9 g Li_3N react.
   a. How many moles of Li_3N react?
   b. How many moles of LiOH are produced?
   c. Calculate the number of grams of LiOH that are produced.

43. Calcium carbonate reacts with phosphoric acid to produce calcium phosphate, carbon dioxide, and water.

   $$3CaCO_3(s) + 2H_3PO_4(aq) \longrightarrow$$
   $$Ca_3(PO_4)_2(aq) + 3CO_2(g) + 3H_2O(l)$$

   In a certain reaction, 3.74 g $Ca_3(PO_4)_2$ are produced.
   a. How many moles of calcium phosphate are produced?
   b. How many moles of phosphoric acid were involved in the reaction?
   c. How many grams of phosphoric acid is this?

44. Nitric acid and zinc react to form zinc nitrate, ammonium nitrate, and water.

   $$4Zn(s) + 10HNO_3(aq) \longrightarrow$$
   $$4Zn(NO_3)_2(aq) + NH_4NO_3(aq) + 3H_2O(l)$$

   In a laboratory experiment involving this reaction, 1.49 g HNO_3 reacts.
   a. Calculate the number of moles of nitric acid that react.
   b. How many moles of zinc nitrate are produced?
   c. Convert this number of moles of zinc nitrate to grams.

45. Hydrazine (N_2H_4) is used as rocket fuel. It reacts with oxygen to form nitrogen and water.

   $$N_2H_4(l) + O_2(g) \longrightarrow N_2(g) + 2H_2O(g)$$

   a. How many liters of N_2 (at STP) form when 1.0 kg N_2H_4 reacts with 1.0 kg O_2?
   b. How many grams of the excess reagent remain after the reaction?

46. Ammonium nitrate will decompose explosively at high temperatures to form nitrogen, oxygen, and water vapor.

$$2NH_4NO_3(s) \longrightarrow 2N_2(g) + 4H_2O(g) + O_2(g)$$

What is the total number of liters of gas formed when 228 g NH_4NO_3 is decomposed? (Assume STP.)

47. In an experiment, varying masses of sodium metal are reacted with a fixed initial mass of chlorine gas. The amounts of sodium used and the amounts of sodium chloride formed are shown on the following graph.

NaCl Produced by Reacting Sodium With Chlorine

Mass of NaCl produced (g) vs. *Mass of Na (g)*

a. Explain the general shape of the graph.

b. How many moles of sodium are used at the point where the curve becomes horizontal?

c. How many moles of chlorine gas reacted with this amount of sodium?

d. How many grams of chlorine gas is this?

48. A car gets 9.2 kilometers to a liter of gasoline. Assuming that gasoline is 100% octane (C_8H_{18}), which has a specific gravity of 0.69, how many liters of air (21% oxygen by volume at STP) will be required to burn the gasoline for a 1250-km trip? Assume complete combustion.

49. Ethyl alcohol (C_2H_5OH) can be produced by the fermentation of glucose ($C_6H_{12}O_6$) in the presence of an enzyme.

$$C_6H_{12}O_6 \xrightarrow{\text{enzyme}} 2C_2H_5OH + 2CO_2$$

In a particular reaction, it takes 5.0 h to produce 8.0 kg of alcohol.

a. How many moles of alcohol were produced during this time period?

b. Calculate the number of moles of glucose consumed during this time.

c. How many days will it take to consume 1.0×10^3 kg of glucose?

50. A 1004.0-g sample of $CaCO_3$ that is 95.0% pure gives 225 L of CO_2 at STP when reacted with an excess of hydrochloric acid.

$$CaCO_3 + 2HCl \longrightarrow CaCl_2 + CO_2 + H_2O$$

What is the density (in g/L) of the CO_2?

51. The white limestone cliffs of Dover, England, contain a large percentage of calcium carbonate ($CaCO_3$). A sample of limestone weighing 84.4 g reacts with an excess of hydrochloric acid to form calcium chloride.

$$CaCO_3 + 2HCl \longrightarrow CaCl_2 + H_2O + CO_2$$

a. If you assume all the limestone is calcium carbonate, how many moles of calcium carbonate react?

b. How many moles of calcium chloride would you expect to form?

c. Calculate the number of grams of calcium chloride you expect to form.

d. The actual mass of calcium chloride formed is 81.8 g. Why does this amount differ from the amount you expected to form?

52. The equation for one of the reactions in the process of reducing iron ore to the metal is

$$Fe_2O_3(s) + 3CO(g) \longrightarrow 2Fe(s) + 3CO_2(g)$$

For a particular reaction, 454 g of iron(III) oxide reacts.

a. How many moles of iron(III) oxide reacts?

b. How many moles of carbon monoxide are needed to reduce this amount of iron(III) oxide?

c. What mass of CO is required to reduce the iron(III) oxide to iron metal?

53. When a certain amount of silicon dioxide is heated with an excess of carbon, 32.2 g of silicon carbide is produced.

$$SiO_2(s) + 3C(s) \longrightarrow SiC(s) + 2CO(g)$$

a. How many moles of silicon carbide are produced?
b. How many moles of silicon dioxide reacted?
c. Calculate the number of grams of silicon dioxide involved in the reaction.

12.3 Limiting Reagent and Percent Yield

54. What is the significance of the limiting reagent in a chemical process? What happens to the amount of any reagent in excess?

55. In a reaction chamber, 3.0 mol of aluminum reacts with 5.3 mol Cl_2. The reaction is described by the following balanced chemical equation.

$$2Al + 3Cl_2 \longrightarrow 2AlCl_3$$

a. Identify the limiting reagent for the reaction.
b. Calculate the number of moles of product formed.
c. Calculate the number of moles of excess reagent remaining after the reaction.

56. Heating an ore of antimony (Sb_2S_3) in the presence of iron gives the element antimony and iron(II) sulfide.

$$Sb_2S_3(s) + 3Fe(s) \longrightarrow 2Sb(s) + 3FeS(s)$$

When 15.0 g Sb_2S_3 reacts with an excess of Fe, 9.84 g of Sb is produced. What is the percent yield of this reaction?

57. If the reaction below proceeds with a 96.8% yield, how many kilograms of $CaSO_4$ are formed when 5.24 kg SO_2 reacts with an excess of $CaCO_3$ and O_2?

$$2CaCO_3(s) + 2SO_2(g) + O_2(g) \longrightarrow$$
$$2CaSO_4(s) + 2CO_2(g)$$

58. The manufacture of compound F requires five separate chemical reactions. The initial reactant, compound A, is converted to compound B, compound B is converted to compound C, and so forth. The diagram below summarizes the step-

wise manufacture of compound F, including the percent yield for each step. Provide the missing quantities or missing percent yields. Assume that the reactant and product in each step react in a one-to-one mole ratio.

59. Given a certain quantity of reactant, you calculate that a particular reaction should produce 55 g of a product. When you perform the reaction, you find that you have produced 63 g of product. What is your percent yield? What could have caused a percent yield greater than 100%?

60. Which of the following reactions depends on a limiting reagent? Explain why or why not each depends on a limiting reactant. Identify the limiting reagent for those that depend on one.
a. Calcium nitrate and aluminum hydroxide react to produce calcium hydroxide and aluminum nitrate.
b. Mercury(II) oxide is heated to produce mercury and oxygen.
c. Sodium and water react to form sodium hydroxide.
d. Methane (CH_4) reacts with excess oxygen to produce carbon dioxide and water.

Test-Taking Tip

Anticipate the answer. Use what you know to guess what you think the answer should be. Then look to see if your answer, or one much like it, is given as an option.

Regents Practice Exam

Part A

For each statement or question write the number of the word or expression that, of those given, best completes the statement or answers the question.

1. Which of the following totals is always equal on both sides of a chemical equation?
   (1) coefficients
   (2) number of reactants and products
   (3) mass
   (4) number of moles

2. The molar mass of BaO is
   (1) 27 g   (3) 153 g
   (2) 121 g   (4) 169 g

3. If the formula $2Fe_3O_4$ is written in a chemical equation, the number 2 shows the
   (1) relative number of moles of the compound in the reaction
   (2) relative mass of the compound in the reaction
   (3) number of iron atoms in the compound
   (4) ratio of iron and oxygen atoms

Part B-1

For each statement or question write the number of the word or expression that, of those given, best completes the statement or answers the question.

4. Which of the following elements forms an ion with a 2+ charge?
   (1) potassium   (3) aluminum
   (2) sulfur   (4) magnesium

5. Nitric acid is formed by the reaction of nitrogen dioxide with water.

   $$3NO_2(g) + H_2O(l) \longrightarrow NO(g) + 2HNO_3(aq)$$

   How many moles of water are needed to react with 8.4 mol NO_2?
   (1) 2.8 mol   (3) 8.4 mol
   (2) 3.0 mol   (4) 25 mol

6. Phosphorus trifluoride is formed from its elements.

   $$P_4(s) + 6F_2(g) \longrightarrow 4PF_3(g)$$

   How many grams of fluorine are needed to react with 6.20 g of phosphorus to form 17.6 g of phosphorus trifluoride?
   (1) 2.85 g   (3) 11.4 g
   (2) 5.70 g   (4) 23.8 g

Use the following information to answer Questions 7–9.

Magnesium nitride is formed in the reaction of magnesium metal with nitrogen gas.

$$3Mg(s) + N_2(g) \longrightarrow Mg_3N_2(s)$$

In an experiment, 4.0 mol of nitrogen were mixed with 6.0 mol of magnesium. The reaction continued until all of one of the reactants was used up.

7. Which reactant was used up?
   (1) Mg
   (2) N_2
   (3) Mg_3N_2
   (4) Both the reactants were used up.

8. How many moles of product were produced?
   (1) 1.0 mol
   (2) 2.0 mol
   (3) 4.0 mol
   (4) 6.0 mol

9. How many moles of the leftover reactant remained after the reaction was completed?
   (1) 1.0 mol
   (2) 2.0 mol
   (3) 4.0 mol
   (4) 6.0 mol

10. Every stoichiometry calculation uses a balanced chemical equation because
    (1) the sum of the coefficients of the reactants equals the sum of the coefficients of the products
    (2) every chemical reaction obeys the law of conservation of mass
    (3) energy is conserved in all chemical reactions
    (4) the coefficients in the equation express the mass relationships

11. Which of the following statements is true?
    (1) A mole ratio is always written with the larger number in the numerator.
    (2) A mole ratio will always be greater than one.
    (3) A mole ratio can be determined from the subscripts in a balanced equation.
    (4) A mole ratio can be used to find the number of moles of a product if the number of moles of a reactant is known.

Part B-2

Answer each of the following questions.

12. Write a balanced chemical equation for each of the following reactions.
  a. When heated, lead(II) nitrate decomposes to form lead(II) oxide, nitrogen dioxide, and molecular oxygen.
  b. The complete combustion of isopropyl alcohol (C_3H_7OH) produces carbon dioxide and water vapor.
  c. When a mixture of aluminum and iron(II) oxide is heated, metallic iron and aluminum oxide are produced.

13. How many grams of beryllium are in 147 g of the mineral beryl ($Be_3Al_2Si_6O_{18}$)?

14. Balance each of the following chemical equations.
  a. $Ba(NO_3)_2(aq) + Na_2SO_4(aq) \longrightarrow$
  $$BaSO_4(s) + NaNO_3(aq)$$
  b. $AlCl_3(aq) + AgNO_3(aq) \longrightarrow$
  $$AgCl(s) + Al(NO_3)_3(aq)$$
  c. $H_2SO_4(aq) + Mg(OH)_2(aq) \longrightarrow$
  $$MgSO_4(aq) + H_2O(l)$$

15. How many electrons, protons, and neutrons are in an atom of each of the following isotopes?
  a. titanium-47
  b. tin-120
  c. oxygen-18
  d. magnesium-26

16. What is the mass, in grams, of a mole of benzene (C_6H_6)?

17. Write the formula for each of the following compounds.
  a. aluminum carbonate
  b. silicon dioxide
  c. potassium sulfide
  d. manganese(II) chromate
  e. sodium bromide

18. Oxalic acid has an empirical formula of CHO_2. What is the molecular formula of oxalic acid if its molar mass is 90 g/mol?

19. Write a balanced chemical equation for the complete combustion of ribose, $C_5H_{10}O_5$.

20. How many moles is each of the following?
  a. 47.8 g KNO_3
  b. 2.22 g SO_2

21. Name each of the following substances.
  a. SiO_2
  b. K_2SO_4
  c. H_2CO_3
  d. MgS

22. Name each of the following ions.
  a. PO_4^{3-}
  b. Al^{3+}
  c. Se^{2-}
  d. NH_4^+

23. Can a compound contain both ionic and covalent bonds? Explain your answer.

24. Distinguish among single, double, and triple covalent bonds.

25. Identify the larger atom in each of the following pairs.
  a. sodium and chlorine
  b. arsenic and nitrogen
  c. fluorine and cesium

26. The diatomic element P and diatomic element Q react to form the compound P_3Q,

P_2 Q_2 P_3Q

Write a balanced equation for the reaction between element P and element Q.

Part C

Answer each of the following questions.

27. Carbon disulfide is an important industrial solvent. It is prepared by the reaction of coke with sulfur dioxide.
$$5C(s) + 2SO_2(g) \longrightarrow CS_2(l) + 4CO(g)$$
  a. How many moles of CS_2 form when 2.7 mol C reacts?
  b. How many moles of carbon are needed to react with 5.44 mol SO_2?
  c. How many moles of carbon monoxide form at the same time that 0.246 mol CS_2 forms?
  d. How many moles SO_2 are required to make 118 mol CS_2?

28. Methanol (CH_3OH) is used in the production of many chemicals. Methanol is made by reacting carbon monoxide and hydrogen at high temperature and pressure.
$$CO(g) + 2H_2(g) \longrightarrow CH_3OH(g)$$
  a. How many moles of each reactant are needed to produce 3.60 mol CH_3OH?
  b. Calculate the number of moles of each reactant needed to produce 4.00 mol CH_3OH.
  c. How many moles of hydrogen are necessary to react with 2.85 mol CO?

On a hot summer day ice cream can turn quickly into a liquid.

INQUIRY Activity

Observing Gas Pressure

Materials
small glass with a smooth, even rim; water; index card

Procedure

1. Fill the glass to its rim with water.
2. Place the index card on top of the glass.
3. Working over a sink, use one hand to press the index card firmly to the top of the glass. Then quickly invert the glass, keeping your hand in place.

    CAUTION *Wipe up any spill immediately.*

4. Remove your hand from the index card.

Think About It

1. What did you observe when you removed your hand?
2. Measure the volume of water in the glass. How many grams of water are in the glass? (Remember that 1 mL H_2O = 1 g H_2O.)
3. What keeps the water inside the glass?

New York Standards: S1.1b, 3.1jj, 3.4b, 3.4c

Connecting to Your World

You are walking your dog in the woods. Suddenly your dog begins to bark and run toward what you think is a black cat. But before you realize that the "cat" is not a cat, the damage is done. The skunk has released its spray! Within seconds you smell that all-too-familiar foul odor. In this section, you will discover some general characteristics of gases that help explain how odors travel through the air, even on a windless day.

Kinetic Theory and a Model for Gases

The word *kinetic* refers to motion. The energy an object has because of its motion is called **kinetic energy.** According to the **kinetic theory,** all matter consists of tiny particles that are in constant motion. The particles in a gas are usually molecules or atoms. The kinetic theory as it applies to gases includes the following fundamental assumptions about gases.

The particles in a gas are considered to be small, hard spheres with an insignificant volume. Within a gas, the particles are relatively far apart compared with the distance between particles in a liquid or solid. Between the particles, there is empty space. No attractive or repulsive forces exist between the particles. The motion of one particle in a gas is independent of the motion of all the other particles.

The motion of the particles in a gas is rapid, constant, and random. As a result, gases fill their containers regardless of the shape and volume of the containers. An uncontained gas can spread out into space without limit. The particles travel in straight-line paths until they collide with another particle, or another object, such as the wall of their container. The particles change direction only when they rebound from collisions with one another or with other objects.

Measurements indicate that the average speed of oxygen molecules in air at 20°C is an amazing 1700 km/h! At these high speeds, the odor from a hot cheese pizza in Washington, D.C., should reach Mexico City in about 115 minutes. That does not happen, however, because the molecules responsible for the odor are constantly striking molecules in air and rebounding in other directions. Their path of uninterrupted travel in a straight line is very short. The aimless path the molecules take is called a random walk.

All collisions between particles in a gas are perfectly elastic. During an elastic collision, kinetic energy is transferred without loss from one particle to another, and the total kinetic energy remains constant. The diagrams in Figure 13.1 on the next page illustrate the assumptions of kinetic theory as applied to gases.

Guide for Reading

Key Concepts
- What are the three assumptions of the kinetic theory as it applies to gases?
- How does kinetic theory explain gas pressure?
- What is the relationship between the temperature in kelvins and the average kinetic energy of particles?

Vocabulary
kinetic energy
kinetic theory
gas pressure
vacuum
atmospheric pressure
barometer
pascal (Pa)
standard atmosphere (atm)

Reading Strategy

Relating Text and Visuals
As you read, look closely at Figure 13.3. Explain how this illustration helps you understand how kinetic energy is distributed among the particles of a gas at two different temperatures.

Word *Origins*

Kinetic comes from the Greek word *kinetos,* meaning "to move." Kinetic energy is the energy an object has because of its motion. **Some sculptures are kinetic. What characteristic do they share?**

Figure 13.1 Gases share some general characteristics.
a The rapid, constant motion of particles in a gas causes them to collide with one another and with the walls of their container.
b The particles travel in straight-line paths between collisions.
c A gas fills all the available space in its container.

Gas Pressure

A helium-filled balloon maintains its shape because of the pressure of the gas within it. **Gas pressure** results from the force exerted by a gas per unit surface area of an object. What causes this force? Moving bodies exert a force when they collide with other bodies. Although a single particle in a gas is a moving body, the force it exerts is extremely small. Yet it is not hard to imagine that simultaneous collisions involving many particles would produce a measurable force on an object. 🔑 **Gas pressure is the result of simultaneous collisions of billions of rapidly moving particles in a gas with an object.** If there are no particles, there cannot be collisions. Consequently, there is no pressure. An empty space with no particles and no pressure is called a **vacuum.**

A gas pressure that you are familiar with is that caused by a mixture of gases—air. Air exerts pressure on Earth because gravity holds the particles in air in Earth's atmosphere. **Atmospheric pressure** results from the collisions of atoms and molecules in air with objects. Atmospheric pressure decreases as you climb a mountain because the density of Earth's atmosphere decreases as the elevation increases.

A **barometer** is a device that is used to measure atmospheric pressure. Figure 13.2 shows an early type of mercury barometer. The height of the mercury column in the tube depends on the pressure exerted by particles in air colliding with the surface of the mercury in the dish. Atmospheric pressure depends on weather and on altitude. In fair weather at sea level, the atmospheric pressure is sufficient to support a mercury column about 760 mm high.

760 mm Hg (barometric pressure)

Vacuum

Atmospheric pressure

253 mm Hg

Sea level   **On top of Mount Everest**

Figure 13.2 At sea level, air exerts enough pressure to support a 760-mm column of mercury. On top of Mount Everest, at 9000 m, the air exerts only enough pressure to support a 253-mm column of mercury.
Calculating *What is the decrease in pressure from sea level to the top of Mount Everest?*

The SI unit of pressure is the **pascal (Pa).** It represents a very small amount of pressure. For example, normal atmospheric pressure is about 100,000 Pa, that is, 100 kilopascals (kPa). Two older units of pressure are still commonly used. These units are millimeters of mercury (mm Hg) and atmospheres. One **standard atmosphere (atm)** is the pressure required to support 760 mm of mercury in a mercury barometer at 25°C. The numerical relationship among the three units is given below.

$$1 \text{ atm} = 760 \text{ mm Hg} = 101.3 \text{ kPa}$$

In the case of gases, it is important to be able to relate measured values to standards. Recall that the standard temperature and pressure (STP) are defined as a temperature of 0°C and a pressure of 101.3 kPa, or 1 atm.

SAMPLE PROBLEM 13.1

Converting Between Units of Pressure

A pressure gauge records a pressure of 450 kPa. What is this measurement expressed in atmospheres and millimeters of mercury?

1 Analyze *List the knowns and the unknowns.*

Knowns
- pressure = 450 kPa
- 1 atm = 101.3 kPa
- 1 atm = 760 mm Hg

Unknowns
- pressure = ? atm
- pressure = ? mm Hg

For converting kPa $\longrightarrow$ atm, the appropriate conversion factor is

$$\frac{1 \text{ atm}}{101.3 \text{ kPa}}$$

For converting kPa $\longrightarrow$ mm Hg, the appropriate conversion factor is

$$\frac{760 \text{ mm Hg}}{101.3 \text{ kPa}}$$

2 Calculate *Solve for the unknowns.*

$$450 \text{ kPa} \times \frac{1 \text{ atm}}{101.3 \text{ kPa}} = 4.4 \text{ atm}$$

$$450 \text{ kPa} \times \frac{760 \text{ mm Hg}}{101.3 \text{ kPa}} = 3400 \text{ mm Hg} = 3.4 \times 10^3 \text{ mm Hg}$$

3 Evaluate *Do the results make sense?*

Because the first conversion factor is much less than 1 and the second much greater than 1, it makes sense that the values expressed in atm and mm Hg are respectively smaller and larger than the value expressed in kPa.

Practice Problems

1. What pressure, in kilopascals and in atmospheres, does a gas exert at 385 mm Hg?

2. The pressure at the top of Mount Everest is 33.7 kPa. Is that pressure greater or less than 0.25 atm?

CHEMath

Using a Calculator

After you analyze a sample problem, you can use a calculator to solve for the unknown. A calculator provides the four basic arithmetic functions of addition (+), subtraction (−), multiplication (×), and division (÷). You can also raise to a power (x^2), take the square root $(\sqrt{x})$, and take the logarithm *(log)*. You will need to be able to enter measurements written in scientific notation. On many calculators, you will use the *EE* key or *EXP* key to enter such measurements.

Math **Handbook**

For help using a calculator, go to page R62.

Interactive Textbook

Problem-Solving 13.1 Solve Problem 1 with the help of an interactive guided tutorial.

with ChemASAP

Kinetic Energy and Temperature

As a substance is heated, its particles absorb energy, some of which is stored within the particles. This stored portion of the energy, or potential energy, does not raise the temperature of the substance. The remaining absorbed energy speeds up the particles—that is, increases their kinetic energy. This increase in kinetic energy results in an increase in temperature.

Average Kinetic Energy The particles in any collection of atoms or molecules at a given temperature have a wide range of kinetic energies. Most of the particles have kinetic energies somewhere in the middle of this range. Therefore, average kinetic energy is used when discussing the kinetic energy of a collection of particles in a substance. At any given temperature the particles of all substances, regardless of physical state, have the same average kinetic energy. For example, the ions in table salt, the molecules in water, and the atoms in helium all have the same average kinetic energy at room temperature even though the three substances are in different physical states.

Figure 13.3 shows the distribution of kinetic energies of water molecules at two different temperatures. The blue curve shows the distribution of kinetic energy among the water molecules in cold water. The red curve shows the distribution of kinetic energy among the water molecules in hot water. In both cases, most of the molecules have intermediate kinetic energies, which are close to the average value. Notice that at the higher temperature there is a wider range of kinetic energies.

There is a relationship between the average kinetic energy of the particles in a substance and the substance's temperature. An increase in the average kinetic energy of the particles causes the temperature of a substance to rise. As a substance cools, the particles tend to move more slowly, and their average kinetic energy declines.

Figure 13.3 The red and blue curves show the kinetic energy distributions of a typical collection of molecules at two different temperatures.

INTERPRETING GRAPHS

a. Inferring Which point on each curve represents the average kinetic energy?
b. Analyzing Data Compare the shapes of the curves for cold water and hot water.
c. Predicting What would happen to the shape of the curve if the water temperature were even higher? Even lower?

Distribution of Molecular Kinetic Energy

Many molecules have an intermediate kinetic energy

Few molecules have a very high kinetic energy

Lower temperature (cold water)

Higher temperature (hot water)

Percent of molecules

Kinetic energy

Figure 13.4 In this vacuum chamber, scientists cooled sodium vapor to nearly absolute zero. To keep the atoms from sticking to the walls of the chamber, the scientists used magnetism and gravity to trap the atoms 0.5 cm above the coil in the center of the chamber. The coil is shown at about two times its actual size.

You could reasonably expect the particles of all substances to stop moving at some very low temperature. The particles would have no kinetic energy at that temperature because they would have no motion. Absolute zero (0 K, or −273.15°C) is the temperature at which the motion of particles theoretically ceases. Absolute zero has never been produced in the laboratory. However, near-zero temperatures of about 0.0000000005 K (0.5×10^{-9} K), which is 0.5 nanokelvin, have been achieved in the vacuum chamber shown in Figure 13.4.

Average Kinetic Energy and Kelvin Temperature The Kelvin temperature scale reflects the relationship between temperature and average kinetic energy. **The Kelvin temperature of a substance is directly proportional to the average kinetic energy of the particles of the substance.** For example, the particles in helium gas at 200 K have twice the average kinetic energy as the particles in helium gas at 100 K. The effects of temperature on particle motion in liquids and solids are more complex than in gases.

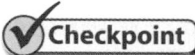 **Checkpoint** *What happens to the temperature of a substance when the average kinetic energy of its particles decreases?*

interactive
Textbook

Animation 14 Observe particles in motion and discover the connection between temperature and kinetic energy.

— with **ChemASAP**

13.1 Section Assessment

3. **Key Concept** Briefly describe the assumptions of kinetic theory as applied to gases.

4. **Key Concept** Use kinetic theory to explain what causes gas pressure.

5. **Key Concept** How is the Kelvin temperature of a substance related to the average kinetic energy of its particles?

6. Convert the following pressures to kilopascals.
    a. 0.95 atm   **b.** 45 mm Hg

7. A cylinder of oxygen gas is cooled from 300 K (27°C) to 150 K (−123°C). By what factor does the average kinetic energy of the oxygen molecules in the cylinder decrease?

Writing ➤ **Activity**

Describing Motion in a Gas Write a paragraph describing the behavior of an oxygen molecule in a sealed container of air. Include what happens when the molecule collides with another molecule or the walls of the container.

interactive
Textbook

Assessment 13.1 Test yourself on the concepts in Section 13.1.

— with **ChemASAP**

New York Standards: S1.1b, 3.1jj–kk, 4.2c

Guide for Reading

🔑 Key Concepts

- What factors determine the physical properties of a liquid?
- What is the relationship between evaporation and kinetic energy?
- When can a dynamic equilibrium exist between a liquid and its vapor?
- Under what conditions does boiling occur?

Vocabulary

vaporization
evaporation
vapor pressure
boiling point
normal boiling point

Reading Strategy

Using Prior Knowledge Before you read, write a definition for the term *boiling point*. After you read this section, compare and contrast the definition of *boiling point* in the text with your original definition.

Connecting to Your World

The Kilauea volcano in Hawaii is the most active volcano in the world. It has been erupting for centuries. The hot lava oozes and flows, scorching everything in its path, occasionally overrunning nearby houses. When the lava cools, it solidifies into rock. The properties of liquids are related to intermolecular interactions. In this section you will learn about some of the properties of liquids.

A Model for Liquids

According to the kinetic theory, both the particles in gases and the particles in liquids have kinetic energy. This energy allows the particles in gases and liquids to flow past one another, as shown in Figure 13.5. Substances that can flow are referred to as fluids. The ability of gases and liquids to flow allows them to conform to the shape of their containers.

There is a key difference between gases and liquids. According to the kinetic theory, there are no attractions between the particles in a gas. But the particles in a liquid are attracted to each other. These intermolecular attractions keep the particles in a liquid close together, which is why liquids have a definite volume. 🔑 **The interplay between the disruptive motions of particles in a liquid and the attractions among the particles determines the physical properties of liquids.**

Intermolecular attractions also reduce the amount of space between the particles in a liquid. Thus liquids are much more dense than gases. Increasing the pressure on a liquid has hardly any effect on its volume. The same is true of solids. For that reason, liquids and solids are known as condensed states of matter.

 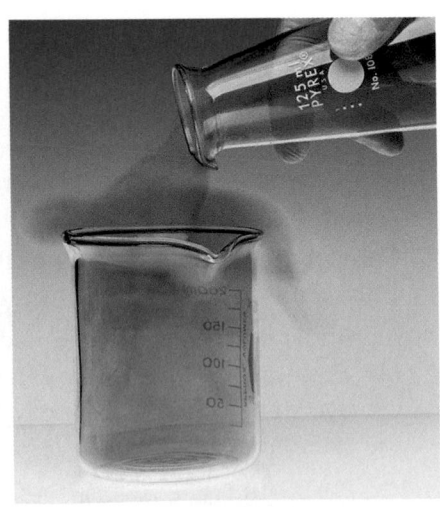

Figure 13.5 Both liquids and gases can flow. The liquid on the left is colored water. The gas on the right is bromine vapor. If a gas is denser than air, it can be poured from one container into another. These pictures were taken in a fume hood because bromine is both toxic and corrosive.
Predicting *Over time, what will happen to the gas in the uncovered beaker? Explain.*

ⓐ Open container   **ⓑ** Closed container

Evaporation

As you probably know from experience, water in an open container like the one in Figure 13.6a eventually moves into the air. The conversion of a liquid to a gas or vapor is called **vaporization.** When such a conversion occurs at the surface of a liquid that is not boiling, the process is called **evaporation.** Most of the molecules in a liquid don't have enough kinetic energy to overcome the attractive forces and escape into the gaseous state. ⟜ **During evaporation, only those molecules with a certain minimum kinetic energy can escape from the surface of the liquid.** Even some of the particles that do escape collide with molecules in the air and rebound into the liquid.

You may have noticed that a liquid evaporates faster when heated. This occurs because heating the liquid increases the average kinetic energy of its particles. The added energy enables more particles to overcome the attractive forces keeping them in the liquid state. As evaporation occurs, the particles with the highest kinetic energy tend to escape first. The particles left in the liquid have a lower average kinetic energy than the particles that have escaped. The process is similar to removing the fastest runner from a race. The remaining runners have a lower average speed. As evaporation takes place, the liquid's temperature decreases. Therefore, evaporation is a cooling process.

You have observed the effects of evaporative cooling on hot days. When you perspire, water molecules in your perspiration absorb heat from your body and evaporate from your skin's surface. This evaporation leaves the remaining perspiration cooler. The perspiration that remains cools you further by absorbing more body heat.

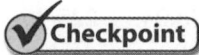 **Checkpoint** *What happens to the rate of evaporation when a liquid is heated?*

Figure 13.6 The process of evaporation has a different outcome in an open system, such as a lake, and a closed system, such as a terrarium. **ⓐ** In an open container, molecules that evaporate escape from the container. **ⓑ** In a closed container, the molecules cannot escape. They collect as a vapor above the liquid. Some molecules condense back into a liquid.

Interactive Textbook

Animation 15
Observe the phenomenon of evaporation from a molecular perspective.
—— with **ChemASAP**

Vapor Pressure

The evaporation of a liquid in a closed container differs from evaporation in an open container. No particles can escape into the outside air from the closed container in Figure 13.6b. When a partially filled container of liquid is sealed, some of the particles at the surface of the liquid vaporize. These particles collide with the walls of the sealed container and produce a vapor pressure. **Vapor pressure** is a measure of the force exerted by a gas above a liquid. Over time, the number of particles entering the vapor increases and some of the particles condense and return to the liquid state. The following equation summarizes the process.

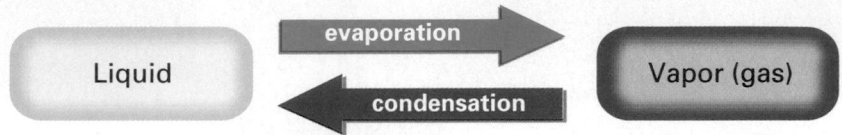

Eventually, the number of particles condensing will equal the number of particles vaporizing. The vapor pressure will then remain constant. **In a system at constant vapor pressure, a dynamic equilibrium exists between the vapor and the liquid. The system is in equilibrium because the rate of evaporation of liquid equals the rate of condensation of vapor.**

At equilibrium, the particles in the system continue to evaporate and condense, but there is no net change in the number of particles in the liquid or vapor. The sealed terrarium in Figure 13.6b is an example of a closed container at equilibrium. The moisture on the inner walls of the terrarium is a sign that equilibrium has been established. Particles that once evaporated are condensing, but other particles are evaporating to take their place.

Vapor Pressure and Temperature Change An increase in the temperature of a contained liquid increases the vapor pressure. This happens because the particles in the warmed liquid have increased kinetic energy. As a result, more of the particles will have the minimum kinetic energy necessary to escape the surface of the liquid. The particles escape the liquid and collide with the walls of the container at a greater frequency. Table 13.1 gives the vapor pressures of some common liquids at various temperatures. The vapor pressure data indicates how volatile a given liquid is, or how easily it evaporates. Of the three liquids shown, diethyl ether is the most volatile and water is the least volatile.

Table 13.1						
Vapor Pressure (in kPa) of Three Substances at Different Temperatures						
	0°C	**20°C**	**40°C**	**60°C**	**80°C**	**100°C**
Water	0.61	2.33	7.37	19.92	47.34	101.33
Ethanol	1.63	5.85	18.04	47.02	108.34	225.75
Diethyl ether	24.70	58.96	122.80	230.65	399.11	647.87

Vapor Pressure Measurements The vapor pressure of a liquid can be determined with a device called a manometer. Figure 13.7 shows how a simple manometer works. One end of a U-shaped glass tube containing mercury is attached to a container. The other end of the tube is open to the surrounding atmosphere. When there is only air in the container, the pressure is the same on both sides of the tube and the mercury level is the same in each arm of the tube. When a liquid is added to the container, the pressure in the container increases due to the vapor pressure of the liquid. The vapor pressure of the liquid pushes the mercury on the container side of the U-tube. The levels of mercury in the U-tube are no longer the same. You can determine the vapor pressure in mm of Hg by measuring the difference between the two levels of mercury. As the vapor pressure increases, so does the difference between the two levels.

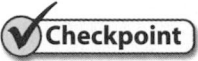 **Checkpoint** *What two physical changes occur in a partially filled, sealed container of liquid?*

Boiling Point

The rate of evaporation of a liquid from an open container increases as the liquid is heated. Heating allows a greater number of particles at the liquid's surface to overcome the attractive forces that keep them in the liquid state. The remaining particles in the liquid move faster and faster as they absorb the added energy. Thus, the average kinetic energy of the particles in the liquid increases and the temperature of the liquid increases. **When a liquid is heated to a temperature at which particles throughout the liquid have enough kinetic energy to vaporize, the liquid begins to boil.** Bubbles of vapor form throughout the liquid, rise to the surface, and escape into the air. The temperature at which the vapor pressure of the liquid is just equal to the external pressure on the liquid is the **boiling point** (bp).

Figure 13.7 The vapor pressure of a contained liquid can be measured in a manometer. The vapor pressure is equal to the difference in height of the mercury in the two arms of the U-tube. **Calculating** *What is the difference in vapor pressure between ethanol at 0°C and ethanol at 20°C?*

12.2 mm Hg
= 1.63 kPa

Ethanol   Mercury

Ethanol at 0°C

43.9 mm Hg
= 5.85 kPa

Ethanol   Mercury

Ethanol at room temperature (20°C)

Sea Level Atmospheric pressure at the surface of water at 70°C is greater than its vapor pressure. Bubbles of vapor cannot form in the water, and it does not boil.

Sea Level At the boiling point, the vapor pressure is equal to atmospheric pressure. Bubbles of vapor form in the water, and it boils.

Atop Mount Everest At higher altitudes, the atmospheric pressure is lower than it is at sea level. Thus the water boils at a lower temperature.

101.3 kPa
70°C

101.3 kPa
100°C

34 kPa
70°C

Figure 13.8 A liquid boils when the vapor pressure of particles within the liquid equals the atmospheric pressure. The boiling point varies with altitude.

Figure 13.9 On the graph, the intersection of a curve with the 101.3-kPa line indicates the boiling point of that substance at standard pressure.

INTERPRETING GRAPHS

a. Analyzing Data What is the boiling point of chloroform at 101.3 kPa?

b. Analyzing Data What is the vapor pressure of ethanol at 40°C?

c. Analyzing Data What would atmospheric pressure need to be for ethanoic acid to boil at 80°C?

Boiling Point and Pressure Changes Because a liquid boils when its vapor pressure is equal to the external pressure, liquids don't always boil at the same temperature. Figure 13.8 shows how a change in altitude affects the boiling point of water. Because atmospheric pressure is lower at higher altitudes, boiling points decrease at higher altitudes. In Denver, which is 1600 m above sea level, the average atmospheric pressure is 85.3 kPa. So water boils at about 95°C. In a pressure cooker, the vapor cannot escape and the vapor pressure increases. So water boils at a temperature above 100°C and food can cook more quickly.

Look at the vapor pressure versus temperature graph in Figure 13.9. You can use the graph to show how the boiling point of a liquid is related to vapor pressure. At a lower external pressure, the boiling point decreases. The particles in the liquid need less kinetic energy to escape from the liquid. At a higher external pressure, the boiling point increases. The particles in the liquid need more kinetic energy to escape from the liquid.

Vapor Pressure and Boiling Point

Table 13.2

The Normal Boiling Points of Several Substances	
Name and formula	**Boiling Point (°C)**
Carbon disulfide (CS_2)	46.0
Chloroform ($CHCl_3$)	61.7
Methanol (CH_4O)	64.7
Tetrachloromethane (CCl_4)	76.8
Ethanol (C_2H_6O)	78.5
Water (H_2O)	100.0

Boiling is a cooling process similar to evaporation. During boiling, the particles with the highest kinetic energy escape first when the liquid is at the boiling point. Turning off the source of external heat drops the liquid's temperature below its boiling point. Supplying more heat allows more particles to acquire enough kinetic energy to escape. However, the temperature of the boiling liquid never rises above its boiling point. If heat is supplied at a greater rate, the liquid only boils faster. The vapor produced is at the same temperature as that of the boiling liquid. Although the vapor has the same average kinetic energy as the liquid, its potential (or stored energy) is much higher. Thus, a burn from steam is more severe than one from an equal mass of boiling water at the same temperature.

Normal Boiling Point Because a liquid can have various boiling points depending on pressure, the **normal boiling point** is defined as the boiling point of a liquid at a pressure of 101.3 kPa. For example, the normal boiling point of water is 100°C. Table 13.2 lists the normal boiling points of six molecular compounds.

Interactive Textbook

Animation 16 Relate vapor pressure and boiling point to intermolecular attractive forces.

— with **ChemASAP**

13.2 Section Assessment

8. 🔑 **Key Concept** What factors help determine the physical properties of liquids?

9. 🔑 **Key Concept** In terms of kinetic energy, explain how a molecule in a liquid evaporates.

10. 🔑 **Key Concept** A liquid is in a closed container and has a constant vapor pressure. What is the relationship between the rate of evaporation of the liquid and the rate of condensation of the vapor in the container?

11. 🔑 **Key Concept** What condition must exist for a liquid to boil?

12. Use Figure 13.9 to determine the boiling point of each liquid.
    a. ethanoic acid at 27 kPa
    b. chloroform at 80 kPa
    c. ethanol at 50 kPa

13. Explain why the boiling point of a liquid varies with atmospheric pressure.

14. Explain how evaporation lowers the temperature of a liquid.

> **Writing** ▶ **Activity**

Contrast Paragraph Look for high-altitude cooking directions on packages of cake, brownie, or muffin mixes. Contrast them with standard directions.

Interactive Textbook

Assessment 13.2 Test yourself on the concepts in Section 13.2.

— with **ChemASAP**

13.3 The Nature of Solids

Guide for Reading

Key Concepts

- How are the structure and properties of solids related?
- What determines the shape of a crystal?

Vocabulary

melting point

crystal

unit cell

allotropes

amorphous solid

glass

Reading Strategy

Building Vocabulary After you have read the section, give an example of a substance that is and one that is not an *amorphous solid*.

Connecting to Your World In 1985, scientists discovered a new form of carbon. They called this form of carbon buckminsterfullerene, or buckyball for short. The molecules in buckyball are hollow spheres. The carbon atoms are arranged so that the pattern on the surface of the sphere resembles the surface of a soccer ball. In this section, you will learn how the arrangement of particles in solids determines some general properties of solids.

A Model for Solids

The general properties of solids reflect the orderly arrangement of their particles and the fixed locations of their particles. In most solids, the atoms, ions, or molecules are packed tightly together. These solids are dense and not easy to compress. Because, the particles in solids tend to vibrate around fixed points, solids do not flow.

When you heat a solid, its particles vibrate more rapidly as their kinetic energy increases. The organization of particles within the solid breaks down, and eventually the solid melts. The **melting point** (mp) is the temperature at which a solid changes into a liquid. At this temperature, the disruptive vibrations of the particles are strong enough to overcome the attractions that hold them in fixed positions. The melting and freezing points of a substance are at the same temperature. At that temperature, the liquid and solid phases are in equilibrium.

Crystal Structure and Unit Cells

Most solid substances are crystalline. In a **crystal** the particles are arranged in an orderly, repeating, three-dimensional pattern called a crystal lattice. Figure 13.10 shows part of the crystal lattice in sodium chloride. **The shape of a crystal reflects the arrangement of the particles within the solid.**

Figure 13.10 The orderly arrangement of sodium and chloride ions within a sodium chloride crystal determines the shape of the crystal. The closely packed ions vibrate around fixed points on the crystal.

The type of bonding that exists between particles in crystals determines their melting points. In general, ionic solids have high melting points because relatively strong forces hold them together. By contrast, molecular solids have relatively low melting points. Not all solids melt, however. Wood and cane sugar, for example, decompose when heated.

Crystal Systems A crystal has sides, or faces. The angles at which the faces of a crystal intersect are always the same for a given substance and are characteristic of that substance. Crystals are classified into seven groups, or crystal systems, which have the characteristic shapes shown in Figure 13.11. The edges are labeled a, b, and c. The angles are labeled α, β, and γ. The seven crystal systems differ in terms of the angles between the faces and in the number of edges of equal length on each face.

Figure 13.11 Crystals are classified into seven crystal systems. **Classifying *In which of the systems are all three angles equal to 90°?***

Galena

$a = b = c$
$\alpha = \beta = \gamma = 90°$
Cubic

Zircon

$a = b \neq c$
$\alpha = \beta = \gamma = 90°$
Tetragonal

Topaz

$a \neq b \neq c$
$\alpha = \beta = \gamma = 90°$
Orthorhombic

Gypsum

$a \neq b \neq c$
$\beta = \gamma = 90° \neq \alpha$
Monoclinic

Amazonite

$a \neq b \neq c$
$\alpha \neq \beta \neq \gamma \neq 90°$
Triclinic

Tourmaline

$a = b \neq c$
$\alpha = \beta = 90°, \gamma = 120°$
Hexagonal

Calcite

$a = b = c$
$\alpha = \beta = \gamma \neq 90°$
Rhombohedral

The shape of a crystal depends on the arrangement of the particles within it. The smallest group of particles within a crystal that retains the geometric shape of the crystal is known as a **unit cell.** A crystal lattice is a repeating array of any one of fourteen kinds of unit cells. There are from one to four types of unit cells that can be associated with each crystal system. Figure 13.12 shows the three kinds of unit cells that can make up a cubic crystal system.

Allotropes Some solid substances can exist in more than one form. A good example is the element carbon. Diamond is one crystalline form of carbon. It forms when carbon crystallizes under tremendous pressure (thousands of atmospheres). A different crystalline form of carbon is graphite. The lead in a pencil is not the element lead; it is graphite. In graphite, the carbon atoms are packed in sheets rather than in the extended three-dimensional array characteristic of diamond.

In 1985, a third form of carbon was discovered in ordinary soot. This form of carbon is called buckminsterfullerene, or buckyball. The 60 carbon atoms in molecules of buckyball are bonded together to form a hollow sphere, or cage. The atoms are arranged in a pattern of hexagons and pentagons on the surface of the cage, similar to the pattern on the surface of a soccer ball. Since 1985, other molecules of carbon with hollow cages have been discovered. The one with 70 carbon atoms is shaped like a football. As a group, these forms of carbon are called fullerenes.

The physical properties of diamond, graphite, and fullerenes are quite different. Diamond has a high density and is very hard. Graphite has a relatively low density and is soft and slippery. The hollow cages in fullerenes give them great strength and rigidity. Diamond, graphite, and buckyballs are allotropes of carbon. **Allotropes** are two or more different molecular forms of the same element in the same physical state. Although allotropes are composed of atoms of the same element, they have different properties because their structures are different. Only a few elements have allotropes. In addition to carbon, these include the nonmetals phosphorus, sulfur, and oxygen (O_2 and O_3), and the metalloids boron and antimony.

Figure 13.12 The unit cell in a cubic crystal system may be simple cubic, body-centered cubic, or face-centered cubic. In the space-filling models and line drawings, the spheres represent atoms or ions.

Simple cubic

In a simple cubic unit cell, the atoms or ions are arranged at the corners of an imaginary cube.

Body-centered

In a body-centered cubic unit cell, the atoms or ions are at the corners and in the center of an imaginary cube.

Face-centered

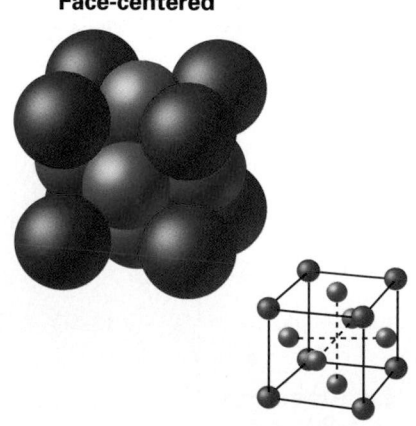

In a face-centered cubic unit cell, the atoms or ions are in the center of each face of the imaginary cube.

Diamond

Graphite

Fullerene

In diamond, each carbon atom in the interior of the diamond is strongly bonded to four others. The array is rigid and compact.

In graphite, the carbon atoms are linked in widely spaced layers of hexagonal (six-sided) arrays.

In buckminsterfullerene, 60 carbon atoms form a hollow sphere. The carbons are arranged in pentagons and hexagons.

Non-Crystalline Solids Not all solids are crystalline in form; some solids are amorphous. An **amorphous solid** lacks an ordered internal structure. Rubber, plastic, and asphalt are amorphous solids. Their atoms are randomly arranged. Other examples of amorphous solids are glasses. A **glass** is a transparent fusion product of inorganic substances that have cooled to a rigid state without crystallizing. Glasses are sometimes called supercooled liquids. The irregular internal structures of glasses are intermediate between those of a crystalline solid and those of a free-flowing liquid. Glasses do not melt at a definite temperature. Instead, they gradually soften when heated. This softening with temperature is critical to the glassblower's art. When a crystalline solid is shattered, the fragments tend to have the same surface angles as the original solid. By contrast, when an amorphous solid, such as glass, is shattered, the fragments have irregular angles and jagged edges.

Figure 13.13 Diamond, graphite, and fullerenes are allotropes of carbon. **Classifying** *Based on the arrangements of their atoms, explain why the properties of fullerenes are closer to those of diamond than of graphite?*

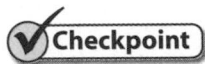 *What property of glass is important to glassblowers?*

13.3 Section Assessment

15. 🔑 **Key Concept** In general, how are the particles arranged in solids?

16. 🔑 **Key Concept** What does the shape of a crystal tell you about the structure of a crystal?

17. How do allotropes of an element differ?

18. What phases are in equilibrium at a substance's melting point?

19. How do the melting points of ionic solids generally compare with those of molecular solids?

20. What is the difference between a crystal lattice and a unit cell?

Elements ➤ **Handbook**

Glass Read about optical glass on page R20. What are the general physical properties of glass? How does optical glass differ from other types of glass? What are some uses of optical glass?

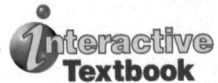
Textbook

Assessment 13.3 Test yourself on the concepts in Section 13.3.

—— with **ChemASAP**

The Behavior of Liquids and Solids

Purpose
To explore and explain some behaviors of liquids and solids.

Materials
- plastic Petri dish
- water
- ice
- rubbing alcohol
- graph paper, 1-cm
- calcium chloride

Procedure

1. In your notebook, make a copy of the table shown below. Add a column for your observations. In the experiments, you will place substances labeled A and B inside the Petri dish and substances labeled C on top of the dish.
2. For Experiment 1, place one drop of water in the Petri dish. Replace the cover and place a small piece of ice on top of the cover.
3. After a few minutes, observe the interior surface of the Petri dish cover and the contents of the dish. Record your observations. Clean and dry the Petri dish and cover.
4. Repeat Steps 2 and 3 for Experiments 2–5, using the materials listed in the table. For Experiment 4, place the Petri dish on the graph paper so that you can place the water and the calcium chloride about 3 cm apart.

Experiment	Substance A	Substance B	Substance C
1	drop of water		ice cube
2	drop of water		drop of water
3	drop of rubbing alcohol		drop of water
4	drop of water	piece of CaCl₂	
5		several pieces of CaCl₂	ice cube

Analyze
Using your experimental data, record the answers to the following questions beneath your data table.

1. Explain your observations in Experiment 1 in terms of the behavior of liquids.
2. Why is ice not needed for cloud formation in Experiment 2?
3. What differences do you observe about the behavior of rubbing alcohol in Experiment 3 and the behavior of water in the previous experiments? Explain.
4. What happens to solid calcium chloride in a humid environment?
5. Propose an explanation for no cloud formation in Experiment 5.

You're The Chemist

1. **Analyze It!** Place a drop of water and a drop of rubbing alcohol about 3 cm apart in a Petri dish. Cover the dish and place it on a piece of graph paper. Be careful not to mix the contents. Observe what happens to the size of the water drop over time.
2. **Analyze It!** Add a drop of bromthymol blue (BTB) to a drop of vinegar. What happens?
3. **Design It!** Vinegar is a solution of water and ethanoic acid, CH_3COOH. Design and carry out an experiment to see if ethanoic acid will evaporate from a drop of vinegar. Does ethanoic acid evaporate?
4. **Design It!** Design and carry out an experiment to see if ammonia will evaporate from a drop of aqueous ammonia.

13.4 Changes of State

 New York Standards: M2.1a, 3.1kk

Connecting to Your World

Familiar weather events can remind you that water exists on Earth as a liquid, a solid, and a vapor. A spring shower brings liquid raindrops and a winter blizzard delivers solid snowflakes. On a humid summer day, you may be uncomfortable because there is a high concentration of water vapor in the air. As water cycles through the atmosphere, the oceans, and Earth's crust, it undergoes repeated changes of state. In this section, you will learn what conditions can control the state of a substance.

Sublimation

If you hang wet laundry on a clothesline on a very cold day, the water in the clothes quickly freezes to ice. Eventually, however, the clothes become dry although the ice never thaws. The ice changes directly to water vapor without melting and passing through the liquid state. The change of a substance from a solid to a vapor without passing through the liquid state is called **sublimation.** Sublimation can occur because solids, like liquids, have a vapor pressure. **Sublimation occurs in solids with vapor pressures that exceed atmospheric pressure at or near room temperature.**

Iodine is another example of a substance that undergoes sublimation. This violet-black solid ordinarily changes into a purple vapor without passing through a liquid state. Notice in Figure 13.14 how dark crystals of iodine deposit on the underside of a watch glass placed on top of a beaker containing solid iodine that is being heated. The iodine vapor sublimes from iodine crystals in the bottom of the beaker and condenses to form crystals on the watch glass.

Sublimation has many useful applications. If freshly brewed coffee is frozen and the water vapor is removed with a vacuum pump, the result is freeze-dried coffee. Solid carbon dioxide (dry ice) is often used as a coolant for goods, such as ice cream, that must remain frozen during shipment. Dry ice has a low temperature of −78°C. Because it sublimes, it does not produce a liquid as ordinary ice does when it melts. Solid air fresheners contain a variety of substances that sublime at room temperature. Sublimation is also useful for separating substances. Organic chemists use sublimation to separate mixtures and to purify compounds.

Guide for Reading

Key Concepts
- When can sublimation occur?
- How are the conditions at which phases are in equilibrium represented on a phase diagram?

Vocabulary
sublimation
phase diagram
triple point

Reading Strategy
Predicting In your notebook, predict what causes ice cubes that are left in the freezer for a long time to get smaller.

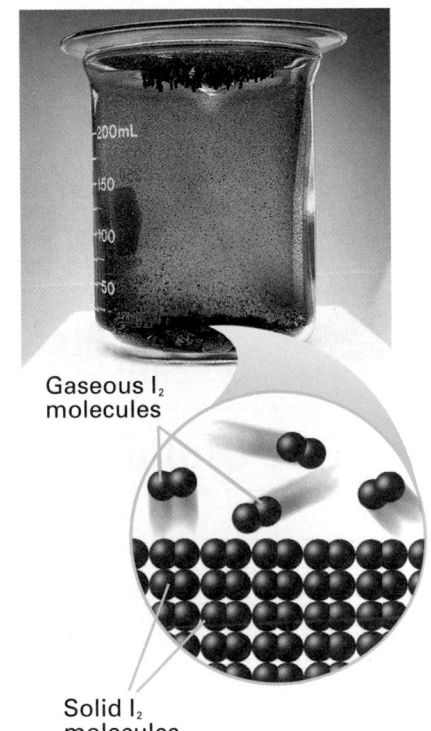

Gaseous I_2 molecules

Solid I_2 molecules

Figure 13.14 When solid iodine is heated, the crystals sublime, going directly from the solid to the gaseous state. When the vapor cools, it goes directly from the gaseous to the solid state.

Sublimation

Purpose
To observe the sublimation of air freshener.

Materials
- small pieces of solid air freshener
- small shallow container
- 2 clear 8 oz plastic cups
- hot tap water
- ice
- 3 thick cardboard strips

Procedure

1. Place a few pieces of air freshener in one of the cups. **CAUTION** *Work in a well-ventilated room.*

2. Bend the cardboard strips and place them over the rim of the cup that has the air freshener pieces.

3. Place the second cup inside the first. The base of the second cup should not touch the air freshener. Adjust the cardboard as necessary. This assembly is your sublimator.

4. Fill the top cup with ice. Do not get any ice or water in the bottom cup.

5. Fill the shallow container about one-third full with hot tap water.

6. Carefully place your sublimator in the hot water. Observe what happens.

Ice

Shallow container with hot water

Air freshener

Analyze and Conclude

1. Define sublimation.

2. What do you think would happen if the water in the shallow container were at room temperature? If it were boiling?

3. Why is it possible to separate the substances in some mixtures by sublimation?

Interactive Textbook

Simulation 14 Predict the physical states present at different points on a phase diagram.

—with **ChemASAP**

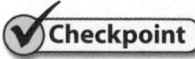

Go Online

NSTA *SciLINKS*

For: Links on Phase Diagrams
Visit: www.SciLinks.org
Web Code: cdn-1134

Phase Diagrams

The relationships among the solid, liquid, and vapor states (or phases) of a substance in a sealed container can be represented in a single graph. The graph is called a **phase diagram.** A phase diagram gives the conditions of temperature and pressure at which a substance exists as solid, liquid, and gas (vapor). 🔑 **The conditions of pressure and temperature at which two phases exist in equilibrium are indicated on a phase diagram by a line separating the phases.**

Figure 13.15 shows the phase diagram for water. In each of the colored regions on the phase diagram, water is in a single phase. The curving line that separates water's vapor phase from its liquid phase are the equilibrium conditions for liquid and vapor. The line also illustrates how the vapor pressure of water varies with temperature. The other two curving lines give the conditions for equilibrium between liquid water and ice and between water vapor and ice. The point on the diagram at which all three curves meet is called the triple point. The **triple point** describes the only set of conditions at which all three phases can exist in equilibrium with one another. For water, the triple point is a temperature of 0.016°C and a pressure of 0.61 kPa (0.0060 atm). Figure 13.16 shows water at its triple point.

By referring to Figure 13.15, you can determine what happens if you melt ice or boil water at pressures less than 101.3 kPa. A decrease in pressure lowers the boiling point and raises the melting point. An increase in pressure will raise the boiling point and lower the melting point.

✓ **Checkpoint** *What are the variables that are plotted on a phase diagram?*

Phase Diagram of Water

Pressure (kPa)

101.3

0.61 - - - Triple point

Solid   Liquid   Vapor

Normal melting point

Normal boiling point

0 0.016   100

Temperature (°C)

Figure 13.15 The phase diagram of water shows the relationship among pressure, temperature, and physical states of water.

INTERPRETING GRAPHS

a. Analyzing Data At the triple point of water, what are the values of temperature and pressure?
b. Inferring What states of matter are present at the triple point of water?
c. Analyzing Data Assuming standard pressure, at what temperature is there an equilibrium between water vapor and liquid water? Between liquid water and ice?

Look at Figure 13.15. Follow the equilibrium line between liquid water and water vapor to the triple point. Below the triple point, the vapor and liquid cannot exist in equilibrium. Increasing the pressure won't change the vapor to a liquid. The solid and the vapor are in equilibrium at temperatures below 0.016°C. With an increase in pressure, the vapor begins to behave more like a solid. For example, it is no longer easily compressed.

Figure 13.20 also illustrates how an increase in pressure affects the melting point of ice. For years, the accepted hypothesis for how ice skaters move along the ice was the following. The blades of the skates exert pressure, which lowers the melting point of the ice. The ice melts and a film of water forms under the blades of the skates. This film acts as a lubricant, enabling the skaters to glide gracefully over the ice. This hypothesis fails to explain why skiers also glide along very nicely on another solid form of water—snow. Wide skis exert much less pressure per unit area of snow than narrow skate blades exert on ice. Recent research shows that the surface of ice has a slippery, water-like surface layer that exists well below ice's melting point. Even ice that is at −129°C has this layer. A new hypothesis proposes that the liquid-like surface layer provides the lubrication needed for smooth skating and skiing.

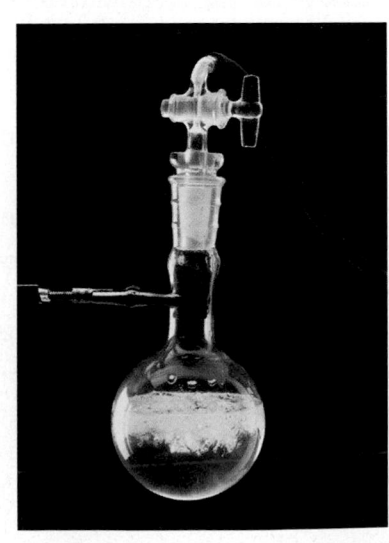

Figure 13.16 At the triple point, ice, liquid water, and water vapor can exist at equilibrium. Freezing, melting, boiling, and condensation can all occur at the same time, as shown in the flask.

Solid State Chemist

By now you are familiar with chemical reactions in aqueous solutions and the gaseous state. But did you know that chemical reactions can also take place in solids, without a liquid or a gas?

Reactions that take place in the solid state are extremely useful. These reactions occur during the manufacture of semiconductors for the electronics industry. The device that ignites the gas in a gas grill is made of a type of ceramic called a piezoelectric. This type of ceramic produces a voltage when subjected to mechanical pressure. There is a class of light-sensitive solids called photopolymers. These solids are used to make plates for printing presses that use dry inks instead of water-based inks. A solid-state reaction takes place in lenses that are designed to darken when exposed to light.

Solid state chemists often study crystal structures, superconductors, and semiconductors. They may also study the electrical, magnetic, and optical properties of solid compounds.

Solid state chemists often work at major universities, teaching and doing basic research. Corporations employ them to do pure research or to develop applications for new discoveries in this field. Companies in the petroleum, electronic, and computer industries are a few of the places a solid state chemist might be employed.

To work in this field usually requires an undergraduate or graduate degree in chemistry or chemical engineering. Courses studied include chemistry, physics, and mathematics.

Go Online
PHSchool.com

For: Careers in Chemistry
Visit: www.PHSchool.com
Web Code: cdb-1134

13.4 Section Assessment

21. **Key Concept** What properties must a solid have to undergo sublimation?

22. **Key Concept** What do the curved lines on a phase diagram represent?

23. Describe one practical use of sublimation.

24. What does the triple point on a phase diagram describe?

25. Using Figure 13.15, estimate the boiling point of water at a pressure of 50 kPa.

Connecting ▶ Concepts

Types of Bonding Would you expect a substance that sublimates at or near room temperature to be a molecular substance or an ionic substance? Use what you learned about bonding in Chapters 7 and 8 to explain your answer.

Interactive Textbook

Assessment 13.4 Test yourself on the concepts in Section 13.4.

— with **ChemASAP**

Thin Films

A thin film consists of layers of atoms deposited on a surface at a uniform depth of 10^{-9} m to 10^{-6} m. Engineers can produce thin films with specific electrical properties by varying the element deposited and the thickness of the deposit **Interpreting** *Thin films are sometimes referred to as super crystals. What does this imply about their structure?*

Semiconductor microchips Thin films of conducting materials, insulating materials, and semiconducting materials are layered and then etched to make a chip that contains thousands of microcircuits.

Smart windows Layers of transparent thin films, sandwiched between glass, change tint when electrically charged. The original tint returns when the electrical charge is removed.

CDs and DVDs The reflective surface of CDs are bands of thin films that carry digital information as notches on the sufrace of the film. DVDs increase information storage by using two or more thin-film layers.

PDAs The display of a PDA contains thousands of liquid crystals attached to transparent, thin-film transistors (TFT). Images are created as each TFT sends a charge to its linked liquid crystal.

Computer monitors Using thin-film transistors and a liquid-crystal display, flatscreen monitors provide sharp images, save space, and are about 60% more efficient than cathode ray monitors.

Key Concepts

13.1 The Nature of Gases

- Particles in a gas are considered to be small, hard spheres with an insignificant volume. The motion of the particles in a gas is rapid, constant, and random. All collisions between particles in a gas are perfectly elastic.

- Gas pressure is the result of simultaneous collisions of billions of rapidly moving particles in a gas with an object.

- The Kelvin temperature of a substance is directly proportional to the average kinetic energy of the particles of the substance.

13.2 The Nature of Liquids

- The interplay between the disruptive motions of particles in a liquid and the attractions among the particles determines the physical properties of liquids.

- During evaporation, only those molecules with a certain minimum kinetic energy can escape from the surface.

- In a system at constant vapor pressure, a dynamic equilibrium exists between the vapor and the liquid. The rates of evaporation and condensation are equal.

- At a temperature at which particles throughout a liquid have enough kinetic energy to vaporize, the liquid begins to boil.

13.3 The Nature of Solids

- The general properties of solids and the shapes of crystals reflect the orderly arrangement and the fixed locations of particles within the solids.

13.4 Changes of State

- Sublimation occurs in solids that have vapor pressures that exceed atmospheric pressure at or near room temperature.

- Conditions of pressure and temperature at which two phases exist in equilibrium are indicated on a phase diagram by a line separating the two regions representing the phases.

Vocabulary

- allotrope (p. 398)
- amorphous solid (p. 399)
- atmospheric pressure (p. 386)
- barometer (p. 386)
- boiling point (p. 393)
- crystal (p. 396)
- evaporation (p. 391)

- gas pressure (p. 386)
- glass (p. 399)
- kinetic energy (p. 385)
- kinetic theory (p. 385)
- melting point (p. 396)
- normal boiling point (p. 395)
- pascal (Pa) (p. 387)
- phase diagram (p. 402)

- standard atmosphere (atm) (p. 387)
- sublimation (p. 401)
- triple point (p. 402)
- unit cell (p. 398)
- vacuum (p. 386)
- vaporization (p. 391)
- vapor pressure (p. 392)

Key Equation

- 1 atm = 760 mm Hg = 101.3 kPa

Organizing Information

Use these terms to construct a concept map that organizes the major ideas of this chapter.

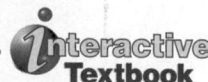
Textbook

Concept Map 13 Create your Concept Map using the computer.

with **ChemASAP**

13.1 The Nature of Gases

25. What is meant by elastic collision?

26. Which of the following statements about gases are true?
   a. Gases fill their containers completely.
   b. Gases exert pressure.
   c. Gases have mass.
   d. The pressure of a gas is independent of its temperature.
   e. Gases are compressible.
   f. The distances between gas particles are relatively large.

27. List the various units used to measure pressure, and identify the SI unit.

28. Change 1656 kPa to atm.

29. Convert 190 mm Hg to the following.
   a. kilopascals
   b. atmospheres of pressure

30. Explain the relationship between the absolute temperature of a substance and the kinetic energy of its particles.

31. How is the average kinetic energy of water molecules affected when you pour hot water from a kettle into cups that are the same temperature as the water?

32. What does the abbreviation STP represent?

33. What is significant about the temperature absolute zero?

34. By what factor does the average kinetic energy of gas molecules in an aerosol container increase when the temperature is raised from 27°C (300 K) to 627°C (900 K)?

35. What causes atmospheric pressure, and why is it much lower on the top of a mountain than it is at sea level?

36. What everyday evidence suggests that all matter is in constant motion?

37. Are perfectly elastic collisions possible between objects that you can see?

13.2 The Nature of Liquids

38. Explain why liquids and gases differ
   a. in physical state.
   b. in compressibility.

39. Compare the evaporation of a liquid in a closed container with that of a liquid in an open container.

40. Explain vapor pressure and dynamic equilibrium.

41. Explain why increasing the temperature of a liquid increases its rate of evaporation.

42. Would you expect an equilibrium vapor pressure to be reached above a liquid in an open container? Why?

43. Describe the effect that increasing temperature has on the vapor pressure of a liquid.

44. Distinguish between the boiling point and the normal boiling point of a liquid.

45. Use the graph to answer each question.

Vapor Pressure vs. Temperature for Water

   a. What is the vapor pressure of water at 40°C?
   b. At what temperature is the vapor pressure of water 600 mm Hg?
   c. What is the significance of the vapor pressure of water at 100°C?

46. Explain how boiling is a cooling process.

Review and Assessment *continued*

Blue questions emphasize Regents Exam content

Use the drawing to answer Questions 47 and 49. The same liquid is in each flask.

(a)   **(b)**

47. In which flask is the vapor pressure lower? Give a reason for your answer.

48. In which flask is the liquid at the higher temperature? Explain your answer.

49. How can the vapor pressure in each flask be determined?

50. In a series of liquids, as the intermolecular forces of attraction strengthen, would you expect the vapor pressure to increase or decrease? Explain.

51. Describe evaporation, vapor pressure, and boiling point.

52. Mount McKinley (6194 m) in Alaska is the tallest peak in North America. The atmospheric pressure at its peak is 330 mm Hg. Find the boiling point of water there. Use Figures 13.11 and 13.12.

53. Why is the equilibrium that exists between a liquid and its vapor in a closed container called a dynamic equilibrium?

54. What happens to the average kinetic energy of the water molecules in your body when you get a fever?

55. Your lab partner measures the boiling point of an open beaker of water as 108.2°C. Even though you know that water can be made to boil at this temperature, you ask your partner to repeat the measurement. Explain.

56. How does perspiration help cool your body on a hot day?

57. Why do different liquids have different boiling points?

58. If the volume of the container in which there is a liquid-vapor equilibrium is changed, the vapor pressure is not affected. Why?

59. The vapor pressure in a sealed beaker containing a large amount of water is the same as that in a similar sealed beaker filled with only a little water at the same temperature, even though many more water molecules are evaporating in the first beaker. Explain how.

60. Why are pressure cookers recommended for high-altitude cooking?

61. A sample of a gas mixture contains oxygen, nitrogen, and water vapor. By what physical process can the water vapor be removed from the sample?

62. Relative humidity is defined by the following equation.

$$Relative\ humidity = \frac{(a)}{(b)} \times 100\%$$

where (a) is the pressure of water vapor in the air and (b) is the equilibrium vapor pressure of water in air at the same temperature. Explain if the relative humidity can ever exceed 100%.

63. Measured values of the vapor pressure of mercury at temperatures in the range of normal air temperatures are listed in chemistry and physics handbooks. Knowing this, should you consider an air-pressure reading made with a mercury barometer more or less than the pressure of the atmosphere? Explain.

13.3 The Nature of Solids

64. Name at least one physical property that would permit you to distinguish a molecular solid from an ionic solid.

65. Describe what happens when a solid is heated to its melting point.

66. Molecular solids usually have lower melting points than ionic solids. Why?

67. The melting points and boiling points of ammonia, methanol, water, and phenol are given in the following table. Predict the physical state of each of these substances at the indicated temperature.

a. phenol at 99°C

b. ammonia at −25°C

c. methanol in an ice-water bath

d. methanol in a boiling-water bath

e. ammonia at −100°C

f. phenol at 25°C

Substance	Melting Point (°C)	Boiling Point (°C)
ammonia	−77.7	−33.4
methanol	−97.7	64.7
water	0	100
phenol	40.9	181.9

68. Explain what happens at the melting point of a substance.

69. Is the average kinetic energy of the particles in a block of ice at 0°C the same as or different from the average kinetic energy of the particles in a gas-filled weather balloon at 0°C? Explain.

70. The ions in sodium chloride are arranged in a face-centered cubic pattern. Sketch a layer of the ions in a crystal of sodium chloride.

71. Refer to Figure 13.15 to answer the following questions.
    a. How many simple-cubic unit cells share a single vertex atom or ion?
    b. From your answer to Question a., what part of a vertex atom or ion belongs to a single simple-cubic unit cell?
    c. From your answer to Question b., how many atoms are in a single, simple-cubic unit cell?
    d. How many atoms are in a single body-centered cubic unit cell?
    e. How many atoms are in a single face-centered cubic unit cell?

72. How many pentagons and hexagons share a vertex carbon atom in buckminsterfullerene?

13.4 Changes of State

73. Any liquid stays at a constant temperature while it is boiling. Why?

74. Refer to Figure 13.12 to answer these questions about chloroform, ethanoic acid, water, and ethanol.

a. What is the boiling point of ethanoic acid?

b. Which liquid has the highest vapor pressure at 40°C?

c. At standard atmospheric pressure, which of the substances are in the gaseous state at 70°C?

d. Water boils at 100°C at standard pressure. How would the pressure on ethanol and on ethanoic acid have to change for these liquids to boil at 100°C?

75. The table gives the vapor pressure of isopropyl alcohol (rubbing alcohol) at various temperatures.

Temperature (°C)	Vapor pressure (kPa)
0	1.11
25	6.02
50	23.9
75	75.3
100	198
125	452

a. Graph the data. Connect the data points using a smooth curve.

b. What is the estimated boiling point of isopropyl alcohol?

c. What is the boiling point of isopropyl alcohol when the external pressure is increased to twice standard pressure?

76. A teacher wants to demonstrate that unheated water can boil at room temperature in a beaker within bell jar connected to a vacuum pump. However, the vacuum pump is faulty and can reduce pressures only to 15 kPa. Explain if the teacher can use this pump to perform the demonstration successfully.

Test-Taking Tip

Interpreting Graphs A line graph helps you see the relationship between two variables. Before you answer a question about a graph, identify the variables and the general relationship between the variables based on the shape of the curve.

Regents Practice Exam

Part A

For each statement or question write the number of the word or expression that, of those given, best completes the statement or answers the question.

1. When heat is added to a substance, the
   (1) temperature of the substance does not change
   (2) temperature of the substance decreases
   (3) temperature of the substance increases
   (4) average kinetic energy of the particles decreases

2. Solids have a fixed volume because the particles in a solid
   (1) do not move at all
   (2) can slide past each other
   (3) are free to move throughout the container
   (4) cannot move from one place to another

3. Which metal ranks highest in the activity series of metals?
   (1) magnesium
   (2) aluminum
   (3) potassium
   (4) lithium

4. At a given temperature and pressure, which of the following choices does *not* help determine the physical state of a substance?
   (1) the structure of particles
   (2) the arrangement of particles
   (3) interactions between particles
   (4) differences in kinetic energy

Part B-1

For each statement or question write the number of the word or expression that, of those given, best completes the statement or answers the question.

5. The correct formula for copper(I) sulfite is
   (1) $CuSO_3$
   (2) Cu_2SO_3
   (3) $CuSO_4$
   (4) Cu_2SO_4

6. Which of the following sequences has the states of CH_3OH correctly ordered in terms of increasing average kinetic energy?
   (1) $CH_3OH(s)$, $CH_3OH(g)$, $CH_3OH(l)$
   (2) $CH_3OH(g)$, $CH_3OH(l)$, $CH_3OH(s)$
   (3) $CH_3OH(l)$, $CH_3OH(g)$, $CH_3OH(s)$
   (4) $CH_3OH(s)$, $CH_3OH(l)$, $CH_3OH(g)$

7. Which of the following statements is true?
   (1) In an open container, the rate of evaporation of a liquid always equals the rate of condensation because a dynamic equilibrium exists between the liquid and its vapor in an open container.
   (2) In a closed container, the rate of evaporation of a liquid always equals the rate of condensation because a dynamic equilibrium exists between the liquid and its vapor in a closed container.
   (3) In an open container, the rate of evaporation of a liquid does not equal the rate of condensation because a dynamic equilibrium exists between the liquid and its vapor in an open container.
   (4) In a closed container, the rate of evaporation of a liquid does not equal the rate of condensation because a dynamic equilibrium exists between the liquid and its vapor only in an open container.

8. Water boils at a temperature below 100°C on top of a mountain because
   (1) atmospheric pressure increases with an increase in altitude
   (2) atmospheric pressure decreases with an increase in altitude
   (3) atmospheric pressure increases with an decrease in altitude
   (4) the normal boiling temperature of water is less than 100°C

9. Gases are more compressible than liquids because there is
   (1) less space between particles in a gas than between particles in a liquid
   (2) the same amount of space between particles in a gas than between particles in a liquid
   (3) more space between particles in a gas than between particles in a liquid
   (4) gas particles have more kinetic energy than the particles in a liquid

Part B-2

Answer each of the following questions.

10. Which atom in each pair has the larger atomic radius?
    a. O and S   **b.** K and Br

11. Write the complete electron configuration of each of the following ions.
    a. Ca^{2+} **b.** S^{2-}

12. How many unshared pairs of electrons are in each molecule?
    a. H_2O **b.** CO

13. Identify the molecular compound in each pair of substances.
    a. NaCl or CO   **b.** PBr_3 or LiOH

14. Write formulas for the following ions.
    a. iron(III)   **b.** cadmium

15. Calculate the percent by mass of the metal in each of the following compounds.
    a. Fe_2S_3 **b.** $Al(OH)_3$

16. How many moles are in 888 g of sulfur dioxide?

17. How many moles is 63.4 g NH_3?

18. Balance the following chemical equations.
    a. $V_2O_5 + H_2 \longrightarrow V_2O_3 + H_2O$
    b. $(NH_4)_2Cr_2O_7 \longrightarrow Cr_2O_3 + N_2 + H_2O$

19. When hydrogen sulfide gas is bubbled into a solution of cadmium nitrate in water, the products are nitric acid and a precipitate of cadmium sulfide. Write a balanced chemical equation from this word statement. Include physical states for all reactants and products. (Hydrogen sulfide gas is quite soluble in water.)

20. Classify each of the following reactions as combination (synthesis), decomposition, single replacement, double replacement, or combustion.
    a. $2Li(s) + Br_2(l) \longrightarrow 2LiBr(s)$
    b. $2C_2H_6(g) + 7O_2(g) \longrightarrow 4CO_2(g) + 6H_2O(g)$

21. The complete decomposition of sucrose (table sugar) caused by strong heating may be represented as shown.

$$C_{12}H_{22}O_{11}(s) \longrightarrow 11H_2O(l) + 12C(s)$$

For the decomposition of 1.00 mol of sucrose:
    a. How many moles of H_2O are produced?
    b. What is the total number of moles of products produced?

Use the graph to answer Questions 22 and 23.

Vapor Pressure Graph of Three Substances

22. What is the boiling point of ethanol at a pressure of 101.3 kPa?

23. Can chloroform be heated to 90°C in an open container?

Part C

Answer each of the following questions.

24. When you remove the lid from a food container that has been left in a freezer for several months, you discover a large collection of ice crystals on the underside of the lid. Explain what has happened.

25. Aerosol spray cans have warning labels telling consumers not to dispose of the cans by incineration. What is the danger? Explain.

26. What role does atmospheric pressure play when someone is drinking a liquid through a straw?

27. Pouring liquid nitrogen onto a balloon decreases the volume of the balloon dramatically, as shown in the photograph. Afterward, the balloon reinflates. Use kinetic theory to explain this sequence of events. The temperature of liquid nitrogen is −196°C.

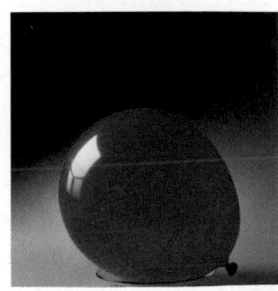

The tank of compressed gas allows this diver to observe the sea turtle in its underwater environment.

INQUIRY Activity

Observing Volume Changes

Materials
round non-latex balloon, marking pen, freezer, metric tape measure, sunny window

Procedure

1. Inflate the balloon and tie it closed. Use the marking pen to draw a line around the middle of the balloon. This line is the circumference of the balloon. You will use the circumference to track any change in the volume of the balloon.

2. Place the balloon in the freezer for half an hour. Remove it and quickly measure and record the circumference of the balloon in centimeters.

3. Place the balloon in a sunny window for half an hour. Measure and record the circumference of the balloon in centimeters.

Think About It

1. How did the volume of the balloon change when you placed it in the freezer?

2. What happened to the volume of the balloon when you placed it in a sunny window?

3. Use your results to suggest a relationship between the temperature and volume of a gas.

Properties of Gases

New York Standards: 3.4b–c

Connecting to Your World

In organized soccer, there are rules about equipment. For international competitions, the ball's mass must be not more than 450 grams and not less than 410 grams. The pressure of the air inside the ball must be no lower than 0.6 atmospheres and no higher than 1.1 atmospheres at sea level. A ball that is properly inflated will rebound faster and travel farther than a ball that is under-inflated. If the pressure is too high, the ball may burst when it is kicked. In this section, you will study variables that affect the pressure of a gas.

Guide for Reading

Key Concepts
- Why are gases easier to compress than solids or liquids are?
- What are the three factors that affect gas pressure?

Vocabulary
compressibility

Reading Strategy
Relating Cause and Effect A cause makes something happen. As you read, write down three possible causes for an increase in gas pressure.

Compressibility

When a car comes to a sudden stop, the people in the car will continue to move forward unless they are restrained. The driver and any passengers are more likely to survive a collision if they are wearing seat belts to restrict their forward movement. Cars also contain air bags as a second line of defense. A sudden reduction in speed triggers a chemical reaction inside an air bag. One product of the reaction is nitrogen gas, which causes the bag to inflate. An inflated air bag keeps the driver from colliding with the steering wheel, as shown in Figure 14.1. An inflated air bag keeps a passenger from colliding with the dashboard or windshield.

Recall that a gas can expand to fill its container, unlike a solid or liquid. The reverse is also true. Gases are easily compressed, or squeezed into a smaller volume. **Compressibility** is a measure of how much the volume of matter decreases under pressure. Why does a collision with an inflated air bag cause much less damage than a collision with a steering wheel or dashboard? When a person collides with an inflated air bag, the impact forces the molecules of gas in the bag closer together. The compression of the gas absorbs the energy of the impact.

Figure 14.1 A crash dummy can be used to test the effectiveness of an air bag. Because gases can be compressed, the air bag absorbs some of the energy from the impact of a collision. Air bags work best when combined with seat belts.

Figure 14.2 There are only a few nitrogen and oxygen molecules in this model of air. At room temperature, the distance between molecules in a container of air at standard pressure is about 10 times the diameter of a molecule.

Kinetic theory can explain why gases are compressed more easily than liquids or solids. 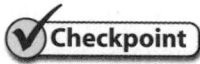 **Gases are easily compressed because of the space between the particles in a gas.** Remember that the volume of the particles in a gas is small compared to the overall volume of the gas. So the distance between particles in a gas is much greater than the distance between particles in a liquid or solid. Under pressure, the particles in a gas are forced closer together, or compressed.

At room temperature, the distance between particles in an enclosed gas is about 10 times the diameter of a particle. Figure 14.2 is a model of an air sample at room temperature. Only oxygen and nitrogen—the two main gases in air—are represented. Note how few particles can fit in this relatively large space when the distance between particles is reasonable for the size of the particles. It isn't practical to represent the actual distances between particles in all the molecular drawings of gases in this book. The drawings would be too large to easily fit on a page. For the drawings to fit on a page, the particles must be drawn closer together.

✓ **Checkpoint** *How does the volume of the particles in a gas compare to the overall volume of the gas?*

Factors Affecting Gas Pressure

Kinetic theory can help explain other properties of gases, such as their ability to expand and take the shape and volume of their containers. Recall these assumptions about the particles in a gas. The particles move along straight-line paths until they collide with other particles or the walls of their container. The motion of the particles is constant and random. Because there are no significant forces of attraction or repulsion among particles in a gas, particles in a gas can move freely.

Four variables are generally used to describe a gas. The variables and their common units are pressure (P) in kilopascals, volume (V) in liters, temperature (T) in kelvins, and the number of moles (n). **The amount of gas, volume, and temperature are factors that affect gas pressure.**

Amount of Gas An air-filled raft blasts through a narrow opening between rocks and plummets over a short waterfall into churning white water below. The raft bends and twists, absorbing some of the pounding energy of the river. The strength and flexibility of the raft are impressive and rely on the pressure of the gas inside the raft. The raft must be made of a material that is strong enough to withstand the pressure of the air inside the raft. The material must also keep air from leaking out of the raft. The volume of the inflated raft in Figure 14.3 is dramatically larger than the volume of the raft before it is inflated. As air is added, the raft expands to its intended volume. The pressure of the air inside the raft keeps the raft inflated.

You can use kinetic theory to predict and explain how gases will respond to a change of conditions. If you inflate an air raft, for example, the pressure inside the raft will increase. Collisions of particles with the inside walls of the raft result in the pressure that is exerted by the enclosed gas. By adding gas, you increase the number of particles. Increasing the number of particles increases the number of collisions, which explains why the gas pressure increases.

Figure 14.4 shows what happens when gas is added to an enclosed, rigid container. Because the container is rigid, the volume of the gas is constant. Assume also that the temperature of the gas does not change. Under these conditions, doubling the number of particles of gas doubles the pressure. Tripling the number of particles triples the pressure, and so on. With a powerful pump and a strong container, you can generate very high pressures by adding more and more gas. However, once the pressure exceeds the strength of the container, the container will burst. Removing gas from a rigid container has the opposite effect. As the amount of gas is reduced, the pressure inside the container is reduced.

Figure 14.3 The volume of this air-filled raft is much larger than its volume before it was inflated. Using a pump to force air into a raft increases the pressure of the air inside the raft. The increased pressure causes the raft to inflate to its intended size.

100 kPa   200 kPa   600 kPa

Figure 14.4 When a gas is pumped into a closed rigid container, the pressure increases as more particles are added. If the number of particles is doubled, the pressure will double. **Predicting** *What would happen to the pressure in the container if the number of particles were tripled? If the number of particles were cut in half?*

Push button opens valve

Paint disperses as fine spray

Valve

Gas propellant (high pressure)

Outside air (atmospheric pressure)

Paint

Gas pressure forces paint up tube

Figure 14.5 The pressure of the gas inside a new can of spray paint is greater than the air pressure outside the can. When gas rushes though an opening in the top of the can, it propels, or forces, paint out of the can. As the can is used, the pressure of the propellant decreases.
Relating Cause and Effect *What happens when the pressure of the propellant equals the air pressure outside the can?*

If the pressure of the gas in a sealed container is lower than the outside air pressure, air will rush into the container when the container is opened. This movement causes the whoosh you hear when you open a vacuum-packed container. When the pressure of a gas in a sealed container is higher than the outside air pressure, the gas will flow out of the container when the container is unsealed.

Aerosol cans depend on the movement of a gas from a region of high pressure to a region of lower pressure. Aerosol cans may contain whipped cream, hair mousse, or spray paint. Figure 14.5 shows how a can of spray paint works. The can contains a gas stored at high pressure. The air outside the can is at a lower pressure. Pushing the spray button creates an opening between the inside of the can and the air outside. The gas flows through the opening to the lower pressure region outside. The movement of the gas propels, or forces, the paint out of the can. As the gas is depleted, the pressure inside the can decreases until the gas can no longer propel paint from the can.

Volume You can raise the pressure exerted by a contained gas by reducing its volume. The more the gas is compressed, the greater is the pressure that the gas exerts inside the container. When gas is in a cylinder, as in an automobile engine, a piston can be used to reduce its volume. The snug-fitting piston keeps gas from escaping as the cylinder moves down and up.

Figure 14.6 shows a cylinder of gas under two different conditions. When the cylinder has a volume of 1 L, the gas exerts a pressure of 100 kPa. When the volume is halved to 0.5 L, the pressure is doubled to 200 kPa. Increasing the volume of the contained gas has the opposite effect. If the volume is doubled, the particles can expand into a volume that is twice the original volume. With the same number of particles in twice the volume, the pressure of the gas is cut in half.

100 kPa

100 kPa

200 kPa

200 kPa

Volume = 1 L

Volume = 0.5 L

Figure 14.6 A piston can be used to force a gas in a cylinder into a smaller volume. When the volume is decreased, the pressure the gas exerts is increased.
Interpreting Diagrams *What happens to the gas pressure when the volume is reduced from 1 L to 0.5 L?*

Figure 14.7 An increase in temperature causes an increase in the pressure of an enclosed gas. The container can explode if there is too great an increase in the pressure.

Temperature A sealed bag of potato chips bulges at the seams when placed in a sunny location. The bag bulges because an increase in the temperature of an enclosed gas causes an increase in its pressure. You can use kinetic theory to explain what happens. As a gas is heated, the temperature increases and the average kinetic energy of the particles in the gas increases. Faster-moving particles impact the walls of their container with more energy.

Look at Figure 14.7. The volume of the container and the amount of gas is constant. When the Kelvin temperature of the enclosed gas doubles from 300 K to 600 K, the pressure of the enclosed gas doubles from 100 kPa to 200 kPa. A gas in a sealed container may generate enormous pressure when heated. For that reason, an aerosol can, even an "empty" one, may explode if thrown onto a fire. By contrast, as the temperature of an enclosed gas decreases, the pressure decreases. The particles, on average, move more slowly and have less kinetic energy. They strike the container walls with less force. Halving the Kelvin temperature of a gas in a rigid container decreases the gas pressure by half.

14.1 Section Assessment

1. 🔑 **Key Concept** Why is a gas easy to compress?

2. 🔑 **Key Concept** List three factors that can affect gas pressure.

3. Why does a collision with an air bag cause less damage than a collision with a steering wheel?

4. How does a decrease in temperature affect the pressure of a contained gas?

5. If the temperature is constant, what change in volume would cause the pressure of an enclosed gas to be reduced to one quarter of its original value?

6. Assuming the gas in a container remains at a constant temperature, how could you increase the gas pressure in the container a hundredfold?

Writing ▶ Activity

Explaining Aerosol Cans Write a paragraph explaining how the compressed gas in an aerosol can force paint out of the can. Describe how the gas pressure inside the can changes as the paint is sprayed, and identify the variable that causes this change. Refer to Figure 14.5.

Textbook

Assessment 14.1 Test yourself on the concepts in Section 14.1.

with ChemASAP

New York Standards: M2.1a, M3.1a, 3.4c

Guide for Reading

 Key Concepts

- How are the pressure, volume, and temperature of a gas related?
- When is the combined gas law used to solve problems?

Vocabulary

Boyle's law
Charles's law
Gay-Lussac's law
combined gas law

Reading Strategy

Relating Text and Visuals
As you read, look closely at Figure 14.9. Explain how a combination of photographs and drawings helps you understand the relationship between the temperature and volume of a gas.

Connecting to Your World   This hot air balloon was designed to carry a passenger around the world. Because warm air is less dense than cooler air, the pilot heats the air inside the balloon to make the balloon rise. The pilot releases hot air through a vent in the top of the balloon to make the balloon descend. In this section, you will study some laws that will allow you to predict gas behavior under specific conditions, such as in a hot air balloon.

Boyle's Law: Pressure and Volume

How would an increase in pressure affect the volume of a contained gas? **If the temperature is constant, as the pressure of a gas increases, the volume decreases.** In turn, as the pressure decreases, the volume increases. Robert Boyle was the first person to study this pressure-volume relationship in a systematic way. In 1662, Boyle proposed a law to describe the relationship. **Boyle's law** states that for a given mass of gas at constant temperature, the volume of the gas varies inversely with pressure.

Look at Figure 14.8. A gas with a volume of 1.0 L (V_1) is at a pressure of 100 kPa (P_1). As the volume increases to 2.0 L (V_2), the pressure decreases to 50 kPa (P_2). The product $P_1 \times V_1$ (100 kPa $\times$ 1.0 L = 100 kPa·L) is the same as the product $P_2 \times V_2$ (50 kPa $\times$ 2.0 L = 100 kPa·L). As the volume decreases to 0.5 L (V_3), the pressure increases to 200 kPa (P_3). Again, the product of the pressure and the volume equals 100 kPa·L.

Figure 14.8 The pressure of a gas changes as the volume changes.

INTERPRETING GRAPHS

a. Observing When the volume is 2.0 L, what is the pressure?

b. Predicting What would the pressure be if the volume were increased to 3.0 L?

c. Drawing Conclusions Based on the shape of the graph, describe the general pressure-volume relationship.

In an inverse relationship, the product of the two variable quantities is constant. So the product of pressure and volume at any two sets of pressure and volume conditions is always constant at a given temperature. The mathematical expression of Boyle's law is as follows.

$$P_1 \times V_1 = P_2 \times V_2$$

The graph of an inverse relationship is always a curve, as in Figure 14.8.

Interactive Textbook

Simulation 15 Examine the relationship between gas volume and pressure.

— with **ChemASAP**

SAMPLE PROBLEM 14.1

Using Boyle's Law

A balloon contains 30.0 L of helium gas at 103 kPa. What is the volume of the helium when the balloon rises to an altitude where the pressure is only 25.0 kPa? (Assume that the temperature remains constant.)

1 **Analyze** *List the knowns and the unknown.*

Knowns
- $P_1 = 103$ kPa
- $V_1 = 30.0$ L
- $P_2 = 25.0$ kPa

Unknown
- $V_2 = ?$ L

Use Boyle's law ($P_1 \times V_1 = P_2 \times V_2$) to calculate the unknown value (V_2).

2 **Calculate** *Solve for the unknown.*
Rearrange Boyle's law to isolate V_2.

$$V_2 = \frac{V_1 \times P_1}{P_2}$$

Substitute the known values for P_1, V_1, and P_2 into the equation and solve.

$$V_2 = \frac{30.0 \text{ L} \times 103 \text{ kPa}}{25.0 \text{ kPa}}$$

$$= 1.24 \times 10^2 \text{ L}$$

Math Handbook

For help with algebraic equations, go to page R69.

3 **Evaluate** *Does the result make sense?*
A decrease in pressure at constant temperature must correspond to a proportional increase in volume. The calculated result agrees with both kinetic theory and the pressure-volume relationship. Also, the units have canceled correctly and the answer is expressed to the proper number of significant figures.

Practice Problems

7. Nitrous oxide (N_2O) is used as an anesthetic. The pressure on 2.50 L of N_2O changes from 105 kPa to 40.5 kPa. If the temperature does not change, what will the new volume be?

8. A gas with a volume of 4.00 L at a pressure of 205 kPa is allowed to expand to a volume of 12.0 L. What is the pressure in the container if the temperature remains constant?

Interactive Textbook

Problem Solving 14.8 Solve Problem 8 with the help of an interactive guided tutorial.

— with **ChemASAP**

$P_1 = 100$ kPa

$V_1 = 1$ L
$T_1 = 265$ K

$P_2 = 100$ kPa

$V_2 = 1.4$ L
$T_2 = 373$ K

Figure 14.9 When the gas in the blue balloon is cooled at constant pressure, the volume of the gas decreases. When the gas is heated at constant pressure, the volume increases.
Calculating *What is the ratio of volume to temperature for each set of conditions? Round your answer to two significant figures.*

Charles's Law: Temperature and Volume

Figure 14.9 compares the volume of a balloon in ice water to the volume of the same balloon in hot water. The amount of gas and the pressure are constant. **As the temperature of an enclosed gas increases, the volume increases, if the pressure is constant.**

In 1787, the French physicist Jacques Charles studied the effect of temperature on the volume of a gas at constant pressure. When he graphed his data, Charles observed that a graph of gas volume versus temperature (in °C) is a straight line for any gas. When he extrapolated, or extended, the line to zero volume ($V = 0$), the line always intersected the temperature axis at −273.15°C. This value is equal to 0 on the Kelvin temperature scale.

The observations that Charles made are summarized in Charles's law. **Charles's law** states that the volume of a fixed mass of gas is directly proportional to its Kelvin temperature if the pressure is kept constant. Look at the graph in Figure 14.10. When the temperature is 300 K, the volume is 1.0 L. When the temperature is 900 K, the volume is 3.0 L. In both cases, the ratio of V to T is 0.0033.

Figure 14.10 This graph shows how the volume changes as the temperature of a gas changes.

INTERPRETING GRAPHS

a. Observing What is the unit of temperature?
b. Drawing Conclusions What happens to the volume as the temperature rises?
c. Predicting If the temperature of a gas were 0 K, what would the volume of the gas be?

Charles's Law

The ratio V_1/T_1 is equal to the ratio V_2/T_2. Because this ratio is constant at all conditions of temperature and volume, when the pressure is constant, you can write Charles's law as follows.

$$\frac{V_1}{T_1} = \frac{V_2}{T_2}$$

The ratio of the variables is always a constant in a direct relationship, and the graph is always a straight line. It is not a direct relationship if the temperatures are expressed in degrees Celsius. So when you solve gas law problems, the temperature must always be expressed in kelvins.

Simulation 16 Examine the relationship between gas volume and temperature.

— with **ChemASAP**

SAMPLE PROBLEM 14.2

Using Charles's Law

A balloon inflated in a room at 24°C has a volume of 4.00 L. The balloon is then heated to a temperature of 58°C. What is the new volume if the pressure remains constant?

1 Analyze *List the knowns and the unknown.*

Knowns
- $V_1 = 4.00$ L
- $T_1 = 24$°C
- $T_2 = 58$°C

Unknown
- $V_2 = ?$ L

Use Charles's law ($V_1/T_1 = V_2/T_2$) to calculate the unknown value (V_2).

2 Calculate *Solve for the unknown.*

Because you will use a gas law, express the temperatures in kelvins.

$$T_1 = 24°C + 273 = 297 \text{ K}$$

$$T_2 = 58°C + 273 = 331 \text{ K}$$

Rearrange Charles's law to isolate V_2.

$$V_2 = \frac{V_1 \times T_2}{T_1}$$

Substitute the known values for T_1, V_1, and T_2 into the equation and solve.

$$V_2 = \frac{4.00 \text{ L} \times 331 \text{ K}}{297 \text{ K}}$$

$$= 4.46 \text{ L}$$

3 Evaluate *Does the result make sense?*

The volume increases as the temperature increases. This result agrees with both the kinetic theory and Charles's law.

Practice Problems

9. If a sample of gas occupies 6.80 L at 325°C, what will its volume be at 25°C if the pressure does not change?

10. Exactly 5.00 L of air at −50.0°C is warmed to 100.0°C. What is the new volume if the pressure remains constant?

Problem Solving 14.10 Solve Problem 10 with the help of an interactive guided tutorial.

— with **ChemASAP**

100 kPa   200 kPa

300 K   600 K

Gay-Lussac's Law: Pressure and Temperature

When tires are not inflated to the recommended pressure, fuel efficiency and traction decrease. Treads can wear down faster. Most importantly, improper inflation can lead to tire failure. A driver should not check tire pressure after driving a long distance because the air in a tire heats up during a drive. **As the temperature of an enclosed gas increases, the pressure increases, if the volume is constant.**

Joseph Gay-Lussac (1778–1850), a French chemist, discovered the relationship between the pressure and temperature of a gas in 1802. His name is on the gas law that describes the relationship. **Gay-Lussac's law** states that the pressure of a gas is directly proportional to the Kelvin temperature if the volume remains constant. Look at Figure 14.11. When the temperature is 300 K, the pressure is 100 kPa. When the temperature is doubled to 600 K, the pressure doubles to 200 kPa. Because Gay-Lussac's law involves direct proportions, the ratios P_1/T_1 and P_2/T_2 are equal at constant volume. You can write Gay-Lussac's law as follows.

$$\frac{P_1}{T_1} = \frac{P_2}{T_2}$$

Gay-Lussac's law can be applied to reduce the time it takes to cook food. One cooking method involves placing food above a layer of water and heating the water. The water vapor, or steam, that is produced cooks the food. Steam that escapes from the pot is at a temperature of about 100°C when the pressure is near one atmosphere. In a pressure cooker, like the one shown in Figure 14.12, steam is trapped inside the cooker. The temperature of the steam reaches about 120°C. The food cooks faster at this higher temperature, but the pressure rises, which increases the risk of an explosion. A pressure cooker has a valve that allows some vapor to escape when the pressure exceeds the set value.

✓ Checkpoint *How does a pressure cooker affect the time needed to cook food?*

Figure 14.12 In a pressure cooker, food cooks faster than in an ordinary pot with a lid.

SAMPLE PROBLEM 14.3

Simulation 17 Examine the relationship between gas pressure and temperature.

— with **ChemASAP**

Using Gay-Lussac's Law

Aerosol cans carry warnings on their labels that say not to incinerate (burn) them or store the cans above a certain temperature. This problem will show why it is dangerous to dispose of aerosol cans in a fire. The gas in a used aerosol can is at a pressure of 103 kPa at 25°C. If the can is thrown onto a fire, what will the pressure be when the temperature reaches 928°C?

1 Analyze *List the knowns and the unknown.*

Knowns
- $P_1 = 103$ kPa
- $T_1 = 25$°C
- $T_2 = 928$°C

Unknown
- $P_2 = ?$ kPa

Use Gay-Lussac's law ($P_1/T_1 = P_2/T_2$) to calculate the unknown (P_2). Remember, because this problem involves temperatures and a gas law, the temperatures must be expressed in kelvins.

2 Calculate *Solve for the unknown.*

First convert degrees Celsius to kelvins.

$$T_1 = 25°C + 273 = 298 \text{ K}$$

$$T_2 = 928°C + 273 = 1201 \text{ K}$$

Rearrange Gay-Lussac's law to isolate P_2.

$$P_2 = \frac{P_1 \times T_2}{T_1}$$

Substitute the known values for P_1, T_2, and T_1 into the equation and solve.

$$P_2 = \frac{103 \text{ kPa} \times 1201 \text{ K}}{298 \text{ K}}$$

$$= 415 \text{ kPa}$$

$$= 4.15 \times 10^2 \text{ kPa}$$

3 Evaluate *Does the result make sense?*

From the kinetic theory, one would expect the increase in temperature of a gas to produce an increase in pressure if the volume remains constant. The calculated value does show such an increase.

Practice Problems

11. A sample of nitrogen gas has a pressure of 6.58 kPa at 539 K. If the volume does not change, what will the pressure be at 211 K?

12. The pressure in a car tire is 198 kPa at 27°C. After a long drive, the pressure is 225 kPa. What is the temperature of the air in the tire? Assume that the volume is constant.

Problem Solving 14.12
Solve Problem 12 with the help of an interactive guided tutorial.

— with **ChemASAP**

The Combined Gas Law

There is a single expression that combines Boyle's, Charles's, and Gay-Lussac's laws. The **combined gas law** describes the relationship among the pressure, temperature, and volume of an enclosed gas. ☛ **The combined gas law allows you to do calculations for situations in which only the amount of gas is constant.**

$$\frac{P_1 \times V_1}{T_1} = \frac{P_2 \times V_2}{T_2}$$

SAMPLE PROBLEM 14.4

Using the Combined Gas Law

The volume of a gas-filled balloon is 30.0 L at 313 K and 153 kPa pressure. What would the volume be at standard temperature and pressure (STP)?

① Analyze *List the knowns and the unknown.*

Knowns
- V_1 = 30.0 L
- T_1 = 313 K
- P_1 = 153 kPa
- T_2 = 273 K (standard temperature)
- P_2 = 101.3 kPa (standard pressure)

Unknown
- V_2 = ? L

Use the known values and the combined gas law to calculate the unknown (V_2).

② Calculate *Solve for the unknown.*

Rearrange the combined gas law to isolate V_2.

$$V_2 = \frac{V_1 \times P_1 \times T_2}{P_2 \times T_1}$$

Substitute the known quantities into the equation and solve.

$$V_2 = \frac{30.0\ \text{L} \times 153\ \cancel{\text{kPa}} \times 273\ \cancel{\text{K}}}{101.3\ \cancel{\text{kPa}} \times 313\ \cancel{\text{K}}} = 39.5\ \text{L}$$

③ Evaluate *Does the result make sense?*

A decrease in temperature and a decrease in pressure have opposite effects on the volume of gas in a balloon. To evaluate the increase in volume, multiply the original volume (30.0 L) by the ratio of P_1 to P_2 (1.51) and the ratio of T_2 to T_1 (0.872). The result is 39.5 L.

Practice Problems

13. A gas at 155 kPa and 25°C has an initial volume of 1.00 L. The pressure of the gas increases to 605 kPa as the temperature is raised to 125°C. What is the new volume?

14. A 5.00-L air sample has a pressure of 107 kPa at a temperature of −50°C. If the temperature is raised to 102°C and the volume expands to 7.00 L, what will the new pressure be?

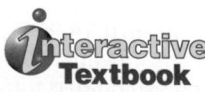

Problem Solving 14.14
Solve Problem 14 with the help of an interactive guided tutorial.

── with ChemASAP

Weather balloons, like the one in Figure 14.13, carry a package of data-gathering instruments up into the atmosphere. At an altitude of about 27,000 meters, the balloon bursts. The combined gas law can help to explain this situation. Both outside temperature and pressure drop as the balloon rises. These changes have opposite effects on the volume of the weather balloon. A drop in temperature causes the volume of an enclosed gas to decrease. A drop in outside pressure causes the volume to increase. Given that the balloon bursts, the drop in pressure must affect the volume more than the drop in temperature does.

The combined gas law can also help you solve gas problems when only two variables are changing. It may seem challenging to remember four different expressions for the gas laws. But you actually only need to remember one expression—the combined gas law. You can derive the other laws from the combined gas law by holding one variable constant.

To illustrate, suppose you hold the temperature constant ($T_1 = T_2$). Rearrange the combined gas law so that the two temperature terms are on the same side of the equation. Because $T_1 = T_2$, the ratio of T_1 to T_2 is equal to one. Multiplying by 1 does not change a value in an equation. So when the temperature is constant, you can delete the temperature ratio from the rearranged combined gas law. What you are left with is the mathematical expression of Boyle's law.

$$P_1 \times V_1 = P_2 \times V_2 \times \frac{T_1}{T_2}$$

$$P_1 \times V_1 = P_2 \times V_2$$

A similar process yields Charles's law when pressure remains constant and Gay-Lussac's law when volume remains constant.

Figure 14.13 Weather balloons carry instruments that can gather data about Earth's atmosphere. **Predicting** *Explain why helium is more likely than air to be used in weather balloons.*

14.2 Section Assessment

15. 🔑 **Key Concept** How are the pressure and volume of a gas related at constant temperature?

16. 🔑 **Key Concept** If pressure is constant, how does a change in temperature affect the volume of a gas?

17. 🔑 **Key Concept** What is the relationship between the temperature and pressure of a contained gas at constant volume?

18. 🔑 **Key Concept** In what situations is the combined gas law useful?

19. Write the mathematical equation for Boyle's law and explain the symbols.

20. A given mass of air has a volume of 6.00 L at 101 kPa. What volume will it occupy at 25.0 kPa if the temperature does not change?

21. Explain how Charles's law can be derived from the combined gas law.

22. The volume of a weather balloon increases as the balloon rises in the atmosphere. Why doesn't the drop in temperature at higher altitudes cause the volume to decrease?

Connecting ▶ Concepts

Phase Changes Use what you learned about phase changes in Section 13.4 to try to explain this statement: Scientists cannot collect temperature and volume data for an enclosed gas at temperatures near absolute zero.

Interactive Textbook

Assessment 14.2 Test yourself on the concepts in Section 14.2.

with **ChemASAP**

Guide for Reading

Key Concepts
- What is needed to calculate the amount of gas in a sample at given conditions of volume, temperature, and pressure?
- Under what conditions are real gases most likely to differ from ideal gases?

Vocabulary
ideal gas constant
ideal gas law

Reading Strategy
Building Vocabulary After you read this section, explain the difference between *ideal* and *real* as these terms are applied to gases.

Connecting to Your World

Solid carbon dioxide, or dry ice, is used to protect products that need to be kept cold during shipping. The adjective *dry* refers to a key advantage of shipping with dry ice. Dry ice doesn't melt. It sublimes. Dry ice can exist because gases don't obey the assumptions of kinetic theory at all conditions. In this section, you will learn how real gases differ from the ideal gases on which the gas laws are based.

Ideal Gas Law

With the combined gas law, you can solve problems with three variables: pressure, volume, and temperature. The combined gas law assumes that the amount of gas does not vary. You cannot use the combined gas law to calculate the number of moles of a gas in a fixed volume at a known temperature and pressure. **To calculate the number of moles of a contained gas requires an expression that contains the variable n.** The combined gas law can be modified to include the number of moles.

The number of moles of gas is directly proportional to the number of particles. The volume occupied by a gas at a specified temperature and pressure also must depend on the number of particles. So moles must be directly proportional to volume as well. You can introduce moles into the combined gas law by dividing each side of the equation by n.

$$\frac{P_1 \times V_1}{T_1 \times n_1} = \frac{P_2 \times V_2}{T_2 \times n_2}$$

This equation shows that $(P \times V)/(T \times n)$ is a constant. This constant holds for ideal gases—gases that conform to the gas laws.

If you know the values for P, V, T, and n for one set of conditions, you can calculate a value for the constant. Recall that 1 mol of every gas occupies 22.4 L at STP (101.3 kPa and 273 K). You can use these values to find the value of the constant, which has the symbol R and is called the ideal gas constant. Insert the values of P, V, T, and n into $(P \times V)/(T \times n)$.

$$R = \frac{P \times V}{T \times n} = \frac{101.3 \text{ kPa} \times 22.4 \text{ L}}{273 \text{ K} \times 1 \text{ mol}} = 8.31 \text{ (L·kPa)/(K·mol)}$$

The **ideal gas constant** (R) has the value 8.31 (L·kPa)/(K·mol). The gas law that includes all four variables—P, V, T, and n—is called the **ideal gas law**. It is usually written as follows.

$$P \times V = n \times R \times T \text{ or } PV = nRT$$

Using the Ideal Gas Law to Find the Amount of a Gas

A deep underground cavern contains 2.24×10^6 L of methane gas (CH_4) at a pressure of 1.50×10^3 kPa and a temperature of 315 K. How many kilograms of CH_4 does the cavern contain?

1 **Analyze** *List the knowns and the unknown.*

Knowns
- $P = 1.50 \times 10^3$ kPa
- $V = 2.24 \times 10^6$ L
- $T = 315$ K
- $R = 8.31$ (L·kPa)/(K·mol)
- molar mass$_{CH_4}$ = 16.0 g

Unknown
- ? kg CH_4

Calculate the number of moles (n) using the ideal gas law. Use the molar mass to convert moles to grams. Then convert grams to kilograms.

2 **Calculate** *Solve for the unknown.*

Rearrange the equation for the ideal gas law to isolate n.

$$n = \frac{P \times V}{R \times T}$$

Substitute the known quantities into the equation to find the number of moles of methane.

$$n = \frac{(1.50 \times 10^3 \text{ kPa}) \times (2.24 \times 10^6 \text{ L})}{8.31 \dfrac{\text{L} \times \text{kPa}}{\text{K} \times \text{mol}} \times 315 \text{ K}} = 128 \text{ mol } CH_4$$
$$= 1.28 \times 10^6 \text{ mol } CH_4$$

A mole-mass conversion gives the number of grams of methane.

$$1.28 \times 10^6 \text{ mol } CH_4 \times \frac{16.0 \text{ g } CH_4}{1 \text{ mol } CH_4} = 20.5 \times 10^6 \text{ g } CH_4$$
$$= 2.05 \times 10^7 \text{ g } CH_4$$

Convert this answer to kilograms.

$$2.05 \times 10^7 \text{ g } CH_4 \times \frac{1 \text{ kg}}{10^3 \text{ g}} = 2.05 \times 10^4 \text{ kg } CH_4$$

3 **Evaluate** *Does the result make sense?*

Although the methane is compressed, its volume is still very large. So it is reasonable that the cavern contains a large mass of methane.

Practice Problems

23. When the temperature of a rigid hollow sphere containing 685 L of helium gas is held at 621 K, the pressure of the gas is 1.89×10^3 kPa. How many moles of helium does the sphere contain?

24. A child's lungs can hold 2.20 L. How many grams of air do her lungs hold at a pressure of 102 kPa and a body temperature of 37°C? Use a molar mass of 29 g for air, which is about 20% O_2 (32 g/mol) and 80% N_2 (28 g/mol).

Engineers use drilling rods to explore for natural gas in the crust below the ocean floor.

Math ▸ **Handbook**

For help with conversion problems, go to page R66.

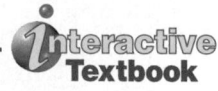

Problem Solving 14.24
Solve Problem 24 with the help of an interactive guided tutorial.

—— with **ChemASAP**

Carbon Dioxide from Antacid Tablets

Purpose
To measure the amount of carbon dioxide gas given off when antacid tablets dissolve in water.

Materials
- 6 effervescent antacid tablets
- 3 rubber balloons (spherical)
- plastic medicine dropper
- water
- clock or watch
- metric tape measure
- graph paper
- pressure sensor (optional)

Procedure

Sensor version available in the Probeware Lab Manual.

1. Break six antacid tablets into small pieces. Keep the pieces from each tablet in a separate pile. Put the pieces from one tablet into the first balloon. Put the pieces from two tablets into a second balloon. Put the pieces from three tablets into a third balloon. **CAUTION** *If you are allergic to latex, do not handle the balloons.*

2. After you use the medicine dropper to squirt about 5 mL of cold water into each balloon, immediately tie off each balloon.

3. Shake the balloons to mix the contents. Allow the contents to warm to room temperature.

4. Measure and record the circumference of each balloon several times during the next 20 minutes.

5. Use the maximum circumference of each balloon to calculate its volume. (*Hint:* Volume of a sphere $= \frac{4\pi r^3}{3}$ and $r = $ circumference$/2\pi$.)

Analyze and Conclude

1. Make a graph of volume versus number of tablets. Use your graph to describe the relationship between the number of tablets used and the volume of the balloon.

2. Assume that the balloon is filled with carbon dioxide gas at 20°C and standard pressure. Calculate the mass and the number of moles of CO_2 in each balloon at maximum inflation.

3. If a typical antacid tablet contains 2.0 g of sodium hydrogen carbonate, how many moles of CO_2 should one tablet yield? Compare this theoretical value with your results.

Ideal Gases and Real Gases

An ideal gas is one that follows the gas laws at all conditions of pressure and temperature. Such a gas would have to conform precisely to the assumptions of kinetic theory. Its particles could have no volume, and there could be no attraction between particles in the gas. As you probably suspect, there is no gas for which these assumptions are true. So an ideal gas does not exist. Nevertheless, at many conditions of temperature and pressure, real gases behave very much like an ideal gas.

The particles in a real gas do have volume, and there are attractions between the particles. Because of these attractions, a gas can condense, or even solidify, when it is compressed or cooled. For example, if water vapor is cooled below 100°C at standard atmospheric pressure, it condenses to a liquid. The behavior of other real gases is similar, although lower temperatures and greater pressures may be required. Such conditions are required to produce the liquid nitrogen in Figure 14.14. ⊂⊃ **Real gases differ most from an ideal gas at low temperatures and high pressures.**

Figure 14.14 In this flask used to store liquid nitrogen, there are two walls with a vacuum in between.

Real Gases Deviate From the Ideal

Figure 14.15 This graph shows how real gases deviate from the ideal gas law at high pressures.

INTERPRETING GRAPHS

a. Observing What are the values of $(PV)/(nRT)$ for an ideal gas at 20,000 and 60,000 kPa?

b. Comparing What variable is responsible for the differences between the two (CH_4) curves?

c. Making Generalizations How does an increase in pressure affect the $(PV)/(nRT)$ ratio for real gases?

Figure 14.15 shows how the value of the ratio (PV/nRT) changes as pressure increases. For an ideal gas, the result is a horizontal line because the ratio is always equal to 1. For real gases at high pressure, the ratio may deviate, or depart, from the ideal. When the ratio is greater than 1, the curve rises above the ideal gas line. When the ratio is less than 1, the curve drops below the line. The deviations can be explained by two factors. As attractive forces reduce the distance between particles, a gas occupies less volume than expected, causing the ratio to be less than 1. But the actual volume of the molecules causes the ratio to be greater than 1.

In portions of the curves below the line, intermolecular attractions dominate. In portions of the curves above the line, molecular volume dominates. Look at the curves for methane (CH_4) at 0°C and at 200°C. At 200°C, the molecules have more kinetic energy to overcome intermolecular attractions. So the curve for CH_4 at 200°C never drops below the line.

14.3 Section Assessment

25. 🔑 **Key Concept** What do you need to calculate the amount of gas in a sample at given conditions of temperature, pressure, and volume?

26. 🔑 **Key Concept** Under what conditions do real gases deviate most from ideal behavior?

27. What is an ideal gas?

28. Determine the volume occupied by 0.582 mol of a gas at 15°C if the pressure is 81.8 kPa.

29. What pressure is exerted by 0.450 mol of a gas at 25°C if the gas is in a 0.650-L container?

30. Use the kinetic theory of gases to explain this statement: No gas exhibits ideal behavior at all temperatures and pressures.

Connecting > **Concepts**

Polarity At standard pressure, ammonia will condense at −33.3°C. At the same pressure, nitrogen does not condense until −195.79°C. Use what you learned about intermolecular attractions and polarity in Section 8.3 to explain this difference.

Textbook

Assessment 14.3 Test yourself on the concepts in Section 14.3.

with **ChemASAP**

Diving In

Divers who depend on the air in their lungs can stay under water for only a few minutes. But with tanks of compressed air, scuba divers can stay under water for hours. They can descend to great depths to explore a coral reef or salvage a sunken ship. Compressed air allows engineers to build, inspect, and repair ships, bridges, and oil platforms.

Interpreting Diagrams *Which of the two main components of air must be in a diver's tank?*

Compressed air

Nitrogen

Heliox

Oxygen

Helium

Trimix

Tank The diver chooses the compressed gas mixture that best suits the depth and length of the planned dive. For deep dives, some or all of the nitrogen may be replaced with helium.

Regulator The regulator automatically adjusts the pressure of the gas mixture to keep the pressure inside the lungs equal to the pressure outside the lungs.

Dive tables help a diver avoid decompression sickness. Divers use the data to control the length and frequency of their dives, and the rate at which they return to the surface.

Table 1 End-of-dive lettergroup At the end of a dive, the diver matches the time and depth of the dive to a letter group. Letter A represents the least amount of nitrogen left in the blood after the dive. The circled numbers show the maximum time a diver can spend at a given depth without having to make a decompression stop during the ascent.

Table 2 Surface interval time The longer a diver spends at the surface, the more nitrogen is excreted through the lungs. A diver can move from Group H to Group A after 8 hours at the surface.

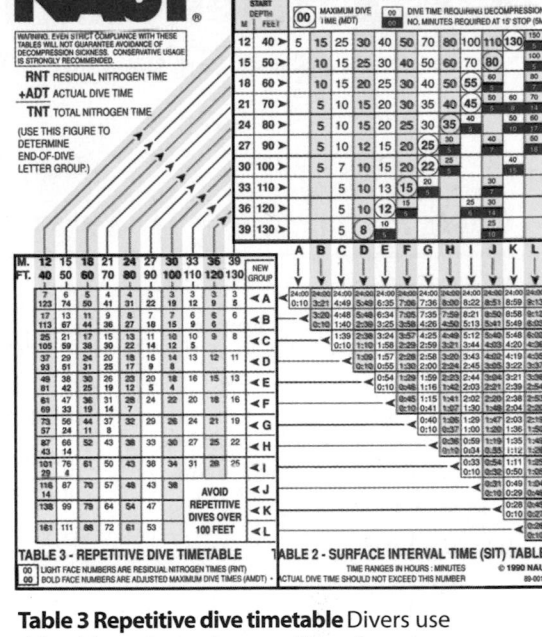

Table 3 **Repetitive dive timetable** Divers use this table to determine an adjusted maximum dive time before doing a second dive. They also use the table to determine a letter group at the end of the second dive.

Dissolved nitrogen As a diver descends, the water exerts greater pressure. More gas pressure is required to keep the lungs expanded. This increased gas pressure causes more nitrogen to dissolve in the diver's blood.

Nitrogen narcosis Below a depth of about 30 meters, dissolved nitrogen interferes with the transmission of nerve impulses. The effects are similar to those of alcohol and include dizziness, slowed reaction time, and an inability to think clearly.

Decompression sickness As the diver returns to the surface, pressure decreases and dissolved nitrogen is released from the blood. Bubbles of nitrogen can block small blood vessels and reduce the supply of oxygen to cells, causing severe pain in the joints, dizziness, and vomiting.

Gases: Mixtures and Movements

Guide for Reading

Key Concepts
- How is the total pressure of a mixture of gases related to the partial pressures of the component gases?
- How does the molar mass of a gas affect the rate at which the gas effuses or diffuses?

Vocabulary
partial pressure
Dalton's law of partial pressures
diffusion
effusion
Graham's law of effusion

Reading Strategy
Previewing Before you read, look at the equation on this page that is highlighted in yellow. In your own words, describe the relationship that the equation is expressing.

Connecting to Your World The top of Mount Everest is more than 29,000 feet above sea level. A list of gear for an expedition to Mount Everest includes climbing equipment such as an ice axe and a climbing harness. It includes ski goggles and a down parka with a hood. All the items on the list are important, but none is as important as the compressed-gas cylinders of oxygen. In this section, you will find out why a supply of oxygen is essential at higher altitudes.

Dalton's Law

Gas pressure results from collisions of particles in a gas with an object. If the number of particles increases in a given volume, more collisions occur. If the average kinetic energy of the particles increases, more collisions occur. In both cases, the pressure increases. Gas pressure depends only on the number of particles in a given volume and on their average kinetic energy. Particles in a mixture of gases at the same temperature have the same average kinetic energy. So the kind of particle is not important.

Table 14.1 shows the composition of dry air, air that does not contain any water vapor. The contribution each gas in a mixture makes to the total pressure is called the **partial pressure** exerted by that gas. In dry air, the partial pressure of nitrogen is 79.11 kPa. **In a mixture of gases, the total pressure is the sum of the partial pressures of the gases.**

$$P_{total} = P_1 + P_2 + P_3 + \dots$$

This equation is a mathematical expression of a law proposed by Dalton. **Dalton's law of partial pressures** states that, at constant volume and temperature, the total pressure exerted by a mixture of gases is equal to the sum of the partial pressures of the component gases.

Interactive Textbook

Animation 17 Observe the behavior of a mixture of nonreacting gases.

with **ChemASAP**

Table 14.1

Composition of Dry Air		
Component	Volume (%)	Partial pressure (kPa)
Nitrogen	78.08	79.11
Oxygen	20.95	21.22
Carbon dioxide	0.04	0.04
Argon and others	0.93	0.95
Total	100.00	101.32

100 kPa   250 kPa   200 kPa   550 kPa

Container A   **Container B**   **Container C**   **Container T**

Figure 14.16 Three gases are combined in container T. The pressure that each gas exerts is independent of the pressure exerted by the other two gases. The pressure in container T is the sum of the pressures in containers A, B, and C.
Interpreting Diagrams *What is the relationship between the number of particles in containers A and C and the partial pressures of the gases in A and C?*

Look at Figure 14.16. Containers A, B, C, and T (for total) have the same volume and are at the same temperature. The gases in containers A, B, and C are combined in container T. Because the volumes are identical, each gas in the mixture exerts the pressure it exerted before the gases were mixed in container T. So the pressure in container T (550 kPa) is the sum of the pressures in containers A, B, and C (100 + 250 + 200 kPa).

If the percent composition of a mixture of gases does not change, the fraction of the pressure exerted by a gas does not change as the total pressure changes. This fact is important for people who must operate at high altitudes. For example, at the top of Mount Everest, the total atmospheric pressure is 33.73 kPa. This is about one-third of its value at sea level. The partial pressure of oxygen is also reduced by one third, to 7.06 kPa. The partial pressure of oxygen must be 10.67 kPa or higher to support respiration in humans. The climber in Figure 14.17 needs an oxygen mask and a cylinder of compressed oxygen to survive.

Figure 14.17 This climber is using a tank of compressed gas to supplement the supply of oxygen available at high altitudes.

Firefighters carry tanks of compressed air. The tanks contain from 19.5% to 23.5% oxygen by volume.

SAMPLE PROBLEM 14.6

Using Dalton's Law of Partial Pressures

Air contains oxygen, nitrogen, carbon dioxide, and trace amounts of other gases. What is the partial pressure of oxygen (P_{O_2}) at 101.30 kPa of total pressure if the partial pressures of nitrogen, carbon dioxide, and other gases are 79.10 kPa, 0.040 kPa, and 0.94 kPa, respectively?

1 **Analyze** *List the knowns and the unknown.*

Knowns
- $P_{N_2} = 79.10$ kPa
- $P_{CO_2} = 0.040$ kPa
- $P_{others} = 0.94$ kPa
- $P_{total} = 101.30$ kPa

Unknown
- $P_{O_2} = ?$ kPa

Use Dalton's law of partial pressures $(P_{total} = P_{O_2} + P_{N_2} + P_{CO_2} + P_{others})$ to calculate the unknown value (P_{O_2}).

2 **Calculate** *Solve for the unknown.*

Rearrange Dalton's law to isolate P_{O_2}. Substitute the values for the partial pressures and solve the equation.

$$P_{O_2} = P_{total} - (P_{N_2} + P_{CO_2} + P_{others})$$
$$= 101.30 \text{ kPa} - (79.10 \text{ kPa} + 0.040 \text{ kPa} + 0.94 \text{ kPa})$$
$$= 21.22 \text{ kPa}$$

3 **Evaluate** *Does the result make sense?*

The partial pressure of oxygen must be smaller than that of nitrogen because P_{total} is only 101.30 kPa. The other partial pressures are small, so an answer of 21.22 kPa seems reasonable.

Practice Problems

31. Determine the total pressure of a gas mixture that contains oxygen, nitrogen, and helium. The partial pressures are: $P_{O_2} = 20.0$ kPa, $P_{N_2} = 46.7$ kPa, and $P_{He} = 26.7$ kPa.

32. A gas mixture containing oxygen, nitrogen, and carbon dioxide has a total pressure of 32.9 kPa. If $P_{O_2} = 6.6$ kPa and $P_{N_2} = 23.0$ kPa, what is P_{CO_2}?

interactive
Textbook

Problem Solving 14.32
Solve Problem 32 with the help of an interactive guided tutorial.

——with **ChemASAP**

Graham's Law

Suppose you open a perfume bottle in one corner of a room. At some point a person standing in the opposite corner will be able to smell the perfume. Molecules in the perfume evaporate and diffuse, or spread out, through the air in the room. **Diffusion** is the tendency of molecules to move toward areas of lower concentration until the concentration is uniform throughout. In Figure 14.18A, bromine vapor is diffusing through the air in a graduated cylinder. The bromine vapor in the bottom of the cylinder has started to move upward toward the area where there is a lower concentration of bromine. In Figure 14.18B, the bromine has diffused almost to the top of the cylinder. If the process is allowed to continue, the bromine vapor will spill out of the cylinder.

There is another process that involves the movement of molecules in a gas. This process is called effusion. During **effusion**, a gas escapes through a tiny hole in its container. With effusion and diffusion, the type of particle is important. 🔑 **Gases of lower molar mass diffuse and effuse faster than gases of higher molar mass.**

Thomas Graham's Contribution The Scottish chemist Thomas Graham studied rates of effusion during the 1840s. From his observations, he proposed a law. **Graham's law of effusion** states that the rate of effusion of a gas is inversely proportional to the square root of the gas's molar mass. This law can also be applied to the diffusion of gases.

Graham's law makes sense if you know how the mass, velocity, and kinetic energy of a moving object are related. The expression that relates the mass (m) and the velocity (v) of an object to its kinetic energy (KE) is $KE = 1/2\,mv^2$. For the kinetic energy to be constant, any increase in mass must be balanced by a decrease in velocity. For example, a ball with a mass of 2 g must travel at 5 m/s to have the same kinetic energy as a ball with a mass of 1 g traveling at 7 m/s. There is an important principle here. If two objects with different masses have the same kinetic energy, the lighter object must move faster.

Word *Origins*

Diffusion and **effusion** come from the Latin *fundere* meaning "to pour." They differ only in their prefixes. The prefix *dis-* means "apart." The prefix *ex-* means "out." **How do these prefixes help to contrast what happens to a gas during diffusion and effusion?**

For: Links on Diffusion/Effusion
Visit: www.SciLinks.org
Web Code: cdn-1144

Figure 14.18 The diffusion of one substance through another is a relatively slow process. ⓐ Bromine vapor is diffusing upward through the air in a graduated cylinder. ⓑ After several hours, bromine vapors are near the top of the cylinder. **Predicting** *What will happen as the bromine continues to diffuse?*

Figure 14.19 The character balloons used in parades are filled with helium gas so that they will float.

Comparing Effusion Rates The balloon in Figure 14.19 is used in holiday parades. It is filled with helium so that it will float above the crowd along the parade route. There is a drawback to using helium in a balloon. Both helium atoms and the molecules in air can pass freely through the tiny pores in a balloon. But a helium-filled balloon will deflate sooner than an air-filled balloon. Kinetic theory can explain this difference.

If the balloons are at the same temperature, the particles in each balloon have the same average kinetic energy. But helium atoms are less massive than oxygen or nitrogen molecules. So the molecules in air move more slowly than helium atoms with the same kinetic energy. Because the rate of effusion is related only to a particle's speed, Graham's law can be written as follows for two gases, A and B.

$$\frac{\text{Rate}_A}{\text{Rate}_B} = \sqrt{\frac{\text{molar mass}_B}{\text{molar mass}_A}}$$

The rates of effusion of two gases are inversely proportional to the square roots of their molar masses. You can use the expression to compare the rates of effusion of nitrogen (molar mass = 28.0 g) and helium (molar mass = 4.0 g). Helium effuses (and diffuses) nearly three times faster than nitrogen at the same temperature.

$$\frac{\text{Rate}_{He}}{\text{Rate}_{N_2}} = \sqrt{\frac{28.0\ g}{4.0\ g}} = \sqrt{7.0} = 2.7$$

Textbook

Animation 18 Observe the processes of gas effusion and diffusion.

with ChemASAP

14.4 Section Assessment

33. 🔑 **Key Concept** In a mixture of gases, how is the total pressure determined?

34. 🔑 **Key Concept** What is the effect of molar mass on rates of diffusion and effusion?

35. How is the partial pressure of a gas in a mixture calculated?

36. What distinguishes effusion from diffusion? How are these processes similar?

37. How can you compare the rates of effusion of two gases in a mixture?

38. Explain why the rates of diffusion of nitrogen gas and carbon monoxide are almost identical at the same temperature.

Elements ▶ Handbook

Table 14.1 on page 432 and the *Elements in the Atmosphere* table on page R4 provide data on the composition of air. Look at the data included in each table. Identify two ways in which the tables are similar. Describe at least three differences.

Textbook

Assessment 14.4 Test yourself on the concepts in Section 14.4.

with ChemASAP

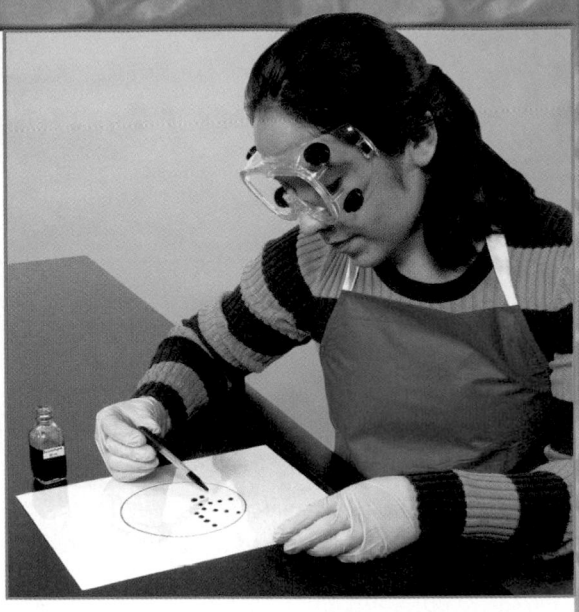

Diffusion

Purpose
To infer diffusion of a gas by observing color changes during chemical reactions.

Materials
- clear plastic cup or Petri dish
- reaction surface
- dropper bottles containing bromthymol blue, hydrochloric acid, and sodium hydrogen sulfite
- ruler
- cotton swab
- NaOH, NH_4Cl, KI, and $NaNO_2$ (optional)

Procedure

1. Use the plastic cup or Petri dish to draw the large circle shown below on a sheet of paper.

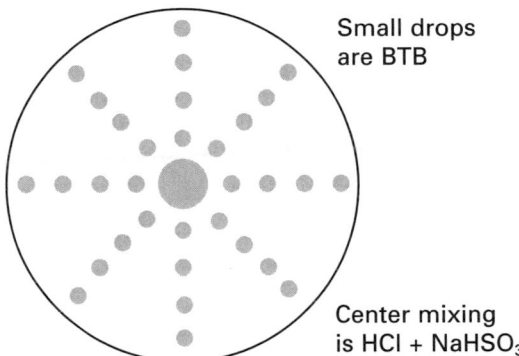

Small drops are BTB

Center mixing is HCl + $NaHSO_3$

2. Place a reaction surface over the grid and add small drops of bromthymol blue (BTB) in the pattern shown by the small circles. Make sure the drops do not touch one another.

3. Mix one drop each of hydrochloric acid (HCl) and sodium hydrogen sulfite ($NaHSO_3$) in the center of the pattern.

4. Place the cup or Petri dish over the grid and observe what happens.

5. If you plan to do You're The Chemist Activity 1, don't dispose of your materials yet.

Analyze and Conclude
Using your experimental data, record the answers to the following questions below your data table.

1. Describe in detail the changes you observed in the drops of BTB over time. Draw pictures to illustrate the changes.

2. Draw a series of pictures showing how one of the BTB drops might look over time if you could view the drop from the side.

3. The BTB changed even though you added nothing to it. If the mixture in the center circle produced a gas, would this explain the change in the drops of BTB? Use kinetic theory to explain your answer.

4. Translate the following word equation into a balanced chemical equation: Sodium hydrogen sulfite reacts with hydrochloric acid to produce sulfur dioxide gas, water, and sodium chloride.

You're The Chemist
The following small-scale activities allow you to develop your own procedures and analyze the results.

1. **Analyze It!** Carefully absorb the center mixture of the original experiment onto a cotton swab and replace it with one drop of NaOH and one drop of NH_4Cl. Describe what happens and explain in terms of kinetic theory. Ammonium chloride reacts with sodium hydroxide to produce ammonia gas, water, and sodium chloride. Write and balance a chemical equation to describe this reaction.

2. **Design It!** Design an experiment to observe the effect of the size of the BTB drops on the rate at which they change. Explain your results in terms of kinetic theory.

3. **Analyze It!** Repeat the original experiment, using KI in place of BTB and mixing sodium nitrite ($NaNO_2$) with hydrochloric acid at the center. Record your results. Write and balance an equation for the reaction. $NaNO_2$ reacts with HCl to produce nitrogen monoxide gas, water, sodium nitrate, and sodium chloride.

Key Concepts

🔑 **14.1 Properties of Gases**
- Gases are easily compressed because of the space between particles in a gas.
- The amount of gas (n), volume (V), and temperature (T) are factors that affect gas pressure (P).

🔑 **14.2 The Gas Laws**
- As the pressure of a gas increases, the volume decreases, if the temperature is constant.
- As the temperature of an enclosed gas increases, the volume increases, if the pressure is constant.
- As the temperature of an enclosed gas increases, the pressure increases, if the volume is constant.

- The combined gas law allows you to do calculations for situations in which only the amount of gas is constant.

🔑 **14.3 Ideal Gases**
- To calculate the number of moles of a contained gas requires an expression that contains the variable n.
- Real gases differ most from an ideal gas at low temperatures and high pressures.

🔑 **14.4 Gases: Mixtures and Movements**
- In a mixture of gases, the total pressure is the sum of the partial pressures of the gases.
- Gases of lower molar mass diffuse and effuse faster than gases of higher molar mass.

Vocabulary

- Boyle's law (p. 418)
- Charles's law (p. 420)
- combined gas law (p. 424)
- compressibility (p. 413)
- Dalton's law of partial pressures (p. 432)
- diffusion (p. 435)
- effusion (p. 435)
- Gay-Lussac's law (p. 422)
- Graham's law of effusion (p. 435)
- ideal gas constant (p. 426)
- ideal gas law (p. 426)
- partial pressure (p. 432)

Key Equations

- Boyle's law: $P_1 \times V_1 = P_2 \times V_2$

- Charles's law: $\dfrac{V_1}{T_1} = \dfrac{V_2}{T_2}$

- Gay-Lussac's law: $\dfrac{P_1}{T_1} = \dfrac{P_2}{T_2}$

- Combined gas law: $\dfrac{P_1 \times V_1}{T_1} = \dfrac{P_2 \times V_2}{T_2}$

- Ideal gas law: $P \times V = n \times R \times T$ or $PV = NRT$

- Dalton's law: $P_{total} = P_1 + P_2 + P_3 + \dots$

- Graham's law: $\dfrac{Rate_A}{Rate_B} = \sqrt{\dfrac{molar\ mass_B}{molar\ mass_A}}$

Organizing Information

Use these terms to construct a concept map that organizes the major ideas of this chapter.

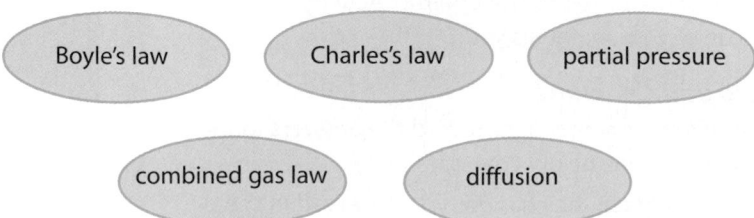

Boyle's law   Charles's law   partial pressure

combined gas law   diffusion

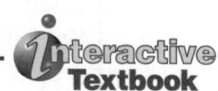

Concept Map 14 Solve the Concept Map with the help of an interactive guided tutorial.

— with **ChemASAP**

14.1 Properties of Gases

39. What happens to the particles in a gas when the gas is compressed?

40. Explain why heating a contained gas that is held at a constant volume increases its pressure.

41. Describe what happens to the volume of a balloon when it is taken outside on a cold winter day. Explain why the observed change happens.

42. A metal cylinder contains 1 mol of nitrogen gas. What will happen to the pressure if another mole of gas is added to the cylinder, but the temperature and volume do not change?

43. If a gas is compressed from 4 L to 1 L and the temperature remains constant, what happens to the pressure?

44. Use the drawing below to help explain why gas pressure decreases when gas is removed from a container with a fixed volume.

200 kPa   Decreasing Pressure

45. How does kinetic theory explain the compressibility of gases?

46. How does the vacuum in the flask used to store liquid nitrogen prevent heat transfer?

47. Oxygen is produced in the laboratory by heating potassium nitrate (KNO_3). The following data table gives the volume of oxygen produced at STP from varying quantities of KNO_3. Use the data to determine the mole ratio for KNO_3 and O_2 in this reaction.

Mass of KNO_3 (g)	Volume of O_2 (cL)
0.84	9.3
1.36	15.1
2.77	30.7
4.82	53.5
6.96	77.3

14.2 The Gas Laws

48. Write the mathematical equation for Charles's law and explain the symbols.

49. The gas in a closed container has a pressure of 3.00×10^2 kPa at 30°C (303 K). What will the pressure be if the temperature is lowered to -172°C (101 K)?

50. Calculate the volume of a gas (in L) at a pressure of 1.00×10^2 kPa if its volume at 1.20×10^2 kPa is 1.50×10^3 mL.

51. A gas with a volume of 4.0 L at 90.0 kPa expands until the pressure drops to 20.0 kPa. What is its new volume if the temperature doesn't change?

52. A gas with a volume of 3.00×10^2 mL at 150.0°C is heated until its volume is 6.00×10^2 mL. What is the new temperature of the gas if the pressure remains constant during the heating process?

53. Write the mathematical equation for the combined gas law, solved for T_2.

54. A sealed cylinder of gas contains nitrogen gas at 1.00×10^3 kPa pressure and a temperature of 20°C. When the cylinder is left in the sun, the temperature of the gas increases to 50°C. What is the new pressure in the cylinder?

55. Pressure and temperature can be related by the following equation.

$$\frac{P_1}{T_1} = \frac{P_2}{T_2}$$

Show how this equation can be derived from the combined gas law.

56. The manufacturer of an aerosol deodorant packaged in a 150-mL container plans to produce a container of the same size that will hold twice as much gas. How will the pressure of the gas in the new product compare with that of the gas in the original container?

57. Why must Kelvin temperature be used in calculations that involve gases?

58. Explain how using a pressure cooker reduces the time required to cook food.

59. The ratio of two variables is always a constant. What can you conclude about the relationship between the two variables?

60. A 3.50-L gas sample at 20°C and a pressure of 86.7 kPa expands to a volume of 8.00 L. The final pressure of the gas is 56.7 kPa. What is the final temperature of the gas, in degrees Celsius?

61. The graph below shows the direct relationship between volume and temperature for three different gas samples. Offer at least one explanation for why the graphs are not identical for the three samples. (*Hint:* What variables other than temperature and volume can be used to describe a gas?)

Volume vs. Temperature Data for Three Gases

62. A 0.10-L container holds 3.0×10^{20} molecules of H_2 at 100 kPa and 0°C.
   a. If the volume of a hydrogen molecule is 6.7×10^{-24} mL, what percentage of the volume of the gas is occupied by its molecules?

b. If the pressure is increased to 100,000 kPa, the volume of the gas is 1×10^{-4} L. What percent of the total volume do the hydrogen molecules now occupy?

14.3 Ideal Gases

63. Describe an ideal gas.

64. Explain why it is impossible for an ideal gas to exist.

65. What is the volume occupied by 1.24 mol of a gas at 35°C if the pressure is 96.2 kPa?

66. What volume will 12.0 g of oxygen gas (O_2) occupy at 25°C and a pressure of 52.7 kPa?

67. If 4.50 g of methane gas (CH_4) is in a 2.00-L container at 35°C, what is the pressure in the container?

68. A helium-filled weather balloon has a volume of 2.4×10^2 L at 99 kPa pressure and a temperature of 0°C. What is the mass of the helium in the balloon?

69. Explain the reasons why real gases deviate from ideal behavior.

70. What real gas comes closest to having the characteristics of an ideal gas? Explain your answer.

71. Many gases that have small molecules, such as N_2 and O_2, have the expected molar volume of 22.41 L at STP. However, other gases behave in a very non-ideal manner, even if extreme pressures and temperatures are not involved. The molar volumes of CH_4, CO_2, and NH_3 at STP are 22.37 L, 22.26 L, and 22.06 L, respectively. Explain the reasons for these large departures from the ideal.

14.4 Gases: Mixtures and Movements

72. In your own words, state Dalton's law of partial pressure.

73. Which gas effuses faster: hydrogen or chlorine? How much faster?

74. Which gas effuses faster at the same temperature: molecular oxygen or atomic argon?

75. Calculate the ratio of the velocity of helium atoms to the velocity of neon atoms at the same temperature.

76. Calculate the ratio of the velocity of helium atoms to the velocity of fluorine molecules at the same temperature.

77. Which of these gases effuses fastest?
  a. Cl_2 **b.** NO_2 **c.** NH_3 **d.** N_2

78. All the oxygen gas from a 10.0-L container at a pressure of 202 kPa is added to a 20.0-L container of hydrogen at a pressure of 505 kPa. After the transfer, what are the partial pressures of oxygen and hydrogen?

79. A mixture of ethyne gas (C_2H_2) and methane gas (CH_4) occupied a certain volume at a total pressure of 16.8 kPa. When the sample burned, the products were CO_2 gas and H_2O vapor. The CO_2 was collected and its pressure was found to be 25.2 kPa in the same volume and at the same temperature as the original mixture. What percentage of the original mixture was methane?

80. How would the number of particles of two gases compare if their partial pressures in a container were identical?

81. **Why does a balloon filled with helium deflate more quickly than a balloon filled with air?**

82. A certain gas effuses four times as fast as oxygen (O_2). What is the molar mass of the gas?

83. During an effusion experiment, a certain number of moles of an unknown gas passed through a tiny hole in 75 seconds. Under the same conditions, the same number of moles of oxygen gas passed through the hole in 30 seconds. What is the molar mass of the unknown gas?

84. Gases will diffuse from a region of higher concentration to a region of lower concentration. Why don't the gases in Earth's atmosphere escape into the near-vacuum of space?

85. Death Valley in California is at 86 m below sea level. Will the partial pressure of oxygen in Death Valley be the same, lower, or higher than the partial pressure of oxygen at sea level? Give a reason for your answer.

86. The following reaction takes place in a sealed 40.0-L container at a temperature of 120°C.

$$4NH_3(g) + 5O_2(g) \longrightarrow 4NO(g) + 6H_2O(g)$$

  a. When 34.0 g of NH_3 reacts with 96.0 g of O_2, what is the partial pressure of NO in the sealed container?
  b. What is the total pressure in the container?

Test-Taking Tip

Constructing a Diagram You may be asked to draw a diagram or make changes to an existing drawing. Sketch lightly at first so you can erase easily if you need to, or do a sketch on a separate piece of paper. Once you are sure of your answer, draw the final diagram.

Regents Practice Exam

Part A

For each statement or question write the number of the word or expression that, of those given, best completes the statement or answers the question.

1. Which of the following elements is a metal?
   (1) arsenic   (3) tungsten
   (2) xenon   (4) sulfur

2. How many electrons, protons, and neutrons are in an atom of lead-206?
   (1) 82 protons and neutrons and 124 electrons
   (2) 82 protons, neutrons, and electrons
   (3) 82 protons and electrons and 124 neutrons
   (4) 206 protons, neutrons, and electrons

3. What is the mathematical relationship between the Kelvin and Celsius temperature scales?
   (1) $K = °C + 273$ (3) $K = °C - 273$
   (2) $°C = K + 273$ (4) $273 = °C + K$

4. Aluminum oxide is formed from its elements. What are the coefficients in the balanced chemical equation for this reaction?

   $$Al(s) + O_2(g) \longrightarrow Al_2O_3(s)$$

   (1) 1, 1, 1   (3) 3, 2, 1
   (2) 4, 3, 2   (4) 2, 3, 1

Part B-1

For each statement or question write the number of the word or expression that, of those given, best completes the statement or answers the question.

5. Which element is most likely to form a compound with strontium?
   (1) neon   (3) selenium
   (2) tin   (4) bromine

6. A gas in a balloon at constant pressure has a volume of 120.0 mL at −123°C. What is its volume at 27.0°C?
   (1) 60.0 mL   (3) 26.5 mL
   (2) 240.0 mL   (4) 546 mL

7. If the Kelvin temperature of a gas is tripled and the volume is doubled, the new pressure will be
   (1) 1/6 the original pressure
   (2) 2/3 the original pressure
   (3) 3/2 the original pressure
   (4) 5 times the original pressure

8. Which of the following changes would increase the pressure of a gas in a closed container?
   (1) Part of the gas is removed.

(2) The container size is increased.
(3) Temperature is increased.
(4) The kinetic energy of the particles is decreased.

9. A real gas behaves most nearly like an ideal gas
   (1) at high pressure and low temperature
   (2) at low pressure and high temperature
   (3) at low pressure and low temperature
   (4) at high pressure and high temperature

Use the following graphs to answer Questions 10 and 11. A graph may be used once, more than once, or not at all.

Graph A

Graph B

Graph C

10. Which graph shows a directly proportional relationship?
    (1) Graph A   (3) Graph C
    (2) Graph B   (4) None of the graphs

11. Which graph shows an inversely proportional relationship?
    (1) Graph A   (3) Graph C
    (2) Graph B   (4) None of the graphs

Part B-2

Answer each of the following questions.

12. A metal sample has a mass of 9.92 g and measures 4.5 cm × 1.3 cm × 1.6 mm. What is the density of the metal?

13. Name each of the following compounds.
    a. $SnBr_2$ c. $Mg(OH)_2$
    b. $BaSO_4$ d. IF_5

14. Calculate the molar mass of each of the following substances.
   a. $Ca(CH_3CO_2)_2$ **c.** $C_{12}H_{22}O_{11}$
   b. H_3PO_4 **d.** $Pb(NO_3)_2$

15. Calculate the molecular formula of each of the following compounds.
   a. The empirical formula is C_2H_4O and the molar mass is 88 g.
   b. The empirical formula is CH and the molar mass is 104 g.

16. What type of reaction is each of the following?
   a. Calcium reacts with water to form calcium hydroxide and hydrogen gas.
   b. Mercury and oxygen are prepared by heating mercury oxide.

17. Write a balanced chemical equation for each of the following reactions.
   a. Tetraphosphorus decoxide reacts with water to form phosphoric acid.
   b. Aluminum hydroxide and hydrogen sulfide form when aluminum sulfide reacts with water.

18. Calculate the percent composition of 2-propanol (C_3H_7OH).

19. Explain why a gas expands until it takes the shape and volume of its container.

20. Use the following drawing to explain how gas pressure is produced.

Container wall

Use the drawing to answer Questions 21 and 22.

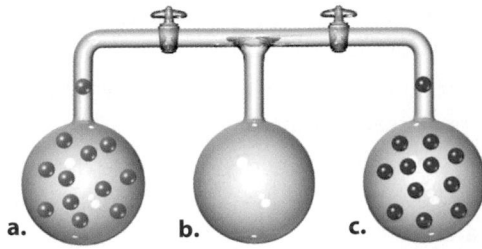

21. Bulb A and bulb C contain different gases. Bulb B contains no gas. If the valves between the bulbs are opened, how will the particles of gas be distributed when the system reaches equilibrium? Assume none of the particles are in the tubes that connect the bulbs.

22. Make a three-bulb drawing with 6 blue spheres in bulb A, 9 green spheres in bulb B, and 12 red spheres in bulb C. Then draw the setup to represent the distribution of gases after the valves are opened and the system reaches equilibrium.

Part C

Answer each of the following questions.

Use this description to answer Questions 23 and 24.

A teacher adds 1 mL of water to an empty metal soda can. The teacher heats the can over a burner until the water boils and then quickly plunges the can upside down in an ice-water bath. The can immediately collapses inward as though crushed in a trash compactor.

23. Use kinetic theory to explain why the can collapsed inward.

24. If the experiment were done with a dry can, would the results be similar? Explain.

25. Why do aerosol containers display the warning, "Do not incinerate?"

26. The photograph shows a tube with cotton balls at each end. The cotton ball at the left was soaked in hydrochloric acid. The cotton ball on the right was soaked with a solution of ammonia. When these compounds react, they form a white solid, ammonium chloride. Based on the location of the ammonium chloride in the tube, which gas moves at a faster rate, hydrogen chloride or ammonia? Explain.

Water and Aqueous Systems

Water is an amazing liquid that makes plant and animal life on Earth possible.

INQUIRY Activity

Observing Surface Tension

Materials

waxed paper, ruler, teaspoon, tap water, cup, liquid dish detergent

Procedure

1. Place a 15-cm square of waxed paper on a flat surface.

2. Drop 1/3 teaspoon of water from a height of about 20 cm onto the center of the paper.

3. Add 1 drop of detergent to 1/2 cup of water and stir.

4. Repeat Steps 1 and 2 using the diluted detergent in place of water.

5. You may wish to repeat this activity with squares of aluminum foil, clear wrap, and writing paper.

Think About It

1. What do you observe when you drop water onto the waxed paper surface?

2. What do you observe when you use diluted detergent instead of water?

3. Use your results to suggest how the detergent may have changed the physical properties of water.

15.1 Water and Its Properties

New York Standards: M1.1d, 5.2l–n

Connecting to Your World

In December of 1968, when the Apollo 8 astronauts first saw their home planet from a distance of thousands of kilometers, they affectionately called it the big blue marble. Water covers about three-quarters of Earth's surface. In addition to making up Earth's oceans, water forms the polar ice caps and cycles through the atmosphere. All life forms that are known to exist are made mostly of water. In this section, you will learn about the properties of water and what makes this unique substance essential to life on Earth.

Guide for Reading

Key Concepts
- How can you account for the high surface tension and low vapor pressure of water?
- How would you describe the structure of ice?

Vocabulary
surface tension
surfactant

Reading Strategy
Monitoring Your Understanding
Before you read, list what you already know about water and aqueous systems. After you read, write what you have learned. Is what you already knew correct? If not, how do you need to revise that information?

Water in the Liquid State

When you turn on the faucet, you expect that water will stream out to supply all your needs. You couldn't live without water, nor could all the plants and animals, like those in Figure 15.1 that share space on the "big blue marble." Besides the water visible on Earth's surface, immense reserves of water exist deep underground. Water in the form of ice and snow dominates the polar regions of Earth. Icebergs drift in the oceans, and snow blankets the temperate zones in winter. Water vapor from the evaporation of surface water and from steam spouted from geysers and volcanoes is always present in Earth's atmosphere.

Figure 15.1 Water is vital to life. Animals that live on the grasslands depend on watering holes, such as the one shown here.

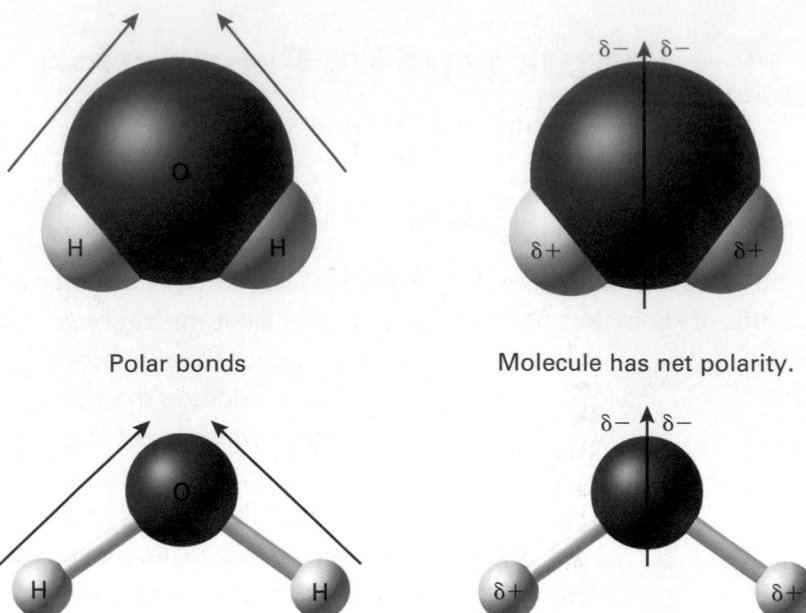

Polar bonds

Molecule has net polarity.

Figure 15.2 In a water molecule, the bond polarities are equal, but the two poles do not cancel each other because a water molecule is bent. The molecule as a whole is polar. **Applying Concepts** *Which element in water has the higher electronegativity?*

Interactive Textbook

Animation 19 See how hydrogen bonding results in the unique properties of water.

—— with **ChemASAP**

Recall that water is a simple triatomic molecule, H_2O. The oxygen atom forms a covalent bond to each of the hydrogen atoms. Because of its greater electronegativity, oxygen attracts the electron pair of the covalent O—H bond to a greater extent than hydrogen. As a result, the oxygen atom acquires a partial negative charge ($\delta-$). The less electronegative hydrogen atoms acquire partial positive charges ($\delta+$). Thus, the O—H bonds are highly polar. How do the polarities of the two O—H bonds affect the polarity of the molecule? The shape of the molecule is the determining factor. The bond angle of the water molecule is approximately 105°, which gives the molecule a bent shape. The two O—H bond polarities do not cancel, so the water molecule as a whole is polar. The net polarity of the water molecule is illustrated in Figure 15.2.

In general, polar molecules are attracted to one another by dipole interactions. The negative end of one molecule attracts the positive end of another molecule. Figure 15.3 shows how this intermolecular attraction among water molecules results in the formation of hydrogen bonds. **Many unique and important properties of water—including its high surface tension and low vapor pressure—result from hydrogen bonding.**

Figure 15.3 The polarity of the water molecule results in hydrogen bonding. **ⓐ** Partial negative charges are on each oxygen atom; partial positive charges are on the hydrogen atom. **ⓑ** Because of polarity, hydrogen bonds form. **Inferring** *To form a hydrogen bond, what must be true about the hydrogen and the element to which it is hydrogen bonded?*

Liquid water

Figure 15.4 Surface tension makes it possible for some insects, such as this water strider, to walk on water. Water molecules at the surface of the water drop above cannot form hydrogen bonds with air molecules, so they are drawn into the body of the liquid, producing surface tension.

Surface Tension Have you ever seen a glass so filled with water that the water surface is not flat but bulges above the rim? Or have you noticed that water forms nearly spherical droplets at the end of a medicine dropper or when sprayed on a greasy surface? The surface of water acts like a skin, as the water strider shown in Figure 15.4 demonstrates. This skinlike property of water's surface is explained by water's ability to form hydrogen bonds. The molecules within the body of the liquid form hydrogen bonds with other molecules that surround them on all sides. The attractive forces on each of these molecules are balanced. However, water molecules at the surface of the liquid experience an unbalanced attraction. You can see in Figure 15.4 that the water molecules are hydrogen-bonded on only one side of the drop. As a result, water molecules at the surface tend to be drawn inward. The inward force, or pull, that tends to minimize the surface area of a liquid is called **surface tension.**

All liquids have a surface tension, but water's surface tension is higher than most. The surface tension of water tends to hold a drop of liquid in a spherical shape. The drop is not a perfect sphere because the force of gravity tends to pull it down, causing it to flatten. This is why, on some surfaces, water tends to bead up rather than spread out. It is possible to decrease the surface tension of water by adding a surfactant. A **surfactant** is any substance that interferes with the hydrogen bonding between water molecules and thereby reduces surface tension. Soaps and detergents are surfactants. Adding a detergent to beads of water on a greasy surface reduces surface tension, causing the beads of water to collapse and spread out.

Vapor Pressure Hydrogen bonding between water molecules also explains water's unusually low vapor pressure. Remember that the vapor pressure of a liquid is the result of molecules escaping from the surface of the liquid and entering the vapor phase. Because hydrogen bonds hold water molecules to one another, the tendency of these molecules to escape is low and evaporation is slow. Imagine what would happen if it were not. All the lakes and oceans, with their large surface areas, would tend to evaporate!

interactive Textbook

Animation 20
Discover how some insects can walk on water.

────── with **ChemASAP**

 What is surface tension?

Quick LAB

Surfactants

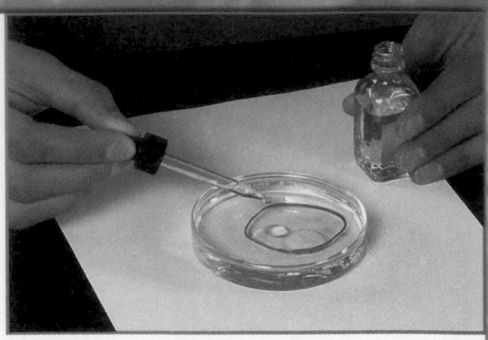

Purpose
To observe an unusual surface property of water that results from hydrogen bonding.

Materials
- shallow dish or Petri dish
- water
- paper clip
- rubber band, approximately 2 inches in diameter
- micropipets or droppers (2)
- vegetable oil
- liquid dish detergent

Procedure
1. Thoroughly clean and dry the dish.
2. Fill the dish almost full with water. Dry your hands.
3. Being careful not to break the surface, gently place the paper clip on the water. Observe what happens.
4. Repeat Steps 1 and 2.
5. Gently place the open rubber band on the water.
6. Slowly add oil drop by drop onto the water encircled by the rubber band until that water is covered with a layer of oil. Observe for 15 seconds.
7. Allow one drop of dish detergent to fall onto the center of the oil layer. Observe the system for 15 seconds.

Analyze and Conclude
1. What happened to the paper clip in Step 3? Why?
2. If a paper clip becomes wet, does it float? Explain your answer.
3. What shape did the rubber band take when the water inside it was covered with oil? Why did it take the observed shape?
4. Describe what happened when dish detergent was dropped onto the layer of oil.

Water in the Solid State

You have seen that water in the liquid state exhibits some unique properties. The same is true for water in the solid state. For example, ice cubes float in your glass of iced tea because solid water has a lower density than liquid water. This is not usual for liquids. As a typical liquid cools, it begins to contract and its density increases gradually. Increasing density means that the molecules of the liquid move closer together so that a given volume of the liquid contains more molecules and thus more mass. If the cooling continues, the liquid eventually solidifies with a density greater than the density of the liquid. Because the density of a typical solid is greater than that of the corresponding liquid, the solid sinks in its own liquid.

As water begins to cool, it behaves initially like a typical liquid. It contracts slightly and its density gradually increases, as shown in Table 15.1. Notice that at 4°C, the density of water is at its maximum of 1.000 g/cm³. When the temperature of the water falls below 4°C, the density of water actually starts to decrease. Below 4°C, water no longer behaves like a typical liquid. Ice, which forms at 0°C, has about a 10 percent lower density than water at 0°C. You may have noticed that ice begins to form at the surface of a pond when the temperature reaches 0°C, but the ice does not sink. It floats at the surface, making ice skating and ice fishing possible. Ice is one of only a few solids that float in their own liquid.

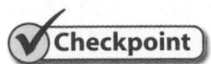 **Checkpoint** *At what temperature does water have its maximum density?*

Table 15.1	
Density of Liquid Water and Ice	
Temperature (°C)	**Density (g/cm³)**
100 (liquid water)	0.9584
50	0.9881
25	0.9971
10	0.9997
4	1.000*
0 (liquid water)	0.9998
0 (ice)	0.9168

*Most dense

Hydrogen bonds

Side view

End view

Ice

Figure 15.5 Extensive hydrogen bonding in ice holds the water molecules farther apart in a more ordered arrangement than in liquid water. The hexagonal symmetry of a snowflake reflects the structure of the ice crystal.

Why is ice less dense than liquid water? As you can see in Figure 15.5, hydrogen bonds hold the water molecules in place in the solid phase. **The structure of ice is a regular open framework of water molecules arranged like a honeycomb.** When ice melts, the framework collapses and the water molecules pack closer together, making liquid water more dense than ice.

The fact that ice floats has important consequences for organisms. A layer of ice on the top of a pond acts as an insulator for the water beneath, preventing it from freezing solid except under extreme conditions. Because the liquid water at the bottom of an otherwise frozen pond is warmer than 0°C, fish and other aquatic life are better able to survive. If ice were denser than liquid water, bodies of water would tend to freeze solid during the winter months, destroying many types of organisms.

Ice melts at 0°C. This is a high melting temperature for a molecule with such a low molar mass. A considerable amount of energy is required to return water molecules in the solid state to the liquid state. The heat absorbed when 1 g of water changes from a solid to a liquid is 334 J. This same amount of energy is needed to raise the temperature of 1 g of liquid water from 0°C to 80°C.

15.1 Section Assessment

1. **Key Concept** What causes the high surface tension and low vapor pressure of water?

2. **Key Concept** How would you describe the structure of ice?

3. What effect does a surfactant have on the surface tension of water?

4. What are two factors that determine how spherical a drop of a liquid will be?

5. The molecules water (H_2O) and methane (CH_4) have similar masses, but methane changes from a gas to a liquid at −161°C. Water becomes a gas at 100°C. What could account for the difference?

Writing ▸ **Activity**

Short Story Use your imagination to write a short children's story about a water strider whose "magic" ability to walk on water saved him from a predator bird. For your young readers, be sure to include an explanation of the life-saving magic.

Textbook

Assessment 15.1 Test yourself on the concepts in Section 15.1.

with **ChemASAP**

15.2 Homogeneous Aqueous Systems

 New York Standards: 3.1oo, 3.1rr, 3.3f

Guide for Reading

 Key Concepts

- What is the difference between a solvent and a solute?
- What happens in the solution process?
- Why are all ionic compounds electrolytes?
- How do you write the formula for a hydrate?

Vocabulary

aqueous solution
solvent
solute
solvation
electrolyte
nonelectrolyte
strong electrolyte
weak electrolyte
hydrate

Reading Strategy

Relating Text and Visuals As you read, look carefully at Figure 15.7. In your notebook, explain in your own words how this illustration helps clarify the process of solvation.

Connecting to Your World

Is it possible to read by the light of a glowing pickle? Although it sounds absurd, an ordinary dill pickle from the deli can be a source of light! Iron or copper electrodes are inserted into the ends of the pickle and connected to a source of alternating electric current. After a time, during which the pickle becomes hot and produces water vapor, the pickle begins to glow. The mechanism by which the light is generated is not fully understood, but it is clear that conduction of electricity by the pickle is an important factor. In this section you will learn what kind of solution conducts electricity.

Solvents and Solutes

Water dissolves so many of the substances that it comes in contact with that you won't find chemically pure water in nature. Even the tap water you drink is a solution that contains varying amounts of dissolved minerals and gases. An **aqueous solution** is water that contains dissolved substances. In a solution, the dissolving medium is the **solvent,** and the dissolved particles are the **solute.** A solvent dissolves the solute. The solute becomes dispersed in the solvent. Solvents and solutes may be gases, liquids, or solids.

Recall that solutions are homogeneous mixtures. They are also stable mixtures. For example, sodium chloride does not settle out when its solutions are allowed to stand, provided other conditions, such as temperature, remain constant. Solute particles can be atoms, ions, or molecules, and their average diameters are usually less than 1 nm (10^{-9} m). Therefore, if you filter a solution through filter paper, both the solute and the solvent pass through the filter, as Figure 15.6 shows.

Substances that dissolve most readily in water include ionic compounds and polar covalent molecules. Nonpolar covalent molecules, such as methane, and compounds found in oil, grease, and gasoline, do not dissolve in water. However, oil and grease will dissolve in gasoline. To understand this difference, you must know more about the structures of the solvent and the solute and what attractions exist between them.

Figure 15.6 A solution cannot be separated by filtration. The small size of the solute particles allows them to pass through filter paper.

Solvated ions

Surface of ionic solid

Figure 15.7 When an ionic solid dissolves, the ions become solvated or surrounded by solvent molecules. **Inferring** *Why do the water molecules orient themselves differently around the anions and the cations?*

The Solution Process

Water molecules are in continuous motion because of their kinetic energy. When a crystal of sodium chloride is placed in water, the water molecules collide with it. Remember that a water molecule is polar, with a partial negative charge on the oxygen atom and partial positive charges on the hydrogen atoms. The polar solvent molecules (H_2O) attract the solute ions (Na^+, Cl^-). **As individual solute ions break away from the crystal, the negatively and positively charged ions become surrounded by solvent molecules and the ionic crystal dissolves.** The process by which the positive and negative ions of an ionic solid become surrounded by solvent molecules is called **solvation.** Figure 15.7 shows a model of the solvation of an ionic solid such as sodium chloride.

In some ionic compounds, the attractions among the ions in the crystals are stronger than the attractions exerted by water. These compounds cannot be solvated to any significant extent and are therefore nearly insoluble. Barium sulfate ($BaSO_4$) and calcium carbonate ($CaCO_3$) are examples of nearly insoluble ionic compounds.

Figure 15.8 shows that oil and water do not mix. But what about oil in gasoline? Both oil and gasoline are composed of nonpolar molecules. The attractive forces that hold two oil molecules together are similar in magnitude to the forces that hold two gasoline molecules together. Oil molecules can easily separate and replace gasoline molecules to form a solution. As a rule, polar solvents such as water dissolve ionic compounds and polar compounds; nonpolar solvents such as gasoline dissolve nonpolar compounds. This relationship can be summed up in the expression "like dissolves like."

Checkpoint *What is meant by solvation?*

Interactive Textbook

Simulation 18 Explore the nature of solute-solvent interactions.

—with **ChemASAP**

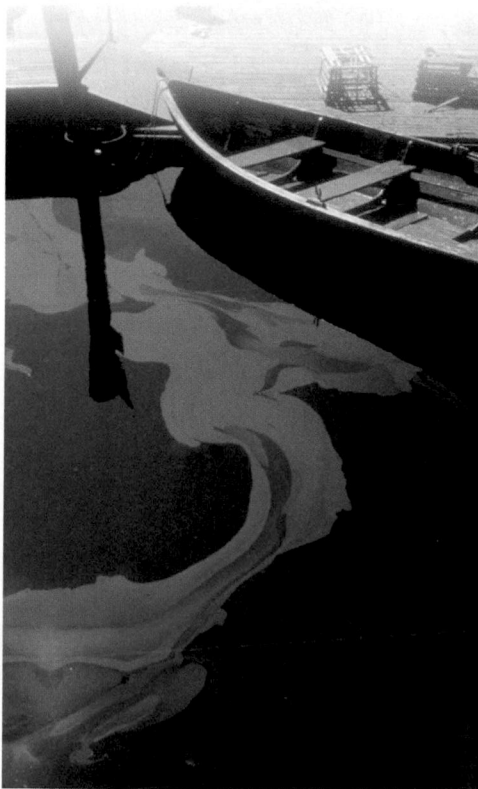

Figure 15.8 Oil and water do not mix. Oil is less dense than water, so it floats on top. The colors result from the bending of light rays by the thin film of oil.

Wastewater Engineer

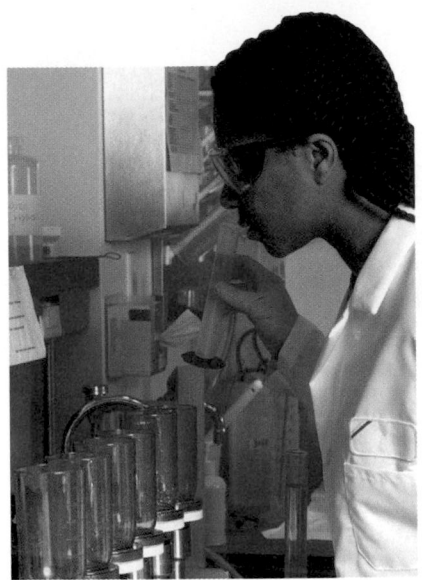

Wastewater must be physically and chemically treated before it is returned to the environment or recycled for human use. A wastewater engineer is responsible for monitoring this process. These engineers control the amount of water treated, the level of treatment, and the quality of water produced. When water is received at a treatment plant, a wastewater engineer oversees primary treatment that involves filtering the water for solids and debris. The engineer then adds microorganisms to the water that convert the remaining dissolved organic matter into solids that can be removed as sludge. If this water is to be released into a river or stream, the engineer then tests the water for levels of remaining organic compounds. If amounts of these compounds fall below recommended levels, the water is safe to be released.

Production of drinking water often requires additional steps. The engineer must test the water for nitrogen and phosphorus compounds that would need to be removed. The engineer then disinfects the water using chlorine, ozone, or other disinfectants, and might add fluoride to strengthen consumers' teeth.

Interpreting the results of tests requires experience and an understanding of the entire chemical, and often biological, environment. Wastewater engineers usually have a degree in engineering. They must take courses in water toxicology, organic chemistry, and environmental biology.

Go Online
PHSchool.com

For: Careers in Chemistry
Visit: PHSchool.com
Web Code: cdb-1152

Electrolytes and Nonelectrolytes

Remember the glowing pickle that you read about in *Connecting to Your World?* The pickle contained an electrolyte. An **electrolyte** is a compound that conducts an electric current when it is in an aqueous solution or in the molten state. Conduction of electricity requires ions that are mobile and thus able to carry an electrical current. **All ionic compounds are electrolytes because they dissociate into ions.** Sodium chloride, copper(II) sulfate, and sodium hydroxide are typical water-soluble electrolytes. Barium sulfate is an ionic compound that cannot conduct electricity in aqueous solution because it is insoluble, but it can conduct in the molten state.

A compound that does not conduct an electric current in either aqueous solution or the molten state is called a **nonelectrolyte.** Many molecular compounds are nonelectrolytes because they are not composed of ions. Most compounds of carbon, such as sugar (sucrose) and rubbing alcohol (1-propanol), are nonelectrolytes.

✓**Checkpoint** *How do electrolytes and nonelectrolytes differ?*

Some polar molecular compounds are nonelectrolytes in the pure state, but become electrolytes when they dissolve in water. This occurs because such compounds ionize in solution. For example, neither ammonia ($NH_3(g)$) nor hydrogen chloride ($HCl(g)$) is an electrolyte in the pure state. Yet an aqueous solution of ammonia conducts electricity because ammonium ions (NH_4^+) and hydroxide ions (OH^-) form when ammonia dissolves in water.

$$NH_3(g) + H_2O(l) \longrightarrow NH_4^+(aq) + OH^-(aq)$$

Similarly, in aqueous solution, hydrogen chloride produces hydronium ions (H_3O^+) and chloride ions (Cl^-). An aqueous solution of hydrogen chloride conducts electricity and is therefore an electrolyte.

$$HCl(g) + H_2O(l) \longrightarrow H_3O^+(aq) + Cl^-(aq)$$

Not all electrolytes conduct an electric current to the same degree. In the simple conductivity test shown in Figure 15.9, a bulb glows brightly when electrodes attached to it are immersed in a sodium chloride solution. The bright glow shows that sodium chloride is a **strong electrolyte** because nearly all the dissolved sodium chloride exists as separate Na^+ and Cl^- ions. The ions move in solution and conduct an electric current. All soluble salts, inorganic acids, and inorganic bases are strong electrolytes.

The bulb glows dimly when the electrodes are immersed in a mercury(II) chloride solution because mercury(II) chloride is a weak electrolyte. A **weak electrolyte** conducts electricity poorly because only a fraction of the solute in the solution exists as ions. Other weak electrolytes are ammonia (NH_3) and organic acids and bases. In a solution of glucose, the bulb does not glow. Glucose ($C_6H_{12}O_6$) is a molecular compound. It does not form ions, so it is a nonelectrolyte.

✔Checkpoint **Name an electrolyte and a nonelectrolyte.**

interactive **Textbook**

Simulation 19 Simulate the behavior of electrolytes and nonelectrolytes in a circuit and at the atomic level.

——with **ChemASAP**

Figure 15.9 A solution conducts electricity if it contains ions. ⓐ Sodium chloride, a strong electrolyte, is nearly 100% dissociated into ions in water. ⓑ Mercury(II) chloride, a weak electrolyte, is only partially dissociated in water. ⓒ Glucose, a nonelectrolyte, does not dissociate in water.

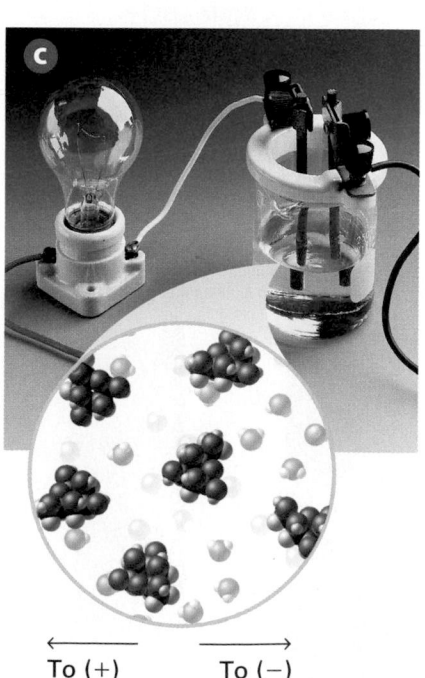

| To (+) electrode | To (−) electrode | To (+) electrode | To (−) electrode | To (+) electrode | To (−) electrode |

Hydrates

When an aqueous solution of copper(II) sulfate is allowed to evaporate, deep-blue crystals of copper(II) sulfate pentahydrate are deposited. The chemical formula for this compound is $CuSO_4 \cdot 5H_2O$. Water molecules are an integral part of the crystal structure of copper(II) sulfate pentahydrate and many other substances. The water contained in a crystal is called the water of hydration or water of crystallization. A compound that contains water of hydration is called a **hydrate**. 🔑 **In writing the formula of a hydrate, use a dot to connect the formula of the compound and the number of water molecules per formula unit.** Crystals of copper(II) sulfate pentahydrate always contain five molecules of water for each copper and sulfate ion pair. The deep-blue crystals are dry to the touch. They are unchanged in composition or appearance in normally moist air. But when heated above 100°C, the crystals lose their water of hydration. Figure 15.10 shows how the blue crystals of $CuSO_4 \cdot 5H_2O$ crumble to a white anhydrous powder that has the formula $CuSO_4$. If anhydrous copper(II) sulfate is treated with water, the blue pentahydrate is regenerated.

$$CuSO_4 \cdot 5H_2O(s) \underset{-heat}{\overset{+heat}{\rightleftharpoons}} CuSO_4(s) + 5H_2O(g)$$

Another compound that changes color in the presence of moisture is cobalt(II) chloride. A piece of filter paper that has been dipped in an aqueous solution of cobalt(II) chloride and then dried is blue in color (anhydrous $CoCl_2$). But as you can see in Figure 15.11, when the paper is exposed to moist air, it turns pink because of the formation of the hydrate cobalt(II) chloride hexahydrate ($CoCl_2 \cdot 6H_2O$). The blue paper could be used to test for the presence of water.

Some familiar hydrates are listed in Table 15.2 and shown in Figure 15.12. Each one contains a fixed quantity of water and has a definite composition.

Figure 15.11 Paper treated with anhydrous cobalt(II) chloride is blue. In the presence of moisture the paper turns pink. **Inferring** *How could you change the pink paper back to blue?*

Table 15.2

Some Common Hydrates		
Formula	**Chemical name**	**Common name**
$MgSO_4 \cdot 7H_2O$	magnesium sulfate heptahydrate	Epsom salt
$Ba(OH)_2 \cdot 8H_2O$	barium hydroxide octahydrate	
$CaCl_2 \cdot 2H_2O$	calcium chloride dihydrate	
$CuSO_4 \cdot 5H_2O$	copper(II) sulfate pentahydrate	blue vitriol
$Na_2SO_4 \cdot 10H_2O$	sodium sulfate decahydrate	Glauber's salt
$KAl(SO_4)_2 \cdot 12H_2O$	potassium aluminum sulfate dodecahydrate	alum
$Na_2B_4O_7 \cdot 10H_2O$	sodium tetraborate decahydrate	borax
$FeSO_4 \cdot 7H_2O$	iron(II) sulfate heptahydrate	green vitriol
$H_2SO_4 \cdot H_2O$	sulfuric acid hydrate (mp 8.6°C)	

Efflorescent Hydrates The forces holding the water molecules in hydrates are not very strong, so the water is easily lost and regained. Because the water molecules are held by weak forces, hydrates often have an appreciable vapor pressure. If a hydrate has a vapor pressure higher than the pressure of water vapor in the air, the hydrate will lose its water of hydration or effloresce. For example, $CuSO_4 \cdot 5H_2O$ has a vapor pressure of about 1.0 kPa at room temperature. The average pressure of water vapor at room temperature is about 1.3 kPa. Copper(II) sulfate pentahydrate is stable until the humidity decreases. When the vapor pressure drops below 1.0 kPa, the hydrate effloresces. Washing soda, or sodium carbonate decahydrate ($Na_2CO_3 \cdot 10H_2O$), is efflorescent. As the crystals lose water of hydration, they effloresce and become coated with a white powder of anhydrous sodium carbonate (Na_2CO_3).

Hygroscopic Hydrates Hydrated salts that have a low vapor pressure remove water from moist air to form higher hydrates. These hydrates and other compounds that remove moisture from air are called hygroscopic. For example, calcium chloride monohydrate spontaneously absorbs a second molecule of water when exposed to moist air.

$$CaCl_2 \cdot H_2O(s) \xrightarrow{\text{moist air}} CaCl_2 \cdot 2H_2O(s)$$

Calcium chloride is used as a desiccant in the laboratory. A desiccant is a substance used to absorb moisture from the air and create a dry atmosphere. For example, anhydrous $CaCl_2$ can be placed in the bottom of a tightly sealed container called a desiccator. Substances that must be kept dry are stored inside. A solid desiccant such as calcium sulfate ($CaSO_4$) can also be added to a liquid solvent to keep it dry. A bottle labeled "dry ethanol" may have solid calcium sulfate at the bottom. The calcium sulfate does not dissolve appreciably in the solvent but absorbs water from the ethanol and keeps it dry. When a desiccant has absorbed all the water it can hold, the salt can be returned to its anhydrous state by heating.

Figure 15.12 Epsom salts can be used as a mild laxative. Borax is a strong cleaner, water softener, and fireproofing agent.

✓Checkpoint *What is a hygroscopic hydrate?*

Suppose you are measuring a mass of Na_2CO_3 for a chemical reaction. You want to use the hydrate of the compound because it is less expensive than the anhydrous compound. To determine what percent of the hydrate is water, first determine the mass of the number of moles of water in one mole of hydrate. Then determine the total mass of the hydrate. The percent by mass of water can be calculated using this equation.

$$\text{percent } H_2O = \frac{\text{mass of water}}{\text{mass of hydrate}} \times 100\%$$

SAMPLE PROBLEM 15.1

Finding the Percent of Water in a Hydrate

Calculate the percent by mass of water in washing soda, sodium carbonate decahydrate ($Na_2CO_3 \cdot 10H_2O$).

1 **Analyze** *List the known and the unknown.*

Known
• Formula of hydrate = $Na_2CO_3 \cdot 10H_2O$

Unknown
• percent H_2O = ? %

To determine the percent by mass, determine the mass of 10 moles of water and the mass of one mole of the hydrated compound. Substitute these values into the following equation and solve.

$$\text{Percent } H_2O = \frac{\text{mass of water}}{\text{mass of hydrate}} \times 100\%$$

2 **Calculate** *Solve for the unknown.*

$$\text{mass of 10 } H_2O = 180 \text{ g}$$

$$\text{mass of } Na_2CO_3 \cdot 10H_2O = 286.0 \text{ g}$$

$$\text{percent } H_2O = \frac{1.80 \times 10^2 \text{ g}}{286.0 \text{ g}} \times 100\% = 62.9\%$$

3 **Evaluate** *Does the result make sense?*

Because the mass of the water accounts for more than half the molar mass of the compound, a percentage greater than 50% should be expected. The answer should have three significant figures.

Practice Problems

6. What is the percent by mass of water in $CuSO_4 \cdot 5H_2O$?

7. Calculate the percent by mass of water in calcium chloride hexahydrate ($CaCl_2 \cdot 6H_2O$).

Math Handbook

For help with percents go to page R72.

interactive Textbook

Problem-Solving 15.6
Solve Problem 6 with the help of an interactive guided tutorial.

— with **ChemASAP**

If you need 5.00 g of anyhydrous Na_2CO_3 for your reaction, how many grams of $Na_2CO_3 \cdot 10H_2O$ could you use instead? You know now that 62.9% of the hydrate is water, so 37.1 g out of every 100 g is Na_2CO_3 (100.0 g − 62.9 g = 37.1 g). Calculate how much hydrate you need as follows.

$$5.00 \text{ g } Na_2CO_3 \times \frac{(100 \text{ g } Na_2CO_3 \cdot 10H_2O)}{37.1 \text{ g } Na_2CO_3} = 13.5 \text{ g } Na_2CO_3 \cdot 10H_2O$$

Figure 15.13 Deliquescent substances can remove water from the air. **a** Sodium hydroxide pellets absorb moisture from the air. **b** Eventually a solution is formed. **Applying Concepts** *Identify the solvent and the solute.*

Deliquescent Compounds Have you ever noticed the small packets of silica gel that are often packaged with electronic equipment and leather goods? Although the structure of silica gel is not the same as a hydrated salt, it is a hygroscopic substance used to absorb moisture from the air to prevent damage to sensitive equipment and materials. Some compounds are so hygroscopic that they become wet when exposed to normally moist air. These compounds are deliquescent, which means that they remove sufficient water from the air to dissolve completely and form solutions. Figure 15.13 shows that pellets of sodium hydroxide are deliquescent. For this reason, containers of NaOH and other chemicals should always be tightly stoppered and the chemicals should never be touched by fingers. The solution formed by a deliquescent substance has a lower vapor pressure than that of the water in the air.

Go Online

For: Links on Deliquescent Compounds
Visit: www.SciLinks.org
Web Code: cdn-1152

15.2 Section Assessment

8. 🔑 **Key Concept** In the formation of a solution, how does the solvent differ from the solute?

9. 🔑 **Key Concept** Describe what happens to the solute and the solvent when an ionic compound dissolves in water.

10. 🔑 **Key Concept** Why are all ionic compounds electrolytes?

11. 🔑 **Key Concept** How do you write the formula for a hydrate?

12. Which of the following substances dissolve to a significant extent in water? Explain your answer in terms of polarity.
   a. CH_4 **b.** KCl   **c.** He
   d. $MgSO_4$ **e.** Sucrose   **f.** $NaHCO_3$

13. Identify the solvent and the solute in vinegar, a dilute aqueous solution of acetic acid.

14. Distinguish between efflorescent and hygroscopic substances.

15. Calculate the percent by mass of water in magnesium sulfate heptahydrate ($MgSO_4 \cdot 7H_2O$).

Connecting ▶ **Concepts**

Percent Composition Review Sample Problem 10.10 in Chapter 10 and compare it with Sample Problem 15.1. How are the procedures the same? Is the percent of copper in $CuSO_4 \cdot 5H_2O$ the same as in $CuSO_4$? Explain.

Interactive Textbook

Assessment 15.2 Test yourself on the concepts in Section 15.2.

with ChemASAP

Small-Scale LAB

Electrolytes

Purpose
To classify compounds as electrolytes by testing their conductivity in aqueous solution.

Materials
- pencil
- paper
- ruler
- reaction surface
- chemicals shown in the grid below
- conductivity tester
- water
- micropipet or dropper
- conductivity probe (optional)

Procedure

 Probeware version available in the Probeware Lab Manual.

On separate sheets of paper, draw two grids similar to the one below. Make each square 2 cm on each side. Place a reaction surface over one of the grids and place a few grains of each solid in the indicated places. Test each solid for conductivity. Then add 1 drop of water to each solid and test the wet mixture for conductivity. Be sure to clean and dry the conductivity leads between each test.

NaCl(s)	MgSO$_4$(s)
Na$_2$CO$_3$(s)	Table Sugar C$_{12}$H$_{22}$O$_{11}$
NaHCO$_3$(s)	Cornstarch (C$_6$H$_{12}$O$_6$)n
KCl(s)	KI(s)

Analyze
Using your experimental data, record the answers to the following questions in the space below your data table.

1. Electrolytes are compounds that conduct electricity in aqueous solution. Which compounds in your table are electrolytes? Which are not electrolytes?

2. Do any of these electrolytes conduct electricity in the solid form? Explain.

3. Are these ionic or covalent compounds? Classify each compound in the grid as ionic or covalent. For a compound to be an electrolyte, what must happen when it dissolves in water?

You're The Chemist
The following small-scale activities allow you to develop your own procedures and analyze the results.

1. **Analyze It!** When an ionic solid dissolves in water, water molecules attract the ions, causing them to come apart, or dissociate. The resulting dissolved ions are electrically charged particles that allow the solution to conduct electricity. The following chemical equations represent this phenomenon.

$$NaCl(s) \longrightarrow Na^+(aq) + Cl^-(aq)$$
$$Na_2CO_3(s) \longrightarrow 2Na^+(aq) + CO_3^{2-}(aq)$$

Write a similar chemical equation for each electrolyte in Figure A. Draw diagrams to explain how the ions conduct electricity.

2. **Design It!** Obtain the following aqueous solutions: HCl, H$_2$SO$_4$, HNO$_3$, CH$_3$COOH, NH$_3$, NaOH, rubbing alcohol, and distilled water. Design and carry out an experiment to test their conductivity. Use your data to classify each substance as a strong electrolyte, weak electrolyte, or nonelectrolyte.

3. **Design It!** Test various liquids for conductivity. Try soft drinks, orange juice, pickle juice, and coffee. Which liquids are electrolytes?

New York Standards: 3.1s, 3.1t, 3.1nn

Connecting to Your World   It wiggles and jiggles. It comes in many colors and flavors. When you pop it in your mouth, it dissolves. It is gelatin, one of the most popular desserts in the United States. In fact, more than a million packages of gelatin are purchased or eaten every day. Gelatin has even traveled into space. In 1996, American astronaut Shannon Lucid shared a gelatin dessert with her Russian crewmates. Gelatin is a heterogeneous mixture called a colloid. In this section, you will learn more about the characteristics of colloids and a related mixture called a suspension.

Guide for Reading

 Key Concepts
- What is the difference between a suspension and a solution?
- What distinguishes a colloid from a suspension and a solution?

Vocabulary

suspension
colloid
Tyndall effect
Brownian motion
emulsion

Reading Strategy

Previewing   Before you read, rewrite the headings of this section as questions. As you read, write answers to your questions.

Suspensions

So far in this chapter, you have learned about homogeneous mixtures that are formed when compounds such as inorganic acids, bases, and ionic salts mix with water. These mixtures are classified as solutions. In contrast, heterogeneous mixtures are not solutions.

If you shake a piece of clay with water, the clay breaks into fine particles. The water becomes cloudy because the clay particles are suspended in the water. But if you stop shaking, the particles begin to settle out. A **suspension** is a mixture from which particles settle out upon standing. A suspension differs from a solution because the particles of a suspension are much larger and do not stay suspended indefinitely. The particles in a typical suspension have an average diameter greater than 1000 nm. By contrast, the particle size in a solution is usually about 1 nm. The larger size of suspended particles means that gravity plays a larger role in causing them to settle out of the mixture. Cooks use suspensions of flour or cornstarch in water to thicken sauces and gravies. These mixtures must be shaken or stirred immediately before use because the suspended particles quickly settle out.

Suspensions are heterogeneous because at least two substances can be clearly identified. In the example of clay particles mixed with water, you can clearly see the dispersed phase (clay) in the dispersion medium (water). Figure 15.14 shows that if muddy water is filtered, the filter traps the suspended clay particles and clear water passes through.

Figure 15.14 A suspension is a heterogeneous mixture. Suspended particles can be removed by filtration. **Comparing and Contrasting** *How does the filtration of a suspension compare with the filtration of a solution?*

Colloids

You read in *Connecting to Your World* that gelatin is a type of mixture called a colloid. A **colloid** is a heterogeneous mixture containing particles that range in size from 1 nm to 1000 nm. The particles are spread throughout the dispersion medium, which can be a solid, liquid, or gas. The first substances to be identified as colloids were glues. Other colloids include such mixtures as gelatin, paint, aerosol sprays, and smoke. Table 15.3 lists some common colloidal systems and gives examples of familiar colloids.

How do the properties of colloids differ from those of suspensions and solutions? Like suspensions, many colloids are cloudy or milky in appearance when they are concentrated. Like solutions, colloids may look clear or almost clear when they are dilute. The important difference between colloids and solutions and suspensions is in the size of the particles. **Colloids have particles smaller than those in suspensions and larger than those in solutions.** These intermediate-sized particles cannot be retained by filter paper as are the larger particles of a suspension, and they do not settle out with time. Colloids can be distinguished by the Tyndall effect and by the observation of Brownian motion. They are also subject to coagulation or clumping together, and they can be emulsified or made stable.

Table 15.3

Some Colloidal Systems

System			
Dispersed phase	**Dispersion medium**	**Type**	**Example**
gas	liquid	foam	whipped cream
gas	solid	foam	marshmallow
liquid	liquid	emulsion	milk, mayonnaise
liquid	gas	aerosol	fog, aerosols
solid	gas	smoke	dust in air
solid	liquid	sols and gels	egg white, jellies, paint, blood, colloidal gold, starch in water, gelatin

Solution   Colloid   Suspension

Figure 15.15 The path of light is visible only when the light is scattered by particles. **a** Fog or mist is a colloid and thus exhibits the Tyndall effect. **b** Particles in colloids and suspensions reflect or scatter light in all directions. Solutions do not scatter light.

The Tyndall Effect Ordinarily you can't see a beam of sunlight unless the light passes through particles of water (mist) or dust in the air. These particles scatter the sunlight. Similarly, a beam of light is visible as it passes through a colloid. The scattering of visible light by colloidal particles is called the **Tyndall effect.** Suspensions also exhibit the Tyndall effect, but solutions do not. The particles in solutions are too small to scatter light. Figure 15.15 shows how the Tyndall effect can differentiate solutions from colloids and suspensions.

Brownian Motion Flashes of light, or scintillations, are seen when colloids are studied under a microscope. Colloids scintillate because the particles reflecting and scattering the light move erratically. The chaotic movement of colloidal particles, which was first observed by the Scottish botanist Robert Brown (1773–1858), is called **Brownian motion.** Brownian motion is caused by collisions of the molecules of the dispersion medium with the small, dispersed colloidal particles. These collisions help prevent the colloidal particles from settling.

Coagulation Colloidal particles also tend to stay suspended because they become charged by adsorbing ions from the dispersing medium onto their surface. Some colloidal particles become positively charged by adsorbing positively charged ions. Other colloidal particles become negatively charged by adsorbing negatively charged ions. All the particles in a particular colloidal system will have the same charge. The repulsion between the like-charged particles prevents the particles from forming heavier aggregates that would have a greater tendency to settle out. Thus, a colloidal system can be destroyed or coagulated by the addition of ions having a charge opposite to that of the colloidal particles. The added ions neutralize the charged colloidal particles. The particles can clump together to form heavier aggregates and precipitate from the dispersion.

For: Links on Brownian Motion
Visit: www.SciLinks.org
Web Code: cdn-1153

 What is Brownian motion?

Figure 15.16 The addition of an egg yolk to a mixture of oil and vinegar produces mayonnaise, a stable emulsion.

Emulsions An **emulsion** is a colloidal dispersion of a liquid in a liquid. An emulsifying agent is essential for the formation of an emulsion and for maintaining the emulsion's stability. For example, oils and greases are not soluble in water. However, they readily form a colloidal dispersion if soap or detergent is added to the water. Soaps and detergents are emulsifying agents. One end of a large soap or detergent molecule is polar and is attracted to water molecules. The other end of the soap or detergent molecule is nonpolar and is soluble in oil or grease. Soaps and other emulsifying agents thus allow the formation of colloidal dispersions between liquids that do not ordinarily mix. Figure 15.16 shows a familiar example of an emulsion—mayonnaise. Mayonnaise is a heterogeneous mixture of oil and vinegar. Such a mixture would quickly separate without the presence of egg yolk, which is the emulsifying agent. Other foods such as milk, margarine, and butter are also emulsions. Cosmetics, shampoos, and lotions are formulated with emulsifiers to maintain consistent quality. Table 15.4 summarizes the properties of solutions, colloids, and suspensions.

Table 15.4

Properties of Solutions, Colloids, and Suspensions			
	System		
Property	**Solution**	**Colloid**	**Suspension**
Particle type	ions, atoms, small molecules	large molecules or particles	large particles or aggregates
Particle size	0.1–1 nm	1–1000 nm	1000 nm and larger
Effect of light	no scattering	exhibits Tyndall effect	exhibits Tyndall effect
Effect of gravity	stable, does not separate	stable, does not separate	unstable, sediment forms
Filtration	particles not retained on filter	particles not retained on filter	particles retained on filter
Uniformity	homogeneous	borderline	heterogeneous

15.3 Section Assessment

16. 🔑 **Key Concept** How does a suspension differ from a solution?

17. 🔑 **Key Concept** What distinguishes a colloid from a suspension and a solution?

18. How can you determine through observation that a mixture is a suspension?

19. Could you separate a colloid by filtering? Explain.

20. How can the Tyndall effect be used to distinguish between a colloid and a solution?

21. What causes Brownian motion? Can the presence of Brownian motion distinguish between a solution and a colloid? Explain.

Elements ▶ **Handbook**

Electrolytes Go to page R8 in the Elements Handbook and read about the importance of electrolytes in the body. Write a paragraph explaining why the concentration of these ions may decline and how they can be restored.

Textbook
Assessment 15.3 Test yourself on the concepts in Section 15.3.

└── with **ChemASAP**

Water Worth Drinking

When you turn on a faucet, you probably don't think about the substances other than water that may end up in your glass. To ensure the safety of the water you drink, the Environmental Protection Agency (EPA) has established drinking water standards that state and local governments must follow. These standards set upper limits on potentially harmful substances that could be present in water. The standards are based on studies of how these substances affect human health. **Inferring *What might happen if water were not treated to kill bacteria and other pathogens?***

1 **Laboratory analysis** identifies natural or synthetic compounds that may be harmful when present in drinking water. Standards are set for these substances in parts per million (ppm) or parts per billion (ppb).

2 If periodic **water samples** indicate too high a level of coliform bacteria, disinfectants such as chlorine must be added to destroy these and other potentially dangerous microorganisms.

3 When water must be **treated with chlorine,** frequent tests ensure that levels of this disinfectant do not fall below 0.5 ppm.

Local water providers test their public water supplies regularly to monitor levels of minerals, chlorine, and microorganisms such as bacteria.

Key Concepts

15.1 Water and Its Properties

- The high surface tension and low vapor pressure of water are the results of hydrogen bonding.

- The structure of ice is a regular open framework of water molecules held together by hydrogen bonds and arranged like a honeycomb.

- Molecules in liquid water are packed closer together than they are in ice.

15.2 Homogeneous Aqueous Systems

- In a solution, a solvent dissolves the solute. The solute becomes dispersed in the solvent.

- In the dissolving process, individual solute ions break away from the crystal. Solvent molecules surround the negatively and positively charged ions in a process called solvation and the ionic crystal dissolves.

- All ionic compounds are electrolytes because they dissociate into ions and thus can conduct electricity.

- The formula of a hydrate consists of the formula of the ionic salt followed by a dot and the number of water molecules associated with one formula unit of the salt.

15.3 Heterogeneous Aqueous Systems

- A suspension differs from a solution because the component particles of a suspension are much larger and do not stay suspended indefinitely.

- Colloids have particles smaller than those in suspensions and larger than those in solutions.

Vocabulary

- aqueous solution (p. 450)
- Brownian motion (p. 461)
- colloid (p. 460)
- electrolyte (p. 452)
- emulsion (p. 462)
- hydrate (p. 454)

- nonelectrolyte (p. 452)
- solute (p. 450)
- solvation (p. 451)
- solvent (p. 450)
- strong electrolyte (p. 453)

- surfactant (p. 447)
- suspension (p. 459)
- surface tension (p. 447)
- Tyndall effect (p. 461)
- weak electrolyte (p. 453)

Key Equation

- Percent $H_2O = \dfrac{\text{mass of water}}{\text{mass of hydrate}} \times 100\%$

Organizing Information

Use these terms to construct a concept map that organizes the major ideas of this chapter.

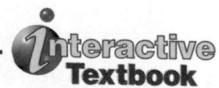

Concept Map 15 Solve the Concept Map with the help of an interactive guided tutorial.

—— with **ChemASAP**

15.1 Water and Its Properties

22. Why does water have high surface tension?

23. Why do the particles at the surface of a liquid behave differently from those in the bulk of the liquid?

24. Describe some observable effects that are produced by the surface tension of a liquid.

25. What is a surfactant? Explain how it works.

26. How can the unusually low vapor pressure of water be explained?

27. Explain why bodies of water with large surface areas such as lakes and oceans do not evaporate rapidly.

28. How does the structure of ice differ from the structure of liquid water?

29. What would be some of the consequences if ice were denser than liquid water?

30. Explain the role of hydrogen bonds in ice.

31. From your knowledge of intermolecular forces, arrange these liquids in order of increasing surface tension: water (H_2O), hexane (C_6H_{14}), ethanol (C_2H_5OH).

32. Water has its maximum density at 4°C. Discuss the consequences of this fact.

33. The following graph shows the density of water over the temperature range 0°C to 20°C.

Density vs. Temperature for Liquid Water

a. What is the maximum density of water?

b. At what temperature does the maximum density of water occur?

c. Would it be meaningful to expand the smooth curve of the graph to the left to temperatures below 0°C? Explain your answer.

34. Explain which properties of water are responsible for these occurrences.

a. Water in tiny cracks in rocks helps break up the rocks when it freezes.

b. Water beads up on a newly waxed car.

c. A longer time is needed for a teaspoon of water to evaporate than a teaspoon of alcohol.

35. Describe what might happen if you put a sealed glass container full of water into a freezer.

36. Describe what would happen to a pond at 0°C if the density of ice were greater than the density of liquid water. Do you think the pond would freeze more quickly? Explain.

37. When the humidity is low and the temperature high, humans must take in large quantities of water or face serious dehydration. Why do you think water is so important for the proper functioning of your body?

38. Make a drawing to show how the oxygen atom in one molecule of water can be connected to as many as four other molecules of water by hydrogen bonds. Write an explanation of your drawing.

39. A problem for firefighters is that much of the water they spray on a fire doesn't soak in but runs off carrying debris and pollution into the environment. Explain how the addition of a surfactant to water used to fight fires could help put out the fire more rapidly and protect the environment.

40. When spring comes, ice melting at the surface of a pond begins a beneficial process that stirs up the water of the pond. Explain why the pond water begins to mix when the ice melts. (*Hint:* Consider the changes in density.)

41. After a winter of alternate periods of freezing and thawing, some roads have broken pavement and potholes. Using what you know of the properties of water, explain why potholes form.

42. Which of the following volumes is greater?
    a. 1 g of ice at 0°C and 1 g of liquid water at 0°C
    b. 1 g of liquid water at 100°C and 1 g of steam at 100°C

15.2 Homogeneous Aqueous Systems

43. Distinguish between a solution and an aqueous solution.

44. Identify the solvent and the solute in a solution of table sugar in water.

45. Why is water an excellent solvent for most ionic and polar covalent compounds but not for nonpolar compounds?

46. Suppose an aqueous solution contains both sugar and salt. Can you separate either of these solutes from the water by filtration? Explain your reasoning.

47. Which of the following substances dissolve appreciably in water? Give reasons for your choice.
    a. HCl   b. NaI
    c. NH_3 d. $MgSO_4$
    e. CH_4 f. $CaCO_3$

48. Explain why gasoline does not dissolve in water.

49. What particles must be present in a solution if it is to conduct electricity?

50. Why does molten sodium chloride conduct electricity?

51. What is the main distinction between an aqueous solution of a strong electrolyte and an aqueous solution of a weak electrolyte?

52. What is meant by a substance's water of hydration?

53. Write formulas for these hydrates.
    a. sodium sulfate decahydrate
    b. calcium chloride dihydrate
    c. barium hydroxide octahydrate

54. Name each hydrate.
    a. $SnCl_4 \cdot 5H_2O$ b. $FeSO_4 \cdot 7H_2O$
    c. $BaBr_2 \cdot 4H_2O$ d. $FePO_4 \cdot 4H_2O$

55. Epsom salt ($MgSO_4 \cdot 7H_2O$) changes to the mono-hydrate form at 150°C. Write an equation for this change.

56. Explain why a hygroscopic substance can be used as a desiccant.

57. Why is it important to keep some hygroscopic substances in tightly sealed containers?

58. Some hydrates are efflorescent. Explain what that means. Under what conditions will a hydrate effloresce?

59. Water is a polar solvent; gasoline is a nonpolar solvent. Decide which compounds are more likely to dissolve in water and which are more likely to dissolve in gasoline.
    a. CCl_4 b. Na_2SO_4
    c. methane (CH_4)   d. KCl

60. The process of solvation involves water molecules surrounding ions in a water solution. In terms of ions and polarity, explain why ions become solvated in aqueous solution.

61. You have a solution containing either sugar or salt dissolved in water.
    a. Can you tell which solute is present by visual inspection? Explain.
    b. Give two ways by which you could easily tell which solute is present. (Tasting the solutions is not a possibility.)

62. Explain why ethanol (C_2H_5OH) will dissolve in both gasoline and water.

63. Are all liquids soluble in each other? Explain.

64. Write equations to show how these substances ionize or dissociate in water.
    a. NH_4Cl b. $Cu(NO_3)_2$
    c. $HC_2H_3O_2$ d. $HgCl_2$

65. Name these hydrates and determine the percent by mass of water in each.
    a. $Na_2CO_3 \cdot H_2O$ b. $MgSO_4 \cdot 7H_2O$

66. How many grams of copper(II) sulfate penta-hydrate would you need to measure in order to have 10.0 g of anhydrous copper(II) sulfate?

67. Find the percent of water in $CaCl_2 \cdot 2H_2O$. What percent of $CaCl_2 \cdot 2H_2O$ is $CaCl_2$?

68. When ethyl alcohol (C_2H_6O) dissolves in water, the volume of the final solution is less than the separate volumes of the water and alcohol added together. Explain this result. Do you think that it might be possible to mix two different liquids and get a mixture volume that is larger than the sum of the volumes of the two components? Explain.

69. Describe as specifically as possible what would happen if a nonpolar molecular liquid were added to water.

70. Cobalt chloride test paper is blue. This paper is made by soaking strips of paper in an aqueous solution of $CoCl_2 \cdot 6H_2O$. The paper strips are then dried in an oven.

$$CoCl_2 \cdot 6H_2O \text{ (pink)} + \text{heat} \longrightarrow$$
$$CoCl_2 \text{ (blue)} + 6H_2O$$

a. When $CoCl_2 \cdot 6H_2O$ is dissolved in water, what is the color of the solution?

b. What is the color of wet cobalt chloride paper?

c. What is the color of dry cobalt chloride paper?

d. What is the percent by mass of water in $CoCl_2 \cdot 6H_2O$?

e. What does cobalt chloride test paper test for?

15.3 **Heterogeneous Aqueous Systems**

71. Explain why muddy water is not a solution.

72. Arrange colloids, suspensions, and solutions in order of increasing particle size.

73. What is the Tyndall effect?

74. Why don't solutions demonstrate the Tyndall effect?

75. What causes Brownian motion?

76. What are two circumstances that help keep colloidal particles in suspension?

77. How can a colloid be destroyed?

78. What makes a colloidal dispersion stable?

79. Match each term with the following descriptions. A description may apply to more than one term.
 a. solution   **b.** colloid   **c.** suspension

 (1) does not settle out on standing
 (2) heterogeneous mixture
 (3) particle size less than 1 nm
 (4) particles can be filtered out
 (5) demonstrates Tyndall effect
 (6) particles are invisible to the unaided eye
 (7) homogenized milk
 (8) salt water
 (9) jelly

80. Why is the midday sky blue while the evening sky in the west is often an orange or red color? (*Hint:* There are colloidal-size particles in the atmosphere.)

Test-Taking Tip

Constructed Response You will probably answer most constructed response questions by writing a sentence or a paragraph. Put as much information into each sentence as possible, but avoid unnecessary words. Your answer should address all the specific points asked for in the question. For longer responses, you may find it helpful to prepare a brief outline.

Regents Practice Exam

Part A

For each statement or question write the number of the word or expression that, of those given, best completes the statement or answers the question.

1. The modern theory of the atom states that the atom consists of a
   (1) negatively charged nucleus surrounded by positively charged electrons
   (2) neutral nucleus surrounded by uncharged electrons
   (3) positively charged nucleus surrounded by negatively charged electrons
   (4) positively charged sphere with electrons embedded in it

2. Water contains polar bonds because the electronegativities of hydrogen and oxygen
   (1) are identical
   (2) are similar
   (3) equal zero
   (4) differ significantly

3. Another name for a solution is a
   (1) compound
   (2) heterogeneous mixture
   (3) homogeneous mixture
   (4) substance

4. How does an atom that contains two valence electrons most likely become stable?
   (1) It loses two electrons.
   (2) It gains two electrons.
   (3) It gains six electrons.
   (4) It loses six electrons.

5. Hydrochloric acid forms many ions in solution. As a result, hydrochloric acid is
   (1) an electrolyte
   (2) a nonelectrolyte
   (3) a nonconductor
   (4) a substance

6. Going from left to right across a period on the periodic table, which of the following properties does *not* increase?
   (1) electronegativity
   (2) atomic size
   (3) first ionization energy
   (4) nonmetallic properties

Part B-1

For each statement or question write the number of the word or expression that, of those given, best completes the statement or answers the question.

7. Particle diagram (1) below represents solute particles in a given volume of solution. Which diagram represents the solute particles in the same volume of solution when the amount of solvent is doubled?

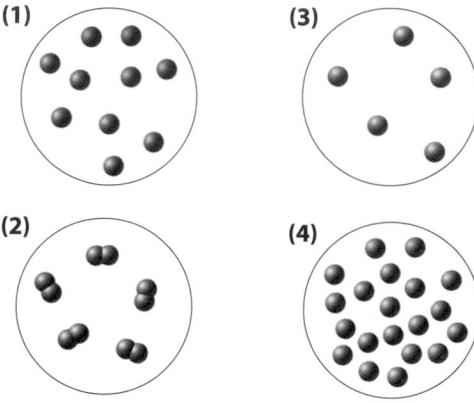

8. Which of the following properties of water is *not* explained by hydrogen bonding?
   (1) boiling point
   (2) colorless
   (3) liquid at room temperature
   (4) melting point

9. How many electrons are contained in a P^{3-} ion?
   (1) 12 (3) 18
   (2) 15 (4) 34

10. When magnesium metal is placed in dilute hydrochloric acid, the metal disappears and bubbles of hydrogen gas form. This reaction is an example of what type of chemical reaction?
    (1) combination (systhesis)
    (2) decomposition
    (3) single-replacement
    (4) double-replacement

11. Drinking water can be made from seawater by changing the liquid water to a vapor then changing the vapor to a liquid again. The solutes in the water are left behind as the water is removed. This process is an example of a
    (1) chemical property
    (2) chemical change
    (3) physical property
    (4) physical change

Part B-2

Answer each of the following questions.

12. How many significant figures are in each measurement?

   a. 56.003 g   **c.** 0.0056 cm

   b. 750 mL   **d.** 0.4005 dg

13. Write the correct electron configuration for the oxide ion. Which noble gas has the same electron configuration?

14. When a hydrogen ion is attracted to the unshared electron pair of a water molecule, the polyatomic hydronium ion (H_3O^+) is formed. Draw the electron dot structure for the hydronium ion.

15. Balance these chemical equations, using the smallest whole-number coefficients.

   a. $CO_2 + H_2O \longrightarrow C_6H_{12}O_6 + O_2$

   b. $Na + H_2O \longrightarrow Na^+ + OH^- + H_2$

16. The formation of water from its elements is given by this equation.

$$2H_2 + O_2 \longrightarrow 2H_2O$$

How many moles each of hydrogen and oxygen are required to produce 4.6 mol of water?

17. The decomposition of hydrogen peroxide is given by this equation.

$$2H_2O_2 \longrightarrow 2H_2O + O_2$$

Calculate the moles of water formed when 2.00×10^{-3} mol of hydrogen peroxide is decomposed.

18. Calculate the volume of CO_2 in liters produced in the complete combustion of 8.00 L of propane at STP, given this balanced equation.

$$C_3H_8 + 5O_2 \longrightarrow 3CO_2 + 4H_2O$$

19. Hydrogen reacts with oxygen to form water.

$$2H_2 + O_2 \longrightarrow 2H_2O$$

   a. How many moles of oxygen are required to produce 10.8 mol H_2O?

   b. How many grams of oxygen are used?

20. How do the following changes in the pressure on the surface of water affect the water's boiling point?

   a. an increase in pressure

   b. a decrease in pressure

Part C

Answer each of the following questions.

Use this description and the data table to answer Questions 21–23.

A student used a meter to measure conductivity. The magnitude of the conductivity value is proportional to the number of ions in the solution. The SI conductivity unit is the microseimens/cm (μS/cm). The table gives the results reported by the student. Each solution had a concentration of 0.02M.

Solution	Conductivity (μS/cm)
potassium chloride, KCl	2050
aluminum chloride, $AlCl_3$	4500
calcium chloride, $CaCl_2$	3540
sodium hydroxide, NaOH	2180
ethanol, C_2H_5OH	0
magnesium bromide, $MgBr_2$	3490
distilled water	0

21. Why do distilled water and the ethanol solution have zero conductivity?

22. Explain why the KCl and NaOH solutions have similar conductivities.

23. The $AlCl_3$ solution has a conductivity that is about twice that of the KCl solution. Explain.

Use the following information to answer Questions 24–27.

One balloon contains 1 mol of He. Two other balloons contain one mole of CH_4, and O_2, respectively. At STP, one mole of any gas occupies 22.4 L.

24. Compare the volumes of each of the balloons.

25. What is the mass of the gas in each balloon?

26. Calculate the density of the gas in each balloon at STP.

27. The density of air at room temperature is about 1.2 g/mL. Indicate whether each balloon will rise or sink when released.

28. Ethanal (CH_3CHO) is produced by reacting ethyne (C_2H_2) with water, as shown by this equation.

$$C_2H_2 + H_2O \longrightarrow CH_3CHO$$

How many grams of CH_3CHO can be produced when 3.76×10^2 g C_2H_2 completely reacts with 2.60×10^2 g H_2O?

Water has shaped these cliffs in Grand Canyon National Park and carried away some of the rock in solution.

INQUIRY Activity

Salt and the Freezing Point of Water

Materials
plastic plate, a 20-cm piece of string or narrow ribbon, water, an ice cube, and some table salt (sodium chloride)

Procedure

1. Remove an ice cube from the freezer and place it on the plate.

2. Moisten the string or ribbon with water and place it in a straight line across the ice cube.

3. Sprinkle some salt along the length of the string on the ice.

4. Wait one to two minutes and then slowly lift the ends of the string. The ice cube should lift off the plate.

5. If you are not successful in lifting the cube with the string, repeat Steps 3 and 4.

Think About It

1. What effect does the salt have on the water/ice?

2. Can you name some practical instances of salt being used to affect the freezing point of water?

3. Do you think sugar or baking soda would work equally well? Try it!

16.1 Properties of Solutions

New York Standards: 3.1nn–oo

Connecting to Your World

It was there one minute and gone the next! An entire house was swallowed up by Earth. A victim of moving groundwater, the house had disappeared into a sinkhole! Groundwater, the rain and melted snow that soaks into the ground, can dissolve huge amounts of rock over time and create beautiful limestone caves. A sinkhole forms when the roof of a cave weakens from being dissolved and suddenly collapses. One recorded sinkhole swallowed a house, several other buildings, five cars, and a swimming pool! In this section, you will learn how the solution process occurs and the factors that influence the process.

Solution Formation

Have you noticed, when making tea, that granulated sugar dissolves faster than sugar cubes, and that both granulated sugar and sugar cubes dissolve faster in hot tea or when you stir? Figure 16.1 illustrates these observations. You will be able to explain these observations, as well as the formation of a sinkhole, once you have gained an understanding of the properties of solutions.

Recall that solutions are homogeneous mixtures that may be solid, liquid, or gaseous. **The compositions of the solvent and the solute determine whether a substance will dissolve. Stirring (agitation), temperature, and the surface area of the dissolving particles determine how fast the substance will dissolve.** These three factors involve the contact of the solute with the solvent.

Guide for Reading

Key Concepts
- What factors determine the rate at which a substance dissolves?
- How is solubility usually expressed?
- What conditions determine the amount of solute that will dissolve in a given solvent?

Vocabulary
saturated solution
solubility
unsaturated solution
miscible
immiscible
supersaturated solution
Henry's law

Reading Strategy
Outlining As you read, make an outline of the most important ideas in this section. Use the red headings as the main topics and the blue headings as subtopics. Add a sentence or a note after each heading to provide key information about each topic.

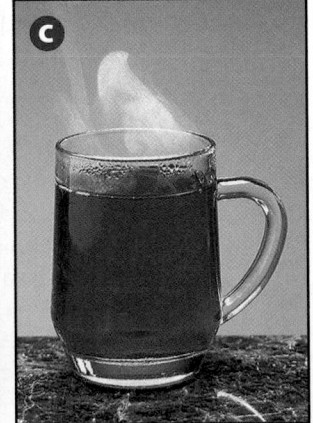

Figure 16.1 Stirring and heating increase the rate at which a solute dissolves. **ⓐ** A cube of sugar in cold tea dissolves slowly. **ⓑ** Granulated sugar dissolves in cold water more quickly than a sugar cube, especially with stirring. **ⓒ** Granulated sugar dissolves very quickly in hot tea.

Go Online

NSTA SciLINKS

For: Links on Solubility
Visit: www.SciLinks.org
Web Code: cdn-1161

Stirring and Solution Formation If a teaspoon of granulated sugar (sucrose) is placed in a glass of tea, the crystals dissolve slowly. If the contents of the glass are stirred, however, the crystals dissolve more quickly. The dissolving process occurs at the surface of the sugar crystals. Stirring speeds up the process because fresh solvent (the water in tea) is continually brought into contact with the surface of the solute (sugar). It's important to realize, however, that agitation (stirring or shaking) affects only the rate at which a solid solute dissolves. It does not influence the amount of solute that will dissolve. An insoluble substance remains undissolved regardless of how vigorously or for how long the solvent/solute system is agitated.

Temperature and Solution Formation Temperature also influences the rate at which a solute dissolves. Sugar dissolves much more rapidly in hot tea than in iced tea. At higher temperatures, the kinetic energy of water molecules is greater than at lower temperatures so they move faster. The more rapid motion of the solvent molecules leads to an increase in the frequency and the force of the collisions between water molecules and the surfaces of the sugar crystals.

Particle Size and Solution Formation The rate at which a solute dissolves also depends upon the size of the solute particles. A spoonful of granulated sugar dissolves more quickly than a sugar cube because the smaller particles in granulated sugar expose a much greater surface area to the colliding water molecules. Remember, the dissolving process is a surface phenomenon. The more surface of the solute that is exposed, the faster the rate of dissolving.

Solubility

If you add 36.0 g of sodium chloride to 100 g of water at 25°C, all of the 36.0 g of salt dissolves. But if you add one more gram of salt and stir, no matter how vigorously or for how long, only 0.2 g of the last portion will dissolve. Why does the remaining 0.8 g of salt remain undissolved? According to the kinetic theory, water molecules are in continuous motion. Therefore, they should continue to bombard the excess solid, removing and solvating the ions. As ions are solvated, they dissolve in the water. Based on this information, you might expect all of the sodium chloride to dissolve eventually. That does not happen, however, because an exchange process is occurring. New particles from the solid are solvated and enter into solution, as shown in Figure 16.2. At the same time an equal number of already dissolved particles crystalize. These particles come out of solution and are deposited as a solid. The mass of undissolved crystals remains constant.

Solvation

Crystallization

Figure 16.2 In a saturated solution, a state of dynamic equilibrium exists between the solution and the excess solute. The rate of solvation (dissolving) equals the rate of crystallization, so the total amount of dissolved solute remains constant. **Inferring** *What would happen if you added more solute?*

What is happening? Particles move from the solid into the solution. Other dissolved particles move from the solution back to the solid. Because these two processes occur at the same rate, no net change occurs in the overall system. As Figure 16.2 illustrates, a state of dynamic equilibrium exists between the solution and the undissolved solute. The system will remain the same as long as the temperature remains constant. Such a solution is said to be saturated. A **saturated solution** contains the maximum amount of solute for a given quantity of solvent at a constant temperature and pressure. For example, 36.2 g of sodium chloride dissolved in 100 g of water is a saturated solution at 25°C. If additional solute is added to this solution, it will not dissolve. The **solubility** of a substance is the amount of solute that dissolves in a given quantity of a solvent at a specified temperature and pressure to produce a saturated solution. ⚬─ **Solubility is often expressed in grams of solute per 100 g of solvent.** Sometimes the solubility of a gas is expressed in grams per liter of solution (g/L). A solution that contains less solute than a saturated solution at a given temperature and pressure is an **unsaturated solution.** If additional solute is added to an unsaturated solution, the solute will dissolve until the solution is saturated.

Some liquids—for example, water and ethanol—are infinitely soluble in each other. Any amount of ethanol will dissolve in a given volume of water, and vice versa. Similarly, ethylene glycol and water mix in all proportions. Pairs of liquids such as these are said to be completely miscible. Two liquids are **miscible** if they dissolve in each other in all proportions. In such a solution, the liquid that is present in the larger amount is usually considered the solvent. Liquids that are slightly soluble in each other—for example, water and diethyl ether—are partially miscible. Liquids that are insoluble in one another are **immiscible.** As you can see in Figure 16.3, oil and vinegar are immiscible, as are oil and water.

 Checkpoint *What is a saturated solution?*

Figure 16.3 Liquids that are insoluble in one another are immiscible. **ⓐ** A thin film of oil spreads over a water surface. Light rays, bent by the film, create patterns of color. **ⓑ** Vinegar, which is water-based, and oil are immiscible.

Figure 16.4 Changing the temperature usually affects the solubility of a substance.

Solubility Varies with Temperature

INTERPRETING GRAPHS

a. Describe What happens to the solubility of KNO$_3$ as the temperature increases?

b. Identify Which substance shows a decrease in solubility as temperature increases? Which substance exhibits the least change in solubility?

c. Apply Concepts Suppose you added some solid sodium chloride (NaCl) to a saturated solution of sodium chloride at 20°C and warmed the mixture to 40°C. What would happen to the added sodium chloride?

Factors Affecting Solubility

You have read that solubility is defined as the mass of solute that dissolves in a given mass of a solvent at a specified temperature. **Temperature affects the solubility of solid, liquid, and gaseous solutes in a solvent; both temperature and pressure affect the solubility of gaseous solutes.**

Temperature The solubility of most solid substances increases as the temperature of the solvent increases. Figure 16.4 shows how the solubility of several substances changes as temperature increases. The mineral deposits around hot springs, such as the one shown in Figure 16.5, result from the cooling of the hot, saturated solution of minerals emerging from the spring. As the solution cools in air, it cannot contain the same concentration of minerals as it did at a higher temperature, so some of the minerals precipitate.

For a few substances, solubility decreases with temperature. For example, the solubility of ytterbium sulfate (Yb$_2$(SO$_4$)$_3$) in water drops from 44.2 g per 100 g of water at 0°C to 5.8 g per 100 g of water at 90°C. Table 16.1 lists the solubilities of some common substances at various temperatures.

Suppose you make a saturated solution of sodium ethanoate (sodium acetate) at 30°C and let the solution stand undisturbed as it cools to 25°C. Because the solubility of this compound is greater at 30°C than at 25°C, you expect that solid sodium ethanoate will crystallize from the solution as the temperature drops. But no crystals form. You have made a supersaturated solution. A **supersaturated solution** contains more solute than it can theoretically hold at a given temperature. The crystallization of a supersaturated solution can be initiated if a very small crystal, called a seed crystal, of the solute is added. The rate at which excess solute deposits upon the surface of a seed crystal can be very rapid, as shown in Figure 16.6. Crystallization can also occur if the inside of the container is scratched.

Figure 16.5 Mineral deposits form around the edges of this hot spring because the hot water is saturated with minerals. As the water cools, some of the minerals crystallize because they are less soluble at the lower temperature.

Figure 16.6 A supersaturated solution crystallizes rapidly when disturbed. ⓐ The solution is clear before a seed crystal is added. ⓑ Crystals begin to form in the solution immediately after the addition of a seed crystal. ⓒ Excess solute crystallizes rapidly. **Applying Concepts** *When the crystallization has ceased, will the solution be saturated or unsaturated?*

Another example of crystallization in a supersaturated solution is the production of rock candy. A solution is supersaturated with sugar. Seed crystals cause the sugar to crystallize out of solution onto a string for you to enjoy!

The effect of temperature on the solubility of gases in liquid solvents is opposite that of solids. The solubilities of most gases are greater in cold water than in hot. For example, Table 16.1 shows that the most important component of air for living beings—oxygen—becomes less soluble in water as the temperature of the solution rises. This fact has some important consequences. When an industrial plant takes water from a lake to use for cooling and then dumps the resulting heated water back into the lake, the temperature of the entire lake increases. Such a change in temperature is known as thermal pollution. Aquatic animal and plant life can be severely affected because the increase in temperature lowers the concentration of dissolved oxygen in the lake water.

Textbook

Simulation 20 Observe the effect of temperature on the solubility of solids and gases in water.

with ChemASAP

Table 16.1

		Solubility (g/100 g H_2O)			
Substance	**Formula**	**0°C**	**20°C**	**50°C**	**100°C**
Barium hydroxide	$Ba(OH)_2$	1.67	31.89	—	—
Barium sulfate	$BaSO_4$	0.00019	0.00025	0.00034	—
Calcium hydroxide	$Ca(OH)_2$	0.189	0.173	—	0.07
Lead(II) chloride	$PbCl_2$	0.60	0.99	1.70	—
Lithium carbonate	Li_2CO_3	1.5	1.3	1.1	0.70
Potassium chlorate	$KClO_3$	4.0	7.4	19.3	56.0
Potassium chloride	KCl	27.6	34.0	42.6	57.6
Sodium chloride	$NaCl$	35.7	36.0	37.0	39.2
Sodium nitrate	$NaNO_3$	74	88.0	114.0	182
Aluminum chloride	$AlCl_3$	30.84	31.03	31.60	33.32
Silver nitrate	$AgNO_3$	122	222.0	455.0	733
Lithium bromide	$LiBr$	143.0	166	203	266.0
Sucrose (cane sugar)	$C_{12}H_{22}O_{11}$	179	230.9	260.4	487
Hydrogen*	H_2	0.00019	0.00016	0.00013	0.0
Oxygen*	O_2	0.0070	0.0043	0.0026	0.0
Carbon dioxide*	CO_2	0.335	0.169	0.076	0.0

*Gas at 101 kPa (one atmosphere) total pressure

Pressure Changes in pressure have little affect on the solubility of solids and liquids, but pressure strongly influences the solubility of gases. Gas solubility increases as the partial pressure of the gas above the solution increases. Carbonated beverages are a good example. These drinks contain large amounts of carbon dioxide (CO_2) dissolved in water. Dissolved CO_2 makes the liquid fizz and your mouth tingle. The drinks are bottled under a high pressure of CO_2 gas, which forces large amounts of the gas into solution. When a carbonated-beverage container is opened, the partial pressure of CO_2 above the liquid decreases. Immediately, bubbles of CO_2 form in the liquid and escape from the open bottle, as shown in Figure 16.7. As a result, the concentration of dissolved CO_2 decreases. If the bottle is left open, the drink becomes "flat" as the solution loses its CO_2.

How is the partial pressure of carbon dioxide gas related to the solubility of CO_2 in a carbonated beverage? The relationship is described by **Henry's law,** which states that at a given temperature, the solubility (S) of a gas in a liquid is directly proportional to the pressure (P) of the gas above the liquid. In other words, as the pressure of the gas above the liquid increases, the solubility of the gas increases. Similarly, as the pressure of the gas decreases, the solubility of the gas decreases. You can write the relationship in the form of an equation.

$$\frac{S_1}{P_1} = \frac{S_2}{P_2}$$

S_1 is the solubility of a gas at one pressure, P_1; S_2 is the solubility at another pressure, P_2.

✓ Checkpoint *How is the solubility of a gas affected by pressure?*

Figure 16.7 Pressure is a factor in the solubility of a gas. **ⓐ** In a sealed bottle, both the pressure of CO_2 above the liquid and the concentration of CO_2 in the liquid are high and equal. **ⓑ** When the cap is removed, the equilibrium is disturbed; the pressure of CO_2 gas above the liquid decreases and carbon dioxide bubbles out of the liquid.

SAMPLE PROBLEM 16.1

Calculating the Solubility of a Gas

If the solubility of a gas in water is 0.77 g/L at 3.5 atm of pressure, what is its solubility (in g/L) at 1.0 atm of pressure? (The temperature is held constant at 25°C.)

1 Analyze *List the knowns and the unknown.*

Knowns
- P_1 = 3.5 atm
- S_1 = 0.77 g/L
- P_2 = 1.0 atm
- Henry's law: $\dfrac{S_1}{P_1} = \dfrac{S_2}{P_2}$

Unknown
- S_2 = ? g/L

2 Calculate *Solve for the unknown.*

Solve Henry's law for S_2. Substitute the known values and calculate.

$$S_2 = \frac{S_1 \times P_2}{P_1} = \frac{0.77 \text{ g/L} \times 1.0 \text{ atm}}{3.5 \text{ atm}} = 0.22 \text{ g/L}$$

Math Handbook

For help with algebraic equations, go to page R69.

3 Evaluate *Does the result make sense?*

The new pressure is approximately one-third of the original pressure, so the new solubility should be approximately one-third of the original. The answer is correctly expressed to two significant figures.

Practice Problems

1. The solubility of a gas in water is 0.16 g/L at 104 kPa. What is the solubility when the pressure of the gas is increased to 288 kPa? Assume the temperature remains constant.

2. A gas has a solubility in water at 0°C of 3.6 g/L at a pressure of 1.0 atm. What pressure is needed to produce an aqueous solution containing 9.5 g/L of the same gas at 0°C?

Interactive Textbook

Problem-Solving 16.2 Solve Problem 2 with the help of an interactive guided tutorial.

— with **ChemASAP**

16.1 Section Assessment

3. 🔑 **Key Concept** What determines whether a substance will dissolve? What determines how fast a substance will dissolve?

4. 🔑 **Key Concept** What units are usually used to express the solubility of a solute?

5. 🔑 **Key Concept** What are two conditions that determine the mass of solute that will dissolve in a given mass of solvent?

6. What would you do to change
  a. a saturated solid/liquid solution to an unsaturated solution?
  b. a saturated gas/liquid solution to an unsaturated solution?

7. The solubility of a gas is 0.58 g/L at a pressure of 104 kPa. What is its solubility if the pressure increases to 250 kPa at the same temperature?

Writing Activity

Procedure Research how to grow crystals. Then write a stepwise procedure for growing rock candy, which is crystallized sugar, or sucrose ($C_{12}H_{22}O_{11}$).

Interactive Textbook

Assessment 16.1 Test yourself on the concepts in Section 16.1.

— with **ChemASAP**

A Solution for Kidney Failure

Your blood transports oxygen and other nutrients to cells throughout your body. It also picks up discarded waste materials from cells and carries them to your kidneys. Kidneys have the important job of filtering potentially toxic materials from blood and excreting them in urine. The body's entire blood supply passes through its two kidneys approximately every 45 minutes. Should the kidneys fail to function, life-threatening poisons would build up in the body. In that case, the treatment is usually hemodialysis, a procedure for cleansing the blood outside the body. **Comparing and Contrasting** *What are some similarities and differences between the way kidneys work and hemodialysis?*

A A tube connects a patient to a dialysis machine. The machine pumps blood from a vein, circulates it through a dialyzing bath, and returns it to another vein.

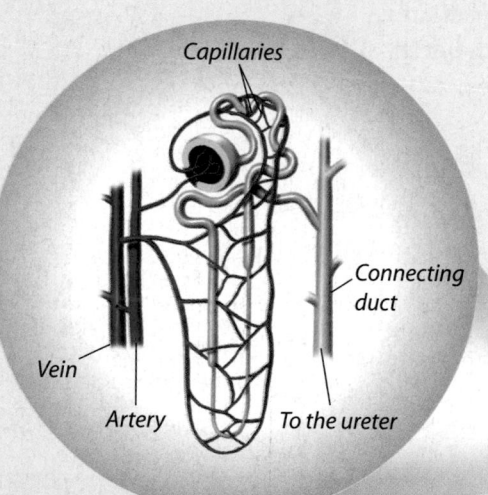

Capillaries

Connecting duct

Vein

Artery

To the ureter

Nephrons Millions of tiny processing units called nephrons filter blood through a network of capillaries. The collecting duct carries toxic materials such as urea to the ureter for excretion.

Kidneys

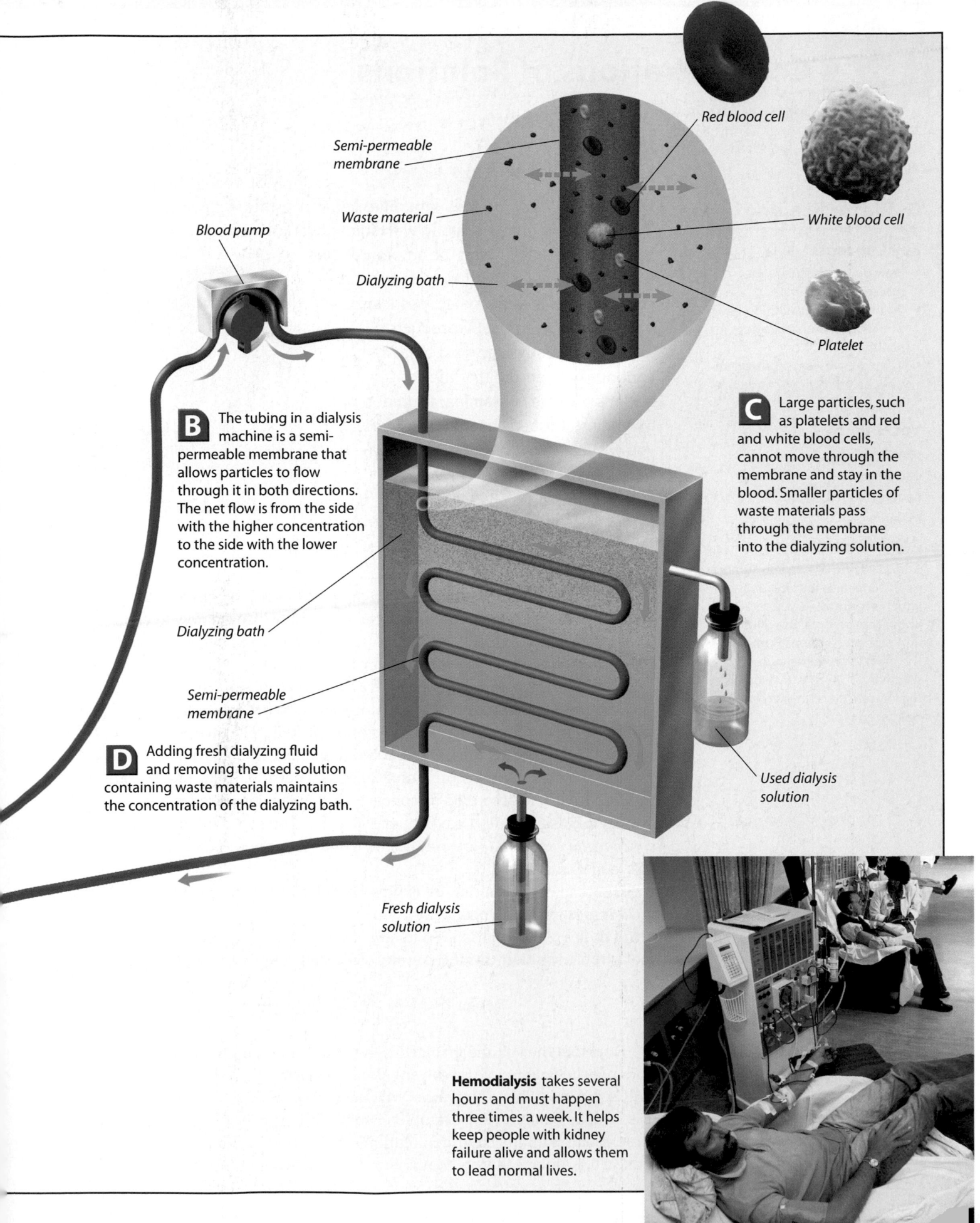

Red blood cell

Semi-permeable membrane

Waste material

White blood cell

Dialyzing bath

Platelet

Blood pump

B The tubing in a dialysis machine is a semi-permeable membrane that allows particles to flow through it in both directions. The net flow is from the side with the higher concentration to the side with the lower concentration.

C Large particles, such as platelets and red and white blood cells, cannot move through the membrane and stay in the blood. Smaller particles of waste materials pass through the membrane into the dialyzing solution.

Dialyzing bath

Semi-permeable membrane

D Adding fresh dialyzing fluid and removing the used solution containing waste materials maintains the concentration of the dialyzing bath.

Used dialysis solution

Fresh dialysis solution

Hemodialysis takes several hours and must happen three times a week. It helps keep people with kidney failure alive and allows them to lead normal lives.

New York Standards: 3.1pp

Connecting to Your World A supply of clean drinking water is important for all communities. What constitutes clean water? The federal government, along with state governments, has set standards limiting the amount of contaminants allowed in drinking water. These contaminants include metals, pesticides, bacteria, and even the by-products of water treatment. Water must be tested continually to ensure that the concentrations of these contaminants do not exceed established limits. In this section, you will learn how solution concentrations are calculated.

Molarity

You have learned that a substance can dissolve to some extent in a particular solvent to form a solution. In this section, you will learn how to express the actual extent of dissolving, that is, the concentration of a solution. The **concentration** of a solution is a measure of the amount of solute that is dissolved in a given quantity of solvent. A **dilute solution** is one that contains a small amount of solute. By contrast, a **concentrated solution** contains a large amount of solute. An aqueous solution of sodium chloride containing 1 g NaCl per 100 g H_2O might be described as dilute when compared with a sodium chloride solution containing 30 g NaCl per 100 g H_2O. But the same solution might be described as concentrated when compared with a solution containing only 0.01 g NaCl per 100 g H_2O. You can see that the terms *concentrated* and *dilute* are only qualitative descriptions of the amount of a solute in solution.

How can concentration be expressed quantitatively? In chemistry, the most important unit of concentration is molarity. **Molarity (*M*)** is the number of moles of solute dissolved in one liter of solution. **To calculate the molarity of a solution, divide the moles of solute by the volume of the solution.**

$$\text{Molarity} \, (M) = \frac{\text{moles of solute}}{\text{liters of solution}}$$

Note that the volume involved is the total volume of the resulting solution, not the volume of the solvent alone. Molarity is also known as molar concentration. When the symbol *M* is accompanied by a numerical value, it is read as "molar." For example, a solution labeled 3*M* NaCl is read as three molar sodium chloride solution. Figure 16.8 demonstrates how to make a 0.5-molar solution, that is, a solution with a molarity of 0.5.

Figure 16.8 The photos show how to make a 0.5-molar (0.5*M*) solution. ⓐ Add 0.5 mol of solute to a 1-L volumetric flask half filled with distilled water. ⓑ Swirl the flask carefully to dissolve the solute. ⓒ Fill the flask with water exactly to the 1-L mark.

SAMPLE PROBLEM 16.2

Calculating the Molarity of a Solution

Intravenous (IV) saline solutions are often administered to patients in the hospital. One saline solution contains 0.90 g NaCl in exactly 100 mL of solution. What is the molarity of the solution?

① Analyze *List the knowns and the unknown.*

Knowns
- solution concentration = 0.90 g NaCl/100 mL
- molar mass NaCl = 58.5 g/mol

Unknown
- solution concentration = ?*M*

Convert the concentration from g/100 mL to mol/L. The sequence is g/100 mL → mol/100 mL → mol/L.

② Calculate *Solve for the unknown.*

Use the molar mass to convert g NaCl/100 mL to mol NaCl/100 mL. Then use the conversion factor between milliliters and liters to convert to mol/L, which is molarity.

$$\text{solution concentration} = \frac{0.90 \text{ g NaCl}}{100 \text{ mL}} \times \frac{1 \text{ mol NaCl}}{58.5 \text{ g NaCl}} \times \frac{1000 \text{ mL}}{1 \text{ L}}$$

$$= 0.15 \text{ mol/L} = 0.15M$$

③ Evaluate *Does the result make sense?*

The answer should be less than 1*M* because a concentration of 0.90 g/100 mL is the same as 9.0 g/1000 mL (9.0 g/1 L), and 9.0 g is less than 1 mol NaCl. The answer is correctly expressed to two significant figures.

Practice Problems

8. A solution has a volume of 2.0 L and contains 36.0 g of glucose ($C_6H_{12}O_6$). If the molar mass of glucose is 180 g/mol, what is the molarity of the solution?

9. A solution has a volume of 250 mL and contains 0.70 mol NaCl. What is its molarity?

Math **Handbook**

For help with dimensional analysis, go to page R66.

Problem-Solving 16.8 Solve Problem 8 with the help of an interactive guided tutorial.

── with **ChemASAP**

Sometimes, you may need to determine the number of moles of solute dissolved in a given volume of solution. You can do this if the molarity of the solution is known. For example, how many moles are in 2.00 L of 2.5M lithium chloride (LiCl)? Rearrange the formula for molarity to solve for the number of moles.

$$\text{Molarity } M = \frac{\text{moles of solute}}{\text{liters of solution}}$$

$$\text{Moles of solute} = \text{molarity } (M) \times \text{liters of solution } (V)$$

$$\text{Moles of LiCl} = 2.5\ M \times 2.00\ \text{L} = \left(\frac{2.5\ \text{mol}}{1\ \cancel{\text{L}}}\right) \times 2.00\ \cancel{\text{L}}$$

$$= 5.0\ \text{mol}$$

Thus 2.00 L of 2.5 M lithium chloride solution contains 5.0 mol LiCl.

SAMPLE PROBLEM 16.3

Finding the Moles of Solute in a Solution

Household laundry bleach is a dilute aqueous solution of sodium hypochlorite (NaClO). How many moles of solute are present in 1.5 L of 0.70M NaClO?

① Analyze *List the knowns and the unknown.*

Knowns
- volume of solution = 1.5 L
- solution concentration = 0.70M NaClO
- moles solute = $M \times \text{L} = \dfrac{\text{mol}}{\text{L}} \times \text{L}$

Unknown
- moles solute = ? mol

The conversion is volume of solution ⟶ moles of solute. Molarity has the units mol/L and is a conversion factor between moles of solute and volume of solution. Multiply the given volume by the molarity expressed in mol/L.

② Calculate *Solve for the unknown.*

$$\text{moles solute} = \frac{0.70\ \text{mol NaClO}}{1\ \cancel{\text{L}}} \times 1.5\ \cancel{\text{L}}$$

$$= 1.1\ \text{mol NaClO}$$

③ Evaluate *Does the result make sense?*

The answer should be greater than 1 mol but less than 1.5 mol because the solution concentration is less than 0.75 mol/L and the volume is less than 2 L. The answer is correctly expressed to two significant figures.

Math ▸ **Handbook**

For help with conversion problems, go to page R66.

Problem-Solving 16.11 Solve Problem 11 with the help of an interactive guided tutorial.

— with **ChemASAP**

Practice Problems

10. How many moles of ammonium nitrate are in 335 mL of 0.425M NH₄NO₃?

11. How many moles of solute are in 250 mL of 2.0M CaCl₂? How many grams of CaCl₂ is this?

Solution A
Concentrated solution

Solution B
Dilute solution

Solute particle

Solvent particle

300 mL
±5%

Figure 16.9 Adding solvent to a concentrated solution lowers the concentration, but the total number of moles of solute present remains the same.

Making Dilutions

Both solutions in Figure 16.9 contain the same solute. You can tell by the darker color of solution A that it is more concentrated than solution B; that is, solution A has the greater molarity. The more dilute solution B was made from solution A by adding more solvent. The procedure for diluting a solution is shown in Figure 16.10. 🔑 **Diluting a solution reduces the number of moles of solute per unit volume, but the total number of moles of solute in solution does not change.**

Moles of solute before dilution = moles of solute after dilution

Recall the definition of molarity.

$$\text{Molarity}\,(M) = \frac{\text{moles of solute}}{\text{liters of solution}}$$

Rearranging the equation gives an expression for moles of solute.

Moles of solute = molarity $(M) \times$ liters of solution (V)

The total number of moles of solute remains unchanged upon dilution, so you can write this equation.

Moles of solute $= M_1 \times V_1 = M_2 \times V_2$

M_1 and V_1 are the molarity and volume of the initial solution, and M_2 and V_2 are the molarity and volume of the diluted solution. Volumes can be in liters or milliliters, as long as the same units are used for both V_1 and V_2.

Figure 16.10 The student is preparing 100 mL of 0.40*M* $MgSO_4$ from a stock solution of 2.0*M* $MgSO_4$. ⓐ She measures 20 mL of the stock solution with a 20-mL pipet. ⓑ She transfers the 20 mL to a 100-mL volumetric flask. ⓒ She carefully adds water to the mark to make 100 mL of solution. **Inferring** *How many significant figures does the new molarity have?*

Figure 16.11 The photo shows a buret, a graduated cylinder, a volumetric flask, and a volumetric pipet. These are just some examples of volume-measuring devices.

SAMPLE PROBLEM 16.4

Preparing a Dilute Solution

How many milliliters of aqueous 2.00M MgSO$_4$ solution must be diluted with water to prepare 100.0 mL of aqueous 0.400M MgSO$_4$?

1 **Analyze** *List the knowns and the unknown.*

Knowns
- M_1 = 2.00M MgSO$_4$
- M_2 = 0.400M MgSO$_4$
- V_2 = 100.0 mL of 0.400M MgSO$_4$
- $M_1 \times V_1 = M_2 \times V_2$

Unknown
- V_1 = ? mL of 2.00M MgSO$_4$

2 **Calculate** *Solve for the unknown.*

Solving for V_1 yields:

$$V_1 = \frac{M_2 \times V_2}{M_1} = \frac{0.400M \times 100.0 \text{ mL}}{2.00M}$$

$$= 20.0 \text{ mL}$$

Thus 20.0 mL of the initial solution must be diluted by adding enough water to increase the volume to 100.0 mL.

3 **Evaluate** *Does the result make sense?*

The concentration of the initial solution is five times larger than the concentration of the diluted solution. Because the moles of solute in each solution are the same, the volume of the solution to be diluted (20.0 mL) should be one-fifth the final volume of the diluted solution. The answer is correctly expressed to three significant figures.

Practice Problems

12. How many milliliters of a solution of 4.00M KI are needed to prepare 250.0 mL of 0.760M KI?

13. How could you prepare 250 mL of 0.20M NaCl using only a solution of 1.0M NaCl and water?

For help with algebraic equations, go to p. R69.

Interactive Textbook

Problem-Solving 16.12 Solve Problem 12 with the help of an interactive guided tutorial.

with ChemASAP

Which of the volume-measuring devices shown in Figure 16.11 should you use to make a dilution? Your choice depends upon how accurate you want the concentration of the solution to be. The dilution described in Sample Problem 16.4 requires a molarity with three significant figures. For this you would need to measure 20.0 mL of the 2.00M MgSO$_4$ solution with a 20-mL volumetric pipet or a buret. A graduated cylinder could not provide the required accuracy. You would transfer the solution to a 100-mL volumetric flask and add distilled water to the flask exactly up to the etched line. The contents would then be exactly 100.0 mL of 0.400M MgSO$_4$. For measurements that require less accuracy, graduated cylinders are appropriate for measuring volumes.

Percent Solutions

Another way to describe the concentration of a solution is by the percent of a solute in the solvent. ➤ **The concentration of a solution in percent can be expressed in two ways: as the ratio of the volume of the solute to the volume of the solution or as the ratio of the mass of the solute to the mass of the solution.**

Concentration in Percent (Volume/Volume) If both the solute and the solvent are liquids, a convenient way to make a solution is to measure the volumes of the solute and the solution. The concentration of the solute is then expressed as a percent of the solution by volume. For example, isopropyl alcohol (2-propanol) is sold as a 91% solution, as shown in Figure 16.12. This solution consists of 91 mL of isopropyl alcohol mixed with enough water to make 100 mL of solution. The concentration can be expressed as 91 percent (volume/volume), or 91% (v/v). The relationship between percent by volume and the volumes of solute and solution is

$$\text{Percent by volume (\% (v/v))} = \frac{\text{volume of solute}}{\text{volume of solution}} \times 100\%$$

Figure 16.12 The label clearly distinguishes this solution of isopropyl alcohol from rubbing alcohol which is a 70% solution of isopropyl alcohol. **Applying Concepts** *How many milliliters of isopropyl alcohol are in 100 mL of 91% alcohol?*

SAMPLE PROBLEM 16.5

Calculating Percent (Volume/Volume)

What is the percent by volume of ethanol (C_2H_6O, or ethyl alcohol) in the final solution when 85 mL of ethanol is diluted to a volume of 250 mL with water?

❶ Analyze *List the knowns and the unknown.*

Knowns
- volume of ethanol = 85 mL
- volume of solution = 250 mL
- Percent by volume (% (v/v)) = $\dfrac{\text{volume of solute}}{\text{volume of solution}} \times 100\%$

Unknown
- % ethanol (v/v) = ? %

❷ Calculate *Solve for the unknown.*
Substitute the known values into the equation and solve.

$$\% \,(v/v) = \frac{85 \text{ mL ethanol}}{250 \text{ mL}} \times 100\%$$
$$= 34\% \text{ ethanol (v/v)}$$

❸ Evaluate *Does the result make sense?*
The volume of the solute is about one-third the volume of the solution, so the answer is reasonable. The answer is correctly expressed to two significant figures.

Practice Problems

14. If 10 mL of propanone (or acetone (C_3H_6O)) is diluted with water to a total solution volume of 200 mL, what is the percent by volume of propanone in the solution?

15. A bottle of the antiseptic hydrogen peroxide (H_2O_2) is labeled 3.0% (v/v). How many mL H_2O_2 are in a 400.0-mL bottle of this solution?

Math ▶ **Handbook**

For help with percents, go to page R72.

Textbook

Problem-Solving 16.14 Solve Problem 14 with the help of an interactive guided tutorial.

—— with **ChemASAP**

Concentration in Percent (Mass/Mass) Another way to express the concentration of a solution is as a percent (mass/mass), which is the number of grams of solute in 100 grams of solution. Percent by mass is sometimes a convenient unit of concentration when the solute is a solid. For example, a solution containing 7 g of sodium chloride in 100 grams of solution is 7 percent (mass/mass), or 7% (m/m).

$$\text{Percent by mass (\% (m/m))} = \frac{\text{mass of solute}}{\text{mass of solution}} \times 100\%$$

Suppose you want to make 2000 g of a solution of glucose in water that has a 2.8% (m/m) concentration of glucose. How much glucose should you use? In a 2.8 percent solution, each 100 g of solution contains 2.8 g of solute. Thus, to find the grams of solute, you can multiply the mass of the solution by the ratio of grams of solute to grams of solution.

$$200 \text{ g solution} \times \frac{2.8 \text{ g glucose}}{100 \text{ g solution}} = 56 \text{ g glucose}$$

How much solvent (water) should be used? The mass of the solvent equals the mass of the solution minus the mass of the solute or 1944 g (2000 g − 56 g). Thus a 2.8% (m/m) glucose solution contains 56 g of glucose dissolved in 1944 g of water.

Information is often expressed as percent composition on food labels. For example, the label on a fruit drink or on maple-flavored pancake syrup should show the percent of fruit juice or maple syrup contained in the product. Such information can be misleading unless the units are given. When you use percentages to express concentration, be sure to state the units (v/v) or (m/m).

16.2 Section Assessment

16. 🔑 **Key Concept** How do you calculate the molarity of a solution?

17. 🔑 **Key Concept** Compare the number of moles of solute before dilution with the number of moles of solute after dilution.

18. 🔑 **Key Concept** What are two ways of expressing the concentration of a solution as a percent?

19. Calculate the molarity of a solution containing 400 g $CuSO_4$ in 4.00 L of solution.

20. How many moles of solute are present in 50.0 mL of 0.20M KNO_3?

21. How many milliliters of a stock solution of 2.00M KNO_3 would you need to prepare 100.0 mL of 0.150M KNO_3?

22. What is the concentration, in percent (v/v), of a solution containing 50 mL of diethyl ether ($C_4H_{10}O$) in 2.5 L of solution?

23. How many grams of K_2SO_4 would you need to prepare 1500 g of 5.0% K_2SO_4 (m/m) solution?

Writing > Activity

Report Write a report comparing the concentration of fruit juice in different types of juice drinks. Is the percent of fruit juice given by % (v/v), or % (m/m)? Explain why these concentrations can be confusing or misleading.

interactive
Textbook

Assessment 16.2 Test yourself on the concepts in Section 16.2.

—— with **ChemASAP**

16.3 Colligative Properties of Solutions

Connecting to Your World

The wood frog is a remarkable creature because it can survive being frozen. Scientists believe that a substance in the cells of this frog acts as a natural antifreeze, which prevents the cells from freezing. Although fluids surrounding the frog's cells may freeze, the cells themselves do not. In this section, you will discover how a solute can change the freezing point of a solution.

Vapor-Pressure Lowering

You probably won't be surprised to learn that the physical properties of a solution differ from those of the pure solvent used to make the solution. After all, tea is not the same as pure water. But it might surprise you to learn that some of these differences in properties have little to do with the specific identity of the solute. Instead, they depend upon the number of solute particles in the solution. A property that depends only upon the number of solute particles, and not upon their identity is called a **colligative property.**

🔑 Three important colligative properties of solutions are vapor-pressure lowering, boiling-point elevation, and freezing-point depression.

Recall that vapor pressure is the pressure exerted by a vapor that is in dynamic equilibrium with its liquid in a closed system. A solution that contains a solute that is nonvolatile (not easily vaporized) always has a lower vapor pressure than the pure solvent, as shown in Figure 16.13. Glucose, a molecular compound, and sodium chloride, an ionic compound, are examples of nonvolatile solutes. When glucose or sodium chloride is dissolved in a solvent, the vapor pressure of the solution is lower than the vapor pressure of the pure solvent. Why is this true?

Guide for Reading

🔑 **Key Concepts**
- What are three colligative properties of solutions?
- What factor determines the amount by which a solution's vapor pressure, freezing point, and boiling point differ from those properties of the solvent?

Vocabulary
colligative property
freezing-point depression
boiling-point elevation

Reading Strategy
Relating Text and Visuals
As you read, look carefully at Figure 16.14. In your notebook, explain how this visual explains why equal molar solutions of different substances can have different freezing point depressions and boiling point elevations.

Figure 16.13 The vapor pressure of a solution of a nonvolatile solute is less than the vapor pressure of a pure solvent. ⓐ In a pure solvent, equilibrium is established between the liquid and the vapor. ⓑ In a solution, solute particles reduce the number of free solvent particles able to escape the liquid. Equilibrium is established at a lower vapor pressure. **Interpreting Diagrams** *How is decreased vapor pressure represented in the diagram?*

ⓐ Solvent particle   ⓑ Solute particle

Pure solvent   Higher vapor pressure   Solution containing nonvolatile solute   Lower vapor pressure

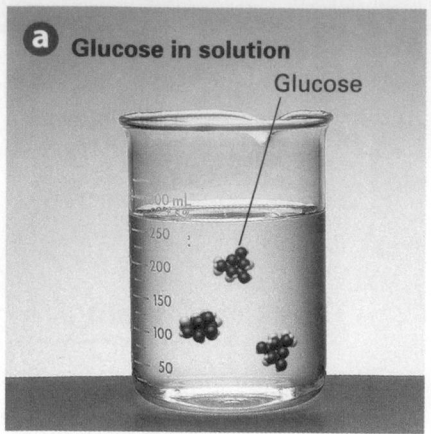

a Glucose in solution

Glucose

b Sodium chloride in solution

Na⁺

Cl⁻

c Calcium chloride in solution

Ca²⁺

Cl⁻

Figure 16.14 Particle concentrations differ for dissolved covalent and ionic compounds in water. **a** Three moles of glucose dissolved in water produce 3 mol of particles because glucose does not dissociate.

b Three moles of sodium chloride dissolved in water produce 6 mol of particles because each formula unit of NaCl dissociates into two ions.

c Three moles of calcium chloride dissolved in water produce 9 mol of particles because each formula unit of $CaCl_2$ dissociates into three ions.

In an aqueous solution of sodium chloride, sodium ions and chloride ions are dispersed throughout the liquid water. Both within the liquid and at the surface, the ions are surrounded by layers of associated water molecules, or shells of water of solvation. The formation of these shells of water of solvation reduces the number of solvent molecules that have enough kinetic energy to escape as vapor. Thus, the solution has a lower vapor pressure than the pure solvent (water) would have at the same temperature.

Ionic solutes that dissociate, such as sodium chloride and calcium chloride, have greater effects on the vapor pressure than does a nondissociating solute such as glucose. Recall that each formula unit of the ionic compound sodium chloride (NaCl) produces two particles in solution, a sodium ion and a chloride ion. Each formula unit of calcium chloride ($CaCl_2$) produces three particles, a calcium ion and two chloride ions. When glucose dissolves, the molecules do not dissociate. Figure 16.14 compares the number of particles in three solutions of the same concentration. The vapor-pressure lowering caused by 0.1 mol of sodium chloride in 1000 g of water is twice that caused by 0.1 mol of glucose in the same quantity of water. In the same way, 0.1 mol $CaCl_2$ in 1000 g of water produces three times the vapor-pressure lowering as 0.1 mol of glucose in the same quantity of water. 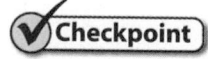 **The decrease in a solution's vapor pressure is proportional to the number of particles the solute makes in solution.**

Checkpoint *Which compound affects the vapor pressure of a solution the least: glucose, sodium chloride, or calcium chloride?*

Freezing-Point Depression

When a substance freezes, the particles of the solid take on an orderly pattern. The presence of a solute in water disrupts the formation of this pattern because of the shells of water of solvation. As a result, more kinetic energy must be withdrawn from a solution than from the pure solvent to cause the solution to solidify. The freezing point of a solution is lower than the freezing point of the pure solvent. The difference in temperature between the freezing point of a solution and the freezing point of the pure solvent is the **freezing-point depression.**

Go Online

NSTA *SciLINKS*

For: Links on Solutions
Visit: www.SciLinks.org
Web Code: cdn-1163

Solutions and Colloids

Purpose
To classify mixtures as solutions or colloids using the Tyndall effect.

Materials
- sodium hydrogen carbonate
- cornstarch
- stirring rod
- distilled water (or tap water)
- flashlight
- masking tape
- 3 jars with parallel sides
- teaspoon
- cup

Procedure

1. In a cup, make a paste by mixing $\frac{1}{2}$ teaspoon cornstarch with 4 teaspoons water.

2. Fill one of the jars with water. Add $\frac{1}{2}$ teaspoon sodium hydrogen carbonate to a second jar and fill with water. Stir to mix. Add the cornstarch paste to the third jar and fill with water. Stir to mix.

3. Turn out the lights in the room. Shine the beam of light from the flashlight at each of the jars and record your observations.

Analyze and Conclude

1. In which of the jars was it possible to see the path of the beam of light?

2. What made the light beam visible?

3. If a system that made the light beam visible were filtered, would the light beam be visible in the filtrate? Explain.

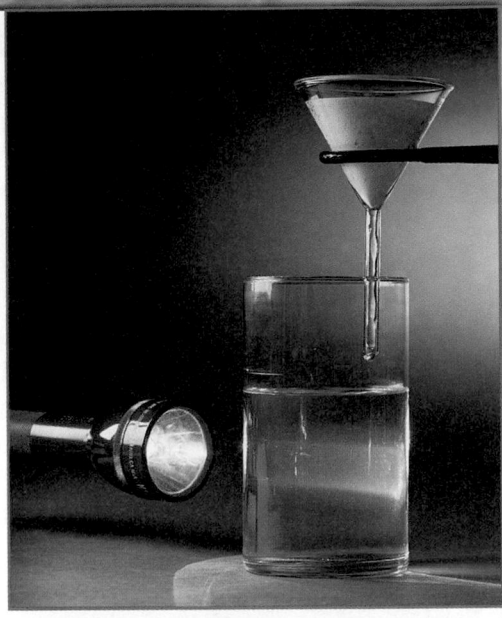

4. Predict what you would observe if you were to replace the sodium hydrogen carbonate with sucrose (cane sugar) or sodium chloride (table salt).

5. Predict what you would observe if you were to replace the cornstarch with flour or diluted milk.

6. Explain how you could use this method to distinguish a colloid from a suspension.

Freezing-point depression is another colligative property. 🔑 **The magnitude of the freezing-point depression is proportional to the number of solute particles dissolved in the solvent and does not depend upon their identity.** The addition of 1 mol of solute particles to 1000 g of water lowers the freezing point by 1.86°C. For example, if you add 1 mol (180 g) of glucose to 1000 g of water, the solution freezes at −1.86°C. However, if you add 1 mol (58.5 g) of sodium chloride to 1000 g of water, the solution freezes at −3.72°C, double the change for glucose. This is because 1 mol NaCl produces 2 mol of particles, and thus doubles the freezing-point depression. The freezing-point depression of aqueous solutions makes walks and driveways safer when people, like the man in Figure 16.15, sprinkle salt on icy surfaces to make the ice melt. The melted ice forms a solution with a lower freezing point than that of pure water. Similarly, ethylene glycol ($C_2H_6O_2$, antifreeze) is added to the water in automobile cooling systems to depress the freezing point of the water below 0°C. Automobiles can thus withstand subfreezing temperatures without freezing up.

Figure 16.15 Surfaces can be free of ice even at temperatures below freezing if salt is applied. **Inferring** *Why would calcium chloride ($CaCl_2$) be a better salt for this purpose than sodium chloride (NaCl)?*

Boiling-Point Elevation

The boiling point of a substance is the temperature at which the vapor pressure of the liquid phase equals atmospheric pressure. As you just learned, adding a nonvolatile solute to a liquid solvent decreases the vapor pressure of the solvent. Because of the decrease in vapor pressure, additional kinetic energy must be added to raise the vapor pressure of the liquid phase of the solution to atmospheric pressure and initiate boiling. Thus the boiling point of a solution is higher than the boiling point of the pure solvent. The difference in temperature between the boiling point of a solution and the boiling point of the pure solvent is the **boiling-point elevation.** The same antifreeze, added to automobile engines to prevent freeze-ups in winter, protects the engine from boiling over in summer.

Remember that boiling-point elevation is a colligative property; it depends on the concentration of particles, not on their identity. Thus you can think about boiling-point elevation in terms of particles. It takes additional kinetic energy for the solvent particles to overcome the attractive forces that keep them in the liquid. Thus the presence of a solute elevates the boiling point of the solvent. **The magnitude of the boiling-point elevation is proportional to the number of solute particles dissolved in the solvent.** The boiling point of water increases by 0.512°C for every mole of particles that the solute forms when dissolved in 1000 g of water.

Elevating the boiling point of a solution has some familiar applications. For example, to make fudge, a lot of sugar and some flavorings are mixed with water and the solution is boiled, as shown in Figure 16.16. As the water slowly boils away, the concentration of sugar in the solution increases. As the concentration increases, the boiling point steadily rises. The fudge recipe may advise using a candy thermometer. At a temperature specified in the recipe, the concentration of the mixture will be such that the fudge will solidify into a delicious treat.

Figure 16.16 As you watch the temperature on a candy thermometer rise, you know that the solution is becoming more concentrated.

16.3 Section Assessment

24. **Key Concept** What are three colligative properties of solutions?

25. **Key Concept** What factor determines how much the vapor pressure, freezing point, and boiling point of a solution differ from those properties of the pure solvent?

26. Would a dilute or a concentrated sodium fluoride solution have a higher boiling point? Explain.

27. An equal number of moles of KI and MgF₂ are dissolved in equal volumes of water. Which solution has the higher
    a. boiling point?
    b. vapor pressure?
    c. freezing point?

28. Explain why the vapor pressure, boiling point, and freezing point of a solution of a nonvolatile solute are not the same as those of the pure solvent.

Connecting ▶ **Concepts**

Vapor Pressure Review what you learned in Chapter 13 about the vapor pressure of liquids and their boiling points. Explain why only nonvolatile solutes cause the elevation of the solvent's boiling point.

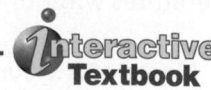

Assessment 16.3 Test yourself on the concepts in Section 16.3.

—— with **ChemASAP**

16.4 Calculations Involving Colligative Properties

 New York Standards: M2.1a, 3.1qq

Connecting to Your World

Cooking instructions for a wide variety of foods, from dried pasta to packaged beans to frozen fruits to fresh vegetables, often call for the addition of a small amount of salt to the cooking water. Most people like the flavor of food cooked with salt. But adding salt can have another effect on the cooking process. Recall that dissolved salt elevates the boiling point of water. Suppose you added a teaspoon of salt to two liters of water. A teaspoon of salt has a mass of about 20 g. Would the resulting boiling point increase be enough to shorten the time required for cooking? In this section, you will learn how to calculate the amount the boiling point of the cooking water would rise.

Guide for Reading

Key Concepts
- What are two ways of expressing the concentration of a solution?
- How are freezing-point depression and boiling-point elevation related to molality?

Vocabulary

molality (*m*)

mole fraction

molal freezing-point depression constant (K_f)

molal boiling-point elevation constant (K_b)

Reading Strategy

Before you read, make a list of the vocabulary terms above. As you read, write the symbols or formulas that apply to each term and describe them using words.

Molality and Mole Fraction

Recall that colligative properties depend only upon solute concentration. **The unit molality and mole fractions are two additional ways in which chemists express the concentration of a solution.** The unit **molality (*m*)** is the number of moles of solute dissolved in 1 kilogram (1000 g) of solvent. Molality is also known as molal concentration.

$$\text{Molality} = \frac{\text{moles of solute}}{\text{kilogram of solvent}}$$

Note that molality is not the same as molarity. Molality refers to moles of solute per kilogram of solvent rather than moles of solute per liter of solution. In the case of water as the solvent, 1 kg or 1000 g equals a volume of 1000 mL, or 1 L.

You can prepare a solution that is 1.00 molal (1*m*) in glucose, for example, by adding 1.00 mol (180 g) of glucose to 1000 g of water. Figure 16.17 shows how a 0.500 molal (0.500*m*) solution in sodium chloride is prepared by dissolving 0.500 mol (29.3 g) of NaCl in 1.000 kg (1000 g) of water.

0.500 mol (29.3 g) NaCl

1.000 kg H_2O

Figure 16.17 To make a 0.500*m* solution of NaCl, use a balance to measure 1.000 kg of water and add 0.500 mol (29.3 g) NaCl. **Calculating** *What would be the molality if only 0.500 kg of water were used?*

Figure 16.18 Ethylene glycol (EG) is added to water as antifreeze in the proportions shown. A mole fraction is the ratio of the number of moles of one substance to the total number of moles of all substances in the solution. **Inferring** *What is the sum of all mole fractions in a solution?*

1.25 mol EG

4.00 mol H₂O

Total moles = Ⓐ + Ⓑ = 5.25 mol

$$\text{Mole fraction EG} = \frac{Ⓐ}{Ⓐ + Ⓑ} = \frac{1.25}{5.25}$$

$$\text{Mole fraction H}_2\text{O} = \frac{Ⓑ}{Ⓐ + Ⓑ} = \frac{4.00}{5.25}$$

SAMPLE PROBLEM 16.6

Using Solution Molality

How many grams of potassium iodide must be dissolved in 500.0 g of water to produce a 0.060 molal KI solution?

1 Analyze *List the knowns and the unknown.*

Knowns
- mass of water = 500.0g = 0.5000 kg
- solution concentration = 0.060m
- molar mass KI = 166.0 g/mol

Unknown
- mass of solute = ? g KI

According to the definition of molal, the final solution must contain 0.060 mol KI per 1000 g H₂O. Use the molality as a conversion factor to convert from mass of water to moles of the solute (KI). Then use the molar mass of KI to convert from mol KI to g KI. The steps are

$$\text{mass of H}_2\text{O} \longrightarrow \text{mol KI} \longrightarrow \text{g KI}.$$

2 Calculate *Solve for the unknown.*

$$0.5000 \text{ kg H}_2\text{O} \times \frac{0.060 \text{ mol KI}}{1.000 \text{ kg H}_2\text{O}} \times \frac{166.0 \text{ g KI}}{1 \text{ mol KI}} = 5.0 \text{ g KI}$$

3 Evaluate *Does the result make sense?*

A 1 molal KI solution is one molar mass of KI (166.0 g) dissolved in 1000 g of water. The desired molal concentration (0.060m) is about $\frac{1}{20}$ of that value, so the mass of KI should be much less than the molar mass. The answer is correctly expressed to two significant figures.

Practice Problems

29. How many grams of sodium fluoride are needed to prepare a 0.400m NaF solution that contains 750 g of water?

30. Calculate the molality of a solution prepared by dissolving 10.0 g NaCl in 600 g of water.

Math Handbook

For help with dimensional analysis, go to page R66.

interactive **Textbook**

Problem-Solving 16.29 Solve Problem 29 with the help of an interactive guided tutorial.

— with **ChemASAP**

The concentration of a solution also can be expressed as a mole fraction, as shown in Figure 16.18. The **mole fraction** of a solute in a solution is the ratio of the moles of that solute to the total number of moles of solvent and solute. In a solution containing n_A mol of solute A and n_B mol of solvent B, the mole fraction of solute A (X_A) and the mole fraction of solvent B (X_B) can be expressed as follows.

$$X_A = \frac{n_A}{n_A + n_B} \qquad X_B = \frac{n_B}{n_A + n_B}$$

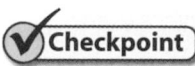 **Checkpoint** *What is a mole fraction?*

SAMPLE PROBLEM 16.7

Calculating Mole Fractions

Ethylene glycol ($C_2H_6O_2$) is added to automobile cooling systems to protect against cold weather. What is the mole fraction of each component in a solution containing 1.25 mol of ethylene glycol (EG) and 4.00 mol of water?

Figure 16.19 The concentration of antifreeze used in an automobile cooling system can be described by mole fractions.

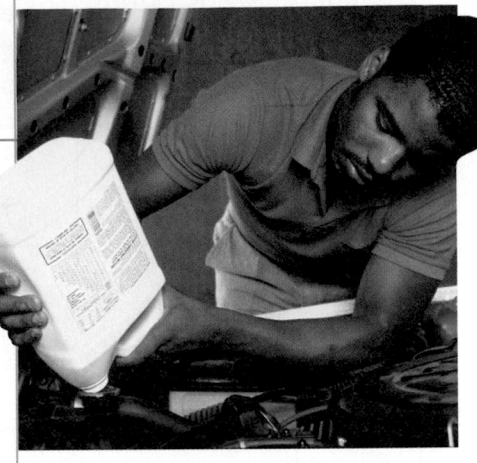

① Analyze *List the knowns and the unknowns.*

Knowns
- moles of ethylene glycol (n_{EG}) = 1.25 mol EG
- moles of water (n_{H_2O}) = 4.00 mol H_2O

Unknowns
- mole fraction EG (X_{EG}) = ?
- mole fraction H_2O (X_{H_2O}) = ?

The mole fraction of ethylene glycol (X_{EG}) in the solution is the number of moles of ethylene glycol divided by the total number of moles in the solution:

$$X_{EG} = \frac{n_{EG}}{n_{EG} + n_{H_2O}}$$

Similarly, the mole fraction of water (X_{H_2O}) in the solution is the number of moles of water divided by the total number of moles in the solution:

$$X_{H_2O} = \frac{n_{H_2O}}{n_{EG} + n_{H_2O}}$$

② Calculate *Solve for the unknowns.*

$$X_{EG} = \frac{n_{EG}}{n_{EG} + n_{H_2O}} = \frac{1.25 \text{ mol}}{1.25 \text{ mol} + 4.00 \text{ mol}} = 0.238$$

$$X_{H_2O} = \frac{n_{H_2O}}{n_{EG} + n_{H_2O}} = \frac{4.00 \text{ mol}}{1.25 \text{ mol} + 4.00 \text{ mol}} = 0.762$$

Math → Handbook

For help with using a calculator, go to page R62.

③ Evaluate *Does the result make sense?*

The mole fraction is a dimensionless quantity. The sum of the mole fractions of all the components in a solution must equal 1. Note that $X_{EG} + X_{H_2O} = 1.000$. Each answer is correctly expressed to three significant figures.

Practice Problems

31. What is the mole fraction of each component in a solution made by mixing 300 g of ethanol (C_2H_5OH) and 500 g of water?

32. A solution contains 50.0 g of carbon tetrachloride (CCl_4) and 50.0 g of chloroform ($CHCl_3$). Calculate the mole fraction of each component in the solution.

Interactive Textbook

Problem-Solving 16.31 Solve Problem 31 with the help of an interactive guided tutorial.

— with **ChemASAP**

Table 16.2

K_f Values for Some Common Solvents

Solvent	K_f (°C/m)
Water	1.86
Acetic acid	3.90
Benzene	5.12
Nitrobenzene	7.00
Phenol	7.40
Cyclohexane	20.2
Camphor	37.7

Interactive Textbook

Simulation 21 Discover the principle underlying the colligative properties of solutions.

with ChemASAP

Freezing-Point Depression and Boiling-Point Elevation

The graph in Figure 16.20 shows that the freezing point of a solvent is lowered and its boiling point is raised by the addition of a nonvolatile solute. **The magnitudes of the freezing-point depression (ΔT_f) and the boiling-point elevation (ΔT_b) of a solution are directly proportional to the molal concentration (m), when the solute is molecular, not ionic.**

$$\Delta T_f \propto m \quad \Delta T_b \propto m$$

The change in the freezing temperature (ΔT_f) is the difference between the freezing point of the solution and the freezing point of the pure solvent. Similarly, the change in the boiling temperature (ΔT_b) is the difference between the boiling point of the solution and the boiling point of the pure solvent. The term m is the molal concentration of the solution.

With the addition of a constant, the proportionality between the freezing point depression (ΔT_f) and the molality m can be expressed as an equation.

$$\Delta T_f = K_f \times m$$

The constant, K_f, is the **molal freezing-point depression constant,** which is equal to the change in freezing point for a 1-molal solution of a nonvolatile molecular solute. The value of K_f depends upon the solvent. Its units are °C/m. Table 16.2 lists the K_f values for water and some other solvents.

The boiling-point elevation of a solution can also be expressed as an equation.

$$\Delta T_b = K_b \times m$$

The constant, K_b, is the **molal boiling-point elevation constant,** which is equal to the change in boiling point for a 1-molal solution of a nonvolatile molecular solute. The value of K_b depends upon the solvent. Its units are °C/m. Table 16.3 lists the K_b values for water and some other solvents.

Figure 16.20 The graph shows the relationship between vapor pressure and temperature for pure water and aqueous solutions.

INTERPRETING GRAPHS

a. Identify What is the freezing point of water? What is the boiling point?

b. Describe How do the freezing and boiling points of the solution compare to those of pure water?

c. Apply Concepts Does adding a solute to water allow it to remain as a liquid over a longer or shorter temperature range? Explain.

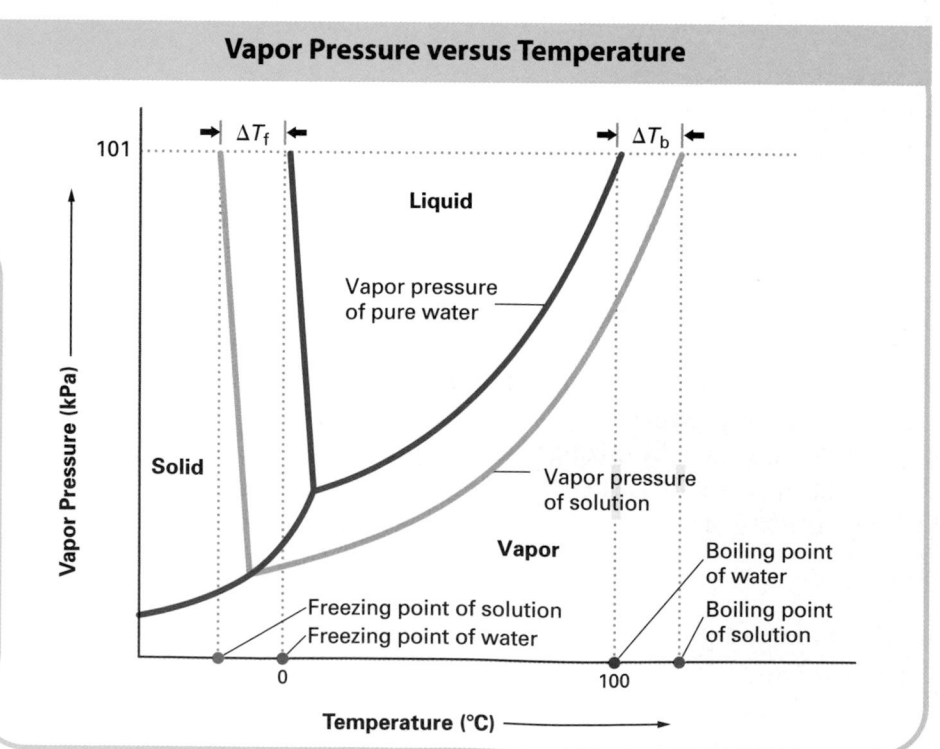

Vapor Pressure versus Temperature

Sample Problem 16.8 shows how these equations can be used for calculating ΔT_f and ΔT_b of solutions if the solute is a molecular compound. For ionic compounds, both the freezing-point depression and the boiling-point elevation depend upon the number of ions produced by each formula unit. This number is used to calculate an effective molality, as shown in Sample Problem 16.9.

Table 16.3

K_b Values for Some Common Solvents

Solvent	K_b (°C/m)
Water	0.512
Ethanol	1.19
Benzene	2.53
Cyclohexane	2.79
Acetic acid	3.07
Phenol	3.56
Nitrobenzene	5.24
Camphor	5.95

SAMPLE PROBLEM 16.8

Calculating the Freezing-Point Depression of a Solution

Antifreeze protects a car from freezing. It also protects it from overheating. Calculate the freezing-point depression and the freezing point of a solution containing 100 g of ethylene glycol ($C_2H_6O_2$) antifreeze in 0.500 kg of water.

1 Analyze *List the knowns and the unknown.*

Knowns
- mass of solute = 100 g $C_2H_6O_2$
- mass of solution = 0.500 kg H_2O
- K_f for H_2O = 1.86°C/m
- $\Delta T_f = K_f \times m$

Unknown
- ΔT_f = °C
- freezing point = ?°C

Calculate the number of moles of solute and the molality. Then calculate the freezing-point depression and freezing point.

2 Calculate *Solve for the unknown.*

$$\text{moles } C_2H_6O_2 = 100 \text{ g } C_2H_6O_2 \times \frac{1 \text{ mol}}{62.0 \text{ g } C_2H_6O_2} = 1.61 \text{ mol}$$

$$m = \frac{\text{mol solute}}{\text{kg solvent}} = \frac{1.61 \text{ mol}}{0.500 \text{ kg}} = 3.22m$$

$$\Delta T_f = K_f \times m = 1.86°C/m \times 3.22m = 5.99°C$$

The freezing point of the solution is 0.00°C − 5.99°C = −5.99°C.

3 Evaluate *Does the result make sense?*

A 1-molal solution reduces the freezing temperature by 1.86°C, so a decrease of 5.99°C for an approximately 3-molal solution is reasonable. The answer is correctly expressed with three significant figures.

> **Math Handbook**
>
> For help with algebraic equations, go to page R69.

Practice Problems

33. What is the freezing point depression of an aqueous solution of 10.0 g of glucose ($C_6H_{12}O_6$) in 50.0 g H_2O?

34. Calculate the freezing-point depression of a benzene solution containing 400 g of benzene and 200 g of the molecular compound acetone (C_3H_6O). K_f for benzene is 5.12°C/m.

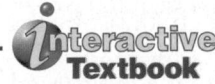

interactive Textbook

Problem–Solving 16.33 Solve Problem 33 with the help of an interactive guided tutorial.

with **ChemASAP**

SAMPLE PROBLEM 16.9

Calculating the Boiling Point of an Ionic Solution

What is the boiling point of a 1.50m NaCl solution?

1 Analyze *List the knowns and the unknown.*

Knowns
- concentration = 1.50m NaCl
- K_b for H_2O = 0.512°C/m
- $\Delta T_b = K_b \times m$

Unknown
- boiling point = ?°C

Each formula unit of NaCl dissociates into two particles, Na^+ and Cl^-. Based on the total number of dissociated particles, the effective molality is $2 \times 1.50m = 3.00m$. Calculate the boiling-point elevation and then add it to 100°C.

Math Handbook

For help with significant figures, go to page R59.

2 Calculate *Solve for the unknown.*

$$\Delta T_b = K_b \times m = \frac{0.512°C}{m} \times 3.00m = 1.54°C$$

The boiling point of the solution is 100°C + 1.54°C = 101.54°C

3 Evaluate *Does the result make sense?*

The boiling point increases about 0.5°C for each mole of solute particles, so the total change is reasonable. Because the boiling point of water is defined as exactly 100°C, this value does not limit the number of significant figures in the solution of the problem.

Problem-Solving 16.36 Solve Problem 36 with the help of an interactive guided tutorial.

— with **ChemASAP**

Practice Problems

35. What is the boiling point of a solution that contains 1.25 mol CaCl$_2$ in 1400 g of water?

36. What mass of NaCl would have to be dissolved in 1.000 kg of water to raise the boiling point by 2.00°C?

16.4 Section Assessment

37. 🔑 **Key Concept** What are two ways of expressing the ratio of solute particles to solvent particles?

38. 🔑 **Key Concept** How are freezing-point depression and boiling-point elevation related to molality?

39. How many grams of sodium bromide must be dissolved in 400.0 g of water to produce a 0.500 molal solution?

40. Calculate the mole fraction of each component in a solution of 2.50 mol ethanoic acid (CH$_3$COOH) in 10.00 mol of water.

41. What is the freezing point of a solution of 12.0 g of CCl$_4$ dissolved in 750.0 g of benzene? The freezing point of benzene is 5.48°C; K_f is 5.12°C/m.

Elements Handbook

Element Distribution Look at the table on page R4 of the Elements Handbook showing the distribution of elements in the oceans. What generalization can you make about the temperature at which ocean water will freeze? What effect does the presence of dissolved elements in the ocean have on the rate of evaporation of ocean water?

Assessment 16.4 Test yourself on the concepts in Section 16.4.

— with **ChemASAP**

Small-Scale LAB

Making a Solution

Purpose
To make a solution and use carefully measured data to calculate the solution's concentration.

Materials
- solid NaCl
- water
- 50-mL volumetric flask
- balance

Procedure
Measure the mass of a clean, dry, volumetric flask. Add enough solid NaCl to approximately fill one-tenth of the volume of the flask. Measure the mass of the flask again. Half fill the flask with water and shake it gently until all the NaCl dissolves. Fill the flask with water to the 50-mL mark and measure the mass again.

Analyze
Using your experimental data, record the answers to the following questions below your data table.

1. Percent by mass tells how many grams of solute are present in 100 g of solution.

$$\% \text{ by mass} = \frac{\text{mass of solute}}{\text{mass of solute} + \text{solvent}} \times 100\%$$

   a. Calculate the mass of the solute (NaCl).
   b. Calculate the mass of the solvent (water).
   c. Calculate the percent by mass of NaCl in the solution.

2. Mole fraction tells how many moles of solute are present for every 1 mol of total solution.

$$\text{Mole fraction} = \frac{\text{mol NaCl}}{\text{mol NaCl} + \text{mol H}_2\text{O}}$$

   a. Calculate the moles of NaCl solute.
      Molar mass NaCl = 58.5 g/mol
   b. Calculate the moles of water.
      Molar mass H_2O = 18 g/mol
   c. Calculate the mole fraction of your solution.

3. Molality (m) tells how many moles of solute are present in 1 kg of solvent.

$$m = \frac{\text{mol NaCl}}{\text{kg H}_2\text{O}}$$

Calculate the molality of your solution.

4. Molarity (M) tells how many moles of solute are dissolved in 1 L of solution.

$$M = \frac{\text{mol NaCl}}{\text{L solution}}$$

   a. Calculate the liters of solution. 1000 mL = 1 L
   b. Calculate the molarity of the NaCl solution.

5. Density tells how many grams of solution are present in 1 mL of solution.

$$\text{Density} = \frac{\text{g solution}}{\text{mL solution}}$$

Calculate the density of the solution.

You're The Chemist
The following small-scale activities allow you to develop your own procedures and analyze the results.

1. **Analyze It** Use a small-scale pipet to extract a sample of your NaCl solution and deliver it to a massed empty plastic bottle. Measure the mass of the bottle and fill it with water to the 50-mL line. Measure the mass of the bottle again. Calculate the concentration of this dilute solution using the same units you used to calculate the concentration of the NaCl solution. Are the results you obtained reasonable?

2. **Design It!** Design and carry out an experiment to make a solution of table sugar quantitatively. Calculate the concentration of the table sugar solution using the same units you used to calculate the concentration of the NaCl solution. Is the effective molality of the table sugar solution the same as the effective molality of a sodium chloride solution of the same concentration? Recall that effective molality is the concentration value used to calculate boiling-point elevation and freezing-point depression.

Key Concepts

16.1 Properties of Solutions

- Whether or not a substance dissolves depends upon the nature of the solvent and the solute. Factors that determine how fast a substance dissolves are stirring, temperature, and surface area.
- Solubility is usually expressed in grams of solute per 100 g of solvent.
- The amount of solute that dissolves in a given solvent depends upon the temperature and pressure.

16.2 Concentrations of Solutions

- To calculate the molarity of a solution, divide the moles of solute by the volume of the solution in liters.
- Diluting a solution does not change the total number of moles of solute in solution.

- The concentration of a solution in percent is the ratio of the volume of the solute to the volume of the solution times 100% or the ratio of the mass of the solute to the mass of the solution times 100%.

16.3 Colligative Properties of Solutions

- Three colligative properties of solutions are vapor-pressure lowering, freezing-point depression, and boiling-point elevation.
- The magnitude of each colligative property is directly proportional to the number of solute molecules or ions present.

16.4 Calculations Involving Colligative Properties

- Molality and mole fractions are two additional ways of expressing the concentration of a solution.
- Freezing-point depression and boiling-point elevation are proportional to molality.

Vocabulary

- boiling-point elevation (p. 490)
- concentrated solution (p. 480)
- concentration (p. 480)
- colligative property (p. 487)
- dilute solution (p. 480)
- freezing-point depression (p. 488)

- Henry's law (p. 476)
- immiscible (p. 473)
- miscible (p. 473)
- molal freezing-point depression constant (K_f) (p. 494)
- molal boiling-point elevation constant (K_b) (p. 494)
- molality (m) (p. 491)

- molarity (M) (p. 480)
- mole fraction (p. 492)
- saturated solution (p. 473)
- solubility (p. 473)
- supersaturated solution (p. 474)
- unsaturated solution (p. 473)

Key Equations

- Henry's law: $\dfrac{S_1}{P_1} = \dfrac{S_2}{P_2}$

- Molarity (M) = $\dfrac{\text{moles of solute}}{\text{liters of solution}}$

- $M_1 \times V_1 = M_2 \times V_2$

- Percent by volume = $\dfrac{\text{volume of solute}}{\text{volume of solution}} \times 100\%$

- Percent by mass = $\dfrac{\text{mass of solute}}{\text{mass of solution}} \times 100\%$

- Molality = $\dfrac{\text{moles of solute}}{\text{kilogram of solvent}}$

- Mole fractions: $X_A = \dfrac{n_A}{n_A + n_B}$ $X_B = \dfrac{n_B}{n_A + n_B}$

- $\Delta T_f = K_f \times m$

- $\Delta T_b = K_b \times m$

16.1 Properties of Solutions

42. Name and distinguish between the two components of a solution.

43. Explain why the dissolved component does not settle out of a solution.

44. Define the following terms: solubility, saturated solution, and unsaturated solution.

45. If a saturated solution of sodium nitrate is cooled, what change might you observe?

46. Can a solution with undissolved solute be supersaturated? Explain.

47. What mass of $AgNO_3$ can be dissolved in 250 g of water at 20°C? Use Table 16.1.

48. What is the effect of pressure on the solubility of gases in liquids?

49. The solubility of methane, the major component of natural gas, in water at 20°C and 1.00 atm pressure is 0.026 g/L. If the temperature remains constant, what will be the solubility of this gas at the following pressures?
    a. 0.60 atm   **b.** 1.80 atm

50. You are given a clear aqueous solution containing KNO_3. How would you determine experimentally if the solution is unsaturated, saturated, or supersaturated?

51. Plot a graph of solubility versus temperature for the three gases listed in Table 16.1.

52. The solubility of KCl in water is 34.0 g KCl/100 g H_2O at 20°C. A warm solution containing 50.0 g KCl in 130 g H_2O is cooled to 20°C.
    a. How many grams of KCl remain dissolved?
    b. How many grams came out of solution?

53. A solution contains 26.5 g NaCl in 75.0 g H_2O at 20°C. Determine if the solution is unsaturated, saturated, or supersaturated. (The solubility of NaCl at 20°C is 36.0 g/100 g H_2O.)

54. How many grams of $NaNO_3$ will precipitate if a saturated solution of $NaNO_3$ in 200 g H_2O at 50°C is cooled to 20°C?

55. One way to express the solubility of a compound is in terms of moles of compound that will dissolve in 1 kg of water. Solubility depends on temperature. Plot a graph of the solubility of potassium nitrate (KNO_3) from the following data.

Temperature (C°)	Solubility (mol/kg)
0	1.61
20	2.80
40	5.78
60	11.20
80	16.76
100	24.50

From your graph estimate
a. the solubility of KNO_3 at 76°C and at 33°C.
b. the temperature at which its solubility is 17.6 mol/kg of water.
c. the temperature at which the solubility is 4.24 mol/kg of water.

16.2 Concentrations of Solutions

56. Knowing the molarity of a solution is more meaningful than knowing whether a solution is dilute or concentrated. Explain.

57. Calculate the molarity of each solution.
    a. 1.0 mol KCl in 750 mL of solution
    b. 0.50 mol $MgCl_2$ in 1.5 L of solution

58. How many milliliters of 0.500M KCl solution would you need to dilute to make 100.0 mL of 0.100M KCl?

59. Calculate the moles and grams of solute in each solution.
    a. 1.0 L of 0.50M NaCl
    b. 5.0×10^2 mL of 2.0M KNO_3
    c. 250 mL of 0.10M $CaCl_2$

60. Calculate the grams of solute required to make the following solutions.
    a. 2500 g of saline solution (0.90% NaCl (m/m))
    b. 0.050 kg of 4.0% $MgCl_2$ (m/m)

61. What is the concentration (in % (v/v)) of the following solutions?
    a. 25 mL of ethanol (C_2H_5OH) is diluted to a volume of 150 mL with water.
    b. 175 mL of isopropyl alcohol (C_3H_7OH) is diluted with water to a total volume of 275 mL.

NEW YORK

62. Hydrogen peroxide is often sold commercially as a 3.0% (m/v) aqueous solution.
   a. If you buy a 250-mL bottle of 3.0% H_2O_2 (m/v), how many grams of hydrogen peroxide have you purchased?
   b. What is the molarity of this solution?

63. When an excess of zinc is added to 800 mL of a hydrochloric acid solution, the solution evolves 1.21 L of hydrogen gas measured over water at 21°C and 747.5 mm Hg. What was the molarity of the acid? The vapor pressure of water at 21°C is 18.6 mm Hg.

64. How many milliliters of $1.50M$ HNO_3 contain enough nitric acid to dissolve an old copper penny with a mass of 3.94 g?

$$3Cu + 8HNO_3 \longrightarrow 3Cu(NO_3)_2 + 2NO + 4H_2O$$

65. The Na_2SO_4 in a 250-mL sample of solution reacts with an excess of $BaCl_2$, and 5.28 g $BaSO_4$ is precipitated.
   a. Write a balanced chemical equation for this reaction.
   b. How many moles of $BaSO_4$ are produced?
   c. How many moles of Na_2SO_4 reacted?
   d. What is the molarity of the Na_2SO_4 solution?

16.3 Colligative Properties of Solutions

66. What are colligative properties? Identify three colligative properties and explain why each occurs.

67. Which has the higher boiling point?
   a. seawater or distilled water
   b. $1.0M$ KNO_3 or $1.5M$ KNO_3
   c. $0.100M$ KCl or $0.100M$ $MgCl_2$

68. How does the freezing point of a $1m$ solution of calcium nitrate compare to a $1.5m$ solution of sodium nitrate?

69. Explain how a decrease in the vapor pressure of a solution results in an increase in its boiling point.

70. In old-fashioned ice cream makers, a mixture of rock salt (NaCl) and ice is used to cool the creamy mixture as it is stirred. What is the purpose of the salt?

71. How many moles of ions are present when 0.10 mol of each compound is dissolved in water?
   a. K_2SO_4 **b.** $Fe(NO_3)_3$ **c.** $Al_2(SO_4)_3$ **d.** $NiSO_4$

72. Why might calcium chloride spread on icy roads be more effective at melting ice than an equal number of moles of sodium chloride?

16.4 Calculations Involving Colligative Properties

73. Distinguish between a $1M$ solution and a $1m$ solution.

74. Describe how you would make an aqueous solution of methanol (CH_3OH) in which there are 2 mol of methanol to every 5 mol of solution.

75. What is the boiling point of each solution?
   a. 0.50 mol glucose in 1000 g H_2O
   b. 1.50 mol NaCl in 1000 g H_2O

76. What is the freezing point of each solution?
   a. 1.40 mol Na_2SO_4 in 1750 g H_2O
   b. 0.060 mol $MgSO_4$ in 100 g H_2O

77. Determine the freezing points of each $0.20m$ aqueous solution.
   a. K_2SO_4 **b.** $CsNO_3$ **c.** $Al(NO_3)_3$

78. Different numbers of moles of two different solutes, A and B, were added to identical quantities of water. The graph shows the freezing point of each of the solutions formed.

Freezing Point of Solutions

   a. Explain the relative slopes of the two lines between 0 and 2 mol of solute added.
   b. Why does the freezing point for solution A not continue to drop as amounts of solute A are added beyond 2.4 mol?

79. Calculate the freezing- and boiling-point changes for a solution containing 12.0 g of naphthalene ($C_{10}H_8$) in 50.0 g of benzene.

80. Describe how you would prepare an aqueous solution of acetone (CH_3COCH_3) in which there is 1 mol acetone for every 4 mol of solution.

81. The solubility of sodium hydrogen carbonate ($NaHCO_3$) in water at 20°C is 9.6 g/100 g H_2O. What is the mole fraction of $NaHCO_3$ in a saturated solution? What is the molality of the solution?

82. A solution is labeled 0.150m NaCl. What are the mole fractions of the solute and solvent in this solution?

83. A mixture of ethylene glycol (EG) and water is used as antifreeze in automobile engines. The freezing point and specific gravity of the mixture vary with the percent by mass of (EG) in the mixture. Specific gravity relates the mass of a substance to the mass of an equal volume of water. On the following graph, point A represents 20% (EG) by mass; point B, 40%; and point C, 60%.

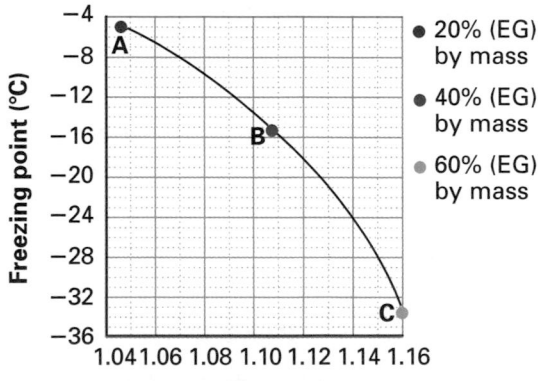

a. What is the specific gravity of the antifreeze mixture that freezes at −25°C?

b. What is the freezing point of a mixture that has a specific gravity of 1.06?

c. Estimate the freezing point of a mixture that is 30% by mass (EG).

84. Calculate the freezing point and the boiling point of a solution that contains 15.0 g of urea (CH_4N_2O) in 250 g of water. Urea is a covalently bonded compound.

85. Calculate the mole fractions in a solution that is 25.0 g of ethanol (C_2H_5OH) and 40.0 g of water.

86. Estimate the freezing point of an aqueous solution of 20.0 g of glucose ($C_6H_{12}O_6$) dissolved in 500.0 g of water.

87. An aqueous solution freezes at −2.47°C. What is its boiling point?

88. What is the molar mass of a nondissociating compound if 5.76 g of the compound in 750 g of benzene gives a freezing-point depression of 0.460°C?

89. The molarity of an aqueous solution of sugar ($C_{12}H_{22}O_{11}$) is 1.62m. Calculate the mole fractions of sugar and water.

90. Which will have a greater boiling point elevation: 3.00 g $Ca(NO_3)_2$ in 60.0 g of water, or 6.00 g $Ca(NO_3)_2$ in 30.0 g of water?

91. Suppose you have an unknown compound and want to identify it by means of its molar mass. Design an experiment that uses the concept of freezing-point depression to obtain the molar mass. What laboratory measurements would you need to make? What calculations would be needed?

Test-Taking Tip

Interpreting Data Tables Tables present a large amount of data in a small space. They allow you to make comparisons and to analyze the information present. Start by reading the title (if there is one). Then read the headings. Try to figure out the relationship between the different columns and rows of information. Ask yourself some questions: *What information is related in the table? How are the relationships represented?*

Regents Practice Exam

Part A

For each statement or question write the number of the word or expression that, of those given, best completes the statement or answers the question.

The numbered choices below refer to Questions 1–4. A numbered choice may be used once, more than once, or not at all.

(1) moles/liter of solution
(2) volume of solute/volume of solution $\times$ 100%
(3) grams/mole
(4) mass of solute/mass of solution $\times$ 100%

Which of the above choices is appropriate for each of the following measurements?

   1. percent by volume

   2. molar mass

   3. molarity

   4. percent by mass

   5. What type of reaction is shown in the following chemical equation?

   $$C_2H_6O(l) + 3O_2(g) \longrightarrow 2CO_2(g) + 3H_2O(l)$$

   (1) combination (synthesis)
   (2) combustion
   (3) double-replacement
   (4) decomposition

   6. Molarity relates the moles of solute to the
   (1) mass of the solvent   **(3)** volume of solution
   (2) volume of solvent   **(4)** moles of solvent

   7. A solution always is a
   (1) substance
   (2) liquid
   (3) homogeneous mixture
   (4) heterogeneous mixture

   8. The solubility of a substance in water never depends on the
   (1) temperature
   (2) surface area of the solute
   (3) pressure
   (4) nature of the solute

Part B-1

For each statement or question write the number of the word or expression that, of those given, best completes the statement or answers the question.

   9. An aqueous solution is 65% (v/v) rubbing alcohol. How many milliliters of water are in a 95-mL sample of this solution?
   (1) 62 mL   **(3)** 33 mL
   (2) 1.5 mL   **(4)** 30 mL

   10. Which of the following actions will cause more sugar to dissolve in a saturated sugar water solution?
   (1) Add more sugar while stirring.
   (2) Add more sugar and heat the solution.
   (3) Grind the sugar to a powder; then add while stirring.
   (4) Add more sugar while shaking the solution.

The numbered choices below refer to Questions 11–15. A numbered choice may be used once, more than once, or not at all.

(1) combination (synthesis)
(2) decomposition
(3) double-replacement
(4) single-replacement

Identify the type of chemical reaction for each of the following.

   11. $H_2(g) + Cl_2(g) \longrightarrow 2HCl(g)$
   12. $2H_2O(l) \longrightarrow O_2(g) + 2H_2(g)$
   13. $2K(s) + 2H_2O(l) \longrightarrow 2KOH(aq) + H_2(g)$
   14. $Cl_2(aq) + 2KBr(aq) \longrightarrow 2KCl(aq) + Br_2(aq)$
   15. $Pb(NO_3)_2(aq) + 2NaCl(aq) \longrightarrow$
   $$PbCl_2(s) + 2NaNO_3(aq)$$

   16. Equal numbers of moles of the following compounds were dissolved in the same volume of distilled water. Which solution has the lowest freezing point?
   (1) $MgCl_2$ **(3)** K_2CO_3
   (2) $NaCl$ **(4)** $Al(NO_3)_3$

Part B-2

Answer each of the following questions.

   17. Convert each of the following mass measurements to its equivalent in kilograms.
   a. 347 g   **c.** 9.43 mg
   b. 73 Mg   **d.** 877 mg

18. Name and give the symbols for the elements in the following positions on the periodic table.
    a. Group 7B (Group 9), period 4
    b. Group 3A (Group 13), period 5
    c. Group 1A (Group 1), period 7
    d. Group 6A (Group 16), period 6

19. How many atoms of each element are present in $4Ca(MnO_4)_2$?

20. Terephthalic acid is an organic compound used in the synthesis of polyesters. The empirical formula for this compound is $C_4H_3O_2$, and its molar mass is approximately 166 g. What is the molecular formula of terephthalic acid?

21. The photograph shows one mole each of copper, mercury, sulfur, and iron.
    a. What is the mass of each element?
    b. How many moles is 25.0 g of each element?

22. Balance the following chemical equation.
    $$HI(aq) + Na_2S(aq) \longrightarrow H_2S(g) + NaI(aq)$$

23. Indicate by simple equations how the following substances ionize or dissociate in water.
    a. NH_4Cl **c.** HNO_3 **e.** Na_2SO_4
    b. $Cu(NO_3)_2$ **d.** $HC_2H_3O_2$ **f.** $HgCl_2$

24. Write electron dot structures for the following atoms.
    a. I   **b.** Te   **c.** Sb   **d.** Sr

25. Why does an ideal gas not exist?

26. The solubility of hydrogen chloride gas in the polar solvent water is much greater than its solubility in the nonpolar solvent benzene. Why?

Use the following particle diagrams to answer Questions 27 and 28. The diagrams show water and two aqueous solutions with different concentrations. The red spheres represent the solute particles; the blue spheres represent water.

a.   b.   c.

27. Which choice has the lowest boiling point? Explain your answer.

28. Which choice has the lowest freezing point? Explain your answer.

Write a brief essay to answer Question 29.

29. Describe how you would prepare 100 mL of 0.50*M* KCl starting with a stock solution that is 2.0*M* KCl.

Part C

Answer each of the following questions.

Use the description and the data table to answer Questions 30–33.

A student measured the freezing points of three different aqueous solutions at five different concentrations. The data table summarizes the data.

Molarity (*M*)	Freezing Point Depression (°C)		
	NaCl	CaCl₂	C₂H₅OH
0.5	1.7	2.6	0.95
1.0	3.5	5.6	2.0
1.5	5.3	8.3	3.0
2.0	7.2	11.2	4.1
2.5	9.4	14.0	5.3

30. Graph the data for all three solutes on the same graph, using molarity as the independent variable.

31. Summarize the relationship between molarity and freezing-point depression.

32. Compare the slopes of the three lines and explain any difference.

33. If you collected similar data for KOH and added a fourth line to your graph, which existing line would the new line approximate?

A marshmallow absorbs heat as it is toasted over a fire.

INQUIRY Activity

Observing Heat Flow

Materials

a clean, medium-sized rubber band

Procedure

1. Hook your index fingers through each end of the rubber band. Without stretching the rubber band, place it against your upper lip or forehead. Note the temperature of the rubber band. **CAUTION** *If you are allergic to latex, do not handle rubber bands.*

2. Move the rubber band away from your skin, quickly stretch and hold it, and then place it back against your skin. Note any temperature change.

3. Fully stretch the rubber band, and then allow it to return to its original shape. Place it against your skin and note any temperature change.

4. Repeat Steps 2 and 3 until you are certain of the temperature change in each step.

Think About It

1. Did the rubber band feel cooler or warmer after it was stretched in Step 2?

2. Did the rubber band feel cooler or warmer after it returned to its original shape in Step 3?

3. Think about the temperature changes you observed and form some initial answers to the following questions. What is heat? In what direction does heat flow?

Connecting to Your World

Lava flowing out of an erupting volcano is very hot. Its temperature ranges from 550°C to 1400°C. As lava flows down the side of a volcano, it loses heat and begins to cool slowly. In some instances, the lava may flow into the ocean, where it cools more rapidly. In this section, you will learn about heat flow and why some substances cool down or heat up more quickly than others.

Guide for Reading

Key Concepts
- In what direction does heat flow?
- What happens in endothermic and exothermic processes?
- In what units is heat flow measured?
- On what two factors does the heat capacity of an object depend?

Vocabulary
thermochemistry
chemical potential energy
heat
system
surroundings
law of conservation of energy
endothermic process
exothermic process
heat capacity
specific heat

Reading Strategy
Building Vocabulary As you read the section, write a definition of each vocabulary term in your own words.

Energy Transformations

Energy is the capacity for doing work or supplying heat. Unlike matter, energy has neither mass nor volume. Energy is detected only because of its effects—for example, the motion of the race car in Figure 17.1.

Thermochemistry is the study of energy changes that occur during chemical reactions and changes in state. Every substance has a certain amount of energy stored inside it. The energy stored in the chemical bonds of a substance is called **chemical potential energy.** The kinds of atoms and their arrangement in the substance determine the amount of energy stored in the substance.

During a chemical reaction, a substance is transformed into another substance with a different amount of chemical potential energy. When you buy gasoline, you are actually buying the stored potential energy it contains. The controlled explosions of the gasoline in a car's engine transform the potential energy into useful work, which can be used to propel the car. At the same time, however, heat is also produced, making the car's engine extremely hot. Energy changes occur as either heat transfer or work, or a combination of both.

Heat, represented by q, is energy that transfers from one object to another because of a temperature difference between them. One of the effects of adding heat to an object is an increase in its temperature. It is the radiant heat of the sun's rays that makes a summer day hot. In this example, the air is the object that absorbs heat and increases in temperature. **Heat always flows from a warmer object to a cooler object.** If two objects remain in contact, heat will flow from the warmer object to the cooler object until the temperature of both objects is the same.

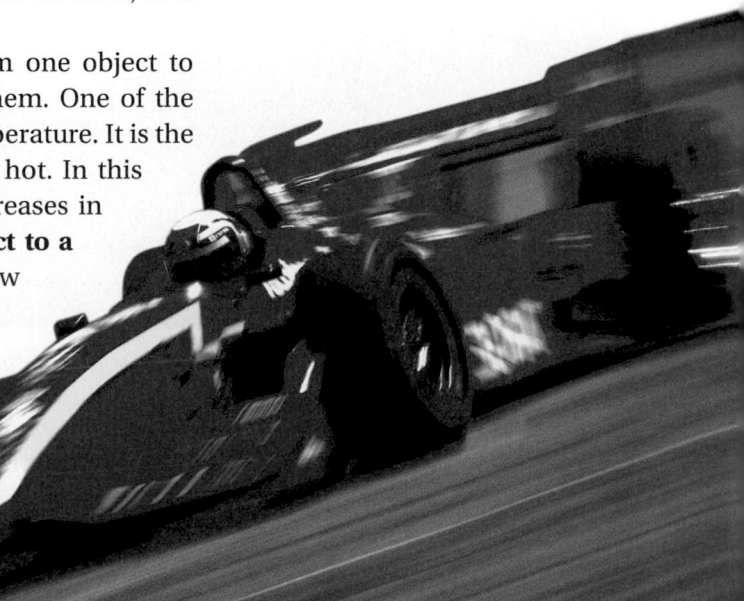

Figure 17.1 When fuel is burned in a car engine, chemical potential energy is released and is used to do work.

Word *Origins*

Exothermic comes from the Greek words *exo*, meaning "outside of," and *therme*, meaning "heat." **Based on the characteristics of endothermic reactions, what do you think the Greek prefix *endo-* means?**

Exothermic and Endothermic Processes

Chemical reactions and changes in physical state generally involve either the release or the absorption of heat. In studying energy changes, you can define a **system** as the part of the universe on which you focus your attention. The **surroundings** include everything else in the universe. In thermochemical experiments, you can consider the region in the immediate vicinity of the system as the surroundings. Together, the system and its surroundings make up the universe. A major goal of thermochemistry is to examine the flow of heat between the system and its surroundings. The **law of conservation of energy** states that in any chemical or physical process, energy is neither created nor destroyed. If the energy of the system decreases during that process, the energy of the surroundings must increase by the same amount so that the total energy of the universe remains unchanged.

In thermochemical calculations, the direction of the heat flow is given from the point of view of the system. An **endothermic process** is one that absorbs heat from the surroundings. 🔑 **In an endothermic process, the system gains heat as the surroundings cool down.** In Figure 17.2a, the system (the person) gains heat from its surroundings (the fire). Heat flowing into a system from its surroundings is defined as positive; *q* has a positive value. An **exothermic process** is one that releases heat to its surroundings. 🔑 **In an exothermic process, the system loses heat as the surroundings heat up.** In Figure 17.2b, the system (the body) loses heat to the surroundings (the perspiration on the skin, and the air). Heat flowing out of a system into its surroundings is defined as negative; *q* has a negative value because the system is losing heat.

✓ **Checkpoint** *What does the law of conservation of energy state?*

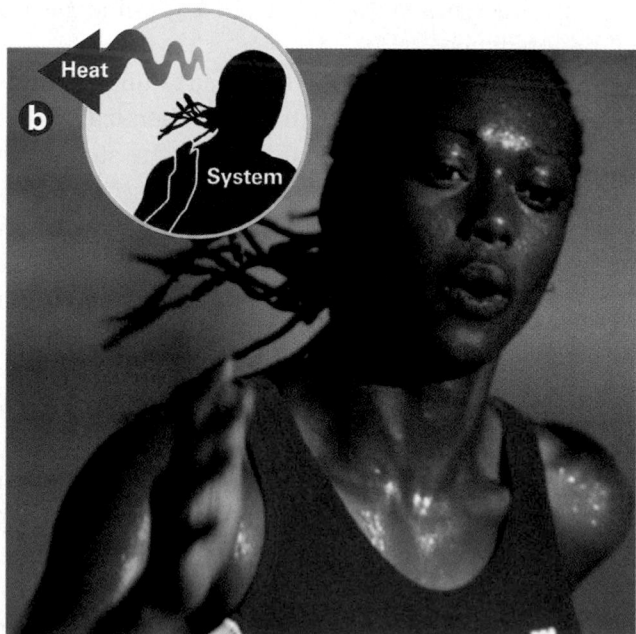

Figure 17.2 Heat flow is defined from the point of view of the system. ⓐ In an endothermic process, heat flows into the system from the surroundings. ⓑ In an exothermic process, heat flows from the system to the surroundings. In both cases, energy is conserved.
Interpreting Diagrams *In which process does q have a negative value?*

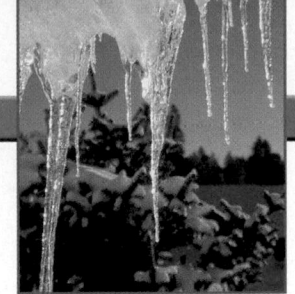

CONCEPTUAL PROBLEM 17.1

Recognizing Exothermic and Endothermic Processes
On a sunny winter day, the snow on a rooftop begins to melt. As the melt-water drips from the roof, it refreezes into icicles. Describe the direction of heat flow as the water freezes. Is this process endothermic or exothermic?

1 **Analyze** *Identify the relevant concepts.*
Heat always flows from a warmer object to a cooler object. An endothermic process absorbs heat from the surroundings. An exothermic process releases heat to the surroundings.

2 **Solve** *Apply concepts to this situation.*
In order for water to freeze, its temperature must decrease. So heat must flow out of the water (the system). Because heat is released from the system to the surroundings (the air), the process is exothermic.

Practice Problems

1. A container of melted paraffin wax is allowed to stand at room temperature until the wax solidifies. What is the direction of heat flow as the liquid wax solidifies? Is the process exothermic or endothermic?

2. When solid barium hydroxide octahydrate (Ba(OH)$_2$·8H$_2$O) is mixed in a beaker with solid ammonium thiocyanate (NH$_4$SCN), a reaction occurs. The beaker quickly becomes very cold. Is the reaction exothermic or endothermic?

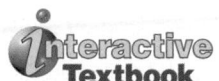
Interactive Textbook

Problem-Solving 17.2 Solve Problem 2 with the help of an interactive guided tutorial.
— with **ChemASAP**

Units for Measuring Heat Flow
Describing the amount of heat flow requires units different than those used to describe temperature. ⚙ **Heat flow is measured in two common units, the calorie and the joule.**

You have probably heard of someone exercising to "burn calories." During exercise your body breaks down sugars and fats into carbon dioxide and water, and this process releases heat. Although there is not an actual fire burning the sugars and fats within your body, chemical reactions accomplish the same result. In breaking down 10 g of sugar, for example, your body releases a certain amount of heat. The same amount of heat would be released if 10 g of sugar were completely burned in a fire.

A calorie (cal) is defined as the quantity of heat needed to raise the temperature of 1 g of pure water 1°C. The word *calorie* is written with a small c except when referring to the energy contained in food. The dietary Calorie, written with a capital C, always refers to the energy in food. One dietary Calorie is actually equal to one kilocalorie, or 1000 calories.

$$1 \text{ Calorie} = 1 \text{ kilocalorie} = 1000 \text{ calories}$$

The statement "10 g of sugar has 41 Calories" means that 10 g of sugar releases 41 kilocalories of heat when completely burned.

The joule is the SI unit of energy. One joule of heat raises the temperature of 1 g of pure water 0.2390°C. You can convert between calories and joules using the following relationships.

$$1 \text{ J} = 0.2390 \text{ cal} \qquad 4.184 \text{ J} = 1 \text{ cal}$$

Heat Capacity and Specific Heat

The amount of heat needed to increase the temperature of an object exactly 1°C is the **heat capacity** of that object. ⊂⊃ **The heat capacity of an object depends on both its mass and its chemical composition.** The greater the mass of the object, the greater its heat capacity. One of the massive steel girders in Figure 17.3, for example, requires much more heat to raise its temperature 1°C than a small steel nail does. Similarly, a cup of water has a much greater heat capacity than a drop of water.

Different substances with the same mass may have different heat capacities. On a sunny day, a 20-kg puddle of water may be cool, while a nearby 20-kg iron sewer cover may be too hot to touch. This situation illustrates how different heat capacities affect the temperature of objects. Assuming that both the water and the iron absorb the same amount of radiant energy from the sun, the temperature of the water changes less than the temperature of the iron because the specific heat capacity of water is larger.

The specific heat capacity, or simply the **specific heat,** of a substance is the amount of heat it takes to raise the temperature of 1 g of the substance 1°C. Table 17.1 gives specific heats for some common substances. Water has a very high specific heat compared with the other substances in the table. You can see from the table that one calorie of heat raises the temperature of 1 g of water 1°C. Metals, however, have low specific heats. One calorie of heat raises the temperature of 1 g of iron 9°C. So water has a specific heat nine times that of iron. Heat affects the temperature of objects with a high specific heat much less than the temperature of those with a low specific heat.

Figure 17.3 A massive steel girder has a higher heat capacity than a steel nail. **Inferring** *What factors affect how quickly the different areas of a construction site will heat up during the day?*

Table 17.1		
Specific Heats of Some Common Substances		
Substance	**Specific Heat**	
	J/(g•°C)	**cal/(g•°C)**
Water	4.18	1.00
Grain alcohol	2.4	0.58
Ice	2.1	0.50
Steam	1.7	0.40
Chloroform	0.96	0.23
Aluminum	0.90	0.21
Iron	0.46	0.11
Silver	0.24	0.057
Mercury	0.14	0.033

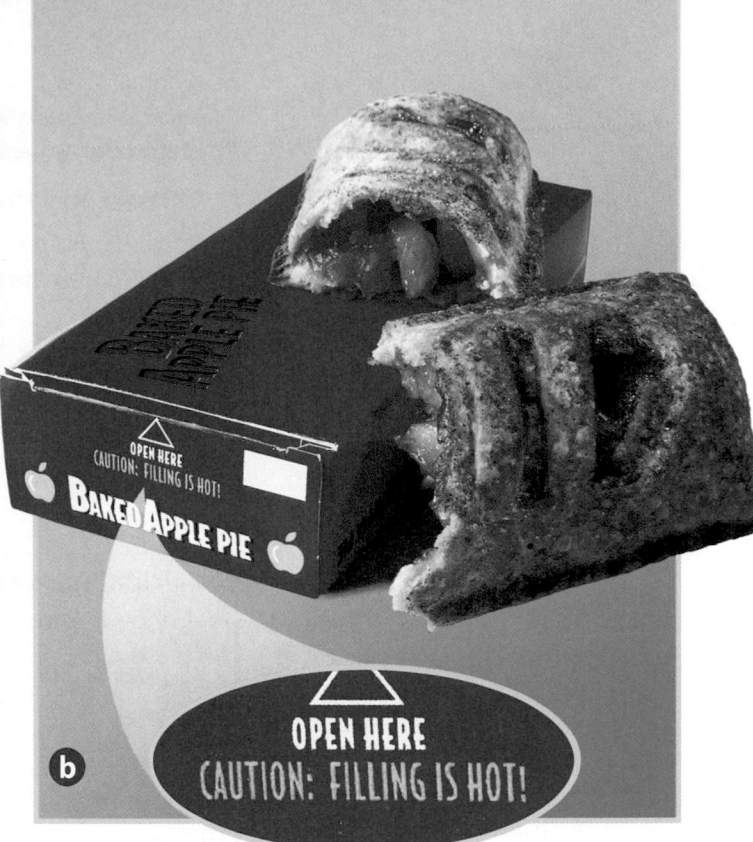

Just as it takes a lot of heat to raise the temperature of water, water also releases a lot of heat as it cools. Water in lakes and oceans absorbs heat from the air on hot days and releases it back into the air on cool days. This property of water is responsible for moderate climates in coastal areas. Figure 17.4 illustrates two other common effects associated with the high specific heat of water. The orange trees in Figure 17.4a have been sprayed with water to protect the fruit from frost damage during icy weather. As the water freezes, it releases heat, which helps prevent the fruit from freezing. In Figure 17.4b, the label on a box of apple pie warns that the "filling is hot." When a freshly baked apple pie comes out of the oven, both the filling and crust are at the same temperature. However, the filling, which is mostly water, has a higher specific heat than the crust. In order to cool down, the filling must give off a lot of heat. This is why you have to be careful not to burn your tongue when eating hot apple pie.

To calculate the specific heat (C) of a substance, you divide the heat input by the temperature change times the mass of the substance.

$$C = \frac{q}{m \times \Delta T} = \frac{\text{heat (joules or calories)}}{\text{mass (g)} \times \text{change in temperature (°C)}}$$

In the equation above, q is heat and m is mass. The symbol ΔT (read "delta T") represents the change in temperature. ΔT is calculated from the equation $\Delta T = T_f - T_i$, where T_f is the final temperature and T_i is the initial temperature. As you can see from the equation, specific heat may be expressed in terms of joules or calories. Therefore, the units of specific heat are either $J/(g \cdot °C)$ or $cal/(g \cdot °C)$.

Figure 17.4 Water releases a lot of heat as it cools. **ⓐ** During freezing weather, farmers protect citrus crops by spraying them with water. The ice that forms has a protective effect as long as its temperature does not drop below 0°C. **ⓑ** Because it is mostly water, the filling of a hot apple pie is much more likely to burn your tongue than the crust.

✓ **Checkpoint** *What is the relationship between specific heat and heat capacity?*

SAMPLE PROBLEM 17.1

Calculating the Specific Heat of a Metal

The temperature of a 95.4-g piece of copper increases from 25.0°C to 48.0°C when the copper absorbs 849 J of heat. What is the specific heat of copper?

1 Analyze *List the knowns and the unknown.*

Knowns
- m_{Cu} = 95.4g
- ΔT = (48.0°C − 25.0°C) = 23.0°C
- q = 849 J

Unknown
- C_{Cu} = ? J/(g·°C)

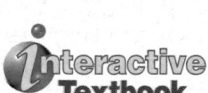

For help with algebraic equations, go to page R69.

2 Calculate *Solve for the unknown.*

Use the known values and the definition of specific heat, $C = \dfrac{q}{m \times \Delta T}$, to calculate the unknown value C_{Cu}.

$$C_{Cu} = \frac{q}{m \times \Delta T} = \frac{849 \text{ J}}{95.4 \text{ g} \times 23.0°C} = 0.387 \text{ J/(g·°C)}$$

3 Evaluate *Does the result make sense?*

Water has a very high specific heat (4.18 J/(g·°C)). Metals, however, have low specific heats, so the calculated value of 0.387 J/(g·°C) seems reasonable.

Practice Problems

3. When 435 J of heat is added to 3.4 g of olive oil at 21°C, the temperature increases to 85°C. What is the specific heat of the olive oil?

4. How much heat is required to raise the temperature of 250.0 g of mercury 52°C?

i nteractive
Textbook

Problem-Solving 17.4 Solve Problem 4 with the help of an interactive guided tutorial.

— with **ChemASAP**

17.1 Section Assessment

5. 🔑 **Key Concept** In what direction does heat flow between two objects?

6. 🔑 **Key Concept** How do endothermic processes differ from exothermic processes?

7. 🔑 **Key Concept** What units are used to measure heat flow?

8. 🔑 **Key Concept** On what factors does the heat capacity of an object depend?

9. Using calories, calculate how much heat 32.0 g of water absorbs when it is heated from 25.0°C to 80.0°C. How many joules is this?

10. A chunk of silver has a heat capacity of 42.8 J/°C and a mass of 181 g. Calculate the specific heat of silver.

11. How many kilojoules of heat are absorbed when 1.00 L of water is heated from 18°C to 85°C?

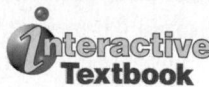

Explanatory Paragraph Use the concept of heat capacity to explain why on a sunny day the concrete deck around an outdoor swimming pool becomes hot, while the water stays cool.

i nteractive
Textbook

Assessment 17.1 Test yourself on the concepts in Section 17.1.

— with **ChemASAP**

17.2 Measuring and Expressing Enthalpy Changes

Connecting to Your World

As you know, a burning match gives off heat. When you strike a match, heat is released to the surroundings in all directions. You can classify this reaction as exothermic. In addition to describing the direction of heat flow, you may also want to determine the quantity of heat that is transferred. How much heat does a burning match release to the surroundings? In this section you will learn how you can measure heat flows in chemical and physical processes by applying the concept of specific heat.

Guide for Reading

Key Concepts
- What basic concepts apply to calorimetry?
- How can you express the enthalpy change for a reaction in a chemical equation?

Vocabulary
calorimetry
calorimeter
enthalpy
thermochemical equation
heat of reaction
heat of combustion

Reading Strategy
Relating Text and Visuals As you read, look at Figure 17.7. Explain how these diagrams help you understand exothermic and endothermic processes.

Calorimetry

Heat that is released or absorbed during many chemical reactions can be measured by a technique called calorimetry. **Calorimetry** is the precise measurement of the heat flow into or out of a system for chemical and physical processes. **In calorimetry, the heat released by the system is equal to the heat absorbed by its surroundings. Conversely, the heat absorbed by a system is equal to the heat released by its surroundings.** The insulated device used to measure the absorption or release of heat in chemical or physical processes is called a **calorimeter.**

Constant-Pressure Calorimeters Foam cups are excellent heat insulators. Because they do not let much heat in or out, they can be used as simple calorimeters. In fact, the heat flows for many chemical reactions can be measured in a constant-pressure calorimeter similar to the one shown in Figure 17.5. Because most chemical reactions and physical changes carried out in the laboratory are open to the atmosphere, these changes occur at constant pressure. The heat content of a system at constant pressure is the same as a property called the **enthalpy** (H) of the system. The heat released or absorbed by a reaction at constant pressure is the same as the change in enthalpy, symbolized as ΔH. Because the reactions presented in this textbook occur at constant pressure, the terms *heat* and *enthalpy change* are used interchangeably. In other words, $q = \Delta H$.

Thermometer

Stirrer

Foam lid
(loose fitting)

Nested
foam cups
(insulation)

Water
(where reaction
takes place)

Figure 17.5 In a simple constant-pressure calorimeter, a thermometer records the temperature change as chemicals react in water. The substances reacting in solution constitute the system. The water constitutes the surroundings.

To measure the enthalpy change for a reaction in aqueous solution in a foam cup calorimeter, you dissolve the reacting chemicals (the system) in known volumes of water (the surroundings). Then measure the initial temperature of each solution and mix the solutions in the foam cup. After the reaction is complete, measure the final temperature of the mixed solutions. Because you know the initial and final temperatures and the heat capacity of water, you can calculate the heat absorbed by the surroundings (q_{surr}) using the formula for specific heat.

$$q_{surr} = m \times C \times \Delta T$$

In this expression, m is the mass of the water; C is the specific heat of water; and $\Delta T = T_f - T_i$. Because the heat absorbed by the surroundings is equal to, but has the opposite sign of, the heat released by the system, the enthalpy change for the reaction (ΔH) can be written as follows.

$$q_{sys} = \Delta H = -q_{surr} = -m \times C \times \Delta T$$

The sign of ΔH is negative for an exothermic reaction and positive for an endothermic reaction.

Constant-Volume Calorimeters Calorimetry experiments can also be performed at constant volume using a device called a bomb calorimeter. In a bomb calorimeter, shown in Figure 17.6, a sample of a compound is burned in a constant-volume chamber in the presence of oxygen at high pressure. The heat that is released warms the water surrounding the chamber. By measuring the temperature increase of the water, it is possible to calculate the quantity of heat released during the combustion reaction.

✓**Checkpoint**) *What formula is used to calculate the enthalpy change in a constant-pressure calorimeter?*

Figure 17.6 Nutritionists use bomb calorimeters to measure the energy content of the foods you eat. To see some of their data (expressed in Calories per serving), you can look at a nutrition label. **Calculating** *According to the nutrition label below, each serving contains 140 Calories. How many kilojoules is this?*

Nutrition Facts
Serving Size 1 Cookie (26g / 0.9oz.)
Servings Per Container 8

Amount Per Serving

Calories 140   Calories from Fat 70

	% Daily Value*
Total Fat 8 g	**12 %**
Saturated Fat 2.5 g	**13 %**
Polyunsaturated Fat 0 g	
Monounsaturated Fat 3 g	
Cholesterol 10 mg	**3 %**
Sodium 80 mg	**3 %**
Total Carbohydrate 16 g	**5 %**
Dietary Fiber 0 g	**0 %**
Sugars 9 g	

Electrical leads — Thermometer
Oxygen intake valve — Insulated outer container
Firing element — Sample to be burned
Oxygen at high pressure — Steel bomb
Stirrer — Water

Enthalpy Change in a Calorimetry Experiment

When 25.0 mL of water containing 0.025 mol HCl at 25.0°C is added to 25.0 mL of water containing 0.025 mol NaOH at 25.0°C in a foam cup calorimeter, a reaction occurs. Calculate the enthalpy change in kJ) during this reaction if the highest temperature observed is 32.0°C. Assume the densities of the solutions are 1.00 g/mL.

1 **Analyze** *List the knowns and the unknown.*

Knowns

- $C_{water} = 4.18$ J/(g·°C)
- $V_{final} = V_{HCl} + V_{NaOH}$
  = 25.0 mL + 25.0 mL = 50.0 mL
- $T_i = 25.0$°C
- $T_f = 32.0$°C
- $Density_{solution} = 1.00$ g/mL

Unknown

- $\Delta H = ?$ kJ

Use dimensional analysis to determine the mass of the water. You must also calculate ΔT. Use $\Delta H = -q_{surr} = -m \times C \times \Delta T$ to solve for ΔH.

2 **Calculate** *Solve for the unknown.*

First, calculate the total mass of the water.

$$m = (50.0 \text{ mL}) \times \left(\frac{1.00 \text{ g}}{\text{mL}}\right) = 50.0 \text{ g}$$

Now calculate ΔT.

$$\Delta T = T_f - T_i = 32.0°C - 25.0°C = 7.0°C$$

Use the values for m, C_{water}, and ΔT to calculate ΔH.

$$\Delta H = -m \times C \times \Delta T = -(50.0 \text{ g})(4.18 \text{ J/(g} \times °C))(7.0°C)$$
$$= -1463 \text{ J} = -1.5 \times 10^3 \text{ J} = -1.5 \text{ kJ}$$

3 **Evaluate** *Does the result make sense?*

The sign of ΔH is negative; the reaction releases 1.5 kJ of heat to the water. The heat released by the system (the reaction) equals the heat absorbed by the surroundings (the water). About 4 J of heat raises the temperature of 1 g of water 1°C; 50 g of water requires about 200 J. To heat 50 g of water 7°C requires about 1400 J, or 1.4 kJ. This estimated answer is very close to the calculated value of ΔH.

Math **Handbook**

For help with dimensional analysis, go to page R66.

Practice Problems

12. When 50.0 mL of water containing 0.50 mol HCl at 22.5°C is mixed with 50.0 mL of water containing 0.50 mol NaOH at 22.5°C in a calorimeter, the temperature of the solution increases to 26.0°C. How much heat (in kJ) was released by this reaction?

13. A small pebble is heated and placed in a foam cup calorimeter containing 25.0 mL of water at 25.0°C. The water reaches a maximum temperature of 26.4°C. How many joules of heat were released by the pebble?

Interactive Textbook

Problem-Solving 17.13
Solve Problem 13 with the help of an interactive guided tutorial.

— with **ChemASAP**

Firefighter

If you are courageous, team-oriented, and have a strong sense of public service, you may wish to consider a career as a firefighter. Firefighters respond to fires,

medical emergencies, and hazardous chemical spills. In responding to a fire, firefighters must know what types of chemicals can be used on different types of fires. Having knowledge of the requirements of different chemical fires and spills enables firefighters to put out rather than feed fires. Regular reviews of fire science literature keep firefighters up to date on current technology developments and policy changes. Firefighters also engage in physical fitness activities to build stamina and improve agility.

Although the job is hazardous and includes unpredictable hours, competition for jobs is relatively high. To become a fire-

fighter, you must be at least 18 years of age with a high school education or equivalent. Selection for positions in fire departments often depends on passing a written test as well as a medical examination. Once hired, training consists of instruction in firefighting and rescue techniques, emergency medical procedures, basic chemistry of fires and firefighting, and instruction in local building codes and fire prevention methods.

Go Online
PHSchool.com

For: Careers in Chemistry
Visit: PHSchool.com
Web Code: cdb-1172

Thermochemical Equations

If you mix calcium oxide with water, the water in the mixture becomes warm. This exothermic reaction occurs when cement, which contains calcium oxide, is mixed with water to make concrete. When 1 mol of calcium oxide reacts with 1 mol of water, 1 mol of calcium hydroxide forms and 65.2 kJ of heat is released. 🔑 **In a chemical equation, the enthalpy change for the reaction can be written as either a reactant or a product.** In the equation describing the exothermic reaction of calcium oxide and water, the enthalpy change can be considered a product.

$$CaO(s) + H_2O(l) \longrightarrow Ca(OH)_2(s) + 65.2 \text{ kJ}$$

This equation is presented visually in Figure 17.7a. A chemical equation that includes the enthalpy change is called a **thermochemical equation.**

The **heat of reaction** is the enthalpy change for the chemical equation exactly as it is written. You will usually see heats of reaction reported as ΔH, which is equal to the heat flow at constant pressure. The physical state of the reactants and products must also be given. The standard conditions are that the reaction is carried out at 101.3 kPa (1 atmosphere) and that the reactants and products are in their usual physical states at 25°C. The heat of reaction, or ΔH, in the above example is -65.2 kJ. Each mole of calcium oxide and water that react to form calcium hydroxide produces 65.2 kJ of heat.

$$CaO(s) + H_2O(l) \longrightarrow Ca(OH)_2(s) \qquad \Delta H = -65.2 \text{ kJ}$$

a Exothermic Reaction

b Endothermic Reaction

Other reactions absorb heat from the surroundings. For example, baking soda (sodium bicarbonate) decomposes when it is heated. The carbon dioxide released in the reaction causes a cake to rise while baking. This process is endothermic.

$$2NaHCO_3(s) + 129 \text{ kJ} \longrightarrow Na_2CO_3(s) + H_2O(g) + CO_2(g)$$

Remember that ΔH is positive for endothermic reactions. Therefore, you can write the reaction as follows.

$$2NaHCO_3(s) \longrightarrow Na_2CO_3(s) + H_2O(g) + CO_2(g) \qquad \Delta H = 129 \text{ kJ}$$

Figure 17.7b shows the enthalpy diagram for this reaction.

Chemistry problems involving enthalpy changes are similar to stoichiometry problems. The amount of heat released or absorbed during a reaction depends on the number of moles of the reactants involved. The decomposition of 2 mol of sodium bicarbonate, for example, requires 129 kJ of heat. Therefore, the decomposition of 4 mol of the same substance would require twice as much heat, or 258 kJ. In this and other endothermic processes, the potential energy of the product(s) is higher than the potential energy of the reactant(s).

The physical state of the reactants and products in a thermochemical reaction must also be stated. To see why, compare the following two equations for the decomposition of 1 mol H_2O.

$$H_2O(l) \longrightarrow H_2(g) + \tfrac{1}{2}O_2(g) \qquad \Delta H = 285.8 \text{ kJ}$$
$$H_2O(g) \longrightarrow H_2(g) + \tfrac{1}{2}O_2(g) \qquad \underline{\Delta H = 241.8 \text{ kJ}}$$
$$\text{difference} = \ \ 44.0 \text{ kJ}$$

Although the two equations are very similar, the different physical states of H_2O result in different ΔH values. In one case, the reactant is a liquid; in the other case, the reactant is a gas. The vaporization of 1 mole of liquid water to water vapor at 25°C requires an extra 44.0 kJ of heat.

$$H_2O(l) \longrightarrow H_2O(g) \qquad \Delta H = 44.0 \text{ kJ}$$

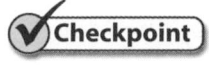 **Checkpoint** *Why must the physical states of the reactants and products be stated in a thermochemical equation?*

Simulation 22 Simulate a combustion reaction and compare the ΔH results for several compounds.
with ChemASAP

Conversion Problems

A conversion factor is a ratio of two quantities that are equal to one another. When doing conversions, write the conversion factors so that the unit of a given measurement cancels, leaving the correct unit for your answer. Note that the equalities needed to write a particular conversion factor may be given in the problem. In other cases, you will need to know or look up the necessary equalities.

> **Math** ▶ **Handbook**
>
> For help with conversion problems, go to page R66.

SAMPLE PROBLEM 17.3

Using the Heat of Reaction to Calculate Enthalpy Change

Using the thermochemical equation in Figure 17.7b on page 515, calculate the amount of heat (in kJ) required to decompose 2.24 mol $NaHCO_3(s)$.

① Analyze *List the knowns and the unknown.*

Knowns
- 2.24 mol $NaHCO_3(s)$ decomposes
- $\Delta H = 129$ kJ (for 2 mol $NaHCO_3$)

Unknown
- $\Delta H = ?$ kJ

Use the thermochemical equation,

$$2NaHCO_3(s) + 129 \text{ kJ} \longrightarrow Na_2CO_3(s) + H_2O(g) + CO_2(g),$$

to write a conversion factor relating kilojoules of heat and moles of $NaHCO_3$. Then use the conversion factor to determine ΔH for 2.24 mol $NaHCO_3$.

② Calculate *Solve for the unknown.*

The thermochemical equation indicates that 129 kJ are needed to decompose 2 mol $NaHCO_3(s)$. Use this relationship to write the following conversion factor.

$$\frac{129 \text{ kJ}}{2 \text{ mol } NaHCO_3(s)}$$

Using dimensional analysis, solve for ΔH.

$$\Delta H = 2.24 \text{ mol } \cancel{NaHCO_3(s)} \times \frac{129 \text{ kJ}}{2 \text{ mol } \cancel{NaHCO_3(s)}}$$

$$= 144 \text{ kJ}$$

③ Evaluate *Does the result make sense?*

Because the $\Delta H = 129$ kJ refers to the decomposition of 2 mol $NaHCO_3(s)$, the decomposition of 2.24 mol should absorb about 10% more heat than 129 kJ, or slightly more than 142 kJ. The answer of 144 kJ is consistent with this estimate.

Practice Problems

14. When carbon disulfide is formed from its elements, heat is absorbed. Calculate the amount of heat (in kJ) absorbed when 5.66 g of carbon disulfide is formed.

$$C(s) + 2S(s) \longrightarrow CS_2(l)$$
$$\Delta H = 89.3 \text{ kJ}$$

15. The production of iron and carbon dioxide from iron(III) oxide and carbon monoxide is an exothermic reaction. How many kilojoules of heat are produced when 3.40 mol Fe_2O_3 reacts with an excess of CO?

$$Fe_2O_3(s) + 3CO(g) \longrightarrow$$
$$2Fe(s) + 3CO_2(g) + 26.3 \text{ kJ}$$

Table 17.2

Heats of Combustion at 25°C		
Substance	**Formula**	**ΔH (kJ/mol)**
Hydrogen	$H_2(g)$	−286
Carbon	$C(s)$, graphite	−394
Methane	$CH_4(g)$	−890
Acetylene	$C_2H_2(g)$	−1300
Ethanol	$C_2H_5OH(l)$	−1368
Propane	$C_3H_8(g)$	−2220
Glucose	$C_6H_{12}O_6(s)$	−2808
Octane	$C_8H_{18}(l)$	−5471
Sucrose	$C_{12}H_{22}O_{11}(s)$	−5645

Table 17.2 lists heats of combustion for some common substances. The **heat of combustion** is the heat of reaction for the complete burning of one mole of a substance. The combustion of natural gas, which is mostly methane, is an exothermic reaction used to heat many homes around the country.

$$CH_4(g) + 2O_2(g) \longrightarrow CO_2(g) + 2H_2O(l) + 890 \text{ kJ}$$

You can also write this equation as follows.

$$CH_4(g) + 2O_2(g) \longrightarrow CO_2(g) + 2H_2O(l) \qquad \Delta H = -890 \text{ kJ}$$

Burning 1 mol of methane releases 890 kJ of heat. The heat of combustion (ΔH) for this reaction is −890 kJ per mole of carbon burned.

Like other heats of reaction, heats of combustion are reported as the enthalpy changes when the reactions are carried out at 101.3 kPa of pressure and the reactants and products are in their physical states at 25°C.

Figure 17.8 The combustion of natural gas is an exothermic reaction. As bonds in methane (the main component of natural gas) and oxygen are broken and bonds in carbon dioxide and water are formed, large amounts of energy are released.

17.2 Section Assessment

16. 🔑 **Key Concept** Calorimetry is based on what basic concepts?

17. 🔑 **Key Concept** How are enthalpy changes treated in chemical equations?

18. When 2 mol of solid magnesium (Mg) combines with 1 mole of oxygen gas (O_2), 2 mol of solid magnesium oxide (MgO) is formed and 1204 kJ of heat is released. Write the thermochemical equation for this combustion reaction.

19. Gasohol contains ethanol (C_2H_5OH)(l), which when burned reacts with oxygen to produce $CO_2(g)$ and $H_2O(g)$. How much heat is released when 12.5 g of ethanol burns?

$$C_2H_5OH(l) + 3O_2(g) \longrightarrow 2CO_2(g) + 3H_2O(l)$$
$$\Delta H = -1368 \text{ kJ}$$

20. Explain the term *heat of combustion*.

Elements ▶ **Handbook**

Group 6A Look up the important chemical reactions involving Group 6A elements. Write two examples of thermochemical equations—one describing an exothermic reaction and another describing an endothermic reaction.

*i*nteractive **Textbook**

Assessment 17.2 Test yourself on the concepts in Section 17.2.

with **ChemASAP**

Solar Power Plants

When you consider energy sources other than coal, oil, or natural gas, you may think of the sun. Solar energy, or energy from the sun, is free, clean, plentiful, and readily available. The daily amount of solar energy received by Earth is about 200,000 times the total world electrical-generating capacity. However, the process of collecting solar energy and using it to generate electricity can be expensive, complex, and space-consuming. Large-scale solar power plants use concentrating solar power (CSP) technologies, which convert solar energy into heat and then electrical energy. **Interpreting Diagrams** *In which part of a power tower is solar energy transformed into heat?*

From sun to socket Because a heliostat field collects solar energy faster than the system can use it, some of the energy is stored (as a molten salt) for later use. Energy storage enables a power tower to supply electricity during cloudy weather or even at night.

Solar power by the tower
A power tower is a CSP technology that uses a vast field of sun-tracking mirrors, called heliostats, to concentrate sunlight on a receiver that sits on top of a tower. Before the solar energy can be used to do work, it must first be transformed into heat by means of a fluid such as steam or a molten salt.

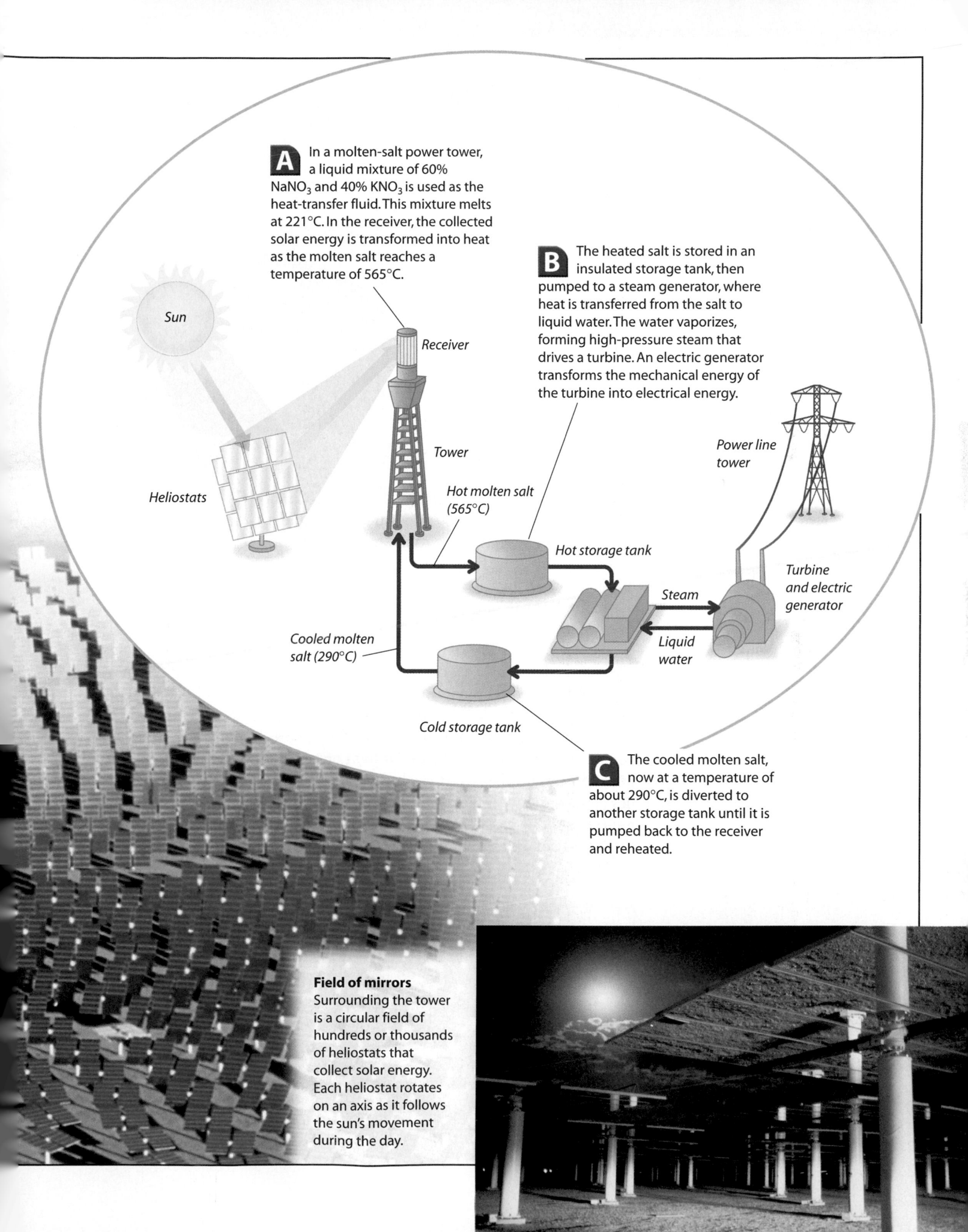

A In a molten-salt power tower, a liquid mixture of 60% $NaNO_3$ and 40% KNO_3 is used as the heat-transfer fluid. This mixture melts at 221°C. In the receiver, the collected solar energy is transformed into heat as the molten salt reaches a temperature of 565°C.

B The heated salt is stored in an insulated storage tank, then pumped to a steam generator, where heat is transferred from the salt to liquid water. The water vaporizes, forming high-pressure steam that drives a turbine. An electric generator transforms the mechanical energy of the turbine into electrical energy.

C The cooled molten salt, now at a temperature of about 290°C, is diverted to another storage tank until it is pumped back to the receiver and reheated.

Sun

Receiver

Tower

Heliostats

Power line tower

Hot molten salt (565°C)

Hot storage tank

Steam

Turbine and electric generator

Cooled molten salt (290°C)

Liquid water

Cold storage tank

Field of mirrors
Surrounding the tower is a circular field of hundreds or thousands of heliostats that collect solar energy. Each heliostat rotates on an axis as it follows the sun's movement during the day.

17.3 Heat in Changes of State

New York Standards: 4.1b, 4.2c

Guide for Reading

🔑 Key Concepts

- How does the quantity of heat absorbed by a melting solid compare to the quantity of heat released when the liquid solidifies?
- How does the quantity of heat absorbed by a vaporizing liquid compare to the quantity of heat released when the vapor condenses?
- What thermochemical changes can occur when a solution forms?

Vocabulary

molar heat of fusion
molar heat of solidification
molar heat of vaporization
molar heat of condensation
molar heat of solution

Reading Strategy

Summarizing After you read this section, construct a flowchart that summarizes the enthalpy changes involved as a substance undergoes phase changes.

Connecting to Your World

An athlete can burn a lot of calories during a race. These calories are either used to do work or are released as heat. When your body heats up, you start to sweat. The evaporation of sweat is your body's way of cooling itself to a normal temperature. This section will help you to understand how the evaporation of sweat from your skin helps to rid your body of excess heat.

Heats of Fusion and Solidification

What happens if you place an ice cube on a table in a warm room? The ice cube is the system, and the table and air around it are the surroundings. The ice absorbs heat from its surroundings and begins to melt. The temperature of the ice and the water produced remains at 0°C until all of the ice has melted. The temperature of the water begins to increase only after all of the ice has melted.

Like ice cubes, all solids absorb heat as they melt to become liquids. The gain of heat causes a change of state instead of a change in temperature. Whenever a change of state occurs by a gain or loss of heat, the temperature of the substance undergoing the change remains constant. The heat absorbed by one mole of a solid substance as it melts to a liquid at a constant temperature is the **molar heat of fusion** (ΔH_{fus}). The **molar heat of solidification** (ΔH_{solid}) is the heat lost when one mole of a liquid solidifies at a constant temperature. 🔑 **The quantity of heat absorbed by a melting solid is exactly the same as the quantity of heat released when the liquid solidifies; that is, $\Delta H_{fus} = -\Delta H_{solid}$.** This relationship is shown in Figure 17.9.

Figure 17.9 Enthalpy changes accompany changes in state. Fusion and vaporization are endothermic processes. Solidification and condensation are exothermic processes.
Interpreting Diagrams
Which arrows represent processes that release heat to the surroundings?

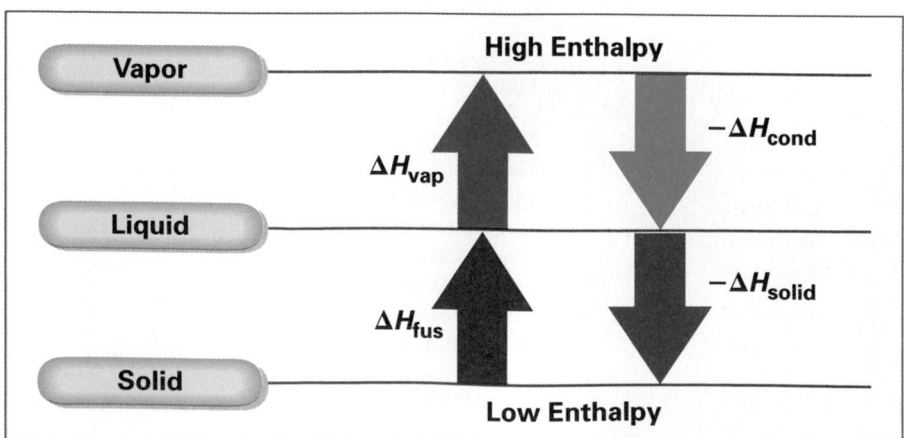

The melting of 1 mol of ice at 0°C to 1 mol of water at 0°C requires the absorption of 6.01 kJ of heat. This quantity of heat is the molar heat of fusion of water. Likewise, the conversion of 1 mol of water at 0°C to 1 mol of ice at 0°C releases 6.01 kJ. This quantity of heat is the molar heat of solidification of water.

$$H_2O(s) \longrightarrow H_2O(l) \quad \Delta H_{fus} = 6.01 \text{ kJ/mol}$$
$$H_2O(l) \longrightarrow H_2O(s) \quad \Delta H_{solid} = -6.01 \text{ kJ/mol}$$

SAMPLE PROBLEM 17.4

Using the Heat of Fusion in Phase-Change Calculations
How many grams of ice at 0°C will melt if 2.25 kJ of heat are added?

① Analyze *List the knowns and the unknown.*

Knowns
- Initial and final temperatures are 0°C
- ΔH_{fus} = 6.01 kJ/mol
- ΔH = 2.25 kJ

Unknown
- m_{ice} = ? g

Use the thermochemical equation

$$H_2O(s) + 6.01 \text{ kJ} \longrightarrow H_2O(l)$$

to find the number of moles of ice that can be melted by the addition of 2.25 kJ of heat. Convert moles of ice to grams of ice.

② Calculate *Solve for the unknown.*
Express ΔH_{fus} and the molar mass of ice as conversion factors.

$$\frac{1 \text{ mol ice}}{6.01 \text{ kJ}} \quad \text{and} \quad \frac{18.0 \text{ g ice}}{1 \text{ mol ice}}$$

Multiply the known enthalpy change (2.25 kJ) by the conversion factors

$$m_{ice} = 2.25 \text{ kJ} \times \frac{1 \text{ mol ice}}{6.01 \text{ kJ}} \times \frac{18.0 \text{ g ice}}{1 \text{ mol ice}}$$
$$= 6.74 \text{ g ice}$$

③ Evaluate *Does the result make sense?*
6.01 kJ is required to melt 1 mol of ice. Because only about one third of this amount of heat (roughly 2 kJ) is available, only about one-third mol of ice, or 18.0 g/3 = 6 g, should melt. This estimate is close to the calculated answer.

Practice Problems

21. How many kilojoules of heat are required to melt a 10.0-g popsicle at 0°C? Assume the popsicle has the same molar mass and heat of fusion as water.

22. How many grams of ice at 0°C could be melted by the addition of 0.400 kJ of heat?

Math **Handbook**

For help with conversion problems, go to page R66.

interactive
Textbook

Problem-Solving 17.21 Solve Problem 21 with the help of an interactive guide tutorial.

with **ChemASAP**

Heat of Fusion of Ice

Purpose
To estimate the heat of fusion of ice.

Materials
- ice
- foam cup
- 100-ml graduated cylinder
- thermometer
- hot water
- temperature probe (optional)

Procedure

Probe version available in the Probeware Lab Manual.

1. Fill the graduated cylinder with hot tap water and let stand for 1 minute. Pour the water into the sink.

2. Use the graduated cylinder to measure 70 mL of hot water. Pour the water into the foam cup. Measure the temperature of the water.

3. Add an ice cube to the cup of water. Gently swirl the cup. Measure the temperature of the water as soon as the ice cube has completely melted.

4. Pour the water into the graduated cylinder and measure the volume.

Analyze and Conclude

1. Calculate the mass of the ice. (*Hint:* The mass of ice melted is the same as the

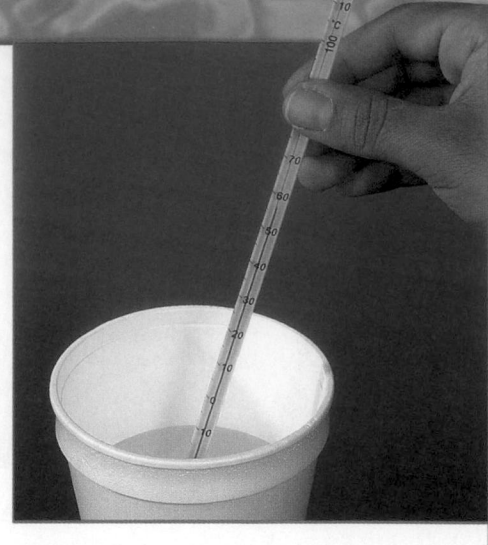

increase in the volume of the water.) Convert this into moles.

2. Calculate ΔH_{fus} of ice (kJ/mol) by dividing the heat transferred from the water by the moles of ice melted.

3. Compare your experimental value of ΔH_{fus} of ice with the accepted value of 6.01 kJ/mol. Account for any error.

4. How might you revise the procedure to achieve more accurate results?

Heats of Vaporization and Condensation

When liquids absorb heat at their boiling points, they become vapors. The amount of heat necessary to vaporize one mole of a given liquid is called its **molar heat of vaporization** (ΔH_{vap}). Table 17.3 lists the molar heats of vaporization for several substances at their normal boiling points.

The molar heat of vaporization of water is 40.7 kJ/mol. This means that it takes 40.7 kJ of energy to convert 1 mol of water molecules in the liquid state to 1 mol of water molecules in the vapor state at the normal boiling point of water (100°C at 101.3 kPa). This process is described in the thermochemical equation below.

$$H_2O(l) \longrightarrow H_2O(g) \qquad \Delta H_{vap} = 40.7 \text{ kJ/mol}$$

Table 17.3

Heats of Physical Change		
Substance	ΔH_{fus} (kJ/mol)	ΔH_{vap} (kJ/mol)
Ammonia (NH$_3$)	5.65	23.4
Ethanol (C$_2$H$_5$OH)	4.60	43.5
Hydrogen (H$_2$)	0.12	0.90
Methanol (CH$_3$OH)	3.16	35.3
Oxygen (O$_2$)	0.44	6.82
Water (H$_2$O)	6.01	40.7

Diethyl ether ($C_4H_{10}O$) is a low-boiling-point liquid (bp = 34.6°C) that is a good solvent and was formerly used as an anesthetic. If diethyl ether is poured into a beaker on a warm, humid day, the ether will absorb heat from the beaker walls and evaporate very rapidly. If the beaker loses enough heat, the water vapor in the air may condense and freeze on the beaker walls. If so, a coating of frost will form on the outside of the beaker. Diethyl ether has a molar heat of vaporization (ΔH_{vap}) of 15.7 kJ/mol.

$$C_4H_{10}O(l) \longrightarrow C_4H_{10}O(g) \qquad \Delta H_{vap} = 15.7 \text{ kJ/mol}$$

Condensation is the exact opposite of vaporization. When a vapor condenses, heat is released. The amount of heat released when 1 mol of vapor condenses at the normal boiling point is called its **molar heat of condensation** (ΔH_{cond}). This value is numerically the same as the corresponding molar heat of vaporization, however the value has the opposite sign. ⚬➤ **The quantity of heat absorbed by a vaporizing liquid is exactly the same as the quantity of heat released when the vapor condenses; that is, $\Delta H_{vap} = -\Delta H_{cond}$.** Figure 17.10 summarizes the enthalpy changes that occur as a solid is heated to a liquid and then to a vapor. You should be able to identify certain trends regarding the temperature during changes of state and the energy requirements that accompany these changes from the graph. The large values for ΔH_{vap} and ΔH_{cond} are the reason hot vapors such as steam can be very dangerous. You can receive a scalding burn from steam when the heat of condensation is released as the steam touches your skin.

$$H_2O(g) \longrightarrow H_2O(l) \qquad \Delta H_{cond} = -40.7 \text{ kJ/mol}$$

✓**Checkpoint**) **What is the molar heat of vaporization?**

ℹ️**nteractive Textbook**

Animation 21 Observe the phase changes as ice is converted to steam when heat is added.

——with **ChemASAP**

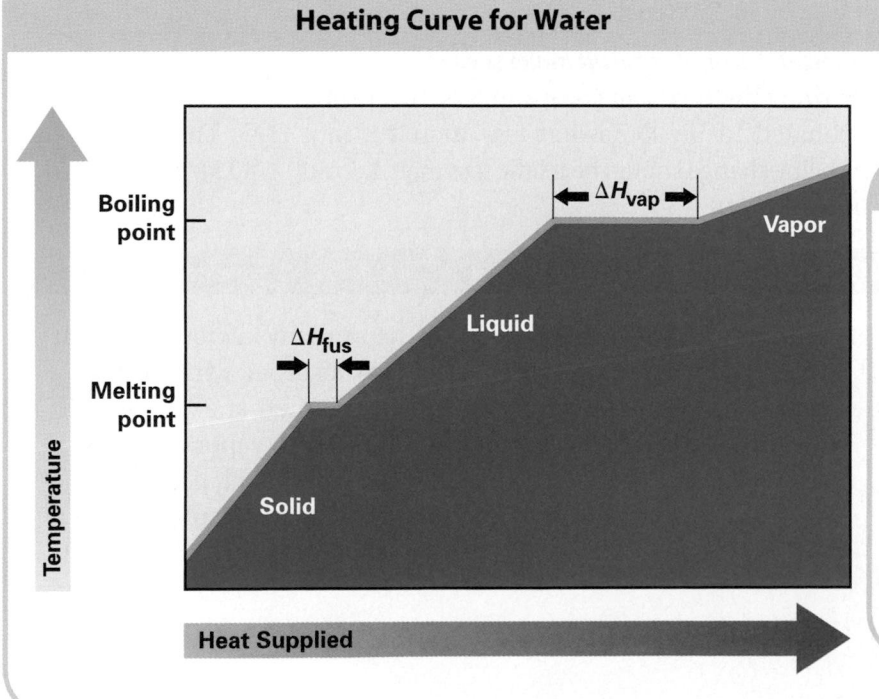

Heating Curve for Water

Figure 17.10 A heating curve graphically describes the enthalpy changes that take place during phase changes.

INTERPRETING GRAPHS
a. Identify In which region(s) of the graph is temperature constant?
b. Describe How does the amount of energy required to melt a given mass of ice compare to the energy required to vaporize the same mass of water? Explain.
c. Apply Concepts Which region of the graph represents the coexistence of solid and liquid? Liquid and vapor?

Using the Heat of Vaporization in Phase-Change Calculations

How much heat (in kJ) is absorbed when 24.8 g $H_2O(l)$ at 100°C and 101.3 kPa is converted to steam at 100°C?

1 **Analyze** *List the knowns and the unknown.*

Knowns

- Initial and final conditions are 100°C and 101.3 kPa
- mass of water converted to steam = 24.8 g
- ΔH_{vap} = 40.7 kJ/mol

Unknown

- ΔH = ? kJ

Refer to the following thermochemical equation.

$$H_2O(l) + 40.7 \text{ kJ/mol} \longrightarrow H_2O(g)$$

ΔH_{vap} is given in kJ/mol, but the quantity of water is given in grams. You must first convert grams of water to moles of water. Then multiply by ΔH_{vap}.

Math Handbook

For help with using a calculator, go to page R62.

2 **Calculate** *Solve for the unknown.*

The required conversion factors come from ΔH_{vap} and the molar mass of water.

$$\frac{1 \text{ mol } H_2O(l)}{18.0 \text{ g } H_2O(l)} \quad \text{and} \quad \frac{40.7 \text{ kJ}}{1 \text{ mol } H_2O(l)}$$

Multiply the mass of water in grams by the conversion factors.

$$\Delta H = 24.8 \text{ g } \cancel{H_2O(l)} \times \frac{1 \text{ mol } \cancel{H_2O(l)}}{18.0 \text{ g } \cancel{H_2O(l)}} \times \frac{40.7 \text{ kJ}}{1 \text{ mol } \cancel{H_2O(l)}}$$

$$= 56.1 \text{ kJ}$$

3 **Evaluate** *Does the result make sense?*

Knowing the molar mass of water is 18.0 g/mol, 24.8 g $H_2O(l)$ can be estimated to be somewhat less than 1.5 mol H_2O. The calculated enthalpy change should be a little less than 1.5 $\cancel{mol}$ × 40 kJ/$\cancel{mol}$ = 60 kJ, and it is.

Practice Problems

Interactive Textbook

Problem-Solving 17.24 Solve Problem 24 with the help of an interactive guided tutorial.

—— with ChemASAP

23. How much heat is absorbed when 63.7g $H_2O(l)$ at 100°C and 101.3 kPa is converted to steam at 100°C? Express your answer in kJ.

24. How many kilojoules of heat are absorbed when 0.46 g of chloroethane (C_2H_5Cl, bp 12.3°C) vaporizes at its normal boiling point? The molar heat of vaporization of chloroethane is 26.4 kJ/mol.

Heat of Solution

If you've ever used a hot pack or a cold pack, then you have felt the enthalpy changes that occur when a solute dissolves in a solvent. 🔑 **During the formation of a solution, heat is either released or absorbed.** The enthalpy change caused by dissolution of one mole of substance is the **molar heat of solution** (ΔH_{soln}). Sodium hydroxide provides a good example of an exothermic molar heat of solution. When 1 mol of sodium hydroxide (NaOH)(*s*) is dissolved in water, the solution can become so hot that it steams. The heat from this process is released as the sodium ions and the hydroxide ions interact with the water. The temperature of the solution increases, releasing 445.1 kJ of heat as the molar heat of solution.

$$NaOH(s) \xrightarrow{H_2O(l)} Na^+(aq) + OH^-(aq)$$
$$\Delta H_{soln} = -445.1 \text{ kJ/mol}$$

A practical application of exothermic dissolving is a hot pack. A hot pack mixes calcium chloride ($CaCl_2$) and water, which produces the heat characteristic of an exothermic reaction.

$$CaCl_2(s) \xrightarrow{H_2O(l)} Ca^{2+}(aq) + 2Cl^-(aq)$$
$$\Delta H_{soln} = -82.8 \text{ kJ/mol}$$

The dissolution of ammonium nitrate (NH_4NO_3) (*s*) is an example of an endothermic process. When ammonium nitrate dissolves in water, the solution becomes so cold that frost may form on the outside of the container. Instant cold packs, which are used to treat muscle aches and sore joints, work by endothermic dissolving. The cold pack in Figure 17.11 contains solid ammonium nitrate crystals and water. Once the solute dissolves in the solvent, the pack becomes cold. In this case, the solution process absorbs energy from the surroundings.

$$NH_4NO_3(s) \xrightarrow{H_2O(l)} NH_4^+(aq) + NO_3^-(aq)$$
$$\Delta H_{soln} = 25.7 \text{ kJ/mol}$$

✓**Checkpoint** *What is the molar heat of solution?*

Figure 17.11 The cold pack shown has two sealed plastic bags, one inside the other. The outer bag contains ammonium nitrate crystals. The inner bag contains liquid water. When the pack is squeezed, the inner bag breaks, allowing the ammonium nitrate and water to mix.
Inferring *How would you define the system and the surroundings in this process?*

> ...ostoite. Use wi...
> ...s minutes. Cold Therapy is no.
> ...auds Syndrome, or Diabetes, withou.
> Supervise children during use.
> ...tion contacts eyes, skin or open wounds, flush
> ...owed, give one or two glasses of milk or water
> ...t poison control immediately. FOR EXTERNAL U!
> **CONTENTS:** Ammonium nitrate and water.

Calculating the Heat Change in Solution Formation

How much heat (in kJ) is released when 2.500 mol NaOH(s) is dissolved in water?

1 **Analyze** *List the knowns and the unknown.*

Knowns
- $\Delta H_{soln} = -445.1$ kJ/mol
- amount of NaOH(s) dissolved = 2.500 mol

Unknown
- $\Delta H = ?$ kJ

Use the heat of solution from the following chemical equation to solve for the amount of heat released (ΔH).

$$\text{NaOH}(s) \xrightarrow{\text{H}_2\text{O}(l)} \text{Na}^+(aq) + \text{OH}^-(aq) + 445.1 \text{ kJ/mol}$$

2 **Calculate** *Solve for the unknown.*

Multiply the number of moles of NaOH by ΔH_{soln}.

$$\Delta H = 2.500 \text{ mol NaOH}(s) \times \frac{-445.1 \text{ kJ}}{1 \text{ mol NaOH}(aq)} = -1113 \text{ kJ}$$

3 **Evaluate** *Does the result make sense?*

ΔH is 2.5 times greater than ΔH_{soln}, as it should be. Also, ΔH should be negative, as the dissolution of NaOH in water is exothermic.

Math Handbook

For help with significant figures go to page R59.

Interactive Textbook

Problem-Solving 17.26 Solve Problem 26 with the help of an interactive guided tutorial.

— with **ChemASAP**

Practice Problems

25. How much heat (in kJ) is released when 0.677 mol NaOH(s) is dissolved in water?

26. How many moles of $NH_4NO_3(s)$ must be dissolved in water so that 88.0 kJ of heat is absorbed from the water?

17.3 Section Assessment

27. 🔑 **Key Concept** How does the molar heat of fusion of a substance compare to its molar heat of solidification?

28. 🔑 **Key Concept** How does the molar heat of vaporization of a substance compare to its molar heat of condensation?

29. 🔑 **Key Concept** What enthalpy changes occur when a solute dissolves in a solvent?

30. Identify each enthalpy change by name and classify each change as exothermic or endothermic.
  a. 1 mol $C_3H_8(l) \longrightarrow$ 1 mol $C_3H_8(g)$
  b. 1 mol Hg(l) $\longrightarrow$ 1 mol Hg(s)
  c. 1 mol $NH_3(g) \longrightarrow$ 1 mol $NH_3(l)$
  d. 1 mol NaCl(s) + 3.88 kJ/mol $\longrightarrow$ 1 mol NaCl(aq)
  e. NaCl(s) $\longrightarrow$ NaCl(l)

31. Why is a burn from steam potentially far more serious than a burn from very hot water?

Connecting ▶ Concepts

Hydrogen Bonding Reread the description of inter-molecular attractions in Section 8.3. Use what you know about hydrogen bonding to explain why water absorbs such a large amount of heat as it vaporizes.

Interactive Textbook

Assessment 17.3 Test yourself on the concepts in Section 17.3.

— with **ChemASAP**

17.4 Calculating Heats of Reaction

New York Standards: 3.3a, 4.1c–d

Connecting to Your World

Emeralds are beautiful gemstones composed of the elements chromium, aluminum, silicon, oxygen, and beryllium. It is possible to break down an emerald into its component elements and measure the resulting enthalpy change—but then the gem would be destroyed. What if you wanted to determine the heat of reaction without actually performing the reaction? In this section you will see how you can calculate heats of reaction from known thermochemical equations and enthalpy data.

Guide for Reading

Key Concepts
- What are two ways that you can determine the heat of reaction when it cannot be directly measured?

Vocabulary
Hess's law of heat summation
standard heat of formation

Reading Strategy
Outlining As you read, make an outline of the most important ideas in this section.

Hess's Law

Sometimes it is hard to measure the enthalpy change for a reaction. For example, the reaction might take place too slowly to actually measure the enthalpy change. Or, the reaction might be an intermediate step in a series of reactions. Or, as mentioned above, you might not want to destroy the material that undergoes the reaction. Fortunately, it is possible to measure a heat of reaction indirectly. **Hess's law of heat summation** states that if you add two or more thermochemical equations to give a final equation, then you can also add the heats of reaction to give the final heat of reaction. **Hess's law allows you to determine the heat of reaction indirectly.**

Figure 17.12 shows a diamond mine. Diamonds are a form of carbon that exists at 25°C. Another is graphite. Because graphite is more stable than diamond, you might predict the following reaction.

$$C(s, \text{diamond}) \longrightarrow C(s, \text{graphite})$$

Fortunately for people who own diamonds, the conversion of diamond to graphite takes millions and millions of years. This enthalpy change cannot be measured directly because the reaction is far too slow. Hess's law, however, provides a way to calculate the heat of reaction.

Figure 17.12 This diamond mine is located in Mpumalanga Province, South Africa.

C(s, graphite)

C(s, diamond)

Figure 17.13 Hess's law is used to determine the enthalpy change for the conversion of diamond to graphite.
Interpreting Diagrams
Which of the reactions shown is an example of decomposition?

C(s, diamond) + $O_2(g)$

? $\Delta H = -1.9$ kJ

C(s, graphite) + $O_2(g)$

$\Delta H = -395.4$ kJ

$\Delta H = 393.5$ kJ

$CO_2(g)$

You can use Hess's law to find the enthalpy change for the conversion of diamond to graphite by using the following combustion reactions and Figure 17.13.

a. $C(s, \text{graphite}) + O_2(g) \longrightarrow CO_2(g)$ $\Delta H = -393.5$ kJ

b. $C(s, \text{diamond}) + O_2(g) \longrightarrow CO_2(g)$ $\Delta H = -395.4$ kJ

Write equation **a** in reverse to give:

c. $CO_2(g) \longrightarrow C(s, \text{graphite}) + O_2(g)$ $\Delta H = 393.5$ kJ

When you write a reverse reaction, you must also change the sign of ΔH. If you now add equations **b** and **c,** you get the equation for the conversion of diamond to graphite. The $CO_2(g)$ and $O_2(g)$ terms on both sides of the summed equations cancel, just as they do in algebra. Now if you also add the values of ΔH for equations **b** and **c,** you get the heat of reaction for this conversion.

$$C(s, \text{diamond}) + O_2(g) \longrightarrow CO_2(g) \quad \Delta H = -395.4 \text{ kJ}$$
$$CO_2(g) \longrightarrow C(s, \text{graphite}) + O_2(g) \quad \Delta H = 393.5 \text{ kJ}$$
$$C(s, \text{diamond}) \longrightarrow C(s, \text{graphite}) \quad \Delta H = -1.9 \text{ kJ}$$

The conversion of diamond to graphite is an exothermic process, so its heat of reaction has a negative sign. Conversely, the change of graphite to diamond is an endothermic process.

Another case in which Hess's law is useful is when reactions yield products in addition to the product of interest. Suppose you want to determine the enthalpy change for the formation of carbon monoxide from its elements. You can write the following equation for this reaction.

$$C(s, \text{graphite}) + \tfrac{1}{2}O_2(g) \longrightarrow CO(g) \qquad \Delta H = ?$$

Although it is easy to write the equation, carrying out the reaction in the laboratory as written is virtually impossible. Carbon dioxide (a "side product") is produced along with carbon monoxide (the "desired product"). Therefore, any measured heat of reaction is related to the formation of both $CO(g)$ and $CO_2(g)$, and not $CO(g)$ alone. However, you can calculate the desired enthalpy change by using Hess's law and the following two reactions that can be carried out in the laboratory.

a. $C(s, \text{graphite}) + O_2(g) \longrightarrow CO_2(g) \qquad \Delta H = -393.5$ kJ

b. $CO(g) + \tfrac{1}{2}O_2(g) \longrightarrow CO_2(g) \qquad \Delta H = -283.0$ kJ

Writing the reverse of equation **b** and changing the sign of ΔH yields equation **c.**

c. $CO_2(g) \longrightarrow CO(g) + \tfrac{1}{2}O_2(g) \qquad \Delta H = 283.0$ kJ

Adding equations **a** and **c** gives the expression for the formation of $CO(g)$ from its elements. The enthalpy diagram for this heat summation is shown in Figure 17.14. Notice that only $\tfrac{1}{2}O_2(g)$ cancels from each equation.

$$C(s, \text{graphite}) + O_2(g) \longrightarrow \cancel{CO_2(g)} \qquad \Delta H = -393.5 \text{ kJ}$$

$$\underline{\cancel{CO_2(g)} \longrightarrow CO(g) + \tfrac{1}{2}O_2(g) \qquad\qquad \Delta H = 283.0 \text{ kJ}}$$

$$C(s, \text{graphite}) + \tfrac{1}{2}O_2(g) \longrightarrow CO(g) \qquad \Delta H = -110.5 \text{ kJ}$$

The formation of $CO(g)$ is exothermic; 110.5kJ of heat is given off when 1 mol $CO(g)$ is formed from its elements.

 Checkpoint *Why can't you directly measure the heat of reaction for the formation of carbon monoxide from its elements?*

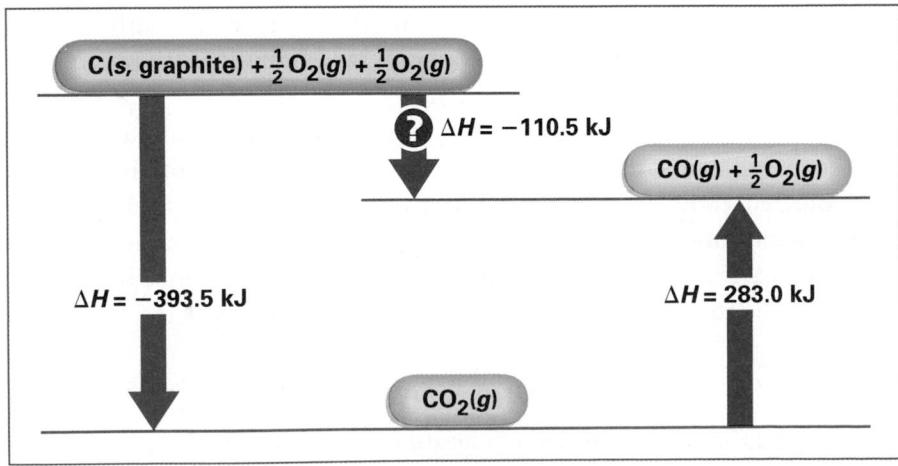

Figure 17.14 Hess's law is used to determine the enthalpy change for the formation of $CO(g)$ from its elements. **Interpreting Diagrams** *How does the diagram represent endothermic and exothermic reactions differently?*

Go Online
NSTA SCILINKS
For: Links on diamond and graphite
Visit: www.SciLinks.org
Web Code: cdn-1174

Table 17.4

Standard Heats of Formation (ΔH_f^0) at 25°C and 101.3 kPa

Substance	ΔH_f^0 (kJ/mol)	Substance	ΔH_f^0 (kJ/mol)
$Al_2O_3(s)$	−1676.0	$H_2O_2(l)$	−187.8
$Br_2(g)$	30.91	$I_2(g)$	62.4
$Br_2(l)$	0.0	$I_2(s)$	0.0
$C(s,$ diamond$)$	1.9	$N_2(g)$	0.0
$C(s,$ graphite$)$	0.0	$NH_3(g)$	−46.19
$CH_4(g)$	−74.86	$NO(g)$	90.37
$CO(g)$	−110.5	$NO_2(g)$	33.85
$CO_2(g)$	−393.5	$NaCl(s)$	−411.2
$CaCO_3(s)$	−1207.0	$O_2(g)$	0.0
$CaO(s)$	−635.1	$O_3(g)$	142.0
$Cl_2(g)$	0.0	$P(s,$ white$)$	0.0
$Fe(s)$	0.0	$P(s,$ red$)$	−18.4
$Fe_2O_3(s)$	−822.1	$S(s,$ rhombic$)$	0.0
$H_2(g)$	0.0	$S(s,$ monoclinic$)$	0.30
$H_2O(g)$	−241.8	$SO_2(g)$	−296.8
$H_2O(l)$	−285.8	$SO_3(g)$	−395.7

Standard Heats of Formation

Enthalpy changes generally depend on conditions of the process. In order to compare enthalpy changes, scientists specify a common set of conditions as a reference point. These conditions, called the standard state, refer to the stable form of a substance at 25°C and 101.3 kPa. The **standard heat of formation** (ΔH_f^0) of a compound is the change in enthalpy that accompanies the formation of one mole of a compound from its elements with all substances in their standard states at 25°C. The ΔH_f^0 of a free element in its standard state is arbitrarily set at zero. Thus, $\Delta H_f^0 = 0$ for the diatomic molecules $H_2(g)$, $N_2(g)$, $O_2(g)$, $F_2(g)$, $Cl_2(g)$, $Br_2(l)$, and $I_2(s)$. Similarly, $\Delta H_f^0 = 0$ for the graphite form of carbon, $C(s,$ graphite$)$. Table 17.4 lists ΔH_f^0 values for some common substances.

Standard heats of formation provide an alternative to Hess's law in determining heats of reaction indirectly. **For a reaction that occurs at standard conditions, you can calculate the heat of reaction by using standard heats of formation.** Such an enthalpy change is called the standard heat of reaction (ΔH^0). The standard heat of reaction is the difference between the standard heats of formation of all the reactants and products.

$$\Delta H^0 = \Delta H_f^0(\text{products}) - \Delta H_f^0(\text{reactants})$$

Figure 17.15 is an enthalpy diagram for the formation of water from its elements at standard conditions. The enthalpy difference between the reactants and products, −285.8 kJ/mol, is the standard heat of formation of liquid water from the gases hydrogen and oxygen. Notice that water has a lower enthalpy than the elements from which it is formed.

Figure 17.15 This enthalpy diagram shows the standard heat of formation of water. **Classifying** *Is this reaction endothermic or exothermic?*

$H_2(g) + \frac{1}{2}O_2(g)$

$\Delta H_f^0 = -285.8$ kJ/mol

$H_2O(l)$

Calculating the Standard Heat of Reaction

What is the standard heat of reaction (ΔH^0) for the reaction of $CO(g)$ with $O_2(g)$ to form $CO_2(g)$?

Carbon Monoxide Detector

① **Analyze** *List the knowns and the unknown.*

Knowns	**Unknown**
(from Table 17.4)	• $\Delta H^0 = ?$ kJ

- $\Delta H_f^0 O_2(g) = 0$ kJ/mol (free element)
- $\Delta H_f^0 CO(g) = -110.5$ kJ/mol
- $\Delta H_f^0 CO_2(g) = -393.5$ kJ/mol

Balance the equation of the reaction of $CO(g)$ with $O_2(g)$ to form $CO_2(g)$. Then determine ΔH^0 using the standard heats of formation of the reactants and products.

② **Calculate** *Solve for the unknown.*

First, write the balanced equation.

$$2CO(g) + O_2(g) \longrightarrow 2CO_2(g)$$

Next, find and add the ΔH_f^0 of all of the reactants, taking into account the number of moles of each.

$$\Delta H_f^0(\text{reactants}) = 2 \text{ mol } CO(g) = \frac{-110.5 \text{ kJ}}{1 \text{ mol } CO(g)} + 0 \text{ kJ}$$

$$= -221.0 \text{ kJ}$$

Then, find the ΔH_f^0 of the product in a similar way.

$$\Delta H_f^0(\text{product}) = 2 \text{ mol } CO_2(g) \times \frac{-393.5 \text{ kJ}}{1 \text{ mol } CO_2(g)}$$

$$= -787.0 \text{ kJ}$$

Finally, solve for the unknown

$$\Delta H^0 = \Delta H_f^0(\text{products}) - \Delta H_f^0(\text{reactants})$$
$$\Delta H^0 = (-787.0 \text{ kJ}) - (-221.0 \text{ kJ})$$
$$\Delta H^0 = -566.0 \text{ kJ}$$

> **Math** **Handbook**
>
> For help with significant figures, go to page R59.

③ **Evaluate** *Does the result make sense?*

The ΔH^0 is negative. Therefore, the reaction is exothermic. This makes sense because combustion reactions always release heat.

Practice Problems

32. Calculate ΔH^0 for the following reactions.
- **a.** $Br_2(g) \longrightarrow Br_2(l)$
- **b.** $CaCO_3(s) \longrightarrow$ $CaO(s) + CO_2(g)$
- **c.** $2NO(g) + O_2(g) \longrightarrow$ $2NO_2(g)$

33. With one exception, the standard heats of formation of $Na(s)$, $O_2(g)$, $Br_2(l)$, $CO(g)$, $Fe(s)$, and $He(g)$ are identical. What is the exception? Explain.

interactive **Textbook**

Problem-Solving 17.32
Solve Problem 32 with the help of an interactive guided tutorial.

—— with **ChemASAP**

Figure 17.16 Standard heats of formation are used to calculate the enthalpy change for the reaction of carbon monoxide and oxygen. **Interpreting Diagrams** *How does this diagram also demonstrate Hess's law?*

Figure 17.16 is an enthalpy diagram that shows how the standard heat of reaction was calculated in Sample Problem 17.7.

$$2CO(g) + O_2(g) \longrightarrow 2CO_2(g)$$

The standard heat of formation of the product, $CO_2(g)$, is -393.5 kJ/mol. The standard heats of formation of the reactants, $CO(g)$ and $O_2(g)$, are -110.5 kJ/mol and 0 kJ/mol, respectively. The diagram shows the difference between ΔH_f^0(product) and ΔH_f^0(reactants) after taking into account the number of moles of each.

17.4 Section Assessment

34. 🔑 **Key Concept** What are two ways that the heat of reaction can be determined when it cannot be directly measured?

35. Calculate the enthalpy change (ΔH) in kJ for the following reaction.

$$2Al(s) + Fe_2O_3(s) \longrightarrow 2Fe(s) + Al_2O_3(s)$$

Use the enthalpy changes for the combustion of aluminum and iron:

$Al(s) + \frac{3}{2}O_2(g) \longrightarrow Al_2O_3(s) \quad \Delta H = -1669.8$ kJ

$2Fe(s) + \frac{3}{2}O_2(g) \longrightarrow Fe_2O_3(s) \quad \Delta H = -824.2$ kJ

36. What is the formula for calculating the standard heat of reaction?

37. What is the standard heat of reaction (ΔH^0) for the decomposition of hydrogen peroxide?

$$2H_2O_2(l) \longrightarrow 2H_2O(l) + O_2(g)$$

Elements ▸ **Handbook**

Sources of Hydrogen Use Hess's law and two thermochemical equations on page R38 to calculate ΔH for the following reaction.

$$2H_2O(g) + CH_4(g) \longrightarrow CO_2(g) + 4H_2(g)$$

ℹ️ **nteractive Textbook**

Assessment 17.4 Test yourself on the concepts in Section 17.4.

— with **ChemASAP**

Heat of Combustion of a Candle

Purpose
To observe a burning candle and calculate the heat associated with the combustion reaction.

Materials
- candle
- aluminum foil
- safety matches
- ruler
- balance
- temperature probe (optional)

Procedure

 Probeware version available in the Probeware Lab Manual.

Measure and record the length of a candle in centimeters. Place the candle on a small piece of aluminum foil and measure the mass of the foil-candle system. Note the time as you light the candle. Let the candle burn for about five minutes. **CAUTION** *Keep clothing away from the flame.* While you wait, begin answering the Analyze questions. After about 5 minutes, extinguish the candle and record the time. Measure the mass of the foil-candle system again. Do not try to measure the mass while the candle is burning.

Analyze
Using your experimental data, answer the following questions.

1. Observe the candle burn and draw a picture of what you see.
2. Examine the flame closely. Is it the wax or the wick that burns?
3. If you said the wax, how does the wax burn without touching the flame? If you said the wick, what is the function of the wax?
4. If you could measure the temperature near the flame, you would find that the air is much hotter above the flame than it is beside it. Why? Explain.
5. Scientists have often wondered if a candle would burn well in zero gravity. How would zero gravity change the shape of the flame?
6. How much length and mass did the candle lose? Are these data more consistent with the wax or the wick burning?

7. Keeping in mind that *wick* is also a verb, explain how a candle works.
8. The formula for candle wax can be approximated as $C_{20}H_{42}$. Write and balance an equation for the complete combustion of the candle wax.
9. Calculate the number of moles of candle wax burned in the experiment.
10. Calculate the heat of combustion of candle wax in kJ/mol. The standard heat of formation of candle wax ($C_{20}H_{42}$) is −2230 kJ/mol. The standard heats of formation of carbon dioxide and water are −394 kJ/mol and −242 kJ/mol, respectively. The heat of combustion of candle wax equals the sum of the heats of formation of the products minus the sum of the heats of formation of the reactants.
11. Calculate the amount of heat (in kJ) released in your reaction. (*Hint:* Multiply the number of moles of candle wax burned in the experiment by the heat of combustion of candle wax.)

You're the Chemist
The following small-scale activities allow you to develop your own procedures and analyze the results.

1. **Design It!** Design an experiment to show that the candle wax does not burn with complete combustion.
2. **Design It!** Design an experiment to show that water is a product of the combustion of a candle.

Key Concepts

17.1 The Flow of Energy—Heat and Work

- Heat always flows from a warmer object to a cooler object.
- A system gains heat in an endothermic process, and loses heat in an exothermic process.
- Heat flow is measured with two common units, the calorie and the joule.
- The heat capacity of an object depends on both its mass and its chemical composition.

17.2 Measuring and Expressing Enthalpy Changes

- In calorimetry, the heat released by a system equals the heat absorbed by its surroundings. Conversely, the heat absorbed by a system equals the heat released by its surroundings.

- The enthalpy change for a reaction can be treated like any other reactant or product.

Heat in Changes of State

- The heat absorbed by a melting solid is exactly the same as the heat lost when the liquid solidifies; that is, $\Delta H_{fus} = -\Delta H_{solid}$.
- The heat absorbed by a vaporizing liquid is exactly the same as the heat lost when the vapor condenses; that is, $\Delta H_{vap} = -\Delta H_{cond}$.
- Heat is either released or absorbed during the formation of a solution.

17.4 Calculating Heats of Reaction

- You can calculate the heat of a reaction by applying Hess's law of heat summation or by using standard heats of formation.

Vocabulary

- calorimeter (p. 511)
- calorimetry (p. 511)
- chemical potential energy (p. 505)
- endothermic process (p. 506)
- enthalpy (p. 511)
- exothermic process (p. 506)
- heat (p. 505)
- heat capacity (p. 508)
- heat of combustion (p. 517)

- heat of reaction (p. 514)
- Hess's law of heat summation (p. 527)
- law of conservation of energy (p. 506)
- molar heat of condensation (p. 523)
- molar heat of fusion (p. 520)
- molar heat of solidification (p. 520)
- molar heat of solution (p. 525)

- molar heat of vaporization (p. 522)
- specific heat (p. 508)
- standard heat of formation (p. 530)
- surroundings (p. 506)
- system (p. 506)
- thermochemical equation (p. 514)
- thermochemistry (p. 505)

Key Equations

- 1 Calorie = 1 kilocalorie = 1000 calories
- $C = \dfrac{q}{m \times \Delta T}$

- $q_{sys} = \Delta H = -q_{surr} = -m \times C \times \Delta T$
- $\Delta H^0 = \Delta H_f^0(\text{products}) - \Delta H_f^0(\text{reactants})$

Organizing Information

Use these terms to construct a concept map that organizes the major ideas of this chapter.

Concept Map 17 Solve the Concept Map with the help of an interactive guided tutorial.

— with **ChemASAP**

specific heat   standard heats of formation   heats of changes of state

endothermic and exothermic reactions   thermochemistry   heat capacity

thermochemical equations   calorimetry   Hess's law

17.1 The Flow of Energy—Heat

38. Explain in your own words the law of conservation of energy.

39. Define potential energy in terms of chemistry.

40. What factors determine heat capacity?

41. What is the relationship between a calorie and a Calorie?

42. Make the following conversions.
   a. 8.50×10^2 cal to Calories
   b. 444 cal to joules
   c. 1.8 kJ to joules
   d. 4.5×10^{-1} kJ to calories

43. Why do you think it is important to define the system and the surroundings?

44. Describe the sign convention that is used in thermochemical calculations.

45. Two substances in a glass beaker chemically react, and the beaker becomes too hot to touch.
   a. Is the reaction exothermic or endothermic?
   b. If the two substances are defined as the system, what constitutes the surroundings?

46. Classify these processes as exothermic or endothermic.
   a. condensing steam
   b. evaporating alcohol
   c. burning alcohol
   d. baking a potato

47. Equal masses of two substances absorb the same amount of heat. The temperature of substance A increases twice as much as the temperature of substance B. Which substance has the higher specific heat? Explain.

48. Your fingers quickly begin to feel cold when you touch an ice cube. What important thermochemical principle does this change illustrate?

17.2 Measuring and Expressing Heat Changes

49. What name is given to a heat change at constant pressure?

50. What is the function of a calorimeter?

51. There are some obvious sources of error in experiments that use foam cups as calorimeters. Name at least three.

52. What device would you use to measure the heat released at constant volume?

53. Give the standard conditions for heat of combustion.

54. What information is given in a thermochemical equation?

55. An orange contains 445 kJ of energy. What mass of water could this same amount of energy raise from 25.0°C to the boiling point?

56. You place a bottle containing 2.0 L of mineral water at 25°C into a refrigerator to cool to 7°C.
   a. How many kJ of heat is lost by the water?
   b. How many kJ of heat is absorbed by the refrigerator?
   c. What assumptions did you make in your calculations?

17.3 Heat in Changes of State

57. Explain why ice melts at 0°C without an increase of temperature, even though heat flows from the surroundings to the system (the ice).

58. Calculate the quantity of heat released or absorbed in the following changes.
   a. 3.50 mol of water freezes at 0°C.
   b. 0.44 mol of steam condenses at 100°C.
   c. 1.25 mol NaOH(s) dissolves in water.
   d. 0.15 mol $C_2H_5OH(l)$ vaporizes at 78.3°C.

59. Sodium acetate dissolves readily in water according to the following equation.

$$NaC_2H_3O_2(s) \longrightarrow NaC_2H_3O_2(aq)$$
$$\Delta H = -17.3 \text{ kJ/mol}$$

Would this process increase or decrease the temperature of the water?

60. If 3.20 kcal of heat is added to 1.00 kg of ice at 0°C, how much liquid water at 0°C is produced, and how much ice remains?

61. Calculate the heat change in joules when 45.2 g of steam at 100°C condenses to water at the same temperature.

CHAPTER
17
Review and Assessment *continued*
Blue questions emphasize Regents Exam content
NEW YORK

62. The amounts of heat required to change different quantities of carbon tetrachloride $(CCl_4)(l)$ into vapor are given in the table.

Mass of CCl₄	Heat	
(g)	(J)	(cal)
2.90	652	156
7.50	1689	404
17.0	3825	915
26.2	5894	1410
39.8	8945	2140
51.0	11453	2740

a. Graph the data, using heat in calories as the dependent variable.

b. What is the slope of the line?

c. The heat of vaporization of $CCl_4(l)$ is 53.8 cal/g. How does this value compare with the slope of the line?

63. An ice cube with a mass of 40.0 g melts in water originally at 25.0°C.

a. How much heat does the ice cube absorb from the water when it melts? Report your answer in joules and kilojoules.

b. Calculate the number of grams of water that can be cooled to 0°C by the melting ice cube.

64. The molar heat of vaporization of ethanol $(C_2H_5OH(l))$ is 43.5 kJ/mol. Calculate the heat required to vaporize 25.0 g of ethanol at its boiling point.

65. How much heat must be removed from a 45.0-g sample of naphthalene $(C_{10}H_8)$ at its freezing point to bring about solidification? The heat of fusion of naphthalene is 191.2 kJ/mol.

66. Why is vaporization an endothermic process but condensation is an exothermic process?

67. Evaluate this statement: The heat content of a substance is higher in the liquid phase than in the vapor phase at the same temperature.

68. The temperature of a person with an extremely high fever can be lowered with a sponge bath of isopropyl alcohol (C_3H_7OH). The heat of vaporization of this alcohol is 46.4 kJ/mol.

a. How many kilojoules of heat are removed from a person's skin when 175 g of isopropyl alcohol evaporates?

b. How many kilograms of water would this energy loss cool in lowering the temperature from 40.0°C to 36.0°C?

69. The enthalpy of vaporization of water at various temperatures is given in the graph. From this graph, estimate the amount of heat required to convert 1 L of water to steam on the summit of Mount Everest (29,002 ft), where the boiling temperature of water is 70°C.

17.4 Calculating Heats Reaction

70. Explain Hess's law of heat summation.

71. A considerable amount of heat is required for the decomposition of aluminum oxide.

$$2Al_2O_3(s) \longrightarrow 4Al(s) + 3O_2(g)$$
$$\Delta H = 3352 \text{ kJ}$$

a. What is the heat change for the formation of 1 mol of aluminum oxide from its elements?

b. Is the formation of aluminum oxide exothermic or endothermic?

72. Add and simplify the following thermochemical equations.

$$Pb(s) + 2Cl_2(g) \longrightarrow PbCl_4(l)$$
$$\Delta H = -329.2 \text{ kJ}$$

$$PbCl_2(s) \longrightarrow Pb(s) + Cl_2(g)$$
$$\Delta H = 359.4 \text{ kJ}$$

a. What is the heat change for the formation of lead(IV) chloride by the reaction of lead(II) chloride with chlorine?

$$PbCl_2(s) + Cl_2(g) \longrightarrow PbCl_4(l)$$
$$\Delta H = ?$$

b. Is the reaction exothermic or endothermic?

73. What is the standard heat of formation of a free element in its standard state?

74. Consider the statement, "the more negative the value of ΔH_f^0, the more stable the compound." Is this statement true or false? Explain.

75. Add and simplify the following thermochemical equations.

$$2PCl_3(g) + 2Cl_2(g) \longrightarrow 2PCl_5(s)$$
$$\Delta H = -176 \text{ kJ}$$

$$2P(s) + 3Cl_2(g) \longrightarrow 2PCl_3(g)$$
$$\Delta H = -574 \text{ kJ}$$

a. What is the heat change for the formation of phosphorus trichloride by the reaction of phosphorus with chlorine?

$$2P(s) + 5Cl_2(g) \longrightarrow 2PCl_5(s)$$

b. Is the reaction exothermic or endothermic?

76. Calculate the change in enthalpy (in kJ) for the following reactions.
a. $CH_4(g) + 2O_2(g) \longrightarrow CO_2(g) + 2H_2O(l)$
b. $2CO(g) + O_2(g) \longrightarrow 2CO_2(g)$

77. What is the standard heat of formation of a compound?

78. Use standard heats of formation (ΔH_f^0) to calculate the change in enthalpy for these reactions.
a. $2C(s, \text{graphite}) + O_2(g) \longrightarrow 2CO(g)$
b. $2H_2O_2(l) \longrightarrow 2H_2O(l) + O_2(g)$
c. $4NH_3(g) + 5O_2(g) \longrightarrow 4NO(g) + 6H_2O(g)$

79. The combustion of ethane (C_2H_4) is an exothermic reaction.

$$C_2H_4(g) + 3O_2(g) \longrightarrow 2CO_2(g) + 2H_2O(l)$$
$$\Delta H = -1.39 \times 10^3 \text{ kJ}$$

Calculate the amount of heat liberated when 4.79 mol C_2H_4 reacts with excess oxygen.

80. Add and simplify the following thermochemical equations.

$$2N_2(g) + 6H_2O(l) \longrightarrow 4NH_3(g) + 3O_2(g)$$
$$\Delta H = 1.53 \times 10^3 \text{ kJ}$$

$$4NH_3(g) + 5O_2(g) \longrightarrow 4NO(g) + 6H_2O(l)$$
$$\Delta H = -1.17 \times 10^3 \text{ kJ}$$

a. What is the heat change for the formation of nitrogen monoxide by the reaction of nitrogen with oxygen?

$$N_2(g) + O_2(g) \longrightarrow 2NO(g)$$

b. Is the reaction endothermic or exothermic?

81. When 1.000 mol of $N_2(g)$ reacts completely with 3.000 mol of $H_2(g)$, 2.000 mol of $NH_3(g)$ and 92.38 kJ of heat are produced.

$$N_2(g) + 3H_2(g) \longrightarrow 2NH_3(g) + 92.38 \text{ kJ}$$

Use this thermochemical equation to calculate ΔH for the following reactions.
a. $2N_2(g) + 6H_2(g) \longrightarrow 4NH_3(g)$
b. $\frac{3}{2}N_2(g) + \frac{9}{2}H_2(g) \longrightarrow 3NH_3(g)$
c. $\frac{1}{2}N_2(g) + \frac{3}{2}H_2(g) \longrightarrow NH_3(g)$

82. Using the following equations:

$$Ca(s) + 2C(s) \longrightarrow CaC_2(s)$$
$$\Delta H = -62.8 \text{ kJ}$$

$$CO_2(g) \longrightarrow C(s) + O_2(g)$$
$$\Delta H = 393.5 \text{ kJ}$$

$$CaCO_3(s) + CO_2(g) \longrightarrow CaC_2(s) + 2\frac{1}{2}O_2(g)$$
$$\Delta H = 1538 \text{ kJ}$$

determine the heat of reaction (in kJ) for:

$$Ca(s) + C(s) + \frac{3}{2}O_2(g) \longrightarrow CaCO_3(s)$$

83. The sugar glucose $(C_6H_{12}O_6)$ is an important nutrient for living organisms to meet their energy needs. The standard heat of formation (ΔH_f^0) of glucose is -1260 kJ/mol. Calculate how much heat (in kJ/mol) is released at standard conditions if 1 mol of glucose undergoes the following reaction.

$$C_6H_{12}O_6(s) + 6O_2(g) \longrightarrow 6CO_2(g) + 6H_2O(l)$$

Test-Taking Tip

Eliminate Wrong Answers If you don't know which response is correct, start by eliminating those you know are wrong. If you can rule out some choices, you'll have fewer left to consider and you'll increase your chances of choosing the correct answer.

Regents Practice Exam

Part A

For each statement or question write the number of the word or expression that, of those given, best completes the statement or answers the question.

1. A chemical reaction that absorbs energy is
   (1) endothermic   (3) oxidation
   (2) exothermic   (4) spontaneous

2. What is the name given to a transfer of energy from one object to a cooler object?
   (1) thermal   (3) heat
   (2) temperature   (4) kinetic energy

3. Heat of reaction equals what relationship between the potential energy of the products and the potential energy of the reactants?
   (1) the sum   (3) the product
   (2) the difference   (4) the quotient

4. Which of the following choices is *not* a type of energy?
   (1) thermal   (3) chemical
   (2) kinetic   (4) temperature

5. The type of energy stored in the bonds of compounds is
   (1) chemical   (3) kinetic
   (2) electrical   (4) mechanical

6. Thermochemical calculations can be made because in chemical reactions
   (1) mass is conserved
   (2) energy is lost
   (3) energy is gained
   (4) energy is conserved

Part B-1

For each statement or question write the number of the word or expression that, of those given, best completes the statement or answers the question.

7. The ΔH_{fus} of ethanol (C_2H_5OH) is 4.60 kJ/mol. How many kilojoules are required to melt 24.5 g of ethanol at its freezing point?
   (1) 2.45 kJ   (3) 245 kJ
   (2) 5.33 kJ   (4) 18.8 kJ

8. How much heat, in kilojoules, must be added to 178 g of water to increase the temperature of the water by 5.0°C?
   (1) 890 kJ   (3) 3.7 kJ
   (2) 36 kJ   (4) 0.093 kJ

9. If ΔH for the reaction $2HgO(s) \longrightarrow 2Hg(l) + O_2(g)$ is 181.66 kJ, then ΔH for the reaction $2Hg(l) + O_2(g) \longrightarrow 2HgO(s)$ is
   (1) 90.83 kJ   (3) 181.66 kJ
   (2) −90.83 kJ   (4) −181.66 kJ

10. The formation of rust is an example of what type of chemical reaction?
    (1) combination (synthesis)
    (2) decomposition
    (3) single-replacement
    (4) double-replacement

11. What element is found in Group 5A (15) and period 4 of the periodic table?
    (1) tin   (3) vanadium
    (2) antimony   (4) arsenic

12. What group on the periodic table contains elements with seven valence electrons?
    (1) Group 7A (17)
    (2) Group 1A (1)
    (3) Group 7B (7)
    (4) Group 2A (2)

Part B-2

Answer each of the following questions.

13. Explain the difference between an independent variable and a dependent variable.

14. Write the correct chemical symbol for each of the following elements.
    a. chromium   d. calcium
    b. copper   e. cesium
    c. carbon   f. chlorine

15. Express the results of the following calculations with the correct number of significant figures.
    a. 6.723 cm × 1.04 cm
    b. 8.934 L + 0.2005 L + 1.55 L
    c. 864 g ÷ 2.4 g
    d. 9.258 mm − 4.82 mm

16. List three kinds of subatomic particles in an atom. Describe each kind in terms of charge, relative mass, and location with respect to the nucleus.

17. List the following atoms in order of increasing atomic radius: phosphorus, germanium, arsenic.

18. How many chloride ions would be required to react with these positive ions to make an electrically neutral unit?
 a. strontium ion
 b. calcium ion
 c. aluminum ion
 d. lithium ion

19. How does a polar covalent bond differ from a nonpolar covalent bond? Which type of bond is found in molecular oxygen (O_2)? In carbon monoxide (CO)?

20. Write formulas for each of the following compounds.
 a. potassium nitride
 b. aluminum sulfide
 c. calcium nitrate
 d. calcium sulfate

21. Write a balanced chemical equation for the double-replacement reaction between sodium chloride and silver acetate.

22. How many moles of oxygen are formed by the decomposition of 25.0 mol of hydrogen peroxide?
$$2H_2O_2(l) \longrightarrow 2H_2O(l) + O_2(g)$$

23. A gas has a volume of 8.57 L at 273 K. What will be the volume at 355 K if its pressure does not change?

Use the graph and table to answer Questions 24–27. Assume 1.00 mol of substance is present in each container.

Substance	Freezing point (K)	ΔH_{fus} (kJ/mol)	Boiling point (K)	ΔH_{vap} (kJ/mol)
Ammonia	195.3	5.65	239.7	23.4
Benzene	278.7	9.87	353.3	30.8
Methanol	175.5	3.16	337.2	35.3
Neon	24.5	0.33	27.1	1.76

24. Calculate the heat absorbed in region A for neon.

25. Calculate the heat absorbed in region C for benzene.

26. Calculate the heat absorbed in regions B and C for methanol. [specific heat = 81.6 J/(g·°C)]

27. Calculate the heat absorbed in regions A, B, and C for ammonia. [specific heat = 35.1 J/(g·°C)]

Part C

Answer each of the following questions.

28. What always happens when two objects of different temperatures come in contact? Give an example from your own experience.

29. When lightning flashes, nitrogen and oxygen combine to form nitrogen monoxide. The nitrogen monoxide reacts with oxygen to form nitrogen dioxide. Write balanced chemical equations for these two reactions.

Temperture vs. Heat supplied

Chemical reactions, like stock car racers, have measurable speeds.

INQUIRY ▶ Activity

Temperature and Reaction Rates

Materials

masking tape, four plastic cups, hot and cold tap water, ice, a thermometer, four effervescent antacid tablets, a clock or watch with a second hand, graph paper, and a pen or pencil.

Procedure

1. Mark an A, B, C, or D on four separate pieces of masking tape. Label each plastic cup with one of the lettered pieces of tape.

2. Fill each cup three-quarters full as follows: (A) cold tap water plus some ice, (B) cold tap water, (C) half-and-half mixture of cold tap water and hot tap water, (D) hot tap water.

3. Measure and record the temperature of the water in cup A.

4. Drop a tablet into cup A and measure the time it takes for the reaction (bubble evolution) to end. Repeat Steps 3 and 4 using the remaining three cups.

5. Draw a line or bar graph of temperature versus reaction time.

Think About It

1. Do the tablets react faster at higher temperatures? Explain why or why not.

2. What results would you expect if you crushed the tablets into a powder before adding them to the water? Explain your prediction. If time permits, check this prediction experimentally.

18.1 Rates of Reaction

New York Standards: 3.4d, 3.4f, 3.4g

Connecting to Your World

Metal objects can be damaged by corrosion, but this process can be useful to hungry soldiers, truck drivers, and others who want a hot meal but do not have a place to cook it. Products now on the market use the heat given off by the corrosion reaction of an iron-magnesium alloy with salt water to produce a hot meal. Normally the reaction takes place at such a slow rate that the heat released from the process cannot be used. But when the rate is increased by the addition of salt water, heat is produced rapidly. In this section, you will learn some ways in which the rate of a reaction can be increased.

Guide for Reading

Key Concepts
- How is the rate of a chemical change expressed?
- What four factors influence the rate of a chemical reaction?

Vocabulary
rate
collision theory
activation energy
activated complex
transition state
inhibitor

Reading Strategy

Outlining As you read, make an outline of the most important ideas in this section. Use the red headings as the main topics and the blue as subtopics. Add a sentence or a note after each heading to provide key information about each topic.

Collision Theory

When you strike a match, it erupts into flame almost instantly and burns quickly. Some other reactions occur more slowly. For example, millions of years were required for dead plants beneath Earth's surface to be converted to coal. These examples show that the speed of chemical reactions can vary from instantaneous to extremely slow.

The concept of speed is already familiar to you. The winning sprinter in Figure 18.1 covers 100 meters in 11.5 seconds. She runs at a speed of 8.70 m/s. Another sprinter takes 15.0 seconds to cover the same distance. She runs at a speed of 6.67m/s. Both 8.70 m/s and 6.67 m/s express rates of travel.

Start   Distance (m)   Finish

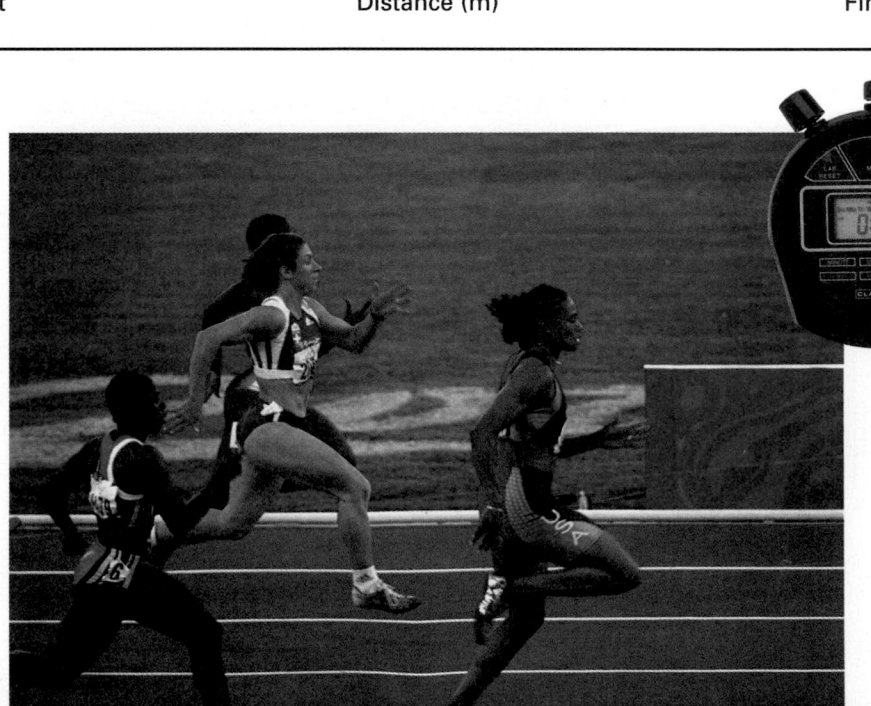

$$\text{Rate} = \frac{\text{Distance (m)}}{\text{Time (s)}} = ? \frac{m}{s}$$

Figure 18.1 Speed is measured as a change in distance in a given interval of time. A world-class sprinter might cover 100 meters in 11.5 seconds; the speed, or rate, is 100 m/11.5 s = 8.70 m/s.

541

Figure 18.2 Change occurs at different rates. **Interpreting Photographs** *List the changes shown above in order of speed from slowest to fastest.*

A **rate** is a measure of the speed of any change that occurs within an interval of time. The interval of time may range from fractions of a second to centuries. Figure 18.2 shows some familiar examples of rates of change. If one half of a 1-molar piece of iron turns to rust in one year, the rate at which iron rusts might be expressed as 0.5 mol/yr. 🔑 **In chemistry, the rate of chemical change or the reaction rate is usually expressed as the amount of reactant changing per unit time.** The progress of a typical reaction is illustrated in Figure 18.3.

Rates of chemical reactions are related to the properties of atoms, ions, and molecules through a model called collision theory. According to **collision theory,** atoms, ions, and molecules can react to form products when they collide with one another, provided that the colliding particles have enough kinetic energy. Particles lacking the necessary kinetic energy to react bounce apart unchanged when they collide. Figure 18.4 is a model for the reaction of hydrogen and oxygen molecules to form water.

You can use two balls of soft modeling clay to illustrate collision theory. If you throw the balls of clay together gently, they don't stick to one another. This is analogous to colliding particles of low energy that fail to react. The same balls of clay thrown together with great force, however, stick tightly to each other. This is analogous to the collision of two high-energy particles that results in the formation of a product.

Figure 18.3 As time passes, the amount of reactant (red squares) decreases and the amount of product (blue spheres) increases. Rates of chemical reactions are often measured as a change in the number of moles during an interval of time. **Interpreting Diagrams** *Assuming equal time intervals between the boxes, how can you tell that the rate of conversion of reactant to product is not constant throughout this reaction?*

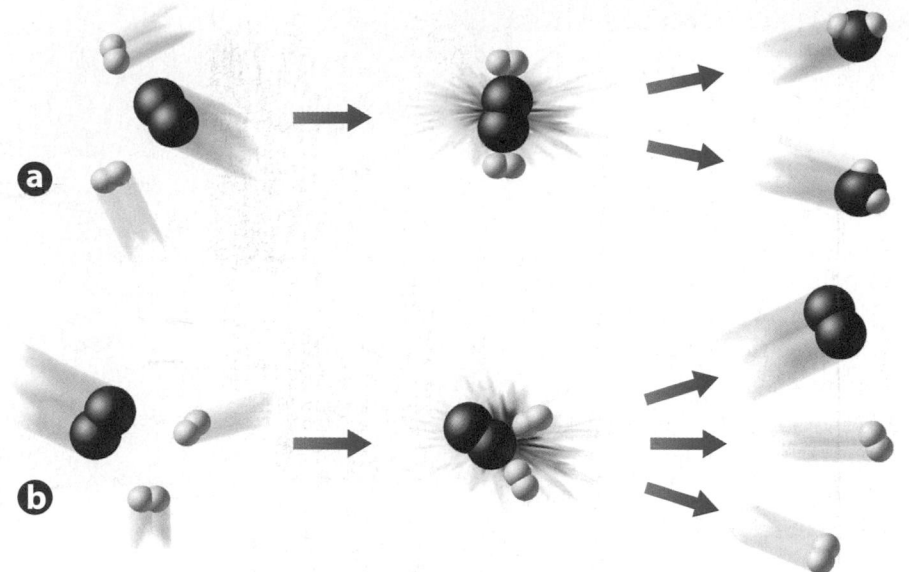

Figure 18.4 If colliding particles have enough kinetic energy and collide at the right orientation, they can react to form a new product. **ⓐ** An effective collision of reactant molecules produces product molecules. **ⓑ** An ineffective collision of reactant molecules produces no reaction, and the reactants bounce apart unchanged.

You can also use modeling clay to illustrate another point about chemical reactions. If you roll clay into a rope and begin to shake one end more and more vigorously, you will come to a point where the clay rope will break. Similarly, if enough energy is applied to a molecule, the bonds holding the molecule together can break apart. Substances, when supplied with sufficient energy, decompose to simpler substances or reorganize themselves into new substances. The minimum energy that colliding particles must have in order to react is called the **activation energy.** In a sense, the activation energy for a chemical reaction is a barrier that reactants must cross to be converted to products. You can see in the energy diagram in Figure 18.5 that when two reactant particles with the necessary activation energy collide, a new entity called the activated complex may form.

Energy Changes in a Reaction

Activated complex

Activation energy

Energy of reactants

Reactants

Energy released by reaction

Energy of products

Products

Energy ⟶

Reaction progress ⟶

Figure 18.5 The activation-energy barrier must be crossed before reactants are converted to products.

INTERPRETING GRAPHS

a. Navigate Which are at a higher energy, the reactants or products?
b. Read Is energy absorbed or released in progressing from the reactants to the activated complex?
c. Interpret Once the activated complex is formed, will it always proceed to form products? Explain.

Does Steel Burn?

Purpose
To determine whether steel will burn.

Materials
- #0000 steel wool pad
- tissue paper
- tongs
- Bunsen burner
- heat-resistant pad
- pencil and paper

Procedure

1. Roll a small piece of steel wool into a very tight, pea-sized ball. Use the tissue paper to protect your fingers from small steel fibers while handling the steel wool.

2. Holding the ball with tongs, heat the steel wool in the blue-tip flame of the burner for no longer than 10 seconds. In this and subsequent steps, place pieces of heated steel wool on the heat-resistant pad to cool. Observe all appropriate safety precautions when working with the burner and the heated materials. Record your observations.

3. Gently roll a second piece of steel wool into a loose, pea-sized ball. Holding the loose ball with the tongs, heat the wool in the burner flame for no longer than 10 seconds. Record your observations.

4. Pull a few individual fibers of steel wool from the pad. Hold one end of the loose fibers with the tongs and heat them in the flame of the burner for no longer than 10 seconds. Again record your observations.

Analyze and Conclude

1. What differences did you observe when the tight ball, the loose ball, and the loose fibers were heated in the flame? Give a reason for any differences you observed.

2. Write the balanced equation for any chemical reaction you may have observed (assume that the steel wool is composed mainly of iron).

3. How do your results differ from those observed in the rusting of an automobile body?

4. Explain why steel wool is a hazard in shops where there are hot plates, open flames, or sparking motors.

An **activated complex** is an unstable arrangement of atoms that forms momentarily at the peak of the activation-energy barrier. An activated complex forms only if the colliding particles have sufficient energy and if the atoms are oriented properly. The lifetime of an activated complex is typically about 10^{-13} s. Its brief existence ends with the re-formation of the reactants or with the formation of products. The two outcomes are equally likely. Thus the activated complex is sometimes called the **transition state.**

Collision theory explains why some naturally occurring reactions are immeasurably slow at room temperature. Carbon and oxygen react when charcoal burns, but this reaction has a high activation energy. At room temperature, the collisions of oxygen and carbon molecules are not energetic enough to break the O—O and C—C bonds. These bonds must be broken to form the activated complex. Thus the reaction rate of carbon with oxygen at room temperature is essentially zero.

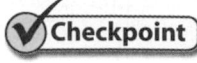 **Checkpoint** *What are two events that might occur after the formation of an activated complex?*

Factors Affecting Reaction Rates

Every chemical reaction proceeds at its own rate. Some reactions are naturally fast and some are naturally slow under the same conditions. However, by varying the conditions of the reaction, the rate of almost any reaction can be modified. **The rate of a chemical reaction depends upon temperature, concentration, particle size, and the use of a catalyst.** Collision theory helps explain why changing one or more of these factors may affect the rate of a chemical reaction.

Temperature Usually, raising the temperature speeds up reactions, while lowering the temperature slows down reactions. At higher temperatures, the motions of the reactant particles are faster and more chaotic than they are at lower temperatures. Increasing the temperature increases both the frequency of collisions and the number of particles that have enough kinetic energy to slip over the activation-energy barrier to become products. An increase in temperature, therefore, causes products to form faster.

A familiar example of the effect of temperature on reaction rate is the burning of charcoal. At room temperature, a bag of charcoal in contact with air does not burn. But when a starter flame touches the charcoal, atoms of the reactants (carbon and oxygen) collide with higher energy and greater frequency. Some collisions are at a high enough energy to form the product (carbon dioxide). The heat released by the reaction then supplies enough energy to get more carbon and oxygen over the activation-energy barrier. When the starter flame is removed, the reaction continues.

Concentration In a crowded room where people are moving about rapidly, you may find yourself bumping into people more frequently than if you were one of a few occupants. Similarly, the number of particles in a given volume affects the rate at which reactions occur. Cramming more particles into a fixed volume increases the concentration of reactants and consequently the frequency of collision. Increased collision frequency leads to a higher reaction rate. The lighted splint in Figure 18.6 only glows in air, which is 20% oxygen. It may soon be extinguished. But when the glowing splint is plunged into pure oxygen, it immediately bursts into flame. The increased concentration of oxygen greatly speeds up the combustion reaction. This is why flames are forbidden in areas where bottled oxygen is in use.

interactive Textbook

Animation 22 Explore several factors that control the speed of a reaction.

— with **ChemASAP**

Go Online

NSTA SCiLINKS

For: Links on Reaction Rates
Visit: www.SciLinks.org
Web Code: cdn-1181

Figure 18.6 The rate of a reaction depends upon the concentrations of the reactants. **a** In air, a lighted splint glows and soon goes out. **b** When placed in pure oxygen, the splint bursts into flame. **Inferring** *What accounts for the difference in reactivity?*

Figure 18.7 In 1932, an explosion destroyed this Chicago grain elevator. The minute size of the reactant particles (grain dust), and the mixture of the grain dust with oxygen in the air caused the reaction to be explosive.

Particle Size If you put a bundle of sticks on a campfire, they burn quickly. A log, however, burns more slowly. Small pieces of wood have more surface area than a log, and surface area plays an important role in determining the rate of reaction. The same is true for other chemical reactions. The total surface area of a solid or liquid reactant affects the reaction rate. The smaller the particle size, the larger is the surface area for a given mass of particles. An increase in surface area increases the amount of the reactant exposed for reaction, which further increases the collision frequency and the reaction rate.

One way to increase the surface area of solid reactants is to dissolve them. In a solution, particles are separated and more accessible to other reactants. You can also increase the surface area of a solid by grinding it into a fine powder. Small dustlike particles, however, can be dangerous when suspended in air. As coal miners know, large chunks of coal pose little danger, but coal dust mixed with air is an explosive hazard because of its large surface area. The same is true of dust in a flour mill or a grain elevator, as the dramatic photograph in Figure 18.7 shows.

Catalysts Increasing the temperature is not always the best way to increase the rate of a reaction. A catalyst is often better. Recall that a catalyst is a substance that increases the rate of a reaction without being used up during the reaction. Catalysts permit reactions to proceed along a lower energy path, as Figure 18.8 shows. Notice that the activation energy barrier for the catalyzed reaction is lower than that of the uncatalyzed reaction. With a lower activation-energy barrier, more reactants have the energy to form products within a given time. For instance, the rate of the combination reaction of hydrogen and oxygen at room temperature is negligible, but with a trace of finely divided platinum (Pt) as a catalyst, the reaction is rapid.

$$2H_2(g) + O_2(g) \xrightarrow{\text{Pt}} 2H_2O(l)$$

Because a catalyst is not consumed during a reaction, it does not appear as a reactant or product in the chemical equation. Instead, the catalyst is often written above the yield arrow, as in the equation above.

Simulation 23 Explore the effects of concentration, temperature, and a catalyst on reaction rate.

with ChemASAP

The Effect of a Catalyst on Activation Energy

Activation energy without catalyst

Activation energy with catalyst

Reactants

Reaction without catalyst

Reaction with catalyst

Products

Reaction progress ⟶

Energy ⟶

Figure 18.8 A catalyst increases the rate of a reaction by lowering the activation-energy barrier.

INTERPRETING GRAPHS

a. Navigate How does the catalyst affect the magnitude of the activation energy?
b. Read Does the catalyst change the amount of energy released in the reaction?
c. Interpret Along which of the two reaction paths are reactants converted more rapidly to products?

Catalysts are crucial for many life processes. Your body temperature is only 37°C and cannot be raised significantly without danger. Without catalysts, few reactions in the body would proceed fast enough. Enzymes are biological catalysts that increase the rates of biological reactions. When you eat a meal containing protein, enzymes in your digestive tract break down the protein molecules in a few hours. Without enzymes, the digestion of protein at 37°C would take many years!

An **inhibitor** is a substance that interferes with the action of a catalyst. Some inhibitor molecules work by reacting with, or "poisoning," the catalyst itself. Thus the inhibitor reduces the amount of functional catalyst available. Reactions slow or even stop when a catalyst is poisoned.

18.1 Section Assessment

1. **Key Concept** How is the rate of a chemical reaction expressed?

2. **Key Concept** What are four factors that affect the rate of a chemical reaction?

3. Suppose a thin sheet of zinc containing 0.2 mol of the metal is completely converted to zinc oxide (ZnO) in one month. How would you express the rate of conversion of the zinc?

4. Does every collision between reacting particles lead to products? Explain.

5. Refrigerated food stays fresh for long periods. The same food stored at room temperature quickly spoils. Why?

Writing ▶ Activity

Write a Report Catalytic converters are required on all cars manufactured in the United States. Find out what substances are used as the catalysts. What chemical reactions does the catalyst facilitate? Write a report summarizing your findings.

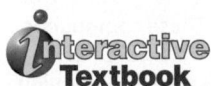
Interactive Textbook

Assessment 18.1 Test yourself on the concepts in Section 18.1.

── with **ChemASAP**

Don't Let Good Food Go Bad

For thousands of years, people have dried fruits and vegetables and salted or smoked meat and fish to keep them from spoiling. These methods slow oxidation and the action of microorganisms. When food oxidizes, or reacts with oxygen, it becomes rancid and turns brown. Microorganisms such as bacteria, yeast, and molds destroy or contaminate food, making it unfit to eat. Today, methods for preserving food also include refrigeration and the addition of preservatives— antioxidants and antimicrobials. **Inferring** *Why is it a good practice to keep food in closed containers?*

Refrigeration Storing foods in a refrigerator keeps them fresh longer. Low temperatures slow microbial action. Meat kept at freezing temperatures has a lifetime of months.

Antioxidants The preservatives BHT (butylated hydroxytoluene) an BHA (butylated hydroxyanisole), added to packaging or to the food inside, keep the food from becoming stale quickly.

Sulfites and sulfur dioxide These compounds are antioxidants and antimicrobials used in drying fruits and preserving fruit juices. Canning and pickling slow the action of microbes and limit contact with air.

Oxygen-free packaging Many food packages contain nitrogen or another nonreactive gas rather than air. Excluding oxygen prolongs shelf life.

18.2 Reversible Reactions and Equilibrium

Connecting to Your World

For years, scientists tried to produce nitrogen compounds for fertilizers to increase the amount of available foodstuffs. Unfortunately, none of these efforts proved to be commercially successful. Finally, in the early 1900s, two German chemists, Fritz Haber and Karl Bosch, refined the process of making ammonia from elemental nitrogen and hydrogen. Their success came from controlling the temperature and pressure under which the two gases are reacted. In this section, you will learn how changing the reaction conditions can influence the yield of a chemical reaction.

Reversible Reactions

From what you have already learned, you may have inferred that chemical reactions go completely from reactants to products, just as the chemical equation indicates. This is not usually the case. Some reactions are reversible. A **reversible reaction** is one in which the conversion of reactants to products and the conversion of products to reactants occur simultaneously. One example of a reversible reaction is the following:

Forward reaction: $2SO_2(g) + O_2(g) \longrightarrow 2SO_3(g)$

Reverse reaction: $2SO_2(g) + O_2(g) \longleftarrow 2SO_3(g)$

In the first reaction, which is read from left to right, sulfur dioxide and oxygen produce sulfur trioxide. In the second reaction, which is read from right to left, sulfur trioxide decomposes into oxygen and sulfur dioxide. The first reaction is called the forward reaction. The second is called the reverse reaction. The two equations can be combined into one using a double arrow. The double arrow tells you that this reaction is reversible.

$$2SO_2(g) + O_2(g) \rightleftharpoons 2SO_3(g)$$

Sulfur   Oxygen   Sulfur
dioxide   trioxide

Figure 18.9 shows that this equation represents two opposite reactions.

Guide for Reading

Key Concepts
- How do the amounts of reactants and products change in a chemical system at equilibrium?
- What three stresses can cause a change in the equilibrium position of a chemical system?
- What does the value of K_{eq} indicate about the position of equilibrium?

Vocabulary
reversible reaction
chemical equilibrium
equilibrium position
Le Châtelier's principle
equilibrium constant

Reading Strategy

Previewing Before you read this section, rewrite the headings as how, why, and what questions about reversible reactions and equilibrium. As you read, write answers to the questions.

SO₂ and O₂   2SO₂ + O₂ ⇌ 2SO₃   SO₃
(not at equilibrium)   (at equilibrium)   (not at equilibrium)

Figure 18.9 Molecules of SO_2 and O_2 react to give SO_3. Molecules of SO_3 decompose to give SO_2 and O_2. At equilibrium, all three types of molecules are present in the mixture.

Figure 18.10 These graphs show how the concentrations of O_2, SO_2, and SO_3 vary with time. Left: Initially, SO_2 and O_2 are present. Right: Initially, only SO_3 is present.

INTERPRETING GRAPHS

a. Navigate Where on the graphs can you find the initial concentrations of the reactants and products? The equilibrium concentrations?
b. Read Which gas is most abundant at equilibrium?
c. Interpret How do the equilibrium concentrations of O_2, SO_2, and SO_3 compare?

Changes in Concentrations of Reactants and Products

Word *Origins*

Equilibrium comes from the Latin word *aequilibrium,* meaning "in balance." In a chemical system at equilibrium, the rate of the forward reaction is balanced by the rate of the reverse reaction.

If the prefix *dis*-means "opposite or absence of," what does a state of disequilibrium indicate?

What actually happens when sulfur dioxide and oxygen gases are mixed in a sealed chamber? The two reactants begin to react to form sulfur trioxide at a particular rate. Because no sulfur trioxide is present at the beginning of the reaction, the initial rate of the reverse reaction is zero. As sulfur trioxide begins to form, however, the decomposition of sulfur trioxide begins. This reverse reaction proceeds slowly at first, but its rate increases as the concentration of sulfur trioxide increases. Simultaneously, the rate of the forward reaction decreases because sulfur dioxide and oxygen are being used up. Eventually sulfur trioxide is decomposing to sulfur dioxide and oxygen as fast as sulfur dioxide and oxygen are forming sulfur trioxide. When the rates of the forward and reverse reactions are equal, the reaction has reached a state of balance called **chemical equilibrium.** Changes in concentrations of the three components during the course of the reaction are shown in the graphs in Figure 18.10. The graph on the left shows the progress of a reaction that starts with specific concentrations of SO_2 and O_2, but with zero concentration of SO_3. The graph on the right shows concentrations for a reaction that begins with an initial concentration of SO_3 and zero concentrations for SO_2 and O_2. Notice that after a certain time, all concentrations remain constant. **At chemical equilibrium, no net change occurs in the actual amounts of the components of the system.** The amount of SO_3 in the equilibrium mixture is the maximum amount that can be produced by this reaction under the conditions of the reaction.

The unchanging amounts of SO_2, O_2, and SO_3 in the reaction mixture at equilibrium might cause you to think that both reactions have stopped. This is not the case. Chemical equilibrium is a dynamic state. Both the forward and reverse reactions continue, but because their rates are equal, no net change occurs in their concentrations. The escalators in Figure 18.11 are like the double arrows in a dynamic equilibrium equation. The number of people using the up escalator must equal the number of people using the down escalator for the number of people on both floors to remain constant.

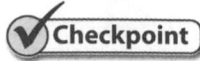 *Why is chemical equilibrium called a dynamic state?*

Although the rates of the forward and reverse reactions are equal at chemical equilibrium, the concentrations of the components on both sides of the chemical equation are not necessarily the same. In fact, they can be dramatically different. Figure 18.10 shows the equilibrium concentrations of SO_2, O_2, and SO_3. The concentration of SO_3 is significantly greater than the concentrations of SO_2 and O_2. The relative concentrations of the reactants and products at equilibrium constitute the **equilibrium position** of a reaction. The equilibrium position indicates whether the reactants or products are favored in a reversible reaction. If A reacts to give B and the equilibrium mixture contains significantly more of B—say 1% A and 99% B—then the formation of B is said to be favored.

$$A \rightleftharpoons B$$
$$\quad 1\% \qquad 99\%$$

On the other hand, if the mixture contains 99% A and 1% B at equilibrium, then the formation of A is favored.

$$A \rightleftharpoons B$$
$$\quad 99\% \qquad 1\%$$

Notice that the equilibrium arrows are not of equal length; the longer of the two arrows indicates the favored direction of a reaction.

In principle, almost all reactions are reversible to some extent under the right conditions. In practice, one set of components is often so favored at equilibrium that the other set cannot be detected. If one set of components (reactants) is completely converted to new substances (products), you can say that the reaction has gone to completion, or is irreversible. When you mix chemicals expecting to get a reaction but no products can be detected, you can say that there is no reaction. Reversible reactions occupy a middle ground between the theoretical extremes of irreversibility and no reaction.

A catalyst speeds up both the forward and the reverse reactions equally because the reverse reaction is exactly the opposite of the forward reaction. The catalyst lowers the activation energy of the reaction by the same amount in both the forward and reverse directions. Catalysts do not affect the amounts of reactants and products present at equilibrium; they simply decrease the time it takes to establish equilibrium.

Checkpoint *What is chemical equilibrium?*

Interactive Textbook

Animation 23 Take a close look at a generalized reversible reaction.

with **ChemASAP**

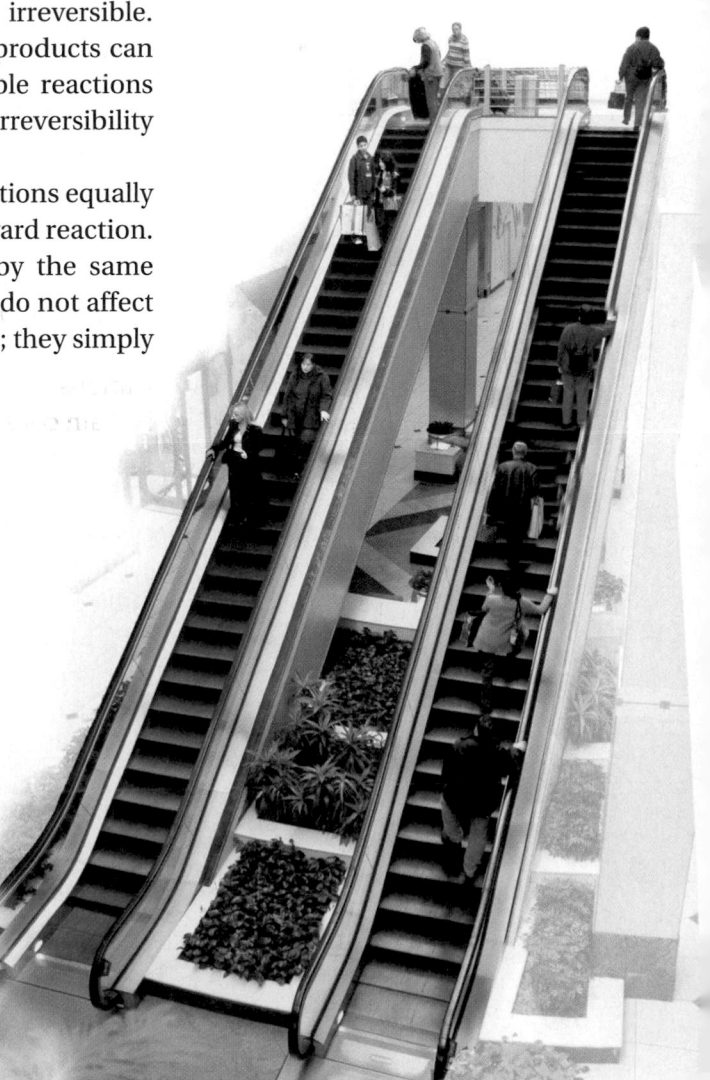

Figure 18.11 If the rate at which shoppers move from the first floor to the second is equal to the rate at which shoppers move from the second floor to the first, then the number of shoppers on each floor remains constant. **Applying Concepts** *Is it necessary that an equal number of shoppers be on each floor? Explain.*

Factors Affecting Equilibrium: Le Châtelier's Principle

A delicate balance exists in a system at equilibrium. Changes of almost any kind can disrupt this balance. When the equilibrium of a system is disturbed, the system makes adjustments to restore equilibrium. However, the equilibrium position of the restored equilibrium is different from the original equilibrium position; that is, the amounts of products and reactants may have increased or decreased. Such a change is called a shift in the equilibrium position.

The French chemist Henri Le Châtelier (1850–1936) studied how the equilibrium position shifts as a result of changing conditions. He proposed what has come to be called **Le Châtelier's principle:** If a stress is applied to a system in dynamic equilibrium, the system changes in a way that relieves the stress. **Stresses that upset the equilibrium of a chemical system include changes in the concentration of reactants or products, changes in temperature, and changes in pressure.**

The following examples of applications of Le Châtelier's principle all involve reversible reactions. For simplicity and clarity, the components to the left of the reaction arrow will be considered the reactants and the components to the right of the reaction arrow will be considered the products. Blue arrows indicate the shifts resulting from additions to or removals from the system. The arrows always point in the direction of the resulting shift in the equilibrium position—that is, toward the favored side.

Concentration Changing the amount, or concentration, of any reactant or product in a system at equilibrium disturbs the equilibrium. The system adjusts to minimize the effects of the change. Consider the decomposition of carbonic acid (H_2CO_3) in aqueous solution to form the products carbon dioxide and water. The system has reached equilibrium. At equilibrium the amount of carbonic acid is less than 1%.

$$\underset{<1\%}{H_2CO_3(aq)} \overset{\underset{\text{Direction of shift}}{\text{Add } CO_2}}{\underset{\underset{\text{Direction of shift} \rightarrow}{\text{Remove } CO_2}}{\rightleftharpoons}} \underset{>99\%}{CO_2(aq) + H_2O(l)}$$

Adding more carbon dioxide disturbs the equilibrium. It increases the concentration of CO_2 in the mixture and causes the rate of the reverse reaction to increase. As more reactant (H_2CO_3) is formed, the rate of the forward reaction also begins to increase. In time, the rates of the forward and reverse reactions again become equal, and a new equilibrium is established with a higher concentration of reactant (H_2CO_3). Adding a product to a reaction at equilibrium pushes a reversible reaction in the direction of reactants.

If, on the other hand, carbon dioxide is removed, the concentration of CO_2 decreases. This causes the rate of the reverse reaction to decrease. As less reactant (H_2CO_3) is being formed, the rate of the forward reaction also begins to decrease. When the rates of the forward and reverse reactions again become equal, equilibrium is restored but at a different equilibrium position. Removing a product always pushes a reversible reaction in the direction of products.

Farmers use this technique to increase the yield of eggs laid by hens. Hens lay eggs and then proceed to hatch them. If the eggs are removed after they are laid (removing the product), the hen will lay more eggs (increasing the yield). Similarly as products are removed from a reaction mixture, the system continually changes to restore equilibrium by producing more products. But because the products are being removed, the reaction can never reestablish equilibrium. The reaction continues to produce products until the reactants are used up. Another example of this concept is found in the body. Blood contains dissolved carbonic acid in equilibrium with carbon dioxide and water. The body uses the removal of products to keep the concentration of carbonic acid within a safe range. When the athletes in Figure 18.12 exhale carbon dioxide, the equilibrium shifts toward carbon dioxide and water, thus reducing the amount of carbonic acid. The same principle applies to adding or removing reactants. When a reactant is added to a system at equilibrium, the reaction shifts in the direction of the formation of products. When a reactant is removed, the reaction shifts in the direction of formation of reactants.

Checkpoint *According to Le Châtelier's principle, how does a system at equilibrium respond to a stress?*

Interactive Textbook

Simulation 24 Simulate Le Châtelier's principle for the synthesis of ammonia.

— with **ChemASAP**

Figure 18.12 The rapid exhalation of CO_2 during and after vigorous exercise helps reestablish the body's correct $CO_2:H_2CO_3$ equilibrium. This keeps the acid concentration in the blood within a safe range.

Temperature Increasing the temperature causes the equilibrium position of a reaction to shift in the direction that absorbs heat. The heat absorption reduces the applied temperature stress. For example, consider the following exothermic reaction that occurs when SO_3 is produced from the reaction of SO_2 and O_2.

$$2SO_2(g) + O_2(g) \overset{\substack{\text{Add heat} \\ \leftarrow \text{Direction of shift}}}{\underset{\substack{\text{Remove heat (cool)} \\ \text{Direction of shift} \rightarrow}}{\rightleftharpoons}} 2SO_3(g) + \text{heat}$$

Heat can be considered to be a product, just like SO_3. Heating the reaction mixture at equilibrium pushes the equilibrium position to the left, which favors the reactants. As a result, the product yield decreases. Cooling, or removing heat, pulls the equilibrium to the right, and the product yield increases.

Pressure A change in the pressure on a system affects only gaseous equilibria that have an unequal number of moles of reactants and products. An example is the reaction you read about in *Connecting to Your World:* hydrogen and nitrogen react to form ammonia. Imagine that the three gases are at equilibrium in a cylinder that has a piston attached to a plunger—similar to a bicycle pump but with the hose sealed. A catalyst has been included to speed up the reaction. What happens to the pressure when you push the plunger down? The pressure on the gases momentarily increases because the same number of molecules is contained in a smaller volume. The system immediately relieves some of the pressure increase by reducing the number of gas molecules. For every two molecules of ammonia made, four molecules of the reactants are used up (three molecules of hydrogen and one of nitrogen). Therefore, the equilibrium position shifts to make more ammonia. There are then fewer molecules in the system. The pressure decreases, although it will not decrease all the way to the original pressure. As you can see in Figure 18.13, increasing the pressure on the system results in a shift in the equilibrium position that favors the formation of product.

$$N_2(g) + 3H_2(g) \overset{\substack{\text{Increase pressure} \\ \text{Direction of shift} \rightarrow}}{\underset{\substack{\text{Reduce pressure} \\ \leftarrow \text{Direction of shift}}}{\rightleftharpoons}} 2NH_3(g)$$

Figure 18.13 Pressure affects a mixture of nitrogen, hydrogen, and ammonia at equilibrium. **ⓐ** The system is at equilibrium. **ⓑ** Equilibrium is disturbed by an increase in pressure. **ⓒ** A new equilibrium position is established with fewer gas molecules. **Interpreting Diagrams** *What effect does a decrease in volume have on the number of gas molecules?*

Ammonia molecule (NH_3)

Hydrogen molecule (H_2)

Nitrogen molecule (N_2)

ⓐ
Initial equilibrium condition
(11 gas molecules)

ⓑ
Pressure increased,
equilibrium disturbed

ⓒ
New equilibrium
condition at increased
pressure (9 gas molecules)

The equilibrium position for this reaction can be made to favor the reactants instead of the product. Imagine pulling the plunger of the piston device back up so the volume containing the gases increases. This increase in volume decreases the pressure on the system. To restore the higher starting pressure, the system can produce more gas molecules by the decomposition of some ammonia molecules. Decomposition of two molecules of gaseous NH_3 produces four molecules of reactants (three H_2 and one N_2). Pressure at the new equilibrium is higher than when the pressure was first decreased, but not as high as it was at the starting equilibrium. Lowering the pressure on the system thus results in a shift of the equilibrium to favor the reactants.

A stress on this physical equilibrium could result in a loss of balance.

CONCEPTUAL PROBLEM 18.1

Applying Le Châtelier's Principle

What effect do each of the following changes have on the equilibrium position for this reversible reaction?

$$PCl_5(g) + heat \rightleftharpoons PCl_3(g) + Cl_2(g)$$

a. addition of Cl_2
b. increase in pressure
c. removal of heat
d. removal of PCl_3 as it is formed

1 Analyze *Identify the relevant concepts.*
a.–d. The stress placed on each system is known. The effect of each stress is unknown. By Le Châtelier's principle, the equilibrium system will shift in a direction that minimizes the imposed stress. Analyze the effect of each change on the reaction.

2 Solve *Apply concepts to this situation.*
a. The addition of Cl_2, a product, shifts the equilibrium to the left, forming more PCl_5.

b. The equation shows 2 mol of gaseous product and 1 mol of gaseous reactant. The increase in pressure is relieved if the equilibrium shifts to the left, because a decrease in the number of moles of gaseous substances produces a decrease in pressure.
c. The removal of heat causes the equilibrium to shift to the left, because the reverse reaction is heat-producing.
d. The removal of PCl_3 causes the equilibrium to shift to the right to produce more PCl_3.

Practice Problem

6. How is the equilibrium position of this reaction affected by the following changes?
$$C(s) + H_2O(g) + heat \rightleftharpoons CO(g) + H_2(g)$$

a. lowering the temperature
b. increasing the pressure
c. removing hydrogen
d. adding water vapor

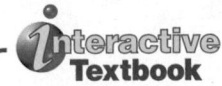

Problem-Solving 18.6 Solve Problem 6 with the help of an interactive guided tutorial.

—— with **ChemASAP**

Equilibrium Constants

Chemists express the position of equilibrium in terms of numerical values. These values relate the amounts of reactants to products at equilibrium. In a general reaction, a mol of reactant A and b mol of reactant B react to give c mol of product C and d mol of product D at equilibrium.

$$aA + bB \rightleftharpoons cC + dD$$

The **equilibrium constant** (K_{eq}) is the ratio of product concentrations to reactant concentrations at equilibrium, with each concentration raised to a power equal to the number of moles of that substance in the balanced chemical equation. The expression for the equilibrium constant can be written this way.

$$K_{eq} = \frac{[C]^c \times [D]^d}{[A]^a \times [B]^b}$$

The exponents in the equilibrium-constant expression are the coefficients in the balanced chemical equation. The square brackets indicate the concentrations of substances in moles per liter (mol/L). The value of K_{eq} depends on the temperature of the reaction. If the temperature changes, the value of K_{eq} also changes.

The size of the equilibrium constant shows whether products or reactants are favored at equilibrium. ◯ **A value of K_{eq} greater than 1 means that products are favored over reactants; a value of K_{eq} less than 1 means that reactants are favored over products.**

$K_{eq} > 1$, products favored at equilibrium

$K_{eq} < 1$, reactants favored at equilibrium

When the numerical value of an equilibrium constant is calculated, the cancellation of units may or may not lead to a unit for the constant. Chemists have agreed to report all equilibrium constants without stated units. Sample Problem 18.1 shows how to calculate the equilibrium constant for the reaction illustrated in Figure 18.14.

Figure 18.14 Dinitrogen tetroxide is a colorless gas; nitrogen dioxide is a brown gas. The flask on the left is in a dish of hot water; the flask on the right is in ice. **Interpreting Illustrations** *How does an increase in temperature affect the equilibrium of a mixture of these gases?*

● **Nitrogen dioxide (NO_2)**
▢ **Dinitrogen tetroxide (N_2O_4)**

Warm   Cool

Expressing and Calculating K_{eq}

The colorless gas dinitrogen tetroxide (N_2O_4) and the dark brown gas nitrogen dioxide (NO_2) exist in equilibrium with each other.

$$N_2O_4(g) \rightleftharpoons 2NO_2(g)$$

A liter of a gas mixture at equilibrium at 10°C contains 0.0045 mol of N_2O_4 and 0.030 mol of NO_2. Write the expression for the equilibrium constant and calculate the equilibrium constant (K_{eq}) for the reaction.

1 **Analyze** *List the knowns and the unknowns.*

Knowns
- $[N_2O_4]$ = 0.0045 mol/L
- $[NO_2]$ = 0.030 mol/L
- $K_{eq} = \dfrac{[C]^c \times [D]^d}{[A]^a \times [B]^b}$

Unknowns
- K_{eq} (algebraic expression) = ?
- K_{eq} (numerical value) = ?

2 **Calculate** *Solve for the unknowns.*

To write the equilibrium constant expressions, place the concentration of the product in the numerator and the concentration of the reactant in the denominator. Raise each to the power equal to its coefficient in the chemical equation. Substitute the given concentrations and calculate K_{eq}.

$$K_{eq} = \frac{[NO_2]^2}{[N_2O_4]} = \frac{(0.030 \text{ mol/L})^2}{0.0045 \text{ mol/L}}$$

$$= \frac{(0.030 \text{ mol/L} \times 0.030 \text{ mol/L})}{0.0045 \text{ mol/L}} = 0.20$$

3 **Evaluate** *Does the result make sense?*

Each concentration is raised to the correct power. The numerical value of the constant is correctly expressed to two significant figures.

Math **Handbook**

For help with using a calculator, go to page R62.

Practice Problems

7. The reaction $N_2(g) + 3H_2(g) \rightleftharpoons 2NH_3(g)$ produces ammonia, a fertilizer. At equilibrium, a 1-L flask contains 0.15 mol H_2, 0.25 mol N_2, and 0.10 mol NH_3. Calculate K_{eq} for the reaction.

8. For the same mixture, under the same conditions described in Problem 8, calculate K_{eq} for this reaction $2NH_3(g) \rightleftharpoons N_2(g) + 3H_2(g)$. How is the K_{eq} for a forward reaction related to the K_{eq} for a reverse reaction?

interactive Textbook

Problem Solving 18.7 Solve Problem 7 with the help of an interactive guided tutorial.

with **ChemASAP**

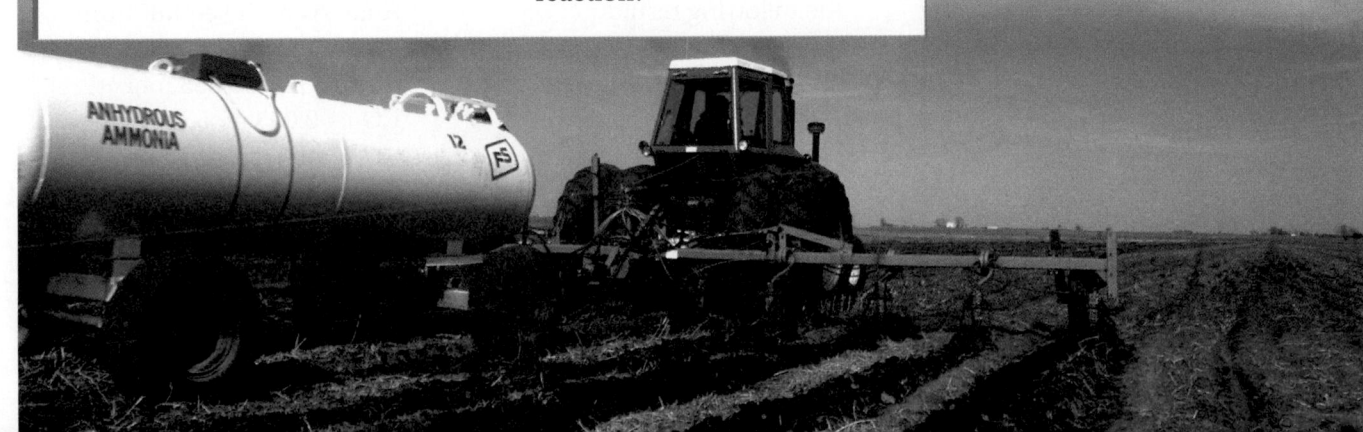

Finding the Equilibrium Constant

One mol of colorless hydrogen gas and 1.00 mol of violet iodine vapor are sealed in a 1-L flask and allowed to react at 450°C. At equilibrium, 1.56 mol of colorless hydrogen iodide is present, together with some of the reactant gases. Calculate K_{eq} for the reaction.

$$H_2(g) + I_2(g) \rightleftharpoons 2HI(g)$$

1 Analyze *List the knowns and the unknowns.*

Knowns
- [H_2] (initial) = 1.00 mol/L
- [I_2] (initial) = 1.00 mol/L
- [HI] (equilibrium) = 1.56 mol/L
- $K_{eq} = \dfrac{[C]^c \times [D]^d}{[A]^a \times [B]^b}$

Unknowns
- K_{eq} (algebraic expression) = ?
- K_{eq} (numerical value) = ?

2 Calculate *Solve for the unknowns.*

The balanced equation indicates that 1.00 mol H_2 and 1.00 mol I_2 are needed to form 2.00 mol HI. Making 1.56 mol of HI, therefore, consumes $\frac{1}{2} \times 1.56$ mol of each or 0.78 mol of H_2 and 0.78 mol of I_2. Calculate how much H_2 and I_2 remain in the flask at equilibrium.

$$\text{mol } H_2 = \text{mol } I_2 = (1.00 \text{ mol} - 0.78 \text{ mol}) = 0.22 \text{ mol}$$

Write the expression for K_{eq}: $K_{eq} = \dfrac{[HI]^2}{[H_2] \times [I_2]}$

Substitute the equilibrium concentrations of the reactants and products into the equation and calculate.

$$K_{eq} = \frac{(1.56 \text{ mol/L})^2}{0.22 \text{ mol/L} \times 0.22 \text{ mol/L}} = \frac{1.56 \text{ mol/L} \times 1.56 \text{ mol/L}}{0.22 \text{ mol/L} \times 0.22 \text{ mol/L}} = 50$$

3 Evaluate *Does the result make sense?*

Each concentration is raised to the correct power. The numerical value of the constant is correctly rounded to two significant figures.

Practice Problems

9. Suppose the following system reaches equilibrium.

   $$N_2(g) + O_2(g) \rightleftharpoons 2NO(g)$$

   Analysis of the equilibrium mixture in a 1-L flask gives the following results: $N_2 = 0.50$ mol, $O_2 = 0.50$ mol, and $NO = 0.020$ mol. Calculate K_{eq} for the reaction.

10. At 750°C the following reaction reaches equilibrium in a 1-L flask.

    $$H_2(g) + CO_2(g) \rightleftharpoons H_2O(g) + CO(g)$$

    Analysis of the equilibrium mixture gives the following results: $H_2 = 0.053$ mol, $CO_2 = 0.053$ mol, $H_2O = 0.047$ mol, and $CO = 0.047$ mol. Calculate K_{eq} for the reaction.

Math ▶ **Handbook**

For help with using a calculator, go to page R62.

interactive **Textbook**

Problem Solving 18.9 Solve Problem 9 with the help of an interactive guided tutorial.

—with **ChemASAP**

You can also calculate the equilibrium concentrations of the reactants and products if you know the equilibrium constant and if you have some information about the initial or final concentration of one of the constituents. For example, bromine chloride (BrCl) decomposes to form bromine and chlorine according to this equation.

$$2BrCl(g) \rightleftharpoons Br_2(g) + Cl_2(g)$$

At a certain temperature, the equilibrium constant for this reaction is 11.1. Suppose that pure BrCl is placed in a 1-L container and allowed to come to equilibrium. Analysis then shows that the reaction mixture contains 4.00 moles of Cl_2. How many moles of Br_2 and BrCl are also present in the equilibrium mixture?

According to the equation, when BrCl decomposes, equal numbers of moles of Br_2 and Cl_2 are formed. At equilibrium, 4.00 mol of Cl_2 is present, so 4.00 mol of Br_2 must also be present. Because the volume of the container is 1 L, the concentrations of Br_2 and Cl_2 are each 4.00 mol/L. These concentrations can be used in the equilibrium constant expression to calculate the concentration of BrCl.

Figure 18.15 Chlorine and bromine are two of the halogens. **Comparing and Contrasting** *How are they similar? In what ways are they different?*

$$11.1 = \frac{[Br_2] \times [Cl_2]}{[BrCl]^2}$$

Rearrange the equation to solve for $[BrCl]^2$ and substitute the known values.

$$[BrCl]^2 = \frac{[Br_2] \times [Cl_2]}{11.1} = \frac{(4.00 \text{ mol/L}) \times (4.00 \text{ mol/L})}{11.1} = 1.44 \text{ mol}^2/L^2$$

$$[BrCl] = \sqrt{1.44 \text{ mol}^2/L^2} = 1.20 \text{ mol/L}$$

The concentration of the reactant (BrCl) is less than the concentrations of the products, so the products (Br_2 and Cl_2) are slightly favored at equilibrium. This is to be expected because $K_{eq} > 1$. Yellow chlorine gas and brown liquid bromine with its vapor are shown in Figure 18.15.

18.2 Section Assessment

11. 🔑 **Key Concept** How do the amounts of reactants and products change after a reaction has reached chemical equilibrium?

12. 🔑 **Key Concept** What are three stresses that can upset the equilibrium of a chemical system?

13. 🔑 **Key Concept** What does the value of the equilibrium constant tell you about the amounts of reactants and products present at equilbrium?

14. How can a balanced chemical equation be used to write an equilibrium-constant expression?

15. Can a pressure change shift the equilibrium position in every reversible reaction? Explain.

16. Using the following equilibrium constants for several reactions, determine in which reactions the products are favored. Why?
    a. $K_{eq} = 1 \times 10^2$ b. $K_{eq} = 0.003$ c. $K_{eq} = 3.5$

Connecting ▶ **Concepts**

Percent Yield Recall the concept of percent yield of a chemical reaction in Section 12.3. Could the fact that a reaction is reversible and establishes equilibrium affect the percent yield of a reaction? Explain.

Interactive Textbook

Assessment 18.2 Test yourself on the concepts in Section 18.2.

with **ChemASAP**

Guide for Reading

🔑 Key Concepts
- What is the relationship between the solubility product constant and the solubility of a compound?
- How can you predict whether precipitation will occur when two salt solutions are mixed?

Vocabulary
solubility product constant
common ion
common ion effect

Reading Strategy

Predicting Based on what you know about equilibrium and the dissociation of ionic compounds in aqueous solution, predict the form of the equilibrium constant expression for the dissolving of an ionic compound in water. After you read the section, check the accuracy of your prediction and clarify any misconceptions you may have had.

Connecting to Your World

X-rays allow physicians to make observations of bones and internal organs without invasive surgery. Sometimes chemical substances are used to improve the clarity of the X-ray image. Barium sulfate is ingested by a patient before X-ray images of the digestive tract are taken. Barium sulfate absorbs the X-rays, thereby producing light areas on the developed X-ray film. However, barium salts are usually toxic. In this section, you will learn why patients can ingest this poisonous substance without harm.

The Solubility Product Constant

Ionic compounds differ in their solubilities. Most salts of the alkali metals are soluble in water. More than 35 g of sodium chloride will dissolve in only 100 g of water. Many classes of ionic compounds, however, are insoluble. For example, compounds that contain phosphate, sulfide, sulfite, or carbonate ions are often insoluble. Exceptions are compounds in which these ions are combined with ammonium ions or alkali metal ions. Table 18.1 summarizes the solubilities of many ionic compounds in water.

Most insoluble salts will actually dissolve to some extent in water. These salts are said to be slightly, or sparingly, soluble in water. For example, Figure 18.16 shows what happens when the "insoluble" salt silver chloride is mixed with water. A very small amount of silver chloride actually dissolves in the water.

$$AgCl(s) \rightleftharpoons Ag^+(aq) + Cl^-(aq)$$

You can write an equilibrium expression for this process.

$$K_{eq} = \frac{[Ag^+] \times [Cl^-]}{[AgCl]}$$

As long as some undissolved AgCl (solid) is present, the concentration of the AgCl is a constant. Thus the concentration of AgCl, a constant, can be combined with the equilibrium constant to form a new constant.

$$K_{eq} \times [AgCl] = [Ag^+] \times [Cl^-] = K_{sp}$$

Cl⁻

Ag⁺

Figure 18.16 Silver chloride is slightly soluble in water.
Predicting *Would adding solid silver chloride to this test tube disturb the equilibrium?*

Table 18.1

Solubilities of Ionic Compounds in Water		
Compounds	**Solubility**	**Exceptions**
Salts of Group 1A metals and ammonia	Soluble	Some lithium compounds
Ethanoates, nitrates, chlorates, and perchlorates	Soluble	Few exceptions
Sulfates	Soluble	Compounds of Pb, Ag, Hg, Ba, Sr, and Ca
Chlorides, bromides, and iodides	Soluble	Compounds of Ag and some compounds of Hg and Pb
Sulfides and hydroxides	Most are insoluble	Alkali metal sulfides and hydroxides are soluble. Compounds of Ba, Sr, and Ca are slightly soluble.
Carbonates, phosphates, and sulfites	Insoluble	Compounds of the alkali metals and of ammonium ions

This new constant, called the **solubility product constant** (K_{sp}), equals the product of the concentrations of the ions each raised to a power equal to the coefficient of the ion in the dissociation equation. The coefficients for the dissociation of silver chloride are each 1. The value of K_{sp} for silver chloride at 25°C is 1.8×10^{-10}.

$$K_{sp} = [Ag^+] \times [Cl^-]$$
$$K_{sp} = 1.8 \times 10^{-10}$$

What does the size of the solubility product constant tell you about the solubility of the compound? 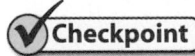 **The smaller the numerical value of the solubility product constant, the lower the solubility of the compound.** The solubility product constants for some common sparingly soluble salts are given in Table 18.2 on the next page. The mineral deposits around sink drains, such as the one shown in Figure 18.17, are composed of compounds such as calcium carbonate ($K_{sp} = 4.5 \times 10^{-9}$). The low solubility of such compounds makes them difficult to remove.

✓Checkpoint *What does the solubility product constant expression consist of?*

Figure 18.17 Scale, formed by the precipitation of slightly soluble salts, often builds up around kitchen and bathroom faucets. **Applying Concepts** *Why are insoluble substances hard to remove?*

Table 18.2

Solubility Product Constants (K_{sp}) at 25°C

Salt	K_{sp}	Salt	K_{sp}	Salt	K_{sp}
Halides		**Sulfates**		**Hydroxides**	
AgCl	1.8×10^{-10}	$PbSO_4$	6.3×10^{-7}	$Al(OH)_3$	3.0×10^{-34}
AgBr	5.0×10^{-13}	$BaSO_4$	1.1×10^{-10}	$Zn(OH)_2$	3.0×10^{-16}
AgI	8.3×10^{-17}	$CaSO_4$	2.4×10^{-5}	$Ca(OH)_2$	6.5×10^{-6}
$PbCl_2$	1.7×10^{-5}	**Sulfides**		$Mg(OH)_2$	7.1×10^{-12}
$PbBr_2$	2.1×10^{-6}	NiS	4.0×10^{-20}	$Fe(OH)_2$	7.9×10^{-16}
PbI_2	7.9×10^{-9}	CuS	8.0×10^{-37}	**Carbonates**	
PbF_2	3.6×10^{-8}	Ag_2S	8.0×10^{-51}	$CaCO_3$	4.5×10^{-9}
CaF_2	3.9×10^{-11}	ZnS	3.0×10^{-23}	$SrCO_3$	9.3×10^{-10}
Chromates		FeS	8.0×10^{-19}	$ZnCO_3$	1.0×10^{-10}
$PbCrO_4$	1.8×10^{-14}	CdS	1.0×10^{-27}	Ag_2CO_3	8.1×10^{-12}
Ag_2CrO_4	1.2×10^{-12}	PbS	3.0×10^{-28}	$BaCO_3$	5.0×10^{-9}

The chromate ion is responsible for the brilliant yellow color of lead(II) chromate.

SAMPLE PROBLEM 18.3

Finding the Ion Concentrations in a Saturated Solution

What is the concentration of lead ions and chromate ions in a saturated lead chromate solution at 25°C? ($K_{sp} = 1.8 \times 10^{-14}$)

1 **Analyze** *List the knowns and the unknowns.*

Knowns
- $K_{sp} = 1.8 \times 10^{-14}$
- $K_{sp} = [Pb^{2+}] \times [CrO_4^{2-}]$
- $PbCrO_4(s) \rightleftharpoons Pb^{2+}(aq) + CrO_4^{2-}(aq)$

Unknowns
- $[Pb^{2+}] = ? \, M$
- $[CrO_4^{2-}] = ? \, M$

For each Pb^{2+} ion formed, one CrO_4^{2-} ion is formed.

2 **Calculate** *Solve for the unknowns.*

$$K_{sp} = [Pb^{2+}] \times [CrO_4^{2-}] = 1.8 \times 10^{-14}$$

At equilibrium $[Pb^{2+}] = [CrO_4^{2-}]$. Substitute $[Pb^{2+}]$ for $[CrO_4^{2-}]$ in the expression for K_{sp} to get an equation with one unknown.

$$K_{sp} = [Pb^{2+}] \times [Pb^{2+}] = [Pb^{2+}]^2 = 1.8 \times 10^{-14}$$

Solve for $[Pb^{2+}]$.

$$[Pb^{2+}] = [CrO_4^{2-}] = \sqrt{1.8 \times 10^{-14}} = 1.3 \times 10^{-7} M$$

3 **Evaluate** *Does the result make sense?*

The product $[Pb^{2+}] \times [CrO_4^{2-}]$ is close to the value of K_{sp}. The answer should have two significant figures.

Practice Problems

17. Lead(II) sulfide (PbS) has a K_{sp} of 3×10^{-28}. What is the concentration of lead(II) ions in a saturated solution of PbS?

18. What is the concentration of calcium ions in a saturated calcium carbonate solution at 25°C? ($K_{sp} = 4.5 \times 10^{-9}$)

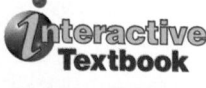

interactive Textbook

Problem Solving 18.17 Solve Problem 17 with the help of an interactive guided tutorial.

—with ChemASAP

Figure 18.18 Lead(II) chromate is slightly soluble in water. **ⓐ** A saturated solution of PbCrO₄ is pale yellow. **ⓑ** When a few drops of lead nitrate (Pb(NO₃)₂) are added to the solution, it becomes cloudy as more lead(II) chromate precipitates.
Applying Concepts *Explain what happened in* **ⓑ** *by considering the addition of lead nitrate as a stress on the PbCrO₄ equilibrium.*

The Common Ion Effect

In a saturated solution of lead(II) chromate, an equilibrium is established between the solid lead(II) chromate and its ions in solution.

$$PbCrO_4(s) \rightleftharpoons Pb^{2+}(aq) + CrO_4^{2-}(aq) \quad K_{sp} = 1.8 \times 10^{-14}$$

What do you think would happen if you added some lead nitrate to this solution? The concentration of lead ion would increase. Immediately, the product of $[Pb^{2+}]$ and $[CrO_4^{2-}]$ would be greater than K_{sp}. Applying Le Châtelier's principle, the stress of the additional Pb^{2+} can be relieved if the reaction shifts to the left. Figure 18.18 demonstrates that lead ions combine with chromate ions in solution to form additional solid PbCrO₄. Lead chromate continues to precipitate from the solution until the product of $[Pb^{2+}]$ and $[CrO_4^{2-}]$ once again equals 1.8×10^{-14}.

K_{sp} for the original solution: $[Pb^{2+}][CrO_4^{2-}] = 1.8 \times 10^{-14}$

K_{sp} after addition of Pb(NO₃)₂: $[Pb^{2+}]_{[CrO_4^{2-}]} = 1.8 \times 10^{-14}$

In this example, the lead ion is called a common ion. A **common ion** is an ion that is found in both salts in a solution. Adding lead nitrate to a saturated solution of PbCrO₄ causes the solubility of PbCrO₄ to decrease. The lowering of the solubility of an ionic compound as a result of the addition of a common ion is called the **common ion effect.** Adding sodium chromate to the solution of PbCrO₄ would also produce the common ion effect. The additional chromate ion, a different common ion, would similarly cause the solubility equilibrium to shift to the left and produce more PbCrO₄.

Recall from *Connecting to Your World* that patients must ingest toxic barium sulfate (BaSO₄) when having an X-ray taken. Table 18.2 shows that the K_{sp} of barium sulfate is 1.1×10^{-10}. Considering this low value, it is understandable that barium cannot harm the patient because so little of it is in solution and able to enter the bloodstream. The solubility can be further reduced by adding sodium sulfate (Na₂SO₄), a nontoxic soluble compound that provides the common ion SO₄²⁻.

 Checkpoint *What is the common ion effect?*

Go Online NSTA *SciLINKS*

For: Links on the Common Ion Effect
Visit: www.SciLinks.org
Web Code: cdn-1182

SAMPLE PROBLEM 18.4

Finding Equilibrium Ion Concentrations in the Presence of a Common Ion

Photographic film is covered with a light-sensitive emulsion containing silver bromide. The K_{sp} of silver bromide is 5.0×10^{-13}. What is the bromide-ion concentration of a 1.00-L saturated solution of AgBr to which 0.020 mol of $AgNO_3$ is added?

1 **Analyze** *List the knowns and the unknown.*

Knowns
- $K_{sp} = 5.0 \times 10^{-13}$
- moles of $AgNO_3$ added = 0.020 mol
- volume of solution = 1 L
- $AgBr(s) \rightleftharpoons Ag^+(aq) + Br^-(aq)$
- $K_{sp} = [Ag^+] \times [Br^-]$

Unknown
- $[Br^-] = ? \, M$

Express the concentrations of the two ions in one unknown. Let the equilibrium concentration of bromide ion from the dissociation be x. Then the equilibrium concentration of silver ion is $x + 0.020$.

2 **Calculate** *Solve for the unknown.*

Because of the small value of K_{sp}, you can make a simplifying assumption: x will be negligibly small compared to 0.020. Thus the $[Ag^+]$ at equilibrium is approximately equal to $0.020M$. Solve for x and substitute these values into the K_{sp} expression.

$$K_{sp} = [Ag^+] \times [Br^-] = [Ag^+] \times x$$

$$x = \frac{K_{sp}}{[Ag^+]} = \frac{(5.0 \times 10^{-13})}{[Ag^+]}$$

$$= \frac{(5.0 \times 10^{-13})}{0.020}$$

$$= [Br^-] = 2.5 \times 10^{-11}M$$

The equilibrium concentration of bromide ion is $2.5 \times 10^{-11}M$.

3 **Evaluate** *Does the result make sense?*

Because the $[Ag^+]$ is so high, $[Br^-]$ should be very low, approaching the numerical value for K_{sp}. The answer should have two significant figures, and the simplifying assumption was justified.

Math Handbook

For help with algebraic equations, go to page R69.

Practice Problems

19. What is the concentration of sulfide ion in a 1.0-L solution of iron(II) sulfide to which 0.04 mol of iron(II) nitrate is added? The K_{sp} of FeS is 8×10^{-19}.

20. The K_{sp} of $SrSO_4$ is 3.2×10^{-7}. What is the equilibrium concentration of sulfate ion in a 1.0-L solution of strontium sulfate to which 0.10 mol of $Sr(CH_3CO_2)_2$ has been added?

interactive Textbook

Problem Solving 18.19 Solve Problem 19 with the help of an interactive guided tutorial.

with ChemASAP

The solubility product (K_{sp}) can be used to predict whether a precipitate will form when solutions are mixed. **If the product of the concentrations of two ions in the mixture is greater than the K_{sp} of the compound formed from the ions, a precipitate will form.** After precipitation, the solution will be saturated with the precipitated compound. If the product of the concentrations is less than the K_{sp}, no precipitate will form and the solution is unsaturated.

Suppose you have 0.50 L of 0.002M Ba(NO_3)$_2$ and mix it with 0.50 L of 0.008 M Na_2SO_4. You then have one liter of solution. The insoluble compound that could precipitate is barium sulfate. To predict whether a precipitate of $BaSO_4$ will form, you need to determine the concentration of the ions after the dilution that occurs on mixing. Precipitation will occur if the product of the concentrations of the two ions (Ba^{2+} and SO_4^{2-}) exceeds the K_{sp} of $BaSO_4$, which is 1.1×10^{-10}. Because each solution was diluted with an equal volume of the other solution, the concentrations of both Ba^{2+} and SO_4^{2-} after mixing will be half of their original concentrations. Thus in the combined solution, $[Ba^{2+}] = 0.001M$ and $[SO_4^{2-}] = 0.004M$. These concentrations can now be multiplied together as a trial product and the result compared with the K_{sp}.

$$[Ba^{2+}] \times [SO_4^{2-}] = (0.001M) \times (0.004M) = 4 \times 10^{-6}$$

The K_{sp} of barium sulfate is 1.1×10^{-10}, so the trial product is larger than the K_{sp}. A precipitate will form. Barium sulfate will precipitate until the product of the concentrations of the ions remaining in solution equals 1.1×10^{-10}. Figure 18.19 shows the mixing of the solutions and the precipitation of barium sulfate.

Figure 18.19 A precipitate of barium sulfate forms as barium nitrate (Ba(NO_3)$_2$) and sodium sulfate (Na_2SO_4) solutions are mixed. **Applying Concepts** *What is the product of the concentrations of barium ion and sulfate ion after precipitation is complete?*

18.3 Section Assessment

21. **Key Concept** What is the relationship between the solubility product constant and the solubility of a compound?

22. **Key Concept** How can you predict whether a precipitate will form when two salt solutions are mixed?

23. Write the solubility product expression for Ag_2CO_3.

24. What is the concentration of lead ions and sulfide ions in a saturated solution of lead sulfide (PbS) solution at 25°C? ($K_{sp} = 3.0 \times 10^{-28}$)

25. The K_{sp} of barium sulfate is 1.1×10^{-10}. What is the sulfate-ion concentration of a 1.00 L saturated solution of $BaSO_4$ to which 0.015 mol of Ba(NO_3)$_2$ is added?

26. Would precipitation occur when 500 mL of a 0.02M solution of $AgNO_3$ is mixed with 500 mL of a 0.001M solution of NaCl? Explain.

27. Which compound, FeS ($K_{sp} = 8.0 \times 10^{-19}$) or CuS ($K_{sp} = 8.0 \times 10^{-37}$), has the higher solubility?

28. What is the K_{sp} of nickel(II) sulfide if the equilibrium concentrations of Ni^{2+} and S^{2-} in a saturated solution of NiS are each $1 \times 10^{-10}M$?

Connecting **Concepts**

Spectator Ions Refer to the discussion of spectator ions and net ionic equations in Section 11.3. In a precipitation reaction, would the addition of a spectator ion lead to the formation of more precipitate because of the common ion effect? Explain.

Textbook

Assessment 18.3 Test yourself on the concepts in Section 18.3.

with **ChemASAP**

New York Standards: 3.1ll–mm, 4.1b

Guide for Reading

Key Concepts
- What are two characteristics of spontaneous reactions?
- What part does entropy play in chemical reactions?
- What two factors determine the spontaneity of a reaction?
- Is the Gibbs free-energy change positive or negative in a spontaneous process?

Vocabulary
free energy
spontaneous reaction
nonspontaneous reaction
entropy
law of disorder
Gibbs free-energy change

Reading Strategy

Relating Text and Visuals As you read about spontaneous and nonspontaneous reactions, study Figure 18.25. Summarize three ways in which the energy terms of the free energy equation result in a spontaneous reaction and three ways in which they result in a non-spontaneous reaction.

Connecting to Your World

Fires in homes, barns, and other places sometimes seem to start on their own, without any application of heat from an external source. These fires could be caused by spontaneous combustion. Inside a pile of oily rags or a stack of hay that has not been thoroughly dried, decomposition causes heat to build up. If the existing conditions do not allow the heat to escape, the temperature can build up enough to cause a fire. In this section, you will learn about the conditions that will produce a spontaneous chemical reaction.

Free Energy and Spontaneous Reactions

Many chemical and physical processes release energy that can be used to bring about other changes. For example, some of the energy liberated in a chemical reaction can be harnessed to do work, such as driving the pistons of an internal-combustion engine. **Free energy** is energy that is available to do work. Just because free energy is available to do work, however, does not mean that it can be used efficiently. The internal-combustion engine in a car is only about 30% efficient; that is, only about 30% of the free energy released by burning gasoline is used to propel the car. The remaining 70% is lost as friction and waste heat. However, no process can be made 100 percent efficient. Even in living things, which are among the most efficient users of free energy, processes are seldom more than 70% efficient.

Another complication, in addition to energy efficiency, is that energy can be obtained from a reaction only if the reaction actually, rather than theoretically, occurs. In other words, although a balanced equation can be written for a chemical reaction, the reaction may not actually take place. For example, you can write an equation for the decomposition of carbon dioxide to carbon and oxygen.

$$CO_2(g) \longrightarrow C(s) + O_2(g)$$

This equation, which represents the reverse of combustion, is balanced. However, experience tells you that the reaction represented by the equation does not tend to occur. Carbon and oxygen react to form carbon dioxide, not the reverse. So the world of balanced chemical equations is really divided into two groups. One group contains equations representing reactions that actually occur; the other contains equations representing reactions that do not tend to occur, or at least not efficiently.

Figure 18.20 Fireworks displays are the result of highly favored spontaneous reactions. A large quantity of free energy is released.

The first, and more important group involves processes that are spontaneous. A **spontaneous reaction** occurs naturally and favors the formation of products at the specified conditions. ⬤ **Spontaneous reactions produce substantial amounts of products at equilibrium and release free energy.** The colorful fireworks display shown in Figure 18.20 is an example of a spontaneous reaction. In contrast, a **nonspontaneous reaction** is a reaction that does not favor the formation of products at the specified conditions. Nonspontaneous reactions do not give substantial amounts of products at equilibrium.

Consider again the reversible decomposition of carbonic acid in water.

$$H_2CO_3(aq) \underset{<1\%}{\overset{}{\rightleftharpoons}} \underset{>99\%}{CO_2(g) + H_2O(l)}$$

Carbonic acid is the reactant in the forward reaction. If you could start with pure carbonic acid in water and let the system come to equilibrium, more than 99% of the reactant would be converted to the products carbon dioxide and water. These products are highly favored at equilibrium. The natural tendency is for carbonic acid to decompose to carbon dioxide and water. Thus the forward reaction is spontaneous and releases free energy. In the reverse reaction, carbon dioxide and water are the reactants, and carbonic acid is the product. If you permit a solution of carbon dioxide in water to come to equilibrium, less than 1% of the reactants combines to form carbonic acid. The reactants show little natural tendency to go to products. Thus the combination of carbon dioxide and water to form carbonic acid is nonspontaneous. In nearly all reversible reactions, one reaction is favored over the other.

Another example, shown in Figure 18.21, is the spontaneous reaction of aqueous cadmium nitrate with aqueous sodium sulfide to produce aqueous sodium nitrate and solid yellow cadmium sulfide. Cadmium sulfide is highly favored in this equilibrium. The reverse reaction, the production of cadmium nitrate and sodium sulfide from cadmium sulfide and sodium nitrate, is nonspontaneous.

$$Cd(NO_3)_2(aq) + Na_2S(aq) \rightleftharpoons CdS(s) + 2NaNO_3(aq)$$

$Cd(NO_3)_2(aq)$

$Na_2S(aq)$

$CdS(s)$
precipitate
and $NaNO_3(aq)$

Figure 18.21 A precipitate of cadmium sulfide (CdS) forms spontaneously when solutions of sodium sulfide (Na_2S) and cadmium nitrate ($Cd(NO_3)_2$) are mixed. **Inferring *Is free energy released in this reaction?***

Figure 18.22 Many nonspontaneous reactions are required for a plant to grow. Nonspontaneous reactions can occur when they are coupled with spontaneous reactions. **Inferring** *What is another requirement for this photosynthesis reaction?*

$$6CO_2 + 6H_2O \xrightarrow{\text{light energy}} C_6H_{12}O_6 + 6O_2$$

It is important to note that the terms *spontaneous* and *nonspontaneous* do not refer to how fast reactants go to products. Some spontaneous reactions go so slowly that they appear to be nonspontaneous. The reaction of sugar and oxygen, for example, produces carbon dioxide and water. However, a bowl of sugar on a table does nothing, and you might assume that the equilibrium among sugar, oxygen, carbon dioxide, and water greatly favors the sugar and oxygen. The equilibrium does favor the products, but at room temperature the reaction is so slow that it takes thousands of years to reach equilibrium. When you supply energy in the form of heat, however, the reaction is fast. Then it is obvious that the formation of carbon dioxide and water is highly favored.

Some reactions that are nonspontaneous at one set of conditions may be spontaneous at other conditions. Changing the temperature or pressure, for example, may determine whether or not a reaction is spontaneous. The nonspontaneous photosynthesis reaction summarized in Figure 18.22 could not be driven to completion without the energy supplied by sunlight.

Sometimes a nonspontaneous reaction can be made to occur if it is coupled to a spontaneous reaction—a reaction that releases free energy. Coupled reactions are a common feature of the complex biological processes that take place in living organisms. Within cells, a series of spontaneous reactions release the energy stored in glucose. As you will learn in Chapter 24, molecules in cells can capture and transfer free energy to nonspontaneous reactions, such as the formation of proteins.

✓ Checkpoint *If a reaction releases free energy, is the reaction spontaneous or nonspontaneous?*

Go Online
NSTA *SciLINKS*

For: Links on Entropy
Visit: www.SciLinks.org
Web Code: cdn-1184

Entropy

Recall that heat (enthalpy) changes accompany most chemical and physical processes. The combustion of carbon, for example, is exothermic and spontaneous. The heat released during this reaction is 393.5 kJ for each mole of carbon (graphite) burned.

$$C(s, \text{graphite}) + O_2(g) \longrightarrow CO_2(g) + 393.5 \text{ kJ/mol}$$

You might expect that only exothermic reactions would be spontaneous. Some processes, however, may be spontaneous even though they absorb heat. For example, consider the physical process of melting ice to water. As it turns from a solid to a liquid, 1 mol of ice at 25°C absorbs 6.0 kJ of heat from its surroundings.

$$H_2O(s) + 6.0 \text{ kJ/mol} \longrightarrow H_2O(l)$$

Ice melts spontaneously at 25°C, even though the water produced contains more heat than the ice from which it forms. Considering only enthalpy changes, the energy of the water seems higher than the energy of the ice. That would seem to violate the rule that in spontaneous processes, the direction of the change in energy is from higher energy to lower energy; that is, free energy is released. Yet this process occurs anyway. Some factor other than the enthalpy change must help determine whether a physical or chemical process is spontaneous.

The other factor is related to order. You are probably familiar with everyday ideas about order and disorder. For example, a handful of marbles is relatively ordered in the sense that all the marbles are collected in one place. It is improbable that when permitted to fall, the marbles will end up in the same neat arrangement. Instead, the marbles scatter on the ground. They become disordered. Scattered marbles have a higher entropy than a handful of marbles. **Entropy** is a measure of the disorder of a system.

The concept that physical and chemical systems attain the lowest possible energy has a companion idea called the **law of disorder,** which states that the natural tendency is for systems to move in the direction of maximum disorder or randomness. You already know something about this natural tendency toward disorder. Maybe the photographs in Figure 18.23 look familiar to you. More than likely, your bedroom is neat and clean at the beginning of the week. But unless you put energy (work) into maintaining it, your room becomes messy by the end of the week.

The law of disorder (entropy change) also operates at the level of atoms and molecules and so it is a factor in determining the direction of chemical reactions. ⚷ **An increase in entropy favors the spontaneous chemical reaction; a decrease favors the nonspontaneous reaction.** Figure 18.24 on the following page illustrates some generalities that will help you to predict the course of many reactions.

Figure 18.23 The entropy of a recently cleaned and orderly room is low. However, over time a room tends to become disorderly. Entropy has a tendency to increase. **Applying Concepts** *Which has the greater entropy, an assembled jigsaw puzzle, or the pieces in the box?*

Figure 18.24 Entropy is a measure of the disorder of a system.

ⓐ Increasing Entropy

ⓐ For a given substance, the entropy of the gas is greater than the entropy of the liquid or the solid. Similarly, the entropy of the liquid is greater than that of the solid. Thus entropy increases in reactions in which solid reactants form liquid or gaseous products. Entropy also increases when liquid reactants form gaseous products.

ⓑ Increasing Entropy

ⓑ Entropy increases when a substance is divided into parts. For instance, entropy increases when a crystalline ionic compound, such as sodium chloride, dissolves in water. This is because the solute particles—sodium ions and chloride ions—are more separated in solution than they are in the crystal form.

ⓒ Increasing Entropy

Electricity

Electricity

$2H_2O(l) \longrightarrow 2H_2(g) + O_2(g)$

Electrolysis of water

ⓒ Entropy tends to increase in chemical reactions in which the total number of product molecules is greater than the total number of reactant molecules.

ⓓ Increasing Entropy

ⓓ Entropy tends to increase when temperature increases. As the temperature increases, the molecules move faster and faster, which increases the disorder.

Table 18.3

How Changes in Enthalpy and Entropy Affect Reaction Spontaneity		
Enthalpy change	**Entropy**	**Spontaneous reaction?**
Decreases (exothermic)	Increases (more disorder in products than in reactants)	Yes
Increases (endothermic)	Increases	Only if unfavorable enthalpy change is offset by favorable entropy change
Decreases (exothermic)	Decreases (less disorder in products than in reactants)	Only if unfavorable entropy change is offset by favorable enthalpy change
Increases (endothermic)	Decreases	No

Enthalpy, Entropy, and Free Energy

In every chemical reaction, heat is either released or absorbed and entropy or randomness either increases or decreases. How do these two energy factors determine the course of a reaction? 🔘 **The size and direction of enthalpy changes and entropy changes together determine whether a reaction is spontaneous; that is, whether it favors products and releases free energy.** An exothermic reaction accompanied by an increase in entropy is definitely spontaneous because both factors are favorable. The combustion of carbon, for example, is exothermic. Entropy also increases as solid carbon is converted to gaseous carbon dioxide. Because both factors are favorable, the reaction must be spontaneous. The reverse reaction—production of carbon and oxygen from carbon dioxide—is nonspontaneous; neither the enthalpy nor the entropy change is favorable.

A reaction is also spontaneous if a decrease in entropy is offset by a large release of heat. Similarly, an endothermic, or heat-absorbing, reaction is spontaneous if an entropy increase offsets the heat absorption. For example, enthalpy change and entropy change work in opposition when ice melts. The melting of ice is endothermic, but the process is still spontaneous above 0°C. At such temperatures, the absorption of heat is more than offset by a favorable entropy change.

Table 18.3 summarizes how entropy and enthalpy changes affect the spontaneity of chemical reactions. Notice that either of the two variables, but not both, can be unfavorable for a spontaneous process.

Nonspontaneous reactions, those in which the products are not favored, can have enthalpy changes, entropy changes, or both working against them. For example, a reaction might be highly endothermic with a large decrease in entropy. In that case, both changes work against the formation of products and the reaction is nonspontaneous. In another case, a reaction may be exothermic but involve a decrease in entropy large enough to offset the favorable enthalpy change. This reaction will also be nonspontaneous. Alternatively, an endothermic reaction could have an increase in entropy too small to overcome the unfavorable enthalpy change. Figure 18.25 on the following page summarizes the relationship among enthalpy, entropy, and free-energy changes for spontaneous reactions.

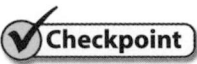 **Checkpoint** *What two energy factors determine the course of a reaction?*

 Textbook

Simulation 25 Simulate how enthalpy and entropy changes combine to determine the spontaneity of a reaction.

—— with **ChemASAP**

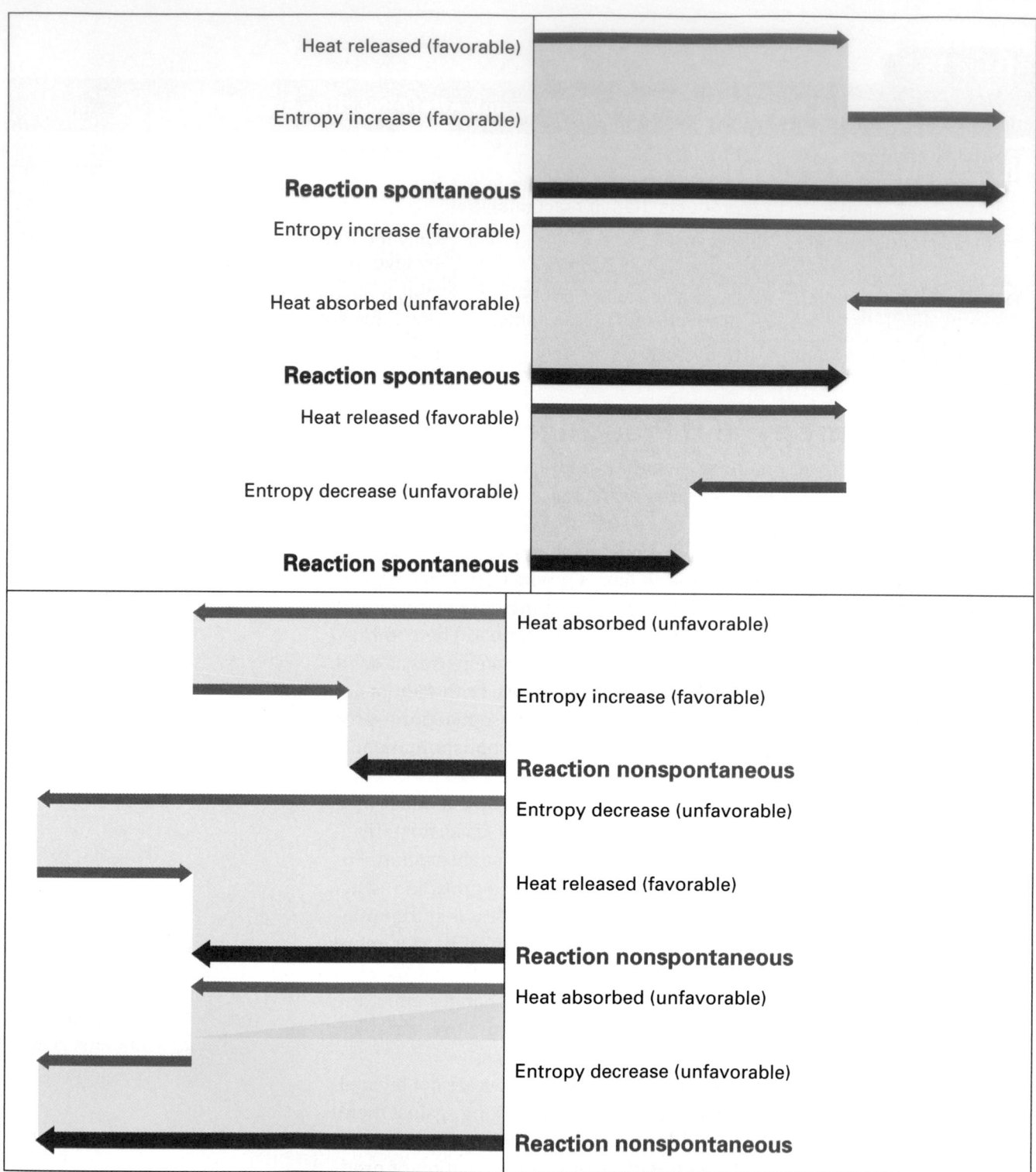

Heat released (favorable)

Entropy increase (favorable)

Reaction spontaneous

Entropy increase (favorable)

Heat absorbed (unfavorable)

Reaction spontaneous

Heat released (favorable)

Entropy decrease (unfavorable)

Reaction spontaneous

Heat absorbed (unfavorable)

Entropy increase (favorable)

Reaction nonspontaneous

Entropy decrease (unfavorable)

Heat released (favorable)

Reaction nonspontaneous

Heat absorbed (unfavorable)

Entropy decrease (unfavorable)

Reaction nonspontaneous

Figure 18.25 The combination of the enthalpy change and the change in entropy for a reaction determines whether or not the reaction is spontaneous.

Gibbs Free-Energy

Recall that in every spontaneous process, some energy becomes available to do work. This energy, called the **Gibbs free-energy change,** is the maximum amount of energy that can be coupled to another process to do useful work. The change in Gibbs free energy is related to the change in entropy (ΔS) and the change in enthalpy (ΔH) of the system by the free-energy equation.

$$\Delta G = \Delta H - T\Delta S$$

The temperature (T) is in kelvins.

All spontaneous processes release free energy. **The numerical value of ΔG is negative in spontaneous processes because the system loses free energy.** Nonspontaneous processes require that work be expended to make them go forward at the specified conditions. Therefore, the numerical value of ΔG is positive for a nonspontaneous process. However, a reaction that is nonspontaneous under one set of conditions may be spontaneous under another set of conditions.

To see the effect of temperature on the spontaneity of a reaction, consider this chemical reaction. Solid calcium carbonate decomposes to give calcium oxide and carbon dioxide.

$CaCO_3$
(formula unit) $\longrightarrow$ CaO
(formula unit) $+$ CO_2
(molecule)

Decomposition reaction

In this reaction, the entropy increases because one of the products formed from the solid reactant is a gas. However, the reaction is endothermic and the entropy increase is not great enough to offset the unfavorable enthalpy change. Thus the reaction is nonspontaneous at ordinary temperatures. The effect of an entropy increase, however, is magnified as the temperature increases. At temperatures above 850°C, the favorable entropy-temperature term $T\Delta S$ in the equation $\Delta G = \Delta H - T\Delta S$ outweighs the unfavorable enthalpy term ΔH. Under these conditions, the decomposition of calcium carbonate becomes spontaneous. Calcium oxide obtained from this spontaneous reaction is used to neutralize acid soil, as shown in Figure 18.26.

Figure 18.26 Soil that becomes too acidic for proper plant growth can be neutralized by the addition of lime, which is the common name for calcium oxide (CaO).

18.4 Section Assessment

29. **Key Concept** What are two characteristics of spontaneous reactions?

30. **Key Concept** What part does entropy play in determining whether a chemical reaction is spontaneous or nonspontaneous?

31. **Key Concept** What two factors determine the spontaneity of a reaction?

32. **Key Concept** What is the sign (+ or −) of the Gibbs free-energy change in a spontaneous process?

33. Where does released free energy typically end up? Does free energy lost as heat ever serve a useful function? Explain.

34. Suppose the products in a spontaneous process are more ordered than the reactants. Is the entropy change favorable or unfavorable?

35. Explain why, under certain circumstances, a nonspontaneous reaction becomes spontaneous?

Elements ▶ Handbook

Explosives Among this class of compounds are the reactants in rapid, violent reactions. Read about some common explosives on page R26 of the Elements Handbook. Choose a reaction and explain why it fits the definition of a spontaneous reaction.

𝑖nteractive Textbook

Assessment 18.4 Test yourself on the concepts in Section 18.4.

with ChemASAP

Enthalpy and Entropy

Purpose
To observe and measure energy changes during the formation of a solution and to describe and explain these changes in terms of entropy and enthalpy.

Materials
- alcohol thermometer
- four 1-oz plastic cups
- plastic spoon
- solid chemical shown in the table
- crushed ice
- water
- stirring rod

Procedure

Place two level spoonfuls of water in a plastic cup and measure the temperature (T_1) of the water. Add one level spoonful of solid NaCl to the cup, stir gently, and measure the highest or lowest temperature (T_2). Record this information on a separate sheet of paper in a table similar to the one below. Repeat the experiment two more times, using NH_4Cl and $CaCl_2$. Record the temperatures.

Mixture	T_1	T_2	ΔT
a. $NaCl(s) + H_2O(l)$			
b. $NH_4Cl(s) + H_2O(l)$			
c. $CaCl_2(s) + H_2O(l)$			

Analysis
Using your experimental data, record the answers to the following questions in or below your data table.

1. Calculate ΔT for each mixture. $\Delta T = T_2 - T_1$

2. An exothermic process gives off heat (warms up). An endothermic process absorbs heat (cools off). Which solutions are endothermic and which are exothermic? What is the sign of ΔH in each case?

3. Which solution(s) had little or no change in temperature?

4. When sodium chloride dissolves in water, the ions dissociate.

$$NaCl(s) \longrightarrow Na^+(aq) + Cl^-(aq)$$

Write ionic equations, similar to the one above, that describe how NH_4Cl and $CaCl_2$ each dissociate as they dissolve in water. Include heat as a reactant or product in each equation.

5. Which solids in this experiment rapidly dissolved in water? Does the dissolving process usually occur with an increase or decrease in entropy? What is the sign of ΔS in each case?

6. Consider the equation $\Delta G = \Delta H - T\Delta S$. For each dissolving process, substitute the sign of ΔS and ΔH into the equation and determine the sign of ΔG. For which process might ΔG be either positive or negative?

You're The Chemist
The following small-scale activities allow you to develop your own procedures and analyze the results.

1. **Analyze It!** Mix a tablespoon of ice (solid water) with a tablespoon of solid NaCl. Stir gently, then measure and record the lowest temperature reached. Compare this mixture with the mixture of solid NaCl and liquid water. What is the difference in temperature?

2. **Analyze It!** Is the process of melting ice exothermic or endothermic? Does this explain the difference in temperature in Activity 1? Explain.

3. **Design It!** What effect does mixing other salts with crushed ice have on temperature? Try substituting different salts in Activity 1.

4. **Design It!** What effect does dissolving other salts in liquid water have on temperature? Try dissolving the following salts in liquid water: potassium chloride (KCl), sodium hydrogen carbonate ($NaHCO_3$), and sodium phosphate (Na_3PO_4).

New York Standards: 3.4f

Guide for Reading

 Key Concepts
- What is the general relationship between the value of the specific rate constant, k, and the speed of a chemical reaction?
- What do the hills and valleys in a reaction progress curve represent?

Vocabulary
rate law
specific rate constant
first-order reaction
elementary reaction
reaction mechanism
intermediate

Reading Strategy
Monitoring Your Understanding After you read the section, identify what you don't yet understand. Reread the section or ask for help, then write your clarified understanding.

Connecting to Your World

The Tour de France is one of the most famous bicycle races in the world. It is held from mid-July to early August. During the course of the race, cyclists travel almost 4000 kilometers and cross steep mountains at heights of 1600 meters or more. To cross these high mountains requires extra amounts of energy. A chemical reaction can be thought of as a process involving peaks and valleys also. In this section, you will learn about the energy requirements for a chemical reaction to progress from initial reactants to final products.

Rate Laws

The rate of a reaction depends in part on the concentrations of the reactants. For a reaction in which reactant A forms product B in one step, you can write a simple equation.

$$A \longrightarrow B$$

The rate at which A forms B can be expressed as the change in A (ΔA) with time, where concentration A_1 is the initial concentration of A at time t_1 and concentration A_2 is the concentration of A at a later time, t_2.

$$\text{Rate} = -\frac{\Delta A}{\Delta t} = -\frac{\text{concentration } A_2 - \text{concentration } A_1}{t_2 - t_1}$$

Because A, the reactant, is decreasing, the concentration of A is smaller at a later time than initially and so ΔA will always be negative. The negative sign in the expression is needed to make the rate positive, as all rates must be. The rate of disappearance of A is proportional to the concentration of A.

$$-\frac{\Delta A}{\Delta t} \propto [A]$$

The proportionality becomes an equation with the insertion of a constant (k).

$$\text{Rate} = -\frac{\Delta A}{\Delta t} = k \times [A]$$

This equation, called a **rate law,** is an expression for the rate of a reaction in terms of the concentration of reactants. The **specific rate constant** (k) for a reaction is a proportionality constant relating the concentrations of reactants to the rate of the reaction. The magnitude of the specific rate constant depends on the conditions of the reaction and is determined experimentally. **The value of the specific rate constant, k, is large if the products form quickly; the value is small if the products form slowly.**

Animation 24 Observe the characteristics of a first-order reaction.

— with **ChemASAP**

Figure 18.27 The graph shows how the concentration of a reactant changes as a reaction proceeds.

INTERPRETING GRAPHS

a. Navigate What is the dependent variable?
b. Read What happens to the relative concentration of reactant A as time progresses?
c. Interpret The short colored lines illustrate the reaction rates at two distinct points of time. Is the *initial rate* or the *subsequent rate* faster?

The Rate of a First-Order Reaction

The rate of blooming for the century plant *(Agave americana)* is one time per 10 to 15 years.

The order of a reaction is the power to which the concentration of a reactant must be raised to give the experimentally observed relationship between concentration and rate. In a **first-order reaction,** the reaction rate is directly proportional to the concentration of only one reactant. The conversion of A to B in a one-step reaction is an example of a first-order reaction; the reaction rate is proportional to the concentration of A raised to the first power: $[A]^1 = [A]$. As a first-order reaction progresses, the rate of reaction decreases, as shown in Figure 18.27. This decrease occurs because the concentration of reactant is decreasing. On a graph, the rate ($\Delta A/\Delta t$) at any point equals the slope of the tangent to the curve at that point. For a first-order reaction, a reduction of [A] by one-half reduces the reaction rate by one-half.

In some kinds of reactions, such as double-replacement, two substances react to give products. The coefficients in the general equation for such a reaction are represented by lowercase letters.

$$a\text{A} + b\text{B} \longrightarrow c\text{C} + d\text{D}$$

For a one-step reaction of A with B, the rate of reaction is dependent on the concentrations of both A and B.

$$\text{Rate} = k[\text{A}]^a[\text{B}]^b$$

When each of the exponents a and b in the rate law equals 1, the reaction is said to be first-order in A, first-order in B, and second-order overall. The overall order of a reaction is the sum of the exponents for the individual reactants.

For any one-step reaction, the experimentally determined exponents in the rate law are the same as the coefficients a and b in the chemical equation. However, the exponents in the rate law and the coefficients in the equation do not correspond in most real reactions because most reactions are more complex than the one-step reactions used in the examples. The actual order of a reaction must be determined by experiment.

Checkpoint *How can you determine the rate of a reaction from a graph of reactant concentration versus time?*

Finding the Order of a Reaction from Experimental Data

The rate law for the one-step reaction $a\text{A} \longrightarrow \text{B}$ is of the form: Rate $= k[\text{A}]^a$. From the data in the following table, find the order of the reaction with respect to A and the overall order of the reaction.

Initial concentration of A (mol/L)	Initial rate (mol/L·s)
0.050	3.0×10^{-4}
0.10	12×10^{-4}
0.20	48×10^{-4}

1 Analyze *Identify the relevant concepts.*

The initial concentration, the initial rate data, and the form of the rate law are given. This is a one-step reaction. Use these data to find the desired orders by inspection.

2 Solve *Apply concepts to this situation.*

If a reaction is first-order in A, then $a = 1$ in the rate equation. In that case, the initial rate is directly proportional to the initial [A]. However, the reaction cannot be first-order in A because a doubling of A causes the rate to increase by four times. This suggests that $a = 2$, because $2^2 = 4$. Increasing [A] fourfold should, therefore, increase the rate sixteenfold ($4^2 = 16$). When the initial concentration of A is increased from 0.050 mol/L to 0.20 mol/L, the initial rate increases from 3.0×10^{-4} mol/L·s to 48×10^{-4} mol/L·s, which is a sixteenfold increase. The reaction is thus second-order in A and the reaction must be second-order overall because A is the only reactant.

Practice Problems

36. Show that the unit of k for a first-order reaction is a reciprocal unit of time, such as a reciprocal second (s^{-1}).

37. Suppose a first-order reaction initially proceeds at a rate of 0.5 mol/L·s. What is the rate when half the starting material remains? When one-fourth of the starting material remains?

Interactive Textbook

Problem Solving 18.37 Solve Problem 37 with the help of an interactive guided tutorial.

— with **ChemASAP**

CHEMath

Graphing

Relationships between variables are easier to see when data is displayed in a graph. The independent variable is plotted on the *x*-axis (horizontal axis). The dependent variable is plotted on the *y*-axis (vertical axis).

A graph may show a trend. For example, as the value of the independent variable increases, the value of the dependent variable may either increase or decrease.

A straight-line graph with a positive slope indicates a direct proportion between the variables. A smooth curve dropping from left to right shows that two variables are inversely proportional.

Math → Handbook

For help with making and interpreting graphs, go to page R74.

Reaction Mechanisms

If enough information were available, you could graph all the energy changes that occur as reactants are converted to products in a chemical reaction. Such a graph would constitute a reaction progress curve. The simplest reaction progress curve is for an elementary reaction, such as the one shown in Figure 18.5. An **elementary reaction** is a reaction in which reactants are converted to products in a single step. Such a reaction has only one activation-energy peak between reactants and products and thus only one activated complex. Most chemical reactions consist of a number of elementary reactions. The series of elementary reactions or steps that take place during the course of a complex reaction is called a **reaction mechanism.** The reaction progress curve for a complex reaction resembles a series of peaks and valleys, as you can see in Figure 18.28. ⟳ **The peaks correspond to the energies of the activated complexes. Each valley corresponds to the energy of an intermediate.** An **intermediate** is a product of one of the steps in the reaction mechanism. It becomes a reactant in the next step. Intermediates have a significant lifetime compared with an activated complex. They have real ionic or molecular structures and some stability. They are reactive enough, however, to take part in the next step of the reaction mechanism.

Intermediates do not appear in the overall chemical equation for a reaction. The reaction mechanism for the decomposition of nitrous oxide (N_2O), for example, is believed to occur in two elementary steps:

$$N_2O(g) \longrightarrow N_2(g) + O(g)$$
$$N_2O(g) + O(g) \longrightarrow N_2(g) + O_2(g)$$
$$\overline{2N_2O(g) \longrightarrow 2N_2(g) + O_2(g)}$$

Notice that in the first elementary step, oxygen atoms are formed. These are an intermediate product in this step of the mechanism. They are a reactant in the second step, and they disappear when the two elementary reactions are summed to give the final chemical equation. This illustrates an important general point: The overall chemical equation for a complex reaction gives no information about the reaction mechanism. Reaction mechanisms must be determined experimentally.

Figure 18.28 A reaction progress curve shows an activation-energy peak for each elementary reaction. Valleys indicate the formation of intermediates.

INTERPRETING GRAPHS

a. Navigate How many elementary reactions are part of this reaction?

b. Read How many intermediates are formed?

c. Interpret How would a catalyst affect the energy of the reactants and the energy of the products of this reaction?

Energy Changes for a Multi-Step Reaction

Activated complex

Intermediate

Energy →

Reactants

Products

Reaction progress →

Professor of Chemistry

If you study chemistry in college, your teacher probably will be a Professor of Chemistry. Chemistry professors train the next generation of chemists. In addition to their classroom teaching, they often undertake fundamental research projects to learn more about the how and why of chemical interactions.

For example, a professor who is interested in reaction rates could study a particular reaction and determine its rate and reaction mechanism. Both graduate and undergraduate students gain valuable experience by assisting the professor in carrying out the work in the laboratory. Together, professor and students publish the results of their research in scientific journals. Much of the basic research reported in journals is done in university laboratories.

Many chemistry professors specialize in one kind of chemistry, for example, inorganic chemistry, organic chemistry, biochemistry, or

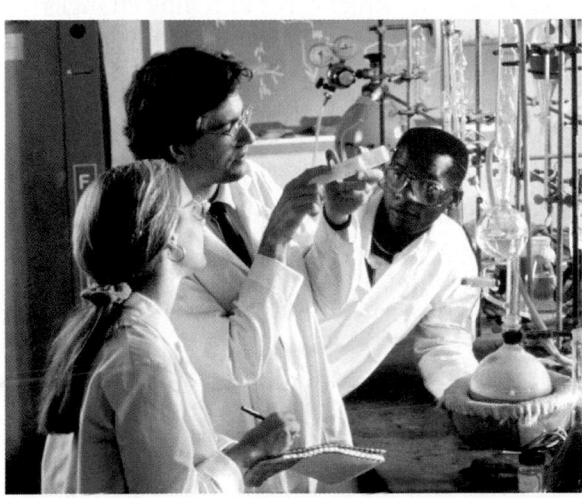

analytical chemistry. As experts in their particular field, they may share what they know by writing books.

A new member of the Chemistry faculty might start at the level of Instructor. The usual steps in advancement are Assistant Professor, Associate Professor, and then Professor. The minimum qualification for Instructor is usually a PhD in chemistry. Often candidates for a position also have completed a number of years of post-doctoral research at a university.

For: Careers in Chemistry
Visit: PHSchool.com
Web Code: cdb-1185

18.5 Section Assessment

38. **Key Concept** How does the size of the specific rate constant (k) for a reaction relate to the speed of the reaction?

39. **Key Concept** What do the hills and valleys in a reaction progress curve represent?

40. Define each of the following terms as applied to chemical reactions.
   a. elementary reaction **b.** intermediate
   c. reaction mechanism **d.** activation energy

41. Show that the unit of k for a reaction that is second-order in A and second-order overall can be expressed in L/(mol·s).

42. The rate law for this reaction is first-order in NO and O_3, and second-order overall.

$$NO(g) + O_3(g) \longrightarrow NO_2(g) + O_2(g)$$

Write the complete rate law for this reaction.

Writing ▶ **Activity**

Write a Report Because of its potential impact on human health and agriculture, ozone depletion in the stratosphere is an area of continuing scientific interest and study. Research and write a report on the reaction mechanisms for the depletion of ozone in the stratosphere caused by the presence of CFCs.

Interactive Textbook

Assessment 18.5 Test yourself on the concepts in Section 18.5.

with ChemASAP

Key Concepts

18.1 Rates of Reaction

- The rate of a chemical reaction is usually expressed as the change in the amount of a reactant per unit time.

- Factors that influence the rate of a chemical reaction are temperature, concentration, particle size, and the use of a catalyst.

18.2 Reversible Reactions and Equilibrium

- Chemical equilibrium is a state in which the forward and reverse reactions take place at the same rate. At chemical equilibrium, no net change occurs in the system.

- Stresses that can alter the equilibrium position of a reaction are changes in the concentrations of reactants or products, changes in temperature, and changes in pressure.

- A K_{eq} value greater than 1 means that products are favored over reactants; a K_{eq} less than 1 means that reactants are favored over products.

18.3 Solubility Equilibrium

- The smaller the numerical value of the solubility product constant, the lower the solubility of the compound.

- A precipitate will form if the product of the concentrations of two ions in a mixture is greater than the K_{sp} of the compound formed from the ions.

18.4 Entropy and Free Energy

- Spontaneous reactions produce substantial amounts of product and release free energy.

- An increase in entropy favors the spontaneous reaction; a decrease favors the nonspontaneous reaction.

- The size and direction of enthalpy changes and entropy changes together determine whether a reaction is spontaneous.

- The numerical value of ΔG is negative in spontaneous processes because the system loses free energy.

18.5 The Progress of Chemical Reactions

- The value of the specific rate constant, k, in the rate equation is large if products form quickly from reactants.

- Graphs of the progress of a reaction show peaks that correspond to the energies of activated complexes and valleys that correspond to the energies of intermediates and products.

Vocabulary

- activated complex (p. 544)
- activation energy (p. 543)
- chemical equilibrium (p. 550)
- collision theory (p. 542)
- common ion (p. 563)
- common ion effect (p. 563)
- elementary reaction (p. 578)
- entropy (p. 569)
- equilbrium constant (p. 556)
- equilibrium position (p. 551)
- first-order reaction (p. 576)
- free energy (p. 566)
- Gibbs free-energy change (p. 572)
- inhibitor (p. 547)
- intermediate (p. 578)
- law of disorder (p. 569)
- Le Châtelier's principle (p. 552)
- nonspontaneous reaction (p. 567)
- rate (p. 542)
- rate law (p. 575)
- reaction mechanism (p. 578)
- reversible reaction (p. 549)
- solubility product constant (p. 561)
- specific rate constant (p. 575)
- spontaneous reaction (p. 567)
- transition state (p. 544)

Key Equations

- $K_{eq} = \dfrac{[C]^c \times [D]^d}{[A]^a \times [B]^b}$

- $\Delta G = \Delta H - T\Delta S$

- rate $= k[A]^a[B]^b$

18.1 Rates of Reaction

43. Explain the collision theory of reactions.

44. How is the activation energy of a reaction like a wall or barrier?

45. How is the rate of a reaction influenced by a catalyst? Explain how a catalyst works.

46. Which of these statements is true?
a. All chemical reactions can be sped up by increasing the temperature.
b. Once a chemical reaction gets started, the reacting particles no longer have to collide for products to form.
c. Enzymes are biological catalysts.

47. An increase in temperature raises the energy of the collisions between reactant molecules. An increase in the concentration of reactants increases the number of collisions. What is the effect of a catalyst on the collisions between molecules?

18.2 Reversible Reactions and Equilibrium

48. In your own words, define a reversible reaction.

49. How do the rates of the forward and reverse reactions compare at a state of dynamic chemical equilibrium?

50. What is Le Châtelier's principle? Use it to explain why carbonated drinks go flat when their containers are left open.

51. Write the expression for the equilibrium constant for each reaction.
a. $4H_2(g) + CS_2(g) \rightleftharpoons CH_4(g) + 2H_2S(g)$
b. $PCl_5(g) \rightleftharpoons PCl_3(g) + Cl_2(g)$

52. Comment on the favorability of product formation in each reaction.
a. $H_2(g) + F_2(g) \rightleftharpoons 2HF(g)$ $K_{eq} = 1 \times 10^{13}$
b. $SO_2(g) + NO_2(g) \rightleftharpoons$
   $NO(g) + SO_3(g)$ $K_{eq} = 1 \times 10^2$
c. $2H_2O(g) \rightleftharpoons 2H_2(g) + O_2(g)$ $K_{eq} = 6 \times 10^{-28}$

53. For the reaction $A + B \rightleftharpoons C$, the activation energy of the forward reaction is 5 kJ and the total energy change is −20 kJ. What is the activation energy of the reverse reaction?

54. A large box is divided into two compartments with a door between them. Equal quantities of two different monatomic gases are placed in the compartments, as shown in (a). The door between the compartments is opened and the gas particles start to mix, as in (b). Why would it be highly unlikely for the situation in (b) to progress to the situation shown in (c)?

a.   b.   c.

55. What would be the effect on the equilibrium position if the volume is decreased in the following reaction?
$$4HCl(g) + O_2(g) \rightleftharpoons 2Cl_2(g) + 2H_2O(g)$$

56. Write the equilibrium-constant expression for the following reaction.
$$2SO_2(g) + O_2(g) \rightleftharpoons 2SO_3(g)$$

57. A mixture at equilibrium at 827°C contains 0.552 mol CO_2, 0.552 mol H_2, 0.448 mol CO, and 0.448 H_2O. The balanced equation is
$$CO_2(g) + H_2(g) \rightleftharpoons CO(g) + H_2O(g)$$
What is the value of K_{eq}?

58. The freezing of liquid water at 0°C can be represented as follows.
$$H_2O(l, d = 1.00 \text{ g/cm}^3) \rightleftharpoons$$
$$H_2O(s, d = 0.92 \text{ g/cm}^3)$$
Explain why the application of pressure causes ice to melt.

59. Suppose equilibrium exists for the following reaction at 425 K.
$$Fe_3O_4(s) + 4H_2(g) \rightleftharpoons 3Fe + 4H_2O(g)$$
How would the equilibrium concentration of H_2O be affected by these actions?
a. adding more $H_2(g)$ to the mixture
b. adding more Fe(s)
c. removing $H_2(g)$
d. adding a catalyst

60. Predict what will happen if a catalyst is added to a slow reversible reaction. What happens to the equilibrium position?

18.3 Solubility Equilibrium

61. Write the solubility product expression for each salt.
   a. NiS
   b. $BaCO_3$

62. What does the solubility product constant (K_{sp}) represent?

63. Use Table 18.2 to rank these salts from most soluble to least soluble.
   a. CuS
   b. $BaSO_4$
   c. $SrCO_3$
   d. AgI

64. How does the addition of a common ion affect the solubility of another substance?

65. What must be true about the concentration of two ions if precipitation occurs when solutions of the two ions are mixed?

66. What is the concentration of carbonate ions in a saturated solution of $SrCO_3$? $K_{sp} = 9.3 \times 10^{-10}$.

67. What is the equilibrium concentration of barium ion in a 1.0-L saturated solution of barium carbonate to which 0.25 mol K_2CO_3 has been added?

18.4 Entropy and Free Energy

68. How does the free energy of a reaction help predict whether the reaction will be spontaneous?

69. What is the meaning of entropy?

70. The products in a spontaneous process are more ordered than the reactants. Is this entropy change favorable or unfavorable?

71. Which system has the lower entropy?
   a. 50 ml of liquid water or 50 ml of ice
   b. 10 g of sodium chloride crystals or a solution containing 10 g of sodium chloride

72. Predict the direction of the entropy change in each reaction.
   a. $CaCO_3(s) \longrightarrow CaO(s) + CO_2(g)$
   b. $NH_3(g) + HCl(g) \longrightarrow NH_4Cl(s)$

73. Is it true that all spontaneous processes are exothermic? Explain your answer.

74. At normal atmospheric pressure, steam condenses to liquid water even though this entropy change is unfavorable. Explain.

75. What two factors together determine whether a reaction is spontaneous?

76. Which of the following statements tells you that a reaction is definitely spontaneous?
   a. The reaction is exothermic.
   b. Entropy is increased in the reaction.
   c. Free energy is released in the reaction.

77. Would you expect the entropy to increase in each of the following reactions? Explain.
   a. $C(s) + O_2(g) \longrightarrow CO_2(g)$
   b. $2Al_2O_3(s) \longrightarrow 4Al(s) + 3O_2(g)$
   c. $2N(g) \longrightarrow N_2(g)$
   d. $N_2(g) \longrightarrow 2N(g)$

78. Sketch an energy profile curve (potential energy diagram) for a reaction that has an activation energy of 22 kJ, and the total energy change is -103 kJ.

79. Make a list of five things you did today that resulted in an increase in entropy.

18.5 The Progress of Chemical Reactions

80. What is meant by each of the following terms?
   a. specific rate constant
   b. first-order reaction
   c. rate law

81. Half of the reactant in a first-order reaction disappears in 50 minutes. How many minutes are required for the reaction to be 75% complete?

82. Write an equation and sketch a potential-energy diagram for the overall reaction with the following mechanism.

$$2NO(g) \longrightarrow N_2O_2(g) \text{ (fast)}$$
$$N_2O_2(g) + O_2(g) \longrightarrow 2NO_2(g) \text{ (slow)}$$

83. Consider the decomposition of N_2O_5 in carbon tetrachloride (CCl_4) at 45°C.

$$2N_2O_5(soln) \longrightarrow 4NO_2(g) + O_2(g)$$

The reaction is first order in N_2O_5, with the specific rate constant 6.08×10^{-4}/s. Calculate the reaction rate at each of the following conditions.

a. $[N_2O_5] = 0.200$ mol/L
b. $[N_2O_5] = 0.319$ mol/L

84. Ammonium ions and nitrite ions react in water to form nitrogen gas.

$$NO_2^-(aq) + NH_4^+(aq) \longrightarrow N_2(g) + 2H_2O(l)$$

From the following data, decide the order of the reaction with respect to NH_4^+ and NO_2^-, and the overall order of the reaction.

Initial concentration of NO₂⁻ (mol/L)	Initial concentration of NH₄⁺ (mol/L)	Initial rate (mol/L·s)
0.0100	0.200	5.4×10^{-7}
0.0200	0.200	10.8×10^{-7}
0.0400	0.200	21.5×10^{-7}
0.0600	0.200	32.3×10^{-7}
0.200	0.0202	10.8×10^{-7}
0.200	0.0404	21.6×10^{-7}
0.200	0.0606	32.4×10^{-7}
0.200	0.0808	43.3×10^{-7}

85. The following data were collected for the decomposition of compound AB into its elements. The reaction is first-order in AB.

[AB] (mol/L)	Time (s)
0.300	0
0.246	50
0.201	100
0.165	150
0.135	200
0.111	250
0.090	300
0.075	350

a. Make a graph of concentration (*y*-axis) versus time (*x*-axis).
b. Determine the rate of this reaction at $t = 100$ seconds and $t = 250$ seconds.

86. The decomposition of hydrogen peroxide is catalyzed by iodide ions. The mechanism is thought to be as follows.

$$H_2O_2(aq) + I^-(aq) \longrightarrow H_2O(l) + IO^-(aq) \text{ (slow)}$$

$$IO^-(aq) + H_2O_2(aq) \longrightarrow$$
$$H_2O(l) + O_2(g) + I^-(aq) \text{ (fast)}$$

a. What is the reactive intermediate?
b. Does I^- qualify as a catalyst? Explain.
c. What is the minimum number of activated complexes needed to describe the reaction?
d. Which of the two reactions has the smaller specific rate constant?
e. Write the balanced equation for the reaction.

87. When table sugar, or sucrose, is dissolved in an acidic solution, the sucrose slowly decomposes into two simpler sugars: fructose and glucose. Use the graph to answer these questions.

Rate of Sucrose Decomposition

a. How many grams of sucrose decompose in the first 30 minutes?
b. How many grams of sucrose decompose in the 30-minute interval between 90 and 120 minutes?
c. In general, what happens to the rate of decomposition with time?

Test-Taking Tip

Multiple Parts Sometimes two phrases in a true/false question are connected by a word such as *because* or *therefore*, or by a group of words like *and so*. These words imply a relationship between one part of the sentence and another. They usually imply that one thing caused another thing to happen. Statements that include such words can be false even if both parts of the statement are true by themselves.

Regents Practice Exam

Part A

For each statement or question write the number of the word or expression that, of those given, best completes the statement or answers the question.

1. Systems in nature always undergo changes that favor
   (1) lower energy and lower entropy
   (2) higher energy and higher entropy
   (3) lower energy and higher entropy
   (4) higher energy and lower entropy

2. The collision theory states that a reaction is most likely to occur if reactant particles collide
   (1) frequently, with little energy
   (2) with proper energy
   (3) with little energy but at a proper orientation
   (4) at any time, with any energy

3. Which of the following choices does *not* affect the rate of reaction?
   (1) catalyst   (3) stirring
   (2) concentration   (4) temperature

4. At equilibrium, the rate of the forward reaction
   (1) constantly increases
   (2) is greater than the rate of the reverse reaction
   (3) is less than the rate of the reverse reaction
   (4) equals the rate of the reverse reaction

5. LeChâtelier's principle explains
   (1) why a reaction reaches equilibrium
   (2) the effect of a stress on a system at equilibrium
   (3) the effect of a stress on a system not at equilibrium
   (4) which reaction proceeds at a faster rate

Part B-1

For each statement or question write the number of the word or expression that, of those given, best completes the statement or answers the question.

6. Which of the following compounds should *not* readily dissolve in water?
   (1) $KI(s)$ (3) $NH_4Cl(s)$
   (2) $C_2H_6(g)$ (4) $Na_3PO_4(s)$

7. The water solubility of which of the following substances would most likely decrease with an increase in temperature?
   (1) $NH_4Cl(s)$ (3) $KI(s)$
   (2) $NH_3(g)$ (4) $NaCl(s)$

8. The purpose of a catalyst is to
   (1) lower the activation energy for a reaction
   (2) raise the activation energy for a reaction
   (3) make the reaction more endothermic
   (4) make the reaction more exothermic

Use the table to answer Questions 9 and 10.

ΔS	ΔH	ΔG	Spontaneous?
+	−	−	Yes
+	+	+ or −	At high T
−	+	+	No
−	−	+ or −	At low T

9. Which of the following reactions would you expect to be spontaneous at relatively low temperatures?
   (1) $H_2O(l) \longrightarrow H_2O(g)$
   (2) $H_2O(g) \longrightarrow H_2O(l)$
   (3) $H_2O(s) \longrightarrow H_2O(l)$
   (4) Both (1) and (2)

10. Which of the following reactions would you expect to be spontaneous at relatively high temperatures?
    (1) $H_2O(l) \longrightarrow H_2O(g)$
    (2) $H_2O(g) \longrightarrow H_2O(l)$
    (3) $H_2O(s) \longrightarrow H_2O(l)$
    (4) Both (1) and (2)

11. The reaction in which ammonia is formed from nitrogen and hydrogen reaches equilibrium.

    $$N_2(g) + 3H_2(g) \rightleftharpoons 2NH_3$$

    Which of the following statements is true about this equilibrium?
    (1) The amount of ammonia compared to the amount of reactants constantly increases.
    (2) The amount of reactants compared to the amount of ammonia constantly increases.
    (3) No reaction is occurring.
    (4) The rate at which ammonia forms equals the rate at which nitrogen and hydrogen form.

Part B-2

Answer each of the following questions.

12. Write electron configurations and draw electron dot structures for the following elements.
    a. Ge   **c.** O   **e.** Cl
    b. Ca   **d.** Ar   **f.** P

13. What is wrong with saying that solid potassium chloride is composed of KCl molecules?

14. Name each of the following ions.
  a. Cu^{2+} **c.** P^{3-} **e.** Na^+ **g.** O^{2-}
  b. F^- **d.** H^+ **f.** I^- **h.** Mg^{2+}

15. Name the following compounds and give the charge on the negative ion for each.
  a. $NaClO_4$ **c.** $Ca_3(PO_4)_2$ **e.** Na_2SO_4
  b. $KMnO_4$ **d.** $MgCO_3$ **f.** $K_2Cr_2O_7$

16. Which items from the following list would you expect to form positive ions, and which would you expect to form negative ions?
  a. Cl   **c.** P   **e.** Cu   **g.** K
  b. Ca   **d.** Se   **f.** Sn   **h.** Fe

17. Find the mass in grams of each of the following quantities.
  a. 4.50 mol Fe
  b. 1.2 mol glucose ($C_6H_{12}O_6$)
  c. 0.0642 mol ammonium phosphate

18. Aqueous silver nitrate reacts with aqueous potassium iodide to form a precipitate of silver iodide. Write the complete balanced chemical equation for this reaction.

19. When heated, potassium chlorate decomposes into potassium chloride and oxygen gas.
  a. Write the balanced chemical equation for this reaction.
  b. How many moles of oxygen are formed when 4.88 mol $KClO_3$ decompose?

20. Give the name and abbreviation of two units of pressure.

21. What happens to the pressure of a contained gas in each of the following instances?
  a. More gas particles are added.
  b. The temperature of the gas is decreased.
  c. The volume of the container is reduced.

22. Calculate the percent by mass of water in barium bromide tetrahydrate ($BaBr_2 \cdot 4H_2O$).

23. How many moles of solute are in 2.40 L of $0.66M$ KCl?

24. How many liters of a stock solution of $6.00M$ HCl would you need to prepare 15.0 L of $0.500M$ HCl?

25. A small amount of ethanol (C_2H_5OH) is dissolved in a large beaker of water.

  a. Identify the solute and the solvent in this solution.
  b. Is the freezing point of the solution above or below 0°C?

26. How much heat is evolved when 12.4 g of steam at 100°C condenses to liquid water at 100°C?

27. Why is the rate of a chemical reaction affected by a change in temperature?

28. Is the boiling point of a liquid compound a constant? Explain.

29. When solid sodium hydroxide dissolves in water, the solution becomes warm. Is this process endothermic or is it exothermic?

30. The complete combustion of ethene is shown by the following chemical equation.
$$C_2H_4(g) + 3O_2(g) \longrightarrow 2CO_2(g) + 2H_2O(g)$$
$$\Delta H = -1411 \text{ kJ}$$

How many kilojoules of heat are released when 3.28 mol of ethene are burned?

31. The particle diagrams below represent different degrees of entropy. Arrange the diagrams in order of increasing entropy.

Part C

Answer each of the following questions.

32. Explain each of the following statements.
  a. A campfire is "fanned" to help get it going.
  b. An explosion at a grain elevator is blamed on dust.
  c. A pinch of powdered manganese dioxide causes hydrogen peroxide to decompose even though the manganese dioxide is not changed.

33. When the gas to a stove is turned on, the gas does not burn unless lit by a flame. Once lit, however, the gas burns until turned off. Explain these observations in terms of activation energy.

Tomatoes contain ascorbic acid (vitamin C), an important nutrient and antioxidant.

INQUIRY Activity

Effect of Foods on Baking Soda

Materials
variety of fruits and vegetables (e.g., a celery stalk, a banana, a grape, a tomato, a lemon, an apple, an orange, a grapefruit), knife, paper towels, large paper plate, and baking soda (sodium hydrogen carbonate, $NaHCO_3$)

Procedure

1. Carefully cut the fruits and vegetables into small pieces and place them on the plate. **Caution** *Never taste anything in the laboratory, including food products.* Make sure the pieces are well separated from each other. Be sure to wipe any juice off the knife after cutting each fruit and vegetable.

2. Sprinkle a pinch of baking soda on each sample.

Think About It

1. What do you observe?

2. Which fruits and vegetables showed a reaction with the baking soda and which ones did not?

19.1 Acid-Base Theories

Connecting to Your World

Bracken Cave, near San Antonio, Texas, is home to twenty to forty million bats, which is probably the largest colony of mammals in the world. Visitors to the cave must wear protective goggles and respirators to protect themselves from the dangerous levels of ammonia in the cave. Ammonia is a byproduct of the bats' urine. In this section, you will learn why ammonia is considered a base.

Properties of Acids and Bases

Acids and bases play a central role in much of the chemistry that affects your daily life. Your body needs acids and bases to function properly. Vinegar, carbonated drinks, and foods such as citrus fruits contain acids. The electrolyte in a car battery is an acid. Most manufacturing processes use acids or bases. Bases are present in many commercial products, including antacids and household cleaning agents. Figure 19.1 shows some of the many products that contain acids and bases.

Acids Acids have several distinctive properties with which you are probably familiar. Acidic compounds give foods a tart or sour taste. For example, vinegar imparts a tart taste to salad dressing. Vinegar contains ethanoic acid, sometimes called acetic acid. Lemons, which taste sour enough to make your mouth pucker, contain citric acid.

Aqueous solutions of acids are electrolytes. Recall from Chapter 15 that electrolytes conduct electricity. Some acid solutions are strong electrolytes, and others are weak electrolytes. Acids cause certain chemical dyes, called indicators, to change color. Many metals, such as zinc and magnesium, react with aqueous solutions of acids to produce hydrogen gas. Acids react with compounds containing hydroxide ions to form water and a salt. **Acids taste sour, will change the color of an acid-base indicator, and can be strong or weak electrolytes in aqueous solution.**

Guide for Reading

Key Concepts
- What are the properties of acids and bases?
- How did Arrhenius define an acid and a base?
- What distinguishes an acid from a base in the Brønsted-Lowry theory?
- How did Lewis define an acid and a base?

Vocabulary
monoprotic acids
diprotic acids
triprotic acids
conjugate acid
conjugate base
conjugate acid-base pair
hydronium ion (H_3O^+)
amphoteric
Lewis acid
Lewis base

Reading Strategy
Building Vocabulary As you read the section, write a definition and the formula of an example of each type of substance listed in the key terms list.

Figure 19.1 Many items contain acids or bases, or produce acids and bases when dissolved in water. **ⓐ** Citrus fruit contain citric acid. **ⓑ** Tea contains tannic acid. **ⓒ** Antacids use bases to neutralize excess stomach acid. **ⓓ** The base calcium hydroxide is a component of mortar.

Table 19.1	
Some Common Acids	
Name	**Formula**
Hydrochloric acid	HCl
Nitric acid	HNO_3
Sulfuric acid	H_2SO_4
Phosphoric acid	H_3PO_4
Ethanoic acid	CH_3COOH
Carbonic acid	H_2CO_3

Bases Bases have properties with which you are less familiar. Bases have a bitter taste, but tasting most bases is hazardous. Soap is a familiar material that has the properties of a base. If you have tasted soap, you know that it has a bitter taste. The slippery feel of soap is another property of bases.

Like acids, aqueous solutions of bases are electrolytes and will cause an indicator to change color. Water and a salt are formed when a base that contains hydroxide ions reacts with an acid. With a few exceptions, none of the foods you eat are bases. Milk of magnesia (a suspension of magnesium hydroxide in water) is a base used to treat the problem of excess stomach acid. 🔑 **Bases taste bitter, feel slippery, will change the color of an acid-base indicator, and can be strong or weak electrolytes in aqueous solution.**

✓**Checkpoint** *Give an example of a base.*

Arrhenius Acids and Bases

Although chemists had recognized the properties of acids and bases for many years, they were not able to propose a theory to explain this behavior. Then, in 1887, the Swedish chemist Svante Arrhenius (1859–1927) proposed a revolutionary way of defining and thinking about acids and bases. 🔑 **Arrhenius said that acids are hydrogen-containing compounds that ionize to yield hydrogen ions (H^+) in aqueous solution. He also said that bases are compounds that ionize to yield hydroxide ions (OH^-) in aqueous solution.**

Arrhenius Acids Table 19.1 lists some common acids. Acids that contain one ionizable hydrogen, such as nitric acid (HNO_3), are called **monoprotic acids.** Acids that contain two ionizable hydrogens, such as sulfuric acid (H_2SO_4), are called **diprotic acids.** Acids that contain three ionizable hydrogens, such as phosphoric acid (H_3PO_4), are called **triprotic acids.** Not all compounds that contain hydrogen are acids, however. Also, not all the hydrogens in an acid may be released as hydrogen ions. Only the hydrogens in very polar bonds are ionizable. In such bonds, hydrogen is joined to a very electronegative element. When a compound that contains such bonds dissolves in water, it releases hydrogen ions because the hydrogen ions are stabilized by solvation. An example is the hydrogen chloride molecule, shown in Figure 19.2. Hydrogen chloride is a polar covalent molecule. It ionizes to form an aqueous solution of hydronium ions and chloride ions.

$$\overset{\delta+}{H}-\overset{\delta-}{Cl}(g) \xrightarrow{H_2O} H^+(aq) + Cl^-(aq)$$

Hydrogen chloride · · · Hydrogen ion · Chloride ion (hydrochloric acid)

Figure 19.2 Hydrochloric acid is actually an aqueous solution of hydrogen chloride. The hydrogen ion forms hydronium ions, making this compound an acid.

HCl
Hydrogen chloride

+

H_2O
Water

H_3O^+
Hydronium ion

+

Cl^-
Chloride ion

In contrast, the four hydrogens in methane (CH_4) are attached by weakly polar C—H bonds. Methane has no ionizable hydrogens and is not an acid. Ethanoic (acetic) acid (CH_3COOH), used in the manufacture of plastics, pharmaceuticals, and photographic chemicals, is different. Although this molecule contains four hydrogens, ethanoic acid is a monoprotic acid. The structural formula shows why.

Go Online

NSTA SciLINKS

For: Links on Acids and Bases in the home
Visit: www.SciLinks.org
Web Code: cdn-1191

$$\begin{array}{ccc} & H & O \\ & | & \| \\ H-&C-&C-O-H \\ & | & \\ & H & \end{array}$$

Ethanoic acid
(CH_3COOH)

The three hydrogens attached to the carbon are in weakly polar bonds. They do not ionize. Only the hydrogen bonded to the highly electronegative oxygen can be ionized. As you gain more experience looking at written formulas for acids, you will be able to recognize which hydrogen atoms can be ionized.

Arrhenius Bases Table 19.2 lists some common bases. The base with which you are perhaps most familiar is sodium hydroxide (NaOH). Sodium hydroxide is commonly known as lye. Sodium hydroxide is an ionic solid. It dissociates into sodium ions and hydroxide ions in aqueous solution.

$$NaOH(s) \xrightarrow{H_2O} Na^+(aq) + OH^-(aq)$$

Sodium   Sodium   Hydroxide
hydroxide   ion   ion

Because of its extremely caustic nature, sodium hydroxide is a major component of consumer products used to clean clogged drains.

Potassium hydroxide (KOH) is another ionic solid that dissociates to form potassium ions and hydroxide ions in aqueous solution.

$$KOH(s) \xrightarrow{H_2O} K^+(aq) + OH^-(aq)$$

Potassium   Potassium   Hydroxide
hydroxide   ion   ion

Sodium and potassium are Group 1A elements. The elements in Group 1A, the alkali metals, react with water to produce solutions that are basic. Sodium metal reacts violently with water to form sodium hydroxide and hydrogen gas. The following equation illustrates the reaction of sodium metal with water.

$$2Na(s) + 2H_2O(l) \longrightarrow 2NaOH(aq) + H_2(g)$$

Sodium   Water   Sodium   Hydrogen
metal   hydroxide

Table 19.2

Some Common Bases		
Name	**Formula**	**Solubility in water**
Potassium hydroxide	KOH	High
Sodium hydroxide	NaOH	High
Calcium hydroxide	$Ca(OH)_2$	Very low
Magnesium hydroxide	$Mg(OH)_2$	Very low

Figure 19.3 Milk of magnesia is a base used as an antacid. Bases are usually hazardous when taken internally, but the low solubility of milk of magnesia makes it safe to use.

Figure 19.4 Sodium carbonate decahydrate ($Na_2CO_3 \cdot 10H_2O$) is used as a laundry aid. Its common name is washing soda.

Sodium hydroxide and potassium hydroxide are very soluble in water. Concentrated solutions of these compounds can be readily prepared. Such solutions, like other basic solutions, would have a bitter taste and slippery feel. However, they are extremely caustic to the skin and can cause deep, painful, slow-healing wounds if not immediately washed off.

Calcium hydroxide ($Ca(OH)_2$) and magnesium hydroxide ($Mg(OH)_2$) are compounds of Group 2A metals. These compounds are not very soluble in water. Their solutions are always very dilute, even when saturated. The concentration of hydroxide ions in such solutions is correspondingly low. A saturated solution of calcium hydroxide contains only 0.165 g $Ca(OH)_2$ per 100 g of water. Magnesium hydroxide is much less soluble than calcium hydroxide. A saturated solution contains only 0.0009 g $Mg(OH)_2$ per 100 g of water. Suspensions of magnesium hydroxide in water contain low concentrations of hydroxide ion. People take these suspensions internally as milk of magnesia, shown in Figure 19.3, which is an antacid and a mild laxative.

Brønsted-Lowry Acids and Bases

The Arrhenius definition of acids and bases is not a very comprehensive one. It defines acids and bases rather narrowly and does not include certain substances that have acidic or basic properties. For example, aqueous solutions of sodium carbonate ($Na_2CO_3(aq)$) and ammonia ($NH_3(aq)$) are basic. Neither of these compounds is a hydroxide, however, and neither would be classified as a base under the Arrhenius definition. In 1923, the Danish chemist Johannes Brønsted (1879–1947) and the English chemist Thomas Lowry (1874–1936) independently proposed a new definition. **The Brønsted-Lowry theory defines an acid as a hydrogen-ion donor, and a base as a hydrogen-ion acceptor.** All the acids and bases included in the Arrhenius theory are also acids and bases according to the Brønsted-Lowry theory. Some compounds not included in the Arrhenius theory are classified as bases in the Brønsted-Lowry theory.

Why Ammonia is a Base The behavior of ammonia as a base can be understood by using the Brønsted-Lowry theory. Ammonia gas is very soluble in water. When ammonia dissolves in water, it acts as a base because it accepts a hydrogen ion from water.

$$NH_3(aq) \; + \; H_2O(l) \; \rightleftharpoons \; NH_4^+(aq) + OH^-(aq)$$

Ammonia	Water	Ammonium ion	Hydroxide ion
(hydrogen-ion acceptor, Brønsted-Lowry base)	(hydrogen-ion donor, Brønsted-Lowry acid)		(makes the solution basic)

In this reaction, ammonia is the hydrogen-ion acceptor and therefore is a Brønsted-Lowry base. Water, the hydrogen-ion donor, is a Brønsted-Lowry acid. Hydrogen ions are transferred from water to ammonia, as is shown in Figure 19.5. This causes the hydroxide-ion concentration to be greater than it is in pure water. As a result, solutions of ammonia are basic.

Checkpoint *Why is ammonia considered to be a Brønsted-Lowry base?*

NH_3	H_2O	$NH_4{}^+$	OH^-
Ammonia	Water	Ammonium ion	Hydroxide ion

Figure 19.5 Ammonia dissolves in water to form ammonium ions and hydroxide ions. In this reaction, the water molecule donates a hydrogen ion to the ammonia molecule.
Explaining *Why is ammonia not classified as an Arrhenius base?*

Conjugate Acids and Bases Because all gases become less soluble in water as temperature increases, increasing the temperature of an aqueous solution of ammonia releases ammonia gas. As ammonia gas leaves the solution, the equilibrium in the equation shifts to the left. The ammonium ion ($NH_4{}^+$) reacts with OH^- to form NH_3 and H_2O. When the reaction goes from right to left, $NH_4{}^+$ gives up a hydrogen ion; it acts as a Brønsted-Lowry acid. The hydroxide ion accepts an H^+; it acts as a Brønsted-Lowry base. Overall, then, this equilibrium has two acids and two bases.

$$NH_3(aq) + H_2O(l) \rightleftharpoons NH_4{}^+(aq) + OH^-(aq)$$

Base   Acid   Conjugate acid   Conjugate base

When ammonia dissolves and then reacts with water, $NH_4{}^+$ is the conjugate acid of the base NH_3. A **conjugate acid** is the particle formed when a base gains a hydrogen ion. Similarly, OH^- is the conjugate base of the acid water. A **conjugate base** is the particle that remains when an acid has donated a hydrogen ion. Conjugate acids and bases are always paired with a base or an acid, respectively. A **conjugate acid-base pair** consists of two substances related by the loss or gain of a single hydrogen ion. The ammonia molecule and ammonium ion are a conjugate acid-base pair. The water molecule and hydroxide ion are also a conjugate acid-base pair.

$$NH_3(aq) + H_2O(l) \rightleftharpoons NH_4{}^+(aq) + OH^-(aq)$$

Base   Acid   Conjugate acid   Conjugate base

The Brønsted-Lowry theory also applies to acids. Consider the dissociation of hydrogen chloride in water.

$$HCl(g) + H_2O(l) \rightleftharpoons H_3O^+(aq) + Cl^-(aq)$$

Acid   Base   Conjugate acid   Conjugate base

In this reaction, hydrogen chloride is the hydrogen-ion donor. Thus it is a Brønsted-Lowry acid. Water is the hydrogen-ion acceptor and therefore water is a Brønsted-Lowry base. A water molecule that gains a hydrogen ion becomes a positively charged **hydronium ion (H_3O^+).** The chloride ion is the conjugate base of the acid HCl. The hydronium ion is the conjugate acid of the base water.

Table 19.3

Several Conjugate Acid-Base Pairs

Acid	Base
HCl	Cl^-
H_2SO_4	$HSO_4{}^-$
H_3O^+	H_2O
$HSO_4{}^-$	$SO_4{}^{2-}$
CH_3COOH	CH_3COO^-
H_2CO_3	$HCO_3{}^-$
$HCO_3{}^-$	$CO_3{}^{2-}$
$NH_4{}^+$	NH_3
H_2O	OH^-

H_2SO_4
Sulfuric acid

H_2O
Water

H_3O^+
Hydronium ion

HSO_4^-
Hydrogen sulfate ion

Figure 19.6 shows the reaction that occurs when sulfuric acid dissolves in water. The solution formed consists of hydronium ions and hydrogen sulfate ions.

Sometimes water accepts a hydrogen ion. At other times, it donates a hydrogen ion. A substance that can act as both an acid and a base is said to be **amphoteric.** Water is amphoteric. In the reaction with HCl, water accepts a proton and is therefore a base.

Lewis Acids and Bases

A third theory of acids and bases was proposed by Gilbert Lewis (1875–1946). **Lewis proposed that an acid accepts a pair of electrons during a reaction, while a base donates a pair of electrons.** This concept is more general than either the Arrhenius theory or the Brønsted-Lowry theory. A **Lewis acid** is a substance that can accept a pair of electrons to form a covalent bond. A **Lewis base** is a substance that can donate a pair of electrons to form a covalent bond. A hydrogen ion (Brønsted-Lowry acid) can accept a pair of electrons in forming a bond. A hydrogen ion, therefore, is also a Lewis acid. A Brønsted-Lowry base, or a substance that accepts a hydrogen ion, must have a pair of electrons available and, therefore, is also a Lewis base. Consider the reaction of H^+ and OH^-.

$$H^+ \; + \; ^-\!\!:\!\ddot{O} - H \; \longrightarrow \; \underset{H \qquad H}{\ddot{O}}$$

Lewis Lewis
acid base

In this reaction, a hydroxide ion is a Lewis base. It is also a Brønsted-Lowry base. The hydrogen ion is both a Lewis acid and a Brønsted-Lowry acid. The Lewis definition also includes some compounds not classified as Brønsted-Lowry acids or bases.

Ammonia dissolved in water is another example of a Lewis acid and Lewis base. In this reaction, the hydrogen ion from the dissociation of water is an electron-pair acceptor and is a Lewis acid. Ammonia is an electron-pair donor and is a Lewis base.

Animation 25 Compare the three important definitions of acids and bases.

with ChemASAP

Table 19.4

Acid-Base Definitions		
Type	**Acid**	**Base**
Arrhenius	H^+ producer	OH^- producer
Brønsted-Lowry	H^+ donor	H^+ acceptor
Lewis	electron-pair acceptor	electron-pair donor

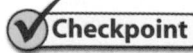 **Checkpoint** *What is a Lewis acid and a Lewis base?*

CONCEPTUAL PROBLEM 19.1

Identifying Lewis Acids and Bases

Ammonia is widely used in fertilizers, plastics, and explosives. Identify the Lewis acid and the Lewis base in this reaction involving ammonia.

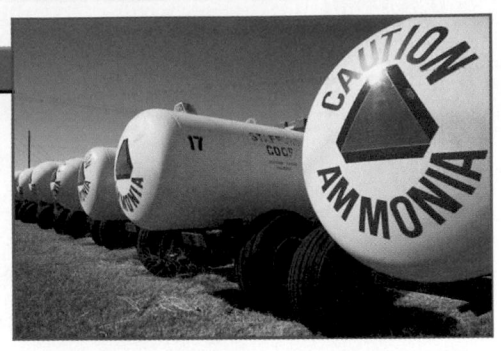

1 **Analyze** *Identify the relevant concepts.*
The Lewis acid–Lewis base definitions, which are to be used in solving the problem, are based on the acceptance and donation of a pair of electrons.

2 **Solve** *Apply concepts to this situation.*
Ammonia is donating a pair of electrons. Boron trifluoride is accepting a pair of electrons. Lewis bases donate electrons, so ammonia is acting as a Lewis base. Lewis acids accept a pair of electrons, so boron trifluoride is acting as a Lewis acid.

Practice Problems

1. Identify the Lewis acid and Lewis base in each reaction.

a.

b. $AlCl_3 + Cl^- \longrightarrow AlCl_4^-$

2. Would you predict PCl_3 to be a Lewis acid or a Lewis base in typical reactions? Explain your prediction.

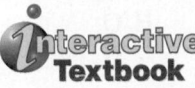

Problem-Solving 19.1 Solve Problem 1 with the help of an interactive guided tutorial.

— with ChemASAP

19.1 Section Assessment

3. 🔑 **Key Concept** What are the properties of acids and bases?

4. 🔑 **Key Concept** How did Arrhenius define an acid and a base?

5. 🔑 **Key Concept** How are acids and bases defined by the Brønsted-Lowry theory?

6. 🔑 **Key Concept** What is the Lewis theory of acids and bases?

7. a. What is a conjugate acid-base pair?
b. Write equations for the ionization of HNO_3 in water and the reaction of CO_3^{2-} with water. For each equation, identify the hydrogen-ion donor and hydrogen-ion acceptor. Then label the conjugate acid-base pairs in each equation.

8. Identify the following acids as monoprotic, diprotic, or triprotic. Explain your reasoning.
a. H_2CO_3 **b.** H_3PO_4 **c.** HCl   **d.** H_2SO_4

Writing ► **Activity**

Write a Report Household drain cleaners contain pellets of sodium hydroxide (NaOH) and small metal particles. Use the library or Internet to find out how drain cleaners work. Include the identity of the metal particles in your written report.

Assessment 19.1 Test yourself on the concepts in Section 19.1.

— with ChemASAP

19.2 Hydrogen Ions and Acidity

 New York Standards: 3.1ss–tt

Guide for Reading

Key Concepts
- How are [H⁺] and [OH⁻] related in an aqueous solution?
- How is the hydrogen-ion concentration used to classify a solution as neutral, acidic, or basic?
- What is the most important characteristic of an acid-base indicator?

Vocabulary
self-ionization
neutral solution
ion-product constant for water (K_w)
acidic solution
basic solution
alkaline solutions
pH

Reading Strategy
Relating Text and Visuals
As you read about pH, look carefully at the diagram in Figure 19.10. Make sure that you can explain why the differences in [H⁺] and [OH⁻] exist in acidic, neutral, and basic solutions.

Connecting to Your World A patient is brought to a hospital unconscious and with a fruity odor on his breath. The doctor suspects the patient has fallen into a diabetic coma. To confirm her diagnosis, she orders several tests, including one of the acidity of the patient's blood. The results from this test will be expressed in units of pH, not molar concentration. In this section, you will learn how the pH scale is used to indicate the acidity of a solution and why the pH scale is used.

Hydrogen Ions from Water

As you already know, water molecules are highly polar and are in continuous motion, even at room temperature. Occasionally, the collisions between water molecules are energetic enough to transfer a hydrogen ion from one water molecule to another. A water molecule that loses a hydrogen ion becomes a negatively charged hydroxide ion (OH⁻). A water molecule that gains a hydrogen ion becomes a positively charged hydronium ion (H_3O^+).

The reaction in which water molecules produce ions is called the **self-ionization** of water. This reaction can be written as a simple dissociation.

$$H_2O(l) \rightleftharpoons H^+(aq) + OH^-(aq)$$
$$\text{Hydrogen ion} \qquad \text{Hydroxide ion}$$

In water or aqueous solution, hydrogen ions (H⁺) are always joined to water molecules as hydronium ions (H_3O^+). Hydrogen ions in aqueous solution have several names. Some chemists call them protons. Others prefer to call them hydrogen ions or hydronium ions. In this textbook, either H⁺ or H_3O^+ is used to represent hydrogen ions in aqueous solution. Figure 19.7 shows how two water molecules react to form one hydronium ion and one hydroxide ion.

Figure 19.7 The self-ionization of water. A proton (hydrogen ion) transfers from one water molecule to another water molecule. The result is one hydronium ion (H_3O^+) and one hydroxide ion (OH⁻).

The self-ionization of water occurs to a very small extent. In pure water at 25°C, the equilibrium concentration of hydrogen ions ($[H^+]$) and the equilibrium concentration of hydroxide ions ($[OH^-]$) are each only $1 \times 10^{-7} M$. This means that the concentrations of H^+ and OH^- are equal in pure water. Any aqueous solution in which $[H^+]$ and $[OH^-]$ are equal is described as a **neutral solution.**

Ion Product Constant for Water

In any aqueous solution, when $[H^+]$ increases, $[OH^-]$ decreases. When $[H^+]$ decreases, $[OH^-]$ increases. Le Châtelier's principle, which you learned about in Chapter 18, applies here. If additional ions (either hydrogen ions or hydroxide ions) are added to a solution, the equilibrium shifts. The concentration of the other type of ion decreases. More water molecules are formed in the process.

$$H^+(aq) + OH^-(aq) \rightleftharpoons H_2O(l)$$

⚷ For aqueous solutions, the product of the hydrogen-ion concentration and the hydroxide-ion concentration equals 1.0×10^{-14}.

$$[H^+] \times [OH^-] = 1.0 \times 10^{-14}$$

This equation is true for all dilute aqueous solutions at 25°C. As you will see, the concentrations of H^+ and OH^- may change when substances are added to water. However, the product of $[H^+]$ and $[OH^-]$ is always 1×10^{-14}.

The product of the concentrations of the hydrogen ions and hydroxide ions in water is called the **ion-product constant for water (K_w).**

$$K_w = [H^+] \times [OH^-] = 1.0 \times 10^{-14}$$

Not all solutions are neutral. When some substances dissolve in water, they release hydrogen ions. For example, when hydrogen chloride dissolves in water, it forms hydrochloric acid.

$$HCl(g) \xrightarrow{H_2O} H^+(aq) + Cl^-(aq)$$

In such a solution, the hydrogen-ion concentration is greater than the hydroxide-ion concentration. The hydroxide ions are present from the self-ionization of water. An **acidic solution** is one in which $[H^+]$ is greater than $[OH^-]$. The $[H^+]$ of an acidic solution is greater than $1 \times 10^{-7} M$.

When sodium hydroxide dissolves in water, it forms hydroxide ions in solution.

$$NaOH(s) \xrightarrow{H_2O} Na^+(aq) + OH^-(aq)$$

In such a solution, the hydrogen-ion concentration is less than the hydroxide-ion concentration. Remember, the hydrogen ions are present from the self-ionization of water. A **basic solution** is one in which $[H^+]$ is less than $[OH^-]$. The $[H^+]$ of a basic solution is less than $1 \times 10^{-7} M$. Basic solutions are also known as **alkaline solutions.** Some uses for acids and bases are shown in Figure 19.8.

 Checkpoint *What is a basic solution?*

Figure 19.8 Acids and bases have many uses in the home and in industry. **ⓐ** Unrefined hydrochloric acid, commonly called muriatic acid, is used to clean stone buildings and swimming pools. **ⓑ** Sodium hydroxide, or lye, is commonly used as a drain cleaner. **Predicting** *How will each chemical affect the hydrogen-ion and hydroxide-ion concentration of an aqueous solution?*

Finding the [OH⁻] of a Solution

Colas are slightly acidic. If the [H⁺] in a solution is $1.0 \times 10^{-5}M$, is the solution acidic, basic, or neutral? What is the [OH⁻] of this solution?

1 Analyze *List the knowns and the unknowns.*

Knowns
- $[\text{H}^+] = 1.0 \times 10^{-5}M$
- Ion-product constant for water:
$$K_w = [\text{H}^+] \times [\text{OH}^-] = 1 \times 10^{-14}$$

Unknowns
- solution = acidic, basic, or neutral?
- $[\text{OH}^-] = ?M$

2 Calculate *Solve for the unknowns.*

$[\text{H}^+]$ is $1.0 \times 10^{-5}M$. Because this is greater than $1.0 \times 10^{-7}M$, the solution is acidic.

By definition $K_w = [\text{H}^+] \times [\text{OH}^-]$. Therefore, $[\text{OH}^-] = \dfrac{K_w}{[\text{H}^+]}$.

Substituting the known numerical values, compute [OH⁻] as follows.

$$[\text{OH}^-] = \frac{1.0 \times 10^{-14}}{1.0 \times 10^{-5}} = 1.0 \times 10^{-9}M$$

3 Evaluate *Do the results make sense?*

If $[\text{H}^+]$ is greater than $1.0 \times 10^{-7}M$, the [OH⁻] must be less than $1.0 \times 10^{-7}M$. At $1 \times 10^{-9}M$, [OH⁻] is less than $1 \times 10^{-7}M$.

Practice Problems

9. Classify each solution as acidic, basic, or neutral.
   a. $[\text{H}^+] = 6.0 \times 10^{-10}M$
   b. $[\text{OH}^-] = 3.0 \times 10^{-2}M$
   c. $[\text{H}^+] = 2.0 \times 10^{-7}M$
   d. $[\text{OH}^-] = 1.0 \times 10^{-7}M$

10. If the hydroxide-ion concentration of an aqueous solution is $1 \times 10^{-3}M$, what is the [H⁺] in the solution? Is the solution acidic, basic, or neutral?

Math Handbook

For help with scientific notation, go to page R56.

Interactive Textbook

Problem-Solving 19.10 Solve Problem 10 with the help of an interactive guided tutorial.

— with **ChemASAP**

The pH Concept

Expressing hydrogen-ion concentration in molarity is cumbersome. A more widely used system for expressing [H⁺] is the pH scale, proposed in 1909 by the Danish scientist Søren Sørensen (1868–1939). On the pH scale, which ranges from 0 to 14, neutral solutions have a pH of 7. A pH of 0 is strongly acidic. A solution with a pH of 14 is strongly basic.

Calculating pH The **pH** of a solution is the negative logarithm of the hydrogen-ion concentration. The pH may be represented mathematically using the following equation.

$$\text{pH} = -\log[\text{H}^+]$$

In a neutral solution, the $[H^+] = 1 \times 10^{-7} M$. The pH of a neutral solution is 7.

$$pH = -\log(1 \times 10^{-7})$$
$$= -(\log 1 + \log 10^{-7})$$
$$= -(0.0 + (-7.0))$$
$$= 7.0$$

You can calculate the pH of a solution using the log function key on a calculator. (You can review finding the logarithm of a number on a calculator in the Math Handbook on page R78.)

Figure 19.9 shows how the hydrogen-ion concentration of a solution is used to classify the solution as neutral acidic, or basic. **A solution in which $[H^+]$ is greater than $1 \times 10^{-7} M$ has a pH less than 7.0 and is acidic. The pH of pure water or a neutral aqueous solution is 7.0. A solution with a pH greater than 7 is basic and has a $[H^+]$ of less than $1 \times 10^{-7} M$.**

- Acidic solution: pH < 7.0 $[H^+]$ greater than $1 \times 10^{-7} M$
- Neutral solution: pH = 7.0 $[H^+]$ equals $1 \times 10^{-7} M$
- Basic solution: pH > 7.0 $[H^+]$ less than $1 \times 10^{-7} M$

Go Online

For: Links on pH
Visit: www.SciLinks.org
Web Code: cdn–1192

[H₃O⁺] and [OH⁻] in Acidic, Neutral, and Basic Solutions

Figure 19.9 The hydrogen-ion concentrate of a solution is used to classify the solution as acidic, neutral, or basic.

INTERPRETING GRAPHS

a. Identify What is $[H_3O^+]$ in a neutral solution?
b. Describe How does $[H_3O^+]$ compare with $[OH^-]$ in an acidic solution?
c. Compare and Contrast In terms of ion concentrations, how are basic solutions different from acidic solutions?

The pH values of several common aqueous solutions are listed in Table 19.5. The table also summarizes the relationship among $[H^+]$, $[OH^-]$, and pH. You may notice that pH can sometimes be read from the value of $[H^+]$. If $[H^+]$ is written in scientific notation and has a coefficient of 1, then the pH of the solution equals the exponent, with the sign changed from minus to plus. For example, a solution with $[H^+] = 1 \times 10^{-2} M$ has a pH of 2.0 and a solution with $[H^+] = 1 \times 10^{-13} M$ has a pH of 13.0.

If the pH is an integer number, it is also possible to directly write the value of $[H^+]$. A solution with a pH of 9.0 has a $[H^+] = 1 \times 10^{-9} M$. A pH of 4 indicates a $[H^+]$ of $1 \times 10^{-4} M$.

Table 19.5

Relationship among [H⁺], [OH⁻], and pH

	[H⁺] (mol/L)	[OH⁻] (mol/L)	pH	Aqueous system
Increasing acidity ↑	1×10^{0}	1×10^{-14}	0.0	←1*M* HCl
	1×10^{-1}	1×10^{-13}	1.0	←0.1*M* HCl
	1×10^{-2}	1×10^{-12}	2.0	←Gastric juice / ←Lemon juice
	1×10^{-3}	1×10^{-11}	3.0	
	1×10^{-4}	1×10^{-10}	4.0	←Tomato juice
	1×10^{-5}	1×10^{-9}	5.0	←Black coffee
	1×10^{-6}	1×10^{-8}	6.0	←Milk
Neutral	1×10^{-7}	1×10^{-7}	7.0	←Pure water
Increasing basicity ↓	1×10^{-8}	1×10^{-6}	8.0	⌐Blood
	1×10^{-9}	1×10^{-5}	9.0	⌐Sodium bicarbonate, sea water
	1×10^{-10}	1×10^{-4}	10.0	
	1×10^{-11}	1×10^{-3}	11.0	←Milk of magnesia
	1×10^{-12}	1×10^{-2}	12.0	←Household ammonia / ←Washing soda
	1×10^{-13}	1×10^{-1}	13.0	←0.1*M* NaOH
	1×10^{-14}	1×10^{0}	14.0	←1*M* NaOH

Calculating pOH The pOH of a solution equals the negative logarithm of the hydroxide-ion concentration.

$$pOH = -\log[OH^-]$$

A neutral solution has a pOH of 7. A solution with a pOH less than 7 is basic. A solution with a pOH greater than 7 is acidic. A simple relationship between pH and pOH allows you to find either one when the other is known.

$$pH + pOH = 14$$

$$pH = 14 - pOH$$

$$pOH = 14 - pH$$

pH and Significant Figures For pH calculations, you should express the hydrogen-ion concentration in scientific notation. For example, a hydrogen-ion concentration of 0.0010*M*, rewritten as $1.0 \times 10^{-3}M$ in scientific notation, has two significant figures. The pH of this solution is 3.00, with the two numbers to the right of the decimal point representing the two significant figures in the concentration. A solution with a pH of 3.00 is acidic, as shown in Figure 19.10.

Figure 19.10 The pH scale shows the relationship between pH and the hydrogen-ion concentration. **Interpreting Diagrams** *What happens to [H⁺] as pH increases?*

Most pH values are not whole numbers. For example, milk of magnesia has a pH of 10.5. Using the definition of pH, this means that $[H^+]$ must equal $1 \times 10^{-10.5}M$. Thus $[H^+]$ must be less than $1 \times 10^{-10}M$ (pH 10.0), but greater than $1 \times 10^{-11}M$ (pH 11.0). If $[H^+]$ is written in scientific notation but its coefficient is not 1, then you use a calculator with a log function key to calculate pH.

SAMPLE PROBLEM 19.2

Calculating pH from $[H^+]$

What is the pH of a solution with a hydrogen-ion concentration of $4.2 \times 10^{-10}M$?

1 Analyze *List the knowns and the unknown.*

Knowns
- $[H^+] = 4.2 \times 10^{-10}M$
- $pH = -\log[H^+]$

Unknown
- $pH = ?$

2 Calculate *Solve for the unknown.*

$$pH = -\log[H^+]$$
$$= -\log(1.0 \times 10^{-10})$$
$$= -(\log 1.0 + \log 10^{-10})$$
$$= -(0.00 + (-10.00))$$
$$= -(-10.00)$$
$$= 10.00$$

Using a calculator, $\log (4.2 \times 10^{-10}) = -9.37675$
$$pH = -(-9.38) = 9.38.$$

3 Evaluate *Do the results make sense?*

The calculated pH is between 9 ($[H^+] = 1 \times 10^{-9}M$) and 10 ($[H^+] = 1 \times 10^{-10}M$). The pH is rounded to two decimal places because the hydrogen-ion concentration has two significant figures.

Practice Problems

11. Find the pH of each solution.
  a. $[H^+] = 1 \times 10^{-4}M$
  b. $[H^+] = 0.0015M$

12. What are the pH values of the following solutions, based on their hydrogen-ion concentrations?
  a. $[H^+] = 1.0 \times 10^{-12}M$
  b. $[H^+] = 0.045M$

You can calculate the hydrogen-ion concentration of a solution if you know the pH. For example, if the solution has a pH of 3.00, then $[H^+] = 1 \times 10^{-3}M$. When the pH is not a whole number, you will need a calculator with a y^x function key to calculate the hydrogen-ion concentration. For example, if the pH is 3.70, the hydrogen-ion concentration is greater than $1 \times 10^{-4}M$ (pH 4.0) and less than $1 \times 10^{-3}M$ (pH 3.0). To get an accurate value, use a calculator as shown in the following example.

CHEMath

Logarithms

The common logarithm (log) of a number (N) is the exponent (*x*) to which the base 10 must be raised to yield the number. If $N = 10^x$, then $\log N = x$.

The use of logarithms allows a large range of values to be conveniently expressed as small, nonexponential numbers. For example, $\log 10^3 = 3$ and $\log 10^6 = 6$. Although there is a range of three orders of magnitude ($10 \times 10 \times 10$ or 1000) between the numbers 10^3 and 10^6, the range of the log values is only 3.

The concentration of hydrogen ions in most aqueous solutions, although small, can vary over many orders of magnitude. Scientists use pH, a logarithmic scale which ranges between 1 and 14, to more conveniently express the hydrogen ion concentration of a solution.

Math ▶ **Handbook**

For help calculating logarithms, go to page R78.

nteractive Textbook

Problem-Solving 19.12 Solve Problem 12 with the help of an interactive guided tutorial.

—— with **ChemASAP**

Using pH to Find [H⁺]

The pH of an unknown solution is 6.35. What is its hydrogen-ion concentration?

1 **Analyze** *List the knowns and the unknown.*

Knowns
- pH = 6.35
- pH = $-\log[H^+]$

Unknown
- $[H^+] = ?M$

Math **Handbook**

For help calculating logarithms, go to page R78.

2 **Calculate** *Solve for the unknown.*

First, rearrange the equation for the definition of pH to solve for the unknown.

$$-\log[H^+] = pH$$

Next, substitute the value of pH.

$$-\log[H^+] = 6.35$$

Change the signs on both sides of the equation.

$$\log[H^+] = -6.35$$

Finally, determine the number that has a log of -6.35, the antilog of -6.35, using the 10^x key on the calculator. The antilog of -6.35 is 4.5×10^{-7}. Therefore, $[H^+] = 4.5 \times 10^{-7}M$.

3 **Evaluate** *Do the results make sense?*

The hydrogen ion concentration must be between $1 \times 10^{-6}M$ (pH = 6) and $1 \times 10^{-7}M$ (pH = 7). The answer is rounded to two significant figures because the pH was measured to two decimal places.

Practice Problems

13. Calculate [H⁺] for each solution.
   a. pH = 5.00
   b. pH = 12.83

14. What are the hydrogen-ion concentrations for solutions with the following pH values?
   a. 4.00
   b. 11.55

interactive Textbook

Problem-Solving 19.14 Solve Problem 14 with the help of an interactive guided tutorial.

with ChemASAP

Measuring pH

People need to be able to measure the pH of the solutions they use. From maintaining the correct acid-base balance in a swimming pool, to creating soil conditions ideal for plant growth, to making medical diagnoses, pH measurements have valuable applications. For preliminary pH measurements and for small-volume samples, an indicator such as the one shown in Figure 19.11 is often used. For precise and continuous measurements, a pH meter is preferred.

Figure 19.11 Acid-base indicators respond to pH changes over a specific range. Phenolphthalein changes from colorless to pink at pH 7–9.

If you know the [OH⁻] of a solution, you can find its pH. The ion-product for water defines the relationship between [H⁺] and [OH⁻]. Therefore, you can determine [H⁺] by dividing K_w by the known [OH⁻].

SAMPLE PROBLEM 19.4

Calculating pH from [OH⁻]

What is the pH of a solution if [OH⁻] $= 4.0 \times 10^{-11}M$?

① Analyze *List the knowns and the unknown.*

Knowns
- [OH⁻] $= 4.0 \times 10^{-11}M$
- $K_w = [OH^-] \times [H^+] = 1 \times 10^{-14}$
- $pH = -\log[H^+]$

Unknown
- pH = ?

② Calculate *Solve for the unknown.*

To calculate pH, first calculate [H⁺] by using the definition of K_w.

$$K_w = [OH^-] \times [H^+]$$

$$[H^+] = \frac{K_w}{[OH^-]} = \frac{1.0 \times 10^{-14}}{4.0 \times 10^{-11}} = 0.25 \times 10^{-3}M$$

$$= 2.5 \times 10^{-4}M$$

With the value of [H⁺] determined, use the definition of pH to solve for the pH.

$$pH = -\log[H^+] = -\log(2.5 \times 10^{-4})$$

A calculator indicates that $\log 2.5 \times 10^{-4}M = -3.60205$, therefore

$$pH = -(-3.60)$$

$$= 3.60$$

③ Evaluate *Do the results make sense?*

A solution in which [OH⁻] is less than $1 \times 10^{-7}M$ would be acidic because [H⁺] would be greater than $1 \times 10^{-7}M$. The pH is expressed to 2 decimal places because [OH⁻] is expressed to 2 significant figures.

Practice Problems

15. Calculate the pH of each solution.
  a. [OH⁻] $= 4.3 \times 10^{-5}M$
  b. [OH⁻] $= 4.5 \times 10^{-11}M$

16. Calculate the pH of each solution.
  a. [H⁺] $= 5.0 \times 10^{-5}M$
  b. [H⁺] $= 8.3 \times 10^{-10}M$

Interactive Textbook
Problem-Solving 19.15 Solve Problem 15 with the help of an interactive guided tutorial.
___ with **ChemASAP**

Acid-Base Indicators An indicator (HIn) is an acid or a base that undergoes dissociation in a known pH range. 🔑 **An indicator is a valuable tool for measuring pH because its acid form and base form have different colors in solution.** The following generalized equation represents the dissociation of an indicator (HIn).

$$\text{HIn}(aq) \underset{\text{H}^+}{\overset{\text{OH}^-}{\rightleftharpoons}} \text{H}^+(aq) + \text{In}^-(aq)$$

Acid form   Base form

The acid form dominates the dissociation equilibrium at low pH (high [H⁺]), and the base form dominates the equilibrium at high pH (high [OH⁻]).

Color Ranges of Acid-Base Indicators

For each indicator, the change from dominating acid form to dominating base form occurs in a narrow range of approximately two pH units. Within this range, the color of the solution is a mixture of the colors of the acid and the base forms. Knowing the pH range over which this color change occurs can give you a rough estimate of the pH of a solution. At all pH values below this range, you would see only the color of the acid form. At all pH values above this range, you would see only the color of the base form. You could get a more precise estimate of the pH of the solution by repeating the experiment with indicators that have different pH ranges for their color changes. Many different indicators are needed to span the entire pH spectrum. Figure 19.12 shows the pH ranges of some commonly used indicators.

Indicators have certain characteristics that limit their usefulness. The listed pH values of indicators are usually given for 25°C. At other temperatures, an indicator may change color at a different pH. If the solution being tested is not colorless, the color of the indicator may be distorted. Dissolved salts in a solution may also affect the indicator's dissociation. Using indicator strips can help overcome these problems. An indicator strip is a piece of paper or plastic impregnated with an indicator. The paper is dipped into an unknown solution and compared with a color chart to measure the pH. Some indicator paper is impregnated with multiple indicators. The colors that result, which cover a wide pH range, are shown in Figure 19.13.

Figure 19.13 You can find acidic and basic substances in your home. ❶ Universal indicator solution has been added to solutions of known pH in the range from 1 to 12 to produce a set of reference colors. ❷ Universal indicator has been added to samples of vinegar, soda water, and ammonia solution. **Interpreting Photographs** *Use the reference colors to assign pH values to vinegar, soda water, and ammonia solution.*

Figure 19.14 Altering soil pH can affect the development of plants. **a** In acidic soils, hydrangeas produce blue flowers. **b** In basic soils, hydrangeas produce pink flowers. Evergreen plants **c** suffer from chlorosis, a yellowing of the foliage **d** if soil pH is too basic.

pH Meters A pH meter makes rapid, accurate pH measurements. Most chemistry laboratories have a pH meter. A pH meter connected to a computer or chart recorder can be used to make a continuous recording of pH changes. As you can see in Figure 19.15, the pH meter gives a direct readout of pH.

A pH meter is often easier to use than liquid indicators or indicator strips. Measurements of pH obtained with a pH meter are typically accurate to within 0.01 pH unit of the true pH. The color and cloudiness of the unknown solution do not affect the accuracy of the pH value obtained. Hospitals use pH meters to find small but meaningful changes of pH in blood and other body fluids. Sewage, industrial effluents, and soil pH are also easily monitored with a pH meter.

Figure 19.15 A pH meter provides a quick and accurate way to measure the pH of a solution. **a** Water is neutral, having a pH of 7. **b** The pH of vinegar, a dilute aqueous solution of ethanoic (acetic) acid, is about 3. **c** The pH of milk of magnesia, an aqueous suspension of magnesium hydroxide, is 10.5.
Applying Concepts *What are some advantages of using a pH meter rather than an indicator?*

Quick LAB

Indicators from Natural Sources

Purpose
To measure the pH of various household materials by using a natural indicator to make an indicator chart.

Materials
- knife
- red cabbage leaves
- 1-cup measure
- hot water
- 2 jars
- clean white cloth
- teaspoon
- tape
- 3 sheets of plain white paper
- pencil
- ruler
- 10 clear plastic cups
- white vinegar (CH_3COOH)
- baking soda ($NaHCO_3$)
- household ammonia
- dropper
- various household items listed in Step 5

Procedure

1. Put $\frac{1}{2}$ cup of finely chopped red cabbage leaves in a jar and add $\frac{1}{2}$ cup of hot water. Stir and crush the leaves with a spoon. Continue the extraction until the water is distinctly colored.

2. Strain the extract through a piece of cloth into a clean jar. This liquid is your natural indicator.

3. Tape three sheets of paper end to end. Draw a line along the center and label it at 5-cm intervals with the numbers 1 to 14. This is your pH scale.

4. Pour your indicator to about 1-cm depth into each of three plastic cups. To one cup, add several drops of vinegar, to the second add a pinch of baking soda, and to the third add several drops of ammonia. The resulting colors indicate pH values of about 3, 9, and 11, respectively. Place these colored positions on your pH scale.

5. Repeat Step 4 for household items such as table salt, borax, milk, lemon juice, laundry detergent, dish detergent, milk of magnesia, mouthwash,

toothpaste, shampoo, and carbonated beverages.

Analyze and Conclude

1. What was the color of the indicator at acidic, neutral, and basic conditions?

2. What chemical changes were responsible for the color changes?

3. Label the materials you tested as acidic, basic, or neutral.

4. Which group contains items used for cleaning or for personal hygiene?

19.2 Section Assessment

17. **Key Concept** What is the relationship between $[H^+]$ and $[OH^-]$ in an aqueous solution?

18. **Key Concept** What is true about the relative concentrations of hydrogen ions and hydroxide ions in each kind of solution?
    a. basic   b. acidic   c. neutral

19. **Key Concept** What is true about the colors of a pH indicator?

20. Determine the pH of each solution.
    a. $[H^+] = 1 \times 10^{-6}M$ b. $[H^+] = 0.00010M$
    c. $[OH^-] = 1 \times 10^{-2}M$ d. $[OH^-] = 1 \times 10^{-11}M$

21. What are the hydroxide-ion concentrations for solutions with the following pH values?
    a. 6.00   b. 9.00   c. 12.00

Group 7A Elements Hypochlorite salts are used to disinfect swimming pools. Use page R32 of the Elements Handbook to research how the pH of swimming pool water is regulated to maintain the necessary concentration of hypochlorous acid, HOCl.

interactive Textbook

Assessment 19.2 Test yourself on the concepts in Section 19.2.

—— with **ChemASAP**

19.3 Strengths of Acids and Bases

 New York Standards: 3.4h–i

Connecting to Your World

Lemons and grapefruits have a sour taste because they contain citric acid. When you make lemonade, or cut up a grapefruit, you probably do not wear safety goggles or chemical-resistant clothing even though you are working with an acid. However, some acids require such precautions. For example, sulfuric acid is a widely used industrial chemical that can quickly cause severe burns if it comes into contact with skin. In this section, you will learn what makes some acids weak acids and other acids strong acids.

Guide for Reading

Key Concepts
- How does the value of an acid dissociation constant relate to the strength of an acid?
- How can you calculate an acid dissociation constant (K_a) of a weak acid?

Vocabulary
strong acids
weak acids
acid dissociation constant (K_a)
strong bases
weak bases
base dissociation constant (K_b)

Reading Strategy
Comparing and Contrasting
Compare the concentrations of H^+ and OH^- in solutions of strong acids and weak acids. Explain these differences. Do the same for strong bases and weak bases.

Strong and Weak Acids and Bases

Acids are classified as strong or weak depending on the degree to which they ionize in water. In general, **strong acids** are completely ionized in aqueous solution. Hydrochloric acid and sulfuric acid are strong acids.

$$HCl(g) + H_2O(l) \longrightarrow H_3O^+(aq) + Cl^-(aq) \text{ (100\% ionized)}$$

Weak acids ionize only slightly in aqueous solution. The ionization of ethanoic acid (acetic acid), a typical weak acid, is not complete.

$$\underset{\text{Ethanoic acid}}{CH_3COOH(aq)} + \underset{\text{Water}}{H_2O(l)} \rightleftharpoons \underset{\text{Hydronium ion}}{H_3O^+(aq)} + \underset{\text{Ethanoate ion}}{CH_3COO^-(aq)}$$

Table 19.6 shows the relative strengths of some common acids and bases.

Table 19.6

Relative Strengths of Common Acids and Bases		
Substance	**Formula**	**Relative Strength**
Hydrochloric acid	HCl	Strong Acid
Nitric acid	HNO₃	
Sulfuric acid	H₂SO₄	
Phosphoric acid	H₃PO₄	Increasing strength of acid
Ethanoic acid	CH₃COOH	
Carbonic acid	H₂CO₃	
Hypochlorous acid	HClO	Neutral Solution
Neutral Solution		
Ammonia	NH₃	
Sodium silicate	Na₂SiO₃	Increasing strength of base
Calcium hydroxide	Ca(OH)₂	
Sodium hydroxide	NaOH	Strong Base
Potassium hydroxide	KOH	

Acid Dissociation Constant In an aqueous solution of ethanoic acid, fewer than 1% of ethanoic acid molecules are ionized at any instant. Therefore, ethanoic acid is considered a weak acid. Figure 19.16 compares the extent of dissociation of strong, weak, and very weak acids. A strong acid completely dissociates in water. As a result, $[H_3O^+]$ is high. Hydrochloric acid and sulfuric acid are examples of strong acids. On the other hand, weak acids, such as boric acid and carbonic acid, remain largely undissociated. The $[H_3O^+]$ of a weak acid is low.

You can write the equilibrium-constant expression from the balanced chemical equation. The equilibrium-constant expression for ethanoic acid is shown below.

$$K_{eq} = \frac{[H_3O^+] \times [CH_3COO^-]}{[CH_3COOH] \times [H_2O]}$$

Figure 19.16 Dissociation of an acid (HA) in water yields H_3O^+ and A^-. The bar graphs compare the extent of dissociation of strong, weak, and very weak acids.

INTERPRETING GRAPHS

a. Explain In the graph for the strong acid, why are the heights of the H_3O^+ and A^- bars the same as the height of HA bar?

b. Inferring In the graph for the weak acid, why is the height of the H_3O^+ bar the same as the distance from the top of the second HA bar to the dotted line?

c. Apply Concepts Draw a bar graph for the dissociation of the weak diprotic acid, oxalic acid. Be sure to include the first and second dissociation.

Dissociation of a Strong Acid, Weak Acid, and Very Weak Acid

Strong Acid

HA(aq) + H₂O(l) ⟶ H₃O⁺(aq) + A⁻(aq)

Weak Acid

HA(aq) + H₂O(l) ⇌ H₃O⁺(aq) + A⁻(aq)

Very Weak Acid

HA(aq) + H₂O(l) ⇌ H₃O⁺(aq) + A⁻(aq)

Table 19.7

	Dissociation Constants of Weak Acids	
Acid	**Ionization**	**K_a (25°C)**
Oxalic acid	$HOOCCOOH(aq) \rightleftharpoons H^+(aq) + HOOCCOO^-(aq)$	5.6×10^{-2}
	$HOOCCOO^-(aq) \rightleftharpoons H^+(aq) + OOCCOO^{2-}(aq)$	5.1×10^{-5}
Phosphoric acid	$H_3PO_4(aq) \rightleftharpoons H^+(aq) + H_2PO_4^-(aq)$	7.5×10^{-3}
	$H_2PO_4^-(aq) \rightleftharpoons H^+(aq) + HPO_4^{2-}(aq)$	6.2×10^{-8}
	$HPO_4^{2-}(aq) \rightleftharpoons H^+(aq) + PO_4^{3-}(aq)$	4.8×10^{-13}
Methanoic acid	$HCOOH(aq) \rightleftharpoons H^+(aq) + HCOO^-(aq)$	1.8×10^{-4}
Benzoic acid	$C_6H_5COOH(aq) \rightleftharpoons H^+(aq) + C_6H_5COO^-(aq)$	6.3×10^{-5}
Ethanoic acid	$CH_3COOH(aq) \rightleftharpoons H^+(aq) + CH_3COO^-(aq)$	1.8×10^{-5}
Carbonic acid	$H_2CO_3(aq) \rightleftharpoons H^+(aq) + HCO_3^-(aq)$	4.3×10^{-7}
	$HCO_3^-(aq) \rightleftharpoons H^+(aq) + CO_3^{2-}(aq)$	4.8×10^{-11}

For dilute solutions, the concentration of water is a constant. It can be combined with K_{eq} to give an acid dissociation constant. An **acid dissociation constant (K_a)** is the ratio of the concentration of the dissociated (or ionized) form of an acid to the concentration of the undissociated (nonionized) form. The dissociated form includes both the H_3O^+ and the anion.

$$K_{eq} \times [H_2O] = K_a = \frac{[H_3O^+] \times [CH_3COO^-]}{[CH_3COOH]}$$

The acid dissociation constant (K_a) reflects the fraction of an acid in the ionized form. For this reason, dissociation constants are sometimes called ionization constants. If the value of the dissociation constant is small, then the degree of dissociation or ionization of the acid in the solution is small. 🔑 **Weak acids have small K_a values. The stronger an acid is, the larger is its K_a value.** A larger value of K_a means the dissociation or ionization of the acid is more complete. For example, nitrous acid (HNO_2) has a K_a of 4.4×10^{-4}, whereas ethanoic acid (acetic acid) has a K_a of 1.8×10^{-5}. This means that nitrous acid is more ionized in solution than ethanoic acid. Nitrous acid is a stronger acid than ethanoic acid.

Therefore, a strong acid has a higher $[H_3O^+]$ and a large dissociation constant. Conversely, a weak acid has a low $[H_3O^+]$ and a small dissociation constant. Diprotic and triprotic acids lose their hydrogens one at a time. Each ionization reaction has a separate dissociation constant. Thus, phosphoric acid (H_3PO_4) has three dissociation constants to go with its three ionizable hydrogens. Table 19.7 shows the ionization reactions and dissociation constants of some common weak acids, ranked by the value of the first dissociation constant of each acid.

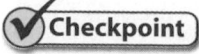 **Checkpoint** *What distinguishes a strong acid from a weak acid?*

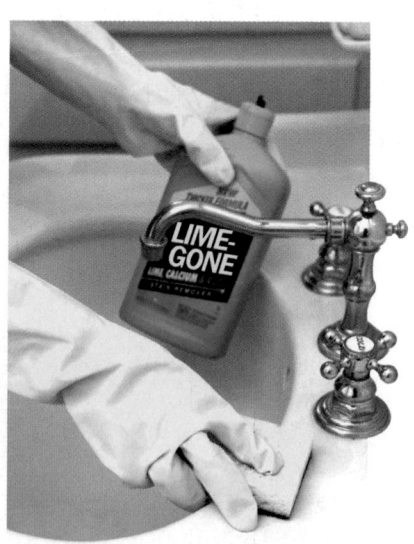

Figure 19.17 A solution of phosphoric acid is used to remove lime deposits from plumbing fixtures. Lime deposits are calcium carbonate.

Base Dissociation Constant Just as there are strong acids and weak acids, there are also strong bases and weak bases. **Strong bases** dissociate completely into metal ions and hydroxide ions in aqueous solution. Some strong bases, such as calcium hydroxide and magnesium hydroxide, are not very soluble in water. The small amounts of these bases that do dissolve dissociate completely.

Weak bases react with water to form the hydroxide ion and the conjugate acid of the base. Ammonia is an example of a weak base.

$$NH_3(aq) + H_2O(l) \rightleftharpoons NH_4^+(aq) + OH^-(aq)$$
Ammonia   Water   Ammonium   Hydroxide
                                    ion   ion

The equilibrium of this equation greatly favors the reverse reaction. Only about 1% of the ammonia is present as NH_4^+, the conjugate acid of NH_3. The concentrations of NH_4^+ and OH^- are low and equal. The equilibrium-constant expression for the reaction of ammonia with water is

$$K_{eq} = \frac{[NH_4^+] \times [OH^-]}{[NH_3] \times [H_2O]}$$

The concentration of water is constant in dilute solutions. It can be combined with K_{eq} to give a base dissociation constant (K_b).

$$K_{eq} \times [H_2O] = K_b = \frac{[NH_4^+] \times [OH^-]}{[NH_3]}$$

In general, the **base dissociation constant (K_b)** is the ratio of the concentration of the conjugate acid times the concentration of the hydroxide ion to the concentration of the conjugate base. The general form of this equation is as follows.

$$K_b = \frac{[\text{conjugate acid}] \times [OH^-]}{[\text{conjugate base}]}$$

The magnitude of K_b indicates the ability of a weak base to compete with the very strong base OH^- for hydrogen ions. Because bases such as ammonia are weak relative to the hydroxide ion, K_b for such bases is usually small. The K_b for ammonia is 1.8×10^{-5}. The smaller the value of K_b, the weaker is the base.

Figure 19.18 Window cleaners use an ammonia solution to clean glass because it is a weak base. Being a weak base also makes ammonia relatively safe to use.

 Checkpoint *Which is larger, the K_a of a weak acid or the K_a of a strong acid?*

Table 19.8

Concentration of Some Common Laboratory Acids and Bases

Acid or base	Concentration	
	Moles/liter (molarity)	Grams/liter
Concentrated hydrochloric acid	12	438
Dilute hydrochloric acid	6	219
Concentrated sulfuric acid	18	1764
Dilute sulfuric acid	6	588
Concentrated phosphoric acid	15	1470
Concentrated nitric acid	16	1008
Dilute nitric acid	6	378
Ethanoic acid, glacial	17	1020
Ethanoic acid, dilute	6	360
Dilute sodium hydroxide	6	240
Concentrated aqueous ammonia	15	255
Dilute aqueous ammonia	6	102

Concentration and Strength The words *concentrated* and *dilute* indicate how much of an acid or base is dissolved in solution. These terms refer to the number of moles of the acid or base in a given volume. The words *strong* and *weak* refer to the extent of ionization or dissociation of an acid or base. They indicate how many of the particles ionize or dissociate into ions. Hydrochloric acid (HCl)(*aq*) is a strong acid; it is completely dissociated into ions. Gastric juice in the stomach is a dilute solution of hydrochloric acid. A relatively small number of HCl molecules are present in a given volume of gastric juice, but they are all dissociated into ions. A sample of hydrochloric acid added to a large volume of water becomes more dilute, but it is still a strong acid. Vinegar is a dilute solution of a weak acid, ethanoic acid. Pure ethanoic acid (glacial acetic acid) is still a weak acid, even though it is highly concentrated. Solutions of ammonia can be dilute or concentrated, depending on the amount of ammonia dissolved in a given volume of water. In any solution of ammonia, however, whether concentrated or dilute, ammonia will be a weak base because the amount of ionization will be small. Table 19.8 lists the concentrations of acids and bases commonly found in the laboratory.

Calculating Dissociation Constants

You can calculate the acid dissociation constant (K_a) of a weak acid or the base dissociation constant (K_b) of a weak base from experimental data. **☞ To find the K_a of a weak acid or the K_b of a weak base, substitute the measured concentrations of all the substances present at equilibrium into the expression for K_a or K_b.** For a weak acid, you can determine these concentrations experimentally if you know the initial molar concentration of the acid and the pH (or $[H_3O^+]$) of the solution at equilibrium.

In general, for an acid in water you can find K_a by substituting the concentrations of the acid, [HA], the negative ion from the dissociation of the acid, [A⁻], and the hydrogen ion, [H⁺], into the equation below.

$$K_a = \frac{[\text{H}^+][\text{A}^-]}{[\text{HA}]}$$

SAMPLE PROBLEM 19.5

Calculating a Dissociation Constant

A 0.1000M solution of ethanoic acid is only partially ionized. From measurements of the pH of the solution, [H⁺] is determined to be $1.34 \times 10^{-3} M$. What is the acid dissociation constant (K_a) of ethanoic acid?

1 Analyze *List the knowns and the unknown.*

Knowns
- [ethanoic acid] = 0.1000M
- [H⁺] = $1.34 \times 10^{-3} M$
- $\text{CH}_3\text{COOH}(aq) + \text{H}_2\text{O}(l) \rightleftharpoons \text{H}_3\text{O}^+(aq) + \text{CH}_3\text{COO}^-(aq)$
- $K_a = \dfrac{[\text{H}^+] \times [\text{CH}_3\text{COO}^-]}{[\text{CH}_3\text{COOH}]}$

Unknown
- $K_a = ?$

Math   Handbook

For help with scientific notation, go to page R56.

2 Calculate *Solve for the unknown.*

Each molecule of CH_3COOH that ionizes gives an H⁺ and a CH_3COO^- ion. Therefore, at equilibrium [H⁺] = [CH_3COO^-] = $1.34 \times 10^{-3} M$. The equilibrium concentration of CH_3COOH is the initial concentration minus the concentration of the ionized acid or $(0.1000 - 0.00134)M = 0.0987M$.

Concentration	[CH₃COOH]	[H⁺]	[CH₃COO⁻]
Initial	0.1000	0	0
Change	-1.34×10^{-3}	1.34×10^{-3}	1.34×10^{-3}
Equilibrium	0.0987	1.34×10^{-3}	1.34×10^{-3}

Substitute the equilibrium values into the expression for K_a.

$$K_a = \frac{[\text{H}^+] \times [\text{CH}_3\text{COO}^-]}{[\text{CH}_3\text{COOH}]} = \frac{(1.34 \times 10^{-3}) \times (1.34 \times 10^{-3})}{0.0987}$$

$$= 1.82 \times 10^{-5}$$

3 Evaluate *Does the result make sense?*

The value of K_a is consistent with that of a weak acid.

Practice Problems

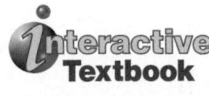
Textbook

Problem-Solving 19.23 Solve Problem 23 with the help of an interactive guided tutorial.

with ChemASAP

22. In an exactly 0.1M solution of methanoic acid, [H⁺] = $4.2 \times 10^{-3}M$. Calculate the K_a of methanoic acid.

23. In an exactly 0.2M solution of a monoprotic weak acid, [H⁺] = $9.86 \times 10^{-4}M$. What is the K_a for this acid?

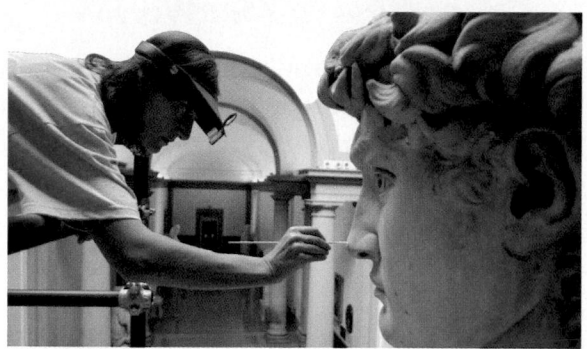
Stone Conservator

As more is learned about the damaging effects of airborne pollutants, such as acid rain, there is a growing concern to preserve historic buildings and pieces of sculpture from damage. Stone conservators work to prevent and repair the damage to stone used in buildings and sculptures.

Stone conservators must clean statues properly to remove pollution deposits. One method they use is to apply a thin, clay mudpack to the stone's surface to pull out the deposits. Lasers are also used to remove pollution from stone. When making repairs, stone conservators sometimes use surgical microscopes to examine the surfaces of statues. If the stone

was originally painted, the original paint is chemically analyzed to determine its composition. In addition, conservators research and apply methods to preserve the stone once it has been repaired. One preservation technique is to seal the stone to prevent water, which carries dissolved gases and salts, from seeping into the pores of the stone.

Stone conservators often work for museums, universities, or private companies that specialize in the cleaning and restoration of stone objects. They must have knowledge of both chemistry and art because they often work closely with both chemists and museum personnel. A stone conservator's level of education may range from a bachelor's degree to a doctorate.

Go Online
PHSchool.com

For: Careers in Chemistry
Visit: PHSchool.com
Web Code: cdb-1193

19.3 Section Assessment

24. 🔑 **Key Concept** Compare a strong acid and a weak acid in terms of the acid dissociation constant.

25. 🔑 **Key Concept** How do you determine the K_a of a weak acid or the K_b of a weak base?

26. Which acid in Table 19.6 would you expect to have the lowest ionization constant?

27. Acid HX has a very small value of K_a. How do the relative amounts of H^+ and HX compare at equilibrium?

28. Write the equations for the ionization or dissociation of the following acids and bases in water.
    a. nitric acid   b. ethanoic acid
    c. ammonia   d. magnesium hydroxide

29. Compare the terms *strong/weak* and *concentrated/dilute* as they pertain to acids and bases.

Writing ▶ **Activity**

Cause and Effect Paragraph The chief cause of tooth decay is the weak acid called lactic acid ($C_3H_6O_3$). Lactic acid is formed in the mouth by the action of specific bacteria, such as *Streptococcus mutans*, on sugars present in sticky plaque on tooth surfaces. Research current efforts to thwart tooth decay. Write a report summarizing your findings.

Textbook

Assessment 19.3 Test yourself on the concepts in Section 19.3.

with ChemASAP

19.4 Neutralization Reactions

Guide for Reading

🔑 Key Concepts
- What are the products of the reaction of an acid with a base?
- What is the endpoint of a titration?

Vocabulary
neutralization reactions

equivalence point

standard solution

titration

end point

Reading Strategy
Identifying a Sequence
A sequence is the order in which a series of events occurs. As you read about acid-base titrations, list the steps that should be used in carrying out a precise titration. Include the reactants and how they are measured, the indicator, and what to look for as the titration nears its end point.

Figure 19.19 For fish and other aquatic animals to survive, the water in which they live must be maintained at the proper pH.

Connecting to Your World

Nearly all of the adult population suffers from acid indigestion at some time. Although hydrochloric acid is always present in the stomach, an excess can cause heartburn and a feeling of nausea. A common way to relieve the pain of acid indigestion is to take antacids to neutralize the stomach acid. The active ingredient in many antacids is sodium hydrogen carbonate, aluminum hydroxide, or magnesium hydroxide. In this section, you will learn what a neutralization reaction is.

Acid-Base Reactions

If you mix a solution of a strong acid containing hydronium (hydrogen) ions with a solution of a strong base that has an equal number of hydroxide ions, a neutral solution results. The final solution has properties that are characteristic of neither an acidic nor a basic solution. Consider these examples:

$$HCl(aq) + NaOH(aq) \longrightarrow NaCl(aq) + H_2O(l)$$
$$H_2SO_4(aq) + 2KOH(aq) \longrightarrow K_2SO_4(aq) + 2H_2O(l)$$

In each example, a strong acid reacts with a strong base. If solutions of these substances are mixed in the mole ratios specified by the balanced equation, neutral solutions will result. Similar reactions of weak acids and/or weak bases do not usually produce neutral solutions. In general, however, reactions in which an acid and a base react in an aqueous solution to produce a salt and water are called **neutralization reactions.** The formation of water in a neutralization reaction is shown in Figure 19.20.

Neutralization reactions are one way to prepare pure samples of salts. You could prepare potassium chloride, for example, by mixing equal molar quantities of hydrochloric acid and potassium hydroxide. An aqueous solution of potassium chloride would result. You could heat the solution to evaporate the water, leaving the salt potassium chloride. Table 19.9 lists some common salts and their applications.

🔑 **In general, the reaction of an acid with a base produces water and one of a class of compounds called salts.** When you hear the word *salt*, you may think of the substance that flavors your French fries or scrambled eggs. Table salt (sodium chloride) is one example of a salt, but there are many more. Salts are compounds consisting of an anion from an acid and a cation from a base.

Table 19.9

	Some Salts and Their Applications	
Name	**Formula**	**Applications**
Ammonium sulfate	$(NH_4)_2SO_4$	Fertilizer
Barium sulfate	$BaSO_4$	Gastrointestinal studies; white pigment
Calcium chloride	$CaCl_2$	De-icing roadways and sidewalks
Potassium chloride	KCl	Sodium-free salt substitute
Silver bromide	AgBr	Photographic emulsions
Sodium hydrogen carbonate (baking soda)	$NaHCO_3$	Antacid
Sodium carbonate decahydrate (washing soda)	$Na_2CO_3 \cdot 10H_2O$	Glass manufacture; water softener
Sodium chloride (table salt)	NaCl	Body electrolyte; chlorine manufacture

Hydronium ion H_3O^+ + Hydroxide ion OH^- ⟶ Water H_2O + Water H_2O

Figure 19.20 In a neutralization reaction, hydronium ions (H_3O^+) combine with hydroxide ions (OH^-) to form neutral water.

The properties of acids, bases, and salts help explain many diverse phenomena. The usefulness of antacids, for example, depends on the process of acid-base neutralization. Farmers use a similar process to control the pH of soil.

Titration

Acids and bases sometimes, but not always, react in a 1:1 mole ratio.

$$HCl(aq) + NaOH(aq) \longrightarrow NaCl(aq) + H_2O(l)$$
1 mol   1 mol   1 mol   1 mol

When sulfuric acid reacts with sodium hydroxide, however, the ratio is 1:2. Two moles of the base sodium hydroxide are required to neutralize one mole of H_2SO_4.

$$H_2SO_4(aq) + 2NaOH(aq) \longrightarrow Na_2SO_4(aq) + 2H_2O(l)$$
1 mol   2 mol   1 mol   2 mol

Similarly, hydrochloric acid and calcium hydroxide react in a 2:1 ratio.

$$2HCl(aq) + Ca(OH)_2(aq) \longrightarrow CaCl_2(aq) + 2H_2O(l)$$
2 mol   1 mol   1 mol   2 mol

You will notice in the preceding examples that the number of moles of hydrogen ions provided by the acid are equivalent to the number of hydroxide ions provided by the base. When an acid and base are mixed, the **equivalence point** is when the number of moles of hydrogen ions equals the number of moles of hydroxide ions.

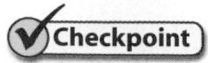 *What is the equivalence point of a reaction between an acid and a base?*

Finding the Number of Moles of an Acid in Neutralization

How many moles of sulfuric acid are required to neutralize 0.50 mol of sodium hydroxide?

1 **Analyze** *List the knowns and the unknown.*

Knowns
- mol NaOH = 0.50 mol
- $H_2SO_4(aq) + 2NaOH(aq) \longrightarrow Na_2SO_4(aq) + 2H_2O(l)$
- $\dfrac{\text{mol } H_2SO_4}{\text{mol NaOH}} = \dfrac{1}{2}$

Unknown
- moles H_2SO_4 = ? mol

2 **Calculate** *Solve for the unknown.*

The mole ratio of H_2SO_4 to NaOH is 1:2. The necessary number of moles of H_2SO_4 is calculated using this ratio.

$$0.50 \ \cancel{\text{mol NaOH}} \times \frac{1 \text{ mol } H_2SO_4}{2 \ \cancel{\text{mol NaOH}}} = 0.25 \text{ mol } H_2SO_4$$

3 **Evaluate** *Does the result make sense?*

Because the mole ratio of H_2SO_4 to NaOH is 1:2, the expected number of moles of H_2SO_4 should be half the given number of moles of NaOH. The answer should have two significant figures.

Math Handbook

For help with dimensional analysis, go to page R66.

interactive **Textbook**

Problem-Solving 19.30 Solve Problem 30 with the help of an interactive guided tutorial.

—— with **ChemASAP**

Practice Problems

30. How many moles of potassium hydroxide are needed to completely neutralize 1.56 mol of phosphoric acid?

31. How many moles of sodium hydroxide are required to neutralize 0.20 mol of nitric acid?

You can determine the concentration of acid (or base) in a solution by performing a neutralization reaction. You must use an appropriate acid-base indicator to show when neutralization has occurred. As you can see in Figure 19.21, the juice of the red cabbage is an acid-base indicator. In the laboratory, phenolphthalein is often the preferred indicator for acid-base neutralization reactions. Solutions that contain phenolphthalein turn from colorless to deep pink as the pH of the solution changes from acidic to basic. In slightly basic solutions, the indicator is very faintly pink.

Figure 19.21 Red cabbage juice is used as an acid-base indicator. As the solution changes from highly acidic to basic, the color changes from red to violet to green to yellow. **Predicting** *Would the yellow solution have a high or low pH?*

Figure 19.22 The titration of an acid with a base is shown here. ⓐ A known volume of an acid (plus a few drops of phenolphthalein indicator) in a flask is placed beneath a buret filled with a base of known concentration. ⓑ Base is slowly added from the buret to the acid while the flask is gently swirled. ⓒ A change in the color of the indicator signals that neutralization has occurred.

The steps in a neutralization reaction are as follows.

1. A measured volume of an acid solution of unknown concentration is added to a flask.
2. Several drops of the indicator are added to the solution while the flask is gently swirled.
3. Measured volumes of a base of known concentration are mixed into the acid until the indicator just barely changes color.

The process of adding a known amount of solution of known concentration to determine the concentration of another solution is called **titration.** The solution of known concentration is called the **standard solution.** Use a buret to add the standard solution. A titration is continued until the indicator shows that neutralization has just occurred. The point at which the indicator changes color is the **end point** of the titration. The titration of an acid of unknown concentration with a standard base is shown in Figure 19.22. You can use a similar procedure to find the concentration of a base using a standard acid.

Figure 19.23 shows how the pH of a solution changes during the titration of a strong acid (HCl) with a strong base (NaOH). The pH of the initial acid solution is low. As the base is added, the pH increases because some of the acid is neutralized. As the titration approaches the point of neutralization, at a pH of 7, the pH increases dramatically as hydrogen ions are used up. Once past the point of neutralization, additional base produces a further increase of pH. 🔑 **The point of neutralization is the end point of the titration.** At this point, the contents of the beaker consist of only H_2O and NaCl, which is the salt derived from the strong acid HCl and the strong base NaOH, plus a trace of indicator.

ⓘ**nteractive**
Textbook

Simulation 26 Simulate the titration of several acids and bases and observe patterns in the pH at equivalence.

— with **ChemASAP**

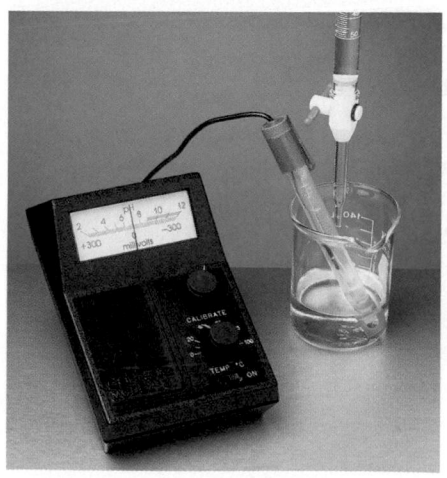

Titration of a Strong Acid with a Strong Base

pH vs. 0.10M NaOH added (mL)

Equivalence point

Figure 19.23 In this titration of a strong acid with a strong base, 0.10M NaOH is slowly added from a buret to 50.0 mL of 0.10M HCl in the beaker. The equivalence point, the midpoint on the vertical portion of the pH titration curve, occurs at 50.0 mL of NaOH added. **Interpreting Diagrams** *What is true concerning [H$^+$] and [OH$^-$] at the equivalence point?*

Determining the Concentration of an Acid by Titration

A 25-mL solution of H_2SO_4 is completely neutralized by 18 mL of 1.0M NaOH. What is the concentration of the H_2SO_4 solution?

1 **Analyze** *List the knowns and the unknown.*

Knowns
- molarity base = 1.0M NaOH
- volume base = 18 mL = 0.018 L
- volume acid = 25 mL = 0.025 L
- $H_2SO_4(aq) + 2NaOH(aq) \longrightarrow Na_2SO_4(aq) + 2H_2O(l)$

Unknown
- molarity acid = ?M H_2SO_4

Use the molarity to convert the volume of base to moles of base. Use the mole ratio to find the number of moles of H_2SO_4. Calculate the molarity by dividing the number of moles of H_2SO_4 by the number of liters of H_2SO_4.

The conversion steps are as follows:

$$\text{L NaOH} \longrightarrow \text{mol NaOH} \longrightarrow \text{mol } H_2SO_4 \longrightarrow M\, H_2SO_4$$

Math ▶ **Handbook**

For help with dimensional analysis, go to page R66.

2 **Calculate** *Solve for the unknown.*

$$0.018 \text{ L NaOH} \times \frac{1.0 \text{ mol NaOH}}{1 \text{ L NaOH}} \times \frac{1 \text{ mol } H_2SO_4}{2 \text{ mol NaOH}} = 0.0090 \text{ mol } H_2SO_4$$

$$\text{molarity} = \frac{\text{moles}}{\text{liters}} = \frac{0.0090 \text{ mol}}{0.025 \text{ L}} = 0.36 \ M$$

The $[H_2SO_4]$ is 0.36M.

3 **Evaluate** *Does the result make sense?*

Because the volume of acid was greater than the volume of base, the concentration is less than 1.0M. The answer has two significant figures.

Interactive Textbook

Problem-Solving 19.33
Solve Problem 33 with the help of an interactive guided tutorial.

— with **ChemASAP**

Practice Problems

32. How many milliliters of 0.45M HCl will neutralize 25.0 mL of 1.00M KOH?

33. What is the molarity of H_3PO_4 if 15.0 mL is completely neutralized by 38.5 mL of 0.150M NaOH?

19.4 Section Assessment

34. 🔑 **Key Concept** What are the products of a reaction between an acid and a base?

35. 🔑 **Key Concept** What occurs at the endpoint of a titration?

36. How many moles of HCl are required to neutralize aqueous solutions of these bases?
  a. 2 mol NH_3 **b.** 0.1 mol $Ca(OH)_2$

37. Write complete balanced equations for the following acid-base reactions?
  a. $H_2SO_4(aq) + KOH(aq) \longrightarrow$
  b. $H_3PO_4(aq) + Ca(OH)_2(aq) \longrightarrow$
  c. $HNO_3(aq) + Mg(OH)_2(aq) \longrightarrow$

Connecting ▶ **Concepts**

Types of Reactions Reread the information on types of chemical reactions in Section 11.2. Which type of reaction are all acid-base neutralizations? Explain your answer.

Interactive Textbook

Assessment 19.4 Test yourself on the concepts in Section 19.4.

— with **ChemASAP**

Small-Scale LAB

Ionization Constants of Weak Acids

Purpose
To measure ionization constants of weak acids such as bromocresol green (BCG).

Materials
- ruler
- reaction surface
- pH buffer and BCG

Procedure

1. On separate sheets of paper, draw two grids similar to the one below. Make each square 2 cm on each side.
2. Place a reaction surface over one of the grids and place one drop of BCG in each square.
3. Place one drop of pH buffer in each square corresponding to its pH value.
4. Use the second grid as a data table to record your observations for each solution.

pH

1	2	3
4	5	6
7	8	9
10	11	12

Analyze
Using your experimental data, record the answers to the following questions below your data table.

1. What is the color of the lowest-pH solutions?
2. What is the color of the highest-pH solutions?
3. At which pH does the bromcresol green change from one color to the other? At which pH does an intermediate color exist?

An acid-base indicator is usually a weak acid with a characteristic color. Because bromcresol green is an acid, it is convenient to represent its rather complex formula as HBCG. HBCG ionizes in water according to the following equation.

$$HBCG + H_2O = BCG^- + H_3O^+$$
(yellow) (blue)

The K_a expression is

$$K_a = \frac{[BCG^-] \times [H_3O^+]}{[HBCG]}$$

When $[BCG^-] = [HBCG]$, $K_a = [H_3O^+]$.

4. What color is the conjugate acid of BCG^-?
5. What color is the conjugate base of HBCG?
6. What color is an equal mixture of the conjugate acid and conjugate base of bromcresol green? At what pH does this equal mixture occur?

You're The Chemist
The following small-scale activities allow you to develop your own procedures and analyze the results.

1. **Design It!** Design and carry out an experiment to measure the K_a of several more acid-base indicators. Record the colors of the conjugate acids (low pH) and the conjugate bases (high pH). Determine the K_a for each acid.
2. **Analyze It!** Explain in your own words how to measure the K_a of a colored acid-base indicator. Explain what you would do and how you would interpret your results.

19.5 Salts in Solution

Guide for Reading

 Key Concepts
- When is the solution of a salt acidic or basic?
- What are the components of a buffer?

Vocabulary

salt hydrolysis

buffer

buffer capacity

Reading Strategy

Predicting Based on what you have learned about acid-base neutralization reaction, predict the possible pH range of solutions of salts of strong acids and weak bases. Account for this pH range. Do the same for salts of weak acids and strong bases.

Connecting to Your World

The internal pH of most living cells is close to 7. Because the chemical processes of the cell are very sensitive to pH levels, even a slight change in pH can be harmful. Human blood, for example, normally maintains a pH very close to 7.4. A person cannot survive for more than a few minutes if the blood pH drops to 6.8 or rises to 7.8. In this section, you will learn about chemical processes that ensure that blood is kept near 7.4.

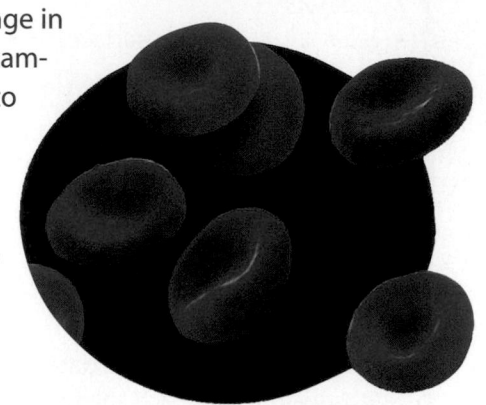

Salt Hydrolysis

A salt consists of an anion from an acid and a cation from a base. It forms as a result of a neutralization reaction. Although solutions of many salts are neutral, some are acidic and others are basic. Solutions of sodium chloride and of potassium sulfate are neutral. A solution of ammonium chloride is acidic. A solution of sodium ethanoate (sodium acetate) is basic. Figure 19.24 shows a titration curve obtained by adding a solution of sodium hydroxide, a strong base, to a solution of ethanoic (acetic) acid, a weak acid. An aqueous solution of sodium ethanoate exists at the equivalence point.

$$CH_3COOH(aq) + NaOH(aq) \longrightarrow CH_3COONa(aq) + H_2O(l)$$

Ethanoic acid $\qquad$ Sodium hydroxide $\qquad$ Sodium ethanoate $\qquad$ Water

The pH at the equivalence point is 8.7—basic.

Figure 19.24 The titration curve for a weak acid and a strong base is compared with the titration curve for a strong acid and a strong base.

INTERPRETING GRAPHS

a. Identify What is the pH of the equivalence point of each titration?

b. Describe Why is the same amount of base used in each titration?

c. Apply Concepts Explain why the equivalence points of the two titrations are different.

Titrations of Weak Acid–Strong Base and Strong Acid–Strong Base

(a) — Weak acid–strong base

(b) — Strong acid–strong base

For a strong acid–strong base titration, the pH at the equivalence point is 7, or neutral. This difference exists because some salts promote hydrolysis. In **salt hydrolysis,** the cations or anions of a dissociated salt remove hydrogen ions from or donate hydrogen ions to water. Depending on the direction of the hydrogen-ion transfer, solutions containing hydrolyzing salts may be either acidic or basic. Hydrolyzing salts are usually derived from a strong acid and a weak base, or from a weak acid and a strong base. Sodium carbonate, washing soda, is the salt of the strong base sodium hydroxide and carbonic acid, a weak acid. Ammonium nitrate, used in fertilizers, is the salt of the weak base ammonia and nitric acid, a strong acid. Soap is the salt of a strong base, usually sodium hydroxide, and stearic acid, a weak acid present in fats. ◗━ **In general, salts that produce acidic solutions contain positive ions that release protons to water. Salts that produce basic solutions contain negative ions that attract protons from water.**

Sodium ethanoate (CH_3COONa) is the salt of a weak acid (ethanoic acid, CH_3COOH) and a strong base (sodium hydroxide, $NaOH$). In solution, the salt is completely ionized.

$$CH_3COONa(aq) \longrightarrow CH_3COO^-(aq) + Na^+(aq)$$

Sodium ethanoate   Ethanoate ion   Sodium ion

The ethanoate ion is a Brønsted-Lowry base, which means it is a hydrogen-ion acceptor. It establishes an equilibrium with water, forming electrically neutral ethanoic acid and negative hydroxide ions.

$$CH_3COO^-(aq) + H_2O(l) \rightleftharpoons CH_3COOH(aq) + OH^-(aq)$$

(hydrogen-ion   (hydrogen-ion   (makes the
acceptor, Brønsted-   donor, Brønsted-   solution
Lowry base)   Lowry acid)   basic)

This process is called hydrolysis because it splits a hydrogen ion off a water molecule. The resulting solution contains a hydroxide-ion concentration greater than the hydrogen-ion concentration. Thus the solution is basic.

Ammonium chloride (NH_4Cl) is the salt of a strong acid (hydrochloric acid, HCl) and a weak base (ammonia, NH_3). It is completely ionized in solution.

$$NH_4Cl(aq) \longrightarrow NH_4^+(aq) + Cl^-(aq)$$

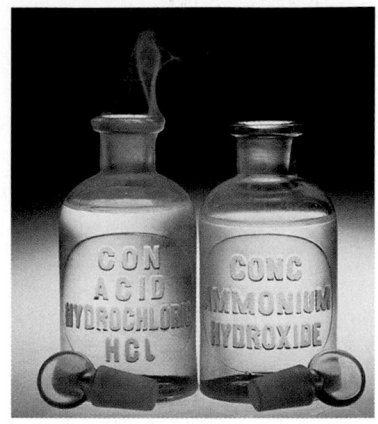

Figure 19.25 Vapors of the strong acid $HCl(aq)$ and the weak base $NH_3(aq)$ combine to form the acidic white salt ammonium chloride (NH_4Cl).

Figure 19.26 A few drops of universal indicator solution have been added to each of these 0.10M aqueous salt solutions. The color of the indicator shows the following. ⓐ Ammonium chloride (NH_4Cl), is acidic (pH about 5.3). ⓑ Sodium chloride (NaCl) is neutral (pH 7). ⓒ Sodium ethanoate (CH_3COONa) is basic (pH about 8.7).

The ammonium ion (NH_4^+) is a strong enough acid to donate a hydrogen ion to a water molecule, although the equilibrium is strongly to the left.

$$NH_4^+\,(aq) \quad + \quad H_2O(l) \rightleftharpoons NH_3(aq) + H_3O^+(aq)$$

| (hydrogen-ion donor, Brønsted-Lowry acid) | (hydrogen-ion acceptor, Brønsted-Lowry base) | (makes the solution acidic) |

This process is also called hydrolysis. It results in the formation of unionized ammonia and hydronium (hydrogen) ions. The $[H_3O^+]$ is greater than the $[OH^-]$. Thus, a solution of ammonium chloride is acidic. To determine if a salt solution is acidic or basic, remember the following rules:

Strong acid + **Strong base** $\longrightarrow$ Neutral solution

Strong acid + **Weak base** $\longrightarrow$ **Acidic** solution

Weak acid + **Strong base** $\longrightarrow$ **Basic** solution

Buffers

The addition of 10 mL of 0.10M sodium hydroxide to 1 L of pure water increases the pH by 4.0 pH units (from 7.0 to 11.0). A solution containing 0.20 mol/L each of ethanoic acid and sodium ethanoate has a pH of 4.76. When moderate amounts of either acid or base are added to this solution, however, the pH changes little. The addition of 10 mL of 0.10M sodium hydroxide to 1 L of this solution, for example, increases the pH by only 0.01 pH unit, from 4.76 to 4.77. Figure 19.27 shows what happens when 1.0 mL of 0.01M HCl solution is added to an unbuffered solution.

The solution of ethanoic acid and sodium ethanoate is an example of a typical buffer. A **buffer** is a solution in which the pH remains relatively constant when small amounts of acid or base are added. ⟳ **A buffer is a solution of a weak acid and one of its salts, or a solution of a weak base and one of its salts.**

A buffer solution is better able to resist drastic changes in pH than is pure water. Figure 19.28 illustrates how a buffer works. Ethanoic acid (CH_3COOH) and its anion (CH_3COO^-) act as reservoirs of neutralizing power. They react with any hydroxide ions or hydrogen ions added to the solution. For example, consider the buffer solution in which the sodium ethanoate (CH_3COONa) is completely ionized.

$$CH_3COONa(aq) \longrightarrow CH_3COO^-(aq) + Na^+(aq)$$

| Sodium ethanoate | Ethanoate ion | Sodium ion |

Figure 19.27 A buffer is a solution in which the pH remains relatively constant. ⓐ The indicator shows that the buffered solution on the left and the unbuffered solution on the right are basic—pH about 8. ⓑ After the addition of 1.0 mL of 0.01M HCl solution, the pH of the buffered solution shows no visible change. The pH of the unbuffered solution, however, is now about 3—the solution is acidic.

buffered   unbuffered

buffered   unbuffered

$$CH_3COO^- \quad CH_3COOH \xleftarrow{\ H^+\ } CH_3COO^- \quad CH_3COOH \xrightarrow{\ OH^-\ } CH_3COO^- \quad CH_3COOH$$

$$\boxed{CH_3COOH \longleftarrow H^+ + CH_3COO^-} \qquad \boxed{CH_3COOH + OH^- \longrightarrow CH_3COO^- + H_2O}$$

When an acid is added to the solution, the ethanoate ions (CH_3COO^-) act as a hydrogen-ion "sponge." This creates ethanoic acid, which does not ionize extensively in water; thus the pH does not change appreciably.

$$CH_3COO^-(aq) + H^+(aq) \rightleftharpoons CH_3COOH(aq)$$
$$\text{Ethanoate} \qquad \text{Hydrogen} \qquad \text{Ethanoic acid}$$
$$\text{ion} \qquad\qquad \text{ion}$$

A base is a source of hydroxide ions. When a base is added to the solution, the ethanoic acid and the hydroxide ions react to produce water and the ethanoate ion.

$$CH_3COOH(aq) + OH^-(aq) \rightleftharpoons CH_3COO^-(aq) + H_2O(l)$$
$$\text{Ethanoic acid} \qquad \text{Hydroxide} \qquad \text{Ethanoate} \qquad \text{Water}$$
$$\qquad\qquad \text{ion} \qquad\qquad \text{ion}$$

The ethanoate ion is not a strong enough base to accept hydrogen ions from water extensively. Again, the pH does not change very much.

An ethanoate buffer solution cannot control the pH when too much acid is added, because no more ethanoate ions are present to accept hydrogen ions. The ethanoate buffer also becomes ineffective when too much base is added. Do you know why this is so? When too much base is added, no more ethanoic acid molecules are present to donate hydrogen ions. When too much acid or base is added, the buffer capacity of a solution is exceeded. The **buffer capacity** is the amount of acid or base that can be added to a buffer solution before a significant change in pH occurs.

Two buffer systems are crucial in maintaining human blood pH within a very narrow range (pH 7.35–7.45). One is the carbonic acid–hydrogen carbonate buffer system. The other is the dihydrogen phosphate–monohydrogen phosphate buffer system. Table 19.10 lists several important buffer systems.

Figure 19.28 The buffer described here is made of ethanoic acid (CH_3COOH) and sodium ethanoate, which is the source of ethanoate ions (CH_3COO^-). To begin, the concentrations of ethanoic acid and ethanoate ions are equal. When either H^+ or OH^- is added, the buffer produces additional ethanoic acid or ethanoate ions. In both situations, the ratio of [CH_3COOH] to [CH_3COO^-] and consequently, the pH, changes very little.

interactive **Textbook**

Animation 26 Discover the chemistry behind buffer action.

— with **ChemASAP**

Table 19.10

Important Buffer Systems		
Buffer name	**Buffer species**	**Buffer pH (components 0.1M)**
Ethanoic acid–ethanoate ion	CH_3COOH/CH_3COO^-	4.76
Dihydrogen phosphate ion–hydrogenphosphate ion	$H_2PO_4^-/HPO_4^{2-}$	7.20
Carbonic acid–hydrogen carbonate ion (solution saturated with CO_2)	H_2CO_3/HCO_3^-	6.46
Ammonium ion–ammonia	NH_4^+/NH_3	9.25

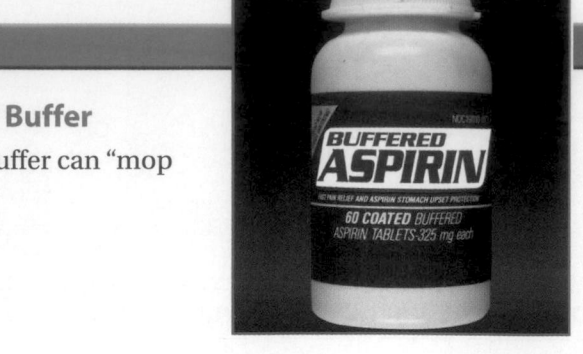

CONCEPTUAL PROBLEM 19.2

Using Equations to Illustrate the Action of a Buffer

Show how the carbonic acid–hydrogen carbonate buffer can "mop up" added hydrogen ions and hydroxide ions.

1 Analyze *Identify the relevant concepts.*

The definition of a buffer, in terms of its ability to act as a reservoir of neutralizing power, should be illustrated. One component in a buffer can react with H^+; this component is a proton acceptor. Another component can react with OH^-; this component is a proton donor.

2 Solve *Apply concepts to this situation.*

The carbonic acid–hydrogen carbonate buffer is a solution of carbonic acid (H_2CO_3) and hydrogen carbonate ions (HCO_3^-). When a base is added to this buffer, it reacts with H_2CO_3 (a proton donor) to produce neutral water. The pH changes very little.

$$H_2CO_3(aq) + (OH^-)(aq) \rightleftharpoons HCO_3^-(aq) + H_2O(l)$$

| Carbonic acid | Hydroxide ion | Hydrogen carbonate ion | Water |

When an acid is added to the buffer, it reacts with HCO_3^- (a proton acceptor) to produce unionized carbonic acid. Again the pH changes very little.

$$HCO_3^-(aq) + H^+(aq) \rightleftharpoons H_2CO_3(aq)$$

| Hydrogen carbonate ion | Hydrogen ion | Carbonic acid |

Practice Problems

38. Write reactions to show what happens when the following occur.
 a. Acid is added to a solution of HPO_4^{2-}.
 b. Base is added to a solution of $H_2PO_4^-$.

39. Write an equation that shows what happens when acid is added to the ethanoic acid–ethanoate buffer.

Interactive Textbook

Problem-Solving 19.39 Solve Problem 39 with the help of an interactive guided tutorial.

— with **ChemASAP**

19.5 Section Assessment

40. 🔑 **Key Concept** What type of salt produces an acidic solution? A basic solution?

41. 🔑 **Key Concept** What substances are combined to make a buffer?

42. Which of these salts would form an acidic aqueous solution?
 a. $KC_2H_3O_2$ **b.** $LiCl$ **c.** $NaHCO_3$ **d.** $(NH_4)_2SO_4$

43. Using equations, show what happens when acid is added to an ammonium ion–ammonia buffer. What happens when base is added?

Writing ▶ **Activity**

Explanatory Paragraph To maintain a proper pH, your blood contains buffers. Research the buffer systems in your blood and write a paragraph on how one of them works.

Interactive Textbook

Assessment 19.5 Test yourself on the concepts in Section 19.5.

— with **ChemASAP**

622 Chapter 19

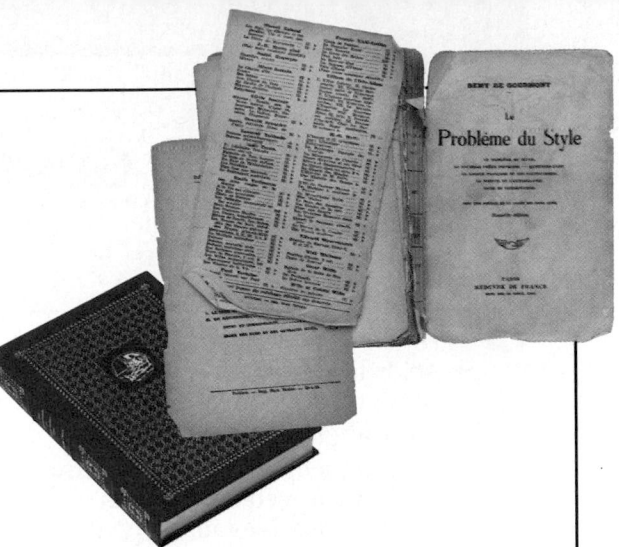

Rescuing Crumbling Books

Millions of books printed since the mid-nineteenth century slowly decay as they sit on library shelves. The cause is the acidity of the paper, which comes from alum (aluminum sulfate), used to prevent inks from soaking into paper. Libraries around the world are working with chemists to find ways to remove the acid from these books. One such method involves placing a book in a vacuum chamber, removing all the moisture from the pages, and applying a gas to neutralize the acid. **Inferring** *Why might a library decide to use the method shown below?*

Deterioration The pages of this book are so fragile that they crumble at a touch. Deacidifying the paper will extend the life of the book.

Deacidification In the tank system above, many books are treated at the same time. The machine moves the books gently in deacidification fluid, bathing each page. After the fluid is pumped away, a vacuum dries the treated books.

Restoration King James of England issued this charter to establish a colony in Virginia and find a water passage to the Pacific Ocean. It was severely damaged from prolonged exposure to moisture and a poor storage environment, after which chemists washed and deacidified each page.

Key Concepts

🔑 19.1 Acid-Base Theories

- Acids taste sour, bases taste bitter and feel slippery. Both are electrolytes and cause indicators to change colors.
- In an aqueous solution, an Arrhenius acid yields hydrogen ions and an Arrhenius base yields hydroxide ions.
- A Brønsted-Lowry acid is a hydrogen-ion donor; a Brønsted-Lowry base is a hydrogen-ion acceptor.
- A Lewis acid is an electron-pair acceptor; a Lewis base is an electron-pair donor.

🔑 19.2 Hydrogen Ions and Acidity

- For an aqueous solution, the product of $[H^+]$ and $[OH^-]$ equals 1×10^{-14}.
- On the pH scale, 0 is strongly acidic, 7 is neutral, and 14 is strongly basic.
- The acid and base form of an indicator have different colors in solution.

🔑 19.3 Strengths of Acids and Bases

- The stronger an acid is, the larger its K_a value.
- To find K_a of a weak acid or K_b of a weak base, substitute the concentrations of the substances into the equilibrium expression.

🔑 19.4 Neutralization Reactions

- An acid and a base react to produce a salt and water.
- The point of neutralization is the endpoint of a titration.

🔑 19.5 Salts in Solution

- Salts that produce acidic solutions contain positive ions that release protons to water; salts that produce basic solutions have negative ions that attract protons from water.
- A buffer is a solution of a weak acid or weak base and one of its salts.

Vocabulary

- acid dissociation constant (K_a) (p. 607)
- acidic solution (p. 595)
- alkaline solution (p. 595)
- amphoteric (p. 592)
- base dissociation constant (K_b) (p. 608)
- basic solution (p. 595)
- buffers (p. 620)
- buffer capacity (p. 621)
- conjugate acid (p. 591)
- conjugate acid-base pair (p. 591)
- conjugate base (p. 591)
- diprotic acid (p. 588)
- end point (p. 615)
- equivalence point (p. 613)
- hydronium ion (H_3O^+) (p. 591)
- ion-product constant for water (K_w) (p. 595)
- Lewis acid (p. 592)
- Lewis base (p. 592)
- monoprotic acids (p. 588)
- neutral solution (p. 595)
- neutralization reaction (p. 612)
- pH (p. 596)
- salt hydrolysis (p. 619)
- self-ionization (p. 594)
- standard solution (p. 615)
- strong acid (p. 605)
- strong base (p. 608)
- titration (p. 615)
- triprotic acid (p. 588)
- weak acid (p. 605)
- weak base (p. 608)

Key Equations

- $K_w = [H^+] \times [OH^-] = 1.0 \times 10^{-14}$
- $pH = -\log[H^+]$
- $pOH = -\log[OH^-]$
- $K_a = \dfrac{[H^+][A^-]}{[HA]}$

Organizing Information

Use these terms to construct a concept map that organizes the major ideas of this chapter.

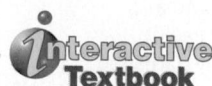

Concept Map 19 Create your Concept Map using the computer.

—with **ChemASAP**

19.1 Acid-Base Theories

44. How did Arrhenius describe acids and bases?

45. Classify each as an Arrhenius acid or an Arrhenius base.
   a. $Ca(OH)_2$ **b.** HNO_3 **c.** KOH
   d. C_2H_5COOH **e.** HBr **f.** H_2SO_4

46. Write the reaction for the dissociation of each compound in water.
   a. potassium hydroxide
   b. magnesium hydroxide

47. Write balanced equations for the reaction of each metal with water to form a base and hydrogen gas.
   a. lithium   **b.** barium

48. Identify each reactant in the following equations as a hydrogen-ion donor (acid) or a hydrogen-ion acceptor (base).
   a. $HNO_3 + H_2O \rightleftharpoons H_3O^+ + NO_3^-$
   b. $CH_3COOH + H_2O \rightleftharpoons H_3O^+ + CH_3COO^-$
   c. $NH_3 + H_2O \rightleftharpoons NH_4^+ + OH^-$
   d. $H_2O + CH_3COO^- \rightleftharpoons CH_3COOH + OH^-$

49. Label the conjugate acid–base pairs in each equation in Problem 48.

50. What is a Lewis acid? A Lewis base? In what sense is the Lewis theory more general than the Arrhenius and Brønsted-Lowry theories?

51. Write equations showing that the hydrogen phosphate ion (HPO_4^{2-}) is amphoteric.

52. Write the formula and name of the conjugate acid of each Brønsted-Lowry base.
   a. ClO_2^- **b.** $H_2PO_4^-$ **c.** H_2O **d.** NH_3

53. Use the Brønsted-Lowry and Lewis definitions of acids and bases to identify each reactant as an acid or a base.
   a. $KOH + HBr \rightleftharpoons KBr + H_2O$
   b. $HCl + H_2O \rightleftharpoons Cl^- + H_3O^-$

54. Write the formula for the conjugate base of each acid.
   a. H_2SO_4 **b.** HCN **c.** H_2O **d.** NH_4^+

55. Arrhenius, Brønsted-Lowry, and Lewis all developed theories to explain acids and bases.
   a. Which theory is easiest for you to understand?
   b. How can all three theories be accepted by chemists?

19.2 Hydrogen Ions and Acidity

56. Write an equation showing how water forms a positive ion and a negative ion.

57. What are the concentrations of H^+ and OH^- in pure water at 25°C?

58. How is the pH of a solution calculated?

59. Why is the pH of pure water at 25°C equal to 7.00?

60. Calculate the pH for the following solutions and indicate whether each solution is acidic or basic.
   a. $[H^+] = 1 \times 10^{-2}M$
   b. $[OH^-] = 1 \times 10^{-2}M$
   c. $[OH^-] = 1 \times 10^{-8}M$

61. What are the hydroxide-ion concentrations for solutions with the following pH values?
   a. 4.00   **b.** 8.00   **c.** 12.00

62. Calculate the pH or $[H^+]$ for each solution.
   a. $[H^+] = 2.4 \times 10^{-6}M$ **b.** pH = 13.20

63. Arrange these solutions in order of decreasing pH.
   a. $0.1M$ NaOH   **b.** $0.1M$ HCl   **c.** water

64. Prove the relationship pH + pOH = 14. (*Hint:* Use the expression for K_w.)

65. In the following graph, which quantity might correspond to the y-axis: concentration of H^+ or pH? Explain your answer.

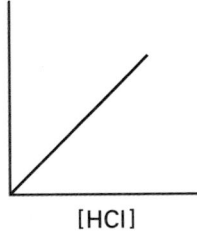

[HCl]

66. The following equilibria are involved in the solubility of carbon dioxide in water.

$$CO_2(g) \rightleftharpoons CO_2(aq)$$
$$CO_2(aq) + H_2O(l) \rightleftharpoons H_2CO_3(aq)$$
$$H_2CO_3(aq) \rightleftharpoons H^-(aq) + HCO_3^{2-}(aq)$$
$$HCO_3^{2-}(aq) \rightleftharpoons H^-(aq) + CO_3^{2-}(aq)$$

If sea water is slightly alkaline, would you expect the concentration of dissolved CO_2 to be higher or lower than in pure water? Explain.

67. Calculate the pH of a $0.010M$ solution of sodium cyanide (NaCN). The K_b of CN^- is 2.1×10^{-5}.

68. Calculate the $[OH^-]$ or pH of each solution.
    a. pH = 4.60
    b. pH = 9.30
    c. $[OH^-] = 1.8 \times 10^{-2} M$
    d. $[OH^-] = 7.3 \times 10^{-9} M$

19.3 Strengths of Acids and Bases

69. Identify each compound as a strong or weak acid or base.
    a. NaOH   b. HCl   c. NH_3 d. H_2SO_4

70. "Strong" is a term that shows that many ions form in solution. Why are $Mg(OH)_2$ and $Ca(OH)_2$ considered to be strong bases even though their saturated solutions are only mildly basic?

71. Write the expression for K_a for each acid. Assume only one hydrogen is ionized.
    a. HF   b. H_2CO_3

72. Is it possible to have a concentrated weak acid? Explain.

73. The pH of a $0.50 M \, HNO_2$ solution is 1.83. What is the K_a of this acid?

74. Criticize the accuracy of each of these statements.
    a. Indicators such as methyl red provide accurate and precise measurements of pH.
    b. According to the Arrhenius definition of acids and bases, ammonia qualifies as a base.
    c. The strength of an acid or base changes as its concentration changes.

75. The K_w of water varies with temperature, as indicated in the table below.

Temperature (°C)	K_w	pH
0	1.137×10^{-15}	a.
10	2.917×10^{-15}	b.
20	6.807×10^{-15}	c.
30	1.469×10^{-14}	d.
40	2.917×10^{-14}	e.
50	5.470×10^{-14}	f.

   a. Find the pH of water for each temperature in the table. Use these data to prepare a graph of pH versus temperature.
   b. Using the graph, estimate the pH of water at 5°C.
   c. At what temperature is the pH of water approximately 6.85?

19.4 Neutralization Reactions

76. Write a general word equation for a neutralization reaction.

77. Identify the products and write balanced equations for each neutralization reaction.
    a. $HNO_3(aq) + KOH(aq) \longrightarrow$
    b. $HCl(aq) + Ca(OH)_2(aq) \longrightarrow$
    c. $H_2SO_4(aq) + NaOH(aq) \longrightarrow$

78. Explain the role of an indicator in a titration.

79. What is the molarity of sodium hydroxide if 20.0 mL of the solution is neutralized by each of the following $1.00 M$ solutions?
    a. 28.0 mL of HCl   b. 17.4 mL of H_3PO_4

80. Write an equation for the reaction of each antacid with hydrochloric acid.
    a. magnesium hydroxide
    b. calcium carbonate
    c. aluminum hydroxide

81. The following data were collected from a titration of 50.00 mL of ethanoic acid (CH_3COOH) of unknown concentration with $0.100 M$ NaOH. Plot these data (pH on the y-axis) to obtain a titration curve.

Volume of NaOH (mL)	pH	Volume of NaOH (mL)	pH
0		50.00	8.73
10.00	4.15	50.01	8.89
25.00	4.76	51.00	11.00
40.00	5.36	60.00	11.96
49.00	6.45	75.00	12.30
49.99	8.55	100.00	12.52

   a. What is the pH at the end of this titration?
   b. Use Figure 19.12 on page 602 to identify one or more indicators that could be used to determine the end point in this titration.

Use the following graph and information to answer Questions 82–87.

The graph shows the number of millimoles (mmol) of water formed by the dropwise addition of an HCl solution to a sample of NaOH solution of unknown concentration.

Millimoles of Water vs. Volume of 1.0*M* HCl

82. Write a balanced chemical equation for the reaction.

83. At what point on the graph is the reaction complete? How do you know?

84. Approximately how many milliliters of HCl were used to complete the reaction?

85. If the acid is 1.0*M*, how many moles of HCl are contained in this volume of acid?

86. According to the equation, how many moles of NaOH are used up when the reaction is complete?

87. If 25.0 mL of NaOH solution was used, what is the concentration of the base?

88. Suppose you slowly add 0.1*M* NaOH to 50.0 mL of 0.1*M* HCl. What volume of NaOH must be added for the resulting solution to become neutral? Explain your reasoning.

Use the following information to answer Questions 89–91.

An 80.0-mL sample of H_2SO_4 solution reacts completely with 0.424 g Na_2CO_3 according to the following chemical equation.

$$H_2SO_4(aq) + Na_2CO_3(aq) \longrightarrow$$
$$H_2O(l) + CO_2(g) + Na_2SO_4(aq)$$

89. How many moles of Na_2CO_3 react?

90. How many moles of H_2SO_4 are used in the reaction?

91. What is the molarity of the H_2SO_4 solution?

19.5 Salts in Solution

92. What kinds of salts hydrolyze water? Explain why solutions of salts that hydrolyze water do not have a pH of 7.

93. Write an equation showing the reaction between water and sodium hydrogen carbonate. Use this equation to explain why an aqueous solution of sodium hydrogen carbonate is basic.

94. Predict whether an aqueous solution of each salt will be acidic, basic, or neutral.
   a. $NaHCO_3$ **b.** NH_4NO_3 **c.** KCl
   d. Na_2CO_3 **e.** Na_2SO_4 **f.** NH_4Cl

95. Use the phosphate buffer ($H_2PO_4^-/HPO_4^{2-}$) to illustrate how a buffer system works. Show, by means of equations, how the pH of a solution can be kept almost constant when small amounts of acid or base are added.

96. How would the equilibrium between hypochlorous acid and the hypochlorite ion be affected by the addition of each of the following compounds?

$$HOCl(aq) + OH^-(aq) \rightleftharpoons OCl^-(aq) + H_2O(l)$$

   a. HCl   **b.** NaOH

97. Write an equation to show that an aqueous solution of sodium ethanoate will be basic.

98. Chlorine bleach is a solution of sodium hypochlorite and is considered a hazardous household solution. The hazards arise from the solution's basicity and from the active bleaching ingredient, ClO^-. What is the $[OH^-]$ in an aqueous solution that is 5% NaClO by mass? What is the pH of the solution? (The density of the solution is 1.0 g/mL.)

Test-Taking Tip

Eliminate Wrong Answers If you don't know which response is correct, start by eliminating those you know are wrong. If you can rule out some choices, you'll have fewer left to consider and you'll increase your chances of choosing the correct answer.

Regents Practice Exam

Part A

For each statement or question write the number of the word or expression that, of those given, best completes the statement or answers the question.

1. What are the products of a neutralization reaction?
   (1) a salt and an acid
   (2) a base and water
   (3) an acid and a base
   (4) a salt and water

2. What does an Arrhenius acid produce when it is placed in water?
   (1) hydrogen ions   (3) a salt
   (2) hydroxide ions   (4) a proton acceptor

3. Which of the following choices is *not* an electrolyte?
   (1) an Arrhenius acid
   (2) an Arrhenius base
   (3) water
   (4) a salt

4. The main purpose of a titration is to determine
   (1) the volume of a solution of known concentration
   (2) the volume of a solution of unknown concentration
   (3) the concentration of a solution of known volume
   (4) the concentration of a solution of unknown volume

Part B-1

For each statement or question write the number of the word or expression that, of those given, best completes the statement or answers the question.

5. Which of the following compounds is *not* an electrolyte?
   (1) $NaCl(l)$ (3) $SiO_2(s)$
   (2) $KNO_2(aq)$ (4) $NaCl(aq)$

6. The pH of a sample of orange juice is 3.5. A sample of tomato juice has a pH of 4.5. Compared to the $[H^+]$ of orange juice, the $[H^+]$ of tomato juice is
   (1) 1.0 times higher   (3) 10 times higher
   (2) 10 times lower   (4) 1.0 times lower

7. How many moles of NaOH are required to neutralize 2.4 mol H_2SO_4?
   (1) 1.2 mol   (3) 3.6 mol
   (2) 2.4 mol   (4) 4.8 mol

8. Calculate the molarity of an HCl solution if 25.0 mL of the solution is neutralized by 15.5 mL of $0.800M$ NaOH.
   (1) $0.248M$ (3) $1.29M$
   (2) $0.496M$ (4) $0.645M$

The numbered choices below refer to Questions 9–11. A numbered choice may be used once, more than once, or not at all.

   (1) PQ   (2) P_2Q_3 (3) PQ_3 (4) P_3Q

Which of the choices is the general formula for the salt formed in each of the following neutralization reaction? P is a positive ion; Q is a negative ion.

9. $H_3PO_4 + NaOH \longrightarrow$

10. $H_2SO_4 + Mg(OH)_2 \longrightarrow$

11. $HNO_3 + Al(OH)_3 \longrightarrow$

12. If the pH of a solution increases from 4 to 5, the hydronium ion concentration
    (1) increases by a factor of one
    (2) decreases by a factor of one
    (3) increases tenfold
    (4) decreases tenfold

Part B-2

Answer each of the following questions.

13. Write the product of each of these combination (synthesis) reactions.
    a. $K(s) + O_2(g) \longrightarrow$
    b. $Ca(s) + S(s) \longrightarrow$
    c. $F_2(g) + Al(s) \longrightarrow$

14. Which state of matter is not part of the process of sublimation?

15. What type of bond is responsible for the high boiling point of water?

16. How many grams of potassium chloride are in 45.0 g of a 5.00% (by mass) solution?

17. How would you prepare 400.0 mL of a $0.680M$ KOH solution?

18. How many liters of $8.0M$ HCl are needed to prepare 1.50 L of $2.5M$ HCl?

19. How many joules of heat are required to melt a 55.0-g ice cube at 0°C?

20. The specific heat capacity of iron is 0.46 J/(g • °C). How many kilojoules of energy are needed to raise the temperature of a 432-g iron bar 14°C?

21. In each of the following pairs, which item has the higher entropy?
   a. NaCl(*s*) or NaCl(*aq*)
   b. CO_2(*s*) or CO_2(*g*)
   c. hot water or cold water

22. How would each of the following changes affect the position of equilibrium of this reaction?

$$2H_2(g) + O_2(g) \rightleftharpoons 2H_2O(g) + heat$$

   a. increasing the pressure
   b. adding a catalyst
   c. increasing the concentration of $H_2(g)$
   d. cooling the reaction mixture
   e. removing water vapor from the container

23. Perform the following conversions.
   a. 25 mg to g
   b. 3.95 m to pm
   c. 1.98×10^5 mL to kL

Part C

Answer each of the following questions.

24. One source of air pollution is the oxidizing of the sulfur that is found in most fossil fuels. Sulfur completely burns in oxygen to form sulfur trioxide.
   a. Write a balanced chemical equation for this reaction.
   b. If 87.4 g of sulfur burn, how many moles of sulfur have burned?

c. How many moles of oxygen are needed for this reaction?
   d. How many grams of oxygen is this?

25. Which of the following processes are endothermic?
   a. burning wax
   b. evaporating water
   c. melting wax
   d. roasting a marshmallow

26. Which of the following choices represent a direct relationship? Assume all other factors remain constant.
   a. A balloon becomes larger when is taken to a location that has a high altitude.
   b. A mylar balloon becomes underinflated when taken outside on a cold day.
   c. The pressure in an automobile tire rises when the tire is heated by the road.

27. A form of hydrochloric acid called muriatic acid is sometimes used to clean brick and other masonry surfaces. Muriatic acid is sold as a 12*M* hydrochloric acid solution. A bricklayer wants to make 1.50 L of 2.50*M* muriatic acid.
   a. How many moles of HCl are in the acid the bricklayer wants to prepare?
   b. What volume of concentrated muriatic acid is used to make the prepared solution?

Oxidation-Reduction Reactions

Rust is the result of the iron in this ship reacting with oxygen and water.

INQUIRY Activity

Rusting

Materials

fine sandpaper, 7 iron finishing nails (approximately 6 cm long), paper towels, scissors, water, saucer, pliers, copper wire, zinc strip, petroleum jelly, table salt, plastic wrap

Procedure

1. Use sandpaper to polish seven nails. Wipe them clean with a paper towel.

2. Place two wet paper towels on the saucer.

3. Nail 1: Using pliers, bend into a U shape. Nail 2: Wrap one end with copper wire. Nail 3: Wrap one end with a strip of zinc. Nail 4: Cover the entire nail with a thin coat of petroleum jelly. Nail 5: Moisten with water and sprinkle with salt. Nail 6: Leave untreated. Nail 7: Leave untreated.

4. Place nails 1 through 6 on the wet paper towel. Make sure the nails do not touch. Cover them with a piece of plastic wrap. Place nail 7 (the control) on top of the plastic wrap. During a 24-hour period, record your observations in a table.

Think About It

1. What changes took place with the nails over 24 hours?

2. How can you account for these changes?

3. How can you account for differences in the appearance of the nails after 24 hours?

20.1 The Meaning of Oxidation and Reduction

New York Standards: 3.2d–e, 3.2g, 3.3b

Connecting to Your World During winter in cold climates, salt is often spread on roads to lower the freezing point of water and thereby prevent the buildup of slippery ice. Salt may make driving safer, but the salt that clings to the metallic parts of cars can cause them to corrode or rust relatively quickly. This corrosion is one example of a chemical reaction called oxidation-reduction. In this section, you will learn about oxidation-reduction reactions.

Guide for Reading

Key Concepts
- How is the gain or loss of oxygen in a chemical reaction linked to oxidation and reduction?
- How is the gain or loss of electrons linked to oxidation and reduction?
- What happens to iron when it corrodes?

Vocabulary
oxidation-reduction reactions
redox reactions
oxidation
reduction
reducing agent
oxidizing agent

Reading Strategy
Comparing and Contrasting As you read, compare the older definitions of oxidation and reduction with the current definitions.

What Are Oxidation and Reduction?

The combustion of gasoline in an automobile engine and the burning of wood in a fireplace are reactions that require oxygen as they release energy. The reactions that break down food in your body and release energy use oxygen from the air you breathe.

Oxygen and Redox Early chemists saw oxidation only as the combination of an element with oxygen to produce an oxide. The burning of a fuel is also an oxidation reaction that uses oxygen. For example, when methane (CH_4), a component of natural gas, burns in air, it oxidizes and forms oxides of carbon and hydrogen, as shown in Figure 20.1. One oxide of carbon is carbon dioxide, CO_2.

Not all oxidation processes that use oxygen involve burning. For example, when elemental iron turns to rust, it slowly oxidizes to compounds such as iron(III) oxide (Fe_2O_3). Bleaching stains in fabrics is an example of oxidation that does not involve burning. Common liquid household bleach contains sodium hypochlorite (NaClO), a substance that releases oxygen, which oxidizes stains to a colorless form. Powder bleaches may contain calcium hypochlorite ($Ca(ClO)_2$), sodium perborate ($NaBO_3$), or sodium percarbonate ($2Na_2CO_3 \cdot 3H_2O_3$). Hydrogen peroxide (H_2O_2) also releases oxygen when it decomposes. It is both a bleach and a mild antiseptic that kills bacteria by oxidizing them.

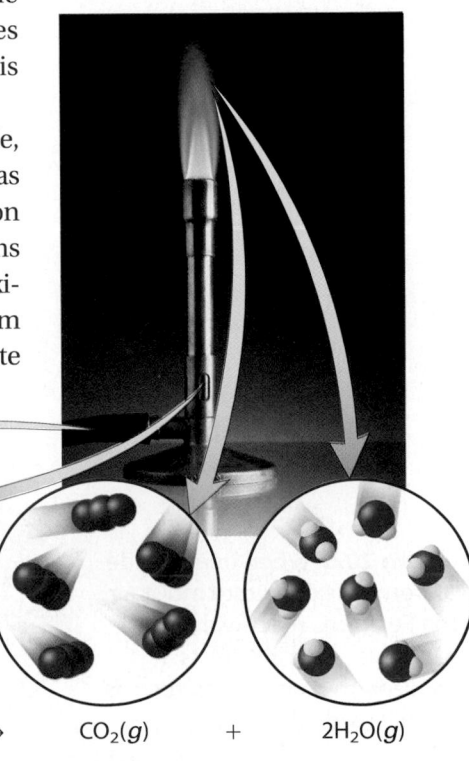

Figure 20.1 A Bunsen burner oxidizes the methane in natural gas to carbon dioxide and water.

$$CH_4(g) \quad + \quad 2O_2(g) \quad \longrightarrow \quad CO_2(g) \quad + \quad 2H_2O(g)$$

Figure 20.2 When charcoal, which is mostly carbon, is burned in air, carbon dioxide and heat are produced.

$$C(s) \quad + \quad O_2(g) \quad \longrightarrow \quad CO_2(g)$$

The oxide of hydrogen is water, H_2O. Charcoal, shown in Figure 20.2, also oxidizes when it burns, forming CO_2.

A process called reduction is the opposite of oxidation. Originally, reduction meant the loss of oxygen from a compound. The reduction of iron ore to metallic iron involves the removal of oxygen from iron(III) oxide. The reduction is accomplished by heating the ore with carbon, usually in the form of coke. The equation for the reduction of iron ore is shown below.

$$2Fe_2O_3(s) + 3C(s) \longrightarrow 4Fe(s) + 3CO_2(g)$$

Iron (III)   Carbon   Iron   Carbon
oxide   dioxide

The reduction of iron also includes an oxidation process. As iron(III) oxide is reduced to iron by losing oxygen, carbon oxidizes to carbon dioxide by gaining oxygen. Oxidation and reduction always occur simultaneously. **The substance gaining oxygen is oxidized, while the substance losing oxygen is reduced.** No oxidation occurs without reduction, and no reduction occurs without oxidation. Reactions that involve these processes are therefore called oxidation-reduction reactions. **Oxidation-reduction reactions** are also known as **redox reactions.**

✓**Checkpoint** *What is another name for redox reactions?*

Figure 20.3 When items made of iron are exposed to moist air, the Fe atoms react with O_2 molecules. The iron rusts; it is oxidized to compounds such as iron(III) oxide (Fe_2O_3).

$$4Fe(s) \quad + \quad 3O_2(g) \quad \longrightarrow \quad 2Fe_2O_3(s)$$

Iron   Oxygen   Iron(III) oxide

Electron Shift in Redox Reactions The modern concepts of oxidation and reduction have been extended to include many reactions that do not even involve oxygen. You learned in Chapter 6 that, with the exception of fluorine, oxygen is the most electronegative element. As a result, when oxygen bonds with an atom of a different element (other than fluorine), electrons from that atom shift toward oxygen. Redox reactions are currently understood to involve any shift of electrons between reactants. **Oxidation** is now defined to mean complete or partial loss of electrons or gain of oxygen. **Reduction** is now defined to mean complete or partial gain of electrons or loss of oxygen.

Oxidation	Reduction
Loss of electrons	Gain of electrons
Gain of oxygen	Loss of oxygen

Word *Origins*

Reduction comes from the Latin word *reducere*, meaning "to lead back." Reduction of metal oxides by the removal of oxygen leads to a smaller mass of the metal compared to the original metal oxide. **Sometimes when a company reorganizes, it undergoes a "reduction in force." What does this mean?**

Redox Reactions That Form Ions During a reaction between a metal and a nonmetal, electrons are transferred from atoms of the metal to atoms of the nonmetal. For example, when magnesium metal is heated with the nonmetal sulfur, the ionic compound magnesium sulfide is produced as shown in Figure 20.4. Two electrons are transferred from a magnesium atom to a sulfur atom. The magnesium atoms become more stable by the loss of electrons. The sulfur atoms become more stable by the gain of electrons.

$$\cdot Mg\cdot \ + \ \cdot \ddot{\underset{..}{S}}\colon \ \longrightarrow \ Mg^{2+} \ + \ \colon\ddot{\underset{..}{S}}\colon^{2-}$$

| Magnesium atom | Sulfur atom | Magnesium ion | Sulfide ion |

Because it loses electrons, the magnesium atom is said to be oxidized to a magnesium ion. Simultaneously, the sulfur atom gains two electrons and is reduced to a sulfide ion. The overall process is represented as the two component processes below.

Oxidation: $\cdot Mg\cdot \longrightarrow Mg^{2+} + 2e^-$ (loss of electrons)

Reduction: $\cdot \ddot{\underset{..}{S}}\colon + 2e^- \longrightarrow \colon\ddot{\underset{..}{S}}\colon^{2-}$ (gain of electrons)

Figure 20.4 When magnesium and sulfur are heated together, they undergo an oxidation-reduction reaction to form magnesium sulfide. **Applying Concepts** *Where did the electrons lost by magnesium go?*

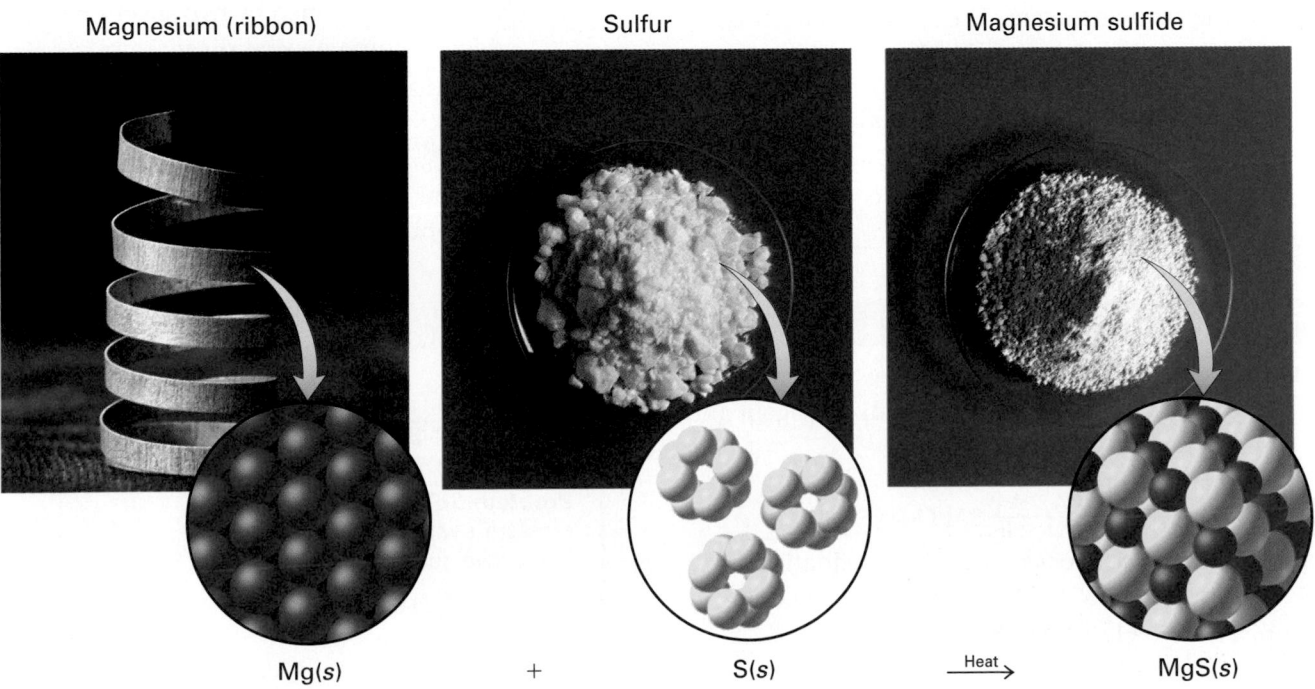

| Magnesium (ribbon) | Sulfur | Magnesium sulfide |

Mg(*s*)   +   S(*s*) $\xrightarrow{\text{Heat}}$ MgS(*s*)

Losing electrons is oxidation. Gaining electrons is reduction. The substance that loses electrons is called the **reducing agent.** By losing electrons to sulfur, magnesium reduces the sulfur. Magnesium is thus the reducing agent. The substance that accepts electrons is called the **oxidizing agent.** By accepting electrons from magnesium, sulfur oxidizes the magnesium. Sulfur is the oxidizing agent. Another way of identifying oxidizing and reducing agents is to remember that the species that is reduced is the oxidizing agent and the species oxidized is the reducing agent.

oxidized

$$Mg(s) \ + \ S(s) \longrightarrow MgS(s)$$

reduced

Magnesium (reducing agent)   Sulfur (oxidizing agent)   Magnesium sulfide

You might find it helpful to use the following mnemonic device to remember the definitions of oxidation and reduction: "*LEO* the lion goes *GER.*" LEO stands for Losing Electrons is Oxidation; GER stands for Gaining Electrons is Reduction.

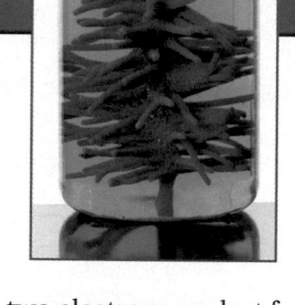

CONCEPTUAL PROBLEM 20.1

Identifying Oxidized and Reduced Reactants

Silver nitrate reacts with copper to form copper nitrate and silver. From the equation below, determine what is oxidized and what is reduced. Identify the oxidizing agent and the reducing agent.

$$2AgNO_3(aq) + Cu(s) \longrightarrow Cu(NO_3)_2(aq) + 2Ag(s)$$

1 **Analyze** *Identify the relevant concepts.*

The species that loses electrons is oxidized and is the reducing agent. The species that gains electrons is reduced and is the oxidizing agent.

2 **Solve** *Apply concepts to this situation.*

Rewrite the equation in ionic form. It is then easier to analyze the reaction.

$$2Ag^+ + 2NO_3^- + Cu \longrightarrow Cu^{2+} + 2NO_3^- + 2Ag$$

In this reaction, two electrons are lost from a copper atom (Cu) when it becomes a Cu^{2+} ion. These electrons are gained by two silver ions (Ag^+), which become neutral silver atoms.

Oxidation: $Cu \longrightarrow Cu^{2+} + 2e^-$ (loss of electrons)

Reduction: $2Ag^+ + 2e^- \longrightarrow 2Ag$ (gain of electrons)

The Cu is the reducing agent. The Ag^+ is the oxidizing agent.

Practice Problems

1. Determine what is oxidized and what is reduced in each reaction. Identify the oxidizing agent and reducing agent in each case.
   a. $2Na(s) + S(s) \longrightarrow Na_2S(s)$
   b. $4Al(s) + 3O_2(g) \longrightarrow 2Al_2O_3(s)$

2. Identify these processes as either oxidation or reduction.
   a. $2I^- \longrightarrow I_2 + 2e^-$ **b.** $Zn^{2+} + 2e^- \longrightarrow Zn$

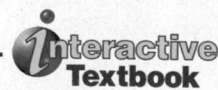

Problem-Solving 20.1 Solve Problem 1 with the help of an interactive guided tutorial.

with **ChemASAP**

Table 20.1	
Processes Leading to Oxidation and Reduction	
Oxidation	**Reduction**
Complete loss of electrons (ionic reactions)	Complete gain of electrons (ionic reactions)
Shift of electrons *away* from an atom in a covalent bond	Shift of electrons *toward* an atom in a covalent bond
Gain of oxygen	Loss of oxygen
Loss of hydrogen by a covalent compound	Gain of hydrogen by a covalent compound
Increase in oxidation number	Decrease in oxidation number

Go Online

NSTA *SciLINKS*

For: Links on Oxidation and Reduction
Visit: www.SciLinks.org
Web Code: cdn-1202

Redox With Covalent Compounds When a metal and a nonmetal react and form ions, it is easy to identify complete transfers of electrons. But some reactions involve covalent compounds, that is, compounds in which complete electron transfer does not occur. One such example is the reaction of hydrogen with oxygen.

$$2H_2(g) + O_2(g) \longrightarrow 2H_2O(l)$$

Consider what happens to the bonding electrons in the formation of a water molecule. In each reactant hydrogen molecule, the bonding electrons are shared equally between the hydrogen atoms. In water, however, the bonding electrons are pulled toward oxygen because it is much more electronegative than hydrogen. The result is a shift of bonding electrons away from hydrogen, even though there is not a complete transfer. Hydrogen is oxidized because it undergoes a partial loss of electrons.

In oxygen, the other reactant, the bonding electrons are shared equally between oxygen atoms in the reactant oxygen molecule. However, when oxygen bonds to hydrogen in the water molecule, there is a shift of electrons toward oxygen. Oxygen is thus reduced because it undergoes a partial gain of electrons.

H—H
electrons
shared
equally

O—O
electrons
shared
equally

H—O
H
shift of bonding electrons away from hydrogen and toward oxygen

Figure 20.5 This artist is using an oxyhydrogen torch to cut and weld steel to make a sculpture. When hydrogen burns in oxygen, the redox reaction generates temperatures of about 2600°C.

In the reaction of hydrogen and oxygen to produce water, hydrogen is the reducing agent because it is oxidized. Oxygen is the oxidizing agent because it is reduced. This redox reaction is highly exothermic—that is, it releases a great deal of energy, as shown in Figure 20.5.

In some reactions involving covalent reactants or products, the partial electron shifts are less obvious. Some general guidelines are thus helpful. For example, for carbon compounds, the addition of oxygen or the removal of hydrogen is always oxidation. Table 20.1 above lists processes that constitute oxidation and reduction. The last entry in the table identifies oxidation numbers.

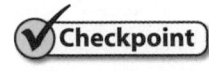 **Checkpoint** *What happens to the bonding electrons in the formation of water?*

Figure 20.6 Oxidation-reduction reactions cause corrosion. The copper on this roof reacted with water vapor, carbon dioxide, and other substances in the air to form a patina. This patina consists of a pale-green film of basic copper(II) carbonate. Because patinas enhance the surface appearance of objects, they are valued by architects and artists.

For: Links on Corrosion
Visit: www.SciLinks.org
Web Code: cdn-1201

Corrosion

Billions of dollars are spent yearly to prevent and to repair damage caused by the corrosion of metals. 🔑 **Iron, a common construction metal often used in the form of the alloy steel, corrodes by being oxidized to ions of iron by oxygen.** Water in the environment accelerates the rate of corrosion. Oxygen, the oxidizing agent, is reduced to oxide ions (in compounds such as Fe_2O_3) or to hydroxide ions. The following equations describe the corrosion of iron to iron hydroxides in moist conditions.

$$2Fe(s) + O_2(g) + 2H_2O(l) \longrightarrow 2Fe(OH)_2(s)$$

$$4Fe(OH)_2(s) + O_2(g) + 2H_2O(l) \longrightarrow 4Fe(OH)_3(s)$$

Corrosion occurs more rapidly in the presence of salts and acids. These substances produce electrically conducting solutions that make electron transfer easier. The corrosion of some metals can be a desirable feature, as Figure 20.6 shows.

Resistance to Corrosion Not all metals corrode easily. Gold and platinum are called noble metals because they are very resistant to losing their electrons by corrosion. Other metals lose electrons easily but are protected from extensive corrosion by the oxide coating formed on their surface. For example, aluminum oxidizes quickly in air to form a coating of very tightly packed aluminum oxide particles. This coating protects the aluminum object from further corrosion, as shown in Figure 20.7. Iron also forms a coating when it corrodes, but the coating of iron oxide that forms is not tightly packed. Water and air can penetrate the coating and attack the iron metal below it. The corrosion continues until the iron object becomes only a pile of rust.

Figure 20.7 Oxidation causes the complete corrosion of some metals. ⓐ Iron reacts with water and oxygen to form iron(III) oxide, or rust. ⓑ Aluminum, however, resists such corrosion because it forms a protective coating of aluminum oxide.
Applying Concepts *How does the aluminum oxide on aluminum differ from the iron(III) oxide formed on corroding iron?*

Figure 20.8 Bridges like this one become unsafe because of corrosion.

Controlling Corrosion The corrosion of objects such as shovels or knives is a common problem but not usually a serious one. In contrast, the corrosion of a steel support pillar of a bridge, as in Figure 20.8, or the hull of an oil tanker is much more serious and costly. To prevent corrosion in such cases, the metal surface may be coated with oil, paint, plastic, or another metal, as shown in Figure 20.9. These coatings exclude air and water from the surface, thus preventing corrosion. If the coating is scratched or worn away, however, the exposed metal will begin to corrode.

In another method of corrosion control, one metal is "sacrificed," or allowed to corrode, in order to save a second metal. For example, to protect an iron object, a piece of magnesium (or another active metal) may be placed in electrical contact with the iron. When oxygen and water attack the iron object, the iron atoms lose electrons as the iron begins to be oxidized.

Figure 20.9 Painting a surface (left) protects it from the effects of the environment. Chromium metal also serves as a protective coating and imparts an attractive, mirrorlike finish (right). Like aluminum, chromium forms a corrosion-resistant oxide film on its surface.

Figure 20.10 Zinc blocks, the white rectangles in the photograph, are attached to the steel (iron) hull of this ship. The zinc blocks oxidize (corrode) instead of the iron, preventing the hull from corroding.

However, because magnesium is a better reducing agent than iron and is more easily oxidized, the magnesium immediately transfers electrons to the iron, preventing their oxidation to iron ions. So, the magnesium is "sacrificed" by oxidation and protects the iron in the process.

Sacrificial zinc and magnesium blocks are sometimes attached to piers and ship hulls to prevent corrosion damage in areas submerged in water, as shown in Figure 20.10. Underground pipelines and storage tanks may be connected to magnesium blocks for protection. It is easier and cheaper to replace a block of magnesium or zinc than to replace a bridge or a pipeline.

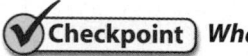 **Checkpoint** *What are two ways to control corrosion?*

20.1 Section Assessment

3. **Key Concept** Define oxidation and reduction in terms of the gain or loss of oxygen.

4. **Key Concept** Define oxidation and reduction in terms of the gain or loss of electrons.

5. **Key Concept** What happens to the atoms in an iron nail that corrodes?

6. How do you identify the oxidizing agent and the reducing agent in a redox reaction?

7. Use electron transfer or electron shift to identify what is oxidized and what is reduced in each reaction. Use the electronegativity values in Table 6.2 in Chapter 6, for molecular compounds.
   a. $2Na(s) + Br_2(l) \longrightarrow 2NaBr(s)$
   b. $H_2(g) + Cl_2(g) \longrightarrow 2HCl(g)$
   c. $2Li(s) + F_2(g) \longrightarrow 2LiF(s)$
   d. $S(s) + Cl_2(g) \longrightarrow SCl_2(g)$
   e. $N_2(g) + 2O_2(g) \longrightarrow 2NO_2(g)$
   f. $Mg(s) + Cu(NO_3)_2(aq) \longrightarrow Mg(NO_3)_2(aq) + Cu(s)$

8. Identify the reducing agent and the oxidizing agent for each reaction in Problem 7.

Writing ▶ Activity

Write a Report Shipwrecks of Spanish galleons sometimes contain gold or silver treasures. Why is the recovered gold hardly ever changed while the silver has turned black? Research and write a report on how the thick layers of tarnish are removed from the silver artifacts.

 Interactive Textbook

Assessment 20.1 Check your understanding of the important ideas and concepts in Section 20.1.

— with **ChemASAP**

20.2 Oxidation Numbers

 New York Standard: 3.2i

Connecting to Your World   The bursts of bright white light produced by fireworks are the result of metals being burned. Powdered or flaked aluminum or magnesium are included in the fireworks. When these metals are heated to high temperatures in the explosion, they burn with an intense white light. The fireworks shown here are called stars. As elements burn, their oxidation numbers change. In this section, you will learn about how oxidation and reduction are defined in terms of a change in oxidation number.

Guide for Reading

 Key Concepts
- What is the general rule for assigning oxidation numbers?
- How are oxidation and reduction defined in terms of a change in oxidation number?

Vocabulary

oxidation number

Reading Strategy

Using Prior Knowledge Before you read, predict how oxidation and reduction affect the charge on an ion. Check your predictions as you read.

Assigning Oxidation Numbers

An **oxidation number** is a positive or negative number assigned to an atom to indicate its degree of oxidation or reduction. **As a general rule, a bonded atom's oxidation number is the charge that it would have if the electrons in the bond were assigned to the atom of the more electronegative element.** The following set of rules should help you determine oxidation numbers.

Rules for Assigning Oxidation Numbers

1. The oxidation number of a monatomic ion is equal in magnitude and sign to its ionic charge. For example, the oxidation number of the bromide ion (Br^{1-}) is -1; that of the Fe^{3+} ion is $+3$.

2. The oxidation number of hydrogen in a compound is $+1$, except in metal hydrides, such as NaH, where it is -1.

3. The oxidation number of oxygen in a compound is -2, except in peroxides, such as H_2O_2, where it is -1, and in compounds with the more electronegative fluorine, where it is positive.

4. The oxidation number of an atom in uncombined (elemental) form is 0. For example, the oxidation number of the potassium atoms in potassium metal (K) or of the nitrogen atoms in nitrogen gas (N_2) is 0.

5. For any neutral compound, the sum of the oxidation numbers of the atoms in the compound must equal 0.

6. For a polyatomic ion, the sum of the oxidation numbers must equal the ionic charge of the ion.

Figure 20.11 The oxidation number of any element in the free or uncombined state is zero. The elements shown here (left to right) are white phosphorus (stored under water), sulfur, potassium (stored under oil), carbon, and bromine (liquid and vapor). The potassium and phosphorus are stored under a liquid to prevent them from reacting with oxygen in the air.

White phosphorus

Potassium

Bromine

Sulfur

Carbon

In binary ionic compounds, such as NaCl and $CaCl_2$, the oxidation numbers of the atoms equal their ionic charges (Rule 1). The compound sodium chloride is composed of sodium ions (Na^{1+}) and chloride ions (Cl^{1-}). Thus the oxidation number of sodium is +1, and that of chlorine is −1. Notice that the sign is put before the oxidation number.

Because water is a molecular compound, no ionic charges are associated with its atoms. However, oxygen is reduced in the formation of water. Oxygen is more electronegative than hydrogen. So, in water, the two shared electrons in the H—O bond are shifted toward oxygen and away from hydrogen. Imagine that the electrons contributed by the two hydrogen atoms are completely transferred to the oxygen. The charges that would result from this transfer are the oxidation numbers of the bonded elements. The oxidation number of oxygen is −2, and the oxidation number of each hydrogen is +1 (Rules 2 and 3). Oxidation numbers are often written above the chemical symbols in a formula. For example, water can be represented as

$$\overset{+1\ -2}{H_2O}$$

Many elements can have several different oxidation numbers. Use rules 5 and 6 to determine the oxidation number of atoms of these elements, plus other elements not covered in the first four rules. The substances in Figure 20.12 are compounds of chromium, but chromium has a different oxidation number in each compound.

Figure 20.12 Yellow potassium chromate (K_2CrO_4) and orange potassium dichromate ($K_2Cr_2O_7$) each have a chromium-containing polyatomic ion. **Inferring** *What is the oxidation number of chromium in each compound?*

Assigning Oxidation Numbers to Atoms

What is the oxidation number of each kind of atom in the following ions and compounds?

a. SO_2 **b.** CO_3^{2-} **c.** Na_2SO_4 **d.** $(NH_4)_2S$

1 **Analyze** *Identify the relevant concepts.*

Use the set of rules you just learned to assign and calculate oxidation numbers.

2 **Solve** *Apply concepts to this situation.*

a. There are two oxygen atoms and the oxidation number of each oxygen is -2 (Rule 3). The sum of the oxidation numbers for the neutral compound must be 0 (Rule 5). Therefore, the oxidation number of sulfur is $+4$, because $+4 + (2 \times (-2)) = 0$.

$$\overset{+4\ -2}{SO_2}$$

b. The oxidation number of oxygen is -2 (Rule 3).

$$\overset{?\ -2}{CO_3^{2-}}$$

The sum of the oxidation numbers of the carbon and oxygen atoms must equal the ionic charge, -2 (Rule 6). The oxidation number of carbon must be $+4$, because $+4 + (3 \times (-2)) = -2$.

$$\overset{+4\ -2}{CO_3^{2-}}$$

c. The oxidation number of each sodium ion, Na^+, is the same as its ionic charge, $+1$ (Rule 1). The oxidation number of oxygen is -2 (Rule 3).

$$\overset{+1\ ?\ -2}{Na_2SO_4}$$

For the sum of the oxidation numbers in the compound to be 0 (rule 5), the oxidation number of sulfur must be $+6$, because $(2 \times (+1)) + (+6) + (4 \times (-2)) = 0$.

$$\overset{+1\ +6\ -2}{Na_2SO_4}$$

d. Ammonium ions, NH_4^+, have an ionic charge of $+1$, so the sum of the oxidation numbers of the atoms in the ammonium ion must be $+1$. The oxidation number of hydrogen is $+1$ in this ion.

$$\overset{?\ +1}{NH_4^+}$$

$$? + 4(+1) = +1$$

So, the oxidation number of nitrogen must be -3 because $-3 + (+4) = +1$.

Two ammonium ions have a total charge of $+2$. Since the compound $(NH_4)_2S$ is neutral, sulfur must have a balancing oxidation number of -2.

$$\overset{-3\ +1\ -2}{(NH_4)_2S}$$

Practice Problems

9. Determine the oxidation number of each element in the following.

     a. S_2O_3 **b.** Na_2O_2 **c.** P_2O_5 **d.** NO_3^-

10. Determine the oxidation number of chlorine in each of the following substances.

     a. $KClO_3$ **b.** Cl_2 **c.** $Ca(ClO_4)_2$ **d.** Cl_2O

Interactive Textbook

Problem-Solving 20.9 Solve Problem 9 with the help of an interactive guided tutorial.

—— with **ChemASAP**

Figure 20.13 Copper reacts with silver nitrate. **ⓐ** When a copper wire is placed in a silver nitrate solution crystals of silver coat the wire. **ⓑ** The solution slowly turns blue as a result of the formation of copper(II) nitrate. **Drawing Conclusions** *What change occurs in the oxidation number of silver? How does the oxidation number of copper change?*

Oxidation-Number Changes in Chemical Reactions

Figure 20.13 shows what happens when copper wire is placed in a solution of silver nitrate. In this reaction, the oxidation number of silver decreases from +1 to 0 as each silver ion (Ag^{1+}) gains an electron and is reduced to silver metal (Ag^0). Copper's oxidation number increases from 0 to +2 as each atom of copper metal (Cu^0) loses two electrons and is oxidized to a copper(II) ion (Cu^{2+}). Here is the equation with oxidation numbers added:

$$\overset{+1\ +5\ -2}{2AgNO_3(aq)} + \overset{0}{Cu(s)} \longrightarrow \overset{+2\ +5\ -2}{Cu(NO_3)_2(aq)} + \overset{0}{2Ag(s)}$$

Figure 20.14 illustrates a redox reaction that shows what occurs when a shiny iron nail is dipped into a solution of copper(II) sulfate.

You can define oxidation and reduction in terms of a change in oxidation number. **⚷ An increase in the oxidation number of an atom or ion indicates oxidation. A decrease in the oxidation number of an atom or ion indicates reduction.**

Figure 20.14 A redox reaction occurs between iron and copper. **ⓐ** An iron nail dipped in a copper(II) sulfate solution becomes coated with metallic copper. **ⓑ** The iron reduces Cu^{2+} ions in solution and is simultaneously oxidized to Fe^{2+}.

CONCEPTUAL PROBLEM 20.3

Identifying Oxidized and Reduced Atoms

Use changes in oxidation number to identify which atoms are oxidized and which are reduced in the following reaction. Also identify the oxidizing agent and the reducing agent.

$$Cl_2(g) + 2HBr(aq) \longrightarrow 2HCl(aq) + Br_2(l)$$

① **Analyze** *Identify the relevant concepts.*

Use the rules to assign oxidation numbers to each atom in the equation. An increase in oxidation number indicates oxidation. A decrease in oxidation number indicates reduction. The substance that is oxidized in a redox reaction is the reducing agent. The substance that is reduced is the oxidizing agent.

The element chlorine is reduced because its oxidation number decreases (0 to -1). The bromide ion from $HBr(aq)$ is oxidized because its oxidation number increases (-1 to 0). Chlorine is reduced, so Cl_2 is the oxidizing agent. The bromide ion from $HBr(aq)$ is oxidized, so Br^- is the reducing agent.

② **Solve** *Apply concepts to this situation.*

$$\overset{0}{Cl_2}(g) + 2\overset{+1\ -1}{HBr}(aq) \longrightarrow 2\overset{+1\ -1}{HCl}(aq) + \overset{0}{Br_2}(l)$$

Practice Problems

11. Identify which atoms are oxidized and which are reduced in each reaction.
   a. $2H_2(g) + O_2(g) \longrightarrow 2H_2O(l)$
   b. $2KNO_3(s) \longrightarrow 2KNO_2(s) + O_2(g)$

12. Identify the oxidizing agent and the reducing agent in each equation in Practice Problem 11.

20.2 Section Assessment

13. 🔑 **Key Concept** What is the general rule for assigning oxidation numbers?

14. 🔑 **Key Concept** How is a change in oxidation number related to the process of oxidation and reduction?

15. Use the changes in oxidation numbers to identify which atoms are oxidized and which are reduced in each reaction.
   a. $2Na(s) + Cl_2(g) \longrightarrow 2NaCl(s)$
   b. $2HNO_3(aq) + 6HI(aq) \longrightarrow 2NO(g) + 3I_2(s) + 4H_2O(l)$

16. Identify the oxidizing agent and the reducing agent in each reaction in Problem 15.

Connecting ▶ Concepts

Types of Reactions Reread Section 11.2 and identify which of the five types of reactions are most likely redox reactions.

Cold Water Makes a Hot Meal

Researchers have solved a long-standing problem: how to provide astronauts and military personnel with hot meals when there are no cooking facilities or time to cook. They developed the Flameless Ration Heater (FRH). An FRH is very small and weighs only one and a half ounces. It heats precooked, packaged meal rations with no flame or electricity. Simply place an MRE (Meal Ready to Eat) pouch in an FRH and add water. After about 15 minutes, the food is a warm 60°C. **Applying Concepts** *What is the chemical equation for the reaction of magnesium and water?*

How it works An FRH uses corrosion to generate heat. Water oxidizes magnesium to form magnesium hydroxide, hydrogen, and heat. Just 24 grams of magnesium releases 355,000 joules of heat, enough to boil about 1 L of water.

Eating in space Astronauts N. Jan Davis and Stephen K. Robinson on the space shuttle Discovery eat Japanese rice. Astronauts use the FRH to heat packaged meals.

Balancing Redox Equations

Connecting to Your World One of the long pursued goals of alchemists was to change common metals, such as lead or copper, into gold. One tool that the alchemists employed in their quest was *aqua regia*, which means "royal water." *Aqua regia* is a mixture of concentrated hydrochloric (HCl) and nitric (HNO_3) acids. When metallic gold is added to *aqua regia*, oxidation and reduction reactions produce gaseous nitrogen monoxide (NO) and soluble, stable $AuCl_4^-$ ions. In this section, you will learn how to write and balance chemical equations for redox reactions such as this one.

Guide for Reading

Key Concepts
- How are oxidation numbers used to identify redox reactions?
- How are changes in oxidation numbers used to balance a redox equation?
- What is the procedure for balancing a redox equation using half-reactions?

Vocabulary
oxidation-number-change method
half-reaction
half-reaction method

Reading Strategy

Identifying a Sequence As you read, list the steps used to balance a redox equation by the oxidation-number change method and the half-reaction method.

Identifying Redox Reactions

In general, all chemical reactions can be assigned to one of two classes. One class is oxidation-reduction (redox) reactions, in which electrons are transferred from one reacting species to another. Many single-replacement reactions, combination reactions, decomposition reactions, and combustion reactions are redox reactions. Two examples of redox reactions are shown in Figure 20.15. Figure 20.15a shows what happens when potassium metal reacts with water. Figure 20.15b shows the reaction of zinc with hydrochloric acid. The other class includes all other reactions, in which no electron transfer occurs. For example, double-replacement reactions and acid-base reactions are not redox reactions.

Figure 20.15 Many single replacement reactions are redox reactions. **a** Potassium metal reacts violently with water to produce hydrogen gas (which ignites) and potassium hydroxide. **b** Zinc metal reacts vigorously with hydrochloric acid to produce hydrogen gas and zinc chloride. **Applying Concepts** *Explain why each reaction is a redox reaction.*

Figure 20.16 The redox reaction between nitrogen and oxygen that takes place when lightning bolts heat the air to extreme temperatures forms nitrogen monoxide.

During an electrical storm, as shown in Figure 20.16, oxygen molecules and nitrogen molecules in the air react to form nitrogen monoxide. This is an example of a combination reaction. The equation for the reaction is shown below.

$$N_2(g) + O_2(g) \longrightarrow 2NO(g)$$

How can you tell if this is a redox reaction? **⟳ If the oxidation number of an element in a reacting species changes, then that element has undergone either oxidation or reduction. Therefore, the reaction as a whole must be a redox reaction.** In the example above, the oxidation number of nitrogen increases from 0 to +2 while the oxidation number of oxygen decreases from 0 to −2. Therefore, the reaction between nitrogen and oxygen to form nitrogen monoxide is a redox reaction.

Many reactions in which color changes occur are redox reactions. One example is shown in Figure 20.17. Written in ionic form, the unbalanced equation for this reaction is

$$MnO_4^-(aq) \;+\; Br^-(aq) \longrightarrow Mn^{2+}(aq) \;+\; Br_2(aq)$$

| Permanganate ion (purple) | Bromide ion (colorless) | Manganese(II) ion (colorless) | Bromine (brown) |

Figure 20.17 A color change can signal a redox reaction. When a colorless solution containing bromide ions (Br⁻) is added to a solution containing permanganate ions (MnO₄⁻), the distinctive purple color of the permanganate ion is replaced by the pale brown color of bromine.

Identifying Redox Reactions

Use the change in oxidation number to identify whether each reaction is a redox reaction or a reaction of some other type. If a reaction is a redox reaction, identify the element reduced, the element oxidized, the reducing agent, and the oxidizing agent.

a. $Cl_2(g) + 2NaBr(aq) \longrightarrow 2NaCl(aq) + Br_2(g)$

b. $2NaOH(aq) + H_2SO_4(aq) \longrightarrow Na_2SO_4(aq) + 2H_2O(l)$

1 Analyze *Identify the relevant concepts.*

Assign oxidation numbers to show whether or not oxidation numbers change. If changes occur, the reaction is a redox reaction. The element whose oxidation number increases is oxidized and is the reducing agent. The element whose oxidation number decreases is reduced and is the oxidizing agent.

2 Solve *Apply concepts to this situation.*

$$\overset{0}{Cl_2}(g) + 2\overset{+1 \ -1}{NaBr}(aq) \longrightarrow 2\overset{+1 \ -1}{NaCl}(aq) + \overset{0}{Br_2}(g)$$

a.

This is a single-replacement reaction. The chlorine is reduced. The bromide ion is oxidized. This is a redox reaction. Chlorine is the oxidizing agent; bromide ion is the reducing agent.

$$\overset{+1-2+1}{b. \ 2NaOH}(aq) + \overset{+1+6-2}{H_2SO_4}(aq) \longrightarrow$$

$$\overset{+1+6-2}{Na_2SO_4}(aq) + 2\overset{+1 \ -2}{H_2O}(l)$$

This is an acid-base (neutralization) reaction. None of the elements changes in oxidation number. This is not a redox reaction.

Practice Problems

17. Identify which of the following are oxidation-reduction reactions. If a reaction is a redox reaction, name the element oxidized and the element reduced.

a. $Mg(s) + Br_2(l) \longrightarrow MgBr_2(s)$

b. $H_2CO_3(aq) \longrightarrow H_2O(l) + CO_2(g)$

18. Identify which of the following are oxidation-reduction reactions. If a reaction is a redox reaction, name the element oxidized and the element reduced.

a. $CaCO_3(s) + 2HCl(aq) \longrightarrow$
$CaCl_2(aq) + H_2O(l) + CO_2(g)$

b. $CuO(s) + H_2(g) \longrightarrow Cu(s) + H_2O(l)$

Two Ways to Balance Redox Equations

Chemists and chemical engineers must be able to write a correctly balanced equation that accurately represents what happens in a chemical reaction. Many oxidation-reduction reactions are too complex to be balanced by trial and error. Fortunately, two systematic methods are available. These two methods are based on the fact that the total number of electrons gained in reduction must equal the total number of electrons lost in oxidation. One method uses oxidation-number changes, and the other uses half-reactions.

Using Oxidation-Number Changes You can use oxidation numbers to keep track of electron transfers—a type of chemical bookkeeping. In the **oxidation-number-change method,** you balance a redox equation by comparing the increases and decreases in oxidation numbers.

Interactive Textbook

Problem-Solving 20.18 Solve Problem 18 with the help of an interactive guided tutorial.

—with **ChemASAP**

To use the oxidation-number-change method, start with the skeleton equation for the redox reaction. As an example, look at the process used to obtain metallic iron from iron ore in a blast furnace shown in Figure 20.18.

$$Fe_2O_3(s) + CO(g) \longrightarrow Fe(s) + CO_2(g) \text{ (unbalanced)}$$

Step 1 *Assign oxidation numbers to all the atoms in the equation.* Write the numbers above the atoms.

$$\overset{+3\ -2}{Fe_2O_3}(s) + \overset{+2-2}{CO}(g) \longrightarrow \overset{0}{Fe}(s) + \overset{+4-2}{CO_2}(g)$$

Note that the oxidation number is stated as the charge per atom. So although the total positive charge of Fe ions in Fe_2O_3 is 6+, the oxidation number of each Fe ion is +3.

Step 2 *Identify which atoms are oxidized and which are reduced.* In this reaction, iron decreases in oxidation number from +3 to 0, a change of −3. Therefore, iron is reduced. Carbon increases in oxidation number from +2 to +4, a change of +2. Thus, carbon is oxidized.

Step 3 *Use one bracketing line to connect the atoms that undergo oxidation and another such line to connect those that undergo reduction.* Write the oxidation-number change at the midpoint of each line.

$$\overset{+3\ -2}{Fe_2O_3}(s) + \overset{+2-2}{CO}(g) \longrightarrow \overset{0}{Fe}(s) + \overset{+4-2}{CO_2}(g)$$
+2 (oxidation)
−3 (reduction)

Remember that a change in oxidation number represents the number of electrons transferred. Each carbon atom in CO loses 2 electrons in oxidation, and each iron atom in Fe_2O_3 accepts 3 electrons in reduction. As the equation is written, the number of electrons transferred in oxidation does not equal the number transferred in reduction. **In a balanced redox equation, the total increase in oxidation number of the species oxidized must be balanced by the total decrease in the oxidation number of the species reduced.** Step 4 will make the oxidation-number changes equal.

Step 4 *Make the total increase in oxidation number equal to the total decrease in oxidation number by using appropriate coefficients.* In this example, the oxidation-number increase should be multiplied by 3 and the oxidation-number decrease should be multiplied by 2, which gives an increase of +6 and a decrease of −6. This can be done in the equation by placing the coefficient 2 in front of Fe on the right side and the coefficient 3 in front of both CO and CO_2. The formula Fe_2O_3 does not need a coefficient because the formula already indicates 2 Fe.

$$Fe_2O_3(s) + 3CO(g) \longrightarrow 2Fe(s) + 3CO_2(g)$$
$3 \times (+2) = +6$
$2 \times (-3) = -6$

Step 5 *Finally, make sure that the equation is balanced for both atoms and charge.* If necessary, finish balancing the equation by inspection.

$$Fe_2O_3(s) + 3CO(g) \longrightarrow 2Fe(s) + 3CO_2(g)$$

Figure 20.18 In a blast furnace like this one, air is blown through a combination of iron ore and coke. The carbon monoxide produced from the oxidation of coke reduces the Fe^{3+} ions to metallic iron.

CONCEPTUAL PROBLEM 20.5

Balancing Redox Equations by Oxidation-Number Change

Balance this redox equation by using the oxidation-number-change method.

$$K_2Cr_2O_7(aq) + H_2O(l) + S(s) \longrightarrow KOH(aq) + Cr_2O_3(s) + SO_2(g)$$

1 **Analyze** *Identify the relevant concepts.*

You can balance redox equations by determining changes in oxidation numbers and applying the five steps.

2 **Solve** *Apply concepts to this situation.*

Assign oxidation numbers.

Identify the atoms that are oxidized and reduced. Cr is reduced. S is oxidized.

Connect the atoms that change in oxidation number. Indicate the signs and magnitudes of the changes.

$$\overset{+6}{K_2Cr_2O_7}(aq) + H_2O(l) + \overset{0}{S}(s) \longrightarrow KOH(aq) + \overset{+3}{Cr_2O_3}(s) + \overset{+4}{SO_2}(g)$$

Balance the increase and decrease in oxidation numbers. Four chromium atoms must be reduced ($4 \times (-3) = -12$ decrease) for each three sulfur atoms that are oxidized ($3 \times (+4) = +12$ increase). Put the coefficient 3 in front of S and SO_2, and the coefficient 2 in front of $K_2Cr_2O_7$ and Cr_2O_3.

Check the equation and balance by inspection if necessary. The coefficient 4 in front of KOH balances potassium. The coefficient 2 in front of H_2O balances hydrogen and oxygen. The final equation is

$$2K_2Cr_2O_7(aq) + 2H_2O(l) + 3S(s) \longrightarrow 4KOH(aq) + 2Cr_2O_3(s) + 3SO_2(g).$$

Practice Problems

19. Balance each redox equation using the oxidation-number change method.
a. $KClO_3(s) \longrightarrow KCl(s) + O_2(g)$
b. $HNO_2(aq) + HI(aq) \longrightarrow NO(g) + I_2(s) + H_2O(l)$

20. Balance each redox equation using the oxidation-number change method.
a. $Bi_2S_3(s) + HNO_3(aq) \longrightarrow$
$Bi(NO_3)_3(aq) + NO(g) + S(s) + H_2O(l)$
b. $SbCl_5(aq) + KI(aq) \longrightarrow$
$SbCl_3(aq) + KCl(aq) + I_2(s)$

Textbook

Problem-Solving 20.20 Solve Problem 20 with the help of an interactive guided tutorial.

with **ChemASAP**

Table 20.2

Oxidation Numbers of Sulfur in Different Substances

Substance	Oxidation number
H_2SO_4	+6
SO_3	+6
H_2SO_3	+4
SO_2	+4
$Na_2S_2O_3$	+2
SCl_2	+2
S_2Cl_2	+1
S	0
H_2S	−2

Using Half-Reactions A second method for balancing redox equations involves the use of half-reactions. A **half-reaction** is an equation showing just the oxidation or just the reduction that takes place in a redox reaction. In the **half-reaction method,** you write and balance the oxidation and reduction half-reactions separately before combining them into a balanced redox equation. The outcome is the same as with the oxidation-number-change method. **To balance a redox reaction using half-reactions, write separate half-reactions for the oxidation and the reduction. After you balance atoms in each half-reaction, balance electrons gained in the reduction with electrons lost in the oxidation.** The half-reaction method is particularly useful in balancing equations for ionic reactions.

Sulfur is an element that can have several different oxidation numbers, as you can see in Table 20.2. The oxidation of sulfur by nitric acid in aqueous solution is one example of a redox reaction that can be balanced by the half-reaction method.

$$S(s) + HNO_3(aq) \longrightarrow SO_2(g) + NO(g) + H_2O(l) \text{ (unbalanced)}$$

The following steps show how to balance this equation using the half-reaction method.

Step 1 *Write the unbalanced equation in ionic form.* In this case, only HNO_3 is ionized. The products are covalent compounds.

$$S(s) + H^+(aq) + NO_3^-(aq) \longrightarrow SO_2(g) + NO(g) + H_2O(l)$$

Step 2 *Write separate half-reactions for the oxidation and reduction processes.* Sulfur is oxidized in this reaction because its oxidation number increases from 0 to +4. Nitrogen is reduced because its oxidation number decreases from 5 to +2.

$$\text{Oxidation half-reaction:} \quad \overset{0}{S}(s) \longrightarrow \overset{+4}{S}O_2(g)$$

$$\text{Reduction half-reaction:} \quad \overset{+5}{N}O_3^-(aq) \longrightarrow \overset{+2}{N}O(g)$$

Notice that H^+ ions and H_2O are not included in the half-reactions because they are neither oxidized nor reduced. However, they will be used in balancing the half-reactions.

Step 3 *Balance the atoms in the half-reactions.*

a. Balance the oxidation half-reaction. Sulfur is already balanced in the half-reaction, but oxygen is not. This reaction takes place in acid solution, so H_2O and $H^+(aq)$ are present and can be used to balance oxygen and hydrogen as needed. Add two molecules of H_2O on the left to balance the oxygen in the half-reaction.

$$2H_2O(l) + S(s) \longrightarrow SO_2(g)$$

Oxygen is now balanced, but four hydrogen ions ($4H^+$) must be added to the right to balance the hydrogen on the left.

$$2H_2O(l) + S(s) \longrightarrow SO_2(g) + 4H^+(aq)$$

This half-reaction is now balanced in terms of atoms.

b. Balance the reduction half-reaction. Nitrogen is already balanced. Add two molecules of H_2O on the right to balance the oxygen.

$$NO_3^-(aq) \longrightarrow NO(g) + 2H_2O(l)$$

Oxygen is balanced, but four hydrogen ions $(4H^+)$ must be added to the left to balance hydrogen.

$$4H^+(aq) + NO_3^-(aq) \longrightarrow NO(g) + 2H_2O(l)$$

This half-reaction is now balanced in terms of atoms.

Step 4 *Add enough electrons to one side of each half-reaction to balance the charges.* Note that neither half-reaction is balanced for charge. Four electrons are needed on the right side in the oxidation half-reaction.

Oxidation: $2H_2O(l) + S(s) \longrightarrow SO_2(g) + 4H^+(aq) + 4e^-$

Three electrons are needed on the left side in the reduction half-reaction.

Reduction: $4H^+(aq) + NO_3^-(aq) + 3e^- \longrightarrow NO(g) + 2H_2O(l)$

Each half-reaction is now balanced with respect to both atoms and charge.

Step 5 *Multiply each half-reaction by an appropriate number to make the numbers of electrons equal in both.* The number of electrons lost in oxidation must equal the number of electrons gained in reduction. In this case, the oxidation half-reaction is multiplied by 3 and the reduction half-reaction is multiplied by 4. Therefore the number of electrons lost in oxidation and the number of electrons gained in reduction both equal 12.

Oxidation: $6H_2O(l) + 3S(s) \longrightarrow 3SO_2(g) + 12H^+(aq) + 12e^-$

Reduction: $16H^+(aq) + 4NO_3^-(aq) + 12e^- \longrightarrow 4NO(g) + 8H_2O(l)$

Step 6 *Add the balanced half-reactions to show an overall equation.*

$$6H_2O(l) + 3S(s) + 16H^+(aq) + 4NO_3^-(aq) + 12e^- \longrightarrow$$
$$3SO_2(g) + 12H^+(aq) + 12e^- + 4NO(g) + 8H_2O(l)$$

Then subtract terms that appear on both sides of the equation.

$$3S(s) + 4H^+(aq) + 4NO_3^-(aq) \longrightarrow 3SO_2(g) + 4NO(g) + 2H_2O(l)$$

Step 7 *Add the spectator ions and balance the equation.* Recall that spectator ions are present but do not participate in or change during a reaction. Because none of the ions in the reactants appear in the products, there are no spectator ions in this particular example. The balanced equation is correct. However, it can be written to show the HNO_3 as unionized.

$$3S(s) + 4HNO_3(aq) \longrightarrow 3SO_2(g) + 4NO(g) + 2H_2O(l)$$

Balancing a Redox Equation Using the Half-Reaction Method

Step 1 Write the unbalanced equation in ionic form.

Step 2 Write separate half-reactions for the oxidation and reduction processes.

Step 3 Balance the atoms in the half-reactions.

Step 4 Add enough electrons to one side of each half-reaction to balance the charges. (*Hint:* The electrons will be added to opposite sides of a redox reaction.)

Step 5 Multiply each half-reaction by an appropriate number to make the numbers of electrons equal in both.

Step 6 Add the half-reactions to show an overall equation.

Step 7 Add the spectator ions and balance the equation.

Balancing Redox Equations by Half-Reactions

Balance this redox equation using the half-reaction method.

$$KMnO_4(aq) + HCl(aq) \longrightarrow MnCl_2(aq) + Cl_2(g) + H_2O(l) + KCl(aq)$$

1 Analyze *Identify the relevant concepts.*

You can use the seven steps of the half-reaction method.

2 Solve *Apply concepts to this situation.*

Write the equation in ionic form.

$$K^+(aq) + MnO_4^-(aq) + H^+(aq) + Cl^-(aq) \longrightarrow$$
$$Mn^{2+}(aq) + 2Cl^-(aq) + Cl_2(g) +$$
$$H_2O(l) + K^+(aq) + Cl^-(aq)$$

Write half-reactions. Determine the oxidation and reduction process.

Oxidation: $\overset{-1}{Cl^-} \longrightarrow \overset{0}{Cl_2}$

Reduction: $\overset{+7}{MnO_4^-} \longrightarrow \overset{+2}{Mn^{2+}}$

Balance the atoms. The solution is acidic, so use H_2O and H^+ to balance the oxygen and hydrogen. (If the solution is basic, H_2O and OH^- are used.)

Oxidation:
$2Cl^-(aq) \longrightarrow Cl_2(g)$ (atoms balanced)

Reduction:
$MnO_4^-(aq) + 8H^+(aq) \longrightarrow Mn^{2+}(aq) + 4H_2O(l)$ (atoms balanced)

Balance the charges.

Oxidation: $2Cl^-(aq) \longrightarrow Cl_2(g) + 2e^-$
(charges balanced)

Reduction:
$MnO_4^-(aq) + 8H^+(aq) + 5e^- \longrightarrow Mn^{2+}(aq) + 4H_2O(l)$ (charges balanced)

Make the numbers of electrons equal. Multiply the oxidation half-reaction by 5 and the reduction half-reaction by 2.

Oxidation: $10Cl^-(aq) \longrightarrow 5Cl_2(g) + 10e^-$

Reduction:
$2MnO_4^-(aq) + 16H^+(aq) + 10e^- \longrightarrow 2Mn^{2+}(aq) + 8H_2O(l)$

Add the half-reactions.

$10Cl^-(aq) + 2MnO_4^-(aq) + 16H^+(aq) + \cancel{10e^-} \longrightarrow$
$5Cl_2(g) + \cancel{10e^-} + 2Mn^{2+}(aq) + 8H_2O(l)$

The equation, after subtracting terms that appear on both sides:

$10Cl^-(aq) + 2MnO_4^-(aq) + 16H^+(aq) \longrightarrow$
$5Cl_2(g) + 2Mn^{2+}(aq) + 8H_2O(l)$

Add the spectator ions.

$10Cl^- + 2MnO_4^- + 2K^+ + 16H^+ + 6Cl^- \longrightarrow$
$5Cl_2 + 2Mn^{2+} + 4Cl^- + 8H_2O + 2K^+ + 2Cl^-$

Adding spectator and nonspectator Cl^- on each side gives

$16Cl^-(aq) + 2MnO_4^-(aq) + 2K^+(aq) + 16H^+(aq) \longrightarrow 5Cl_2(g) + 2Mn^{2+}(aq) + 6Cl^-(aq) + 8H_2O(l) + 2K^+(aq)$

The equation is balanced for atoms and charge. To show it balanced for the substances given in the question (rather than for ions), rewrite it as

$2KMnO_4(aq) + 16HCl(aq) \longrightarrow 2MnCl_2(aq) + 5Cl_2(g) + 8H_2O(l) + 2KCl(aq)$

Practice Problem

21. The following reaction takes place in basic solution. Balance the equation using the half-reaction method.

$$Zn(s) + NO_3^-(aq) \longrightarrow NH_3(aq) + Zn(OH_4)^{2-}(aq)$$

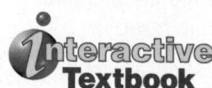

Interactive Textbook

Problem-Solving 20.21 Solve Problem 21 with the help of an interactive guided tutorial.

— with **ChemASAP**

Choosing a Balancing Method

Some redox equations, such as the following example, are simple enough to balance by inspection.

$$Zn(s) + 2AgNO_3(aq) \longrightarrow 2Ag(s) + Zn(NO_3)_2(aq)$$

Balancing by oxidation number change usually works well if the oxidized and reduced species appear only once on each side of the equation and no acids or bases are involved. However, in some redox reactions, the same element is both oxidized and reduced. In the reaction of bromine with a base such as KOH, elemental bromine is simultaneously oxidized from 0 in Br_2 to +5 in $KBrO_3$ and reduced from 0 in Br_2 to −1 in KBr.

$$3Br_2(l) + 6KOH(aq) \longrightarrow 5KBr(aq) + KBrO_3(aq) + 3H_2O(l)$$

You can tell from the coefficients in the balanced equation that it is not easy to balance. Equations such as this one and equations for reactions that take place in acidic or alkaline solution are best balanced by the half-reaction method.

Quick LAB

Bleach It! Oxidize the Color Away

Purpose
To test the effect of oxidizing agents on stains and dyes.

Materials
- spot plate
- dropper
- water
- colorimeter (optional)

Oxidizing agents
- liquid chlorine bleach (5% (m/v) sodium hypochlorite)
- powder bleach
- oxalic acid solution (1% (m/v))
- sodium thiosulfate solution (hypo) (0.2M $Na_2S_2O_3$)
- hydrogen peroxide (3% (v/v) H_2O_2)

Samples
- iodine solution (1% I_2 in 2% (m/v) KI)
- potassium permanganate solution (0.05M $KMnO_4$)
- grape juice
- rusty water
- piece of colored fabric
- colored flower petals
- grass stain on piece of white fabric

Procedure

 Sensor version available in the Probeware Lab Manual.

1. Place samples on a spot plate. Use 4 drops of each liquid or a small piece of each solid.

2. Describe the color and appearance of each sample in Step 1.

3. Add a few drops of the first oxidizing agent to each sample.

4. Describe any immediate change in appearance and any further change after 15 minutes.

5. Repeat Steps 1–4 with each oxidizing agent.

Analyze and Conclude
1. Make a grid and record your observations.

2. Compare the oxidizing power of the oxidizing agents.

3. How do you know that chemical changes have occurred?

Quality Control Chemist

A quality control chemist is responsible for seeing that products meet manufacturing standards. The consistent quality of many products you use is due to the work of a quality control chemist. They work in a wide variety of industries, including those that manufacture air bags for automobiles. They are involved in every aspect of producing the product. They contribute to the original research and development of the product and help refine its manufacturing process. They then develop methods to test the product or to determine why it has failed to perform for the consumer.

Quality control chemists must know how to make and interpret measurements. Experience in analytical chemistry and the ability to develop new analytical methods are particularly important. The specific requirements for the job depend on the industry and company that employs the quality control chemist. A good quality control chemist assures that his or her company's customers receive the highest-quality products.

For: Careers in Chemistry
Visit: PHSchool.com
Web Code: cdb-1203

20.3 Section Assessment

22. **Key Concept** What happens to the oxidation number of a species reacting in a redox reaction?

23. **Key Concept** In any redox reaction, how does the increase in oxidation number of the species oxidized compare to the decrease in the oxidation number of the species reduced?

24. **Key Concept** In balancing a redox reaction using half-reactions, what must be true concerning the number of electrons lost in the oxidation half-reaction compared to the number of electrons gained in the reduction half-reaction?

25. Balance each redox equation, using the oxidation-number-change method.

a. $ClO_3^-(aq) + I^-(aq) \longrightarrow$
$Cl^-(aq) + I_2(aq)$ [acidic solution]

b. $C_2O_4^{2-}(aq) + MnO_4^-(aq) \longrightarrow$
$Mn^{2+}(aq) + CO_2(g)$ [acidic solution]

c. $Br_2(l) + SO_2(g) \longrightarrow$
$Br^-(aq) + SO_4^{2-}(aq)$ [acidic solution]

Elements ▶ Handbook

Sodium, Iodine, and Bromine Review the equations for the production of sodium, bromine, and iodine found on pages R6 and R32 of the Elements Handbook. Identify the oxidizing agent and the reducing agent in each reaction.

Assessment 20.3 Test yourself on the concepts in Section 20.3.

— with **ChemASAP**

Small-Scale LAB

Half-Reactions

Purpose
To observe redox reactions and to write half-reactions that describe them.

Materials
- pencil
- paper
- ruler
- reaction surface
- chemicals listed in the grid

Procedure

On separate sheets of paper, draw two grids similar to the one below.

	HCl	HNO₃	H₂SO₄
Zn			
Mg			
Cu			
Fe			

Make each square 2 cm on each side. Place a reaction surface over one of the grids and add one drop of each acid solution to one piece of each metal, as shown above. Use the second grid as a data table to record your observations for each solution.

Analyze
Using your experimental data, answer the following questions.

1. Which metal is the most reactive? Explain. Which metal did not react with any of the acids? List the metals in order of decreasing reactivity.

2. What is the chemical formula of the gas produced in each reaction?

3. An active metal reacts with an acid to produce hydrogen gas and a salt. Write equations and net ionic equations to describe the reactions you observed. Are all of these redox reactions? Explain.

4. The half-reaction for the oxidation of Zn is shown below.

$$Zn(s) \longrightarrow Zn^{2+}(aq) + 2e^-$$

Write the oxidation half-reaction for the other metals that react.

5. The half-reaction for the reduction of H⁺ from the acid is shown below.

$$2H^+ + 2e^- \longrightarrow H_2(g)$$

Notice that this half-reaction is the same for all the acids. Demonstrate how adding this half-reaction to each oxidation half-reaction results in the overall net ionic equations.

You're The Chemist
The following small-scale activities allow you to develop your own procedures and analyze the results.

1. **Analyze It!** Pennies minted after 1982 are made of zinc with a thin copper coating. Use a penny that has been damaged so that a portion of the zinc shows through to compare the reactivity of the zinc and the copper toward various acids.

2. **Design It!** Many household products, such as toilet-bowl cleaners and vinegar, contain acids. Design and carry out experiments to find out if these products also react with metals.

Study Guide

Key Concepts

🔑 20.1 The Meaning of Oxidation and Reduction

- Oxidation and reduction always occur simultaneously. The substance gaining oxygen is oxidized, while the substance losing oxygen is reduced.

- Losing electrons is oxidation. Gaining electrons is reduction.

- Iron, often used in the form of the alloy steel, corrodes by being oxidized to ions of iron by oxygen.

🔑 20.2 Oxidation Numbers

- As a general rule, a bonded atom's oxidation number is the charge that it would have if the electrons in the bond were assigned to the atom of the more electronegative element.

- An increase in the oxidation number of an atom or ion indicates oxidation. A decrease in the oxidation number of an atom or ion indicates reduction.

🔑 20.3 Balancing Redox Equations

- If the oxidation number of an element in a reacting species changes, then that element has undergone either oxidation or reduction. Therefore, the reaction as a whole must be a redox reaction.

- In a balanced redox equation, the total increase in oxidation number of the species oxidized must be balanced by the total decrease in the oxidation number of the species reduced.

- To balance a redox reaction using half-reactions, write separate half-reactions for the oxidation and the reduction. After you balance atoms in each half-reaction, balance electrons gained in the reduction with electrons lost in the oxidation.

Vocabulary

- half-reaction (p. 650)
- half-reaction method (p. 650)
- oxidation (p. 633)
- oxidation number (p. 639)
- oxidation-number-change method (p. 647)

- oxidation-reduction reaction (p. 632)
- oxidizing agent (p. 634)
- redox reaction (p. 632)
- reducing agent (p. 634)
- reduction (p. 633)

Organizing Information

Use these terms to construct a concept map that organizes the major ideas of this chapter.

Textbook

Concept Map 20 Create your concept map using the computer.

with **ChemASAP**

20.1 The Meaning of Oxidation and Reduction

25. What chemical process must always accompany a reduction process?

26. What happens to an oxidizing agent during a redox reaction?

27. Balance each of the following redox equations and identify whether the first substance in the equation was oxidized or reduced.
a. $Ba(s) + O_2(g) \longrightarrow BaO(s)$
b. $CuO(s) + H_2(g) \longrightarrow Cu(s) + H_2O(l)$
c. $C_2H_4(g) + O_2(g) \longrightarrow CO_2(g) + H_2O(l)$
d. $CaO(s) + Al(s) \longrightarrow Al_2O_3(s) + Ca(s)$

28. Identify each process as either oxidation or reduction.
a. $Al \longrightarrow Al^{3+} + 3e^-$ b. $2Cl^- \longrightarrow Cl_2 + 2e^-$
c. $S^{2-} \longrightarrow S + 2e^-$ d. $Sr \longrightarrow Sr^{2+} + 2e^-$

29. Which of the following would most likely be oxidizing agents and which would most likely be reducing agents? (*Hint:* Think in terms of tendencies to lose or gain electrons.)
a. Cl_2 b. K   c. Ag^+ d. Zn^{2+}

30. Determine which reactant is oxidized and which reactant is reduced in each reaction.
a. $H_2(g) + S(s) \longrightarrow H_2S(g)$
b. $N_2(g) + 3H_2(g) \longrightarrow 2NH_3(g)$
c. $S(s) + O_2(g) \longrightarrow SO_2(g)$
d. $2H_2(g) + O_2(g) \longrightarrow 2H_2O(l)$

31. Identify the oxidizing agent and the reducing agent for each reaction in Problem 30.

32. Identify the element oxidized and the element reduced in each unbalanced redox equation.
a. $MnO_2(s) + HCl(aq) \longrightarrow$
$MnCl_2(aq) + Cl_2(g) + H_2O(l)$
b. $Cu(s) + HNO_3(aq) \longrightarrow$
$Cu(NO_3)_2(aq) + NO_2(g) + H_2O(l)$
c. $P(s) + HNO_3(aq) + H_2O(l) \longrightarrow$
$NO(g) + H_3PO_4(aq)$
d. $Bi(OH)_3(s) + Na_2SnO_2(aq) \longrightarrow$
$Bi(s) + Na_2SnO_3(aq) + H_2O(l)$

33. The following equation represents an oxidation-reduction reaction that uses oxygen. Show how this reaction can also be defined as an oxidation-reduction reaction in terms of electron transfer.
$$Pb(s) + O_2(g) \longrightarrow PbO(s)$$

34. Which of the following equations represents a redox reaction? Explain how you know.
a. $Bi_2O_3(s) + 3C(s) \longrightarrow 2Bi(s) + 3CO(g)$
b. $Cr_2O_3(s) + 3H_2S(g) \longrightarrow Cr_2S_3(s) + 3H_2O(l)$
c. $BCl_3(g) + 3H_2O(l) \longrightarrow H_3BO_3(s) + 3HCl(g)$

35. Explain why the number of electrons lost must equal the number of electrons gained in every redox reaction.

36. Explain why a sodium atom is a reducing agent but a sodium ion is not.

37. Many decomposition, single-replacement, combination, and combustion reactions are also redox reactions. Why is a double-replacement reaction never a redox reaction?

38. Why must every redox reaction have a reducing agent and an oxidizing agent?

39. Which substance in each pair is more likely to be an oxidizing agent?
a. S^{2-} or SO_4^{2-} b. H_2O or H_2O_2
c. NO_2^- or NO_3^- d. $Cr_2O_7^{2-}$ or Cr^{3+}
e. H_2 or H_2O

40. Which is more likely to be a strong reducing agent, a Group 1A (1) metal or a Group 7A (17) nonmetal? Explain.

41. The electronegativity of rhenium, Re, is 1.9, and the electronegativity of selenium is 2.4. If rhenium were to react with selenium to form a compound, which element would be oxidized and which element would be reduced? Explain.

42. Which of the following ions is most likely to be an oxidizing agent? Explain your choice.
$$MnO_4^-, MnO_4^{2-}, Mn^{2+}$$

20.2 Oxidation Numbers

43. What is an oxidation number?

44. Determine the oxidation number of each metal atom.
a. Ca^{2+} b. Al_2S_3 c. Na_2CrO_4
d. V_2O_5 e. MnO_4^- f. FeO

45. Which of these statements is false?
  a. The oxidation number of an uncombined atom is zero.
  b. The sum of the oxidation numbers of the atoms in a polyatomic ion must equal the charge of the ion.
  c. Every element has a single oxidation number.
  d. The oxidation number of oxygen in a compound or a polyatomic ion is almost always -2.

46. Assign oxidation numbers to the atoms in the following ions.
  a. OH^- **b.** PO_4^{3-} **c.** IO_3^- **d.** $H_2PO_4^-$ **e.** HSO_4^-

47. Determine the oxidation number of phosphorus in each molecule or ion.
  a. P_4O_8 **b.** PO_4^{3-} **c.** P_2O_5
  d. P_4O_6 **e.** $H_2PO_4^-$ **f.** PO_3^{3-}

48. What is the oxidation number for chromium in each of the compounds shown below?

K_2CrO_4 $K_2Cr_2O_7$

49. Examine the following hypothetical redox equation.

$$2X + 3H_2Y \longrightarrow X_2Y_3 + 3H_2$$

  a. What is the oxidation number of element X on each side of the equation?
  b. What is the oxidation number of element Y on each side of the equation?
  c. What is oxidized in this equation?
  d. What is reduced in this equation?

50. The highest possible oxidation number that chlorine exhibits in any compound is $+7$, whereas its most negative oxidation number is -1. Write the electron configuration of chlorine, and explain why these are the limiting oxidation numbers for chlorine.

51. The oxidation number of nitrogen can range from a minimum of -3 to a maximum of $+5$. Use this information to explain why the nitride ion, N^{3-}, can act only as a reducing agent, and why the nitrate ion, NO_3^-, can act only as an oxidizing agent.

20.3 Balancing Redox Equations

52. Use the changes in oxidation numbers to identify which atoms are oxidized and which are reduced in each reaction.
  a. $4Al(s) + 3MnO_2(s) \longrightarrow 2Al_2O_3(s) + 3Mn(s)$
  b. $2K(s) + 2H_2O(l) \longrightarrow 2KOH(aq) + H_2(g)$
  c. $2HgO(s) \longrightarrow 2Hg(l) + O_2(g)$
  d. $P_4(s) + 5O_2(g) \longrightarrow P_4O_{10}(s)$

53. Balance each redox equation.
  a. $Al(s) + Cl_2(g) \longrightarrow AlCl_3(s)$
  b. $Al(s) + Fe_2O_3(s) \longrightarrow Al_2O_3(s) + Fe(s)$
  c. $Cl_2(g) + KOH(aq) \longrightarrow$
$$KClO_3(aq) + KCl(aq) + H_2O(l)$$
  d. $HNO_3(aq) + H_2S(g) \longrightarrow S(s) + NO(g) + H_2O(l)$
  e. $KIO_4(aq) + KI(aq) + HCl(aq) \longrightarrow$
$$KCl(aq) + I_2(s) + H_2O(l)$$

54. Identify which of these unbalanced equations represent redox reactions.
  a. $Li(s) + H_2O(l) \longrightarrow LiOH(aq) + H_2(g)$
  b. $K_2Cr_2O_7(aq) + HCl(aq) \longrightarrow KCl(aq) +$
$$CrCl_3(aq) + H_2O(l) + Cl_2(g)$$
  c. $Al(s) + HCl(aq) \longrightarrow AlCl_3(aq) + H_2(g)$
  d. $Cl_2(g) + H_2O(l) \longrightarrow HCl(aq) + HClO(aq)$
  e. $I_2O_5(s) + CO(g) \longrightarrow I_2(s) + CO_2(g)$
  f. $H_2O(l) + SO_3(g) \longrightarrow H_2SO_4(aq)$

55. Balance each redox equation in Problem 54.

56. A device called a Breathalyzer is used to test a person's breath for the alcohol ethanol, C_2H_5OH. In this test ethanol reacts with an acidic solution of orange dichromate ion to form green chromium(III) ion.

$$Cr_2O_7^{2-}(aq) + C_2H_5OH(aq) \longrightarrow$$
$$Cr^{3+}(aq) + CO_2(g)$$

The amount of color change is proportional to the amount of ethanol in the exhaled breath.

a. Balance this equation by the half-reaction method.

b. Does the dichromate ion contain the element that is oxidized or reduced? If so, name the element.

57. The metallic element tungsten, used as a filament in incandescent light bulbs, is obtained by heating tungsten(VI) oxide with hydrogen.

$$WO_3(s) + H_2(g) \longrightarrow W(s) + H_2O(g)$$

a. Balance the equation.
b. What is oxidized in this reaction?
c. Which element undergoes a decrease in oxidation number?

58. Silver tarnishes when it reacts with hydrogen sulfide in the air.

$$Ag(s) + H_2S(g) \longrightarrow Ag_2S(s) + H_2(g)$$

a. Is silver oxidized or reduced in this reaction?
b. Identify what is reduced in this reaction.
c. Balance the equation.

59. The following unbalanced equation represents a reaction that can occur when dinitrogen tetroxide, N_2O_4, is combined with hydrazine, N_2H_4.

$$N_2O_4(l) + N_2H_4(l) \longrightarrow N_2(g) + H_2O(g)$$

Balance the equation and describe in words the electron transfer that takes place.

60. Predict the product(s) and write the balanced equation for each of these redox reactions. Identify the oxidizing agent in each reaction.

a. rubidium + iodine $\longrightarrow$
b. barium + water $\longrightarrow$
c. aluminum + iron(II) sulfate $\longrightarrow$
d. butene (C_4H_8) + oxygen $\longrightarrow$
e. zinc + hydrobromic acid $\longrightarrow$
f. magnesium + bromine $\longrightarrow$

61. How many grams of copper are needed to reduce completely the silver ions in 85.0 mL of $0.150M$ $AgNO_3(aq)$ solution? $Cu(NO_3)_2$ is one of the products.

62. How many milliliters of $0.280M$ $K_2Cr_2O_7(aq)$ solution are needed to oxidize 1.40 g of sulfur? First, balance the equation.

$$K_2Cr_2O_7(aq) + H_2O(l) + S(s) \longrightarrow$$
$$SO_2(g) + KOH(aq) + Cr_2O_3(aq)$$

63. Carbon monoxide can be removed from the air by passing it over solid diiodine pentoxide.

$$CO(g) + I_2O_5(s) \longrightarrow I_2(s) + CO_2(g)$$

a. Balance the equation.
b. Identify the element being oxidized and the element being reduced.
c. How many grams of carbon monoxide can be removed from the air by 0.55 g of diiodine pentoxide (I_2O_5)?

64. The elements fluorine and oxygen can react to form fluorine monoxide, F_2O. Write the balanced chemical equation for this reaction. Check electronegativity values and then identify the elements oxidized and reduced.

65. Combine each of the following pairs of half-reactions into a complete, balanced, ionic redox equation.

a. $Hg^{2+} + 2e^- \longrightarrow Hg$
$Al \longrightarrow Al^{3+} + 3e^-$
b. $MnO_2 + 4H^+ + 2e^- \longrightarrow Mn^{2+} + 2H_2O$
$Fe \longrightarrow Fe^{2+} + 2e^-$
c. $Fe^{3+} + e^- \longrightarrow Fe^{2+}$
$Cd \longrightarrow Cd^{2+} + 2e^-$

Test-Taking Tip

Interpreting Data Tables Tables present a large amount of data in a small space. They allow you to make comparisons and to analyze the information present. To interpret the content in a table, start by reading the title (if there is one). Then read the headings. Try to figure out the relationship between the different columns and rows of information. Ask yourself some questions: *What information is related in the table? How are the relationships represented?*

Regents Practice Exam

Part A

For each statement or question write the number of the word or expression that, of those given, best completes the statement or answers the question.

Use the following choices to answer Questions 1–7. You can use each choice once, more than once, or not at all.

(1) 1   **(2)** 2   **(3)** 3   **(4)** None of these

What is the oxidation number of nitrogen in each of theses species?

1. HNO_3
2. NH_3
3. N_2O_3
4. NO_2^-
5. N_2O
6. NH_4Cl
7. NO

8. Which of the following processes shows oxidation?
   (1) a decrease in oxidation number
   (2) a positive ion becomes a neutral atom
   (3) a loss of valence electrons
   (4) the formation of a negative ion from a neutral atom

9. Which of these general types of reactions is *never* a redox reaction?
   (1) single-replacement
   (2) double-replacement
   (3) combustion
   (4) combination (synthesis)

10. Which of these unbalanced equations represent redox reactions?
    a. $MnO(s) + PbO_2(s) \longrightarrow MnO_4^-(aq) + Pb^{2+}(aq)$ [acidic]
    b. $P_4(s) + S_8(s) \longrightarrow P_2S_5(s)$

    (1) **a.** only
    (2) **b.** only
    (3) neither **a.** nor **b.**
    (4) both **a.** and **b.**

11. A change of state that does not involve a liquid is
    (1) melting
    (2) condensation
    (3) boiling
    (4) sublimation

Part B-1

For each statement or question write the number of the word or expression that, of those given, best completes the statement or answers the question.

12. In which of the following choices is the oxidation number of nitrogen the greatest?
    (1) NO_3^-
    (2) N_2O_4
    (3) N_2O
    (4) NO_2^-

13. Identify the elements oxidized and reduced in this reaction.
    $$2ClO^- + H_2 + 2e^- \longrightarrow 2Cl^- + 2OH^-$$
    (1) Cl is oxidized, H is reduced
    (2) H is oxidized, Cl is reduced
    (3) Cl is oxidized, O is reduced
    (4) O is oxidized, Cl is reduced

14. Which of the following unbalanced half-reactions represents a reduction?
    (1) $Fe^{2+} \longrightarrow Fe^{3+}$
    (2) $Cr_2O_7^{2-} \longrightarrow Cr^{3+}$
    (3) $Mn^{2+} \longrightarrow MnO_4^-$
    (4) $S^{2-} \longrightarrow S$

15. Which of the following choices contains the atom that undergoes oxidation in this reaction?
    $$MnO_4^- + SO_2 \longrightarrow Mn^{2+} + SO_4^{2-}$$
    (1) SO_2
    (2) SO_4^{2-}
    (3) Mn^{2+}
    (4) MnO_4^-

16. Which of the following substances is an electrolyte?
    (1) $S(s)$
    (2) $NH_4Cl(aq)$
    (3) $SiO_2(s)$
    (4) $F_2(g)$

Part B-2

Answer each of the following questions.

17. What is the process a vapor undergoes when it changes to a liquid?

18. How would you make 440 mL of $1.5M$ HCl solution from a solution of $6.0M$ HCl?

19. One mole of LiF and 1.0 mol of $Ca(NO_3)_2$ are dissolved in 1.0 L of water. Which solution has the higher boiling point? Explain.

20. What is the molarity of the solution prepared by dissolving 46.4 g H_3PO_4 in enough water to make 1.25 L of solution?

21. How many milliliters of a $4.00M$ KOH solution are needed to neutralize 45.0 mL of $2.50M$ H_2SO_4 solution?

Use the numbers in the following table to answer Questions 22–25.

Metal	Metal ion
K	K⁺
Ca	Ca²⁺
Na	Na⁺
Mg	Mg²⁺
Al	Al³⁺
Zn	Zn²⁺
Fe	Fe²⁺
Ni	Ni²⁺
Sn	Sn²⁺
Pb	Pb²⁺
Cu	Cu²⁺
Ag	Ag⁺

(Table: a column of Metals K, Ca, Na, Mg, Al, Zn, Fe, Ni, Sn, Pb, Cu, Ag with corresponding Metal ions K^+, Ca^{2+}, Na^+, Mg^{2+}, Al^{3+}, Zn^{2+}, Fe^{2+}, Ni^{2+}, Sn^{2+}, Pb^{2+}, Cu^{2+}, Ag^+. Arrow 1 points up along the metals, arrow 2 points down along the ions. Bracket 3 groups K–Na, bracket 4 groups Fe–Ni, bracket 5 groups Cu–Ag.)

22. Which arrow indicates increasing ease of oxidation? Of reduction?

23. Which number's group of metals are the easiest to oxidize?

24. Which element is more easily reduced, Na or Fe?

25. Which element is more easily oxidized, Mg or Ag?

Use this diagram to answer Questions 26 and 27. It shows the formation of an ion from an atom.

Atom → Ion

26. Does the diagram represent oxidation, or does it represent reduction?

27. Does the oxidation number increase or decrease when the ion forms?

28. Draw a diagram showing the formation of a sulfide ion from a sulfur atom. Make the relative sizes of the atom and ion realistic. Does your drawing represent an oxidation or a reduction?

Part C

Answer each of the following questions.

29. The complete combustion of hydrocarbons involves the oxidation of both carbon atoms and hydrogen atoms by oxygen. The following table lists the moles of O_2 used and the moles of CO_2 and moles of H_2O produced when a series of hydrocarbons called alkanes are burned.

Alkane burned	O₂ used (mol)	CO₂ produced (mol)	H₂O produced (mol)
CH₄	2	1	2
C₂H₆	3.5	2	3
C₃H₈	5	3	4
C₄H₁₀	a. ____	b. ____	c. ____
C₅H₁₂	d. ____	e. ____	f. ____
C₆H₁₄	g. ____	h. ____	i. ____

a. Complete the table.

b. Based on the data, write a balanced generalized equation for the complete oxidation of any alkane. Use the following form, and write the coefficients in terms of x and y.

$$C_xH_y + \underline{\hspace{1cm}} O_2 \longrightarrow \underline{\hspace{1cm}} CO_2 + \underline{\hspace{1cm}} H_2O$$

30. Sodium chlorite is a powerful bleaching agent used in the paper and textile industries. It is prepared by this reaction.

$$4NaOH(aq) + Ca(OH)_2(aq) + C(s) + 4ClO_2(g) \longrightarrow 4NaClO_2(aq) + CaCO_3(s) + 3H_2O(l)$$

a. Identify the element oxidized in this reaction.

b. What element is reduced?

An electrochemical process was used to produce the shiny chrome finish on this motorcycle.

A Lemon Battery

Materials
copper strip (1 cm × 3 cm), zinc strip (1 cm × 3 cm), fine sandpaper, a whole lemon, voltmeter

Procedure

1. Polish the copper and zinc strips with sandpaper.
2. Clean the strips with hot, soapy water and dry them.
3. Push the zinc strip into the lemon. Leave about 1.5 cm of the zinc strip sticking out of the lemon.
4. Push the copper strip into the lemon about 1 cm away from the zinc strip. It should not make contact with the zinc strip. Leave about 1.5 cm of the copper strip sticking out of the lemon.

5. Briefly touch both metal strips at the same time with your tongue and observe what happens. Do not share the lemon battery with another student.
6. Measure the voltage of your lemon battery.

Think About It

1. Describe the sensation you felt on your tongue.
2. Do you think you would feel the same sensation using two copper strips or two zinc strips? Try it!
3. What would you expect to happen if, in place of the lemon, you were to use an orange?
4. If you connected 12 lemon batteries together in series, you would generate a voltage of about 12 V. Could you use this assembly to start a car? Explain.

New York Standards: 3.2j–k

Connecting to Your World On a summer evening, fireflies glow to attract their mates. In the ocean depths, anglerfish emit light to attract prey. Luminous shrimp, squid, jellyfish, and even bacteria also exist. These organisms, and others, are able to give off energy in the form of light as a result of redox reactions. In this section, you will discover that the transfer of electrons in a redox reaction produces energy.

Electrochemical Processes

As you have learned, chemical processes can either release energy or absorb energy. The energy can sometimes be in the form of electricity. Electrochemistry has many applications in the home as well as in industry. Flashlight and automobile batteries are familiar examples of devices used to generate electricity. The manufacture of sodium and aluminum metals and the silverplating of tableware involve the use of electricity. Biological systems also use electrochemistry to carry nerve impulses. In this chapter, you will learn about the relationship between redox reactions and electrochemistry.

A Spontaneous Redox Reaction When a strip of zinc metal is dipped into an aqueous solution of blue copper sulfate, the zinc becomes copper-plated, as shown in Figure 21.1. The net ionic equation involves only zinc and copper.

$$Zn(s) + Cu^{2+}(aq) \longrightarrow Zn^{2+}(aq) + Cu(s)$$

Guide for Reading

🔑 **Key Concepts**
• For any two metals in an activity series, which metal is more readily oxidized?
• What type of chemical reaction is involved in all electrochemical processes?
• How does a voltaic cell produce electrical energy?
• What current technologies use electrochemical processes to produce electrical energy?

Vocabulary
electrochemical process
electrochemical cell
voltaic cells
half-cell
salt bridge
electrode
anode
cathode
dry cell
battery
fuel cells

Reading Strategy
Building Vocabulary As you read the section, write a definition of each key term in your own words.

Figure 21.1 Zinc metal oxidizes spontaneously in a copper-ion solution. **ⓐ** A zinc strip is immersed in a solution of copper sulfate. **ⓑ** As the redox reaction proceeds, copper plates out onto the zinc, and the blue copper sulfate solution is replaced by a solution of zinc sulfate. **Classifying** *How can you classify this reaction?*

Table 21.1

Activity Series of Metals, with Half-Reactions for Oxidation Process

	Element	Oxidation half-reactions
Most active and most easily oxidized	Lithium	$Li(s) \longrightarrow Li^+(aq) + e^-$
	Potassium	$K(s) \longrightarrow K^+(aq) + e^-$
	Barium	$Ba(s) \longrightarrow Ba^{2+}(aq) + 2e^-$
	Calcium	$Ca(s) \longrightarrow Ca^{2+}(aq) + 2e^-$
	Sodium	$Na(s) \longrightarrow Na^+(aq) + e^-$
	Magnesium	$Mg(s) \longrightarrow Mg^{2+}(aq) + 2e^-$
	Aluminum	$Al(s) \longrightarrow Al^{3+}(aq) + 3e^-$
Decreasing activity	Zinc	$Zn(s) \longrightarrow Zn^{2+}(aq) + 2e^-$
	Iron	$Fe(s) \longrightarrow Fe^{2+}(aq) + 2e^-$
	Nickel	$Ni(s) \longrightarrow Ni^{2+}(aq) + 2e^-$
	Tin	$Sn(s) \longrightarrow Sn^{2+}(aq) + 2e^-$
	Lead	$Pb(s) \longrightarrow Pb^{2+}(aq) + 2e^-$
	Hydrogen*	$H_2(g) \longrightarrow 2H^+(aq) + 2e^-$
	Copper	$Cu(s) \longrightarrow Cu^{2+}(aq) + 2e^-$
	Mercury	$Hg(s) \longrightarrow Hg^{2+}(aq) + 2e^-$
Least active and least easily oxidized	Silver	$Ag(s) \longrightarrow Ag^+(aq) + e^-$
	Gold	$Au(s) \longrightarrow Au^{3+}(aq) + 3e^-$

*Hydrogen is included for reference purposes.

Electrons are transferred from zinc atoms to copper ions. This is a redox reaction that occurs spontaneously. As the reaction proceeds, zinc atoms lose electrons as they are oxidized to zinc ions. The zinc metal slowly dissolves. At the same time, copper ions in solution gain the electrons lost by the zinc. They are reduced to copper atoms and are deposited as metallic copper. As the copper ions in solution are gradually replaced by zinc ions, the blue color of the solution fades. Balanced half-reactions for this redox reaction can be written as follows.

$$\text{Oxidation: } Zn(s) \longrightarrow Zn^{2+}(aq) + 2e^-$$

$$\text{Reduction: } Cu^{2+}(aq) + 2e^- \longrightarrow Cu(s)$$

If you look at the activity series of metals in Table 21.1, you will see that zinc is higher on the list than copper. **For any two metals in an activity series, the more active metal is the more readily oxidized.** As Figure 21.1 shows, zinc is more readily oxidized than copper because when dipped into a copper sulfate solution, zinc becomes plated with copper. In contrast, when a copper strip is dipped into a solution of zinc sulfate, the copper does not spontaneously become zinc-plated. This is because copper metal is not oxidized by zinc ions.

When a zinc strip is dipped into a copper sulfate solution, electrons are transferred from zinc metal to copper ions. This flow of electrons is an electric current. Thus the zinc-metal–copper-ion system is an example of the conversion of chemical energy into electrical energy.

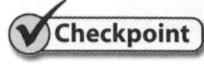 **Checkpoint** *Why doesn't a copper strip that is dipped in zinc sulfate solution become spontaneously zinc-plated?*

Redox Reactions and Electrochemistry An **electrochemical process** is any conversion between chemical energy and electrical energy. **All electrochemical processes involve redox reactions.** If a redox reaction is to be used as a source of electrical energy, the two half-reactions must be physically separated. In the case of the zinc-metal–copper-ion reaction, the electrons released by zinc must pass through an external circuit to reach the copper ions if useful electrical energy is to be produced. In that situation, the system serves as an electrochemical cell. Alternatively, an electric current can be used to produce a chemical change. That system, too, serves as an electrochemical cell. An **electrochemical cell** is any device that converts chemical energy into electrical energy or electrical energy into chemical energy. Redox reactions occur in all electrochemical cells.

Voltaic Cells

In 1800, the Italian physicist Alessandro Volta built the first electrochemical cell that could be used to generate a direct (DC) electric current. Figure 21.2 shows a photograph of Volta's illustration of one of his early cells. **Voltaic cells** (named after their inventor) are electrochemical cells used to convert chemical energy into electrical energy. **Electrical energy is produced in a voltaic cell by spontaneous redox reactions within the cell.** You use a voltaic cell every time you turn on a flashlight or a battery-powered calculator.

Constructing a Voltaic Cell A **half-cell** is one part of a voltaic cell in which either oxidation or reduction occurs. A typical half-cell consists of a piece of metal immersed in a solution of its ions. Figure 21.3 on the following page shows a voltaic cell that makes use of the zinc–copper reaction. In this cell, one half-cell is a zinc rod immersed in a solution of zinc sulfate. The other half-cell is a copper rod immersed in a solution of copper sulfate.

The half-cells are connected by a **salt bridge**—a tube containing a strong electrolyte, often potassium sulfate (K_2SO_4). Salt bridges usually are made of agar, a gelatinous substance. A porous plate may be used instead of a salt bridge. The porous plate allows ions to pass from one half-cell to the other but prevents the solutions from mixing completely. A wire carries the electrons in the external circuit from the zinc rod to the copper rod. A voltmeter or light bulb can be connected in the circuit. The driving force of such a voltaic cell is the spontaneous redox reaction between zinc metal and copper(II) ions in solution.

The zinc and copper rods in this voltaic cell are the electrodes. An **electrode** is a conductor in a circuit that carries electrons to or from a substance other than a metal. The reaction at the electrode determines whether the electrode is labeled as an anode or a cathode. The electrode at which oxidation occurs is called the **anode.** Because electrons are produced at the anode, it is labeled the negative electrode. The electrode at which reduction occurs is called the **cathode.** Electrons are consumed at the cathode. As a result, the cathode is labeled the positive electrode. Neither electrode is really charged, however. All parts of the voltaic cell remain balanced in terms of charge at all times. The moving electrons balance any charge that might build up as oxidation and reduction occur.

Figure 21.2 Volta built his electrochemical cell using piles of silver and zinc plates separated by cardboard soaked in salt water. He used his cell to obtain an electrical current.

$$Zn(s) \longrightarrow Zn^{2+}(aq) + 2e^-$$

ZnSO₄ solution

CuSO₄ solution

$$Cu^{2+}(aq) + 2e^- \longrightarrow Cu(s)$$

Figure 21.3 In this voltaic cell, the electrons generated from the oxidation of Zn to Zn^{2+} flow through the external circuit (the wire) into the copper strip. These electrons reduce the surrounding Cu^{2+} to Cu. To maintain neutrality in the electrolytes, anions flow through the salt bridge.

How a Voltaic Cell Works The electrochemical process that occurs in a zinc–copper voltaic cell can best be described in a number of steps. These steps actually occur at the same time.

1. Electrons are produced at the zinc rod according to the oxidation half-reaction.

$$Zn(s) \longrightarrow Zn^{2+}(aq) + 2e^-$$

Because it is oxidized, the zinc rod is the anode, or negative electrode.

2. The electrons leave the zinc anode and pass through the external circuit to the copper rod. (If a bulb is in the circuit, the electron flow will cause it to light. If a voltmeter is present, it will indicate a voltage.)

3. Electrons enter the copper rod and interact with copper ions in solution. There the following reduction half-reaction occurs.

$$Cu^{2+}(aq) + 2e^- \longrightarrow Cu(s)$$

Because copper ions are reduced at the copper rod, the copper rod is the cathode, or positive electrode, in the voltaic cell.

4. To complete the circuit, both positive and negative ions move through the aqueous solutions via the salt bridge. The two half-reactions can be summed to show the overall cell reaction. Note that the electrons in the overall reaction must cancel.

$$\begin{aligned} Zn(s) &\longrightarrow Zn^{2+}(aq) + 2e^- \\ Cu^{2+}(aq) + 2e^- &\longrightarrow Cu(s) \\ \hline Zn(s) + Cu^{2+}(aq) &\longrightarrow Zn^{2+}(aq) + Cu(s) \end{aligned}$$

When the zinc sulfate and copper(II) sulfate solutions in the voltaic half-cells are both 1.0M, the cell generates an electrical potential of 1.10 volts (V). If different metals are used for the electrodes or if different solution concentrations are used, the voltage will differ.

Representing Electrochemical Cells You can represent the zinc–copper voltaic cell by using the following shorthand form.

$$Zn(s) \mid ZnSO_4(aq) \parallel CuSO_4(aq) \mid Cu(s)$$

The single vertical lines indicate boundaries of phases that are in contact. The zinc rod ($Zn(s)$) and the zinc sulfate solution ($ZnSO_4(aq)$), for example, are separate phases in physical contact. The double vertical lines represent the salt bridge or porous partition that separates the anode compartment from the cathode compartment. The half-cell that undergoes oxidation (the anode) is written first, to the left of the double vertical lines.

Checkpoint *Which half-cell is written first in the shorthand representation of an electrochemical cell?*

Using Voltaic Cells as Energy Sources

Although the zinc-copper voltaic cell is of historical importance, it is no longer used commercially. **Current technologies that use electrochemical processes to produce electrical energy include dry cells, lead storage batteries, and fuel cells.**

Dry Cells When a compact, portable electrical energy source is required, a dry cell is usually chosen. A **dry cell** is a voltaic cell in which the electrolyte is a paste. A type of dry cell that is very familiar to you is the common flashlight battery, which, despite the name, is not a true battery. In such a dry cell, a zinc container is filled with a thick, moist electrolyte paste of manganese(IV) oxide (MnO_2), zinc chloride ($ZnCl_2$), ammonium chloride (NH_4Cl), and water (H_2O). As shown in Figure 21.4a, a graphite rod is embedded in the paste. The zinc container is the anode and the graphite rod is the cathode. The thick paste and its surrounding paper liner prevent the contents of the cell from freely mixing, so a salt bridge is not needed. The half-reactions for this cell are shown below.

Oxidation: $Zn(s) \longrightarrow Zn^{2+}(aq) + 2e^-$ (anode reaction)

Reduction: $2MnO_2(s) + 2NH_4^+(aq) + 2e^- \longrightarrow$
$$Mn_2O_3(s) + 2NH_3(aq) + H_2O(l) \text{ (cathode reaction)}$$

Go Online
NSTA *SciLINKS*
For: Links on Electrochemical Cells
Visit: www.SciLinks.org
Web Code: cdn-1210

a Dry Cell
Positive button (+)
Graphite rod (cathode)
Moist paste of MnO_2, $ZnCl_2$, NH_4Cl, H_2O, and graphite powder
Zinc (anode)
Negative end cap (−)

b Alkaline Battery
Positive button (+)
Steel case
MnO_2 in KOH paste
Graphite rod (cathode)
Absorbent separator
Zinc (anode)
Negative end cap (−)

Figure 21.4 Both dry cells and alkaline batteries are single electrochemical cells that produce about 1.5 V. **a** The dry cell is inexpensive, has a short shelf life, and suffers from voltage drop when in use. **b** The alkaline battery costs more than the dry cell, has a longer shelf life, and does not suffer from voltage drop. **Inferring** *What is oxidized in these cells and what is reduced?*

In an ordinary dry cell, the graphite rod serves only as a conductor and does not undergo reduction, even though it is the cathode. The manganese in MnO_2 is the species that is actually reduced. The electrical potential of this cell starts out at 1.5 V but decreases steadily during use to about 0.8 V. Dry cells of this type are not rechargeable because the cathode reaction is not reversable.

The alkaline battery, shown in Figure 21.4b on the previous page, is an improved dry cell used for the same purposes. In the alkaline battery, the reactions are similar to those in the common dry cell, but the electrolyte is a basic KOH paste. This change in design eliminates the buildup of ammonia gas and maintains the Zn electrode, which corrodes more slowly under alkaline conditions.

✓ **Checkpoint**) **What electrolyte is used in an alkaline battery?**

Lead Storage Batteries People depend on lead storage batteries to start their cars. A **battery** is a group of cells connected together. A 12-V car battery consists of six voltaic cells connected together. Each cell produces about 2 V and consists of lead grids, as shown in Figure 21.5. One set of grids, the anode, is packed with spongy lead. The other set, the cathode, is packed with lead(IV) oxide (PbO_2). The electrolyte for both half-cells in a lead storage battery is concentrated sulfuric acid. Using the same electrolyte for both half-cells allows the cell to operate without a salt bridge or porous separator. The half-reactions are as follows.

Oxidation: $Pb(s) + SO_4^{2-}(aq) \longrightarrow PbSO_4(s) + 2e^-$

Reduction: $PbO_2(s) + 4H^+(aq) + SO_4^{2-}(aq) + 2e^- \longrightarrow$
$$PbSO_4(s) + 2H_2O(l)$$

When a lead storage battery discharges, it produces the electrical energy needed to start a car. The overall spontaneous redox reaction that occurs is the sum of the oxidation and reduction half-reactions.

$$Pb(s) + PbO_2(s) + 2H_2SO_4(aq) \longrightarrow 2PbSO_4(s) + 2H_2O(l)$$

This equation shows that lead sulfate forms during discharge. The sulfate slowly builds up on the plates, and the concentration of sulfuric acid decreases.

The reverse reaction occurs when a lead storage battery is recharged. This reaction occurs whenever the car's generator is working properly.

$$2PbSO_4(s) + 2H_2O(l) \longrightarrow Pb(s) + PbO_2(s) + 2H_2SO_4(aq)$$

This is not a spontaneous reaction. To make the reaction proceed as written, a direct current must pass through the cell in a direction opposite that of the current flow during discharge. In theory, a lead storage battery can be discharged and recharged indefinitely, but in practice its lifespan is limited. This is because small amounts of lead sulfate fall from the electrodes and collect on the bottom of the cell. Eventually, the electrodes lose so much lead sulfate that the recharging process is ineffective or the cell is shorted out. The battery must then be replaced. The processes that occur during the discharge and recharge of a lead-acid battery are summarized in Figure 21.6.

Figure 21.5 One cell of a 12-V lead storage battery is illustrated here. Current is produced when lead at the anode and lead(IV) oxide at the cathode are both converted to lead sulfate. These processes decrease the sulfuric acid concentration in the battery. Reversing the reaction recharges the battery.

Dilute sulfuric acid ($H_2SO_4(aq)$) electrolyte

Lead grid filled with lead(IV) oxide (PbO_2) (cathode)

Lead grid filled with spongy lead (Pb) (anode)

Figure 21.6 The lead-acid battery in an automobile acts as a voltaic cell (top) when it supplies current to start the engine. Some of the power from the running engine is used to recharge the battery which then acts as an electrolytic cell (bottom). You will learn more about electrolytic cells in Section 21.3.

Fuel Cells To overcome the disadvantages associated with lead storage batteries, cells with renewable electrodes have been developed. Such cells, called **fuel cells,** are voltaic cells in which a fuel substance undergoes oxidation and from which electrical energy is continuously obtained. Fuel cells do not have to be recharged. They can be designed to emit no air pollutants and to operate more quietly and more cost-effectively than a conventional electrical generator.

Perhaps the simplest fuel cell is the hydrogen–oxygen fuel cell, which is shown in Figure 21.7 on the following page. In this fuel cell, there are three compartments separated from one another by two electrodes made of porous carbon. Oxygen (the oxidizer) is fed into the cathode compartment. Hydrogen (the fuel) is fed into the anode compartment. The gases diffuse slowly through the electrodes. The electrolyte in the central compartment is a hot, concentrated solution of potassium hydroxide. Electrons from the oxidation half-reaction at the anode pass through an external circuit to enter the reduction half-reaction at the cathode.

Oxidation: $2H_2(g) + 4OH^-(aq) \longrightarrow 4H_2O(l) + 4e^-$ (anode)

Reduction: $O_2(g) + 2H_2O(l) + 4e^- \longrightarrow 4OH^-(aq)$ (cathode)

The overall reaction in the hydrogen–oxygen fuel cell is the oxidation of hydrogen to form water.

$$2H_2(g) + O_2(g) \longrightarrow 2H_2O(l)$$

Other fuels, such as methane (CH_4) and ammonia (NH_3), can be used in place of hydrogen. Other oxidizers, such as chlorine (Cl_2) and ozone (O_3), can be used in place of oxygen.

Figure 21.7 The hydrogen–oxygen fuel cell is a clean source of power. Such cells are often used in spacecraft. **Predicting** *What waste products, if any, are produced?*

Hydrogen

Oxygen

Since the 1960s, astronauts have used fuel cells as an energy source aboard spacecraft. Hydrogen–oxygen fuel cells with a mass of approximately 100 kg each were used in the Apollo spacecraft missions. Fuel cells are well suited for extended space missions because they offer a continuous energy source that releases no pollutants. On space shuttle missions, for example, astronauts drink the water produced by onboard hydrogen–oxygen fuel cells. Fuel cells are also used as auxiliary power sources for submarines and other military vehicles. At present, however, they are too expensive for general use.

21.1 Section Assessment

1. **Key Concept** If the relative activities of two metals are known, which metal is more easily oxidized?

2. **Key Concept** What type of reaction occurs during an electrochemical process?

3. **Key Concept** What is the source of electrical energy produced in a voltaic cell?

4. **Key Concept** What are three examples of technologies that use electrochemical processes to supply electrical energy?

5. Describe the structure of a dry cell. What substance is oxidized? What substance is reduced?

6. What is the electrolyte in a lead storage battery? Write the half-reactions for such a battery.

7. Write the overall reaction that takes place in a hydrogen–oxygen fuel cell. What product(s) are formed? Describe the half-reactions in this cell.

8. Predict the result when a strip of copper is dipped into a solution of iron(II) sulfate.

Writing ▶ **Activity**

Explanatory Paragraph Write a paragraph explaining how a zinc–copper voltaic cell works. Make sure to mention the half-reactions and the overall reaction in your explanation. (*Hint:* Use Figure 21.3 on page 666 as a reference.)

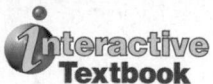
Textbook

Assessment 21.1 Test yourself on the concepts in Section 21.1.

with ChemASAP

21.2 Half-Cells and Cell Potentials

New York Standards: 3.2f, 3.2h, 3.2j–k

Connecting to Your World

Batteries provide current to power lights and many kinds of electronic devices—such as the personal digital assistant shown here. One type of battery that you're probably familiar with is a car battery. The electrical potential between the negative and positive terminals of a car battery is 12 V. Other common batteries are the ones used to power flashlights, radios, and CD players. They are commonly known as AAA, AA, C, and D batteries. The electrical potential in these batteries is 1.5 V. In this section, you will learn how to calculate electrical potential.

Guide for Reading

Key Concepts
- What causes the electrical potential of an electrochemical cell?
- What value is assigned to the electrical potential of a standard hydrogen electrode?
- How can you determine the standard reduction potential of a half-cell?
- How can you interpret the cell potential of a redox reaction in terms of the spontaneity of the reaction?

Vocabulary
electrical potential
reduction potential
cell potential
standard cell potential
standard hydrogen electrode

Reading Strategy
Monitoring Your Understanding
After you read the section, identify what you don't yet understand about half-cells and cell potentials. Reread the section or ask for help. Then write your clarified understanding.

Electrical Potential

The **electrical potential** of a voltaic cell is a measure of the cell's ability to produce an electric current. Electrical potential is usually measured in volts (V). The potential of an isolated half-cell cannot be measured. For example, you cannot measure the electrical potential of a zinc half-cell or of a copper half-cell separately. When these two half-cells are connected to form a voltaic cell, however, the difference in potential can be measured. The electrical potential of a $1 M$ zinc–copper cell is $+1.10$ V.

The electrical potential of a cell results from a competition for electrons between two half-cells. The half-cell that has a greater tendency to acquire electrons will be the one in which reduction occurs. Oxidation occurs in the other half-cell as there is a loss of electrons. The tendency of a given half-reaction to occur as a reduction is called the **reduction potential.** The half-cell in which reduction occurs has a greater reduction potential than the half-cell in which oxidation occurs. The difference between the reduction potentials of the two half-cells is called the **cell potential.**

$$\text{cell potential} = \begin{pmatrix} \text{reduction potential} \\ \text{of half-cell in which} \\ \text{reduction occurs} \end{pmatrix} - \begin{pmatrix} \text{reduction potential} \\ \text{of half-cell in which} \\ \text{oxidation occurs} \end{pmatrix}$$

$$\text{or} \quad E^0_{cell} = E^0_{red} - E^0_{oxid}$$

Figure 21.8 A working voltaic cell can be constructed using a lemon and strips of copper and zinc.

Figure 21.9 The standard hydrogen electrode is arbitrarily assigned a standard reduction potential of 0.00 V at 25°C.

Salt bridge to other half-cell

Platinum wire

Glass sleeve

H₂ (g) (101 kPa)

Platinum foil coated with platinum black

1.00M acid solution

Standard Cell Potential

The **standard cell potential** (E^0_{cell}) is the measured cell potential when the ion concentrations in the half-cells are $1M$, any gases are at a pressure of 101 kPa, and the temperature is 25°C. The symbols E^0_{red} and E^0_{oxid} represent the standard reduction potentials for the reduction and oxidation half-cells, respectively. The relationship between these values follows the general relationship for cell potential given on the previous page.

$$E^0_{cell} = E^0_{red} - E^0_{oxid}$$

Because half-cell potentials cannot be measured directly, scientists have chosen an arbitrary electrode to serve as a reference. The **standard hydrogen electrode** is used with other electrodes so the reduction potentials of the other cells can be measured. 🔵 **The standard reduction potential of the hydrogen electrode has been assigned a value of 0.00 V.** The standard hydrogen electrode, which is illustrated in Figure 21.9, consists of a platinum electrode immersed in a solution with a hydrogen-ion concentration of $1M$. The solution is at 25°C . The electrode itself is a small square of platinum foil coated with finely divided platinum, known as platinum black. Hydrogen gas at a pressure of 101 kPa is bubbled around the platinum electrode. The half-cell reaction that occurs at the platinum black surface is as follows.

$$2H^+ (aq, 1M) + 2e^- \rightleftharpoons H_2(g, 101 \text{ kPa}) \qquad E^0_{H^+} = 0.00 \text{ V}$$

The double arrows in the equation indicate that the reaction is reversible. The symbol $E^0_{H^+}$ represents the standard reduction potential of H^+. The standard reduction potential of H^+ is the tendency of H^+ ions to acquire electrons and be reduced to $H_2(g)$. Whether this half-cell reaction occurs as a reduction or as an oxidation is determined by the reduction potential of the half-cell to which the standard hydrogen electrode is connected.

✓ Checkpoint *What components and conditions are required for a standard hydrogen electrode?*

Standard Reduction Potentials

A voltaic cell can be made by connecting a standard hydrogen half-cell to a standard zinc half-cell, as shown in Figure 21.10. To determine the overall reaction for this cell, first identify the half-cell in which reduction takes place. In all electrochemical cells, reduction takes place at the cathode and oxidation takes place at the anode. A voltmeter gives a reading of +0.76 V when the zinc electrode is connected to the negative terminal and the hydrogen electrode is connected to the positive terminal. The zinc is oxidized, which means that it is the anode. Hydrogen ions are reduced, which means that the hydrogen electrode is the cathode. You can now write the half-reactions and the overall cell reaction.

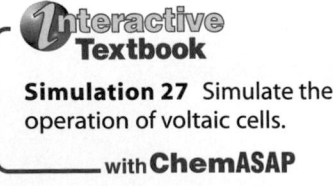

Simulation 27 Simulate the operation of voltaic cells.

__with ChemASAP__

Oxidation:	$Zn(s) \longrightarrow Zn^{2+}(aq) + 2e^-$ (at anode)
Reduction:	$2H^+(aq) + 2e^- \longrightarrow H_2(g)$ (at cathode)
Cell reaction:	$Zn(s) + 2H^+(aq) \longrightarrow Zn^{2+}(aq) + H_2(g)$

$E^0 \text{cell} = +0.76\text{V}$

e⁻ → ... ← e⁻

Anode (−)

Zn

Cathode (+)

H₂ (g) (101 kPa)

Salt bridge

Cotton plugs

1.00M Zn²⁺

1.00M H⁺

Zinc half-cell

Hydrogen half-cell

Figure 21.10 This voltaic cell consists of zinc and hydrogen half-cells. **Interpreting Diagrams** *Where does reduction occur, and what is reduced in this cell?*

You can determine the standard reduction potential of a half-cell by using a standard hydrogen electrode and the equation for standard cell potential. In the zinc–hydrogen cell, zinc was oxidized and hydrogen ions were reduced. Let $E^0_{red} = E^0_{H^+}$ and $E^0_{oxid} = E^0_{Zn^{2+}}$ in the standard cell potential equation.

$$E^0_{cell} = E^0_{red} - E^0_{oxid}$$
$$E^0_{cell} = E^0_{H^+} - E^0_{Zn^{2+}}$$

The cell potential (E^0_{cell}) was measured at $+0.76$ V. The reduction potential of the hydrogen half-cell is a defined standard: $E^0_{H^+}$ always equals 0.00 V. Substituting these values into the preceding equation will give the standard reduction potential for the zinc half-cell.

$$+0.76\text{ V} = 0.00\text{ V} - E^0_{Zn^{2+}}$$
$$E^0_{Zn^{2+}} = -0.76\text{ V}$$

The standard reduction potential for the zinc half-cell is -0.76 V. The value is negative because the tendency of zinc ions to be reduced to zinc metal in this cell is less than the tendency of hydrogen ions to be reduced to hydrogen gas (H_2). Consequently, the zinc ions are not reduced. Instead, the opposite occurs: Zinc metal is oxidized to zinc ions.

Many different half-cells can be paired with the hydrogen half-cell in a similar manner. Using this method, the standard reduction potential for each half-cell can be obtained. For a standard copper half-cell, for example, the measured standard cell potential is $+0.34$ V. Copper is the cathode, and Cu^{2+} ions are reduced to Cu metal when the cell operates. The hydrogen half-cell is the anode, and H_2 gas is oxidized to H^+ ions. You can calculate the standard reduction potential for copper as follows.

$$E^0_{cell} = E^0_{red} - E^0_{oxid}$$
$$E^0_{cell} = E^0_{Cu^{2+}} - E^0_{H^+}$$
$$+0.34\text{ V} = E^0_{Cu^{2+}} - 0.00$$
$$E^0_{Cu^{2+}} = +0.34\text{ V}$$

This value is positive because the tendency for copper ions to be reduced in the cell is greater than the tendency of hydrogen ions to be reduced.

Table 21.2

Reduction Potentials at 25°C with 1M Concentrations of Aqueous Species

Electrode	Half-reaction	E^0 (V)
Li$^+$/Li	Li$^+$ + e$^-$ $\longrightarrow$ Li	−3.05
K$^+$/K	K$^+$ + e$^-$ $\longrightarrow$ K	−2.93
Ba^{2+}/Ba	Ba^{2+} + 2e$^-$ $\longrightarrow$ Ba	−2.90
Ca^{2+}/Ca	Ca^{2+} + 2e$^-$ $\longrightarrow$ Ca	−2.87
Na$^+$/Na	Na$^+$ + e$^-$ $\longrightarrow$ Na	−2.71
Mg^{2+}/Mg	Mg^{2+} + 2e$^-$ $\longrightarrow$ Mg	−2.37
Al^{3+}/Al	Al^{3+} + 3e$^-$ $\longrightarrow$ Al	−1.66
H$_2$O/H$_2$	2H$_2$O + 2e$^-$ $\longrightarrow$ H$_2$ + 2OH$^-$	−0.83
Zn^{2+}/Zn	Zn^{2+} + 2e$^-$ $\longrightarrow$ Zn	−0.76
Cr^{3+}/Cr	Cr^{3+} + 3e$^-$ $\longrightarrow$ Cr	−0.74
Fe^{2+}/Fe	Fe^{2+} + 2e$^-$ $\longrightarrow$ Fe	−0.44
H$_2$O/H$_2$ (pH 7)	2H$_2$O + 2e$^-$ $\longrightarrow$ H$_2$ + 2OH$^-$	−0.42
Cd^{2+}/Cd	Cd^{2+} + 2e$^-$ $\longrightarrow$ Cd	−0.40
PbSO$_4$/Pb	PbSO$_4$ + 2e$^-$ $\longrightarrow$ Pb + SO$_4^{2-}$	−0.36
Co^{2+}/Co	Co^{2+} + 2e$^-$ $\longrightarrow$ Co	−0.28
Ni^{2+}/Ni	Ni^{2+} + 2e$^-$ $\longrightarrow$ Ni	−0.25
Sn^{2+}/Sn	Sn^{2+} + 2e$^-$ $\longrightarrow$ Sn	−0.14
Pb^{2+}/Pb	Pb^{2+} + 2e$^-$ $\longrightarrow$ Pb	−0.13
Fe^{3+}/Fe	Fe^{3+} + 3e$^-$ $\longrightarrow$ Fe	−0.036
H$^+$/H$_2$	2H$^+$ + 2e$^-$ $\longrightarrow$ H$_2$	0.000
AgCl/Ag	AgCl + e$^-$ $\longrightarrow$ Ag + Cl$^-$	+0.22
Hg$_2$Cl$_2$/Hg	Hg$_2$Cl$_2$ + 2e$^-$ $\longrightarrow$ 2Hg + 2Cl$^-$	+0.27
Cu^{2+}/Cu	Cu^{2+} + 2e$^-$ $\longrightarrow$ Cu	+0.34
O$_2$/OH$^-$	O$_2$ + 2H$_2$O + 4e$^-$ $\longrightarrow$ 4OH$^-$	+0.40
Cu$^+$/Cu	Cu$^+$ + e$^-$ $\longrightarrow$ Cu	+0.52
I$_2$/I$^-$	I$_2$ + 2e$^-$ $\longrightarrow$ 2I$^-$	+0.54
Fe^{3+}/Fe^{2+}	Fe^{3+} + e$^-$ $\longrightarrow$ Fe^{2+}	+0.77
Hg$_2^{2+}$/Hg	Hg$_2^{2+}$ + 2e$^-$ $\longrightarrow$ 2Hg	+0.79
Ag$^+$/Ag	Ag$^+$ + e$^-$ $\longrightarrow$ Ag	+0.80
O$_2$/H$_2$O (pH 7)	O$_2$ + 4H$^+$ + 4e$^-$ $\longrightarrow$ 2H$_2$O	+0.82
Hg^{2+}/Hg	Hg^{2+} + 2e$^-$ $\longrightarrow$ Hg	+0.85
Br$_2$/Br$^-$	Br$_2$ + 2e$^-$ $\longrightarrow$ 2Br$^-$	+1.07
O$_2$/H$_2$O	O$_2$ + 4H$^+$ + 4e$^-$ $\longrightarrow$ 2H$_2$O	+1.23
MnO$_2$/Mn^{2+}	MnO$_2$ + 4H$^+$ + 2e$^-$ $\longrightarrow$ Mn^{2+} + 2H$_2$O	+1.28
Cr$_2$O$_7^{2-}$/Cr^{3+}	Cr$_2$O$_7^{2-}$ + 14H$^+$ + 6e$^-$ $\longrightarrow$ 2Cr^{3+} + 7H$_2$O	+1.33
Cl$_2$/Cl$^-$	Cl$_2$ + 2e$^-$ $\longrightarrow$ 2Cl$^-$	+1.36
PbO$_2$/Pb^{2+}	PbO$_2$ + 4H$^+$ + 2e$^-$ $\longrightarrow$ Pb^{2+} + 2H$_2$O	+1.46
MnO$_4^-$/Mn^{2+}	MnO$_4^-$ + 8H$^+$ + 5e$^-$ $\longrightarrow$ Mn^{2+} + 4H$_2$O	+1.51
PbO$_2$/PbSO$_4$	PbO$_2$ + 4H$^+$ + SO$_4^{2-}$ + 2e$^-$ $\longrightarrow$ PbSO$_4$ + 2H$_2$O	+1.69
F$_2$/F$^-$	F$_2$ + 2e$^-$ $\longrightarrow$ 2F$^-$	+2.87

Table 21.2 on the preceding page lists some standard reduction potentials at 25°C. The half-reactions are arranged in increasing order of their tendency to occur in the forward direction—that is, as a reduction. Thus, the half-reactions at the top of the table have the least tendency to occur as reductions. The half-reactions at the bottom of the table have the greatest tendency to occur as reductions. For example, lithium ions (at the top) have very little tendency to be reduced to lithium metal.

Calculating Standard Cell Potentials

To function, a cell must be constructed of two half-cells. The half-cell reaction having the more positive (or less negative) reduction potential occurs as a reduction in the cell. With this in mind, it is possible to write cell reactions and calculate cell potentials for cells without actually assembling them. You can simply use the known standard reduction potentials for the various half-cells (from Table 21.2) to predict the half-cells in which reduction and oxidation will occur. This information can then be used to find the resulting E_{cell}^0 value. ⊙ **If the cell potential for a given redox reaction is positive, then the reaction is spontaneous as written. If the cell potential is negative, then the reaction is nonspontaneous.** This latter reaction will be spontaneous in the reverse direction, however, and the cell potential will then have a numerically equal but positive value.

CONCEPTUAL PROBLEM 21.1

Determining Reaction Spontaneity

Many hearing aid batteries contain zinc and silver oxide. Show that the following redox reaction between Zn and Ag^+ is spontaneous.

$$Zn(s) + 2Ag^+(aq) \longrightarrow Zn^{2+}(aq) + 2Ag(s)$$

❶ Analyze *Identify the relevant concepts.*
Identify the half-reactions, and calculate the standard cell potential ($E_{cell}^0 = E_{red}^0 - E_{oxid}^0$). If E_{cell}^0 is positive, the reaction is spontaneous.

❷ Solve *Apply concepts to this situation.*
The half-reactions from the equation are:

Oxidation: $Zn(s) \longrightarrow Zn^{2+}(aq) + 2e^-$

Reduction: $Ag^+(aq) + e^- \longrightarrow Ag(s)$

Use Table 21.2 to look up the standard reduction potentials for the half-cells.

$$Zn^{2+}(aq) + 2e^- \longrightarrow Zn(s) \quad E_{Zn^{2+}}^0 = -0.76 \text{ V}$$
$$Ag^+(aq) + e^- \longrightarrow Ag(s) \quad E_{Ag^+}^0 = +0.80 \text{ V}$$

Calculate the standard cell potential.

$$E_{cell}^0 = E_{red}^0 - E_{oxid}^0 = E_{Ag^+}^0 - E_{Zn^{2+}}^0$$
$$= 0.80 \text{ V} - (-0.76 \text{ V}) = +1.56 \text{ V}$$

$E_{cell}^0 > 0$, so the reaction is spontaneous.

Practice Problems

9. Determine whether the following redox reaction will occur spontaneously.

$$3Zn^{2+}(aq) + 2Cr(s) \longrightarrow 3Zn(s) + 2Cr^{3+}(aq)$$

10. Is this redox reaction spontaneous as written?

$$Co^{2+}(aq) + Fe(s) \longrightarrow Fe^{2+}(aq) + Co(s)$$

Problem-Solving 12.9 Solve Problem 9 with the help of an interactive guided tutorial.

— with **ChemASAP**

Writing the Cell Reaction

Determine the cell reaction for a voltaic cell composed of the following half-cells.

$$Fe^{3+}(aq) + e^- \longrightarrow Fe^{2+}(aq) \qquad E^0_{Fe^{3+}} = +0.77\,V$$

$$Ni^{2+}(aq) + 2e^- \longrightarrow Ni(s) \qquad E^0_{Ni^{2+}} = -0.25\,V$$

1 Analyze *List the knowns and the unknowns.*

Knowns
- $E^0_{Fe^{3+}} = +0.77\,V$
- $E^0_{Ni^{2+}} = -0.25\,V$

Unknowns
- cell reaction = ?
- $E^0_{cell} = ?\,V$

The half-cell with the more positive reduction potential is the one in which reduction occurs (the cathode). That means that the oxidation reaction occurs at the anode. Add the half-reactions, making certain that the number of electrons lost equals the number of electrons gained.

2 Calculate *Solve for the unknowns.*

The Fe^{3+} half-cell, which has the more positive reduction potential, is the cathode. So in this voltaic cell, Fe^{3+} is reduced and Ni is oxidized. The half-cell reactions, written in the direction in which they actually occur, are as follows.

Oxidation: $Ni(s) \longrightarrow Ni^{2+}(aq) + 2e^-$ (at anode)

Reduction: $Fe^{3+}(aq) + e^- \longrightarrow Fe^{2+}(aq)$ (at cathode)

Before adding the half-reactions, be sure that the electrons cancel—that is, that they are present in equal number on both sides of the equation. Because Ni loses two electrons as it is oxidized, while Fe^{3+} gains only one electron as it is reduced, you must multiply the Fe^{3+} half-cell equation by 2.

$$Ni(s) \longrightarrow Ni^{2+}(aq) + 2e^-$$
$$2[Fe^{3+}(aq) + e^- \longrightarrow Fe^{2+}(aq)]$$
$$\overline{Ni(s) + 2Fe^{3+}(aq) \longrightarrow Ni^{2+}(aq) + 2Fe^{2+}(aq)}$$

3 Evaluate *Does the result make sense?*

The electrons cancelled when the half-reactions were added. The equation for the cell reaction is correctly written.

Practice Problems

11. A voltaic cell is constructed using the following half-reactions.

$$Cu^{2+}(aq) + 2e^- \longrightarrow Cu(s)$$
$$E^0_{Cu^{2+}} = +0.34\,V$$
$$Al^{3+}(aq) + 3e^- \longrightarrow Al(s)$$
$$E^0_{Al^{3+}} = -1.66\,V$$

Determine the cell reaction.

12. A voltaic cell is constructed using the following half-reactions.

$$Ag^+(aq) + e^- \longrightarrow Ag(s)$$
$$E^0_{Ag^+} = +0.80\,V$$
$$Cu^{2+}(aq) + 2e^- \longrightarrow Cu(s)$$
$$E^0_{Cu^{2+}} = +0.34\,V$$

Determine the cell reaction.

interactive **Textbook**

Problem-Solving 12.12 Solve Problem 12 with the help of an interactive guided tutorial.

—with **ChemASAP**

Calculating the Standard Cell Potential

Calculate the standard cell potential for the voltaic cell described in Sample Problem 21.1. The half-reactions are as follows.

$$Fe^{3+}(aq) + e^- \longrightarrow Fe^{2+}(aq) \qquad E^0_{Fe^{3+}} = +0.77 \text{ V}$$

$$Ni^{2+}(aq) + 2e^- \longrightarrow Ni(s) \qquad E^0_{Ni^{2+}} = -0.25 \text{ V}$$

1 Analyze *List the knowns and the unknown.*

Knowns
- $E^0_{Fe^{3+}} = +0.77 \text{ V}$
- $E^0_{Ni^{2+}} = -0.25 \text{ V}$
- cathode: Fe^{3+} half-cell

Unknown
- $E^0_{cell} = ?$

Use the equation $E^0_{cell} = E^0_{red} - E^0_{oxid}$ to calculate standard cell potential.

2 Calculate *Solve for the unknown.*

$$E^0_{cell} = E^0_{red} - E^0_{oxid} = E^0_{Fe^{3+}} - E^0_{Ni^{2+}}$$

$$= +0.77 \text{ V} - (-0.25 \text{ V}) = +1.02 \text{ V}$$

Math ▸ Handbook

For help with significant figures, go to page R59.

3 Evaluate *Does the result make sense?*

If the reduction potential of the reduction is positive, and the reduction potential of the oxidation is negative, E^0_{cell} must be positive.

Practice Problems

13. A voltaic cell is constructed using the following half-reactions.

$$Cu^{2+}(aq) + 2e^- \longrightarrow Cu(s)$$
$$E^0_{Cu^{2+}} = +0.34 \text{ V}$$
$$Al^{3+}(aq) + 3e^- \longrightarrow Al(s)$$
$$E^0_{Al^{3+}} = -1.66 \text{ V}$$

Calculate the standard cell potential.

14. A voltaic cell is constructed using the following half-reactions.

$$Ag^+(aq) + e^- \longrightarrow Ag(s)$$
$$E^0_{Ag^+} = +0.80 \text{ V}$$
$$Cu^{2+}(aq) + 2e^- \longrightarrow Cu(s)$$
$$E^0_{Cu^{2+}} = +0.34 \text{ V}$$

Calculate the standard cell potential.

21.2 Section Assessment

15. **Key Concept** What causes the electrical potential of a cell?

16. **Key Concept** What is the electrical potential of a standard hydrogen electrode?

17. **Key Concept** How can you find the standard reduction potential of a half-cell?

18. **Key Concept** What cell potential values indicate a spontaneous reaction? A nonspontaneous reaction?

19. The standard reduction potential for a cadmium half-cell is −0.40 V. What does this mean?

Connecting ▸ Concepts

Batteries Reread the discussion on batteries in Section 21.1. Use Figure 21.6 and Table 21.2 to calculate the standard cell potential of a voltaic cell in a lead–acid battery.

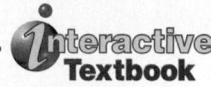
interactive Textbook

Assessment 21.2 Test yourself on the concepts in Section 21.2.

— with **ChemASAP**

21.3 Electrolytic Cells

New York Standards: 3.2j, 3.2l

Guide for Reading

Key Concepts
- How do voltaic and electrolytic cells differ?
- What products are formed by the electrolysis of water?
- What oxidation and reduction reactions occur during the electrolysis of brine?
- How are electrolytic cells used in metal processing?

Vocabulary
electrolysis
electrolytic cell

Reading Strategy

Relating Text and Visuals As you read about electrolytic cells, look at Figure 21.12. Make sure that you can explain the differences between a voltaic cell and an electrolytic cell.

Connecting to Your World

DVDs are used to store all types of data, from multimedia computer programs to the latest popular movie. DVDs have made it possible to store large amounts of data in a very small space. To manufacture a DVD, a laser is used to transfer all the necessary data to the master DVD. Then, metal is deposited on the master using electricity. Once the metal disc is removed from the master, it is used to stamp out the duplicates sold to the public. In this section, you will read about electrochemical processes that require (rather than produce) electrical energy.

Electrolytic vs. Voltaic Cells

In Section 21.1, you learned how a spontaneous chemical reaction can be used to generate a flow of electrons (an electric current). In this section, you will learn how an electric current can be used to make a nonspontaneous redox reaction go forward. The process in which electrical energy is used to bring about such a chemical change is called **electrolysis.** Although you may not have realized it, you are already familiar with some results of electrolysis: silver-plated dishes and utensils, gold-plated jewelry, and chrome-plated automobile parts are a few examples.

The apparatus in which electrolysis is carried out is an electrolytic cell. An **electrolytic cell** is an electrochemical cell used to cause a chemical change through the application of electrical energy. An electrolytic cell uses electrical energy (direct current) to make a nonspontaneous redox reaction proceed to completion. The vast array of electrolytic cells shown in Figure 21.11 are used for the commercial production of chlorine and sodium hydroxide from brine, a concentrated aqueous solution of sodium chloride.

Figure 21.11 To produce chlorine and sodium hydroxide in electrolytic cells, electricity is passed through brine, a sodium chloride solution. The products have many uses, such as disinfecting swimming pools, cleaning drains, manufacturing soap, and producing paper pulp.

a Voltaic Cell   **b** Electrolytic Cell

Figure 21.12 Electrochemical cells can be classified as voltaic or electrolytic. **a** In a voltaic cell, energy is released from a spontaneous redox reaction. The system (cell) does work on the surroundings (lightbulb). **b** In an electrolytic cell, energy is absorbed to drive a non-spontaneous reaction. The surroundings (battery or power supply) do work on the system (cell). **Comparing and Contrasting** *How are voltaic and electrolytic cells similar? How are they different?*

In both voltaic and electrolytic cells, electrons flow from the anode to the cathode in the external circuit. As shown in Figure 21.12, for both types of cells, the electrode at which reduction occurs is the cathode. The electrode at which oxidation occurs is the anode.

The key difference between voltaic and electrolytic cells is that in a voltaic cell, the flow of electrons is the result of a spontaneous redox reaction, whereas in an electrolytic cell, electrons are pushed by an outside power source, such as a battery. The redox process in the voltaic cell is spontaneous; in the electrolytic cell, the redox process is nonspontaneous. Electrolytic and voltaic cells also differ in the assignment of charge to the electrodes. In an electrolytic cell, the cathode is considered to be the negative electrode. This is because it is connected to the negative electrode of the battery. (Remember that in a voltaic cell, the anode is the negative electrode and the cathode is the positive electrode.) The anode in the electrolytic cell is considered to be the positive electrode because it is connected to the positive electrode of the battery. It is important to remember these conventions about the two kinds of cells.

 What charges are assigned to the electrodes in an electrolytic cell? In a voltaic cell?

Oxygen (*g*) Hydrogen (*g*)

Figure 21.13 When an electric current is passed through water, the water decomposes into oxygen gas and hydrogen gas. **Interpreting Photographs** *Which electrode in the photograph is the cathode? The anode?*

Electrolysis of Water

When a current is applied to two electrodes immersed in pure water, nothing happens. There is no current flow and no electrolysis. However, when an electrolyte such as H_2SO_4 or KNO_3 in low concentration is added to the pure water, the solution conducts electricity and electrolysis occurs. This process is illustrated in Figure 21.13. **The products of the electrolysis of water are hydrogen gas and oxygen gas.** Water is reduced to hydrogen at the cathode according to the following reduction half-reaction.

Reduction: $2H_2O(l) + 2e^- \longrightarrow H_2(g) + 2OH^-(aq)$ (at cathode)

Water is oxidized at the anode according to the following oxidation half-reaction.

Oxidation: $2H_2O(l) \longrightarrow O_2(g) + 4H^+(aq) + 4e^-$ (at anode)

The region around the cathode turns basic due to the production of OH^- ions. The region around the anode turns acidic due to an increase in H^+ ions. The overall cell reaction is obtained by adding the half-reactions (after doubling the first one to balance electrons).

$$\text{Reduction:} \quad 2[2H_2O(l) + 2e^- \longrightarrow H_2(g) + 2OH^-(aq)]$$
$$\text{Oxidation:} \quad 2H_2O(l) \longrightarrow O_2(g) + 4H^+(aq) + 4e^-$$
$$\overline{\text{Overall cell reaction:} \quad 6H_2O(l) \longrightarrow 2H_2(g) + O_2(g) +}$$
$$4H^+(aq) + 4OH^-(aq)$$

The ions produced tend to recombine to form water.

$$4H^+(aq) + 4OH^-(aq) \longrightarrow 4H_2O(l)$$

For that reason they are not included in the net reaction.

$$2H_2O(l) \xrightarrow{\text{electrolysis}} 2H_2(g) + O_2(g)$$

Figure 21.14 The electrolytic cell used for the electrolysis of brine. **Interpreting Diagrams** *Which substances are produced by oxidation? By reduction?*

In the diagram:

Battery

Cl₂ ← Anode reaction
$2Cl^-(aq) \rightarrow Cl_2(g) + 2e^-$

Cathode reaction → H₂
$2H_2O(l) + 2e^- \rightarrow$
$H_2(g) + 2OH^-(aq)$

Cl₂   H₂

Na⁺

Cl⁻   OH⁻ ← Na⁺

(+) ← Cl⁻   (−)

Anode   OH⁻   Cathode

Electrolysis of Brine

If the electrolyte in an aqueous solution is more easily oxidized or reduced than water, then the products of electrolysis will be substances other than hydrogen and oxygen. An example is the electrolysis of brine, a concentrated aqueous solution of sodium chloride, which simultaneously produces chlorine gas, hydrogen gas, and sodium hydroxide. The electrolytic cell for this process is shown in Figure 21.14.

⊂⊃ During electrolysis of brine, chloride ions are oxidized to produce chlorine gas at the anode. Water is reduced to produce hydrogen gas at the cathode. Sodium ions are not reduced to sodium metal in the process because water molecules are more easily reduced than are sodium ions. The reduction of water produces hydroxide ions as well as hydrogen gas. Thus the electrolyte in solution becomes sodium hydroxide (NaOH). The half-reactions are

Oxidation: $2Cl^-(aq) \longrightarrow Cl_2(g) + 2e^-$ (at anode)

Reduction: $2H_2O(l) + 2e^- \longrightarrow H_2(g) + 2OH^-(aq)$ (at cathode)

The overall ionic equation is the sum of the two half-reactions.

$$2Cl^-(aq) + 2H_2O(l) \longrightarrow Cl_2(g) + H_2(g) + 2OH^-(aq)$$

The spectator ion Na⁺ can be included in the equation (as part of NaCl and of NaOH) to show the formation of sodium hydroxide during the electrolytic process.

$$2NaCl(aq) + 2H_2O(l) \longrightarrow Cl_2(g) + H_2(g) + 2NaOH(aq)$$

When the sodium hydroxide solution is about 10% (m/v), it is removed from the cell and processed further.

Go Online
NSTA SciLINKS

For: Links on Electrolysis
Visit: www.SciLinks.org
Web Code: cdn-1213

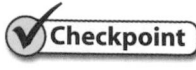 **Checkpoint** *What is the overall ionic equation for the electrolysis of brine?*

Quick LAB

Electrochemical Analysis of Metals

Purpose
To electrochemically oxidize metals and identify them.

Materials
- 9-volt battery
- sodium sulfate solution
- copper penny
- nickel coin
- iron nail
- filter paper
- aluminum foil
- reaction surface

Procedure

1. Stack the following in order on a reaction surface: a 3-cm square of aluminum foil, a 2-cm square of filter paper, 1 drop of Na_2SO_4 solution, and a penny. The penny should be roughly centered on the filter paper, which should be roughly centered on the foil.

2. Apply the negative ($-$) terminal of the 9-volt battery to the aluminum foil and the positive ($+$) terminal to the penny for no more than three seconds.

3. Remove the penny and observe the filter paper.

4. Repeat Steps 1–3, replacing the penny with the nickel coin.

5. Repeat Steps 1–3, replacing the penny with the iron nail.

Analyze and Conclude

1. What colors formed on the filter paper for each object?

2. For each metal object you tested, the battery oxidized the metal to form metal cations with a 2+ charge. Write a half-reaction for each metal oxidation you observed. Did these reactions take place at the anode or the cathode?

3. Explain in your own words why the colors formed in the filter paper?

4. The aluminum foil serves as the cathode, where the reduction of water takes place. Write the half-reaction for the reduction of water?

5. Combine the half-reaction for the oxidation of copper with the half-reaction for the reduction of water to form an overall equation?

Using Electrolysis in Metal Processing

Electrolysis has many important applications in the field of metallurgy. **Electrolytic cells are commonly used in the plating, purifying, and refining of metals.** Many of the shiny, metallic objects you see every day—such as chrome-plated fixtures or nickel-plated coins—were manufactured with the help of electrolytic processes.

Electroplating and Electroforming Electroplating is the deposition of a thin layer of a metal on an object in an electrolytic cell. An object may be electroplated to protect the surface of the base metal from corrosion or to make it more attractive. An object that is to be silver-plated is made the cathode in an electrolytic cell. The anode is the metallic silver that is to be deposited, and the electrolyte is a solution of a silver salt, such as silver cyanide. When a direct current is applied, silver ions move from the anode to the object to be plated.

$$\text{Reduction:} \quad Ag^+(aq) + e^- \longrightarrow Ag(s) \text{ (at cathode)}$$

Animation 27 Take an atomic-level look at how electricity can bring about a chemical change.

—— with **ChemASAP**

The net result is that silver transfers from the silver electrode to the object being plated. Figure 21.15 shows a silver-plated tea set. Many factors contribute to the quality of the metal coating that forms. In the plating solution, the concentration of the cations to be reduced must be carefully controlled. The solution must also contain compounds to control the acidity and to increase the conductivity. Other compounds may be used to make the metal coating brighter or smoother.

Electroforming is a process in which an object is reproduced by making a metal mold of it at the cathode of a cell. For example, a phonograph record can be coated with metal so it will conduct a current. It is then electroplated with a thick coating of metal. This coating can be stripped off and used as a mold to produce copies of the record.

Figure 21.15 Pure silver was electroplated onto steel to produce this silver-plated tea set.

Electrowinning In another process, called electrowinning, impure metals can be purified in electrolytic cells. The cations of molten salts or aqueous solutions are reduced at the cathode to give very pure metals. A common use of electrowinning is in the extraction of aluminum from its ore, bauxite. Bauxite is impure alumina (Al_2O_3). In a method known as the Hall-Heroult process, purified alumina is dissolved in molten cryolite (Na_3AlF_6), and heated to above 1000°C in a carbon-lined tank. The carbon lining, connected to a direct current, serves as the cathode. The anode consists of carbon rods dipped into the tank. At the cathode, Al^{3+} ions are reduced, forming molten aluminum. At the anode, carbon is oxidized, forming carbon dioxide gas.

$$2Al_2O_3(l) + 3C(s) \longrightarrow 4Al(l) + 3CO_2(g)$$

Electrorefining In the process of electrorefining, a piece of impure metal is made the anode of the cell. It is oxidized to the cation and then reduced to the pure metal at the cathode. This technique is used to obtain ultrapure silver, lead, and copper.

Other Processes Other electrolytic processes are centered on the anode rather than the cathode. In electropolishing, for example, the surface of an object at the anode is dissolved selectively to give it a high polish. In electromachining, a piece of metal at the anode is partially dissolved until the remaining portion is an exact copy of the object at the cathode.

21.3 Section Assessment

20. **Key Concept** What is the difference between an electrolytic cell and a voltaic cell?

21. **Key Concept** What products form during the electrolysis of water?

22. **Key Concept** What chemical changes occur during the electrolysis of brine?

23. **Key Concept** What are some applications of electrolysis in the field of metallurgy?

24. What is the charge on the anode of an electrolytic cell? Of a voltaic cell?

25. Which process, oxidation or reduction, always occurs at the cathode of an electrolytic cell?

Elements ▶ **Handbook**

Manufacturing Aluminum Read about the Hall-Heroult process on page R17. Write the half-reactions for the electrolysis that takes place, and explain the function of cryolite in the process.

interactive Textbook

Assessment 21.3 Test yourself on the concepts in Section 21.3.

—— with **ChemASAP**

Electrolysis of Water

Purpose

To electrolyze solutions and interpret your observations in terms of chemical reactions and equations.

Materials

- pencil
- paper
- ruler
- reaction surface
- electrolysis device
- chemicals shown in Figure A

Procedure

1. On separate sheets of paper, draw two grids similar to Figure A. Make each square 2 cm on each side.

2. Place a reaction surface over one of the grids and add one drop of each solution as shown in Figure A.

3. Apply the leads of the electrolysis device to each solution. Be sure to clean the leads between each experiment. Look carefully at the cathode (negative lead) and the anode (positive lead).

4. Use the second grid as a data table to record your observations for each solution.

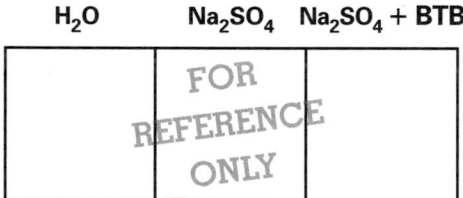

H_2O	Na_2SO_4	Na_2SO_4 + BTB
FOR REFERENCE ONLY		

Figure A

Analyze

Using your experimental data, record the answers to the following questions below your data table.

1. Explain why pure water does not conduct electricity and does not undergo electrolysis.

2. Explain why water with sodium sulfate conducts electricity and undergoes electrolysis.

3. The cathode (negative lead) provides electrons to water and the following half-reaction occurs.

$$2H_2O + 2e^- \longrightarrow H_2(g) + 2OH^-$$

4. Explain how your observations correspond to the products shown in this reaction.

5. The anode (positive lead) takes away electrons from water and the following half-reaction occurs.

$$H_2O \longrightarrow \tfrac{1}{2}O_2(g) + 2H^+ + 2e^-$$

Explain how your observations correspond to the products shown in this reaction.

6. Add the two half-reactions to obtain the overall reaction for the electrolysis of water. Simplify the result by adding the OH^- and H^+ to get HOH, and then canceling anything that appears on both sides of the equation.

You're the Chemist

The following small-scale activities allow you to develop your own procedures and analyze the results.

1. **Analyze It!** Perform the above experiment using the chemicals shown in Figure B. Record your results. The cathode and anode reactions are

$$2H_2O + 2e^- \longrightarrow H_2(g) + 2OH^- \text{ (at cathode)}$$
$$2I^- \longrightarrow I_2(aq) + 2e^- \text{ (at anode)}$$

Explain how your observations correspond to the products shown in these half-reactions.

KI	KI + starch	KI + BTB
FOR REFERENCE ONLY		

Figure B

2. **Design It!** Design an experiment to explore what happens when you electrolyze NaCl, KBr, and $CuSO_4$ with and without BTB. Use half-reactions to predict your results.

3. **Analyze It!** For each half-reaction listed above, look up the E^0 values in Section 21.2. Show that the E^0 values are consistent with what happens in each case.

Electroplating

Electroplating is the use of electrolysis to deposit a thin coating of metal on an object, often to enhance its appearance or value. Metals commonly used for electroplating include gold, silver, copper, nickel, and chromium. The layer of the deposited metal is very thin, usually from 5×10^{-5} cm to 1×10^{-3} cm thick. In addition to jewelry and tableware, common electroplated objects include electronic connectors, circuit boards, and contacts coated with elements such as gold, platinum, ruthenium, or osmium.

Applying Concepts *What are the half-reactions for the electrolytic cell shown below?*

Plating Metals Gold and silver are often used to plate jewelry. Chrome and nickel are used to plate faucets, kitchen appliances, and automotive trim. Zinc coatings are used to protect steel objects from corrosion.

DC power supply

Flow of electrons

Flow of electrons

Cathode: material being plated

Anode: silver rod

Ag^+

CN^-

Electroplating In an electrolytic cell used for plating, the object to be plated (a bracelet) is the cathode. The anode is the plating matel, in this case, a piece of silver. At the anode, silver is oxidized to silver ions. Silver ions in the electrolyte solution reduce to silver metal. The silver metal forms a thin coating on the cathode, producing a plated bracelet.

Key Concepts

🔑 21.1 Electrochemical Cells

- For any two metals in an activity series, the more active metal is the more readily oxidized.

- All electrochemical processes involve redox reactions.

- Energy is produced in a voltaic cell by spontaneous redox reactions within the cell.

- Current electrochemical technologies used to produce electrical energy include dry cells, lead storage batteries, and fuel cells.

🔑 21.2 Half-Cells and Cell Potentials

- The electrical potential of a cell results from a competition for electrons between two half-cells.

- The standard reduction potential of the hydrogen electrode has been assigned a value of 0.00 V.

- You can determine the standard reduction potential of a half-cell by using a standard hydrogen electrode and the equation for standard cell potential.

- If the cell potential for a given redox reaction is positive, then the reaction is spontaneous. If the cell potential is negative, then the reaction is nonspontaneous.

🔑 21.3 Electrolytic Cells

- The key difference between voltaic and electrolytic cells is that in a voltaic cell, the flow of electrons is the result of a spontaneous redox reaction, whereas in an electrolytic cell, electrons are pushed by an outside power source, such as a battery.

- The products of the electrolysis of water are hydrogen gas and oxygen gas.

- During electrolysis of brine, chloride ions are oxidized to produce chlorine gas at the anode; water is reduced at the cathode to produce hydrogen gas.

- Electrolytic cells are commonly used in the plating, purifying, and refining of metals.

Vocabulary

- anode (p. 665)
- battery (p. 668)
- cathode (p. 665)
- cell potential (p. 671)
- dry cell (p. 667)
- electrical potential (p. 671)
- electrochemical cell (p. 665)
- electrochemical process (p. 665)
- electrode (p. 665)
- electrolysis (p. 678)
- electrolytic cell (p. 678)
- fuel cell (p. 669)
- half-cell (p. 665)
- reduction potential (p. 671)
- salt bridge (p. 665)
- standard cell potential (p. 672)
- standard hydrogen electrode (p. 672)
- voltaic cell (p. 665)

Key Equation

- $E^0_{cell} = E^0_{red} - E^0_{oxid}$

Organizing Information

Use these terms to construct a concept map that organizes the major ideas of this chapter.

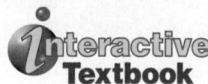

Concept Map 21 Solve the Concept Map with the help of an interactive guided tutorial.

with ChemASAP

CHAPTER 21

Review and Assessment

Blue questions emphasize Regents Exam content

21.1 Electrochemical Cells

23. What is meant by the term *half-reaction*?

24. Write the half-reactions that occur when a strip of aluminum is dipped into a solution of copper(II) sulfate.

25. What would you expect to happen when a strip of lead is placed in an aqueous solution of magnesium nitrate?

26. For each pair of metals listed below, decide which metal is more readily oxidized.
    a. Hg, Cu b. Ca, Al c. Ni, Mg
    d. Sn, Ag e. Pb, Zn f. Cu, Al

27. At which electrode in a voltaic cell does reduction always occur?

28. Explain the function of the salt bridge in a voltaic cell.

29. In a typical flashlight battery, what material is used for the anode? For the cathode?

30. Explain why the specific gravity of the electrolyte in a lead storage battery decreases during the discharge process.

31. Use the shorthand method to represent the electrochemical reaction in a car battery.

32. Fuel cells can be designed to generate electrical energy while emitting no air pollutants, yet they are not widely used. Explain.

33. List the advantages of a fuel cell over a lead storage battery.

34. Describe the composition of the anode, cathode, and electrolyte in a fully discharged lead storage battery.

35. Predict what will happen, if anything, when an iron nail is dipped into a solution of copper sulfate. Write the oxidation and reduction half-reactions for this process and the balanced equation for the overall reaction.

36. What property do lead(II) sulfate and lead dioxide have that makes salt bridges unnecessary in a lead storage battery?

37. In certain cases, more than one reaction is possible at an electrode. How can you determine which reaction actually take place?

38. Lead storage batteries can be recharged. Why are dry cells not rechargeable?

39. For any voltaic cell, chemists consider the electrode that produces electrons to be negative, and they call it the anode. Most dictionaries, however, define the anode as the positively charged electrode. Explain.

40. Which plot is characteristic of a dry cell? Explain.

(a)

(c)

(b)

(d)
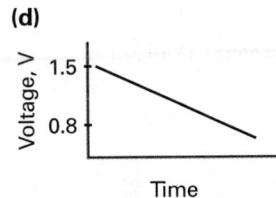

41. This spontaneous redox reaction occurs in the voltaic cell illustrated below.

$$Ni^{2+}(aq) + Fe(s) \longrightarrow Ni(s) + Fe^{2+}(aq)$$

    a. Identify the anode and the cathode.
    b. Assign charges to the electrodes.
    c. Write the half-reactions.
    d. Calculate the standard cell potential when the half-cells are at standard conditions.

42. The cells in an automobile battery are separated from each other. However the electrolyte is the same in all the cells. What would be the consequence of placing all the electrodes into a single container of electrolyte solution rather than into separate compartments?

43. A type of voltaic cell called a *standard cell* is sometimes used as a voltage reference in laboratory instruments. The voltage produced by these cells is constant only as long as the amount of current produced by them is very small and only when they are required to produce that current for brief periods of time.

   a. What happens to the electrodes when the cell is producing current?

   b. What happens to the electrolytes when the cell is producing current?

   c. Which of the above is more likely to alter the standard conditions of the cell?

   d. Predict what happens to the voltage produced by the cell as it supplies current. Does it increase or decrease?

21.2 **Half-Cells and Cell Potentials**

44. How was the standard reduction potential of the hydrogen electrode determined?

45. What is the electric potential of a cell?

46. How does the order of the metals in Table 21.1 compare with the order in Table 21.2? Why?

47. Explain how to determine the standard reduction potential for the aluminum half-cell.

48. **Determine whether these redox reactions will occur spontaneously. Calculate the standard cell potential in each case.**

   a. $Cu(s) + 2H^+(aq) \longrightarrow Cu^{2+}(aq) + H_2(g)$
   b. $2Ag(s) + Fe^{2+}(aq) \longrightarrow 2Ag^+(aq) + Fe(s)$

49. Use the information in Table 21.2 to calculate standard cell potentials for these voltaic cells.
   a. $Ni \mid Ni^{2+} \parallel Cl_2 \mid Cl^-$
   b. $Sn \mid Sn^{2+} \parallel Ag^+ \mid Ag$

50. Calculate E^0_{cell}, and write the overall cell reaction for these cells.
   a. $Sn \mid Sn^{2+} \parallel Pb^{2+} \mid Pb$
   b. $H_2 \mid H^+ \parallel Br_2 \mid Br^-$

51. Identify the better oxidizing agent in each of the following pairs.
   a. Li^+, Ca^{2+}
   b. Fe^{3+}, Hg_2^{2+}
   c. Cu^{2+}, Cu^+
   d. Hg^{2+}, I_2

52. Gold is not included in Table 21.2. In what part of the table does gold belong?

53. **An engineer has proposed a new battery design that uses silver as the electrode in both half-cells. As a chemist, what would you tell the engineer about the proposal?**

54. **In most voltaic cells, the half-cells are connected by a salt bridge or a porous barrier instead of a piece of wire made of copper or some other metal. Why is a metal wire not suitable for connecting the half-cells of a voltaic cell?**

55. **Write the overall cell reactions and calculate E^0_{cell} for voltaic cells composed of the following sets of half-reactions.**
   a. $AgCl(s) + e^- \longrightarrow Ag(s) + Cl^-(aq)$
   $\quad Ni^{2+}(aq) + 2e^- \longrightarrow Ni(s)$
   b. $Al^{3+}(aq) + 3e^- \longrightarrow Al(s)$
   $\quad Cl_2(g) + 2e^- \longrightarrow 2Cl^-(aq)$

56. What relationship does the voltage produced by a redox reaction have to the spontaneity of the reaction?

57. **Use the information in Table 21.2 to determine which of the following cell reactions will proceed spontaneously.**
   a. $Zn + Pb^{2+} \longrightarrow ?$
   b. $Cu + Fe^{2+} \longrightarrow ?$
   c. $Ag^+ + Cu^{2+} \longrightarrow ?$
   d. $H_2 + Cu \longrightarrow ?$
   e. $Fe + Pb^{2+} \longrightarrow ?$
   f. $Na + Cl_2 \longrightarrow ?$

58. **For each spontaneous reaction in Question 57, write the half-reaction that takes place at the anode. Be sure to include the electrons.**

59. **Write the overall balanced equation for each reaction in Question 57 that proceeds spontaneously.**

60. Determine the standard cell potential for each spontaneous reaction in Question 57.

21.3 Electrolytic Cells

61. Describe briefly how you would use an electrolytic cell to plate a teaspoon with silver.

Use the diagram to answer questions 62–64.

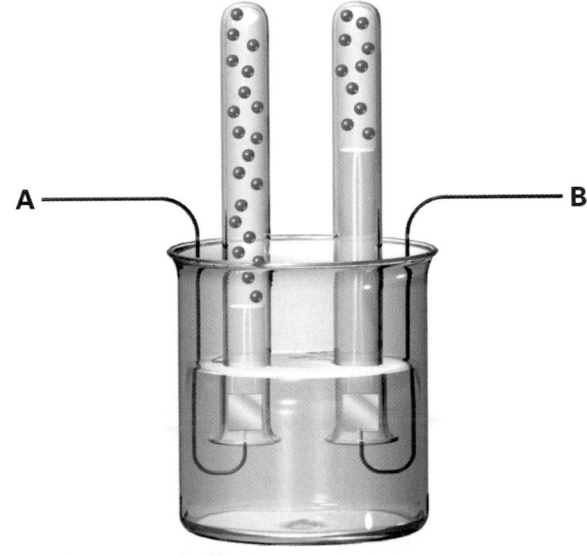

A   B

62. Write an equation for the decomposition of water by electrolysis.

63. At which electrode, A or B, is hydrogen produced?

64. The equation for the electrolysis of brine is

$$2NaCl(aq) + 2H_2O(l) \longrightarrow$$
$$Cl_2(g) + H_2(g) + 2NaOH(aq)$$

How would you modify the electrolysis diagram to make it quantitatively represent the formation of hydrogen and chlorine?

65. Distinguish between voltaic and electrolytic cells.

66. Complete this data table for the electrolysis of water. One mole of any gas occupies 22.4 L at STP.

H$_2$O used	H$_2$ formed	O$_2$ formed
a. 2.0 mol	____ mol	____ mol
b. ____ g	____ g	16.0 g
c. ____ mL	10.0 g	____ g
d. 44.4 g	____ g	____ g
e. ____ g	8.80 L (STP)	____ L (STP)
f. 66.0 mL	____ g	____ L (STP)

67. In one process used to produce aluminum metal, ore containing aluminum oxide is converted to aluminum chloride. Aluminum metal is then produced by the electrolysis of molten aluminum chloride ($AlCl_3$).
  a. Write the half-reactions that take place at each electrode.
  b. Write the equation for the overall cell reaction.
  c. Identify the products produced at each electrode.

68. The reactions that take place in voltaic cells produce electric current, and the reactions in electrolytic cells can be made to take place when an electric current is applied. What common feature do these redox reactions share?

69. Answer the following questions for the electrolysis of molten (liquid) sodium chloride.
  a. Write the equation for the reaction that takes place at the anode.
  b. Write the equation for the reaction that takes place at the cathode.

70. Describe the process that is occurring in the following illustration.

Regents Practice Exam

Part A

For each statement or question write the number of the word or expression that, of those given, best completes the statement or answers the question.

1. Which of the following statements describes electrolysis?
   (1) Reduction occurs at the anode.
   (2) Energy is produced.
   (3) Oxidation occurs at the cathode.
   (4) Positive ions move to the cathode.

2. Magnesium metal is prepared by the electrolysis of molten $MgCl_2$. One half-reaction is $Mg^{2+}(l) + 2e^- \longrightarrow Mg(l)$. Which of the following statements is true about this reaction?
   (1) This half-reaction occurs at the cathode.
   (2) Magnesium ions are oxidized.
   (3) Chloride ions are reduced at the anode.
   (4) Chloride ions gain electrons during this process.

3. Convert 4.32×10^5 joules to kilojoules.
   (1) 4.32×10^{-1} kJ   (3) 4.32×10^5 kJ
   (2) 4.32×10^2 kJ   (4) 4.32×10^8 kJ

4. Write the half-reaction for the reduction of aluminum ions.
   (1) $Al^{3+} \longrightarrow Al + 3e^-$
   (2) $Al^{3+} + 3e^- \longrightarrow Al$
   (3) $Al + 3e^- \longrightarrow Al^{3+}$
   (4) $Al \longrightarrow Al^{3+} + 3e^-$

Part B-1

For each statement or question write the number of the word or expression that, of those given, best completes the statement or answers the question.

5. Which of the following statements about rusting is true?
   (1) Iron is oxidized.
   (2) Iron brings about the oxidation of oxygen.
   (3) Iron atoms gain electrons.
   (4) The reaction is not a redox reaction.

6. A sample of oxygen gas has a volume of 425 mL at 30°C. What is the new volume of the gas if the temperature is raised to 60°C while the pressure is kept constant?
   (1) 213 mL   (3) 467 mL
   (2) 387 mL   (4) 850 mL

Use the following choices to answer Questions 7–12. You may use each choice once, more than once, or not at all.
   (1) 0   (3) 4
   (2) 2   (4) None of these

Determine the oxidation number of sulfur in each of the following substances or ions.

7. H_2SO_4

8. H_2S

9. SO_2

10. $Na_2S_2O_3$

11. S

12. SO_3^{2-}

13. Identify which of the following choices is an oxidation-reduction reaction.
    (1) $CaCO_3(s) \longrightarrow CaO(s) + CO_2(g)$
    (2) $Ca(s) + Cl_2(g) \longrightarrow CaCl_2(s)$
    (3) $H_2O(l) + CO_2(g) \longrightarrow H_2CO_3(aq)$
    (4) $CaCl_2(aq) + 2AgNO_3(aq) \longrightarrow$
    $ Ca(NO_3)_2(aq) + 2AgCl(s)$

14. For the following redox reaction, name the element oxidized and the element reduced.

    $$Ca(s) + 2H_2O(l) \longrightarrow Ca(OH)_2(aq) + H_2(g)$$

    (1) Ca is oxidized; H is reduced
    (2) H is oxidized; Ca is reduced
    (3) O is oxidized; H is reduced
    (4) Ca is oxidized; O is reduced

15. A reaction that creates ammonia from nitrogen and hydrogen is an exothermic process that takes place in a closed system and reaches equilibrium.

    $$N_2(g) + 3H_2(g) \rightleftharpoons 2NH_3(g) + heat$$

    Which of the following events would shift the equilibrium to the left?
    (1) Ammonia is removed from the system.
    (2) Additional nitrogen is added.
    (3) The pressure is decreased.
    (4) The system is cooled.

16. How many milliliters of concentrated nitric acid (16M) would you need to prepare 500 mL of 1.0M HNO_3?
    (1) 8.0 mL   (3) 32 mL
    (2) 31 mL   (4) 800 mL

Part B-2

Answer each of the following questions.

17. Balance each of the following chemical equations.

   a. $H_2S(g) + HNO_3(aq) \longrightarrow S(s) + NO(g) + H_2O(l)$

   b. $AgNO_3(aq) + Pb(s) \longrightarrow Pb(NO_3)_2(aq) + Ag(s)$

   c. $Cl_2(g) + NaOH(aq) \longrightarrow$
$$NaCl(aq) + NaClO_3(aq) + H_2O(l)$$

18. Write formulas for the following hydrates.

   a. tin(IV) chloride pentahydrate

   b. magnesium sulfate heptahydrate

   c. iron(III) phosphate tetrahydrate

   d. calcium chloride dehydrate

19. Calculate the grams of solute required to make the following solutions.

   a. 250 g of 0.50% NaCl

   b. 500 mL of $2.0M$ KNO_3

20. Calculate the quantity of heat lost or gained in the following changes.

   a. 0.625 mol $NaOH(s)$ dissolves in water.

   b. 1.17 g water freezes at 0°C.

   c. 0.66 g of steam condenses at 100°C.

21. Determine the oxidation number of each element in the following substances.

   a. $CaCr_2O_7$ **c.** $Ca(NO_3)_2$

   b. $KMnO_4$ **d.** $Al(OH)_3$

22. Balance each of the following redox equations.

   a. $Br_2(g) + NaOH(aq) \longrightarrow$
$$NaBrO_3(aq) + NaBr(aq) + H_2O(l)$$

   b. $Fe_2O_3(s) + H_2(g) \longrightarrow Fe(s) + H_2O(l)$

Use the following data table to answer Questions 23–28. Hydrogen is included as a reference point for the metals.

Activity Series of Selected Metals	
Element	**Oxidation half-reaction**
Lithium	$Li(s) \longrightarrow Li^+(aq) + e^-$
Potassium	$K(s) \longrightarrow K^+(aq) + e^-$
Sodium	$Na(s) \longrightarrow Na^+(aq) + e^-$
Aluminum	$Al(s) \longrightarrow Al^{3+}(aq) + 3e^-$
Zinc	$Zn(s) \longrightarrow Zn^{2+}(aq) + 2e^-$
Iron	$Fe(s) \longrightarrow Fe^{2+}(aq) + 2e^-$
Hydrogen	$H_2(g) \longrightarrow 2H^+(aq) + 2e^-$
Copper	$Cu(s) \longrightarrow Cu^{2+}(aq) + 2e^-$

23. Which metal will more easily lose an electron, sodium or potassium?

24. Which metal is more easily oxidized, copper or aluminum?

25. What is the relationship between ease of oxidation and the activity of a metal?

26. Describe what would happen if you placed a clean strip of aluminum in a solution of copper(II) sulfate. Explain your answer.

27. Would a copper strip placed in a solution containing zinc ions react spontaneously with the zinc ions? Explain your reasoning.

28. Based on the positions of zinc and iron in the table, explain how attaching zinc blocks to a steel ship hull protects the steel from corrosion.

29. What is the oxidation number of the italicized element in each formula?

   a. $K_2Cr_2O_7$ **c.** MnO_4^-

   b. KIO_3 **d.** $FeCl_3$

Part C

Answer each of the following questions.

30. This image shows an electrolytic cell. Draw this cell on a separate piece of paper and label the anode, the cathode, and the direction of electron flow.

31. The combustion of natural gas, methane (CH_4), is an exothermic reaction.

$$CH_4(g) + 2O_2(g) \longrightarrow CO_2(g) + 2H_2O(l)$$
$$\Delta H = -890 \text{ kJ}$$

Calculate the amount of heat liberated when 4.80 mol CH_4 reacts with an excess of oxygen.

Hydrocarbon Compounds

An oil rig drills deep into the ocean floor in search of petroleum, a valuable mixture of hydrocarbons.

INQUIRY Activity

What Dissolves What?

Materials

candle wax, vegetable oil, petroleum jelly, rubbing alcohol, mineral oil, water, three square glass plates, nine toothpicks

Procedure

1. Place 3 pea-sized portions of petroleum jelly 10 cm apart on a glass plate.

2. Add 5 drops of rubbing alcohol to one portion of the petroleum jelly, 5 drops of mineral oil to another, and 5 drops of water to the third.

3. Use a clean toothpick to mix each portion as completely as possible. Observe whether the petroleum jelly appears to dissolve.

4. On a second glass plate repeat Steps 1 through 3 using pea-sized portions of candle wax.

5. On a third glass plate, repeat Steps 1 through 3 using pea-sized portions of vegetable oil.

Think About It

1. How did the solubility of these three materials (petroleum jelly, candle wax, and vegetable oil) in water compare with their solubility in mineral oil?

2. Was the solubility of these materials in rubbing alcohol more like that in water or in mineral oil?

3. Use your observations to develop a general statement about the solubility of the materials you tested.

22.1 Hydrocarbons

 New York Standards: 3.1ff–gg

Connecting to Your World

The gasoline used in cars and lawnmowers, the diesel fuel used in trucks and busses, and the kerosene used in lanterns and camping stoves are examples of liquid fuels. Often, a barbecue grill uses a gaseous fuel. A solid fuel, coal, produced the steam for the locomotives that pulled old-time trains. All these fuels are mixtures of compounds called hydrocarbons. In this section, you will learn about the structure and properties of hydrocarbons.

Organic Chemistry and Hydrocarbons

Fewer than 200 years ago, it was thought that only living organisms could synthesize the carbon compounds found in their cells. So these compounds were classified as organic compounds and the study of these compounds as organic chemistry. Many people thought that a mysterious vital force directed the formation of carbon compounds. A German chemist, Friedrich Wöhler (1800–1882), refuted this idea in 1828. He was able to use inorganic substances to synthesize urea—a carbon compound found in urine. Today, organic chemistry includes the chemistry of almost all carbon compounds, regardless of their origin.

In a reference book that lists properties of common compounds, the list of organic compounds is much longer than the list of inorganic compounds. In fact, there are more than a million organic compounds. By definition, a compound contains at least two elements. The simplest organic compounds contain only carbon and hydrogen and are called **hydrocarbons.** The two simplest hydrocarbons are methane and ethane.

Methane (CH_4) is the major component of natural gas. It is sometimes called marsh gas because it is formed by the action of bacteria on decaying plants in swamps and other marshy areas. Livestock and termites also emit substantial quantities of methane as a product of digestion. Recall that a carbon atom has four valence electrons and a hydrogen atom has one valence electron. So one carbon atom can form a single covalent bond with four hydrogen atoms.

$$\cdot\overset{\cdot}{C}\cdot \ + \ 4H\cdot \ \longrightarrow \ H\!:\!\overset{\cdot\cdot}{\underset{\cdot\cdot}{C}}\!:\!H$$

Carbon   Hydrogen   Methane
atom   atoms   molecule

Because carbon has four valence electrons, a carbon atom always forms four covalent bonds. Remembering this principle will help you to write correct structures for organic compounds.

Guide for Reading

Key Concepts

- How is the number of valence electrons in carbon atoms related to the bonds that carbon atoms form?
- What are two possible arrangements of carbon atoms in an alkane?
- In terms of their polarity, what type of molecules are alkanes?

Vocabulary

hydrocarbons
alkane
straight-chain alkanes
homologous series
condensed structural formula
substituent
alkyl group
branched-chain alkane

Reading Strategy

Relating Text and Visuals As you read, look at Figure 22.1. Explain how the formulas and models can help you understand the structure of methane and ethane molecules.

Animation 28 Get a glimpse of the staggering variety of hydrocarbon compounds.

—— with **ChemASAP**

Figure 22.1 Different types of formulas and models can be used to represent hydrocarbons such as methane and ethane. **Interpreting Diagrams** *What does a stick in a ball-and-stick model represent?*

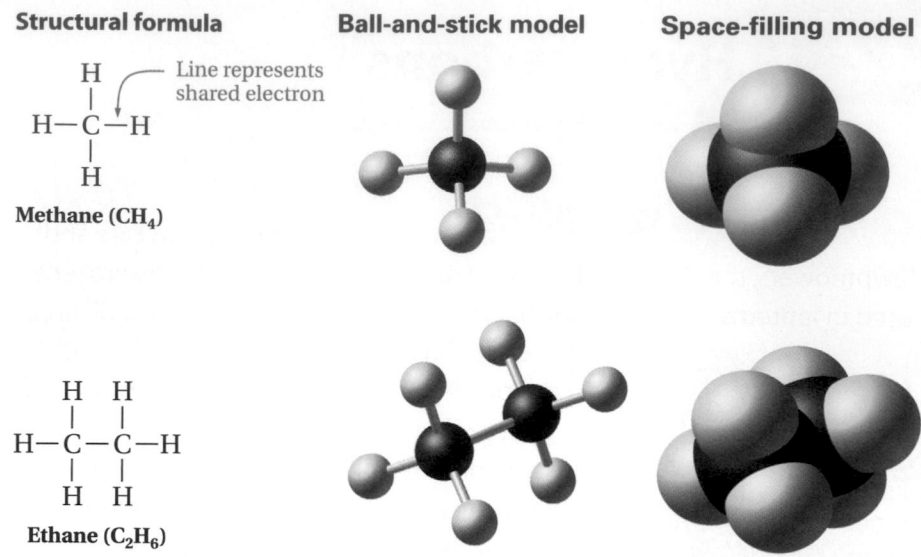

Structural formula | Ball-and-stick model | Space-filling model

Methane (CH₄)

Ethane (C₂H₆)

Methane is not typical of the vast majority of organic compounds, because there isn't a bond between carbon atoms in a methane molecule. There is a carbon-carbon bond in ethane. Like methane, ethane (C_2H_6) is a gas at standard temperature and pressure. In an ethane molecule, two carbon atoms share a pair of electrons. The remaining six valence electrons form bonding pairs with the electrons from six hydrogen atoms.

$$2\cdot\dot{\text{C}}\cdot \;+\; 6\text{H}\cdot \;\longrightarrow\; \cdot\dot{\text{C}}\!:\!\dot{\text{C}}\cdot \;+\; 6\text{H}\cdot \;\longrightarrow\; \text{H}\!:\!\ddot{\text{C}}\!:\!\ddot{\text{C}}\!:\!\text{H}$$

Carbon atoms   Hydrogen atoms   Ethane molecule

The ability of carbon to form stable carbon-carbon bonds is one reason that carbon can form so many different compounds.

Figure 22.1 shows the molecular formulas, structural formulas, ball-and-stick models, and space-filling models for methane and ethane. Structural formulas are a convenient way to show the arrangement of atoms in a molecule. But two-dimensional structural formulas do not provide accurate information about how the atoms in a molecule are arranged in space. Three-dimensional molecular models represent the shapes of molecules more accurately. Throughout this chapter and the next, ball-and-stick models and space-filling models will be used along with structural formulas to represent organic molecules. The bonding theories you studied in Section 8.3—hybrid orbital theory and VSEPR theory—are used to predict the molecular shapes.

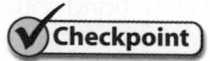 **Checkpoint** *What is the main advantage of a molecular model as compared to a structural formula?*

Alkanes

Methane and ethane are examples of alkanes. An **alkane** is a hydrocarbon in which there are only single covalent bonds. In any alkane, all the carbon-carbon bonds are single covalent bonds, and all the other bonds are carbon-hydrogen bonds. ⬭ **The carbon atoms in an alkane can be arranged in a straight chain or in a chain that has branches.**

Propane

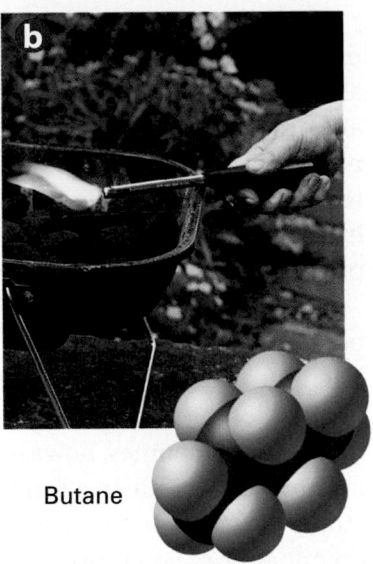

Butane

Figure 22.2 Hydrocarbons are used as fuels. ⓐ Pressurized tanks of propane are used to fuel the burners in hot-air balloons. ⓑ Butane serves as the fuel for many lighters.

Straight-Chain Alkanes Ethane is the simplest of the **straight-chain alkanes,** which contain any number of carbon atoms, one after the other, in a chain. Propane (C_3H_8) has three carbon atoms bonded in a chain with eight electrons shared with eight hydrogen atoms. Butane (C_4H_{10}) has a chain of four carbons and ten hydrogens. Figure 22.2 shows how propane and butane are used.

Table 22.1 shows the straight-chain alkanes containing up to ten carbons. The straight-chain alkanes are an example of a homologous series. A group of compounds forms a **homologous series** if there is a constant increment of change in molecular structure from one compound in the series to the next. A CH_2 group is the increment of change in straight-chain alkanes. This change can be traced in the structural formulas in Table 22.1. Notice in Table 22.1 that the boiling points of the straight-chain alkanes increase as the number of carbons in the chain increase. The melting points also increase in the same way. The change reflects the increase in molar mass from methane to decane.

Word *Origins*

Homologous comes from the Greek prefix *homo,* meaning "same," and *logos,* meaning "word." The homologous series of alkanes have the same general formula $C_n H_{2n+2}$ where *n* is any integer. **What is the formula for a 14-carbon alkane?**

Table 22.1			
The First Ten Straight-Chain Alkanes			
Name	**Molecular formula**	**Structural formula**	**Boiling point (°C)**
Methane	CH_4	CH_4	−161.0
Ethane	C_2H_6	CH_3CH_3	−88.5
Propane	C_3H_8	$CH_3CH_2CH_3$	−42.0
Butane	C_4H_{10}	$CH_3CH_2CH_2CH_3$	0.5
Pentane	C_5H_{12}	$CH_3CH_2CH_2CH_2CH_3$	36.0
Hexane	C_6H_{14}	$CH_3CH_2CH_2CH_2CH_2CH_3$	68.7
Heptane	C_7H_{16}	$CH_3CH_2CH_2CH_2CH_2CH_2CH_3$	98.5
Octane	C_8H_{18}	$CH_3CH_2CH_2CH_2CH_2CH_2CH_2CH_3$	125.6
Nonane	C_9H_{20}	$CH_3CH_2CH_2CH_2CH_2CH_2CH_2CH_2CH_3$	150.7
Decane	$C_{10}H_{22}$	$CH_3CH_2CH_2CH_2CH_2CH_2CH_2CH_2CH_2CH_3$	174.1

The names of the alkanes listed in Table 22.1 follow rules established by the International Union of Pure and Applied Chemistry (IUPAC). Every alkane has a name that ends with the suffix *-ane*. For the straight-chain alkanes with one to four carbon atoms, the official names and the common names are the same. They are methane, ethane, propane, and butane, respectively. A mixture of Latin and Greek prefixes are used to name the hydrocarbons having straight chains longer than four carbon atoms. The prefixes are *pent-* for 5, *hex-* for 6, *hept-* for 7, *oct-* for 8, and so on.

To draw a structural formula for a straight-chain alkane, write the symbol for carbon as many times as necessary to get the proper chain length. Then complete the formula with hydrogens and lines representing covalent bonds. Complete structural formulas show all the atoms and bonds in a molecule. Sometimes, however, shorthand or condensed structural formulas work just as well. In a **condensed structural formula,** some bonds and/or atoms are left out of the structural formula. Although the bonds and atoms do not appear, you must understand that they are there. Table 22.2 shows several ways to draw condensed structural formulas for butane.

✓ **Checkpoint**   *What suffix is used in the name of an alkane?*

Table 22.2

Formulas for Butane	
Formula	**Description**
C_4H_{10}	Molecular formula
$\begin{array}{c} \text{H} \quad \text{H} \quad \text{H} \quad \text{H} \\ | \quad\; | \quad\; | \quad\; | \\ \text{H}-\text{C}-\text{C}-\text{C}-\text{C}-\text{H} \\ | \quad\; | \quad\; | \quad\; | \\ \text{H} \quad \text{H} \quad \text{H} \quad \text{H} \end{array}$	Complete structural formula
$CH_5-CH_2-CH_2-CH_5$	Condensed structural formula; C — H bonds understood
$CH_3CH_2CH_2CH_3$	Condensed structural formula; C — H and — C — C — bonds understood
$CH_3(CH_2)_2CH_3$ Subscript Methylene unit	Condensed structural formula; all bonds understood; parentheses indicate CH_2 units are linked together in a continuous chain (the — CH_2 — unit is called a methylene group); subscript 2 to the right of parenthesis indicates two methylene groups are linked together
$C-C-C-C$	Carbon skeleton; all hydrogens and C — H bonds understood
$\wedge\!\!\!\vee\!\!\!\wedge$	Line-angle formula; all carbons and hydrogens understood; carbon atoms are located at each intersection and at the ends of lines

Drawing Structural Formulas for Alkanes

Draw complete structural formulas for the straight-chain alkanes that have three and four carbons.

1 **Analyze** *Identify the relevant concepts.*
In an alkane, each carbon atom forms four covalent bonds to hydrogen or to other carbon atoms. Because these are straight-chain alkanes, the appropriate number of carbons will be written in a straight line and then connected to each other by single bonds. The chain will then be filled in with hydrogen atoms so that each carbon forms four covalent bonds.

2 **Solve** *Apply concepts to this situation.*
A three-carbon straight-chain alkane has three carbon atoms in a straight line. The center carbon bonds to two hydrogen atoms. Each of the two end carbons bonds to three hydrogen atoms. A four-carbon straight-chain alkane has four carbon atoms in a straight line. Each of the two center carbons bonds to two hydrogen atoms, and each of the two end carbons bond to three hydrogen atoms.

$$
\begin{array}{ccc}
\text{H} & \text{H} & \text{H} \\
| & | & | \\
\text{H}-\text{C}-\text{C}-\text{C}-\text{H} \\
| & | & | \\
\text{H} & \text{H} & \text{H}
\end{array}
\qquad
\begin{array}{cccc}
\text{H} & \text{H} & \text{H} & \text{H} \\
| & | & | & | \\
\text{H}-\text{C}-\text{C}-\text{C}-\text{C}-\text{H} \\
| & | & | & | \\
\text{H} & \text{H} & \text{H} & \text{H}
\end{array}
$$

Practice Problems

1. Draw complete structural formulas for the straight-chain alkanes with five and six carbons.

2. How many single bonds are there in a propane molecule?

Problem-Solving 22.1 Solve Problem 1 with the help of an interactive guided tutorial.

── with **ChemASAP**

Branched-Chain Alkanes Alkanes and other hydrocarbons do not always have carbon atoms bonded in straight chains. Because a carbon atom forms four covalent bonds, it can bond not only to one or two other carbon atoms, but also to three or even four other carbons, resulting in branched chains. In organic chemistry, branches on a hydrocarbon chain are discussed as if they were substituted for a hydrogen atom on the chain. An atom or group of atoms that can take the place of a hydrogen atom on a parent hydrocarbon molecule is called a **substituent.** Look at the diagrams below. The longest continuous carbon chain of a branched-chain hydrocarbon is called the *parent* alkane. All other carbon atoms or groups of carbon atoms are regarded as substituents. In Chapter 23, you will study compounds in which atoms of halogens, oxygen, nitrogen, sulfur, and phosphorus can take the place of a hydrogen atom on the carbon chain.

Figure 22.3 Ball-and-stick and space-filling models show the arrangement of atoms in 4-ethyl-2,3-dimethylheptane. **Interpreting Diagrams** *Based on the ball-and-stick model, how many carbons are there in the longest straight chain?*

A hydrocarbon substituent is called an **alkyl group.** An alkyl group can be one carbon or several carbons long. Alkyl groups are named by removing the *-ane* ending from the parent hydrocarbon name and adding *-yl.* The three smallest alkyl groups are the methyl group (CH_3 —), the ethyl group (CH_3CH_2 —), and the propyl group ($CH_3CH_2CH_2$ —). An alkyl group consists of an alkane with one hydrogen removed.

When a substituent alkyl group is attached to a straight-chain hydrocarbon, branches are formed. An alkane with one or more alkyl groups is called a **branched-chain alkane.** The IUPAC rules for naming branched-chain alkanes are quite straightforward. The name of a branched-chain alkane is based on the name of the longest continuous carbon chain. Each alkyl substituent is named according to the length of its chain and numbered according to its position on the main chain. The compound with the following structural formula can be used as an example. Figure 22.3 shows models of the compound.

$$
\begin{array}{ccccccc}
7 & 6 & 5 & 4 & 3 & 2 & 1 \\
CH_3 - CH_2 - CH_2 - CH - CH - CH - CH_3 \\
& & & | & | & | \\
& & & CH_2 & CH_3 & CH_3 \\
& & & | \\
& & & CH_3
\end{array}
$$

1. Find the longest chain of carbons in the molecule. This chain is considered the parent structure. In the example, the longest chain contains seven carbon atoms. Therefore, the parent hydrocarbon structure is heptane.

2. Number the carbons in the main chain in sequence. To do this, start at the end that will give the groups attached to the chain the smallest numbers. This has already been done in the example. As you can see, numbering the chain from right to left places the substituent groups at carbon atoms 2, 3, and 4. If the chain were numbered from left to right, the groups would be at positions 4, 5, and 6. These higher numbers would violate the rule.

3. Add numbers to the names of the substituent groups to identify their positions on the chain. These numbers become prefixes to the name of the alkyl group. In this example the substituents and positions are 2-methyl, 3-methyl, and 4-ethyl.

4. Use prefixes to indicate the appearance of the same group more than once in the structural formula. Common prefixes are *di-* (twice), *tri-* (three times), *tetra-* (four times), and *penta-* (five times). This example has two methyl substituents. Thus, *dimethyl* will be part of the complete name.

5. List the names of alkyl substituents in alphabetical order. For purposes of alphabetizing, ignore the prefixes *di-*, *tri-*, and so on. In this example, the 4-ethyl group is listed before the 2-methyl and 3-methyl groups (which are combined as 2,3-dimethyl in the name).

6. Use proper punctuation. This is very important in writing the names of organic compounds in the IUPAC system. Commas are used to separate numbers. Hyphens are used to separate numbers and words. The entire name is written without any spaces.

According to the IUPAC rules, the name of the compound in the example is 4-ethyl-2,3-dimethylheptane. Note that the name of the parent alkane, heptane, follows directly after the final prefix, dimethyl. (It would be incorrect to write the name 4-ethyl-2,3-dimethyl heptane.)

CONCEPTUAL PROBLEM 22.2

Naming Branched-Chain Alkanes

Name this compound using the IUPAC system. Notice that the longest chain is not written in a straight line.

$$CH_3$$
$$|$$
$$CH_3 — CH_2 — C — CH_3$$
$$|$$
$$CH_2$$
$$|$$
$$CH_2$$
$$|$$
$$CH_3$$

1 **Analyze** *Identify the relevant concepts.*
The parent structure is the longest chain of carbons. All other groups are substituents. The carbons are numbered to give the first substituent the lowest possible number.

These location numbers become part of the name as prefixes. The names of the substituents are listed in alphabetical order with numbers separated by commas and numbers and words separated by hyphens.

2 **Solve** *Apply concepts to this situation.*
The longest carbon chain in the molecule is hexane (six carbons). There are two methyl substituents on carbon 3, so the prefix is 3,3-dimethyl. The correct IUPAC name is 3,3-dimethylhexane.

Practice Problems

3. Name these compounds according to the IUPAC system.

a.
$$CH_2 — CH_2 — CH — CH_2 — CH_3$$
$$|\qquad\qquad\quad |$$
$$CH_3\qquad\quad CH_2$$
$$\qquad\qquad\quad |$$
$$\qquad\qquad\quad CH_3$$

b.
$$CH_3 — CH_2 — CH — CH_3$$
$$|$$
$$CH_3$$

4. Name these compounds according to the IUPAC system.

a.
$$H\quad CH_3\ H$$
$$|\qquad |\quad |$$
$$CH_3 — C — C — C — CH_3$$
$$|\qquad |\quad |$$
$$CH_3\ H\quad H$$

b.
$$CH_3 — CH — CH_2 — CH_2 — CH_3$$
$$|$$
$$CH_3$$

Problem-Solving 22.3 Solve Problem 3 with the help of an interactive guided tutorial.
——— with **ChemASAP**

With an alkane name and knowledge of the IUPAC rules, it is easy to reconstruct the structural formula.

1. Find the root word (ending in *-ane*) in the hydrocarbon name. Then write the longest carbon chain to create the parent structure.

2. Number the carbons on this parent carbon chain.

3. Identify the substituent groups. Attach the substituents to the numbered parent chain at the proper positions.

4. Add hydrogens as needed.

Drawing Structural Formulas for Branched-Chain Alkanes

The compound 2,2,4-trimethylpentane (isooctane) is found in gasoline. Draw a complete structural formula for isooctane.

 Analyze *Identify the relevant concepts.*
Prefixes indicate the types of substituents, the number of times each appears, and their locations on the parent chain. The part of the name that ends in -*ane* indicates the parent structure. The carbons on the parent chain are numbered so that the carbons to which alkyl substituents are attached have the lowest numbers. Hydrogens are added as needed.

 Solve *Apply concepts to this situation.*
The parent structure is pentane, which has five carbon atoms. There are two methyl groups on carbon 2 and one on carbon 4. Nine hydrogens are added to complete the structure.

Practice Problems

5. Draw structural formulas for 2,3-dimethylhexane.

6. Draw the structural formula for 4-ethyl-2,3,4-trimethyloctane.

interactive Textbook

Problem-Solving 22.6 Solve Problem 4 with the help of an interactive guided tutorial.

— with **ChemASAP**

Properties of Alkanes

The electron pair in a carbon-hydrogen or a carbon-carbon bond is shared almost equally by the nuclei of the atoms forming the bond. **Molecules of hydrocarbons, such as alkanes, are nonpolar molecules.** The attractions between nonpolar molecules are weak van der Waals forces. So alkanes of low molar mass tend to be gases or liquids that boil at a low temperature.

Recall the general rule "like dissolves like." Two nonpolar compounds will form a solution, as will two polar compounds. But a nonpolar compound and a polar compound will not form a solution. For example, because oil is a mixture of hydrocarbons, oil and water do not mix. So the oil from an oil spill will float on top of the water, as shown in Figure 22.4.

Figure 22.4 The nonpolar molecules in this oil spill in Wales are not attracted to the polar water molecules in the ocean. The oil appears brown because a dispersant was added to help the oil and water mix.

Careers *in* Chemistry

Organic Chemist

An organic chemist might be best described as part inventor and part detective. Most organic chemists use existing carbon-based molecules to synthesize new organic compounds. An organic chemist uses scientific theories and scientific methods to design and build a molecule with a specific set of new properties.

To confirm the identity of new molecules, organic chemists use infrared (IR) spectrophotometry and nuclear magnetic resonance (NMR) spectrometry to analyze their structures.

Companies that manufacture medicines, dyes, cosmetics, or foods are among the companies that employ organic chemists.

To become an organic chemist, you will need at least an undergraduate education in chemistry. In addition to courses in organic chemistry, you must have a firm background in physical, inorganic, and analytical chemistry.

If you are interested in the computer-aided design of bioactive molecules, such as new drugs, biochemistry and computer training are also important. An organic chemist must know how to use laboratory equipment and how to handle chemicals safely.

For: Careers in Chemistry
Visit: PHSchool.com
Web Code: cdb-1221

22.1 Section Assessment

7. **Key Concept** Explain why carbon atoms form four covalent bonds.

8. **Key Concept** What are two ways that carbon atoms can be arranged in an alkane?

9. **Key Concept** Describe the polarity of alkane molecules.

10. Write complete structural formulas for the following alkanes.
    a. propane   b. pentane

11. Draw a condensed structural formula for 2,2-dimethylbutane.

12. Explain why mineral oil, which is a mixture of hydrocarbons, does not dissolve in water.

Connecting ▶ **Concepts**

Bond Dissociation Energy Except for combustion reactions, alkanes usually do not react easily. Use what you learned about bond dissociation energy in Section 8.2 to explain why alkane molecules tend to be unreactive.

Textbook

Assessment 22.1 Test yourself on the concepts in Section 22.1.

with ChemASAP

Guide for Reading

Key Concepts
- What are the structural characteristics of alkenes?
- What are the structural characteristics of alkynes?

Vocabulary
saturated compounds
unsaturated compounds
alkenes
alkynes
aliphatic hydrocarbons

Reading Strategy

Comparing and Contrasting
After you read the section, write a paragraph about alkenes and alkynes. How are these compounds similar? How are they different?

Connecting to Your World

A cockroach can transmit bacterial diseases when it comes in contact with food. Roach traps are bated with pheromones, which roaches produce to attract mates. The structure of many pheromones is based on unsaturated hydrocarbons. In this section, you will study two types of unsaturated hydrocarbons—alkenes and alkynes.

A cockroach

Alkenes

Organic compounds that contain the maximum number of hydrogen atoms per carbon atom are called **saturated compounds.** Alkanes are saturated compounds because the only bonds in alkanes are single covalent bonds. Compounds that contain double or triple carbon-carbon bonds are called **unsaturated compounds.** The ratio of hydrogen atoms to carbon atoms is lower in an unsaturated compound than in a saturated compound.

Alkenes are hydrocarbons that contain one or more carbon-carbon double covalent bonds. A carbon-carbon double bond is shown in structural formulas as two parallel lines. **At least one carbon-carbon bond in an alkene is a double covalent bond. Other bonds may be single carbon-carbon bonds and carbon-hydrogen bonds.**

Ethene (C_2H_4) is the simplest alkene. It is often called by the common name ethylene. Figure 22.5 shows the ball-and-stick and space-filling models of ethene. To name an alkene by the IUPAC system, find the longest chain in the molecule that contains the double bond. This chain is the parent alkene. It has the root name of the alkane with the same number of carbons plus the ending -*ene*. The chain is numbered so that the carbon atoms of the double bond have the lowest possible numbers. Substituents on the chain are named and numbered in the same way they are for the alkanes. Some examples of the structures and IUPAC names of simple alkenes are shown below.

Ethene

Figure 22.5 Because rotation is restricted around the double bond, atoms in ethene lie in one plane. **Calculating** *What is the ratio of hydrogen to carbon in ethene?*

Ethene
(ethylene)

Propene
(propylene)

1-butene

2-butene

4-methyl-2-pentene

Table 22.3

Name	Molecular structure	Boiling point (°C)
C$_2$		
Ethane	$CH_3 - CH_3$	−88.5
Ethene	$CH_2 = CH_2$	−103.9
Ethyne	$CH \equiv CH$	−81.8
C$_3$		
Propane	$CH_3CH_2CH_3$	−42.0
Propene	$CH_3CH = CH_2$	−47.0
Propyne	$CH_3C \equiv CH$	−23.3

Boiling Points of Homologous Alkanes, Alkenes, and Alkynes

Alkynes

Hydrocarbons that contain one or more carbon-carbon triple covalent bonds are called **alkynes.** A carbon-carbon triple bond is shown in structural formulas as three parallel lines. ⊙➝ **At least one carbon-carbon bond in an alkyne is a triple covalent bond. Other bonds may be single or double carbon-carbon bonds and single carbon-hydrogen bonds.** Like alkenes, alkynes are unsaturated compounds.

$$- C \equiv C -$$

Alkynes are not plentiful in nature. The simplest alkyne is the gas ethyne (C_2H_2), which has the common name acetylene. Acetylene is the fuel burned in oxyacetylene torches, which are used in welding. Figure 22.6 shows that the single bonds that extend from the carbons in the carbon-carbon triple bond of ethyne are separated by the maximum angle of 180°. This makes ethyne a linear molecule.

Straight-chain and branched-chain alkanes, alkenes, and alkynes are **aliphatic hydrocarbons.** The major attractions between aliphatic molecules are weak van der Waals forces. As a result, the introduction of a double or triple bond into a hydrocarbon does not have a dramatic effect on physical properties such as boiling point. Compare the boiling points in Table 22.3.

Ethyne

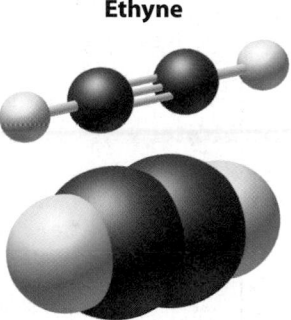

Figure 22.6 The triple bond restricts rotation in an ethyne molecule, which has a linear shape. **Calculating** *What is the ratio of hydrogen to carbon in ethyne?*

22.2 Section Assessment

13. ⊙➝ **Key Concept** Describe the bonding between atoms in an alkene.

14. ⊙➝ **Key Concept** What types of bonds are present in an alkyne?

15. What is the difference between saturated and unsaturated hydrocarbons?

16. Write electron dot structures for ethene and ethyne. Describe the shape of each molecule.

17. Draw and name all the alkenes with the molecular formula C_4H_8.

Connecting ➤ **Concepts**

Saturated and Unsaturated Write a paragraph explaining what saturated and unsaturated hydrocarbons have in common with saturated and unsaturated solutions. Refer to Section 16.1.

Textbook

Assessment 22.2 Test yourself on the concepts in Section 22.2.

——— with **ChemASAP**

22.3 Isomers

New York Standards: 3.1ff–gg, 3.1ii

Guide for Reading

Key Concepts
- How do the properties of structural isomers differ?
- What are the two types of stereoisomers?

Vocabulary

isomers

structural isomers

stereoisomers

geometric isomers

trans configuration

cis configuration

asymmetric carbon

optical isomers

Reading Strategy

Building Vocabulary As you read, write definitions of the four types of isomers described. Be sure your definitions differentiate among the types.

Connecting to Your World The retinal molecule in the rod and cone cells of your eye has a hydrocarbon skeleton. The first step in the process of vision occurs when light enters your eye and strikes a cell containing retinal. The light causes a change in the three-dimensional structure of the retinal molecule. The structures before and after the light strikes are examples of isomers. In this section, you will study different types of isomers.

Structural Isomers

You may have noticed that the structures of some hydrocarbons differ only in the positions of substituent groups or of multiple bonds in their molecules. Look at the structural formulas for butane and 2-methylpropane shown below and at their ball-and-stick models in Figure 22.7. Even though both compounds have the formula C_4H_{10}, their boiling points and other properties differ. Because their structures are different, they are different substances. Compounds that have the same molecular formula but different molecular structures are called **isomers.**

$$CH_3 — CH_2 — CH_2 — CH_3$$
Butane (C_4H_{10})
(bp −0.5°C)

$$CH_3 — \overset{\overset{\displaystyle CH_3}{|}}{CH} — CH_3$$
2-methylpropane (C_4H_{10})
(bp −10.2°C)

Butane and 2-methylpropane represent a category of isomers called structural isomers. **Structural isomers** are compounds that have the same molecular formula, but the atoms are joined together in a different order. **Structural isomers differ in physical properties such as boiling point and melting point. They also have different chemical reactivities.** In general, the more highly branched the hydrocarbon structure, the lower the boiling point of the isomer compared with less branched isomers. For example, 2-methylpropane has a lower boiling point than butane.

Figure 22.7 Both butane and 2-methylpropane have the molecular formula C_4H_{10}. But the atoms in their molecules are arranged in a different order. So these compounds are structural isomers.

Butane

2-methylpropane

Stereoisomers

Remember that molecules are three-dimensional structures. So molecules with the same molecular formula and with atoms joined in exactly the same order may still be isomers. **Stereoisomers** are molecules in which the atoms are joined in the same order, but the positions of the atoms in space are different. 🔑 **Two types of stereoisomers are geometric isomers and optical isomers.**

Geometric Isomers The first category of stereoisomers is based on the presence of a double bond in a molecule. A double bond between two carbon atoms prevents them from rotating with respect to each other. Because of this lack of rotation, groups on either side of the double bond can have different orientations in space. **Geometric isomers** have atoms joined in the same order, but differ in the orientation of groups around a double bond. Look at the models of 2-butene in Figure 22.8. Two arrangements are possible for the methyl groups with respect to the rigid double bond. In the **trans configuration,** the methyl groups are on opposite sides of the double bond. In the **cis configuration,** the methyl groups are on the same side of the double bond. *Trans*-2-butene and *cis*-2-butene have different physical and chemical properties. For example, the density of *cis*-2-butene is 0.616 g/cm³, and the density of *trans*-2-butene is 0.599 g/cm³. The groups attached to the carbons of the double bond do not need to be the same. Geometric isomerism is possible whenever each carbon of the double bond has at least one substituent.

Trans configuration

Cis configuration

Figure 22.8 There is a *trans* and a *cis* configuration of 2-butene because a methyl group is attached to each carbon of the double bond.
Comparing and Contrasting *How are the trans and cis configurations different?*

trans-2-pentene	cis-2-pentene	2-methyl-1-butene (no cis, trans isomers)

Optical Isomers The second category of stereoisomers occurs whenever a carbon atom has four different atoms or groups attached. A carbon with four different atoms or groups attached is an **asymmetric carbon.** Look at the models in Figure 22.9. Because H, F, Cl, and Br atoms are attached to a single carbon atom, the carbon is asymmetric. The relationship between the molecules is similar to the relationship between right and left hands.

Think about an object placed in front of a mirror. If the object is symmetrical, like a ball, then its mirror image can be superimposed. That is, the appearance of the ball and its reflection are indistinguishable. By contrast, a pair of hands is distinguishable even though the hands consist of identical parts. The right hand reflects as a left hand and the left hand reflects as a right hand. The images cannot be superimposed. Many ordinary objects, such as ears, feet, shoes, and bird wings, are similarly related.

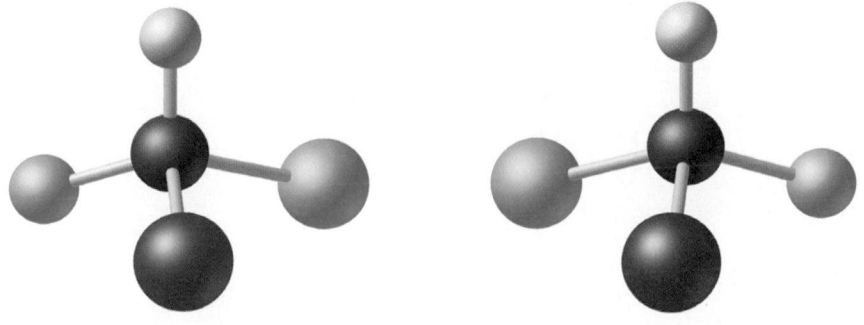

Figure 22.9 In these models, four different atoms are attached to the same carbon atom, making the carbon atom an asymmetric carbon.

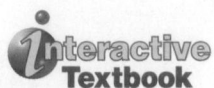
Pairs of molecules that differ only in the way that four different groups are arranged around a central carbon atom are called **optical isomers.** The term *optical* is used to describe this type of isomer because the term is related to the concept of objects and mirror images. The molecules shown in Figure 22.9 are optical isomers. The models cannot be superimposed because they are mirror images of each other. Try to visualize the models in three dimensions. Imagine rotating one model 180°. At first, it might appear that the models are now identical. However, the direction of each bond in space is not the same. For example, the carbon-bromine bond would be pointing away from you rather than toward you. No matter how you turn the models, you cannot make the models look exactly alike. Unless bonds are broken, these molecules cannot be made to look alike.

✓ Checkpoint *How does the presence of a carbon-carbon double bond in a molecule result in geometric isomers?*

CONCEPTUAL PROBLEM 22.4

Identifying Asymmetric Carbon Atoms

Compounds with the following formulas are alcohols. The alcohol represented by the formula in **a.** is the alcohol in rubbing alcohol. Which compound has an asymmetric carbon?

a. CH$_3$CHCH$_3$
       |
       OH

b. CH$_3$CHCH$_2$CH$_3$
       |
       OH

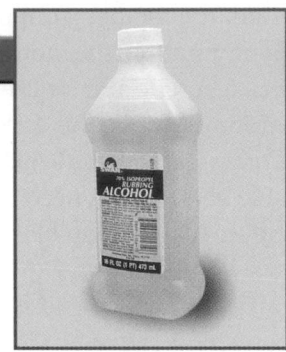

① Analyze *Identify the relevant concepts.*
An asymmetric carbon atom has four different groups attached.

② Solve *Apply concepts to this situation.*
Draw the structures in a more complete form to determine the presence of a carbon atom with four different groups attached.

a. The central carbon has two CH$_3$ groups attached. It is not asymmetric.

b. The central carbon has one H, one OH, one CH$_3$, and one CH$_2$CH$_3$ group attached. Because these four groups are different, the central carbon is asymmetric. In a structural formula, an asymmetric carbon is often marked with an asterisk.

Practice Problems

18. Identify the asymmetric carbon, if any, in each of the following structures.

   a. CH$_3$CHCHO
          |
          Cl

   b. CH$_3$CHOH
          |
          CH$_3$

19. Identify the asymmetric carbon, if any, in each of the following structures.

                CH$_3$
                |
   a. CH$_3$CH$_2$ — C — Br
                |
                F

   b. CH$_2$Cl$_2$

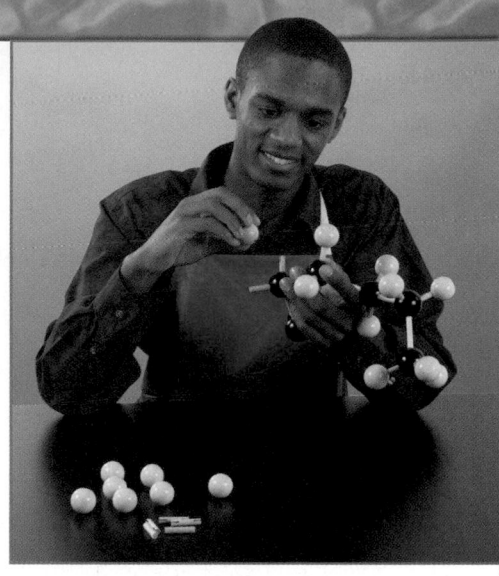

Quick LAB

Structural Isomers of Heptane

Purpose
To build ball-and-stick models and name the nine structural isomers of heptane (C_7H_{16}).

Materials
- ball-and-stick molecular model kit (Colors used to represent elements in the kit may not match colors used to represent elements in this book.)

Heptane

Procedure
1. Build a model for the straight-chain isomer of C_7H_{16}. Draw the structural formula and write the IUPAC name for this isomer.

2. Move one carbon atom from the end of the chain and add a methyl substituent to the chain. Draw the structural formula and name this isomer.

3. Move the methyl group to a new position on the chain. Then draw and name this third isomer. Is there a third position that the methyl group can be moved to on the chain of six carbons to form yet another different isomer?

4. Make other structural isomers by shortening the longest straight chain and using the removed carbons as substituents. Draw the structural formulas and name each isomer.

Analyze and Conclude
1. What are the names of the nine structural isomers of C_7H_{16}?

2. What is the shortest possible straight carbon chain in the isomers?

3. Why does each structural isomer have its own unique name?

22.3 Section Assessment

20. **Key Concept** Explain why you would expect two structural isomers to have different boiling points.

21. **Key Concept** Name the two types of stereoisomers.

22. What structure must be present in a molecule for geometric isomers to exist?

23. **Key Concept** How can an asymmetric carbon be identified?

24. What is the relationship between two molecules that are optical isomers?

25. Draw structural formulas for the following alkenes. If a compound has geometric isomers, draw both the *cis* and *trans* forms.
   a. 1-pentene
   b. 2-hexene
   c. 2-methyl-2-hexene

Writing ▶ Activity

Writing Instructions Write instructions that could be used to decide whether two compounds are isomers and, if so, what type of isomers they might be. (1) How can you tell if two compounds are isomers? (2) How can you tell if two compounds are structural isomers? (3) How can you tell if two compounds can be geometric isomers? (4) How can you tell if two compounds can be optical isomers?

Textbook

Assessment 22.3 Test yourself on the concepts in Section 22.3.

— with **ChemASAP**

Hydrocarbon Isomers

Purpose
To draw line-angle formulas and name some of the isomers in gasoline.

Materials
- toothpicks
- modeling clay

Procedure
Gasoline is a complex mixture of hydrocarbon molecules. Each molecule contains between five and ten carbon atoms. Many of the components of gasoline are isomers with the same molecular formula. These components include the isomers of pentane. Study the formulas and names of the isomers of C_5H_{12} in the chart below. Make a model of each isomer using toothpicks and modeling clay. Compare the models and make accurate drawings on your paper.

Formulas Representing Isomers of C_5H_{12}

Condensed	Line-angle	Space-filling
CH₃CH₂CH₂CH₂CH₃ pentane		
CH₃CHCH₂CH₃ │ CH₃ 2-methylbutane		
CH₃ │ CH₃CCH₃ │ CH₃ 2, 2-dimethylpropane		

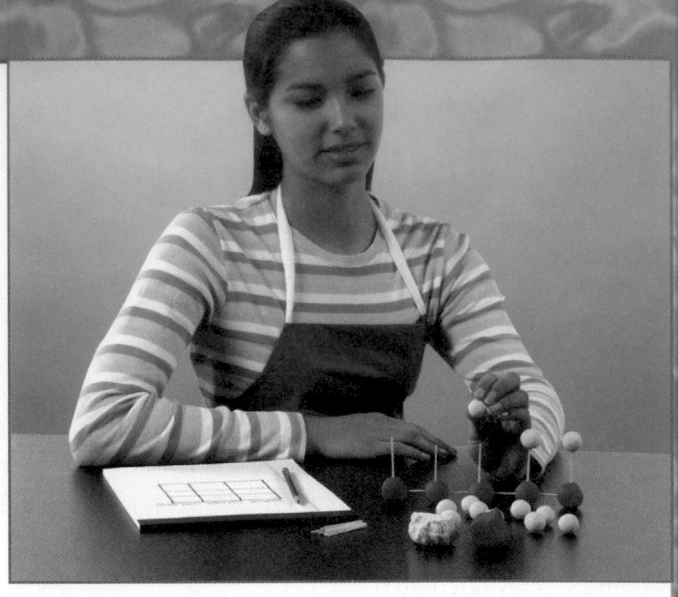

Analyze
Using your experimental data, answer the following questions.

1. Complete structural formulas include all the atoms and all the chemical bonds in a molecule. Draw the complete structural formula for each isomer of C_5H_{12} in the chart.

2. In a line-angle formula, each line represents a carbon-carbon bond. Each end of a line, as well as the intersection of lines, represents a carbon atom. All hydrogen atoms are understood. Knowing that carbon always forms four bonds in organic compounds, explain how to determine the number of hydrogen atoms bonded to each carbon in a line-angle formula.

3. Because butane can vaporize readily, it is used in the formulations of gasolines in cold climates during winter. Draw the condensed structural formulas, the line-angle formulas, and the space-filling formulas for the two isomers of butane (C_4H_{10}). Make models of each isomer.

You're The Chemist
The following small-scale activities allow you to develop your own procedures and analyze the results.

1. **Analyze It!** Gasoline contains isomers of hexane. Draw the line-angle formulas and name the five isomers of C_6H_{14}. Make a model of one isomer and convert that model into the other four.

2. **Design It!** Gasoline also contains small amounts of the six isomers of pentene. Two of the isomers are *cis* and *trans* configurations of the same structural isomer. Experiment with your models to make these isomers. Use two toothpicks to represent a double bond. Draw structural formulas for the *cis* and *trans* isomers, and line-angle formulas for the others.

22.4 Hydrocarbon Rings

New York Standard: 3.1ff

Connecting to Your World

Not everyone loves carrots, but you have probably heard about how good they are for you. One reason carrots are a healthful food choice is that they contain beta-carotene, an important nutrient for vision. Beta-carotene also gives carrots their orange color. The hydrocarbon skeleton of beta-carotene contains hydrocarbon rings. In this section, you will learn about hydrocarbon rings and the properties of compounds formed from these rings.

Cyclic Hydrocarbons

Saturated and unsaturated straight-chain and branched-chain hydrocarbons are not the only types of hydrocarbons. 🔑 **In some hydrocarbon compounds, the carbon chain is in the form of a ring.** Figure 20.10 shows the structures of some of these hydrocarbons. Compounds that contain a hydrocarbon ring are called **cyclic hydrocarbons.**

Guide for Reading

🔑 **Key Concepts**
• What is the general structure of cyclic hydrocarbons?
• What is the most accurate description of the bonding in a benzene ring?

Vocabulary
cyclic hydrocarbons
aromatic compound

Reading Strategy
Relating Text and Visuals As you read, look at the benzene diagrams on page 710. What is the value of the diagram with a circle in a hexagon?

| Cyclopropane (bp −34.4°C) | Cyclobutane (bp −13°C) | Cyclopentane (bp 49.5°C) | Cyclohexane (bp 81.4°C) |

Figure 22.10 The simplest cyclic hydrocarbon has a 3-carbon ring. Rings containing up to 20 carbon atoms are found in nature. Rings with 5 or 6 carbons are the most abundant.

For: Links on Aromatic Hydrocarbons
Visit: www.SciLinks.org
Web Code: cdn-1224

Aromatic Hydrocarbons

There is a class of organic compounds that are responsible for the aromas of spices such as vanilla, cinnamon, cloves, and ginger. These compounds were originally called aromatic compounds because they have distinct, pleasant aromas. Not all compounds currently classified as aromatic have an odor. Molecules of aromatic compounds contain a single ring or a group of rings. Benzene (C_6H_6) is the simplest example of an aromatic compound. An **aromatic compound** is an organic compound that contains a benzene ring or other ring in which the bonding is like that of benzene. Another name for an aromatic compound is an arene. Because of the structure of benzene, the properties of aromatic compounds are quite different from those of aliphatic compounds.

The Structure of Benzene Friedrich Kekulé (1829–1896) made one major contribution to chemistry. He was the first to describe the structure of a benzene molecule. Look at the space-filling model of benzene in Figure 22.11. The benzene molecule is a six-membered carbon ring with a hydrogen atom attached to each carbon. This arrangement leaves one electron from each carbon free to participate in a double bond. Two different structures with alternating double bonds can be written for benzene.

These structural formulas show only the extremes in electron sharing between any two adjacent carbons in benzene. One extreme is a normal single bond. The other extreme is a normal double bond. Recall that when two or more equally valid structures can be drawn for a molecule, resonance occurs. The actual bonding in a benzene ring doesn't alternate between the two extreme resonance structures. Rather, all the bonds in the ring are identical hybrids of single and double bonds. ⟵ **In a benzene molecule, the bonding electrons between carbon atoms are shared evenly around the ring.** Benzene and other molecules that exhibit resonance are more stable than similar molecules that do not exhibit resonance. Thus, benzene is not as reactive as six-carbon alkenes.

Because of the way electrons are distributed, drawing a solid or dashed circle inside a hexagon is a good way to represent benzene. However, it does not show the number of electrons involved. For this reason, the traditional structure, which is the structure shown on the right, is used in this textbook. Remember, though, that each bond in the ring is identical.

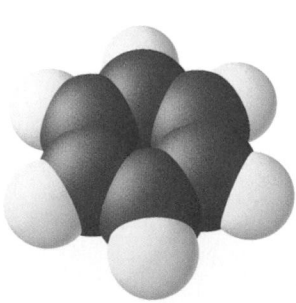

Figure 22.11 This is a space-filling model of benzene. **Applying Concepts** *What is the molecular formula of benzene?*

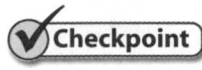 **Checkpoint** *What is the name of the simplest aromatic hydrocarbon and what is its formula?*

Substituted Aromatic Compounds The dyes used to produce the intense colors shown in Figure 22.12 are substituted aromatic compounds. Compounds containing substituents attached to a benzene ring are named as derivatives of benzene. When the benzene ring is a substituent on an alkane, the C_6H_5 group is called a phenyl group.

Methylbenzene (toluene)

$CH_3-CH_2-CH-CH_2-CH_2-CH_3$

3-phenylhexane

Ethylbenzene

Figure 22.12 The molecules of many dyes include benzene rings. Dyes that contain aromatic compounds are called aniline dyes.

Some derivatives of benzene have two substituents. These derivatives are called disubstituted benzenes. There are three structural isomers for the liquid aromatic compound dimethylbenzene ($C_6H_4(CH_3)_2$). Dimethylbenzenes are also called xylenes. The boiling points of the xylenes are a reminder that structural isomers have different physical properties.

1,2-dimethylbenzene
(*o*-xylene)
(bp 144°C)

1,3-dimethylbenzene
(*m*-xylene)
(bp 139°C)

1,4-dimethylbenzene
(*p*-xylene)
(bp 139°C)

In the IUPAC naming system, the possible positions of two substituents in disubstituted benzene are designated as 1,2; 1,3; or 1,4. Common names for disubstituted benzenes use the terms *ortho, meta,* and *para* (abbreviated as *o, m,* and *p*) in place of numbers.

22.4 Section Assessment

26. 🔑 **Key Concept** What is a cyclic hydrocarbon?

27. 🔑 **Key Concept** Describe the bonding between carbon atoms in benzene.

28. The molecules of both cyclohexane and benzene have six carbon atoms bonded in a ring. What is the difference between these two compounds?

29. Name the following compounds.

a. CH_2CH_3

b. CH_2CH_3

$CH_2CH_2CH_3$

> **Writing** ▶ **Activity**
>
> **Explanatory Paragraph** The alternate name for an aromatic compound is arene. Write a paragraph explaining why *arene* is not an entirely accurate choice for an aromatic compound. (*Hint:* What does the suffix *-ene* indicate when used with aliphatic compounds?)

interactive **Textbook**

Assessment 22.4 Test yourself on the concepts in Section 22.4.

with **ChemASAP**

Hydrocarbons From Earth's Crust

New York Standards: 3.1gg, 7.1

Guide for Reading

 Key Concepts
- What type of hydrocarbons are in natural gas?
- What is the first step in the refining of petroleum?
- How is coal classified?
- What is the chemical composition of coal?

Vocabulary

cracking

Reading Strategy

Previewing Before you read, jot down five things you know about petroleum. As you read, explain how what you learn relates to what you already know.

Connecting to Your World The photograph shows a painting in which the artist imagines Saturn's moon Titan as a refueling station in space. A traveler would refill a fuel tank with hydrocarbons from Titan's atmosphere. On Earth, hydrocarbons are also used as fuels. However, they are more difficult to obtain because they are found in Earth's crust, not in Earth's atmosphere. In this section, you will learn about three fossil fuels—natural gas, petroleum, and coal.

Natural Gas

Much of the world's energy is supplied by burning fossil fuels. Fossil fuels are carbon-based because they are derived from the decay of organisms. Millions of years ago, marine organisms died, settled on the ocean floor, and were buried in ocean sediments. Heat, pressure, and bacteria changed the residue into petroleum and natural gas, which contain mostly aliphatic hydrocarbons. Figure 22.13 shows one possible location for these fuels.

 Natural gas is an important source of alkanes of low molar mass. Typically, natural gas is composed of about 80% methane, 10% ethane, 4% propane, and 2% butane. The remaining 4% consists of nitrogen and hydrocarbons of higher molar mass. Natural gas also contains a small amount of the noble gas helium. In fact, natural gas is a major source of helium. Methane, the major constituent of natural gas, is especially prized for combustion because it burns with a hot, clean flame.

$$CH_4(g) + 2O_2(g) \longrightarrow CO_2(g) + 2H_2O(g) + heat$$

Propane and butane are separated from the other gases in natural gas by liquefaction. These heating fuels are sold in liquid form in pressurized tanks as liquid petroleum gas (LPG).

Oxygen is necessary for the efficient combustion of a hydrocarbon. If there is not enough oxygen available, the combustion is incomplete. Complete combustion of a hydrocarbon gives a blue flame. Incomplete combustion gives a yellow flame. This is due to the formation of small, glowing carbon particles that are deposited as soot when they cool. Carbon monoxide, a toxic gas, is also formed along with carbon dioxide and water during incomplete combustion.

Figure 22.13 Wells are drilled to reach natural gas and petroleum. Pressure from the trapped gas may force petroleum up a well pipe, but pumping is usually required.

Petroleum

The organic compounds found in petroleum, or crude oil, are more complex than those in natural gas. Most of the hydrocarbons in petroleum are straight-chain and branched-chain alkanes. Petroleum also contains small amounts of aromatic compounds and sulfur-, oxygen-, and nitrogen-containing organic compounds.

Humans have known about petroleum for centuries; ancient peoples found it seeping from the ground in certain areas. In the late 1850s, a vast deposit of petroleum was discovered in Pennsylvania when a well was drilled to obtain petroleum for use as a fuel. Within decades, petroleum deposits had also been found in the Middle East, Europe, and the East Indies. Petroleum has since been found in other parts of the world as well.

Petroleum is a mixture of hydrocarbons having from one to more than 40 carbon atoms. Without further treatment, petroleum is not very useful. The mixture must be separated, or refined, into parts called fractions, which have many commercial uses. 🔑 **The refining process starts with the distillation of petroleum (crude oil) into fractions according to boiling point.** A schematic of a petroleum refining distillation tower is shown in Figure 22.14. Each distillation fraction contains several different hydrocarbons. The fractions and their composition are listed in Table 22.4.

The amounts of products obtained by fractional distillation are not in proportion to the demand of the market. Gasoline is by far the most commonly used product, so other processes are used to make the supply meet the demand. **Cracking** is a controlled process by which hydrocarbons are broken down or rearranged into smaller, more useful molecules. For example, fractions containing compounds of higher molar mass are "cracked" to produce the more useful short-chain components of gasoline and kerosene. Hydrocarbons are cracked with the aid of a catalyst and with heat. This process also produces low-molar-mass alkanes, which are used to manufacture paints and plastics. Other catalytic processes besides cracking are used to increase the amounts of components that improve the performance of gasoline.

✓ **Checkpoint** *When and where was the first petroleum well drilled?*

Fractionating Column

Figure 22.14 In fractional distillation, the crude oil is heated so that it vaporizes and rises through the fractionating column. The column is hotter at the bottom and cooler at the top. Compounds with the highest boiling points condense near the bottom. Compounds with the lowest boiling points condense near the top.

Table 22.4

Fractions Obtained from Crude Oils			
Fraction	**Composition of carbon chains**	**Boiling range (°C)**	**Percent of crude oil**
Natural gas	C_1 to C_4	Below 20 ⎫	
Petroleum ether (solvent)	C_5 to C_6	30 to 60 ⎬ 10%	
Naphtha (solvent)	C_7 to C_8	60 to 90 ⎭	
Gasoline	C_5 to C_{12}	40 to 175	40%
Kerosene	C_{12} to C_{15}	150 to 275	10%
Fuel oils, mineral oil	C_{15} to C_{18}	225 to 400	30%
Lubricating oil, petroleum jelly greases, paraffin wax, asphalt	C_{16} to C_{24}	Over 400	10%

Figure 22.15 Coal formed when tree ferns and mosses died. The layers of decaying organic material were compressed over millions of years between layers of soil and rock. The first stage in coal formation is peat. Continued pressure and heat transform peat into lignite, bituminous coal, and anthracite coal.

Coal

Geologists think that coal had its origin some 300 million years ago when huge tree ferns and mosses grew abundantly in swampy tropical regions. When the plants died, they formed thick layers of decaying vegetation. Layer after layer of soil and rock eventually covered the decaying vegetation, which caused a buildup of intense pressure. This pressure, together with heat from Earth's interior, slowly turned the plant remains into coal.

Coal Formation The first stage in the formation of coal is an intermediate material known as peat. Peat, shown in Figure 22.15, is a soft, brown, spongy, fibrous material. When first dug out of a bog, peat has a very high water content. After it has been allowed to dry, it produces a low-cost but smoky fuel. If peat is left in the ground, it continues to change. After a long period of time, peat loses most of its fibrous texture and becomes lignite, or brown coal. Lignite is much harder than peat and has a higher carbon content (about 50%). The water content, however, is still high. Continued pressure and heat slowly change lignite into bituminous, or soft coal. Bituminous coal has a lower water content and higher carbon content (70–80%) than lignite. In some regions of Earth's crust, even greater pressures have been exerted. In those places, such as eastern Pennsylvania, soft coal has been changed into anthracite, or hard coal. Anthracite has a carbon content that exceeds 80%, making it an excellent fuel source. ☞ **Coal is classified by its hardness and carbon content.**

Coal, which is usually found in seams from 1 to 3 meters thick, is obtained from both underground and surface mines. In North America, coal mines are usually less than 100 meters underground. Much of the coal is so close to the surface that it is strip-mined, as shown in Figure 22.16. By contrast, many coal mines in Europe and other parts of the world extend 1000 to 1500 meters below Earth's surface.

Peat

Lignite

Bituminous

Anthracite

Figure 22.16 Coal is mined from both surface mines, shown here, and underground mines.

Composition of Coal 🔑 **Coal consists largely of condensed aromatic compounds of extremely high molar mass. These compounds have a high proportion of carbon compared with hydrogen.** Due to the high proportion of aromatic compounds, coal leaves more soot upon burning than do the more aliphatic fuels obtained from petroleum. The majority of the coal that was once burned in North America contained about 7% sulfur, which burns to form the major air pollutants SO_2 and SO_3.

Coal may be distilled to obtain a variety of products: coke, coal tar, coal gas, and ammonia. Coke is the solid material left after coal distillation. It is used as a fuel in many industrial processes and is the crucial reducing agent in the smelting of iron ore. Because it is almost pure carbon, coke produces intense heat and little or no smoke when it burns. Coal gas consists mainly of hydrogen, methane, and carbon monoxide, all of which are flammable. Coal tar can be distilled further into benzene, toluene, naphthalene, phenol, and pitch. The ammonia from distilled coal is converted to ammonium sulfate for use as a fertilizer.

22.5 Section Assessment

30. 🔑 **Key Concept** Describe the hydrocarbons found in natural gas.

31. 🔑 **Key Concept** Describe the first process used in the refining of petroleum.

32. What are the two variables used to classify coal?

33. 🔑 **Key Concept** Describe the chemical composition of coal.

34. How did the three major fossil fuels form?

35. What are the principal sources of aliphatic hydrocarbons? What is the principal source of aromatic hydrocarbons?

36. Explain why cracking is a necessary step in petroleum refining.

Elements ➤ Handbook

Catalytic Converters When fossil fuels burn in an internal combustion engine, the exhaust contains more than carbon dioxide gas and water vapor. Read about catalytic converters on R42. Write a paragraph explaining what happens to pollutants in a catalytic converter.

Interactive Textbook

Assessment 22.5 Test yourself on the concepts in Section 22.5.

— with **ChemASAP**

Technology & Society

A Number You Can't Knock

Engine "knock" is the sound an engine makes when gasoline ignites too soon, possibly because of poor engine timing or the use of low octane fuel. Knocking can cause overheating, loss of power, and engine damage. A gasoline's octane rating is a measure of its ability to resist engine knock. **Applying Concepts** *What happens to the pressure inside the cylinder during Step 2.*

Octane Ratings Octane ratings are based on isooctane, which resists engine knock, and heptane, which is prone to engine knock. Isooctane has a rating of 0. Heptane has a rating of 100. So an octane rating of 89 means that the gasoline blend performs as though it were 89 parts isooctane and 11 parts heptane.

Engine knock Knocking occurs when the fuel ignites by itself in the engine cylinder. Often this ignition occurs prior to spark ignition. The sound comes from the vibration of the piston, connecting rod, and bearings.

1 **Intake** Gasoline and air are mixed in a cylinder of an internal combustion engine.

2 **Compression** The gas–air mixture is compressed. The greater the compression, the greater the engine's power, and the more likely the engine is to knock.

Oil refineries To make gasoline, a refinery separates crude oil into various components. Refinery technicians combine some of the components, performance additives, and dyes to make different grades of fuel.

3 **Combustion** A spark plug ignites the compressed mixture. The combustion products push down a cylinder that turns the crankshaft.

4 **Exhaust** The cylinder clears the chamber of combustion products, such as carbon dioxide.

Key Concepts

22.1 Hydrocarbons
- Because carbon has four valence electrons, carbon atoms always form four covalent bonds.
- The carbon atoms in an alkane can be arranged in a straight chain or in a chain that has branches.
- Molecules of hydrocarbons, such as alkanes, are nonpolar molecules.

22.2 Unsaturated Hydrocarbons
- At least one carbon-carbon bond in an alkene is a double bond. Other bonds may be single carbon-carbon and carbon-hydrogen bonds.
- At least one carbon-carbon bond in an alkyne is a triple bond. Other bonds may be single or double carbon-carbon bonds and single carbon-hydrogen bonds.

22.3 Isomers
- Structural isomers differ in physical properties and have different chemical reactivites.

- Two types of stereoisomers are geometric isomers and optical isomers.

22.4 Hydrocarbon Rings
- Some hydrocarbon compounds have a carbon chain that is in the form of a ring.
- In a benzene molecule, the bonding electrons between carbon atoms are shared evenly around the ring.

22.5 Hydrocarbons From Earth's Crust
- Natural gas is an important source of alkanes of low molar mass.
- The refining of petroleum starts with the distillation of petroleum into fractions according to boiling point.
- Coal consists largely of condensed aromatic compounds of extremely high molar mass. These compounds have a high proportion of carbon compared with hydrogen.

Vocabulary

- aliphatic hydrocarbons (p. 703)
- alkanes (p. 694)
- alkenes (p. 702)
- alkyl group (p. 698)
- alkynes (p. 703)
- aromatic compound (p. 710)
- asymmetric carbon (p. 705)
- branched-chain alkane (p. 698)

- *cis* configuration (p. 705)
- condensed structural formulas (p. 696)
- cracking (p. 713)
- cyclic hydrocarbon (p. 709)
- homologous series (p. 695)
- hydrocarbons (p. 693)
- geometric isomers (p. 705)
- isomers (p. 704)

- optical isomers (p. 706)
- saturated compounds (p. 702)
- stereoisomers (p. 705)
- straight-chain alkanes (p. 695)
- structural isomers (p. 704)
- substituent (p. 697)
- *trans* configuration (p. 705)
- unsaturated compounds (p. 702)

Organizing Information

Use these terms to construct a concept map that organizes the major ideas of this chapter.

Interactive Textbook

Concept Map 22 Create your Concept Map using the computer.

— with **ChemASAP**

Review and Assessment

Blue questions emphasize Regents Exam content

22.1 Hydrocarbons

34. Draw condensed structural formulas for pentane and hexane. Assume that the C—H and C—C bonds are understood.

35. Name the alkanes that have the following molecular or structural formulas.

a. $CH_3CH_2CH_3$ **b.** $CH_3(CH_2)_6CH_3$

c.
$$
\begin{array}{ccccc}
H & H & H & H & H \\
| & | & | & | & | \\
H-C-C-C-C-C-H \\
| & | & | & | & | \\
H & H & H & H & H
\end{array}
$$

36. Draw structures for the alkyl groups derived from methane, ethane, and propane.

37. Give the IUPAC name for each compound.

a. $CH_3 - CH - CH_2$
        | |
        CH_3 CH_3

b. $CH_3 - CH - CH - CH_3$
        | |
        CH_3 CH_3

c. $CH_3 - CH - CH_2 - CH_2$
        | |
        CH_2 CH_3
        |
        CH_3

38. Why are alkane molecules nonpolar?

39. Why are the following names incorrect? What are the correct names?
a. 2-dimethylpentane
b. 1,3-dimethylpropane
c. 3-methylbutane
d. 3,4-dimethylbutane

40. Name the next three higher homologs of ethane.

41. Can an alkane undergo an addition reaction? Explain.

42. Use the data in Table 22.1 to make a graph of boiling point versus number of carbons for the first ten straight-chain alkanes. Does the graph describe a straight line? On the basis of this graph, what would you predict to be the boiling point of undecane, the straight-chain alkane containing eleven carbons? Use a chemistry handbook to find this boiling point of undecane. Compare this boiling point with your prediction.

22.2 Unsaturated Hydrocarbons

43. Give a systematic name for these alkenes.
a. $CH_3CH = CH_2$
b.
$$
\begin{array}{cc}
CH_3 & H \\
C=C \\
H & CH_2CH_3
\end{array}
$$
c. $CH_3CHCH_2CH = CH_2$
              |
              CH_3
d.
$$
\begin{array}{cc}
CH_3 & CH_2CH_3 \\
C=C \\
CH_3 & CH_2CH_3
\end{array}
$$

44. Name and draw a structural formula for each alkene with the molecular formula C_5H_{10}.

45. For each hydrocarbon pictured below, identify the type of bonding and name the compound. Carbon atoms are represented by black spheres, and the blue spheres represent hydrogen atoms.

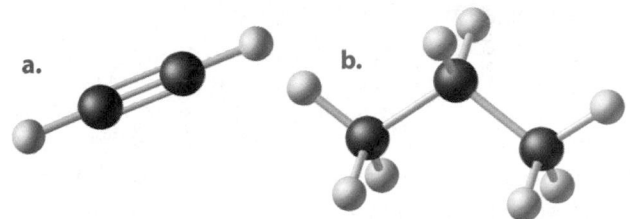

a.   b.

46. You cannot draw a structural formula for methene. Explain.

47. Alkadienes are hydrocarbons with two double bonds. Draw the structural formula of the alkadiene with the molecular formula C_3H_4.

48. The molecular formula C_4H_6 could represent an alkyne, a cycloalkene, or a hydrocarbon with two double bonds. Write the condensed structural formulas for each. Which do you think is the least stable, and why?

22.3 Isomerism

49. Draw all the structural isomers with the molecular formula C_6H_{14}. Name each one. (For convenience, you may wish to draw only the carbon skeleton for each structure.)

CHAPTER 22
Review and Assessment *continued*
Blue questions emphasize Regents Exam content

NEW YORK

50. Draw one structural isomer of each compound.

51. Draw a structural formula or carbon skeleton for each of the following alkenes.
a. 2-pentene   b. 2-methyl-2-pentene
c. 3-ethyl-2-pentene

52. Do all molecules have optical isomers? Explain.

53. Can you draw a structural isomer of hexane (C_6H_{14}) that has an asymmetric carbon? Explain.

54. Are these two structures geometric isomers? Explain.

55. Show how lack of rotation about a carbon–carbon double bond leads to geometric isomerism. Use the isomers of 2-pentene to illustrate your answer.

56. Compare and contrast geometric and optical isomers.

57. The graph shows the number of structural isomers for alkanes with three through ten carbon atoms.

Number of Possible Structural Isomers

a. According to the graph, how many structural isomers are there for the C_6, C_7, C_8, C_9, and C_{10} alkanes?
b. The difference between the number of isomers for C_7 and C_8 is 9. The difference between the number of isomers for C_9 and C_{10} is 40. In each case, one additional carbon atom is added to the molecule. Why is the change in the number of isomers so different?

22.4 Hydrocarbon Rings

58. Draw a structural formula for each compound.
a. 1,4-diethylbenzene
b. 2-methyl-3-phenylpentane
c. 1,3-dimethylbenzene

59. Explain why both of these structures represent 1,2-diethylbenzene.

60. Write structural formulas for the following compounds.
a. propyne
b. cyclohexane
c. 2-phenylpropane
d. 2,2,4-trimethylpentane

61. Draw electron dot structures for each of the following compounds.
a. ethene   b. propane
c. ethyne   d. cyclobutane

62. Compare these three molecular structures. Which would you expect to be most stable? Why?

63. The seven organic chemicals produced in the largest amounts in the United States in a recent year are listed in the following table. Answer the following questions based on the data given.

Chemical	Amount produced (billions of kg)
Ethylene	15.9
Propylene	8.4
Urea	6.8
Ethylene dichloride	6.3
Benzene	5.3
Ethyl benzene	4.3
Vinyl chloride	3.7

a. How many billion kilograms of aromatic compounds were produced?

b. Of the total mass of all seven compounds produced, what percent by mass was made up of aliphatic compounds?

64. Use the labeled features in the molecular structure to answer the following questions.

$$(2)$$
$$CH_2CH_2CH_3$$
$$(1)$$
$$C_6H_5 \qquad H$$
$$(3)$$
$$(5)\ CH_3 \qquad CH{=}CH_2$$
$$Cl{-}C{-}Br$$
$$|$$
$$F$$
$$(4)$$

a. Which label identifies a double bond?

b. Which label identifies a phenyl group?

c. Which label identifies a methyl group?

d. Which label identifies an asymmetric carbon?

e. Which label identifies a propyl group?

65. Why do most cyclic hydrocarbons have higher boiling points than alkanes with the same number of carbons?

66. Draw structural formulas for the following compounds.
a. *cis*-2,3-dimethyl-3-hexene
b. 1-ethyl-2-methylcyclopentane

67. How does an aromatic hydrocarbon differ from a cycloalkane in terms of its bonding?

68. Draw the correct structure for any of the structures below that are incorrect.
a. $CH_3{-}CH{=}CH{-}CH_2{-}CH_3$
b. $CH_3{-}C{=}CH{-}CH_2{-}CH_3$
c. $CH_3{=}CH{-}CH_2{-}CH_3$

69. What structural feature is associated with each of the following hydrocarbons?
a. an alkane
b. an alkene
c. an aromatic hydrocarbon
d. a cycloalkane

70. Each of the following names is wrong. Correct each name and draw the correct structural formula.
a. 4-methylhexane
b. 1,4-diethyl cyclopentane
c. 3,3-methyl-4-ethyloctane

22.5 Hydrocarbons from Earth

71. Write an equation for the complete combustion of octane (C_8H_{18}).

72. Rank these materials in order of increasing hardness: bituminous coal, peat, lignite, and anthracite coal.

73. Describe the chemical structure of coal.

74. How does the amount of sulfur in coal affect its potential use?

75. Methane (CH_4), a widely used fuel, has a heat of combustion (ΔH) of -890 kJ/mol. The ΔH for benzene (C_6H_6) is considerably higher, -3268 kJ/mol, yet benzene is never used as a fuel. Suggest as many thermochemical and environmental reasons as you can why benzene is a less desirable fuel than methane.

76. Fossil fuels such as oil and natural gas are the raw materials for many consumer products. Do you believe it is wise to continue to use the limited supplies of fossil fuels as an energy source?

Test-Taking Tip

Eliminate Wrong Answers If you don't know which response to a question is correct, start by eliminating those you know are wrong. If you can rule out some choices, you'll have fewer choices left to consider and you'll increase your chances of choosing the correct answer.

Regents Practice Exam

Part A

For each statement or question write the number of the word or expression that, of those given, best completes the statement or answers the question.

1. All alkenes
   (1) are saturated
   (2) contain a carbon-carbon triple bond
   (3) contain a multiple bond
   (4) contain only single bonds

2. Saturated compounds contain
   (1) all single bonds
   (2) at least one double bond
   (3) at least one triple bond
   (4) either a double or a triple bond

3. Hydrocarbons contain
   (1) carbon, hydrogen, and oxygen
   (2) carbon and hydrogen only
   (3) single bonds only
   (4) carbon and water

4. Isomers of organic compounds
   (1) have the same structures
   (2) have the same properties
   (3) have the same molecular formula
   (4) are alike in every way

5. A solution is a
   (1) substance
   (2) compound
   (3) homogeneous mixture
   (4) heterogeneous mixture

6. The acidity of a solution is measured by what property of the solution?
   (1) molarity   (3) solute
   (2) pH   (4) solvent

Part B-1

For each statement or question write the number of the word or expression that, of those given, best completes the statement or answers the question.

7. What is the name of the compound with the following structural formula?

$$CH_3 - \underset{\underset{H}{|}}{\overset{\overset{CH_3}{|}}{C}} - \underset{\underset{H}{|}}{\overset{\overset{H}{|}}{C}} - \underset{\underset{H}{|}}{\overset{\overset{CH_3}{|}}{C}} - CH_3$$

(1) 1,2,3,3-tetramethylpropane
(2) heptane
(3) 2,4-dimethylpentane
(4) 1,5-dimethylbutane

8. How many carbon atoms are in a molecule of 4,5-diethyloctane?
   (1) 10   (3) 14
   (2) 12   (4) 16

9. A structural isomer of heptane is
   (1) methylbutane
   (2) 3,3-dimethylpentane
   (3) cycloheptane
   (4) 3-methylhexene

Note that the following questions have only three choices.

The numbered choices below refer to Questions 10–12. A numbered choice may be used once, more than once, or not at all.

   (1) alkene
   (2) alkyne
   (3) alkane

In which of the above classes of hydrocarbons does each of the following compounds belong?

10. C_7H_{16} 11. C_5H_8 12. C_8H_{16}

13. Which of the following structures is a saturated hydrocarbon?

(1)
$$\underset{H}{\overset{CH_3}{\diagdown}} C = C \underset{CH_3}{\overset{H}{\diagup}}$$

(2) $CH_3 - CH_2 - CH_2 - CH_3$

(3)
$$\underset{CH_3}{\overset{H}{\diagdown}} C = C \underset{CH_3}{\overset{H}{\diagup}}$$

Part B-2

Answer each of the following questions.

14. Calculate the volume of a gas at 3 kPa of pressure if the same gas has a volume of 6 L at 0.5 kPa and the temperature is constant.

15. How many kilojoules are absorbed when 56.0 g of liquid water at 100°C is vaporized to steam at 100°C?

16. How many moles of solute are in 750 mL of $1.50M$ KNO_3? How many grams of KNO_3 is this?

17. How do (a) surface area and (b) temperature affect the rate of a chemical reaction?

18. Explain how the equilibrium position of this reaction is affected by the following changes.

$$CaCO_3(s) + heat \longrightarrow CaO(s) + CO_2(g)$$

a. decreasing the temperature
b. removing CO_2

19. A colorless solution of unknown pH turns blue when tested with the acid-base indicator bromthymol blue. The solution remains colorless when tested with phenolphthalein.

a. What is the approximate pH of the solution?
b. How could you determine the pH more accurately?

20. Write the formula for each of the following acids and bases.

a. sulfuric acid
b. cesium hydroxide
c. carbonic acid
d. beryllium hydroxide

21. Write the equation for the dissolving of each of the following compounds in water. (Each compound breaks into its ions.)

a. sodium hydroxide
b. barium hydroxide

22. Give the oxidation number of each element in the following compounds.

a. $CaCO_3$ **c.** $LiIO_3$
b. Cl_2 **d.** Na_2SO_3

23. Identify each of the following processes as either oxidation or reduction.

a. $Fe^{3+} + e^- \longrightarrow Fe^{2+}$
b. $Cl_2 + 2e^- \longrightarrow 2Cl^-$
c. $Fe^{3+} + 3e^- \longrightarrow Fe$
d. $Zn \longrightarrow Zn^{2+} + 2e^-$

24. Determine the oxidation number of nitrogen in the following compounds and ions.

a. N_2O_4 **c.** NH_3 **e.** NH_4^+
b. NO_2 **d.** NO_3^- **f.** NO

25. Balance these redox equations.

a. $C_3H_7OH(l) + O_2(g) \longrightarrow CO_2(g) + H_2O(l)$
b. $BaO(s) + Al(s) \longrightarrow Al_2O_3(s) + Ba(s)$

26. What process always occurs at the cathode of an electrolytic cell? At the cathode of a voltaic cell?

27. Explain why 3-pentene is an incorrect name for an alkene.

28. Explain why 1,1,2,2-tetramethylethene is an incorrect name for an alkene.

Use the space-filling models of pentane isomers to answer Question 29.

29. Write structural formulas for three structural isomers of pentane (C_5H_{12}). Name each isomer.

30. Identify any incorrect formulas among the following compounds. For those that are incorrect, write the correct formula.

a. H_2O_2 **d.** CaS_2
b. $NaIO_4$ **e.** $CaHPO_4$
c. SrO **f.** $BaOH$

Part C

Answer each of the following questions.

31. A silver dollar is heated and placed in a foam cup calorimeter containing 50.0 mL of water at 26.5°C. The water reached a maximum temperature of 27.3°C. How many joules of heat were released by the silver dollar?

32. Butane (C_4H_{10}) is commonly used in lighters. A certain lighter contains 28.3 g of butane.

a. Write a balanced chemical equation for the complete combustion of butane.
b. How many moles of butane are in the lighter?
c. How many moles of oxygen are needed for the complete combustion of the butane?
d. At STP, 1.00 mol of a gas occupies 22.4 L. What volume of oxygen is needed for the reaction?

33. Normal rainwater has a pH of approximately 6.5.

a. Is this rainwater acidic, basic, or neutral?
b. This pH is the result of carbon dioxide and water in the air reacting, forming carbonic acid. What type of reaction is this?
c. Write a balanced chemical equation for this reaction.

23 Functional Groups

The sweet smell of lavender comes, in part, from linalool, an alcohol.

INQUIRY Activity

Making the Slimiest Polymer

Materials

White paper glue, 100-mL graduated cylinder, two large glasses, four paper or foam cups, borax, balance, spoon, 10-mL graduated cylinder

Procedure

1. Mix 60 mL (about 2 oz) of white paper glue with 60 mL of water in a glass.

2. Pour 30 mL of this mixture into each of the four cups.

3. Make a borax solution by stirring 5 g of borax into 100 mL of water in the other glass.

4. Add 5 mL of borax solution to the first cup of glue, 10 mL to the second, 15 mL to the third, and 20 mL to the fourth. Stir the mixture in each cup

and knead it with your fingers until it is smooth.

5. Take the contents of the cup with 5 mL of borax and slowly stretch it into a long strand. Repeat for the other three cups.

Think About It

1. Which amount of borax allowed you to pull the longest strand?

2. Do you think adding less than 5 mL or more than 20 mL of the borax solution would allow you to pull a longer strand?

3. Would the results be different if you did not add water to the glue initially?

Introduction to Functional Groups

New York Standards: 3.1hh, 3.2c

Connecting to Your World

The lights dim and the audience chatter subsides as the musicians enter the hall. All the musicians wear black, and from a distance they look nearly identical. But their differences become apparent when they pick up their instruments. As the conductor signals the beginning of the piece, a single flute is heard. The warm sounds of the stringed instruments join in, and soon each musician contributes a unique sound to the music. In a similar way, one hydrocarbon is nearly identical to another until it picks up a functional group. In this section, you will learn how functional groups determine the character of organic compounds.

Guide for Reading

Key Concepts
- How are organic compounds classified?
- What is a halocarbon?
- How may halocarbons be prepared?

Vocabulary
functional group
halocarbons
alkyl halides
aryl halides
substitution reaction

Reading Strategy
Making and Using Tables As you read, examine the tables carefully. Make a table in your notebook that organizes the material in this section.

Functional Groups

In Chapter 22, you learned about hydrocarbon chains and rings—the essential components of every organic compound. Yet in most chemical reactions involving organic molecules, the saturated hydrocarbon skeletons of the molecules are chemically inert. How, then, can there be hundreds of different kinds of organic reactions?

Most organic chemistry involves substituents, which are groups attached to hydrocarbon chains. The substituents of organic molecules often contain oxygen, nitrogen, sulfur, and/or phosphorus. They are called functional groups because they are the chemically functional parts of the molecules. A **functional group** is a specific arrangement of atoms in an organic compound that is capable of characteristic chemical reactions. Most organic chemistry is functional-group chemistry. **Organic compounds can be classified according to their functional groups.** Figure 23.1 shows several consumer products that contain various functional groups. The symbol R represents any carbon chains or rings attached to the functional group. Because the double and triple bonds of alkenes and alkynes are chemically reactive, they are also considered functional groups. Table 23.1 on the following page lists the functional groups that you will learn about in this chapter and in Chapter 24. You will find it helpful to refer to this table throughout the chapter.

Figure 23.1 Many consumer products contain hydrocarbon derivatives. The hydrocarbon skeletons in these products are chemically similar. Functional groups give each product unique properties and uses.

Table 23.1

Organic Compounds Classified by Functional Group

Compound type	Compound structure	Functional group
Halocarbon	R — X (X = F, Cl, Br, or I)	Halogen
Alcohol	R — OH	Hydroxyl
Ether	R — O — R	Ether
Aldehyde	$\underset{\displaystyle R-C-H}{\overset{\displaystyle O}{\parallel}}$	Carbonyl
Ketone	$\underset{\displaystyle R-C-R}{\overset{\displaystyle O}{\parallel}}$	Carbonyl
Carboxylic acid	$\underset{\displaystyle R-C-OH}{\overset{\displaystyle O}{\parallel}}$	Carboxyl
Ester	$\underset{\displaystyle R-C-O-R}{\overset{\displaystyle O}{\parallel}}$	Ester
Amine	R — NH₂	Amino
Amide	$\underset{\displaystyle R-C-N-R}{\overset{\displaystyle O \quad\ H}{\parallel \quad |}}$	Amido

Halogen Substituents

Halocarbons are a class of organic compounds containing covalently bonded fluorine, chlorine, bromine, or iodine. **A halocarbon is a carbon-containing compound with a halogen substituent.** The IUPAC rules for naming halocarbons are based on the name of the parent hydrocarbon. The halogen groups are added as substituents. Examples of IUPAC names for several simple halocarbons along with their structural formulas and space-filling models are given in Figure 23.2. Common names are in parentheses.

Common names of halocarbons consist of two parts. The first part names the hydrocarbon portion of the molecule as an alkyl group, such as *methyl-* or *ethyl-*. The second part gives the halogen with an *-ide* ending.

Figure 23.2 The IUPAC rules for naming halocarbons are based on the name of the parent hydrocarbon. Structural formulas and space-filling models of halocarbons. ❶ The common name for chloromethane is methyl chloride. ❷ The common name for chloroethene is vinyl chloride. ❸ The common name for chlorobenzene is phenyl chloride.

Chloromethane
(methyl chloride)

Chloroethene
(vinyl chloride)

Chlorobenzene
(phenyl chloride)

Table 23.2

	Names of Some Common Alkyl Groups	
Name	**Alkyl group**	**Remarks**
Isopropyl	CH_3 — $\overset{\overset{\displaystyle CH_3}{\mid}}{\underset{\underset{\displaystyle H}{\mid}}{C}}$ —	The prefix *iso-* is used when there is a methyl group on the carbon second from the unsubstituted end of the longest chain.
Isobutyl	$\overset{\overset{\displaystyle CH_3}{\mid}}{CH_3}$ — CH — CH$_2$— *primary carbon*	The carbon joining this alkyl group to another group is bonded to one other carbon; it is a primary carbon.
Secondary butyl (*sec*-butyl)	CH_3 — CH_2 — $\underset{\underset{\displaystyle \,}{\mid}}{CH}$ — CH_3 *secondary carbon*	The carbon joining this alkyl group to another group is bonded to two other carbons; it is a secondary carbon.
Tertiary butyl (*tert*-butyl)	CH_3 — $\overset{\overset{\displaystyle CH_3}{\mid}}{\underset{\underset{\displaystyle CH_3}{\mid}}{C}}$ — *tertiary carbon*	The carbon joining this alkyl group to another group is bonded to three carbons; it is a tertiary carbon.
Vinyl	$\underset{\displaystyle H}{\overset{\displaystyle H}{}} C = C \underset{\displaystyle H}{\overset{\displaystyle }{}}$	When used as an alkyl group in giving compounds common names, this group is called vinyl.
Phenyl	(benzene ring structure)	Phenyl is derived from benzene.

On the basis of their common names, halocarbons in which a halogen is attached to a carbon of an aliphatic chain are called **alkyl halides.** The number of carbon atoms attached to the alkyl group determines whether the carbon is primary, secondary, or tertiary. Table 23.2 lists the names of alkyl groups other than methyl, ethyl, and propyl. Halocarbons in which a halogen is attached to a carbon of an arene ring are called **aryl halides.**

The attractions between halocarbon molecules are primarily the result of the weak van der Waals interactions called dispersion forces. These attractions increase with the degree of halogen substitution. Thus, more highly halogenated organic compounds have higher boiling points, as illustrated in Table 23.3 on the next page.

Very few halocarbons are found in nature, but they can be readily prepared and used for many purposes. For example, halothane (2-bromo-2-chloro-1,1,1-trifluoroethane) is used as an anesthetic. Hydrofluorocarbons are used as refrigerants in automobile air-conditioning systems.

Figure 23.3 Halothane is a halocarbon that is used as an anesthetic.

✓ Checkpoint *Give an example of a halocarbon.*

Table 23.3

Molecular structure	Name	Molar mass	Boiling point (°C)
CH₄*	Methane	16.0	−161
CH₃Cl	Chloromethane (methyl chloride)	50.5	−24
CH₂Cl₂	Dichloromethane (methylene chloride)	85.0	40
CHCl₃	Trichloromethane (chloroform)	119.5	61
CCl₄	Tetrachloromethane (carbon tetrachloride)	154.0	74

Molecular Masses and Boiling Points of Chloromethanes

* Included for purposes of comparison.

Substitution Reactions

Organic reactions often proceed more slowly than inorganic reactions. This is because organic reactions commonly involve the breaking of relatively strong covalent bonds. Catalysts are often needed. Many organic reactions are complex, often producing a mixture of products. The desired product must then be separated by distillation, crystallization, or other means. A common type of organic reaction is a **substitution reaction,** in which an atom, or a group of atoms, replaces another atom or group of atoms.

A halogen can replace a hydrogen atom on an alkane to produce a **halocarbon.** The symbol X stands for a halogen in this generalized equation.

$$R\!-\!H \ + \ X_2 \ \longrightarrow \ R\!-\!X \ + \ HX$$

Alkane   Halogen   Halocarbon   Hydrogen halide

Sunlight or another source of ultraviolet radiation usually serves as a catalyst. From the generalized equation, you can write a specific one.

$$CH_4 \ + \ Cl_2 \ \xrightarrow{UV\ light} \ CH_3Cl \ + \ HCl$$

Methane   Chlorine   Chloromethane   Hydrogen chloride

Even under controlled conditions, this simple halogenation reaction produces a mixture of mono-, di-, tri-, and tetrachloromethanes.

 Checkpoint *What is a substitution reaction?*

Go Online

NSTA SciLINKS

For: Links on Substitution Reactions
Visit: www.SciLinks.org
Web Code: cdn-1231

Treating benzene with a halogen in the presence of a catalyst causes the substitution of a hydrogen atom in the ring. Iron compounds are often used as catalysts for aromatic substitution reactions. For example, a rusty nail dropped in the reaction flask can act as a catalyst.

$$\text{(benzene)} + Br_2 \xrightarrow{\text{catalyst}} \text{(bromobenzene)} + HBr$$

Halogens on carbon chains are readily displaced by hydroxide ions to produce an alcohol and a salt. The general reaction is as follows.

$$R{-}X \;+\; OH^- \xrightarrow[100°C]{H_2O} R{-}OH \;+\; X^-$$

| Halocarbon | Hydroxide ion | Alcohol | Halide ion |

Chemists usually use aqueous solutions of sodium or potassium hydroxide as the source of hydroxide ions. The chemical equations for two specific examples are shown below.

$$CH_3{-}I(l) \;+\; KOH(aq) \xrightarrow[100°C]{H_2O} CH_3{-}OH(l) \;+\; KI(aq)$$

Iodomethane   Potassium   Methanol   Potassium
(methyl iodide)   hydroxide   iodide

$$CH_3CH_2Br(l) \;+\; NaOH(aq) \xrightarrow[100°C]{H_2O} CH_3CH_2OH(l) \;+\; NaBr(aq)$$

Bromoethane   Sodium   Ethanol   Sodium
(ethyl bromide)   hydroxide   bromide

Fluoro groups are not easily displaced. Thus, fluorocarbons are seldom, if ever, used to make alcohols.

23.1 Section Assessment

1. **Key Concept** How are organic compounds classified?

2. **Key Concept** What is a halocarbon?

3. **Key Concept** How can a halocarbon be prepared?

4. Identify the functional group in each structure.
   a. $CH_3{-}OH$
   b. $CH_3{-}CH_2{-}NH_2$
   c. (benzene ring)$-C(=O){-}OH$
   d. $CH_3{-}CH_2{-}CH_2{-}Br$
   e. $CH_3{-}CH_2{-}O{-}CH_2{-}CH_3$

5. Give the structural formula for each compound.
   a. isopropyl chloride
   b. 1-iodo-2,2-dimethylpentane
   c. *p*-bromotoluene

6. Write the names of all possible dichloropropanes that could form from the chlorination of propane.

Elements ▸ **Handbook**

Halogens Learn more about the chemistry of halogens on pages R32–R35 of the Elements Handbook. Write a short report about the importance of halogens as functional groups in organic chemistry.

Assessment 23.1 Check your understanding of the important ideas and concepts in Section 23.1.

—— with **ChemASAP**

New York Standards: 3.1hh, 3.2c

Guide for Reading

Key Concepts
- How are alcohols classified and named?
- How does the solubility of an alcohol vary with the length of its carbon chain?
- What reactions of alkenes may be used to introduce functional groups into organic molecules?
- What is the general structure of an ether and how are their alkyl groups named?

Vocabulary
alcohol
hydroxyl group
fermentation
denatured alcohol
addition reaction
hydration reaction
hydrogenation reaction
ether

Reading Strategy

Relating Text and Visuals As you read, look carefully at the structural formulas and the space-filling models in the section. In your notebook, explain how each type of representation of a compound helps you to understand organic compounds and their functional groups.

Connecting to Your World

Prior to the 1840s, patients had to endure surgery while they were fully conscious. Today, when having major surgery, a patient often receives a general anesthetic. In addition to causing the patient to lose consciousness, a general anesthetic also causes the patient's muscles to relax. The major benefit of a general anesthetic is that the patient does not experience pain during surgery. The earliest anesthetics, used during the Civil War, belonged to a class of chemical compounds called ethers. In this section, you will read about the chemical characteristics of ethers that make them good anesthetics.

Alcohols

What do mouthwash, perfume, and hairspray have in common? They all contain an alcohol of some type. An **alcohol** is an organic compound with an — OH group.

$$R \overset{\ddot{O}}{\diagup} H$$

Alcohol molecule

The — OH functional group in alcohols is called a **hydroxyl group** or hydroxy function. **Aliphatic alcohols can be classified into structural categories according to the number of R groups attached to the carbon with the hydroxyl group.** If one R group is attached, the alcohol is a primary alcohol; if two R groups, a secondary alcohol; if three R groups, a tertiary alcohol. This nomenclature is summarized below.

Primary alcohol	$R - CH_2 - OH$	Only one R group is attached to C — OH of a primary (abbreviated 1°) alcohol.
Secondary alcohol	$R - \overset{\overset{\textstyle R}{\mid}}{C}H - OH$	Two R groups are attached to C — OH of a secondary (2°) alcohol.
Tertiary alcohol	$R - \overset{\overset{\textstyle R}{\mid}}{\underset{\underset{\textstyle R}{\mid}}{C}} - OH$	Three R groups are attached to C — OH of a tertiary (3°) alcohol.

✓ Checkpoint *What is an alcohol?*

Both IUPAC and common names are used for alcohols. ● **When using the IUPAC system to name continuous-chain and substituted alcohols, drop the -e ending of the parent alkane name and add the ending -ol.** The parent alkane is the longest continuous chain of carbons that includes the carbon attached to the hydroxyl group. In numbering the longest continuous chain, the position of the hydroxyl group is given the lowest possible number. Alcohols containing two, three, and four — OH substituents are named diols, triols, and tetrols, respectively.

Common names of aliphatic alcohols are written in the same way as those of the halocarbons. The alkyl group ethyl, for example, is named and followed by the word alcohol, as in ethyl alcohol. Figure 23.4 shows several products that contain ethyl alcohol. Compounds with more than one — OH substituent are called glycols. The structural formulas for some simple aliphatic alcohols along with their IUPAC and common names are shown below.

Go Online
NSTA SciLINKS

For: Links on Alcohols
Visit: www.SciLinks.org
Web Code: cdn-1232

$CH_3 — OH$
Methanol
(methyl alcohol)

$CH_3 — CH_2 — OH$
Ethanol
(ethyl alcohol)

$CH_3 — CH_2 — CH_2 — OH$
1-propanol
(propyl alcohol)

$$CH_3 — \overset{\displaystyle OH}{\overset{|}{CH}} — CH_3$$
2-propanol
(isopropyl alcohol)

$$CH_3 — \overset{\displaystyle CH_3}{\overset{|}{CH}} — CH_2 — OH$$
2-methyl-1-propanol
(isobutyl alcohol)

$$CH_3 — CH_2 — \overset{|}{CH} — CH_3 \atop OH$$
2-butanol
(*sec*-butyl alcohol)

$$CH_3 — \overset{\displaystyle CH_3}{\underset{\displaystyle OH}{\overset{|}{\underset{|}{C}}}} — CH_3$$
2-methyl-2-propanol
(*tert*-butyl alcohol)

$$\overset{CH_2 — CH_2}{\underset{OH \quad\;\; OH}{|\qquad\;\; |}}$$
1,2-ethanediol
(ethylene glycol)

$$\overset{CH_3 — CH — CH_2}{\underset{OH \quad\; OH}{\qquad |\qquad\;\; |}}$$
1,2-propanediol
(propylene glycol)

$$\overset{CH_2 — CH — CH_2}{\underset{OH \quad\; OH \quad\; OH}{|\qquad\;\; |\qquad\;\; |}}$$
1,2,3-propanetriol
(glycerol)

Phenols are compounds in which a hydroxyl group is attached directly to an aromatic ring. Phenol is the parent compound. Cresol is the common name for the *o*, *m*, and *p* structural isomers of methylphenol. Phenols are commonly used to make plastics, fibers, and drugs.

Figure 23.4 Ethanol (ethyl alcohol) is a common component of many household products.

CH₃—OH

Methanol
(methyl alcohol)

$CH_3—CH_2—OH$

Ethanol
(ethyl alcohol)

$CH_3—CH—CH_3$
$|$
OH

2-propanol
(isopropyl alcohol)

$CH_2—CH_2$
$|\quad\ |$
$OH\quad OH$

1,2-ethanediol
(ethylene glycol)

$CH_2—CH—CH_2$
$|\quad\ |\quad\ |$
$OH\quad OH\quad OH$

1,2,3-propanetriol
(glycerol)

Figure 23.5 These alcohols contain one, two, or three hydroxyl groups. **Classifying** *Which space-filling model depicts a diol? A triol?*

Properties of Alcohols

Alcohols are capable of intermolecular hydrogen bonding. Therefore, they boil at higher temperatures than alkanes and halocarbons containing comparable numbers of atoms.

Because alcohols are derivatives of water (the hydroxyl group is part of a water molecule), they are somewhat soluble. **🔑 Alcohols of up to four carbons are soluble in water in all proportions. The solubility of alcohols with four or more carbons in the chain is usually much lower.** This is because alcohols consist of two parts: the carbon chain and the hydroxyl group. The carbon chain is nonpolar and is not attracted to water. The hydroxyl group is polar and strongly interacts with water through hydrogen bonding. For alcohols of up to four carbons, the polarity of the hydroxyl group is more significant than the nonpolarity of the carbon chain. Thus, these alcohols are soluble in water. As the number of carbon atoms increases above four, however, the nonpolarity of the chain becomes more significant, and the solubility decreases.

Many aliphatic alcohols are used in laboratories, clinics, and industry as shown in Figure 23.6. Isopropyl alcohol (IUPAC: 2-propanol), which is more familiarly known as rubbing alcohol, is a colorless, somewhat odorless liquid (bp 82°C) often used as an antiseptic. It is also used as a base for perfumes, creams, lotions, and other cosmetics. Ethylene glycol (IUPAC: 1,2-ethanediol) is the principal ingredient of certain antifreezes. Its boiling point is 197°C. Its advantages over other liquids with high boiling points are its solubility in water and its freezing point of −17.4°C. If water is added to ethylene glycol, the mixture freezes at an even lower temperature. For example, a 50% (v/v) aqueous solution of ethylene glycol freezes at −36°C. Another aliphatic alcohol, glycerol (IUPAC: 1,2,3-propanetriol), is a viscous, sweet-tasting, water-soluble liquid used as a moistening agent in cosmetics, foods, and drugs. Glycerol is also an important component of fats and oils, which you will learn about in Chapter 24.

Figure 23.6 Aliphatic alcohols are used in many common household products. **ⓐ** Isopropyl alcohol is an effective antiseptic. **ⓑ** Ethylene glycol is the main ingredient in antifreeze. **ⓒ** Many cosmetic products contain glycerol. **Applying Concepts** *How does antifreeze prevent the water in a car's radiator from freezing at 0°C and boiling at 100°C?*

Ethyl alcohol (IUPAC: ethanol), which has a boiling point of 78.5°C, is also called grain alcohol. It is an important industrial chemical. Most ethanol is still produced by yeast fermentation of sugar. **Fermentation** is the production of ethanol from sugars by the action of yeast or bacteria. The bread shown in Figure 23.7 is different from the crackers because of fermentation. The enzymes of the yeast or bacteria serve as catalysts for the transformation. The breakdown of the sugar glucose ($C_6H_{12}O_6$) is an important fermentation reaction.

$$C_6H_{12}O_6(aq) \longrightarrow 2CH_3CH_2OH(aq) + 2CO_2(g)$$

Glucose   Ethanol   Carbon dioxide

Ethanol is the intoxicating substance in alcoholic beverages. It is a depressant that can be fatal if taken in large doses at once. Over time, continuous abuse of alcoholic beverages can damage the liver, which can lead to death.

The ethanol used in industrial applications is denatured. **Denatured alcohol** is ethanol with an added substance to make it toxic (poisonous). That added substance, or denaturant, is often methyl alcohol (IUPAC: methanol). Methyl alcohol is sometimes called wood alcohol because, prior to 1925, it was prepared by the distillation of wood. Wood alcohol is extremely toxic. As little as 10 mL has been reported to cause permanent blindness, and as little as 30 mL has been known to cause death.

Figure 23.7 Cracker and bread dough are both made primarily of flour and water, but bread dough also contains yeast. Carbon dioxide, a product of sugar fermentation by yeast, causes bread to rise. **Inferring** *What happens to the ethanol that is also produced?*

Addition Reactions

The carbon–carbon single bonds in alkanes are not easy to break. In an alkene, however, one of the bonds in the double bond is somewhat weaker and thus is easier to break than a carbon–carbon single bond. So it is sometimes possible for a compound of general structure X—Y to add to a double bond. In an **addition reaction,** a substance is added at the double or triple bond of an alkene or alkyne. ⬡ **Addition reactions of alkenes are an important method of introducing new functional groups into organic molecules.** In the general reaction shown below, X and Y represent the two parts of the compound that are added.

$$\text{C=C} + \text{X—Y} \longrightarrow \begin{array}{c} \text{X} \quad \text{Y} \\ | \quad | \\ \text{—C—C—} \\ | \quad | \end{array}$$

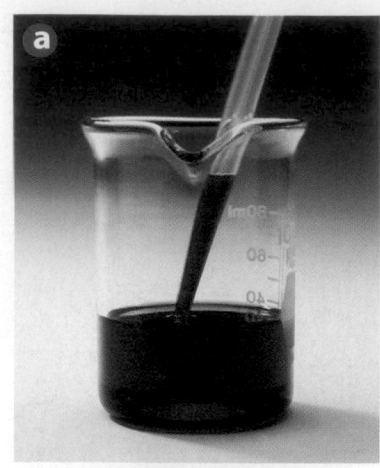

The addition of water to an alkene is a **hydration reaction.** Hydration reactions usually occur when the alkene and water are heated to about 100°C in the presence of a trace of strong acid. The acid, usually hydrochloric acid or sulfuric acid, serves as a catalyst for the reaction. The addition of water to ethene, the equation for which is shown below, is a typical hydration reaction. The parts of ethanol that come from the addition of water are shown in blue.

$$\underset{\substack{\text{Ethene}}}{\overset{\text{H}}{\underset{\text{H}}{}}\text{C}=\text{C}\overset{\text{H}}{\underset{\text{H}}{}}} + \underset{\text{Water}}{\text{H}-\text{OH}} \xrightarrow[100°C]{\text{H}^+} \underset{\substack{\text{Ethanol}}}{\text{H}-\overset{\overset{\text{H}}{|}}{\underset{\underset{\text{H}}{|}}{\text{C}}}-\overset{\overset{\text{OH}}{|}}{\underset{\underset{\text{H}}{|}}{\text{C}}}-\text{H}}$$

When the reagent X—Y is a halogen molecule such as chlorine or bromine, the product of the reaction is a disubstituted halocarbon. The addition of bromine to ethene to form the disubstituted halocarbon 1,2-dibromoethane is an example.

$$\underset{\substack{\text{Ethene}\\ \text{(colorless)}}}{\overset{\text{H}}{\underset{\text{H}}{}}\text{C}=\text{C}\overset{\text{H}}{\underset{\text{H}}{}}} + \underset{\substack{\text{Bromine}\\ \text{(brownish}\\ \text{orange)}}}{\text{Br}-\text{Br}} \longrightarrow \underset{\substack{\text{1,2-dibromoethane}\\ \text{(colorless)}}}{\text{H}-\overset{\overset{\text{Br}}{|}}{\underset{\underset{\text{H}}{|}}{\text{C}}}-\overset{\overset{\text{Br}}{|}}{\underset{\underset{\text{H}}{|}}{\text{C}}}-\text{H}}$$

The addition of bromine to carbon–carbon multiple bonds is often used as a chemical test for unsaturation in an organic molecule. Bromine has a brownish-orange color, but most organic compounds of bromine are colorless. The test for unsaturation is performed by adding a few drops of a 1% solution of bromine in carbon tetrachloride (CCl_4) to the suspected alkene. As Figure 23.8 shows, the loss of the orange color is a positive test for unsaturation. If the orange color remains, the sample is completely saturated.

Hydrogen halides, such as HBr or HCl, also can add to a double bond. Because the product contains only one substituent, it is called a monosubstituted halocarbon. The addition of hydrogen chloride to ethene is an example.

Figure 23.8 Bromine can be used to identify unsaturated compounds. **ⓐ** Bromine has a brownish-orange color. **ⓑ** A few drops of bromine solution are added to an unsaturated organic compound. **ⓒ** The bromine reacts to form a colorless halocarbon.

$$\underset{\substack{\text{Ethene}\\ \text{(ethylene)}}}{\overset{\text{H}}{\underset{\text{H}}{}}\text{C}=\text{C}\overset{\text{H}}{\underset{\text{H}}{}}} + \underset{\substack{\text{Hydrogen}\\ \text{chloride}}}{\text{H}-\text{Cl}} \longrightarrow \underset{\substack{\text{Chloroethane}\\ \text{(ethyl chloride)}}}{\text{H}-\overset{\overset{\text{H}}{|}}{\underset{\underset{\text{H}}{|}}{\text{C}}}-\overset{\overset{\text{Cl}}{|}}{\underset{\underset{\text{H}}{|}}{\text{C}}}-\text{H}}$$

The addition of hydrogen to a carbon–carbon double bond to produce an alkane is called a **hydrogenation reaction.** Hydrogenation reactions usually require a catalyst. Finely divided platinum (Pt) or palladium (Pd) is often used. The manufacture of margarine from unsaturated vegetable oils is a common application of a hydrogenation reaction. Adding hydrogen to unsaturated oils results in the formation of saturated fats that have higher melting points than the unsaturated oils and remain solid at room temperature.

The hydrogenation of a double bond is a reduction reaction. In the examples below, ethene is reduced to ethane, and cyclohexene is reduced to cyclohexane.

Ethene
(ethylene)   Hydrogen   Ethane

Cyclohexene   Hydrogen   Cyclohexane

Under normal conditions, benzene resists hydrogenation. It also resists the addition of a halogen or a hydrogen halide. Under conditions of high temperatures and high pressures of hydrogen, and with certain catalysts however, three molecules of hydrogen gas can reduce one molecule of benzene to form one molecule of cyclohexane.

Benzene   Hydrogen   Cyclohexane

Ethers

Another class of organic compounds may sound familiar to you—ethers. An **ether** is a compound in which oxygen is bonded to two carbon groups. ⟜ The general structure of an ether is R—O—R. The alkyl groups attached to the ether linkage are named in alphabetical order and are followed by the word *ether.*

Ether molecule   Ethylmethyl ether $CH_3CH_2-O-CH_3$ CH_3-O-⟨phenyl⟩

Methylphenyl ether
(anisole)

Some ethers, such as ethylmethyl ether and methylphenyl ether, are nonsymmetric. This is because the R groups attached to the ether oxygen are different. When both R groups are the same, the ether is symmetric. Symmetric ethers are named by using the prefix *di-*. Sometimes, however, the prefix *di-* is dropped and a compound such as diethyl ether is simply called ethyl ether. Figure 23.9 shows examples of a nonsymmetric ether and a symmetric ether.

 Checkpoint *What is an ether?*

a

b

Figure 23.9 Ethers are either nonsymmetric or symmetric. **ⓐ** Ethylmethyl ether is an example of a nonsymmetric ether. **ⓑ** Diphenyl ether is a symmetric ether. Both space-filling and ball-and-stick models of each ether are shown. **Interpreting Visuals** *Describe the differences between a nonsymmetric ether and a symmetric ether.*

Diethyl ether, a volatile liquid (bp 35°C) shown in Figure 23.10, was the first reliable general anesthetic. Originally reported in 1849 by Crawford W. Long, an American physician, diethyl ether was used by doctors for more than a century.

$$CH_3CH_2 \text{—} O \text{—} CH_2CH_3$$

Diethyl ether
(ethyl ether)

Diphenyl ether
(phenyl ether)

Diethyl ether has been replaced by other anesthetics such as halothane because it is highly flammable and often causes nausea.

Ethers usually have lower boiling points than alcohols of comparable molar mass. They have higher boiling points than comparable hydrocarbons and halocarbons. Ethers are more soluble in water than hydrocarbons and halocarbons, but less soluble than alcohols. This is because the oxygen atom in an ether is a hydrogen acceptor. Ethers have no hydroxyl hydrogen atoms to donate in hydrogen bonding. Ethers, therefore, form more hydrogen bonds than hydrocarbons and halocarbons but fewer hydrogen bonds than alcohols.

Figure 23.10 Diethyl ether is a dangerous, highly flammable liquid. It is usually stored in metal cans to keep it away from direct sunlight.

23.2 Section Assessment

7. **Key Concept** How are alcohols classified and named?

8. **Key Concept** How does the solubility of alcohols vary with the length of the carbon chains?

9. **Key Concept** How can functional groups be introduced into organic molecules?

10. **Key Concept** Write the general structure for an ether and explain how ethers are named.

11. Give the structure for the expected organic product from each of the following reactions.

   a.

$$\underset{H}{\overset{CH_3}{}}C{=}C\underset{CH_3}{\overset{H}{}} \; + \; HBr \longrightarrow$$

   b. [benzene ring] $+ \, Cl_2 \xrightarrow{\text{catalyst}}$

   c. [benzene ring] $+ \, 3H_2 \xrightarrow[\text{pressure}]{\text{catalyst}}$

12. Write the common names for the following compounds.

   a. $CH_3CH_2CHCH_3$
      |
      OH

   b. CH_3CHCH_2OH
      |
      CH_3

   c. $CH_3CH_2OCH_2CH_3$

   d. $CH_3CH_2CH_2OCH_2CH_2CH_2CH_3$

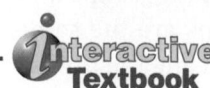

Writing ▶ **Activity**

Portfolio Project Research and write a report on methyl-*tert*-butyl ether (MTBE), which is a gasoline additive. Find out why MTBE was introduced and why there are now efforts to limit its use.

*i*nteractive **Textbook**

Assessment 23.2 Check your understanding of the important ideas and concepts in Section 23.2.

— with **ChemASAP**

23.3 Carbonyl Compounds

New York Standards: 3.1hh, 3.2c

Connecting to Your World

What is your favorite flavor, benzaldehyde or vanillin? Although these two flavors might sound like they belong in the foods of a science-fiction movie, the chances are good that you have eaten these organic molecules, called aldehydes, in ice cream or cookies. Aldehydes and other carbonyl compounds have important everyday uses—even though they may have unfamiliar names. In this section, you will read about the properties that are associated with carbonyl compounds.

Aldehydes and Ketones

Remember that in an alcohol, an oxygen atom is bonded to a carbon group and a hydrogen atom. In an ether, an oxygen atom is bonded to two carbon groups. An oxygen atom can also be bonded to a single carbon atom by a double covalent bond. Such an arrangement is called a carbonyl group. A **carbonyl group** is a functional group with the general structure C=O. **The C=O functional group is present in aldehydes and ketones.** The structural formulas and space-filling models of some carbonyl-group compounds are shown in Figure 23.11.

An **aldehyde** is an organic compound in which the carbon of the carbonyl group is always joined to at least one hydrogen. The general formula for an aldehyde is RCHO.

A **ketone** is an organic compound in which the carbon of the carbonyl group is joined to two other carbons. The general formula for a ketone is RCOR.

Aldehyde   Ketone

ⓐ $H-C-H$ **ⓑ** CH_3-C-H **ⓒ** CH_3-C-CH_3

Guide for Reading

Key Concepts
- What is the structure of a carbonyl group found in aldehydes and ketones?
- What is the general formula for a carboxylic acid?
- What is the general structure of an ester?
- How is dehydrogenation an oxidation reaction?

Vocabulary
carbonyl group
aldehyde
ketone
carboxylic acid
carboxyl group
fatty acids
esters
dehydrogenation reaction

Reading Strategy

Outlining As you read the section, make an outline of the red and blue heads. Under each head, write a few sentences that summarize what you learned from that part of the section.

Figure 23.11 These low molar-mass carbonyl group compounds are completely soluble in water. **ⓐ** Methanal is commonly known as formaldehyde. **ⓑ** Ethanal is commonly known as acetaldehyde. **ⓒ** Propanone is commonly known as acetone. **Interpreting Diagrams** *Use the structures to explain why these compounds are soluble in water.*

Table 23.4

Some Common Aldehydes and Ketones

Condensed formula	Structural formula	IUPAC name	Common name
Aldehydes			
HCHO		Methanal	Formaldehyde
CH_3CHO		Ethanal	Acetaldehyde
C_6H_5CHO		Benzaldehyde	Benzaldehyde
$C_6H_5CH{=}CHCHO$		3-phenyl-2-propenal	Cinnamaldehyde
$CH_3O(OH)C_6H_3CHO$		4-hydroxy-3-meth-oxybenzaldehyde	Vanillin
Ketones			
CH_3COCH_3		Propanone	Acetone (dimethyl ketone)
$C_6H_5COC_6H_5$		Diphenylmethanone	Benzophenone (diphenyl ketone)

The IUPAC system may be used for naming aldehydes and ketones. For either class of compounds, first identify the longest hydrocarbon chain that contains the carbonyl group. Replace the *-e* ending of the hydrocarbon by *-al* to designate an aldehyde. In the IUPAC system, the continuous-chain aldehydes are named methanal, ethanal, propanal, butanal, and so forth.

Ketones are named by changing the ending of the longest continuous carbon chain that contains the carbonyl group from *-e* to *-one*. Table 23.4 illustrates the naming of some common aldehydes and ketones. If the carbonyl group of a ketone could occur at more than one place on the chain, then its position is designated by the lowest possible number.

✓ Checkpoint *What name ending designates a ketone?*

Table 23.5

Boiling Points of Some Compounds with One and Two Carbons

Compound	Formula	Molar mass	Boiling point (C)	Primary intermolecular interactions
One carbon				
Methane	CH_4	16	−161	No hydrogen-bonding or polar-polar interactions
Methanal	HCHO	30	−21	Polar-polar interactions
Methanol	CH_3OH	32	65	Hydrogen bonding
Two carbons				
Ethane	C_2H_6	30	−89	No hydrogen-bonding or polar-polar interactions
Ethanal	CH_3CHO	44	20	Polar-polar interactions
Ethanol	CH_3CH_2OH	46	78	Hydrogen bonding

Properties of Aldehydes and Ketones Aldehydes and ketones can form weak hydrogen bonds between the carbonyl oxygen and the hydrogen atoms of water. The lower members of the series—methanal (formaldehyde), ethanal (acetaldehyde), and propanone (acetone)—are soluble in water in all proportions. As the length of the hydrocarbon chain increases, however, water solubility decreases. When the carbon chain exceeds five or six carbons, solubility of both aldehydes and ketones is very low. As might be expected, all aldehydes and ketones are soluble in nonpolar solvents.

Aldehydes and ketones cannot form intermolecular hydrogen bonds because they lack hydroxyl (—OH) groups. Consequently, they have boiling points that are lower than those of the corresponding alcohols. Aldehydes and ketones can attract each other, however, through polar–polar interactions of their carbonyl groups. As a result, their boiling points are higher than those of the corresponding alkanes. These attractive forces account for the fact that nearly all aldehydes and ketones are either liquids or solids at room temperature. The exception is methanal, which is an irritating, pungent gas. Table 23.5 compares the boiling points of alkanes, aldehydes, and alcohols of similar molar mass.

Uses of Aldehydes and Ketones A wide variety of aldehydes and ketones have been isolated from plants and animals. Many of them, particularly those with high molar masses, have fragrant or penetrating odors. They are usually known by their common names, which can indicate their natural sources or perhaps a characteristic property. Aromatic aldehydes are often used as flavoring agents. Benzaldehyde is the simplest aromatic aldehyde. Also known as oil of bitter almond, benzaldehyde is a constituent of almonds. It is a colorless liquid with a pleasant almond odor. Cinnamaldehyde imparts the characteristic odor of oil of cinnamon.

Figure 23.12 Vanilla beans, the seed pods of the vanilla orchid, are the natural source of this vanilla flavoring for ice cream and other foods.

Figure 23.13 Many types of nail polish remover contain acetone, a common ketone.

Vanilla beans, which are responsible for the popular vanilla flavor, are shown in Figure 23.12.

The simplest aldehyde is methanal, also called formaldehyde. Methanal is very important industrially, having its greatest use in the manufacture of synthetic resins, but it is hard to handle in the gaseous state. Methanal is usually available as a 40% aqueous solution, known as formalin. Formalin can be used to preserve biological specimens. The methanal in solution combines with protein in tissues to make the tissues hard and insoluble in water, preventing the specimen from decaying. Today, formalin is used infrequently as a preservative because it causes cancer.

The most common industrial ketone is propanone, also called acetone. Propanone is a colorless, volatile liquid that boils at 56°C. It is miscible with water in all proportions. Propanone is used as a solvent for resins, plastics, and varnishes and is often found in nail-polish removers as shown in Figure 23.13.

Figure 23.14 Carboxylic acids give a variety of foods—spoiled as well as fresh—a distinctive sour taste. **Predicting** *What would you expect the pH range of aqueous solutions containing carboxylic acids to be?*

Carboxylic Acids

A **carboxylic acid** is a compound with a carboxyl group. A **carboxyl group** consists of a carbonyl group attached to a hydroxyl group.

$$R-\overset{\overset{\displaystyle O}{\|}}{C}-OH$$

Carbonyl group
Hydroxyl group

Carboxyl group
(also written $-CO_2H$ or $-COOH$)

🔑 **The general formula for a carboxylic acid is RCOOH.** Carboxylic acids are weak acids because they ionize slightly in solution to give a carboxylate ion and a hydrogen ion.

$$R-\overset{\overset{\displaystyle O}{\|}}{C}-OH \rightleftharpoons R-\overset{\overset{\displaystyle O}{\|}}{C}-O^- + H^+$$

Carboxylic
acid

Carboxylate
ion

Hydrogen ion
(proton)

In the IUPAC system, carboxylic acids are named by replacing the *-e* ending of the parent alkane with the ending *-oic acid*. Remember, the parent alkane of a carboxylic acid is the hydrocarbon with the longest continuous carbon chain containing the carboxyl group.

Table 23.6

		Saturated Aliphatic Carboxylic Acids		
Formula	**Carbon atoms**	**IUPAC name**	**Common name**	**Melting point (°C)**
HCOOH	1	Methanoic acid	Formic acid	8
CH_3COOH	2	Ethanoic acid	Acetic acid	17
CH_3CH_2COOH	3	Propanoic acid	Propionic acid	−22
$CH_3(CH_2)_2COOH$	4	Butanoic acid	Butyric acid	−6
$CH_3(CH_2)_4COOH$	6	Hexanoic acid	Caproic acid	−3
$CH_3(CH_2)_6COOH$	8	Octanoic acid	Caprylic acid	16
$CH_3(CH_2)_8COOH$	10	Decanoic acid	Capric acid	31
$CH_3(CH_2)_{10}COOH$	12	Dodecanoic acid	Lauric acid	44
$CH_3(CH_2)_{12}COOH$	14	Tetradecanoic acid	Myristic acid	58
$CH_3(CH_2)_{14}COOH$	16	Hexadecanoic acid	Palmitic acid	63
$CH_3(CH_2)_{16}COOH$	18	Octadecanoic acid	Stearic acid	70

Carboxylic acids are abundant and widely distributed in nature. Many have common names derived from a Greek or Latin word that describes their natural sources. For example, the common name for ethanoic acid is acetic acid, which comes from the Latin word *acetum,* meaning vinegar. Common household vinegar contains about 5% (v/v) acetic acid. The formation of acetic acid in wine causes the wine to turn sour, become vinegar, and develop a pungent aroma. One type of vinegar made from wine is shown in Figure 23.14. Many continuous-chain carboxylic acids were first isolated from fats and are called **fatty acids.** Propionic acid, the three-carbon acid, literally means first fatty acid. Common names are used more often than IUPAC names for carboxylic acids. Table 23.6 lists the names and formulas of some common aliphatic carboxylic acids.

The low-molar-mass members of the aliphatic carboxylic acid series are colorless, volatile liquids. They have sharp, unpleasant odors. The higher members of the series are nonvolatile, waxy, odorless solids with low melting points. Stearic acid, an 18-carbon acid obtained from beef fat, is used to make inexpensive wax candles.

Like alcohols, carboxylic acids form intermolecular hydrogen bonds. Thus, carboxylic acids have higher boiling and melting points than other compounds of similar molar mass. All aromatic carboxylic acids are crystalline solids at room temperature.

The carboxyl group in carboxylic acids is polar and readily forms hydrogen bonds with water molecules. Figure 23.15 shows a model of ethanoic acid. Methanoic, ethanoic, propanoic, and butanoic acids are completely miscible with water. The solubility of carboxylic acids of higher molar mass drops sharply, however. Most carboxylic acids dissolve in organic solvents such as ethanol or propanone.

Checkpoint *What is a fatty acid?*

CH_3COOH

Figure 23.15 Ethanoic acid, shown in this formula and space-filling model, is a colorless, volatile liquid. **Applying Concepts** *Is ethanoic acid soluble in water? Why?*

Figure 23.16 Esters impart the characteristic aromas and flavors of many flowers and fruits. Marigolds, raspberries, and bananas all contain esters.

Esters

Esters are probably the most pleasant and delicious organic compounds one can study. Many esters have pleasant, fruity odors. Esters give blueberries, pineapples, apples, pears, bananas, and many other fruits their characteristic aromas. They give many perfumes their fragrances. **Esters** are derivatives of carboxylic acids in which the — OH of the carboxyl group has been replaced by an — OR from an alcohol. **Esters contain a carbonyl group and an ether link to the carbonyl carbon. The general formula for an ester is RCOOR.** The R groups can be short-chain or long-chain aliphatic (alkyl) or aromatic (aryl) groups, saturated or unsaturated.

Carbonyl group
(from the acid)

$$R - C \begin{array}{c} \\ \diagup O \\ \diagdown O - R \end{array}$$

Alkyl or aryl group
(from the alcohol)

Figure 23.16 shows some of the flowers and fruits that contain esters. Simple esters are neutral substances. Although the molecules are polar, they cannot form hydrogen bonds with one another because they do not contain hydrogen attached to oxygen or another electronegative atom. As a result, only weak attractions hold ester molecules to one another. As you might expect, esters have much lower boiling points than the strongly hydrogen-bonded carboxylic acids from which they are derived. The low-formula-mass esters are somewhat soluble in water, but esters containing more than four or five carbons have very limited solubility.

Esters may be prepared from a carboxylic acid and an alcohol. The process is called esterification. The reactants, usually a carboxylic acid and a primary or secondary alcohol, are heated with a mineral acid as a catalyst. The reaction is reversible.

$$R - C \begin{array}{c} \diagup O \\ \diagdown OH \end{array} + RO - H \overset{H^+}{\rightleftharpoons} R - C \begin{array}{c} \diagup O \\ \diagdown OR \end{array} + H - OH$$

Carboxylic   Alcohol   Carboxylate   Water
acid   ester

The formation of the ester ethyl ethanoate from ethanoic acid and ethanol is an example of esterification. The product of this reaction, ethyl ethanoate, is shown in Figure 23.17.

$$CH_3-C\overset{O}{\underset{OH}{\diagup}} + CH_3CH_2O-H \rightleftharpoons[H^+]{} CH_3-C\overset{O}{\underset{OCH_2CH_3}{\diagup}} + H_2O$$

Ethanoic   Ethanol   Ethyl   Water
acid   ethanoate

If an ester is heated with water for several hours, usually very little happens. In strong acid or base solutions, however, the ester breaks down. An ester is hydrolyzed by the addition of water to produce a carboxylic acid and an alcohol. The reaction is rapid in acidic solution.

$$CH_3-\overset{O}{\overset{\|}{C}}-OCH_2CH_3 + H-OH \rightleftharpoons[H^+]{} CH_3-\overset{O}{\overset{\|}{C}}-OH + HOCH_2CH_3$$

Ethyl ethanoate   Ethanoic acid   Ethanol

Hydroxide ions also promote this reaction. The usual agent for ester hydrolysis is an aqueous solution of sodium hydroxide or potassium hydroxide. Because many esters do not dissolve in water, a solvent such as ethanol is added to make the solution homogeneous. The reaction mixture is usually heated. All of the ester is converted to products. The carboxylic acid product is in solution as its sodium or potassium salt.

$$CH_3-\overset{O}{\overset{\|}{C}}-OCH_2CH_3 + NaOH \longrightarrow CH_3-\overset{O}{\overset{\|}{C}}-O^-Na^+ + HOCH_2CH_3$$

Ethyl ethanoate   Sodium ethanoate   Ethanol

If the reaction mixture is acidified, the carboxylic acid forms.

$$CH_3-\overset{O}{\overset{\|}{C}}-O^-Na^+ + HCl \longrightarrow CH_3-\overset{O}{\overset{\|}{C}}-OH + NaCl$$

Sodium ethanoate   Ethanoic acid

Oxidation-Reduction Reactions

All the classes of organic compounds you have just studied are related by oxidation and reduction reactions. Recall from Chapter 20 that oxidation is the gain of oxygen, loss of hydrogen, or loss of electrons and reduction is the loss of oxygen, gain of hydrogen, or gain of electrons. Also remember that one does not occur without the other.

In organic chemistry, the number of oxygen atoms and hydrogen atoms attached to carbon indicates the degree of oxidation of a compound. The fewer hydrogens on a carbon–carbon bond, the more oxidized the bond. Thus, a triple bond (an alkyne) is more oxidized than a double bond (an alkene), which is more oxidized than a single bond (an alkane). In other words, an alkane can be oxidized to an alkene and then to an alkyne; ethane (an alkane) can be oxidized to ethene (an alkene), then to ethyne (an alkyne).

$$CH_3-C\overset{O}{\underset{OCH_2CH_3}{\diagup}}$$

Ethyl
ethanoate

Figure 23.17 Ethyl ethanoate, shown with its structural formula and space-filling model, is a low-molar-mass ester.

Figure 23.18 Oxidation reactions occur in many daily activities. ⓐ These basketball players are energized by oxidation reactions taking place within the cells of their bodies. ⓑ Much of the world relies on hydrocarbon combustion as a source of energy for vehicles.

The loss of hydrogen is a **dehydrogenation reaction.** Strong heating and a catalyst are usually necessary to make dehydrogenation reactions occur. 🔑 **Dehydrogenation is an oxidation reaction because the loss of each molecule of hydrogen involves the loss of two electrons from the organic molecule.** The remaining carbon electrons pair to make a second or third bond.

$$\text{H}-\overset{\overset{\displaystyle H}{|}}{\underset{\underset{\displaystyle H}{|}}{C}}-\overset{\overset{\displaystyle H}{|}}{\underset{\underset{\displaystyle H}{|}}{C}}-\text{H} \quad \xrightarrow[\text{oxidation}]{\substack{\text{loss of hydrogen} \\ \text{(dehydrogenation)}}} \quad \underset{\text{H}}{\overset{\text{H}}{>}}C=C\underset{\text{H}}{\overset{\text{H}}{<}} \quad \xrightarrow[\text{oxidation}]{\substack{\text{loss of hydrogen} \\ \text{(dehydrogenation)}}} \quad \text{H}-\text{C}\equiv\text{C}-\text{H}$$

Least oxidized (most reduced) — Most oxidized (least reduced)

These reactions are reversible. Alkynes can be reduced to alkenes, and alkenes can be reduced to alkanes by addition of hydrogen to a double bond.

$$\text{H}-\text{C}\equiv\text{C}-\text{H} \quad \xrightarrow[\text{reduction}]{\substack{\text{gain of} \\ \text{hydrogen} \\ \text{(hydrogenation)}}} \quad \underset{\text{H}}{\overset{\text{H}}{>}}C=C\underset{\text{H}}{\overset{\text{H}}{<}} \quad \xrightarrow[\text{reduction}]{\substack{\text{gain of} \\ \text{hydrogen} \\ \text{(hydrogenation)}}} \quad \text{H}-\overset{\overset{\displaystyle H}{|}}{\underset{\underset{\displaystyle H}{|}}{C}}-\overset{\overset{\displaystyle H}{|}}{\underset{\underset{\displaystyle H}{|}}{C}}-\text{H}$$

Most oxidized (least reduced) — Most reduced (least oxidized)

Oxidation in organic chemistry also involves the number and degree of oxidation of oxygen atoms attached to carbon. For example, methane, a saturated hydrocarbon, can be oxidized in steps to carbon dioxide. This occurs if it alternately gains oxygen atoms and loses hydrogen atoms. Methane is oxidized to methanol, then to methanal, then to methanoic acid, and finally to carbon dioxide. The same sequence of oxidations occurs for other alkanes. Each series consists of an alkane, alcohol, aldehyde (or ketone), carboxylic acid, and carbon dioxide. The carbon dioxide is most oxidized or least reduced, and the alkane is least oxidized or most reduced.

$$\text{H}-\overset{\overset{\displaystyle H}{|}}{\underset{\underset{\displaystyle H}{|}}{C}}-\text{H} \xrightarrow[\text{oxidation}]{\substack{\text{gain of} \\ \text{oxygen}}} \text{H}-\overset{\overset{\displaystyle OH}{|}}{\underset{\underset{\displaystyle H}{|}}{C}}-\text{H} \xrightarrow[\text{oxidation}]{\substack{\text{loss of} \\ \text{hydrogen}}} \text{H}-\overset{\overset{\displaystyle O}{\parallel}}{C}-\text{H} \xrightarrow[\text{oxidation}]{\substack{\text{gain of} \\ \text{oxygen}}} \text{H}-\overset{\overset{\displaystyle O}{\parallel}}{C}-\text{OH} \xrightarrow[\text{oxidation}]{\substack{\text{loss of} \\ \text{hydrogen}}} \text{O}=\text{C}=\text{O}$$

Methane (most energetic molecule) — Methanol (methyl alcohol) — Methanal (formaldehyde) — Methanoic acid (formic acid) — Carbon dioxide (least energetic molecule)

The more reduced a carbon compound is, the more energy it can release upon its complete oxidation to carbon dioxide. The oxidation of organic compounds is exothermic. The energy-releasing properties of oxidation reactions are extremely important for the production of energy in living systems. They also explain why the combustion of hydrocarbons such as methane is a good source of energy. Figure 23.18 shows how energy production by oxidation reactions is used in both living and nonliving systems.

Primary alcohols can be oxidized to aldehydes, and secondary alcohols can be oxidized to ketones, as shown below.

$$\text{R}-\overset{\overset{\displaystyle OH}{|}}{\underset{\underset{\displaystyle H}{|}}{C}}-\text{H} \xrightarrow[-2\text{H}]{\text{oxidation}} \text{R}-\overset{\overset{\displaystyle O}{\parallel}}{C}-\text{H} \qquad \text{R}-\overset{\overset{\displaystyle OH}{|}}{\underset{\underset{\displaystyle H}{|}}{C}}-\text{R} \xrightarrow[-2\text{H}]{\text{oxidation}} \text{R}-\overset{\overset{\displaystyle O}{\parallel}}{C}-\text{R}$$

Primary alcohol — Aldehyde — Secondary alcohol — Ketone

Tertiary alcohols, however, cannot be oxidized because there is no hydrogen atom present on the carbon bearing the hydroxyl group. A comparison of the structure of primary, secondary, and tertiary alcohols follows.

Go Online

NSTA *SciLINKS*

For: Links on Oxidation and Reduction
Visit: www.SciLinks.org
Web Code: cdn-1233

$$H-\underset{\underset{H}{|}}{\overset{\overset{H}{|}}{C}}-\underset{\underset{H}{|}}{\overset{\overset{H}{|}}{C}}-\underset{\underset{H}{|}}{\overset{\overset{H}{|}}{C}}-OH \qquad H-\underset{\underset{H}{|}}{\overset{\overset{H}{|}}{C}}-\underset{\underset{OH}{|}}{\overset{\overset{H}{|}}{C}}-\underset{\underset{H}{|}}{\overset{\overset{H}{|}}{C}}-H \qquad H-\underset{\underset{H}{|}}{\overset{\overset{H}{|}}{C}}-\underset{\underset{OH}{|}}{\overset{\overset{CH_3}{|}}{C}}-\underset{\underset{H}{|}}{\overset{\overset{H}{|}}{C}}-H$$

Primary alcohol   Secondary alcohol   Tertiary alcohol

The primary alcohols methanol and ethanol can be oxidized to aldehydes by warming them at about 50°C with acidified potassium dichromate ($K_2Cr_2O_7$). In these reactions, methanol produces formaldehyde, and ethanol produces acetaldehyde.

$$H-\underset{\underset{H}{|}}{\overset{\overset{OH}{|}}{C}}-H \xrightarrow[H_2SO_4]{K_2Cr_2O_7} H-\overset{\overset{O}{||}}{C}-H \qquad CH_3-\underset{\underset{H}{|}}{\overset{\overset{OH}{|}}{C}}-H \xrightarrow[H_2SO_4]{K_2Cr_2O_7} CH_3-\overset{\overset{O}{||}}{C}-H$$

Methanol   Methanal   Ethanol   Ethanal
(methyl alcohol) (formaldehyde)   (ethyl alcohol)   (acetaldehyde)
(bp 65°C)   (bp 21°C)   (bp 78°C)   (bp 21°C)

Preparing an aldehyde by this method is often a problem because aldehydes are easily oxidized further to carboxylic acids.

$$R-\overset{\overset{O}{||}}{C}-H \xrightarrow[H_2SO_4]{K_2Cr_2O_7} R-\overset{\overset{O}{||}}{C}-OH$$

Aldehyde   Carboxylic acid

Oxidation of the secondary alcohol 2-propanol by warming it with acidified potassium dichromate produces acetone.

$$CH_3-\underset{\underset{H}{|}}{\overset{\overset{OH}{|}}{C}}-CH_3 \xrightarrow[H_2SO_4]{K_2Cr_2O_7} CH_3-\overset{\overset{O}{||}}{C}-CH_3$$

2-Propanol   Propanone
(isopropyl alcohol) (acetone)

Unlike aldehydes, ketones are resistant to further oxidation, so there is no need to remove them from the reaction mixture during the reaction.

Tests for aldehydes make use of the ease with which these compounds are oxidized. Benedict's and Fehling's reagents are deep-blue alkaline solutions of copper(II) sulfate. Figure 23.19 illustrates Fehling's test for an aldehyde. When an aldehyde is oxidized with Benedict's or Fehling's reagent, a red precipitate of copper(I) oxide (Cu_2O) is formed. The aldehyde is oxidized to its acid, and copper(II) ions (Cu^{2+}) are reduced to copper(I) ions (Cu^+).

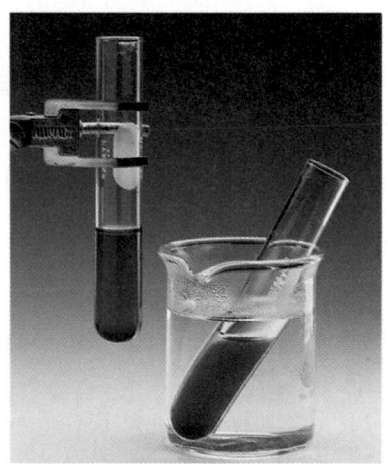

Figure 23.19 When an aldehyde is mixed with Fehling's reagent (left test tube) and heated, the blue copper(II) ions in Fehling's reagent are reduced to form Cu_2O, a red precipitate (right test tube). **Inferring** *What is the oxidation state of copper in the product?*

Quick LAB

Testing for an Aldehyde

Purpose
To distinguish an aldehyde from an alcohol or a ketone using Tollens's reagent.

Materials
- 1M sodium hydroxide
- 5% silver nitrate
- 6M aqueous ammonia
- 4 small test tubes
- test tube rack
- plastic droppers
- glucose solution
- propanone
- ethanol

Procedure

1. Add 1 drop of 1M sodium hydroxide to 2 mL of 5% silver nitrate in a test tube. Add 6M aqueous ammonia drop by drop, gently agitating the tube after each addition until the brownish precipitate dissolves. This will be your Tollens's reagent.

2. Place 10 drops of Tollens's reagent in each of three clean, labeled test tubes.

3. To test tube 1, add 2 drops of glucose solution. To test tube 2, add 2 drops of propanone. To test tube 3, add 2 drops of ethanol. Gently agitate each test tube to mix the contents.

4. Observe the test tubes, leaving them undisturbed for at least 5 minutes.

Analyze and Conclude

1. What evidence of a chemical reaction did you observe in test tube 1? In test tube 2? In test tube 3?

2. Write the equation for any chemical reaction you observed.

3. If you observed a chemical reaction in one or more of the test tubes, what practical uses might the reaction have?

23.3 Section Assessment

13. **Key Concept** Describe the structure of the carbonyl groups that are characteristic of aldehydes and ketones.

14. **Key Concept** What is the general formula for a carboxylic acid?

15. **Key Concept** What is the general structure of an ester?

16. **Key Concept** Explain why dehydrogenation is an oxidation reaction.

17. What products are expected when the following compounds are oxidized?

         OH
         |
a. $CH_3CH_2CCH_3$
         |
         CH_3

         OH
         |
b. $CH_3CH_2CHCH_3$

18. Give the IUPAC name for the aldehyde and the ketone.

                      O
                      ||
a. CH_3CH_2CHO **b.** $CH_3CH_2CH_2CCH_2CH_3$

Connecting   **Concepts**

Acids Review the acids and bases in Chapter 19. Write a paragraph comparing the properties of inorganic acids with those of carboxylic acids. Explain whether carboxylic acids are weak or strong acids.

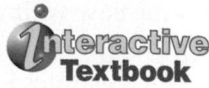
Textbook

Assessment 23.3 Check your understanding of the important ideas and concepts in Section 23.3.

—— with **ChemASAP**

23.4 Polymerization

Connecting to Your World

Snap beads are a favorite toy for toddlers. These colorful plastic shapes of many different colors can be snapped together end-to-end to form chains of different lengths. They can also be snapped together to form loops of various sizes. Chemical compounds called monomers and polymers resemble snap beads. Monomers are like individual snap beads. When snap-bead monomers are joined end-to-end to other snap-bead monomers they form long chains called polymers. In this section, you will learn about some characteristics of monomers and polymers.

Addition Polymers

Most of the reactions that you have learned about so far involve reactants and products of low molar mass. Some of the most important organic compounds that exist, however, are giant molecules called polymers. Each day, you see many different polymers. For example, the materials you know as plastics are polymers. The kinds and uses of plastics are numerous indeed!

A **polymer** is a large molecule formed by the covalent bonding of repeating smaller molecules. The smaller molecules that combine to form a polymer are called **monomers.** Some polymers contain only one type of monomer. Others contain two or more types of monomers. The reaction that joins monomers to form a polymer is called polymerization. Most polymerization reactions require a catalyst.

🔑 **An addition polymer forms when unsaturated monomers react to form a polymer.** Ethene undergoes addition polymerization. The ethene molecules bond to one another to form the long-chain polymer polyethylene.

x is number of ethylene units that combine to form a long chain

Ethene (ethylene)

Polyethylene

x is number of repeating $-CH_2-CH_2-$ units in polymer; parentheses identify the repeating unit

Polyethylene, which is chemically resistant and easy to clean, is an important industrial product. It is used to make familiar items such as the plastic products pictured in Figure 23.20.

Guide for Reading

Key Concepts
- How does an addition polymer form?
- How are condensation polymers formed?

Vocabulary
polymer
monomers

Reading Strategy

Predicting In your notebook, write a prediction about how polymers are formed. As you read the section, correct your prediction, if necessary. After you finish the section, write a short summary of the two main ways polymers are formed.

Figure 23.20 Polyethylene is used for many familiar household items, including plastic bottles, bags, and food containers.

The physical properties of polyethylene can be controlled by shortening or lengthening the carbon chains. Polyethylene that contains relatively short chains ($x = 100$) has the consistency of paraffin wax. Polyethylene with long chains ($x = 1000$) is harder and more rigid.

Polymers of substituted ethenes also are useful. Polypropylene is prepared by the polymerization of propene.

$$x CH_2 = \overset{\displaystyle \overset{CH_3}{|}}{CH} \longrightarrow +CH_2 - \overset{\displaystyle \overset{CH_3}{|}}{CH}\overset{}{)_x}$$

Propene
(propylene)

Polypropylene

Polypropylene, a stiffer polymer than polyethylene, is used extensively in utensils and containers, as well as items such as the whistles shown in Figure 23.21a. Polystyrene is prepared by the polymerization of styrene. Polystyrene, in the form of a rigid foam, is a poor heat conductor, which makes it useful for insulating homes and for manufacturing molded items such as coffee cups and picnic coolers.

$$x CH_2 = CH \longrightarrow +CH_2 - CH)_x$$

Styrene
(vinyl benzene)

Polystyrene

Many halocarbon polymers, including polyvinyl chloride (PVC), have useful properties. Vinyl chloride is the monomer of polyvinyl chloride.

$$x CH_2 = \overset{\displaystyle \overset{Cl}{|}}{CH} \longrightarrow +CH_2 - \overset{\displaystyle \overset{Cl}{|}}{CH}\overset{}{)_x}$$

Chloroethene
(vinyl chloride)

Polyvinyl chloride
(PVC)

Polyvinyl chloride (PVC) is used for the plumbing pipes shown in Figure 23.21b. It is also produced in sheets, sometimes with a fabric backing, for use as a tough plastic upholstery covering.

Figure 23.21 These common polymers are used for various applications. **ⓐ** Polypropylene is used in the manufacture of a variety of items, such as these whistles. **ⓑ** Polyvinyl chloride is used for pipes in plumbing.

Figure **23.22** PTFE is used to coat cookware and to insulate wires, cables, motors, and generators. It also is suspended in motor oils as a friction-reducing agent.

Polytetrafluoroethene (Teflon™ or PTFE) is the product of the polymerization of tetrafluoroethene monomers. PTFE is very resistant to heat and chemical corrosion. You are probably familiar with this polymer as a coating on the nonstick cookware shown in Figure 23.22. Because PTFE is very durable and slick, it is formed into bearings and bushings used in chemical reactors.

$$x CF_2 = CF_2 \longrightarrow + CF_2 - CF_2 +_x$$

Tetrafluoroethene   Teflon (PTFE)

Polyisoprene, harvested from tropical plants such as the rubber tree shown in Figure 23.23, is the polymer that constitutes natural rubber. It is used to make tires, rubber bands, soles of athletic shoes, and many other common items.

$$x CH_2 = CCH = CH_2 \longrightarrow$$
$$\underset{CH_3}{|}$$

$$+ CH_2 \underset{CH_3}{\diagdown} C = C \underset{H}{\diagup} CH_2 +_x$$

Isoprene   Polyisoprene

 Checkpoint *What is polyisoprene?*

Figure **23.23** Rubber is harvested from tropical plants and is used in a variety of products.
Interpreting Photographs
What is the source of natural polyisoprene?

Condensation Polymers

Condensation polymers are formed by the head-to-tail joining of monomer units. This is usually accompanied by the formation of water as a reaction product, thus the name condensation polymers. The formation of a polyester is an example of condensation polymerization. Polyesters are polymers that consist of many repeating units of dicarboxylic acids and dihydroxy alcohols joined by ester bonds. The formation of a polyester can be represented by a block diagram, which shows only the functional groups involved in the polymerization reaction. The squares and circles represent unreactive parts of the organic molecules.

Condensation polymerization requires that there be two functional groups on each monomer molecule.

$$x\text{HO}-\overset{\overset{\text{O}}{\|}}{\text{C}}-\Box-\overset{\overset{\text{O}}{\|}}{\text{C}}-\text{OH} + x\text{HO}-\bigcirc-\text{OH} \longrightarrow \left(\overset{\overset{\text{O}}{\|}}{\text{C}}-\Box-\overset{\overset{\text{O}}{\|}}{\text{C}}-\text{O}-\bigcirc-\text{O}\right)_{\!\!\overline{x}} + 2x\text{H}_2\text{O}$$

Dicarboxylic acid Dihydroxy alcohol Representative polymer unit of a polyester

The polyester polyethylene terephthalate (PET) is formed from terephthalic acid and ethylene glycol.

$$\text{HO}-\overset{\overset{\text{O}}{\|}}{\text{C}}-\underset{\text{}}{\bigcirc}-\overset{\overset{\text{O}}{\|}}{\text{C}}-\text{OH} + \text{HO}-\text{CH}_2\text{CH}_2-\text{OH} \longrightarrow \left(\overset{\overset{\text{O}}{\|}}{\text{C}}-\underset{\text{}}{\bigcirc}-\overset{\overset{\text{O}}{\|}}{\text{C}}-\text{O}-\text{CH}_2\text{CH}_2-\text{O}\right)_{\!\!\overline{x}} + 2x\text{H}_2\text{O}$$

Terephthalic acid Ethylene glycol Representative polymer unit of polyethylene terephthalate (PET)

PET fibers form when the compound is melted and forced through tiny holes in devices called spinnerettes. The fibers, sold as Dacron™, Fortrel®, or Terylene (depending on the manufacturer), are used for tire cord and permanent-press clothing. Figure 23.24 shows how woven Dacron tubing is used to replace major blood vessels. PET fibers are often blended with cotton to make clothes that are more comfortable on hot, humid days than those containing 100% polymer. These clothes retain the wrinkle resistance of 100% polyester. PET melts may also be forced through a narrow slit to produce sheets of Mylar™, a polymer used extensively as magnetic tape for tape recorders and computers.

✓ **Checkpoint** *How are PET fibers made?*

Figure 23.24 Woven Dacron (PET fibers) tubing can be used to replace major blood vessels. ⓐ The blood vessel replacement before surgery. ⓑ The blood vessel after surgery.
Applying Concepts *What properties of Dacron make it useful for this purpose?*

Figure 23.25 Many types of nylon are polyamides. **ⓐ** Flame-resistant clothing is made of Nomex™, a polyamide with aromatic rings. **ⓑ** Nylon fishing lines are lightweight, yet very strong.

Many important polymers are formed by the reaction of carboxylic acids and amines. The amines used to make polymers generally contain the amino functional group —NH_2. The condensation of a carboxylic acid and an amine produces an amide.

$$R-\overset{\overset{\displaystyle O}{\|}}{C}-OH + H-\overset{\overset{\displaystyle H}{|}}{N}-R \longrightarrow R-\overset{\overset{\displaystyle O}{\|}}{C}-\overset{\overset{\displaystyle H}{|}}{N}-R + HO-H$$

  Carboxylic acid   Amine   Amide   Water

Polyamides are polymers in which the carboxylic acid and amine monomer units are linked by amide bonds. The many types of nylon are polyamides. You are probably familiar with a range of nylon products; more nylon products are shown in Figure 23.25. Nylon polymer has a molar mass of about 1×10^4 g/mol and a melting point of 250°C. The representative polymer unit of nylon is derived from 6-aminohexanoic acid, a compound that contains both carboxyl and amino functional groups. The long polymer chain is formed by the successive attachment of the carboxyl group of one molecule of the monomer to the amino group of the next monomer by the formation of an amide bond.

$$x H_2N-CH_2\left(CH_2\right)_{\!4}\overset{\overset{\displaystyle O}{\|}}{C}-OH \xrightarrow{\text{heat}} \left(CH_2\left(CH_2\right)_{\!4}\overset{\overset{\displaystyle O}{\|}}{C}-\overset{\overset{\displaystyle H}{|}}{N}\right)_{\!\!x} + x H_2O$$

  6-Aminohexanoic acid   Representative polymer
                                      unit of nylon

The melted polymer can be spun into very fine, yet very strong, fibers. Nylon fibers are used for carpeting, tire cord, fishing lines, sheer hosiery, and textiles. Nylon is also molded into gears, bearings, and zippers.

 Checkpoint *What are polyamides?*

Polyamides that contain aromatic rings are extremely tough and flame resistant. The aromatic rings make the resulting fiber stiffer and tougher. Nomex™ is a polyamide with a carbon skeleton consisting of aromatic rings derived from isophthalic acid and *m*-phenylenediamine.

$$
HO-\overset{\overset{\displaystyle O}{\|}}{C} \cdots \overset{\overset{\displaystyle O}{\|}}{C}-OH + H_2N \cdots NH_2 \longrightarrow \left(\overset{\overset{\displaystyle O}{\|}}{C} \cdots \overset{\overset{\displaystyle O}{\|}}{C}-\underset{\underset{\displaystyle H}{|}}{N} \cdots \underset{\underset{\displaystyle H}{|}}{N} \right)_x + 2xH_2O
$$

Isophthalic acid   *m*-Phenylenediamine   Representative unit of Nomex

Like nylon, Nomex is a poor conductor of electricity. Because it is more rigid than nylon, it is used to make parts for electrical fixtures. Nomex is also used in the manufacture of flame-resistant clothing for race-car drivers and fire-fighters and in the fabrication of flame-resistant building materials.

Kevlar™ has a structure similar to that of Nomex. It is a polyamide made from terephthalic acid and *p*-phenylenediamine.

$$
HO-\overset{\overset{\displaystyle O}{\|}}{C} \cdots \overset{\overset{\displaystyle O}{\|}}{C}-OH + H_2N \cdots NH_2 \longrightarrow \left(\overset{\overset{\displaystyle O}{\|}}{C} \cdots \overset{\overset{\displaystyle O}{\|}}{C}-\overset{\overset{\displaystyle H}{|}}{N} \cdots \overset{\overset{\displaystyle H}{|}}{N} \right)_x + 2xH_2O
$$

Terephthalic acid   *p*-Phenylenediamine   Representative unit of Kevlar

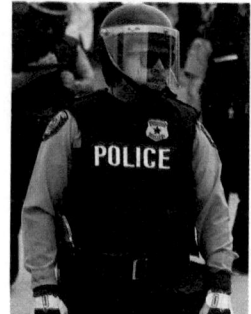

Figure 23.26 Bulletproof vests are made of Kevlar.

Kevlar is used extensively where strength and flame resistance are needed. A properly constructed vest made of Kevlar, shown in Figure 23.26, is strong enough to stop high-speed bullets, yet is light and flexible enough to be worn under normal clothing.

Proteins, which are polyamides of naturally occurring amino acids, rank among the most important of all biological molecules. You will learn about these essential polymers in more detail in Chapter 24.

23.4 Section Assessment

19. **⚷ Key Concept** Describe how addition polymers form.

20. **⚷ Key Concept** Describe how condensation polymers form.

21. What is a polymer? A monomer?

22. Give names and uses for three types of polymers.

23. How is water involved in the formation of condensation polymers?

24. What is formed when a carboxylic acid and an amine combine? Give an example of the type of polymer that is formed by this reaction.

25. What structure must a monomer have if it is to undergo addition polymerization?

Writing ▶ Activity

Write an Analogy Analogies are often used to help explain concepts. Write an analogy that you can use to describe to a middle-school student how a polymer is constructed from monomers. Use diagrams as well as words to describe your analogy.

*i*nteractive **Textbook**

Assessment 23.4 Check your understanding of the important ideas and concepts in Section 23.4.

—— with **ChemASAP**

Polymers

Purpose
To cross-link some polymers and examine their properties.

Materials
- $3\frac{1}{2}$-oz plastic cup
- soda straw
- powdered guar gum
- plastic spoon
- 4% borax solution
- pipet

Procedure
1. Half fill a $3\frac{1}{2}$-oz cup with water.
2. Use a soda straw as a measuring scoop to obtain approximately 2 cm of powdered guar gum. **Caution:** *Do not use your mouth to draw up the guar gum into the straw.* Gently sprinkle the guar gum powder into the water while stirring with a plastic spoon. Add the guar gum powder slowly to prevent it from clumping. Stir the mixture well.
3. While stirring, add one full pipet (about 4 mL) of borax solution. Continue to stir until a change occurs.

Analyze
Using your experimental data, record the answers to the following questions below your observations.
1. Describe the polymer you just made. Is it a liquid or a solid? What special characteristics does it have?
2. Guar gum is a carbohydrate, a polymer with many repeating alcohol functional groups (—OH). Draw a zigzag line to represent a crude polymer chain.
3. Add —OH groups along the chain to represent the alcohol functional groups.
4. Borate ions combine with alcohol to form water and borate complexes of the alcohol.

$$\underset{\substack{\\ ^-O}}{\overset{HO}{\diagdown}}B\overset{OH}{\underset{OH}{\diagup}} + R—OH \longrightarrow \underset{\substack{\\ ^-O}}{\overset{HO}{\diagdown}}B\overset{OH}{\underset{OR}{\diagup}} + HOH$$

Write a similar equation that replaces all of the —OH groups on the borate with —OR groups.

5. If two polymer chains each contain two nearby —OH groups, borate will cross-link the polymer chains by forming a complex with two alcohols on each chain. Draw a structure similar to the one you drew for Question 4, but replace your four R groups with two polymer chains.

You're the Chemist
The following small-scale activities allow you to develop your own procedures and analyze the results.

1. **Design It!** Try using borax to cross-link other common carbohydrate polymers, such as cornstarch or liquid laundry starch. For each polymer, half fill a $3\frac{1}{2}$-oz cup with the chosen carbohydrate polymer and add enough water to bring the liquid to within about 1 cm of the rim. Stir carefully and thoroughly. Add one full pipet (about 4 mL) of borax solution while stirring. Describe the similarities and differences between this cross-linked polymer and the polymer you made previously. Compare the properties of these polymers.

2. **Analyze It!** Cut a 1 cm × 15 cm strip of paper. Use a drop of glue or a stapler to fasten one end of the paper strip to the other end to form a ring. Now cut out some identical-sized strips of paper, and glue or staple them together into an interlocking chain of paper rings. Explain how this chain is like a polymer. Make another paper ring that cross-links your chain to one of your classmates' chains. Explain how these linked chains are like cross-linked polymers.

Organic Dyes

Organic dyes are made from plants or insects and generally produce colors that are soft and natural. Using organic dyes requires two steps: extracting the dyestuff from the plant, and fixing the dye to a surface or material. The earliest recorded use of organic dyes to color fabrics dates from 2600 BC in China. **Interpreting Photographs** *What plant yields a dye that produces salmon pinks to deep reds?*

Dying fabric Long lengths of fabric are bathed in large vats of dye before being wound into bolts and sold.

Tiny cochineal insects (Dactylopius coccus) live in dusty, white clusters on prickly pear cacti. Dried and ground bodies of the female yield a dye that produces colors from pink to **purple.**

The ground root of the madder plant (*Rubia tinctoria*) yields a dye that produces colors from salmon pink to deep **red.** The red coats worn by British soldiers during the Revolutionary War were colored by a dye made from madder root.

The shredded wood and root bark of the Osage orange tree (*Maclura pomifera*) yield a dye that can produce colors ranging from yellow to tan to **green.** During World War I, dye from Osage orange was used to color U.S. uniforms khaki.

The wood of the smoke tree (*Cotinus coggygria*) yields fustic, which produces colors from yellow to gold to **orange.**

Made from the indigo plant (*Indigofera tinctoria*), indigo dye produces a wide variety of blues from pale sky **blue** to dark navy.

Key Concepts

🔑 **23.1 Introduction to Functional Groups**
- Organic compounds can be classified according to their functional groups.
- A halocarbon is a carbon-containing compound with a halogen substituent.
- A halogen can replace a hydrogen atom on an alkane to produce a halocarbon.

🔑 **23.2 Alcohols and Ethers**
- Aliphatic alcohols can be arranged into structural categories according to the number of R groups attached to the carbon with the hydroxyl group.
- When using the IUPAC system to name continuous-chain and substituted alcohols, drop the -*e* ending of the parent alkane name and add the ending -*ol*.
- Alcohols of up to four carbons are soluble in water in all proportions. The solubility of alcohols with four or more carbons in the chain is usually much lower.
- Addition reactions of alkenes are an important method of introducing new functional groups into organic molecules.

- The general structure of an ether is R—O—R. The alkyl groups attached to the ether linkage are named in alphabetical order and are followed by the word *ether*.

🔑 **23.3 Carbonyl Compounds**
- A carbonyl group, with the general structure C=O, is the functional group in aldehydes and ketones.
- The general formula for a carboxylic acid is RCOOH.
- Esters contain a carbonyl group and an ether link to the carbonyl carbon. The general formula for an ester is RCOOR.
- Dehydrogenation is an oxidation reaction because the loss of each molecule of hydrogen involves the loss of two electrons from the organic molecule.

🔑 **23.4 Polymerization**
- An addition polymer forms when unsaturated monomers react to form a polymer.
- Condensation polymers are formed by the head-to-tail joining of monomer units.

Vocabulary

- addition reaction (p. 733)
- alcohol (p. 730)
- aldehyde (p. 737)
- alkyl halide (p. 727)
- aryl halide (p. 727)
- carbonyl group (p. 737)
- carboxyl group (p. 740)
- carboxylic acid (p. 740)
- dehydrogenation reaction (p. 743)
- denatured alcohol (p. 733)
- ester (p. 741)
- ether (p. 735)
- fatty acid (p. 740)
- fermentation (p. 733)
- functional group (p. 725)
- halocarbon (p. 726)
- hydration reaction (p. 734)
- hydrogenation reaction (p. 734)
- hydroxyl group (p. 730)
- ketone (p. 737)
- monomer (p. 747)
- polymer (p. 747)
- substitution reaction (p. 728)

Organizing Information

Use these terms to construct a concept map that organizes the major ideas of this chapter.

Concept Map 23 Create your Concept Map using the computer.

with ChemASAP

23.1 Introduction to Functional Groups

26. What does R in the formula R—CH_2Cl represent?

27. Write a structural formula for each compound.
 a. 1,2,2-trichlorobutane
 b. 1,3,5-tribromobenzene
 c. 1,2-dichlorocyclohexane

28. Name the following halocarbons.
 a. CH_2=$CHCH_2Cl$ c. Br

 $\underset{\text{CH}_3}{|}$ $\underset{\text{Cl}}{|}$
 b. $CH_3CHCH_2CHCH_2Cl$

29. Write structural formulas and give IUPAC names for all the isomers of the following compounds.
 a. $C_3H_6Cl_2$ b. C_4H_9Br

30. Write structural formulas for the organic products that are formed in the following reactions.

 a. ⬡—Br + NaOH $\xrightarrow{\text{heat}}$ _____ + NaBr

 b. ⬡—Cl + NaOH ⟶ _____ + NaCl

 c. $CH_3\underset{\underset{\text{CH}_3}{|}}{CHCl}$ + NaOH ⟶ _____ + NaCl

 d. ⬡ + Br_2 $\xrightarrow{\text{catalyst}}$ _____ + HBr

31. Explain why a carbon–carbon double bond is nonpolar, but a carbon–oxygen double bond is very polar.

32. Write the structural formulas for the products of these reactions.
 a. CH_3CH_2CH=CH_2 + Cl_2 ⟶
 b. CH_3CH_2CH=CH_2 + Br_2 ⟶
 c. ⬡ + HBr ⟶

33. The processes used to synthesize many organic compounds often use compounds that contain double or triple bonds as reactants. Explain why the use of unsaturated reactants might be an advantage over using saturated reactants.

34. Cadaverine (1,5-diaminopentane) and putrescine (1,4-diaminobutane) are unpleasant-smelling compounds that are formed by bacteria in rotting flesh. Draw their structures. What class of organic compounds are these two chemicals?

23.2 Alcohols and Ethers

35. Name the following alcohols.

 a. CH_3—$\underset{\underset{\text{OH}}{|}}{CH}$—$CH_3$

 b. $\underset{\underset{\text{OH}}{|}}{CH_2}$—$\underset{\underset{\text{OH}}{|}}{CH}$—$CH_3$

36. Write the structure for the expected product from each reaction.
 a. CH_2=$CHCH_2CH_3$ + Br_2 ⟶
 b. CH_3CH=$CHCH_3$ + I_2 ⟶
 c. CH_3CH=$CHCH_3$ + H_2 ⟶
 d.

 ⬡ + Cl_2 ⟶

37. Write structures and names of the products obtained upon addition of each of the following reagents to ethene.
 a. HBr   b. Cl_2 c. H_2O d. H_2 e. HCl

38. Name the following ethers.
 a. $CH_3OCH_2CH_3$

 b. ⬡—O—CH_2CH_3

 c. CH_2=$CHOCH$=CH_2

 d. $CH_3\underset{\underset{\text{CH}_3}{|}}{CH}OCH\underset{\underset{\text{CH}_3}{|}}{}CH_3$

39. Classify each compound as an alcohol, a phenol, or an ether.

a.

b.

c.

d.

e. CH_3CH_2CHOH
         |
        CH_3

40. Explain why diethyl ether is more soluble in water than dihexyl ether is. Would you expect propane or diethyl ether to be more soluble in water? Why?

41. Explain why 1-butanol has a higher boiling point than diethyl ether has. Which compound would you expect to be more soluble in water? Why?

42. Cholesterol is a compound in your diet and is also synthesized in the liver. Sometimes it is deposited on the inner walls of blood vessels, causing hardening of the arteries. Describe the structural features and functional groups of this important molecule.

43. Hydrocarbons from petroleum are an important source of raw material for the chemical industry. Using reactions covered in this chapter and any required inorganic chemicals, propose a scheme

for the manufacture of ethylene glycol, a major component of antifreeze, from petrochemical ethene.

23.3 Carbonyl Compounds

44. Name these aldehydes and ketones.

a. CH_3CCH_3

b. CH_3CHCH_2CHO with CH_3 branch

c. $-CH_2CHO$

d. CH_3CHO

e.

f. $CH_3CH_2CCH_2CH_2CH_3$

45. Write a general structure for each type of compound.
   a. halocarbon   **b.** ketone
   c. ester   **d.** amide

46. Predict which compound has the highest boiling point. Molar masses are given in parentheses.
   a. CH_3CHO (44)   **b.** CH_3CH_2OH (46)
   c. $CH_3CH_2CH_3$ (44)

47. Write the structure and name of the expected products for each reaction.

a. $CH_3COOH + CH_3OH \xrightarrow{H^+}$

b. $CH_3CH_2CH_3COOCH_2CH_3 + H_2O \xrightarrow{NaOH}$

c. $CH_3CH_2OH \xrightarrow{K_2Cr_2O_7}$

48. What are the products of each reaction?
   a. $HCOOH + KOH \longrightarrow$
   b. $CH_3CH_2COOH + NaOH \longrightarrow$
   c. $CH_3COOH + NaOH \longrightarrow$

49. For each compound pictured, identify the functional group and name the compound. The red atoms represent oxygen.

a.

b.

c.

d.

50. Write the name and structure for the alcohol that must be oxidized to make each carbonyl compound.

a. HCHO

b. $CH_3\overset{\overset{\displaystyle O}{||}}{C}CH_3$

c. $CH_3\overset{\overset{\displaystyle CH_3}{|}}{C}HCHO$

d. [cyclohexanone structure with O]

51. Write the structures of the expected products for these reactions.

a. $CH_3CH_2COOCH_2CH_3 \xrightarrow{NaOH}$

b. CH_3COO- [benzene ring] $\xrightarrow{KOH}$

c. $CH_3CH_2COOCH_2\overset{\overset{\displaystyle }{|}}{C}HCH_3 \xrightarrow{HCl}$
 $\quad\quad\quad\quad\quad\quad\quad\quad CH_3$

52. Complete the following reactions by writing the structures of the expected products and by naming the reactants and products.

a. $CH_3COOCH_3 + H_2O \xrightarrow{HCl}$

b. $CH_3CH_2CH_2COOCH_2CH_2CH_3 + H_2O \xrightarrow{NaOH}$

c. $HCOOCH_2CH_3 + H_2O \xrightarrow{KOH}$

53. Benzene is poisonous and a proven carcinogen. Yet many compounds containing benzene rings, such as benzaldehyde, are common in the foods you eat. Why are some organic compounds with phenyl groups safe to eat?

54. Propane ($CH_3CH_2CH_3$) and acetaldehyde (CH_3CHO) have the same molar mass, but propane boils at $-42°C$ and acetaldehyde boils at $20°C$. Account for this difference.

55. How would you expect the water solubility of ethanoic and decanoic acids to compare?

23.4 Polymerization

56. Different samples of a polymer such as polyethylene can have different properties. Explain.

57. What is the structure of the repeating units in a polymer that has the following monomers?
a. 1-butene
b. 1,2-dichloroethene

58. Human hair is composed of long-chain polymers. Some of the monomers in these polymers contain sulfur atoms. When two sulfur atoms are adjacent to one another, they form strong, covalent disulfide (S—S) bonds that can link two polymer molecules together. The location of the cross links between the hair polymers affects how curly or straight the hair is and helps to hold the polymers in their shape. Waving lotion that is used in permanent waves is a reducing agent, and neutralizing agent is an oxidizing agent. Using this information, explain in terms of chemistry how a permanent wave can change the shape of hair. Describe what chemical steps should be taken to change the shape of someone's hair from straight to curly.

Test-Taking Tip

Eliminate Wrong Answers If you don't know which response is correct, start by eliminating those you know are wrong. If you can rule out some choices, you'll have fewer left to consider and you'll increase your chances of choosing the correct answer.

Regents Practice Exam

Part A

For each statement or question write the number of the word or expression that, of those given, best completes the statement or answers the question.

1. Which of the following reactions would an alkane *not* undergo?
   (1) addition   (3) substitution
   (2) combustion   (4) oxidation

2. When a compound breaks down into its component elements, the type of reaction is
   (1) combination (synthesis)
   (2) decomposition
   (3) single-replacement
   (4) combustion

3. A C—H bond is
   (1) ionic   (3) polar covalent
   (2) hydrogen   (4) nonpolar covalent

4. The functional group in aldehydes and ketones is
   (1) —OH   (3) —CO—
   (2) —COOH   (4) —COO—

5. The following chemical equation shows an example of what type of reaction?

   $$C_6H_{12}O_6 \longrightarrow 2CH_3CH_2OH + 2CO_2$$

   (1) fermentation   (3) saponification
   (2) polymerization   (4) substitution

6. The organic acid HCOOH and the inorganic acid HCl are alike in that both compounds
   (1) can be produced by an addition reaction
   (2) can be classified as organic under certain circumstances
   (3) produce OH^- ions in solution
   (4) produce H^+ ions in solution

Part B-1

For each statement or question write the number of the word or expression that, of those given, best completes the statement or answers the question.

7. Ethane, methanal, and methanol have similar molar masses. Which series lists the compounds in order of increasing boiling point?
   (1) ethane, methanal, methanol
   (2) methanal, methanol, ethane
   (3) methanol, methanal, ethane
   (4) ethane, methanol, methanal

The numbered choices below refer to Questions 8–11. A numbered choice may be used once, more than once, or not at all.

   (1) alcohol   (3) organic acid
   (2) ketone   (4) ether

To which class of organic compounds does each of the following compounds belong?

8. CH_3CH_2COOH

9. $CH_3CH_2OCH_3$

10. $CH_3CH_2CH_2OH$

11. CH_3COCH_3

The numbered choices below refer to Questions 12–15. A numbered choice may be used once, more than once, or not at all.

   (1) addition   (3) substitution
   (2) polymerization   (4) esterification

What type of reaction is shown by each of the following chemical equations?

12. $CH_2{=}CH_2 + HCl \longrightarrow CH_3CH_2Cl$

13. $CH_3CO_2H + CH_3CH_2OH \xrightarrow{H^+}$
   $$CH_3COOCH_2CH_3 + H_2O$$

14. $x CH_2{=}CH_2 \longrightarrow H{-}(CH_2{-}CH_2{)}_x{-}H$

15. + Br₂ $\xrightarrow{\text{catalyst}}$ Br + HBr

16. Ethanol (CH_3CH_2OH) is miscible in water in all proportions because
   (1) ethanol and water do not mix
   (2) ethanol molecules form hydrogen bonds with water molecules
   (3) there are no intermolecular forces between ethanol molecules
   (4) ethanol contains a functional group

Part B-2

Answer each of the following questions.

17. Using electron dot structures, illustrate the formation of the following ions.
   a. F^- from a fluorine atom
   b. a hydroxide ion from atoms of hydrogen and oxygen

18. Calculate the mass, in grams, of one liter of SO_2 at standard temperature and pressure. One mole of any gas occupies 22.4 L at STP.

19. A sample of 1.40 L of nitrogen gas is in a sealed container at 25.0°C and has a pressure of 1.00×10^2 kPa. What is the new pressure if the gas is heated to 68.7°C?

20. A solution is made by diluting 250 mL of $0.210M$ $Ca(NO_3)_2$ solution with water to a final volume of 450 mL. Calculate the molarity of $Ca(NO_3)_2$ in the diluted solution.

21. In a saturated solution containing undissolved solute, the solute is continually dissolving, but the solution concentration remains constant. Explain.

22. A 500-g aluminum tray at 22°C is heated to 180°C in an oven. How many kJ of heat does the pan absorb if the specific heat of aluminum is $0.90 \text{ J}/(g \times °C)$?

23. Predict the direction of shift in the equilibrium position for each of the following changes in conditions.

$$2NO_2(g) \rightleftharpoons 2NO(g) + O_2(g)$$

a. concentration of O_2 decreased
b. total pressure increased

24. Assign an oxidation number to each atom in the following compounds.
   a. $NaNO_2$ **c.** SeO_2 **e.** K_2PtCl_4
   b. $CoSO_4$ **d.** $Zn(OH)_2$

25. What is the source of the electrical energy produced in a voltaic cell?

26. At which electrode in an electrolytic cell does reduction always occur?

27. Draw a complete structural formula for each of the following compounds.
   a. 2-pentene   **c.** 3-ethyl-2-pentene
   b. 2-methyl-2-pentene

Use the space-filling models to answer Questions 28 and 29.

a.   **b.**   **c.**

28. Using models a, b, and c as guides, draw ball-and-stick models of the three compounds that have the formula C_3H_8O. Name each compound.

29. Two different compounds contain a C=O group and have the molecular formula C_3H_6O. Write a complete structural formula and draw a ball-and-stick model for each compound. Name each compound.

Part C

Answer each of the following questions.

30. Sodium carbonate is often sold as the anhydrous compound $Na_2CO_3(s)$ or as the decahydrate $Na_2CO_3 \cdot 10H_2O(s)$. If the price per kilogram of the anhydrous and decahydrate forms are the same, which compound is the better value?

31. Assume that water enters a power plant at 20°C and leaves at 30°C. Will the amount of dissolved oxygen in the water be greater entering or leaving the plant?

32. Solid sodium borohydride ($NaBH_4$) is under investigation as a source of hydrogen fuel for hydrogen-powered vehicles. The borohydride reacts with water to produce hydrogen gas and sodium borate ($Na_2B_4O_7$). Identify which atoms of the reactants are oxidized, which are reduced, and which are unaffected in this reaction.

24 The Chemistry of Life

All organisms, including you and your classmates, are made of the same types of molecules: carbohydrates, proteins, lipids, and nucleic acids.

INQUIRY Activity

Biological Catalysts

Materials

2 small pieces of red meat, such as ground beef, one raw and one cooked; 2 paper plates; small amount of 3% hydrogen peroxide; dropper

Procedure

1. Place the two meat samples on separate plates. Both samples should be at room temperature. Add a few drops of hydrogen peroxide solution to the raw and the cooked meat samples. **CAUTION** *Never taste any chemical used in the laboratory, including food products.*

2. Observe the samples for about five minutes.

Think About It

1. Do you observe any difference in the appearance of the hydrogen peroxide placed on the raw meat and on the cooked meat?

2. What do you think causes the difference in the appearance of the hydrogen peroxide on the raw and cooked meats?

3. What can you conclude from this experiment?

24.1 A Strategy for Life

New York Standards: 4.1a, 5.2i

Connecting to Your World The air you breathe is composed mainly of nitrogen (N_2) and oxygen (O_2). Earth's early atmosphere may have been very different and most inhospitable to life. It is thought that the atmosphere changed over time as a result of photosynthesis, a process carried out by green organisms such as these cyanobacteria. One of the products of photosynthesis is oxygen, which accumulated in the atmosphere and changed the composition of air. In this section, you will learn about the characteristics of living things, including the organisms in which photosynthesis occurs.

The Structure of Cells

Life! You are certainly familiar with it, but what does it really mean? Until recently, life was defined as the ability of an organism to grow and to reproduce its own kind. However, recent discoveries made at the fringes of life seem to blur this simple definition. As difficult as it is to define life, you can generally regard tiny structures called cells as the fundamental units of life. You will learn about the construction of cells and the chemical processes that cells undergo to obtain the energy they need to survive.

Organisms are composed of as few as one cell or as many as billions of cells. **Two major cell types occur in nature: the cells of bacteria, known as prokaryotic cells, and the cells of all other organisms, known as eukaryotic cells.** The prokaryotic cell is the more ancient of the two. Microscopic examination of fossilized remains shows that prokaryotic cells were present on Earth at least 3 billion years ago. Eukaryotic cells did not appear until about 1 billion years ago. Figure 24.1 shows both types of cells.

Guide for Reading

Key Concepts
- What are the two major types of cells that occur in nature?
- What compound is reduced during photosynthesis? What compounds are formed?

Vocabulary
photosynthesis

Reading Strategy

Relating Text and Visuals As you read, look carefully at Figure 24.3. In your notebook, explain how this illustration helps you understand the relationship between photosynthesis and the carbon compounds used by all organisms.

Figure 24.1 Typical prokaryotic and eukaryotic cells are shown here. Note that only the eukaryotic cell has a nucleus. **Comparing and Contrasting** *How do prokaryotic and eukaryotic cells compare in size?*

Chromosome Cell membrane
Cell wall

Prokaryotic cell
├── 1.0 to 10.0 micrometers (μm) ──┤

Nucleus Endoplasmic reticulum
Mitochondrion
Lysosome
Cytoplasm Cell membrane

Eukaryotic cell
├── 10.0 to 100.0 micrometers (μm) ──┤

Both eukaryotic and prokaryotic cells contain all the chemicals necessary for life, encased in a cell membrane. The cell membrane is a sack that holds the contents of a cell and acts as a selective barrier for the passage of substances into and out of the cell. Eukaryotic cells are considerably larger and more complex than prokaryotic cells, but the chemical processes carried out by both types of cells are very similar.

One major feature that distinguishes eukaryotic cells from prokaryotic cells is the presence of membrane-enclosed organelles. Organelles, meaning little organs, are small structures suspended in the interior cellular fluid, or cytoplasm. The organelles are the sites of many specialized functions in eukaryotic cells. The nucleus, a structure that is important in eukaryotic cell reproduction, is not present in prokaryotic cells. Mitochondria (singular: mitochondrion) are the source of cellular energy in eukaryotic cells that use oxygen. Mitochondria are often referred to as the powerhouses of the cell. Lysosomes are the sites for the digestion of substances taken into a cell. Yet another membrane-enclosed structure in eukaryotic cells is the highly folded, netlike endoplasmic reticulum (ER). Among its various functions, the ER serves as an attachment site for ribosomes. The ribosomes, small organelles that are not membrane-enclosed, are the sites where essential substances called proteins are made.

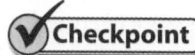 **Checkpoint** *Which organelle is involved in cell reproduction?*

The Energy and Carbon Cycle

Organisms must have energy to survive. The ultimate source of this energy is the sun. Cells of green plants and certain algae contain organelles called chloroplasts that are able to capture solar energy and make food. Figure 24.2 shows a chloroplast from the cell of a corn leaf. Within the chloroplast is a light-capturing system that converts light energy into chemical energy by a process called **photosynthesis.** In addition to sunlight, photosynthetic organisms require carbon dioxide and water. **Photosynthesis uses the energy from sunlight to reduce carbon dioxide to compounds that contain C—H bonds, mainly in the form of glucose ($C_6H_{12}O_6$).** The following equation describes the process.

$$6CO_2 \ + \ 6H_2O \ + \ Energy \longrightarrow C_6H_{12}O_6 \ + \ 6O_2$$

| Carbon dioxide (carbon in more oxidized state) | Water | from sunlight | Glucose (carbon in more reduced state) | Oxygen |

Figure 24.3 illustrates the relationship between photosynthesis and the carbon compounds used by all organisms. In the energy and carbon cycle, photosynthetic organisms produce necessary carbon compounds. Animals, which do not carry out photosynthesis, get these carbon compounds by eating plants or by eating animals that feed on plants. Both plants and animals get energy by unleashing the energy stored in the chemical bonds of these carbon compounds. The nutrients are oxidized back to carbon dioxide and water in the process.

$$C_6H_{12}O_6 \ + \ 6O_2 \longrightarrow 6CO_2 \ + \ 6H_2O \ + \ Energy$$

| Glucose (carbon in more reduced state) | Oxygen | Carbon dioxide (carbon in more oxidized state) | Water | |

Figure 24.2 The reactions of photosynthesis take place on the inner membranes and in the spaces between membranes of a chloroplast.

Figure 24.3 In the energy and carbon cycle, photosynthesis and the oxidation of glucose are responsible for the major transformations and movements of carbon. Plants, such as rain forest trees, release oxygen into the atmosphere through photosynthesis. **Interpreting Diagrams** *In which part of the cycle is oxygen released?*

Thus, although plant life could survive without animals, animal life could never survive without plants. Without photosynthesis, the supply of carbon compounds that animals need to get energy would not exist.

Oxygen also is an important product of photosynthesis. Photosynthetic organisms produce the oxygen found in Earth's atmosphere. The oxygen is required for most organisms to sustain life. The importance of photosynthetic organisms in producing carbon compounds and oxygen is a major reason for the concern about the loss of such organisms through the destruction of rain forests.

All biological processes, including photosynthesis, are based on certain essential kinds of chemical substances. Surprisingly, the great complexity of life arises from just a few types of biological molecules. In the remainder of this chapter, you will learn about the molecular structures of the great classes of biological molecules and the roles they play in the body.

24.1 Section Assessment

1. **Key Concept** What two types of cells occur in nature?

2. **Key Concept** What chemical changes occur during photosynthesis?

3. What are the fundamental units of life?

4. Describe the structure of a eukaryotic cell.

5. What is the function of chloroplasts in green plants and algae?

6. Write an equation that describes the oxidation of glucose.

7. Explain how carbon moves through the environment.

Elements ▸ Handbook

Greenhouse Gases Read the feature on greenhouse gases on page R22. Describe how the energy and carbon cycle normally keeps atmospheric CO_2 levels balanced. What factors have disrupted this balance and caused atmospheric CO_2 levels to rise?

Interactive Textbook

Assessment 24.1 Test yourself on the concepts in Section 24.1.
— with **ChemASAP**

24.2 Carbohydrates

New York Standards: 3.1ii, 3.2c

Guide for Reading

Key Concepts
- Where is glucose found abundantly in nature?
- How can the cyclic forms of two simple sugars be linked?

Vocabulary
carbohydrates
monosaccharides
disaccharide
polysaccharides

Reading Strategy

Previewing Before you read this section, skim the section to find out the types of carbohydrates you will be learning about. List the types of carbohydrates and, as you read, write a description of each one.

Connecting to Your World This cicada is molting—shedding its old exoskeleton and forming a new one. An exoskeleton is the hard protective covering of insects, lobsters, and other arthropods. As an arthropod grows, it must molt to make room for its bigger body. An arthropod's exoskeleton is made of a polymer called chitin, which belongs to a class of organic molecules known as carbohydrates. In this section, you will learn about the structures and functions of carbohydrates.

Monosaccharides

Long-distance runners often prepare for a big race by eating a great deal of bread and pasta, a process known as carbohydrate loading. Breads and pastas are excellent sources of the family of important molecules called carbohydrates. **Carbohydrates** are monomers and polymers of aldehydes and ketones that have numerous hydroxyl groups attached; they are made up of carbon, hydrogen, and oxygen. The name carbohydrate comes from the early observation that many of these compounds have the general formula $C_n(H_2O)_n$ and, as a result, appear to be hydrates of carbon. They are not, in fact, true hydrates.

You would probably call a diet based mainly on bread and pasta a starchy diet. You would be correct. Such foods contain certain carbohydrates called starches. In this section, you will learn about the similarities and differences among some well-known types of carbohydrates.

Carbohydrates are present in most foods, as Figure 24.4 shows. The simplest carbohydrate molecules are called simple sugars, or **monosaccharides.** Glucose and fructose are examples of simple sugars. **Glucose is abundant in plants and animals.** Depending on the source, glucose has also been called corn sugar, grape sugar, or blood sugar. Fructose occurs in a large number of fruits and in honey. Glucose and fructose both have the molecular formula $C_6H_{12}O_6$. However, glucose has an aldehyde functional group, whereas fructose has a ketone functional group. Therefore, they are structural isomers. Both undergo many of the same reactions as ordinary aldehydes and ketones.

Figure 24.4 Carbohydrates are the most abundant sources of energy in food. Fruits contain simple carbohydrates called sugars. Bread and pasta are good sources of complex carbohydrates called starches.

In aqueous solution, simple sugars such as glucose and fructose exist in a dynamic equilibrium between straight-chain and cyclic forms. The cyclic form predominates. The structures for each sugar in both forms are:

Straight-chain and cyclic forms of glucose

Straight-chain and cyclic forms of fructose

Note the aldehyde functional group (—CHO) on the straight-chain form of glucose and the ketone functional group $\left(-\overset{\text{O}}{\underset{\|}{C}}-\right)$ on the straight-chain form of fructose.

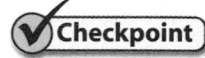 **Checkpoint** *Which form of a simple sugar is favored at equilibrium in aqueous solution?*

Disaccharides and Polysaccharides

Simple sugars form the building blocks of more complex carbohydrates. **The cyclic forms of two simple sugars can be linked by means of a condensation reaction.** For example, the linking of glucose and fructose with the loss of a water molecule produces sucrose—common table sugar. A sugar such as sucrose that forms from two monosaccharides in this way is known as a **disaccharide.** The reaction by which it forms is as follows.

Glucose

Fructose

$-H_2O$

Sucrose

Sucrose is obtained commercially mainly from the juice of sugar cane and sugar beets. The world's production from these sources exceeds 7×10^9 metric tons per year.

The formation of a disaccharide is sometimes the first step in a condensation polymerization reaction that produces extremely large molecules. The polymers produced by the linkage of many monosaccharide monomers are called **polysaccharides.** Starches, the major storage form of glucose in plants, are polysaccharide polymers that consist of glucose monomers. Figure 24.5 shows a portion of a starch molecule.

Word *Origins*

Polysaccharide comes from the Greek words *polys*, meaning "full" or "many," and *sakcharon*, meaning "sugar." A polysaccharide is a compound that is formed by the linking together of many simple sugar molecules. Starches, cellulose, and glycogen are all polysaccharides. **What are the names of some other organic molecules that contain the prefix *poly-*?**

Figure 24.5 Starch and cellulose are similar polymers made up of hundreds of glucose monomers. They differ in the orientation of the bond between the glucose units. Because of this difference, starch is readily digestible, but cellulose is indigestible by most organisms. **Using Models** *What other types of models could you use to show the structural differences between starch and cellulose?*

Starch

Cellulose

A typical linear starch molecule contains hundreds of glucose monomers. Other starches are branched molecules, each branch containing about a dozen glucose units. Glycogen, the energy source stored in the liver and muscle cells of animals, is a more highly branched molecule than plant starches. Glycogen, too, consists of glucose monomers.

Cellulose is probably the most abundant biological molecule on Earth. As you can see in Figure 24.5, cellulose also is a polymer of glucose. The orientation of the bond that links the glucose monomers in cellulose is different, however, from the bond orientation in starch and in glycogen. Starch can be digested by most organisms and is partially soluble in water. Cellulose, however, can be digested by only a few kinds of microorganisms, such as those that live in the digestive tracts of cattle and termites. Cellulose is insoluble in water and is an important structural polysaccharide that provides form, hardness, and rigidity in plants. Plant cell walls are made of cellulose. Cotton is about 80% cellulose.

24.2 Section Assessment

8. 🔑 **Key Concept** Where is glucose found in nature?

9. 🔑 **Key Concept** How can the cyclic forms of two simple sugars be combined?

10. Distinguish between the important structural features of sucrose, glucose, and fructose.

11. Describe the main characteristics of monosaccharides, disaccharides, and polysaccharides.

12. Starch and cellulose have different properties, but both are composed of glucose units. Explain what makes them different.

13. Name a source for each polysaccharide:
   a. starch   **b.** cellulose   **c.** glycogen

14. What is the most abundant carbohydrate on Earth and where is it found?

Connecting ▶ **Concepts**

Polymers Starch is a condensation polymer of glucose. Reread Section 23.4, and describe some other examples of molecules that form by condensation polymerization.

Textbook

Assessment 24.2 Test yourself on the concepts in Section 24.2.

—— with **ChemASAP**

24.3 Amino Acids and Their Polymers

New York Standards: 3.1hh, 3.4f

Connecting to Your World

Many people are lactose intolerant, which means that they cannot digest milk or products containing milk. These people cannot digest milk products because their bodies do not produce enough of the enzyme lactase to digest lactose, the sugar found in milk. The undigested lactose causes bloating and stomach upset. Some people with lactose intolerance can enjoy milk products if they take a pill containing lactase before eating. In this section, you will learn what enzymes are and what function they serve in the body.

Amino Acids

Many biological compounds contain nitrogen in addition to carbon, oxygen, and hydrogen. Some of the most important nitrogen-containing molecules in organisms are amino acids. In fact, the polymers of amino acids, which you will also learn about, make up more than one half of the dry weight of your body.

An **amino acid** is any compound that contains an amino group (—NH₂) and a carboxyl group (—COOH) in the same molecule. For chemists and biochemists, however, the term is usually reserved for the 20 common amino acids that are formed and used by living organisms. **Amino acids have a skeleton that consists of a carboxyl group and an amino group, both of which are covalently bonded to a central carbon atom. The remaining two groups on the central carbon atom are hydrogen and an R group that constitutes the amino acid side chain.**

Central carbon atom — R Side chain

$$H_2N - C - COOH$$

Amino group — H — Carboxyl group

The chemical nature of the side-chain group accounts for the differences in properties among the 20 amino acids. In some amino acids, the side chains are nonpolar aliphatic or aromatic hydrocarbons. In other amino acids, the side chains are neutral but polar. In still others, the side chains are acidic or basic.

Because the central carbon of amino acids is asymmetric, these compounds can exist as optical isomers. As you may recall from Section 22.3, optical isomers may be right- or left-handed. Nearly all the amino acids found in nature are of the left-handed, or L, form.

Guide for Reading

Key Concepts
- What is the general structure of an amino acid?
- Which functional groups are always involved in amide bonds between amino acids?
- What determines the differences in the chemical and physiological properties of peptides and proteins?
- How do enzymes affect the rates of reactions in living things?

Vocabulary
amino acid
peptide
peptide bond
protein
enzymes
substrates
active site

Reading Strategy
Outlining As you read the section, make an outline of the red and blue heads. Under each head, write one or two sentences summarizing what you learned from that part of the section.

Table 24.1 gives the names of the amino acids with their three-letter abbreviations. Examine the abbreviations. You will use them as shortcuts when you read or write about protein structure.

Peptides

A **peptide** is any combination of amino acids in which the amino group of one amino acid is united with the carboxyl group of another amino acid. The amide bond between the carboxyl group of one amino acid and the nitrogen in the amino group of the next amino acid in the peptide chain is called a **peptide bond.**

$$H_2N-\underset{\underset{H}{|}}{\overset{\overset{R}{|}}{C}}-\overset{\overset{O}{\|}}{C}-OH \;+\; H-\underset{\underset{H}{|}}{\overset{\overset{R}{|}}{N}}-\underset{\underset{H}{|}}{\overset{\overset{R}{|}}{C}}-\overset{\overset{O}{\|}}{C}-OH \longrightarrow H_2N-\underset{\underset{H}{|}}{\overset{\overset{R}{|}}{C}}-\overset{\overset{O}{\|}}{C}-\underset{\underset{H}{|}}{\overset{}{N}}-\underset{\underset{H}{|}}{\overset{\overset{R}{|}}{C}}-\overset{\overset{O}{\|}}{C}-OH + H_2O$$

Amino acid   Amino acid   Peptide

Peptide bond

🔑 **The amide bonds between amino acids always involve the central amino and central carboxyl groups. The side chains are not involved in the bonding.**

Note that a free amino group remains at one end of the resulting peptide. The convention is to write the formula of the peptide so that this free amino group is at the left end. There is also a free carboxyl group, which appears at the right end.

More amino acids may be added to the peptide in the same fashion to form long chains by condensation polymerization. The order in which the amino acids of a peptide molecule are linked is called the amino acid sequence of that molecule. The amino acid sequence of a peptide is conveniently expressed using the three-letter abbreviations for the amino acids. For example, Asp—Glu—Gly represents a peptide containing three amino acids. This tripeptide contains aspartic acid, glutamic acid, and glycine, in that order, with the free amino group assumed to be on the left end (on the Asp) and the free carboxyl group on the right end (on the Gly). Note that Asp—Glu—Gly is a different peptide from Gly—Glu—Asp because the order of amino acids is reversed, and thus the free amino group and free carboxyl group are on different amino acids.

✓ **Checkpoint** *By what process can amino acids be added to peptides to form long chains?*

Proteins

In theory, the process of adding amino acids to a peptide chain may continue indefinitely. Any peptide with more than ten amino acids is called a polypeptide. A peptide with more than about 100 amino acids is called a **protein.** On average, a molecule of 100 amino acids has a molar mass of about 10,000 amu. Proteins are an important class of biomolecules. Your skin, hair, nails, muscles, and the hemoglobin molecules in your blood are made of protein. Proteins are needed for almost all chemical reactions that take place in the body.

Table 24.1

Abbreviations for Amino Acids

Amino acid	Abbreviation
Alanine	Ala
Arginine	Arg
Asparagine	Asn
Aspartic acid	Asp
Cysteine	Cys
Glutamine	Gln
Glutamic acid	Glu
Glycine	Gly
Histidine	His
Isoleucine	Ile
Leucine	Leu
Lysine	Lys
Methionine	Met
Phenylalanine	Phe
Proline	Pro
Serine	Ser
Threonine	Thr
Tryptophan	Trp
Tyrosine	Tyr
Valine	Val

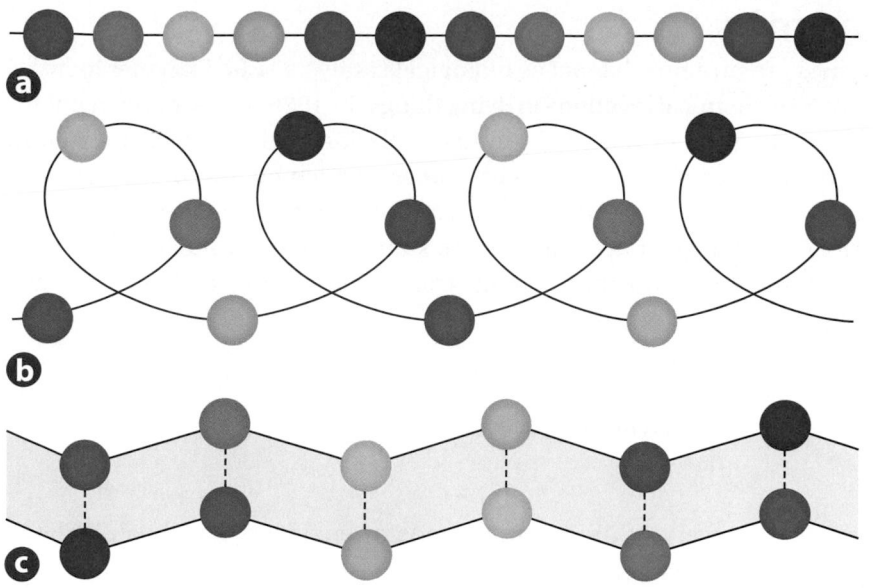

Figure 24.6 Peptides form three-dimensional shapes. **ⓐ** This is a representation of amino acids in a peptide chain. **ⓑ** The chain may coil into a helix. **ⓒ** Two peptide chains may become arranged in a pleated, sheet-like structure.
Applying Concepts *What types of bonds determine the three-dimensional shape of a protein?*

🔑 **Differences in the chemical and physiological properties of peptides and proteins result from differences in the amino acid sequence.** 20 amino acids can be linked in an enormous number of ways in a protein molecule. As many as 20^{100} amino acid sequences are possible for a protein of 100 amino acids containing a combination of the 20 different amino acids.

Protein molecules are folded into relatively stable three-dimensional shapes. Figure 24.6a represents a long peptide chain of a protein. Figure 24.6b shows how sections of peptide chain may coil into a regular spiral, known as a helix. Peptide chains may also be arranged side by side to form a pleated sheet, as shown in Figure 24.6c. Irregular folding of the chains also can occur. The three-dimensional shape of a protein is determined by interactions among the amino acids in its peptide chains. Protein shape is partly maintained by hydrogen bonds between adjacent folded chains. Covalent bonds also form between sulfur atoms of cysteine side chains that are folded near each other. In that way, separate polypeptide chains may be joined into a single protein. Figure 24.7 traces the shape of myoglobin, a protein that stores oxygen in muscle cells. As you can see, the peptide chains of most of the myoglobin molecule are twisted into helixes.

Figure 24.7 The three-dimensional structure of myoglobin, the oxygen storage protein of this muscle tissue, is shown here. Most of the peptide chain of myoglobin is wound into helixes. Myoglobin also contains a nonprotein structure called heme. The heme group is shown as a disk in the myoglobin structure. Heme contains four linked rings with an iron(II) ion (Fe^{2+}) at the center. Molecular oxygen binds to the heme iron.

Water molecule
Heme
Iron(II) ion
Myoglobin
Peptide chain

Enzymes

Enzymes are proteins that act as biological catalysts. ⊙ **Enzymes increase the rates of chemical reactions in living things.** In 1926, the American chemist James B. Sumner reported the first isolation and crystallization of an enzyme. The enzyme he isolated was urease, which hydrolyzes urea, a constituent of urine, into ammonia and carbon dioxide. The strong ammonia smell of wet diapers that are allowed to stand for a long time is the result of the action of bacteria that contain this enzyme. The reaction is shown below.

$$\underset{\text{Urea}}{H_2N-\overset{\overset{\displaystyle O}{\|}}{C}-NH_2(aq)} + \underset{\text{Water}}{H_2O(l)} \xrightarrow{\text{urease}} \underset{\text{Ammonia}}{2NH_3(g)} + \underset{\substack{\text{Carbon} \\ \text{dioxide}}}{CO_2(g)}$$

Since the discovery of urease, thousands of enzymes have been isolated and structurally characterized as proteins.

In addition to being able to promote reactions, enzymes have two other properties of true catalysts. First, they are unchanged by the reaction they catalyze. Second, they do not change the normal equilibrium position of a chemical system. The same amount of product is eventually formed whether or not an enzyme is present. Few reactions in cells ever reach equilibrium, however. The products tend to convert rapidly to another substance in a subsequent enzyme-catalyzed reaction. According to Le Châtelier's principle, such removal of a product pulls the reaction toward completion.

How Enzymes Work Enzymes catalyze most of the chemical changes that occur in the cell. **Substrates** are the molecules on which an enzyme acts. In a typical enzymatic reaction, diagrammed in Figure 24.8, the substrate interacts with side chains of the amino acids on the enzyme. These interactions cause the making and breaking of bonds. A substrate molecule must make contact with and bind to an enzyme molecule before the substrate can be transformed into product. The place on an enzyme where a substrate binds is called the **active site.** An active site is usually a pocket or crevice formed by folds in the peptide chains of the enzyme protein. The peptide chain of an enzyme is folded in a unique way to accommodate the substrate at the active site. The diagram in Figure 24.9 shows this folding for an enzyme called HIV protease, which is produced by the virus that causes AIDS.

Figure 24.8 A substrate fits into a distinctively shaped active site on an enzyme. Bond-breaking occurs at the active site to produce the products of the reaction. **Predicting** *What would happen if access to the active site were blocked by another molecule?*

Because the active site of each enzyme has a distinctive shape, only one specific substrate molecule can fit into the enzyme, in the same way that only one key will fit into a certain lock. Each enzyme catalyzes only one chemical reaction, with only one substrate. An enzyme-substrate complex is formed when an enzyme molecule and a substrate molecule are joined.

To see the efficiency of enzymes, consider an enzyme called carbonic anhydrase. It catalyzes the reversible breakdown of carbonic acid to carbon dioxide and water. One molecule of carbonic anhydrase can catalyze the breakdown of 36 million molecules of carbonic acid in one minute!

$$H_2CO_3(aq) \underset{\text{carbonic}}{\overset{\text{anhydrase}}{\rightleftharpoons}} CO_2(g) + H_2O(l)$$

Carbonic acid   Carbon dioxide   Water

Figure 24.9 This color-enhanced scanning electron micrograph shows HIV (red particle) infecting a human white blood cell (orange). The diagram models the enzyme HIV protease. The green and yellow ribbons trace the two peptide chains of the enzyme. A substrate molecule (purple) is embedded in the active site formed between the two peptide chains.

Coenzymes Some enzymes can directly catalyze the transformation of biological substrates without assistance from other substances. Other enzymes need nonprotein coenzymes, also called cofactors, to assist the transformation. Coenzymes are metal ions or small organic molecules that must be present for an enzyme-catalyzed reaction to occur. Many water-soluble vitamins, such as B vitamins, are coenzymes. Metal ions that act as coenzymes include the cations of magnesium, potassium, iron, and zinc. The enzyme catalase includes an iron(III) ion in its structure. Catalase catalyzes the breakdown of hydrogen peroxide to water and oxygen.

$$2H_2O_2(aq) \xrightarrow{\text{catalase}} 2H_2O(l) + O_2(g)$$

24.3 Section Assessment

15. 🔑 **Key Concept** What are the four groups that surround the central carbon atom in an amino acid?

16. 🔑 **Key Concept** Which functional groups are always involved in amide bonds?

17. 🔑 **Key Concept** What determines the differences in the properties of peptides and proteins?

18. 🔑 **Key Concept** How do enzymes affect the reaction rates in living things?

19. What is meant by the amino acid sequence of a protein?

20. Describe three properties of enzymes.

Connecting ▶ Concepts

Reversible Reactions Reread Section 18.2 on reversible reactions and equilibrium. Use Le Châtelier's principle to explain why few reactions in cells ever reach equilibrium.

Textbook

Assessment 24.3 Test yourself on the concepts in Section 24.3.

with ChemASAP

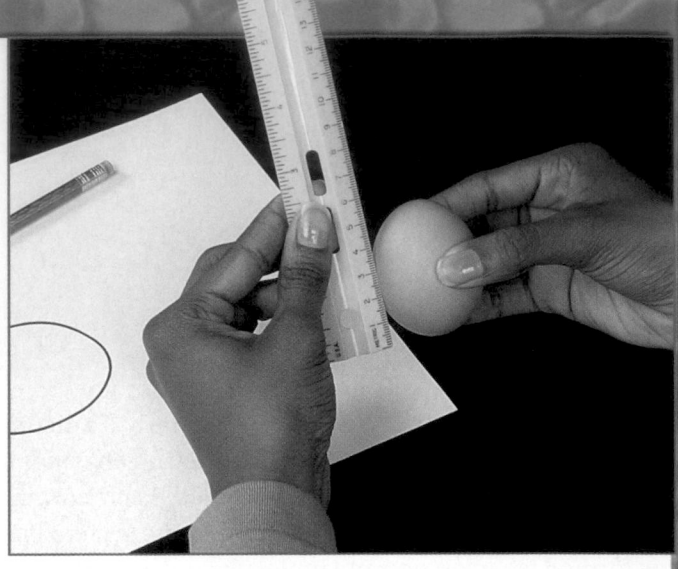

The Egg: A Biochemical Storehouse

Purpose
To explore some physical and chemical properties of a chicken egg

Materials
- chicken egg
- ruler
- balance
- pencil
- paper

Procedure
Obtain a chicken egg. Examine the egg's shape and measure its length and width in centimeters. Measure the mass of the egg. Make an accurate, life-size sketch of your egg and record all your data on the sketch.

Analyze
Using your experimental data, record the answers to the following questions below your drawing.

1. A common way to compare the shapes of eggs is by using a shape index. The shape index is the width of an egg expressed as a percentage of its length.

$$\text{Shape index} = \frac{\text{width}}{\text{length}} \times 100\%$$

   Calculate the shape index of your egg.

2. The volume, original mass (when freshly laid), and surface area of an egg can easily be estimated by using the following equations.

   $V = (0.5236)(lw^2)$ $m = (0.5632)(lw^2)$
   $A = (3.138)(lw^2)^{2/3}$

   V = volume m = original mass
   A = surface area l = length w = width

   Use your data to calculate the volume, original mass, and surface area of your egg. Show your work, and record your results.

3. Compare your measured mass of the egg with your calculated mass. Which is greater? Suggest why the mass of an egg might change over time.

4. Using your measured mass and your calculated volume, calculate the density of your egg. Compare this value with the density of a freshly laid egg ($d = 1.075$ g/cm^3).

You're the Chemist
The following small-scale activities allow you to develop your own procedures and analyze the results.

1. **Design It!** Design an experiment to answer the following question: Does the mass of an egg change over time?

2. **Analyze It!** Using your measured mass, your calculated original mass, and your experiments on the mass loss of an egg over time, estimate the age of your egg. What assumptions must you make?

3. **Design It!** Design and carry out an experiment to measure the volume of your egg. Write down what you did and what you found.

4. **Design It!** Carry out a series of experiments, or consult with your classmates and use their data, to determine if and how the shape index varies with the size of the egg (small, medium, large, extra large, jumbo).

5. **Analyze It!** Determine how the mass of an egg varies with its size (small, medium, large, extra large, jumbo).

6. **Analyze It!** An eggshell contains a calcium carbonate matrix with a protein cuticle. Place one drop of HCl on an eggshell and observe what happens. Write a chemical equation for this reaction. **CAUTION** *HCl is caustic and can burn skin.*

7. **Analyze It!** Proteins can be detected by adding aqueous solutions of copper(II) sulfate and sodium hydroxide to a sample. A violet color indicates the presence of protein. Test powdered milk and an eggshell for protein. What are your results?

8. **Design It!** Design and carry out an experiment to answer the following question. Does temperature affect the mass of an egg over time?

24.4 Lipids

New York Standards: 3.1hh, 3.2c

Connecting to Your World

Candles were an early invention of ancient civilizations. Candlesticks that date to at least 5000 years ago have been found with other artifacts from the civilizations of ancient Egypt and Crete. Before the invention of electric lighting, wax candles were the major source of lighting in homes. In this section, you will read more about waxes and similar compounds that make up the class of biomolecules known as lipids.

Triglycerides

Fats, oils, and other water-insoluble compounds are called **lipids.** The difference between fats and oils is simply that fats are solid at room temperature and oils are liquid. Most fats, such as butter, are obtained from animals. The fats from palm kernels and coconuts, however, are exceptions. Most oils, such as olive oil, are plant products.

Although excessive dietary fat is harmful, you do need some lipids in your diet to stay healthy. Experts recommend that your lipid intake make up less than 30% of your daily caloric intake of food. Lipids such as the butter shown in Figure 24.10 provide an efficient way for your body to store energy. They are also needed to keep your cell membranes healthy. In this section, you will learn about the chemical composition and biological uses of lipids. **Lipids tend to dissolve readily in organic solvents, such as ether and chloroform, rather than in highly polar solvents such as water. This property sets them apart from most biological substances such as carbohydrates and proteins.** Natural fats and oils exist as triesters of glycerol with fatty acids, which are long-chain carboxylic acids (C_{12} through C_{24}). This form of lipid is known as a **triglyceride.** Triglycerides are important as the long-term storage form of energy in the human body. The following equation shows the general reaction for the formation of triglycerides.

Glycerol   3 Fatty acid molecules   Triglyceride (triester of glycerol)   Water

Guide for Reading

Key Concepts
- What physical property distinguishes lipids from other classes of biological molecules?
- How do phospholipid molecules arrange themselves in water?

Vocabulary
lipids
triglyceride
saponification
phospholipids
waxes

Reading Strategy
Building Vocabulary As you read the section, write a definition of each vocabulary term in your own words.

Figure 24.10 Moderate levels of dietary fats and oils are essential to health.

Figure 24.11 These photographs illustrate soapmaking. Once the soap is formed, it is poured into molds. Later it may be milled, or shredded, with scent or color added, and then remolded to produce a finished product.

Like other esters, fats and oils are easily hydrolyzed in the presence of acids and bases. The hydrolysis of oils or fats by boiling with an aqueous solution of an alkali-metal hydroxide is called **saponification.** Saponification is used to make soap. Soaps are thus the alkali metal (Na, K, or Li) salts of fatty acids. A typical saponification reaction is shown below.

$$CH_2-O-\overset{\overset{\displaystyle O}{\|}}{C}-(CH_2)_{16}CH_3$$
$$CH-O-\overset{\overset{\displaystyle O}{\|}}{C}-(CH_2)_{16}CH_3 \ + \ 3NaOH \longrightarrow CHOH \ + \ 3CH_3(CH_2)_{16}-\overset{\overset{\displaystyle O}{\|}}{C}-O^-Na^+$$
$$CH_2-O-\overset{\overset{\displaystyle O}{\|}}{C}-(CH_2)_{16}CH_3$$

Tristearin (triester of glycerol and stearic acid)   Glycerol   Sodium stearate (a soap)

As shown in Figure 24.11, soap can be made by heating a fat, such as beef tallow or coconut oil, with an excess of sodium hydroxide. When sodium chloride is added to the saponified mixture, the sodium salts of the fatty acids separate as a thick curd of crude soap. The crude soap is then purified. Glycerol is an important by-product of saponification reactions. It is recovered by evaporating the water layer.

Hydrophilic head   Hydrophobic tail

✔ **Checkpoint** *What are the products of a saponification reaction?*

Phospholipids

Phospholipids, or lipids that contain phosphate groups, are abundant in cells. Figure 24.12 shows a typical phospholipid molecule, lecithin. The lecithin molecule has a hydrophilic (water-loving) ionic head and oily or hydrophobic (water-hating) hydrocarbon tails. You know the solubility rule, "Like dissolves like." Lecithin, which is partly hydrophobic and partly hydrophilic, behaves in water like both an insoluble hydrocarbon and a soluble ionic compound. In water, the hydrophobic carbon chains aggregate to exclude water. The hydrophilic part is drawn to water, which can solvate it. ⊙ **In water, phospholipids spontaneously form a spherical double layer, called a lipid bilayer, in which the hydrophobic tails of phospholipid molecules are sandwiched between two layers of hydrophilic heads.**

Figure 24.12 A space-filling model of lecithin is shown here. In the simplified representation above, the hydrophilic head is shown as a sphere and the hydrophobic tails as wavy lines.

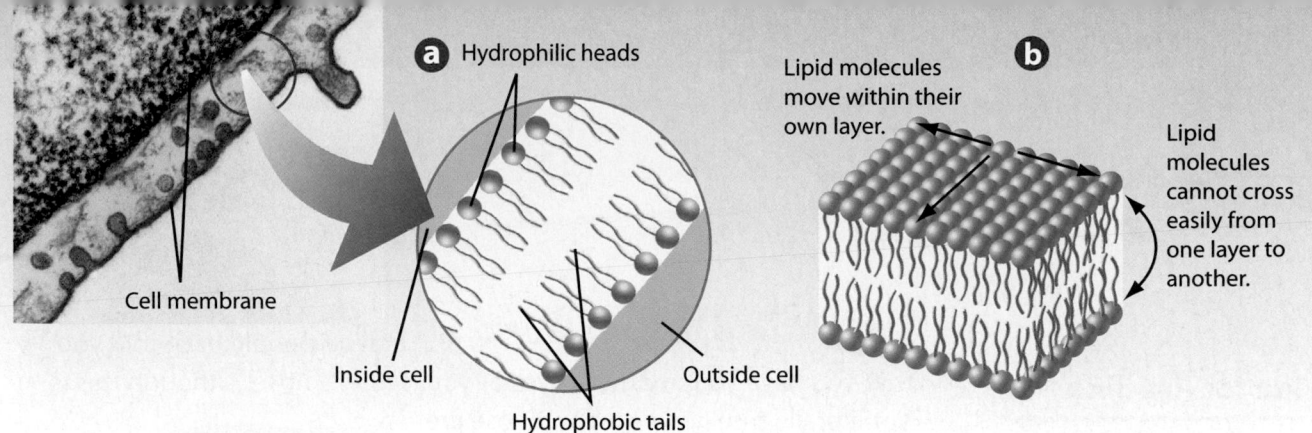

a Hydrophilic heads

Cell membrane

Inside cell

Outside cell

Hydrophobic tails

b Lipid molecules move within their own layer.

Lipid molecules cannot cross easily from one layer to another.

Cell membranes, such as the one shown in Figure 24.13, consist primarily of lipid bilayers. The lipid bilayer of a cell membrane acts as a barrier against the passage of molecules and ions into and out of the cell. However, cells do need to take in certain ions and molecules, such as nutrients, while excluding other materials. Selective absorption is accomplished by the protrusion of protein molecules through the lipid bilayer. These proteins form channels through which specific ions and molecules can selectively pass. Not all membrane proteins extend all the way through the membrane. Proteins, such as enzymes, may be bound to the interior surface of the membrane. Many membrane proteins have attached carbohydrate molecules. The carbohydrate portion is on the exterior of the lipid bilayer, where it can hydrogen-bond with water. The protein portion is on the interior of the lipid bilayer, so it does not contact the water.

Figure 24.13 A cell membrane has a lipid bilayer structure. a The hydrophilic heads are in contact with water, but the hydrophobic tails are not. b The lipid molecules move easily within their own layer but do not readily move to the other layer. **Applying Concepts** *What prevents a lipid molecule from crossing to the opposite side of the bilayer?*

Waxes

Waxes are also part of the lipid family. **Waxes** are esters of long-chain fatty acids and long-chain alcohols. The hydrocarbon chains for both the acid and the alcohol usually contain from 10 to 30 carbon atoms. Waxes are low-melting, stable solids. In many plants, a wax coat protects the surfaces of leaves from water loss and attack by microorganisms. For example, carnauba wax, a major ingredient in car wax and floor polish, is found on the leaves of a South American palm tree. In animals, waxes coat the skin, hair, and feathers and help keep these structures pliable and waterproof.

Go Online

NSTA *SciLINKS*

For: Links on Fats
Visit: www.SciLinks.org
Web Code: cdn-1244

<hr>

24.4 Section Assessment

21. 🔑 **Key Concept** What physical property sets lipids apart from biological substances such as carbohydrates and proteins?

22. 🔑 **Key Concept** How do phospholipids behave in water?

23. Compare the molecular structures of the three main types of lipids.

24. What role do phospholipids and proteins play in cell membranes?

25. What two classes of organic compounds combine to form a wax?

Writing ▶ **Activity**

Explain a Concept Write a paragraph explaining how cells are able to selectively absorb certain ions and molecules while excluding other materials.

Interactive Textbook

Assessment 24.4 Test yourself on the concepts in Section 24.4.

—— with **ChemASAP**

24.5 Nucleic Acids

New York Standards: 3.2c, 5.2m, 7.1

Guide for Reading

Key Concepts
- What are the functions of DNA and RNA?
- How long a base sequence of DNA is required to specify one amino acid in a peptide chain?
- What are gene mutations?
- What forms the basis for a method of identifying a person from biological samples?
- What is recombinant DNA technology?

Vocabulary
nucleic acids
nucleotides
gene

Reading Strategy
Summarizing As you read the section, summarize each red-headed section in a few sentences.

Connecting to Your World Maybe people have told you that you have your mother's eyes or your father's nose. Although this is not literally true (your eyes and nose are your own), you do inherit the instructions for assembling the proteins of your body from your parents. In this section, you will learn what these instructions are called and how they code for proteins.

DNA and RNA

More than 100 years ago, a Swiss biochemist discovered a class of nitrogen-containing compounds in the nuclei of cells. The nuclei were first obtained from dead white blood cells in the pus of infected wounds. The eventual understanding of the biological role of the compounds has led to a revolution in biochemistry.

These nitrogen-containing compounds, called **nucleic acids,** are polymers that are found primarily in cell nuclei. They are indispensable components of every living thing. Two kinds of nucleic acids are found in cells—*d*eoxyribo*nu*cleic *a*cid (DNA) and *ri*bo*nu*cleic *a*cid (RNA). **DNA stores the information needed to make proteins and governs the reproduction and growth of cells and new organisms. RNA has a key role in the transmission of the information stored in DNA and in the synthesis of proteins.**

The monomers that make up the DNA and RNA polymers are called **nucleotides.** Nucleic acids are therefore polynucleotides. As shown below, each nucleotide consists of a phosphate group, a five-carbon sugar, and a nitrogen-containing unit called a nitrogen base.

Phosphate + Sugar + Nitrogen base ⟶ Phosphate — Sugar — Nitrogen base

The sugar unit in the nucleotides of DNA is the five-carbon monosaccharide known as deoxyribose. There are four different nitrogen bases in DNA—adenine, guanine, thymine, and cytosine. These four bases are abbreviated A, G, T, and C, respectively, and are shown in a short segment of a DNA molecule in Figure 24.15. Notice that adenine and guanine each contains a double ring and that thymine and cytosine contain a single ring. Ribose, which has one more oxygen atom than deoxyribose, is the sugar found in the nucleotide monomers of RNA. The base thymine is never found in RNA. Instead, it is replaced by a fifth nitrogen base, called uracil, which is abbreviated U.

Figure 24.14 This photo shows strands of DNA extracted from cellular material.

Figure 24.15 The nucleotide monomers of DNA are linked together through their phosphate groups.

Nitrogen base
Simple sugar
Phosphate group

Adenine
Cytosine
Guanine
Thymine

Chemists studying nucleic acids discovered that the amount of adenine in DNA always equals the amount of thymine (A = T). Similarly, the amount of guanine always equals the amount of cytosine (G = C). The significance of these facts was not apparent until 1953, when James Watson and Francis Crick proposed that the structure of DNA consists of two polynucleotide chains wrapped into a spiral shape. This is the famous double helix of DNA. For the nitrogen bases to fit neatly into the double helix, every double-ringed base on one strand must be paired with a single-ringed base on the opposing strand. The pairing of A with T and G with C not only provides the best possible fit; it also allows the maximum number of hydrogen bonds to form between the opposing bases, as Figure 24.16 shows. Thus, the pairing of A and T (with two hydrogen bonds between the opposing bases) and of G and C (with three hydrogen bonds) makes for the most stable arrangement in the double helix.

Simple sugar
Phosphate group

Thymine   Adenine

T=A

Cytosine   Guanine

C≡G

Figure 24.16 The two DNA strands in a double helix are held together by many hydrogen bonds; there are two hydrogen bonds between each thymine (T) and adenine (A) and three hydrogen bonds between each cytosine (C) and guanine (G). **Interpreting Diagrams** *In the pairing of C with G, how many hydrogen bonds involve nitrogen? How many involve oxygen?*

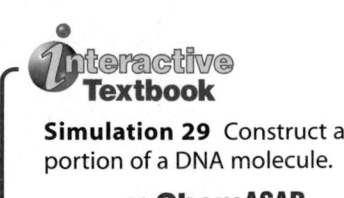

interactive Textbook

Simulation 29 Construct a portion of a DNA molecule.

with **ChemASAP**

A Model of DNA

Purpose
To construct a model of double-stranded DNA

Materials
- cardboard tube from paper-towel roll
- felt-tip markers (two colors)
- metric ruler
- thumbtack
- 10 toothpicks

Procedure

1. The typical cardboard tube has a seam that, when viewed from one end, describes a spiral that moves away from the observer. This spiral is a helix. Outline the spiral seam with a colored marker.

2. Using a different-colored marker, draw a second spiral midway between the lines of the first. These two spirals represent the two strands of double-stranded DNA.

3. Measure along the tube, and mark a dot on each spiral every 5 cm. Label each dot with the letter S to indicate a sugar unit. Make a hole in the spirals at each S mark with the thumbtack. Move down each spiral and mark a letter P to indicate a phosphate group halfway between each two S dots.

4. Color each toothpick along half its length with a marker. A toothpick represents a base pair in the DNA molecule.

5. Starting at the top of the tube, insert a toothpick in one hole at an S label and guide it so it emerges through the hole in the S on the opposite side of the tube. Repeat the process for the other holes.

Analyze and Conclude

1. Are the bases on the interior or the exterior of the double helix? Are they randomly arranged or neatly stacked?

2. Are the phosphate groups on the exterior or the interior of the DNA structure?

3. Are the sugar groups on the interior or the exterior of the DNA molecule?

The Genetic Code

An organism contains many proteins that are characteristic of that particular organism. The proteins of earthworms are different from the proteins of pine trees, which are different from the proteins of humans. How do cells in a given kind of organism know which proteins to make? The cells use the instructions contained in the organism's DNA. A **gene** is a segment of DNA that carries the instructions for making one peptide chain. Thus the products of genes are the peptides and proteins found in an organism.

You can think of DNA as a reference manual that stores the instructions for building proteins. The instructions are written in a simple language that has 4 "letters"—the bases A, T, G, and C. Experimental data show that each "word" in a DNA manual is exactly three letters in length. Each three-letter base sequence, or triplet, codes for one of the 20 common amino acids. The code words are strung together in the DNA molecule to form genes, which specify the order of amino acids in peptides and proteins. ⊂▪ **Three bases of DNA arranged in a specific sequence are required to specify one amino acid in a peptide or protein chain.**

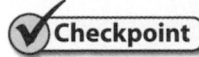 **Checkpoint** *How do cells in a given kind of organism know which proteins to make?*

Table 24.2 provides the DNA code words for the 20 common amino acids. For example, you can see that the DNA code word AAA specifies the amino acid phenylalanine and that the DNA code word CGA specifies the amino acid alanine. Note that most amino acids are specified by more than one code word, but a code word never specifies more than one amino acid. With DNA code words of three letters, 900 bases arranged in a specific sequence would be required to code for a peptide chain made up of 300 amino acids arranged in a specific sequence.

Three code words (ATT, ATC, and ACT) are reserved as end, or termination, code words. The translation of a base sequence of DNA in a gene into the amino acid sequence of a peptide begins after one termination code word and runs continuously until another termination code word is reached. The termination code word signals a stop to the addition of amino acids in the production of the peptide, which is thus completed. You can think of a termination code as being similar to the period at the end of a sentence.

The molar masses of DNA molecules reach into the millions and possibly billions. Even with only four bases, the number of possible sequences of nucleotides in a DNA chain is enormous. The sequence of the nitrogen bases A, T, G, and C in the DNA of an organism constitutes the genetic plan, or blueprint, for that organism. This genetic plan is inherited from parents and passed to offspring. Differences in the number and sequence of the bases in DNA ultimately are responsible for the great diversity of living creatures found on Earth.

Figure 24.17 This space-filling model shows only a tiny segment of a DNA molecule and gives you an idea of the enormous mass of the entire molecule.

Table 24.2

Three-Letter DNA Code Words for the Amino Acids

First Letter in Code Word		Second Letter in Code Word				Third Letter in Code Word
		A	**G**	**T**	**C**	
A		AAA Phe	AGA Ser	ATA Tyr	ACA Cys	**A**
		AAG Phe	AGG Ser	ATG Tyr	ACG Cys	**G**
		AAT Leu	AGT Ser	ATT End	ACT End	**T**
		AAC Leu	AGC Ser	ATC End	ACC Trp	**C**
G		GAA Leu	GGA Pro	GTA His	GCA Arg	**A**
		GAG Leu	GGG Pro	GTG His	GCG Arg	**G**
		GAT Leu	GGT Pro	GTT Gln	GCT Arg	**T**
		GAC Leu	GGC Pro	GTC Gln	GCC Arg	**C**
T		TAA Ile	TGA Thr	TTA Asn	TCA Ser	**A**
		TAG Ile	TGG Thr	TTG Asn	TCG Ser	**G**
		TAT Ile	TGT Thr	TTT Lys	TCT Arg	**T**
		TAC Met	TGC Thr	TTC Lys	TCC Arg	**C**
C		CAA Val	CGA Ala	CTA Asp	CCA Gly	**A**
		CAG Val	CGG Ala	CTG Asp	CCG Gly	**G**
		CAT Val	CGT Ala	CTT Glu	CCT Gly	**T**
		CAC Val	CGC Ala	CTC Glu	CCC Gly	**C**

Gene Mutations

When a change occurs in a DNA code word, the result is a mutation. **Substitutions, additions, or deletions of one or more nucleotides in the DNA molecule are called gene mutations.** The effect of the deletion of a single base from a gene can be illustrated by the following analogy. Suppose a string of letters of the alphabet goes as follows:

PATTHEBADCAT

The letters may not make sense at first glance. However, if you separate them into three-letter words, they form a perfectly sensible statement:

PAT THE BAD CAT

Now delete the first letter, and again separate the string into three-letter segments:

ATT HEB ADC AT

This last sequence is nonsensical. Similarly, the deletion of a base in the DNA base sequence can turn the information into nonsense. A sequence that once may have coded for the proper sequence of amino acids in a necessary protein may be replaced by a sequence that produces a useless or damaging amino acid sequence. The same sort of harmful effect may be obtained by mutations involving substitutions or additions of nucleotides.

Such mutations might result in the production of a faulty protein or of no protein at all. Diseases that result from gene mutations are called genetic disorders. Thousands of genetic disorders have been identified. Sickle cell anemia, which affects mainly people of African descent, results from a mutation in one of the peptide chains of hemoglobin, the oxygen-carrying protein of blood. Figure 24.18 shows the three-dimensional structure of normal hemoglobin. The defective hemoglobin made by the sickle cell gene reduces the oxygen supply to the tissues, triggering the painful episodes of the disease. In methemoglobinemia, another genetic disorder, iron in some of the hemoglobin is in the oxidized iron(III) state rather than the normal reduced iron(II) state. A faulty hemoglobin chain permits the undesirable oxidation of the iron(II) to occur.

Figure 24.18 The abbreviated molecular structure of hemoglobin, the oxygen-transporting protein of blood, is shown here. **a** The hemoglobin molecule consists of four peptide chains, each containing a heme group. **b** In the genetic disorder sickle cell anemia, defective hemoglobin causes red blood cells to take on a distorted shape. **c** Normal red blood cells have a doughnut-like shape.
Interpreting Diagrams *How many nitrogen atoms does a heme group contain?*

Figure 24.19 This scientist is comparing DNA fingerprints. DNA fingerprinting is an important tool in the identification of people. A person's DNA fingerprint contains DNA fragments that are characteristic of his or her father and mother but that would not be identical to those of the father or the mother.

Not all gene mutations are harmful. Occasionally, a mutation can result in the synthesis of a protein that is more efficient than the version that previously existed. Such a mutation could thus be beneficial to the survival of an organism.

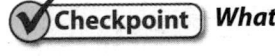 **Checkpoint** *What are diseases that result from gene mutations called?*

DNA Fingerprinting

Only about 5% of a human's DNA is used for coding the information needed for protein synthesis. The remaining 95% consists of repeating, noncoding base sequences that separate or sometimes interrupt gene coding sequences. The role of these stretches of noncoding DNA is unclear. The noncoding sequences are similar for members of the same family but are slightly different for almost every individual. Differences also exist in the coding portions of DNA. The base sequences of DNA are slightly different for different individuals, except for identical twins. Identical twins are exactly alike because they have identical DNA.

The variation in the DNA of individuals forms the basis for a method of identifying a person from samples of his or her hair, skin cells, or body fluid. Because DNA sequences, like fingerprints, are unique for each individual, the DNA method is called DNA fingerprinting. To construct a DNA fingerprint, scientists first isolate the DNA in a sample. Only a tiny sample is needed. Enzymes that cut DNA chains between specific base sequences are used to cleave the DNA in the sample, thus providing a large number of DNA fragments. The fragments are of different lengths and base compositions for different individuals and can be separated and visualized. The pattern, or DNA fingerprint, that emerges can then be compared with a sample of DNA from a known individual, as Figure 24.19 shows.

If the DNA fingerprints are identical, it can be stated with a high degree of certainty that the DNA in the unknown sample is from the known individual. The chance in favor of a DNA fingerprint being unique to one individual can be as high as 1×10^{19} to 1—a high degree of certainty, given that the world's population is only about 6×10^9 people. In practice, however, the chance of positively identifying an individual from a sample of DNA is generally lower than predicted and is often subject to interpretation.

Questions about the certainty of identification by means of DNA fingerprints are often at issue in criminal cases. DNA fingerprints can be obtained from evidence, such as blood, left at the scene of a crime. However, there is no standard for absolute determination of innocence or guilt from DNA fingerprinting, nor is there likely to be. Juries must decide whether the evidence is convincing. Evidence based on DNA fingerprints is permitted in more than half of the states in the United States.

✓ Checkpoint *How do scientists construct a DNA fingerprint from a sample of hair, skin cells, or body fluid?*

Recombinant DNA Technology

Scientists have learned to manipulate genes by various methods. **Recombinant DNA technology consists of methods for cleaving a DNA chain, inserting a new piece of DNA into the gap created by the cleavage, and resealing the chain.** Figure 24.20 illustrates such a method. The altered DNA formed by this method is known as recombinant DNA.

Applications in Medicine The first practical application of recombinant DNA technology was to insert the gene for making human insulin into bacteria. Most people naturally make insulin, a polypeptide that controls levels of blood sugar, but insufficient insulin production results in diabetes. The symptoms of diabetes can often be controlled by insulin injections. In the past, human insulin was not available for this purpose. Pig insulin, which is quite similar in structure to human insulin, was used as a substitute. Some patients, however, were allergic to pig insulin. Today, diabetic patients use the human form of insulin produced by bacteria that have been altered by recombinant DNA technology. Use of this insulin removes the need for the potentially dangerous use of pig insulin.

Other proteins produced by recombinant DNA technology are used as medicinal drugs. For example, an enzyme called tissue plasminogen activator (TPA) is used to dissolve blood clots in patients who have suffered heart attacks. Another protein, interferon, is thought to relieve or delay some of the debilitating effects of multiple sclerosis. Recombinant DNA technology is also being applied to the cure of genetic disorders in a treatment known as gene therapy.

Applications in Agriculture In agriculture, new recombinant DNA techniques can make plants resistant to pests and weed killers and produce fruits and vegetables that are better suited for shipping and storage. Figure 24.21 shows genetically altered tomatoes that have a longer ripening period, which prevents spoilage and allows for their year-round availability. Genetically altered organisms have many potential benefits, but some people have concerns about their safety.

Bacterial DNA

DNA strands broken by enzyme

Foreign gene

Insertion of foreign gene

Foreign gene clipped out by enzyme

DNA strands resealed by enzyme to form recombinant DNA. This DNA is then inserted into bacteria, which use instructions from the foreign gene to create the desired protein.

Figure 24.20 Included here are the elements of an experiment involving recombinant DNA. In this experiment, DNA from one organism is inserted into the DNA of a different organism.

Figure 24.21 These genetically engineered tomatoes were altered to increase the length of time it takes them to ripen.

Cloning Ethical concerns were raised in 1997 when Scottish scientists announced the birth of a lamb named Dolly, shown in Figure 24.22. In normal animal reproduction, an offspring is a genetic mixture of the characteristics of both parents. Dolly, however, was a clone—an offspring of a single individual. A clone is an exact genetic copy of its parent because it is formed using the DNA of only that parent. The birth of Dolly has raised the question of whether humans might eventually be cloned. Many people are concerned about some of the possible outcomes of cloning identical individuals. These reactions are one aspect of more general concerns about the uniqueness of life. Human cloning experiments have been outlawed in several countries.

Figure 24.22 Dolly the sheep had no father. She was cloned from a single cell taken from her mother. Dolly died in February, 2003. **Inferring** *How did Dolly's DNA compare with the DNA in her mother's cells?*

24.5 Section Assessment

26. 🔑 **Key Concept** What functions are performed by DNA and RNA?

27. 🔑 **Key Concept** What does a three-letter base sequence of DNA specify?

28. 🔑 **Key Concept** What are three types of gene mutations?

29. 🔑 **Key Concept** What is the basis for a method of identifying a person from samples of hair, skin cells, or body fluid?

30. 🔑 **Key Concept** What methods are used in recombinant DNA technology?

31. Why do you think cloning is controversial? What are your personal thoughts on this matter?

Connecting Concepts

Scientific Methods Write a paragraph describing how scientific methods might be applied to the process of DNA fingerprinting.

interactive **Textbook**

Assessment 24.5 Test yourself on the concepts in Section 24.5.

——— with **ChemASAP**

Connecting to Your World   The body's metabolic rate is controlled by a hormone called thyroxine that is released by the thyroid gland. When a person's diet does not contain adequate iodine, the thyroid gland is unable to produce and release thyroxine. The gland begins to swell, forming a goiter. In this section, you will learn where some of the nutrients in a person's diet come from and how they are involved in metabolic reactions.

Guide for Reading

Key Concepts

- What is the function of ATP in living cells?
- How does a cell obtain the energy and building blocks needed for the construction of new biological compounds?
- What happens in a cell during anabolism?
- How do nitrogen-fixing bacteria provide plants with a useable form of nitrogen?

Vocabulary

adenosine triphosphate (ATP)

metabolism

catabolism

anabolism

Reading Strategy

Comparing and Contrasting
When you compare and contrast things, you examine how they are alike and different. As you read, list the similarities and differences between catabolism and anabolism.

ATP

All living things need energy to function properly. **Adenosine triphosphate (ATP),** shown in Figure 24.23, is a molecule that transmits this energy in the cells of living organisms. The function of ATP can be compared to a belt connecting an electric motor to a pump. The motor generates energy capable of operating the pump. But if a belt does not connect the motor to the pump, the energy produced by the motor is wasted. You can think of ATP as the belt that couples the production and use of energy by cells. **In living cells, ATP is the energy carrier between the spontaneous reactions that release energy and nonspontaneous reactions that use energy.**

Recall that oxidation reactions, such as the combustion of methane in a furnace or the oxidation of glucose in a living cell, are spontaneous reactions that release energy. This energy can be captured when adenosine diphosphate (ADP) condenses with an inorganic phosphate group to become ATP. The addition of a phosphate group, called phosphorylation, occurs during certain biochemical oxidation reactions.

Figure 24.23 ATP is ADP that has been phosphorylated. ATP provides energy to muscles for moving the body. **Comparing and Contrasting** *How is the structure of ATP similar to that of a DNA nucleotide?*

$$\text{Adenosine} - \overset{\overset{\displaystyle O}{\|}}{\underset{\underset{\displaystyle OH}{|}}{P}} - O - \overset{\overset{\displaystyle O}{\|}}{\underset{\underset{\displaystyle OH}{|}}{P}} - OH \ + \ HO - \overset{\overset{\displaystyle O}{\|}}{\underset{\underset{\displaystyle OH}{|}}{P}} - OH \ \longrightarrow \ \text{Adenosine} - \overset{\overset{\displaystyle O}{\|}}{\underset{\underset{\displaystyle OH}{|}}{P}} - O - \overset{\overset{\displaystyle O}{\|}}{\underset{\underset{\displaystyle OH}{|}}{P}} - O - \overset{\overset{\displaystyle O}{\|}}{\underset{\underset{\displaystyle OH}{|}}{P}} - OH \ + \ H_2O$$

| Adenosine diphosphate (ADP) | Inorganic phosphate (P_i) | Adenosine triphosphate (ATP) | Water |

The formation of ATP efficiently captures energy produced by the oxidation reactions in living cells. Every mole of ATP produced by the phosphorylation of ADP stores about 30.5 kJ of energy. The reverse happens when ATP is hydrolyzed back to ADP: Every mole of ATP that is hydrolyzed back to ADP releases about 30.5 kJ of energy. Cells use this released energy to drive processes that would ordinarily be nonspontaneous. Because of its ability to capture energy from one process and transmit it to another, ATP is sometimes referred to as a high-energy compound; however, the energy produced by the breakdown of ATP to ADP is not particularly high for the breaking of a covalent bond. ATP is important because it occupies an intermediate position in the energetics of the cell. It can be formed by using the energy obtained from a few higher-energy oxidation reactions. The energy that is contained in the bonds of ATP can then be used to drive other cellular processes.

Catabolism

Thousands of chemical reactions take place in the cells of a living organism. The entire set of chemical reactions carried out by an organism is known as the organism's **metabolism.** In metabolism, unneeded cellular components and the nutrients in food are broken down into simpler compounds by chemical reactions collectively called **catabolism.** Catabolic reactions release energy as well as produce simple compounds. **The degradation of complex biological molecules such as carbohydrates, lipids, proteins, and nucleic acids during catabolism provides the energy and the building blocks for the construction of new biological compounds needed by the cell.** Through the formation of ATP, catabolic reactions provide the energy for such needs as body motion and the transport of nutrients to cells where they are required. The oxidation reactions of catabolism also provide energy in the form of heat. These reactions help keep your body temperature constant at 37°C. The need for energy and building blocks is the reason why all organisms, such as the field mouse shown in Figure 24.24, require food.

The complete oxidation of glucose to carbon dioxide and water is one of the most important energy-yielding processes of catabolism. Study Figure 24.25, which summarizes the major steps in the degradation of one glucose molecule to six molecules of carbon dioxide. The complete oxidation actually involves many reactions, which are not shown. As you can see in the figure, the major carbon-containing reactants and products are named, and they are also referred to according to the number of carbons they contain.

Go Online

SCiLINKS

For: Links on Food as Fuel
Visit: www.SciLinks.org
Web Code: cdn-1246

Figure 24.24 Organisms such as this mouse use the energy stored in the chemical bonds of food molecules to power their body processes.

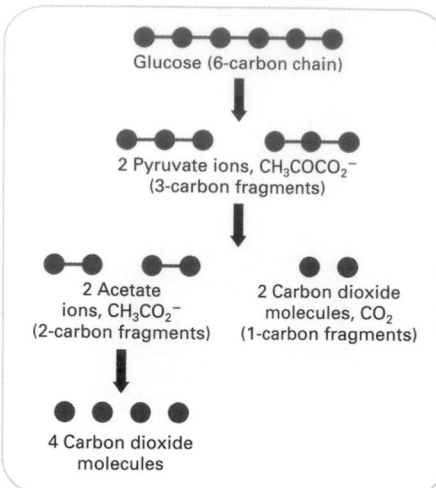

Figure 24.25 The breakdown of glucose to carbon dioxide and water is one of the most important energy-yielding processes of catabolism. **Making Generalizations** *What happens to the number of carbon-carbon bonds from one step to the next?*

The combustion of 1 mole of glucose to 6 moles of carbon dioxide and 6 moles of water, either by fire or by oxidation in a living cell, produces 2.82×10^3 kJ of energy. Cells that use oxygen may produce up to 38 moles of ATP by capturing the energy released by the complete oxidation of a single mole of glucose! The large amount of ATP produced from the oxidation of glucose makes it the likeliest mode of energy production for most kinds of cells. In fact, if glucose is available, brain cells use no other source of carbon compounds for energy production.

✔ **Checkpoint** *How much energy is released by the complete combustion of 1 mole of glucose?*

Anabolism

Some of the simple compounds produced by catabolism are used to synthesize more-complex biological molecules—carbohydrates, lipids, proteins, and nucleic acids—necessary for the health and growth of an organism. The synthesis reactions of metabolism are called **anabolism.** Unlike catabolism, which releases energy, anabolism uses energy.

Figure 24.26 gives an overview of the relationship between catabolism and anabolism. Nutrients and unneeded cell components are degraded to simpler components by the reactions of catabolism. The oxidative reactions of catabolism yield energy captured in the formation of ATP. ⚷ **In anabolism, the products and the energy of catabolism are used to make new cell parts and compounds needed for cellular life and growth.** You already know that energy produced by physical and chemical processes is of little value unless the energy can be captured to do work. If it is not captured, the energy is lost as heat. The chemical energy produced by catabolism must have some means of being used for the chemical work of anabolism. The ATP molecule is that means of transmitting energy.

Figure 24.26 Simple compounds produced by catabolism are used in the synthesis reactions of anabolism. **Applying Concepts** *What part of metabolism releases energy? What part uses energy?*

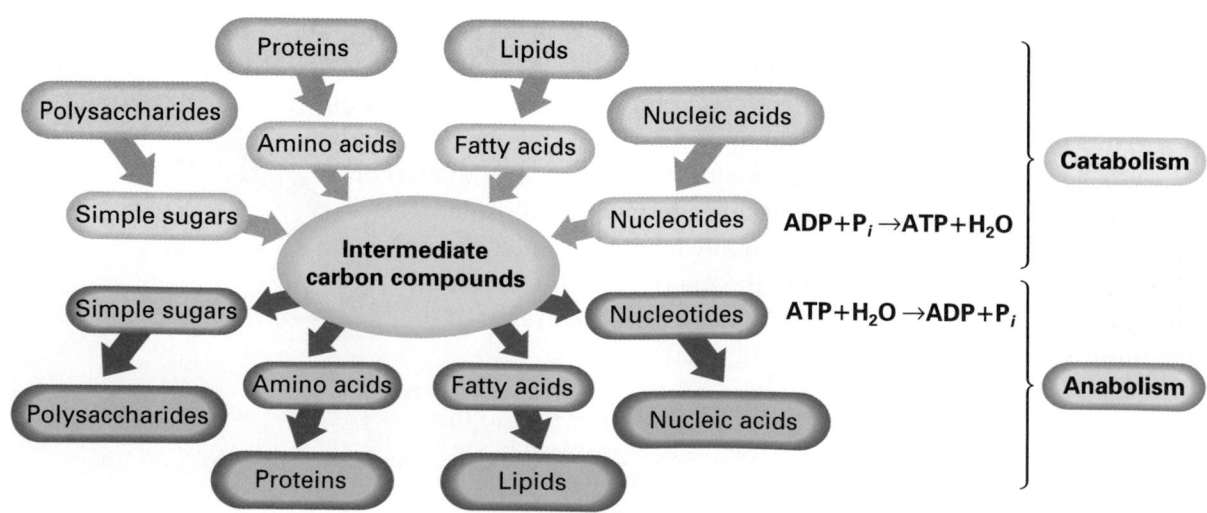

The Nitrogen Cycle

You have learned that the biological molecules taken into an organism's body as nutrients in food are broken down during catabolism. Food contains carbohydrates, proteins, lipids, nucleic acids, vitamins, and minerals. These nutrients are composed mainly of carbon, hydrogen, and oxygen atoms. Many biological compounds, such as proteins, contain nitrogen as well. Although Earth's atmosphere is 78% nitrogen gas, no animals and only a few plants can use this form of nitrogen to make nitrogen-containing compounds. However, certain bacteria can convert nitrogen gas into useable forms in a process called nitrogen fixation. **Nitrogen-fixing bacteria reduce atmospheric nitrogen ($N_2(g)$) to ammonia ($NH_3(g)$), a water-soluble form of nitrogen that can be used by plants.** In soil and biological fluids, most ammonia is present as ammonium ions.

Plants incorporate ammonia into biological nitrogen compounds such as proteins, nucleic acids, and ATP. Because animals cannot synthesize these compounds, they get them by eating plants or other animals that eat plants. When these plants and animals die, they decay with the aid of bacteria. Decaying matter returns nitrogen to the soil as ammonia, nitrite ions (NO_2^-), or nitrate ions (NO_3^-). Moreover, some nitrogen gas is returned to the atmosphere. This flow of nitrogen between the atmosphere and Earth and its living creatures is the nitrogen cycle, shown in Figure 24.27.

Figure 24.27 Nitrogen moves between the atmosphere and the biosphere in the nitrogen cycle.

Atmospheric nitrogen

Animal proteins and other compounds of nitrogen

Industrial fixation

Biological fixation (nitrogen-fixing bacteria)

Denitrifying bacteria

Lightning

Animal wastes, dead plants and animals

Decay (putrefying bacteria)

Plant proteins

Ammonia (NH₃)

Nitrite ions (NO₂⁻)

Nitrite ions (NO₃⁻)

Figure 24.28 The bumps on these plant roots contain bacteria, which live in a symbiotic relationship with the plant. The plant gets nitrogen in a form it can use, and the bacteria get food in the form of sugars that the plant makes during photosynthesis.

Biological Nitrogen Fixation Nitrogen-fixing bacteria are of two types: free-living and symbiotic. Free-living bacteria lead an independent existence in soil. Symbiotic bacteria, such as *Rhizobium,* live in a mutually beneficial arrangement with plants. Symbiotic bacteria live in nodules on the roots of legumes, such as alfalfa, clover, peas, and beans. These root nodules are shown in Figure 24.28. Soil fertility can be improved by plowing nitrogen-rich legumes back into the ground instead of harvesting them.

Industrial Nitrogen Fixation Modern agriculture uses an enormous quantity of nitrogen, which plays a role in the nitrogen cycle. For the past several years, the daily amount of atmospheric nitrogen fixed by industrial processes in the production of fertilizers has probably exceeded the amount fixed by living organisms in Earth's forests and oceans. Nitrogen fertilizers enter the biosphere when they are taken up by plants. In addition, a small amount of atmospheric nitrogen is fixed by lightning discharges, which produce the soluble nitrogen oxides (NO, NO_2, N_2O_4, N_2O_5).

24.6 Section Assessment

32. **Key Concept** What is the role of ATP in energy production and energy use in living cells?

33. **Key Concept** What is the function of catabolism in the cells of living organisms?

34. **Key Concept** How does anabolism make use of the products of catabolism?

35. **Key Concept** What form of nitrogen is supplied to plants by nitrogen-fixing bacteria?

36. How many moles of ATP are formed from the complete oxidation of 1 mol of glucose in a cell that uses oxygen?

Writing ▶ **Activity**

Explain a Process Review the diagram of the nitrogen cycle in Figure 24.27. Write a paragraph that describes how nitrogen moves between the atmosphere and the biosphere. (*Hint:* Use atmospheric nitrogen as the starting point in your description of the process.)

Interactive Textbook

Assessment 24.6 Test yourself on the concepts in Section 24.6.

— with **ChemASAP**

Biomedical Implants

Science, medicine, and technology have combined to create artificial limbs, artificial organs, and other parts for the human body. Some are mechanical devices, some have batteries, and some even contain computers. Scientists are developing replacement wrists and shoulders, researching ways to extend the life of implants, and creating sophisticated implants using robotics. **Inferring** *What do you think would be considered desirable properties for the materials used to make a knee implant?*

Eye implants Small acrylic disks or rings reshape the eye to correct nearsightedness. Plastic or acrylic lens implants are used to treat patients with cataracts.

Cochlear implants An external microphone picks up sound, and a mini-computer translates the sound into signals received by a device implanted in the inner ear.

Heart valve implants Heart valves control blood flow through the heart. Implants replace valves damaged by age or disease.

Knee implants Made of metal and plastic, the first implants used a hinge design. Newer models more closely emulate the complex movements of a knee.

Arm implants Signals from muscles switch motors on or off to move the hand, wrist, or elbow. Researchers hope to develop arm implants that will respond directly to signals from the brain.

CHAPTER 24 Study Guide

Key Concepts

24.1 A Strategy for Life
- Two major cell types occur in nature: prokaryotic cells and eukaryotic cells.
- Photosynthesis uses sunlight to reduce CO_2 to compounds that contain C—H bonds, mainly in the form of glucose.

24.2 Carbohydrates
- Glucose is abundant in plants and animals.
- The cyclic forms of two simple sugars can be linked by means of a condensation reaction.

24.3 Amino Acids and Their Polymers
- An amino acid has a carboxyl group, an amino group, a hydrogen atom, and an R group bonded to a central carbon atom.
- Amide bonds between amino acids involve the amino and carboxyl groups, not side groups.
- Differences in the amino acid sequence result in differences in the properties of peptides.
- Enzymes increase reaction rates.

24.4 Lipids
- Unlike other biological molecules, lipids dissolve readily in organic solvents.
- In water, phospholipids spontaneously form a spherical double layer called a lipid bilayer.

24.5 Nucleic Acids
- DNA stores information needed to make proteins and governs the reproduction of cells. RNA transmits information stored in DNA during protein synthesis.
- A sequence of three bases of DNA is required to specify one amino acid in a peptide.
- Gene mutations occur when nucleotides in DNA are substituted, added, or deleted.
- The variation in DNA forms the basis for identifying a person from biological samples.
- In recombinant DNA technology, DNA is cleaved and a new piece of DNA is inserted.

24.6 Metabolism
- In living cells, ATP is the energy carrier between reactions that release and use energy.
- The degradation of biological molecules during catabolism provides the energy and the building blocks for making new compounds.
- In anabolism, new compounds needed for cellular life and growth are made from the products of catabolism.
- Nitrogen-fixing bacteria reduce atmospheric nitrogen to ammonia.

Vocabulary

- active site (p. 772)
- adenosine triphosphate (p. 786)
- amino acid (p. 769)
- anabolism (p. 788)
- carbohydrates (p. 766)
- catabolism (p. 787)
- disaccharide (p. 767)
- enzymes (p. 772)
- gene (p. 780)
- lipids (p. 775)
- metabolism (p. 787)
- monosaccharides (p. 766)
- nucleic acids (p. 778)
- nucleotides (p. 778)
- peptide (p. 770)
- peptide bond (p. 770)
- phospholipids (p. 776)
- photosynthesis (p. 764)
- polysaccharides (p. 767)
- protein (p. 770)
- saponification (p. 776)
- substrates (p. 772)
- triglyceride (p. 775)
- waxes (p. 777)

Key Equations

- Photosynthesis:
$$6CO_2 + 6H_2O + \text{Energy} \longrightarrow C_6H_{12}O_6 + 6O_2$$

- Oxidation of glucose:
$$C_6H_{12}O_6 + 6O_2 \longrightarrow 6CO_2 + 6H_2O + \text{Energy}$$

Organizing Information

Use these terms to construct a concept map that organizes the major ideas of this chapter.

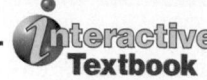

Concept Map 24 Solve the Concept Map with the help of an interactive guided tutorial.

—with **ChemASAP**

lipid   carbohydrate   protein   amino acid   enzyme   substrate   genetic code   photosynthesis   nucleic acid

24.1 A Strategy for Life

34. What is the main difference between a prokaryotic and a eukaryotic cell?

35. Explain what happens in photosynthesis.

36. Write a balanced equation for the complete oxidation of glucose.

37. Describe three organelles found in eukaryotic cells. Give a function of each organelle.

38. Why are the hydrophilic heads located on the outsides of the cell membrane?

39. Suggest a reason why prokaryotic cells are probably more ancient than eukaryotic cells.

40. Explain why photosynthesis might be considered the most important chemical process on Earth.

41. Explain why cell growth stops when the dietary intake of nutrients is insufficient.

24.2 Carbohydrates

42. Name two important monosaccharides.

43. Where in nature are glucose and fructose found?

44. How does the carbonyl functional group differ in glucose and fructose?

45. Which monosaccharides combine to form the disaccharide sucrose?

46. What is the product of the complete hydrolysis of each of the following polysaccharides?
   a. starch   **b.** glycogen

47. What product is formed when cellulose is broken down?

48. Why can't humans digest cellulose, considering that it is made of the same monomers as starch?

49. Describe the differences among monosaccharides, disaccharides, and polysaccharides. Give examples of each type of carbohydrate.

50. You may know that freshly picked corn is sweeter than corn that has been picked and stored for several days. This is because the stored corn contains less sugar than the freshly picked corn. About half of the sugar in fresh-picked corn has been converted to starch only one day after the corn has been picked. The sweetness of corn can be preserved by "blanching" the ears—dipping the ears of corn into boiling water for a few minutes, then cooling them in cold water. Corn that has been blanched and then frozen maintains its sweetness for a long time. Propose a biochemical reason why blanching corn maintains its sweetness.

51. What are the products of the following reaction?

24.3 Amino Acids and Their Polymers

52. What is the name given to the bond connecting two amino acids in a peptide chain?

53. How many peptide bonds does the tripeptide Ser—Gly—Phe have?

54. Describe two common patterns found in the folding of protein chains.

55. Are the structures of the following two tripeptides the same? Explain.
   a. Ala—Ser—Gly
   b. Gly—Ser—Ala

56. Describe what an enzyme does.

57. What is an enzyme-substrate complex? How does it form?

58. What is one function of membrane proteins?

59. How is an enzyme-substrate complex formed in the enzyme's active site?

60. Describe how amino acids join to form a peptide bond.

61. Describe the structural features all amino acids have in common. What structural features differ among the amino acids?

62. Using structural formulas, write a chemical equation for the formation of a dipeptide from two amino acids. What type of bond does the reaction create?

63. Peptide chains fold and bend into three-dimensional shapes. Suggest how a peptide chain is held in this 3-D shape.

24.4 Lipids

64. Distinguish between a fat and an oil.

65. What is a triglyceride?

66. What is a soap?

67. Draw structural formulas for the products of complete hydrolysis of tristearin.

68. Draw and label a simple representation of a lipid bilayer.

69. What two types of compounds combine to form a wax?

70. What is the function of waxes in plants? In animals?

71. The formula for palmitic acid is $CH_3(CH_2)_{14}CO_2H$. A popular soap is mostly sodium palmitate. Write the structure of sodium palmitate.

72. The following compound is hydrolyzed by boiling with sodium hydroxide. What are the saponification products?

$$CH_2-O-\overset{\overset{\displaystyle O}{\|}}{C}-(CH_2)_{14}CH_3$$
$$CH-O-\overset{\overset{\displaystyle O}{\|}}{C}-(CH_2)_{12}CH_3$$
$$CH_2-O-\overset{\overset{\displaystyle O}{\|}}{C}-(CH_2)_{16}CH_3$$

73. What causes the spontaneous formation of a lipid bilayer?

24.5 Nucleic Acids

74. What two types of nucleic acids do cells contain?

75. What are the components of a nucleotide?

76. What is the structural difference between the sugar unit in RNA and the sugar unit in DNA?

77. What type of bonding helps hold a DNA double helix together?

78. Which of the following base pairs are found in a DNA molecule: A—A, A—T, C—G, G—A, A—U, T—U?

79. How many bases specify an amino acid in the genetic code?

80. What are the consequences of a substitution of one base for another in DNA?

81. What is the basis for identifying an individual by DNA fingerprinting?

82. What is recombinant DNA?

83. Consider the following sequence of DNA:

   G—C—C—C—C—A—A—C—G—T—T—A.

   a. Using the code words for amino acids in Table 24.2 on page 781, write the amino acid sequence formed by translation of the DNA sequence into a peptide.

   b. What amino acid sequence would result from the substitution of adenine (A) for the second cytosine (C)?

84. Identify each of the following types of biological molecules.

   a.

   b.

   c.

85. Use Table 24.2 on page 781 to write a base sequence for DNA that codes for the tripeptide Ala—Gly—Ser. Why might your answer be different from the answers of your classmates?

86. A segment of a DNA strand has the following base sequence: C—G—A—T—C—C—A. Write the base sequence that would be found on the other strand in the double helix.

87. Which type of monomer produces each of the following polymers?
   a. protein   **b.** polysaccharide   **c.** nucleic acid

88. Does every code word in DNA specify an amino acid in protein synthesis? Explain.

89. What are some of the outcomes of recombinant DNA research?

90. What is the oxidation state of iron in normal hemoglobin and methemoglobin? What is the consequence of this change in oxidation state?

91. What are the possible consequences of an error in DNA sequence?

92. What is base-pairing? How does base-pairing relate to the structure of DNA?

93. In the DNA double helix, where are the base pairs located in relation to the backbone structure: inside the double helix, or outside the double helix? What must happen before the protein-making machinery of the cell can "read" the code words formed by the DNA bases?

94. Which type of gene mutation do you think will do more damage to an organism: a substitution mutation in which one base is substituted for another base or an addition mutation in which a base is added to a sequence of bases? Explain your reasoning.

95. Suggest a reason why a bean plant might not grow well if planted in sterilized soil.

96. Think about the three-dimensional structure of DNA and suggest a way the molecule might make a copy of itself.

97. What class of polymer is formed from each of the following monomers?
　a. amino acids　　　　**b.** monosaccharides
　c. nucleotides

98. Compare the structure of a DNA nucleotide with an RNA nucleotide.

99. A sequence of nine bases in the gene codes for the amino acid sequence Trp-Met-Met. What is the sequence of bases in this DNA fragment? Use Table 24.2 on page 781 to help you. Could you determine the base sequence for certain if the amino acid sequence were Trp-Met-Leu? Why or why not?

24.6 Metabolism

100. Write an abbreviated, balanced equation for the hydrolysis of ATP to ADP.

101. Where do the complex biomolecules your body degrades during catabolism come from?

102. Compare and contrast catabolism and anabolism.

103. Describe the nitrogen cycle in your own words.

104. What is the source of raw materials used in anabolic reactions?

105. What is meant by industrial nitrogen fixation? What is produced during this process?

106. Some experts recommend that complex carbo-hydrates provide 50–55% of dietary calories. What is the relationship between energy production and complex carbohydrates?

107. Why is it necessary to breathe deeply during vigorous exercise?

108. The complete oxidation of glucose releases 2.82×10^3 kJ/mol of energy, and the formation of ATP from ADP requires 30.5 kJ/mol. What percent of the energy released in the complete oxidation of glucose is captured in the formation of ATP?

109. An average adult expends about 8400 kJ of energy every day. How many moles of ATP must be converted to ADP to provide this amount of energy?

110. What role do coenzymes play in metabolism?

111. Interpret this statement: "Carbon dioxide is an energy-poor molecule, but glucose is an energy-rich molecule."

Test-Taking Tip

Anticipating the Answer You can sometimes figure out the answer to a question before you look at the answer choices. Try to answer the question in your mind before you look at the answer choices. Then read the choices and choose the choice that agrees with the answer in your mind.

Standardized Test Prep

For each statement or question write the number of the word or expression that, of those given, best completes the statement or answers the question.

1. What phrase best describes ATP?

  a. energy producer
  b. energy consumer
  c. energy transmitter
  d. energy pump

2. Which element is *not* found in amino acids?

  a. phosphorus
  b. nitrogen
  c. oxygen
  d. hydrogen

3. For any enzyme to function, the substrate must bind to the

  a. product
  b. cofactor
  c. active site
  d. peptide

4. An organic compound with an —OH functional group is a(n)

  a. aldehyde
  b. alcohol
  c. organic acid
  d. ether

For each question, there are two statements. Decide whether each statement is true or false. Then decide whether Statement II is a correct explanation for Statement I.

	Statement I		**Statement II**
5.	Lipids tend to be insoluble in water.	BECAUSE	Lipids have mainly nonpolar bonds.
6.	Starch and cellulose are both digestible by most organisms.	BECAUSE	Glucose is the monomer in both starch and cellulose.
7.	Many of the reactions in catabolism are oxidation reactions.	BECAUSE	Oxidation reactions tend to be energy-producing reactions.
8.	The sequence of bases in DNA contains the code for making proteins.	BECAUSE	Each pair of bases in DNA codes for a specific amino acid.

Answer each of the following questions.

9. Describe two factors that cause real gases to depart from the ideal gas law.

10. Characterize each of the following compounds as electrolytes or nonelectrolytes.

  a. $NaCl$
  b. $CuSO_4$
  c. CCl_4
  d. H_2O

11. Calculate the boiling point elevation for these aqueous solutions.

  a. $0.507 m$ $NaCl$
  b. $0.204 m$ NH_4Cl
  c. $0.155 m$ $CaCl_2$
  d. $0.222 m$ $NaHSO_4$

12. How much heat (in kJ) is released or absorbed when 0.265 mol of sodium hydrogen carbonate is decomposed according to the following reaction?

$$2NaHCO_3(s) \longrightarrow Na_2CO_3(s) + H_2O(g) + CO_2(g)$$
$$\Delta H = 129 \text{ kJ}$$

13. Explain why the needles on a dried-out fir tree can burn with almost explosive rapidity.

14. What must be true at the end point of an acid-base titration?

15. Calculate the pH of each of the following solutions.

  a. $[H^+] = 7.0 \times 10^{-5} M$
  b. $[OH^-] = 1.8 \times 10^{-9} M$
  c. $[OH^-] = 6.1 \times 10^{-2} M$
  d. $[H^+] = 4.4 \times 10^{-11} M$

16. Identify the element that is being reduced in each of the following reactions.

  a. xenon + fluorine $\longrightarrow$ xenon tetrafluoride
  b. sulfur + oxygen $\longrightarrow$ sulfur trioxide
  c. gaseous chlorine + aqueous sodium bromide $\longrightarrow$ aqueous bromine + aqueous sodium chloride

17. At which electrode in a voltaic cell does oxidation always occur? What is the charge on this electrode?

18. What would you observe when a length of nickel wire is immersed in an aqueous solution of silver nitrate?

19. For each pair of metals shown below, decide which metal is more readily reduced.

  a. Cu, Mg
  b. Cd, Ni
  c. Ag, Sn
  d. Zn, Fe
  e. Ni, Li
  f. Al, Cu

20. Name a structural feature that can allow a molecule to have optical isomers.

21. Write a molecular structure for each of the following compounds.

  a. heptane
  b. 2-methyl-3-hexene
  c. 2-phenylbutane
  d. 1,3-diethylbenzene

22. Give the IUPAC names for each of the following compounds.

a.

c.

H—C—C—C—C—C—H with H, H on first carbon; H, H on second; O on middle (double bond); H, H; H, H

b.

H H H—C—H H H
H—C——C——C—H
H OH H

23. Name the next-highest homolog of each of these compounds.
a. 1-butene   **c.** pentane
b. cyclooctane   **d.** nonane

24. Name the four structural isomers of C_4H_9Cl.

25. Write a molecular formula for each of the following compounds.
a. methyl acetate
b. butanal
c. 2-hydroxypropanoic acid
d. 2-butanone

26. Name each polymer and state at least one of its uses.

a. $-(CF_2-CF_2)_x$ **b.** $H-(CH_2-CH_2)-H$

c. $-(CH_2-CH)_x$ with Cl   **d.** $-(CH_2-CH)_x$ with phenyl

27. Capsaicin, shown below, is the major contributor to the heat of chili peppers. Circle and name the functional groups in capsaicin.

CH_3O
HO—(ring)—$CH_2NHC(CH_2)_4CH=CHCH(CH_3)_2$ with O double bonded

Use the paragraph to answer Questions 28–30.

Because an amino acid contains both a carboxyl group and an amino group, it is amphoteric, that is, it can act as either an acid or a base. Crystalline amino acids have some properties—relatively high melting points and high water solubilities—that are more characteristic of ionic substances than of molecular substances.

28. Write an equation showing glycine acting as an acid in a reaction with water. (Glycine is the simplest amino acid. Its side chain R=H.)

29. Write an equation showing glycine acting as a base in a reaction with water.

30. It is possible for glycine to undergo an internal Brønsted-Lowry acid-base neutralization reaction.
a. Write the resulting structural formula.
b. Explain how this reaction would account for the ionic properties of glycine.

Use the photo to answer Question 31.

31. The photo shows three DNA fingerprints. The DNA in sample E was taken from a crime scene. The DNA in samples S1 and S2 were taken from suspects. Based on the DNA evidence, which suspect did *not* commit the crime?

For Questions 32–35, name the category of organic compounds most closely identified with each biological molecule.

32. proteins

33. nucleic acids

34. lipids

35. carbohydrates

Use these models to answer Question 36.

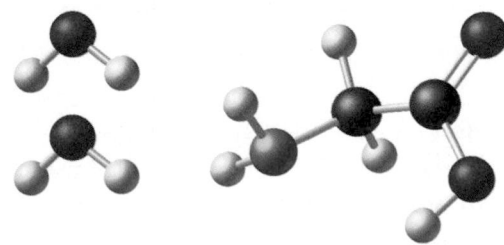

36. Glycine can form hydrogen bonds with water. Draw a glycine molecule with at least two water molecules bonded to each end.

A nuclear submarine uses energy released by nuclear reactions.

INQUIRY Activity

Simulating Radioactive Decay

Materials

a container, a lid, 128 pennies, a flat table or desk surface, a scientific calculator, loose-leaf paper, graph paper, pen or pencil

Procedure

1. Make a two-column data table with the headings "Trial" and "Number of heads."

2. Put 128 pennies in the container and shake them.

3. Carefully pour the pennies onto a flat surface.

4. Pick up, count, and set aside those pennies that are turned heads up. In the table, enter the number of heads for Trial 1.

5. Return the remaining pennies (those that were tails) to the container and repeat Steps 3–5 for a total of five trials.

6. If time permits, repeat the entire experiment four more times and find the average of your data or the data collected by the class.

Think About It

1. Prepare a graph of the number of heads (y-axis) versus the trial number (x-axis). Is the result a straight line or a curve? Add a third column titled "Log of number of heads" to the data table, and use your calculator to complete the table.

2. Prepare a graph of the data in Column 3 (y-axis) versus trial number (x-axis). Is the result a straight line or a curve?

25.1 Nuclear Radiation

 New York Standards: 3.1g, 3.1o–p, 4.4c

Connecting to Your World

Marie Curie was a Polish scientist whose research led to many discoveries about radiation and radioactive elements. In 1903 she and her husband Pierre, along with Antoine Henri Becquerel, won the Nobel Prize in physics for their work on radioactivity. She was also awarded the Nobel Prize in chemistry in 1911 for her research on radioactive elements. Marie Curie's research was essential to understanding and using newly discovered radioactive elements. In 1934 she died from leukemia caused by her long-term exposure to radiation. In this section, you will learn about the various types of radiation and their effects.

Guide for Reading

Key Concepts
- How does an unstable nucleus release energy?
- What are the three main types of nuclear radiation?

Vocabulary
radioactivity
radiation
radioisotopes
alpha particle
beta particle
gamma ray

Reading Strategy

Relating Text and Visuals As you read about types of radiation, look at Figure 25.1. List how the positive, negative, or neutral electric charge of each type of radiation, as described in the text, is related to how the radiation is deflected as it passes by the charged plates.

Radioactivity

In 1896, the French chemist Antoine Henri Becquerel (1852–1908) made an accidental discovery. He was studying the ability of uranium salts that had been exposed to sunlight to fog photographic film plates. During bad weather, Becquerel could not expose the sample to sunlight, but happened to leave it on top of the photographic plate. When he developed the plate, he discovered that the uranium salt still fogged the plate. At that time, two of Becquerel's associates were Marie Curie (1867–1934) and Pierre Curie (1859–1906). The Curies were able to show that rays emitted by the uranium atoms caused the fogging of the plates. Marie Curie named the process by which materials give off such rays **radioactivity.** The penetrating rays and particles emitted by a radioactive source are called **radiation.**

Nuclear reactions, which account for radioactivity, differ from chemical reactions in a number of important ways. In chemical reactions, atoms tend to attain stable electron configurations by losing electrons or sharing electrons. In nuclear reactions, the nuclei of unstable isotopes, called **radioisotopes,** gain stability by undergoing changes. These changes are always accompanied by the emission of large amounts of energy. Unlike chemical reactions, nuclear reactions are not affected by changes in temperature, pressure, or the presence of catalysts. They are also unaffected by the compounds in which the unstable isotopes are present. The nuclear reactions of a given radioisotope cannot be speeded up, slowed down, or turned off.

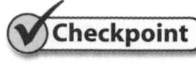 **What is radiation?**

The discovery of radioactivity disproved Dalton's assumption that atoms are indivisible. A radioactive atom, or radioisotope, undergoes drastic changes as it emits radiation. These radioisotopes have unstable nuclei. The stability of a nucleus depends on the ratio of neutrons to protons in the nucleus, and on the overall size of the nucleus. Too many or too few neutrons relative to the number of protons makes a nucleus unstable. ⊙ **An unstable nucleus releases energy by emitting radiation during the process of radioactive decay.** Unstable radioisotopes of one element are transformed into stable (nonradioactive) isotopes of a different element. Radioactive decay is spontaneous and does not require any input of energy.

Types of Radiation

Radiation is emitted during radioactive decay. ⊙ **The three main types of nuclear radiation are alpha radiation, beta radiation, and gamma radiation.** Table 25.1 summarizes the characteristics of these three types of radiation. The different types of radiation can be separated by an electric field as shown in Figure 25.1.

Alpha Radiation The type of radiation called alpha radiation consists of helium nuclei that have been emitted from a radioactive source. Each of these emitted particles, called an **alpha particle,** contains two protons and two neutrons and has a double positive charge. In nuclear equations, an alpha particle is written $^4_2$He or α. The electric charge symbol is generally omitted.

The radioisotope uranium-238 releases alpha radiation and is transformed into another radioisotope, thorium-234. Figure 25.2a illustrates this process.

$$^{238}_{92}\text{U} \xrightarrow[\text{decay}]{\text{Radioactive}} {}^{234}_{90}\text{Th} + {}^4_2\text{He } (\alpha \text{ emission})$$

Uranium-238   Thorium-234   Alpha particle

Note that this nuclear equation is balanced. The sum of the mass numbers (superscripts) on the right equals the sum on the left. The same is true for the atomic numbers (subscripts).

When an atom loses an alpha particle, the atomic number of the product atom is lower by two and its mass number is lower by four. Because of their large mass and charge, alpha particles do not tend to travel very far and are not very penetrating. A sheet of paper or the surface of your skin easily stops them. However, radioisotopes that emit alpha particles are dangerous when ingested. The particles do not have to travel far to penetrate soft tissue and cause damage.

Figure 25.1 These three types of radiation deflect differently as they pass between a pair of electrically charged plates. Alpha particles (α) and beta particles (β) are deflected in opposite directions—alpha particles toward the negative plate and beta particles toward the positive plate. Gamma rays are undeflected. **Applying Concepts** *Why are gamma rays not deflected?*

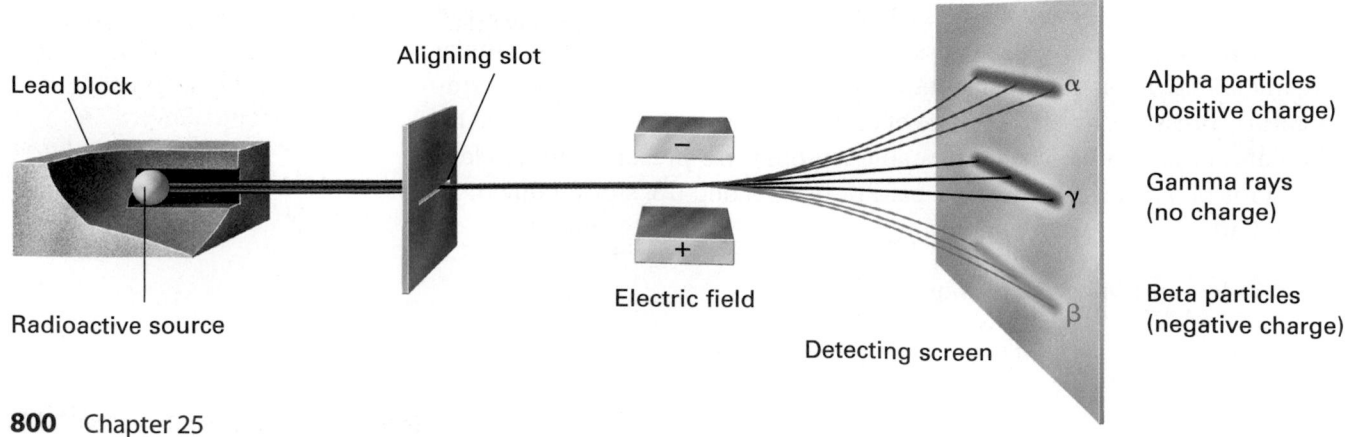

Lead block

Aligning slot

Radioactive source

Electric field

Detecting screen

Alpha particles (positive charge)

Gamma rays (no charge)

Beta particles (negative charge)

Table 25.1

Characteristics of Some Types of Radiation			
Property	**Alpha radiation**	**Beta radiation**	**Gamma radiation**
Composition	Alpha particle (helium nucleus)	Beta particle (electron)	High-energy electro-magnetic radiation
Symbol	$\alpha, {}^{4}_{2}\text{He}$	$\beta, {}^{0}_{-1}\text{e}$	γ
Charge	2+	1−	0
Mass (amu)	4	1/1837	0
Common source	Radium-226	Carbon-14	Cobalt-60
Penetrating power	Low (0.05 mm body tissue)	Moderate (4 mm body tissue)	Very high (penetrates body easily)
Shielding	Paper, clothing	Metal foil	Lead, concrete (incompletely shields)

Beta Radiation An electron resulting from the breaking apart of a neutron in an atom is called a **beta particle.** The neutron breaks apart into a proton, which remains in the nucleus, and a fast-moving electron, which is released.

$$ {}^{1}_{0}\text{n} \longrightarrow {}^{1}_{1}\text{H} \quad + \quad {}^{0}_{-1}\text{e} $$

Neutron   Proton   Electron (beta particle)

The symbol for the electron has a subscript of −1 where the atomic number would be written. This represents the electron's negative charge. The superscript 0 where a mass number would be written represents the extremely small mass of the electron compared to that of a proton.

Carbon-14 emits a beta particle as it undergoes radioactive decay to form nitrogen-14. Figure 25.2b shows this beta emission.

$$ {}^{14}_{6}\text{C} \longrightarrow {}^{14}_{7}\text{N} \quad + \quad {}^{0}_{-1}\text{e} \ (\beta \text{ emission}) $$

Carbon-14   Nitrogen-14   Beta
(radioactive)   (stable)   particle

The nitrogen-14 atom has the same atomic mass number as carbon-14, but its atomic number has increased by 1. It contains an additional proton and one fewer neutron. The nuclear equation is balanced.

ⓐ Alpha decay

Alpha particle
${}^{4}_{2}\text{He}$

${}^{238}_{92}\text{U}$

${}^{234}_{90}\text{Th}$

ⓑ Beta decay

Beta particle
${}^{0}_{-1}\text{e}$

${}^{14}_{6}\text{C}$

${}^{14}_{7}\text{N}$

Figure 25.2 Radiation is emitted during radioactive decay. ⓐ Uranium-238 undergoes alpha decay to form thorium-234. ⓑ Carbon-14 undergoes beta decay to form nitrogen-14. **Interpreting Diagrams** *What particle is emitted in each decay process?*

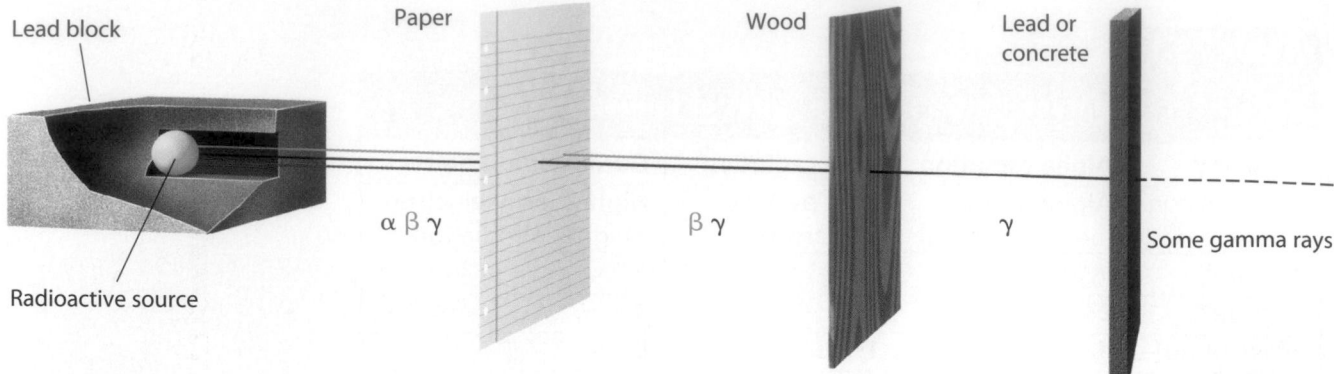

Lead block

Paper

Wood

Lead or concrete

Radioactive source

α β γ

β γ

γ

Some gamma rays

Figure 25.3 Because of their large mass and charge, alpha particles (red) are the least penetrating of the three main types of radiation. Gamma rays (black) have no mass or charge and are the most penetrating.

A beta particle has less charge than an alpha particle and much less mass than an alpha particle. Consequently, beta particles are more penetrating. Beta particles can pass through paper but are stopped by aluminum foil or thin pieces of wood.

Gamma Radiation A high-energy photon emitted by a radioisotope is called a **gamma ray.** The high-energy photons are electromagnetic radiation. Nuclei often emit gamma rays along with alpha or beta particles during radioactive decay. The following example demonstrates this process.

$$_{90}^{230}\text{Th} \longrightarrow {}_{88}^{226}\text{Ra} + {}_{2}^{4}\text{He} + \gamma$$

Thorium-230   Radon-226   Alpha   Gamma
                                  particle   ray

Because gamma rays have no mass and no electrical charge, the emission of gamma radiation does not alter the atomic number or mass number of an atom. Gamma rays are extremely penetrating and can be very dangerous. Gamma rays pass easily through paper, wood, and the human body. They can be stopped, although not completely, by several meters of concrete or several centimeters of lead, as shown in Figure 25.3.

25.1 Section Assessment

1. 🔑 **Key Concept** How does an unstable nucleus release energy?

2. 🔑 **Key Concept** What are the three main types of nuclear radiation?

3. What part of an atom undergoes change during radioactive decay?

4. How is the atomic number of a nucleus changed by alpha decay? By beta decay? By gamma decay?

5. How is the atomic mass number of a nucleus changed by alpha decay? By beta decay? By gamma decay?

6. Which of the three kinds of radiation described in this section is the most penetrating?

Connecting ▶ Concepts

Connecting Concepts Refer back to the rules for balancing chemical equations introduced in Section 11.1. An equation for radioactive decay has different nuclei appearing on each side of the yields sign so the atoms cannot be balanced. What two items must be balanced to achieve a balanced equation for radioactive decay?

Interactive Textbook

Assessment 25.1 Test yourself on the concepts in Section 25.1.

— with **ChemASAP**

25.2 Nuclear Transformations

 New York Standards: 4.4a–b, 4.4d, 5.3a

Connecting to Your World

Weather stripping and insulation help lower heating and cooling bills by conserving energy. They can, however, reduce the exchange of indoor and outdoor air. As a result, radioactive substances such as radon gas can accumulate indoors and pose a health risk. Radon-222 is a radioactive isotope that is present naturally in the soil in some areas. It has a constant rate of decay. In this section, you will learn about decay rates of radioactive substances.

Nuclear Stability and Decay

More than 1500 different nuclei are known. Of those, only 264 are stable and do not decay or change with time. The stability of a nucleus depends on its neutron-to-proton ratio. Figure 25.4 is a graph of the number of neutrons vs. number of protons for all known stable nuclei. The stable nuclei are in a region called the **band of stability.** For elements of low atomic number (below about 20), the ratio of neutrons to protons for stability is about 1. That means the stable nuclei have roughly equal numbers of neutrons and protons. For example, the isotopes $^{12}_{6}C$, $^{14}_{7}N$, and $^{16}_{8}O$ are stable. Above atomic number 20, stable nuclei have more neutrons than protons. The neutron-to-proton ratio reaches about 1.5 for heavy elements. The lead isotope $^{206}_{82}Pb$, for example, with 124 neutrons and 82 protons, is stable. Its neutron-to-proton ratio is $\frac{124}{82}$, or approximately 1.5.

Guide for Reading

Key Concepts
- What determines the type of decay a radioisotope undergoes?
- How much of a sample of a radioisotope remains after each half-life?
- What are two ways that transmutation can occur?

Vocabulary
band of stability
positron
half-life
transmutation
transuranium elements

Reading Strategy
Building Vocabulary Before you read, make a list of the vocabulary terms above. As you read the section, write a definition of each key term in your own words.

Number of Neutrons vs. Number of Protons for Stable Nuclei

Figure 25.4 A neutron-versus-proton plot of all stable nuclei forms a pattern called the band of stability (shown in red).

INTERPRETING GRAPHS

a. Identify What do the dots on the graph represent?
b. Apply Concepts What is the approximate ratio of neutrons to protons for neodymium, whose atomic number is 70?
c. Describe How does the neutron-to-proton ratio change as the number of protons increases?

Table 25.2

Decay Processes

Beta Emission

$$^{66}_{29}Cu \longrightarrow ^{66}_{30}Zn + ^{0}_{-1}e$$

$$^{14}_{6}C \longrightarrow ^{14}_{7}N + ^{0}_{-1}e$$

Electron Capture

$$^{59}_{28}Ni + ^{0}_{-1}e \longrightarrow ^{59}_{27}Co$$

$$^{37}_{18}Ar + ^{0}_{-1}e \longrightarrow ^{37}_{17}Cl$$

Positron Emission

$$^{8}_{5}B \longrightarrow ^{8}_{4}Be + ^{0}_{+1}e$$

$$^{15}_{8}O \longrightarrow ^{15}_{7}N + ^{0}_{+1}e$$

Alpha Emission

$$^{226}_{88}Ra \longrightarrow ^{222}_{86}Rn + ^{4}_{2}He$$

$$^{232}_{90}Th \longrightarrow ^{228}_{88}Ra + ^{4}_{2}He$$

A nucleus may be unstable and undergo spontaneous radioactive decay for several reasons. 🔑 **The neutron-to-proton ratio determines the type of decay that occurs.** Some nuclei have too many neutrons relative to the number of protons. These nuclei decay by turning a neutron into a proton to emit a beta particle (an electron) from the nucleus.

$$^{1}_{0}n \longrightarrow ^{1}_{1}H + ^{0}_{-1}e$$

This process is known as beta emission. It increases the number of protons while decreasing the number of neutrons. Table 25.2 shows examples of beta emission.

Other nuclei are unstable because they have too few neutrons relative to the number of protons. These nuclei increase their stability by converting a proton to a neutron. An electron is captured by a nucleus during this process of electron capture.

A **positron** is a particle with the mass of an electron but a positive charge. During positron emission, a proton changes to a neutron.

All nuclei that have an atomic number greater than 83 are radioactive. These nuclei have both too many neutrons and too many protons to be stable. Therefore they undergo radioactive decay. Most of them emit alpha particles. Alpha emission increases the neutron-to-proton ratio, which tends to increase the stability of the nucleus. In alpha emission the mass number decreases by four and the atomic number decreases by two.

If all the masses in a nuclear reaction were measured accurately enough, you would find that mass is not conserved. An extremely small quantity of mass is converted into energy released in radioactive decay.

Half-Life

Every radioisotope has a characteristic rate of decay measured by its half-life. A **half-life** ($t_{1/2}$) is the time required for one-half of the nuclei of a radioisotope sample to decay to products, as shown in Figure 25.5. 🔑 **After each half-life, half of the existing radioactive atoms have decayed into atoms of a new element.**

Figure 25.5 This decay curve shows that during each half-life, half of the radioactive atoms decay into atoms of another element.

INTERPRETING GRAPHS

a. Identify What percent of the atoms remains after 1 half-life?

b. Describe What percent of the atoms remains after two half-lives?

c. Apply Concepts Approximately how many half-lives does it take for 12.5% of the radioisotope to remain?

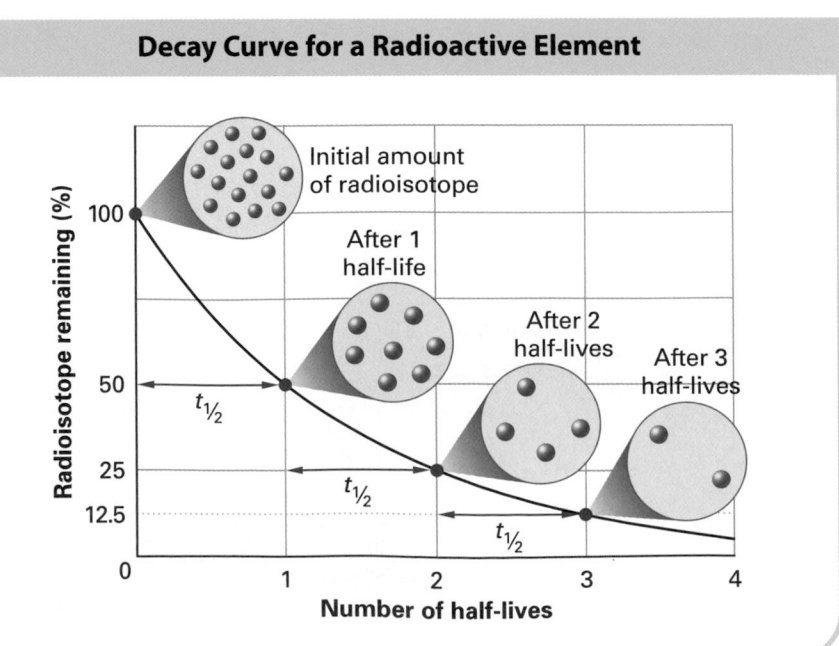

Decay Curve for a Radioactive Element

Table 25.3

Half-Lives and Radiation of Some Naturally Occurring Radioisotopes

Isotope	Half-life	Radiation emitted
Carbon-14	5.73×10^3 years	β
Potassium-40	1.25×10^9 years	β, γ
Radon-222	3.8 days	α
Radium-226	1.6×10^3 years	α, γ
Thorium-234	24.1 days	β, γ
Uranium-235	7.0×10^8 years	α, γ
Uranium-238	4.46×10^9 years	α

Go Online

NSTA SCI*LINKS*

For: Links on Radioactive Dating
Visit: www.scilinks.org
Web Code: cdn-1252

Half-lives can be as short as a fraction of a second or as long as billions of years. Table 25.3 shows the half-lives of some radioisotopes that occur in nature. Scientists use the half-lives of some radioisotopes found in nature to determine the age of ancient artifacts. Many artificially produced radioisotopes have short half-lives, which is useful in nuclear medicine. The short-lived isotopes are not a long-term radiation hazard to the patient.

One isotope that has a long half-life is uranium-238. Uranium-238 decays through a complex series of radioactive isotopes to the stable isotope lead-206. Figure 25.6 illustrates this process. The age of uranium-containing minerals can be estimated by measuring the ratio of uranium-238 to lead-206. Because the half-life of uranium-238 is 4.5×10^9 years, it is possible to use its half-life to date rocks as old as the solar system.

*i*nteractive
Textbook

Simulation 30 Simulate the decay of several isotopes.

—— with **ChemASAP**

✓ **Checkpoint** *What is the half-life of carbon-14?*

Figure 25.6 Uranium-238 decays through a complex series of radioactive intermediates, including radon (Rn) gas. **Interpreting Diagrams** *What is the stable end product of this series?*

Figure 25.7 These archaeologists are digging for artifacts. The age of an artifact can often be determined from its measured carbon-14 content.

Scientists often find the age of an object that was once part of a living system by measuring the amount of carbon-14 ($^{14}_{6}C$) it contains. Carbon-14 has a half-life of 5730 years. Most of Earth's carbon, however, consists of the more stable isotopes $^{12}_{6}C$ and $^{13}_{6}C$. The ratio of $^{14}_{6}C$ to the other carbon isotopes in the environment is fairly constant because high-energy cosmic rays from space constantly produce $^{14}_{6}C$ in the upper atmosphere. Plants grow by producing sugars, cellulose, and other compounds from carbon dioxide in the atmosphere. Animals grow by eating the plants, and sometimes other animals. This keeps the ratio of carbon-14 to other carbon isotopes constant during any living organism's lifetime. When an organism dies, it stops exchanging carbon with the environment and its radioactive $^{14}_{6}C$ atoms decay without being replaced. Therefore, the ratio of $^{14}_{6}C$ to stable carbon in the remains of an organism changes in a predictable way that enables the archaeologists in Figure 25.7 to obtain an estimate of its age.

SAMPLE PROBLEM 25.1

Using Half-lives in Calculations

Carbon-14 emits beta radiation and decays with a half-life ($t_{1/2}$) of 5730 years. Assume you start with a mass of 2.00×10^{-12} g of carbon-14.
a. How long is three half-lives?
b. How many grams of the isotope remain at the end of three half-lives?

1 Analyze *List the knowns and the unknowns.*

Knowns
- $t_{1/2}$ = 5730 years
- initial mass 2.00×10^{-12} g
- number of half-lives = 3

Unknowns
- 3 half-lives = ? years
- mass after 3 half-lives = ? g

First, calculate the time for three half-lives by multiplying the length of each half-life by three. Find the mass remaining by multiplying the original mass by $\frac{1}{2}$ three times.

2 Calculate *Solve for the unknowns.*
a. 3 half-lives = 3 × 5730 years = 17,190 years
b. The initial mass of carbon-14 is reduced by one half for each of the three half-lives, so for three half-lives

$$\text{Remaining mass} = 2.00 \times 10^{-12}\text{g} \times \frac{1}{2} \times \frac{1}{2} \times \frac{1}{2} = 0.250 \times 10^{-12}\text{g}$$

3 Evaluate *Do the results make sense?*
The mass of carbon-14 after three half-lives should be much lower than the original mass. The final answer has the proper units and the proper number of significant figures.

Practice Problems

7. Manganese-56 is a beta emitter with a half-life of 2.6 h. What is the mass of manganese-56 in a 1.0-mg sample of the isotope at the end of 10.4 h?

8. A sample of thorium-234 has a half-life of 24.1 days. Will all the thorium undergo radioactive decay in 48.2 days? Explain.

Math ➤ Handbook

For help with scientific notation, go to page R56 of the Math Handbook.

Problem-Solving 25.7
Solve Problem 7 with the help of an interactive guided tutorial.

— with **ChemASAP**

Transmutation Reactions

The conversion of an atom of one element to an atom of another element is called **transmutation.** There are at least two ways transmutation occurs. **Transmutation can occur by radioactive decay. Transmutation can also occur when particles bombard the nucleus of an atom.** The bombarding particles may be protons, neutrons, or alpha particles.

Many transmutations occur in nature. The production of carbon-14 from naturally occurring nitrogen-14, for example, takes place in the upper atmosphere. Another naturally occurring isotope, uranium-238, undergoes 14 transmutations before reaching a stable isotope. Many other transmutations are done in laboratories or in nuclear reactors. The earliest artificial transmutation was performed in 1919 by Ernest Rutherford (1871–1937). He bombarded nitrogen gas with alpha particles to produce an unstable isotope of fluorine. The results of this reaction are shown in Figure 25.8. The first step of the reaction forms fluorine-18.

$$\underset{\text{Nitrogen-14}}{^{14}_{7}\text{N}} \quad + \quad \underset{\substack{\text{Alpha} \\ \text{particle}}}{^{4}_{2}\text{He}} \quad \longrightarrow \quad \underset{\text{Fluorine-18}}{^{18}_{9}\text{F}}$$

The fluorine isotope quickly decomposes to a stable isotope of oxygen and a proton.

$$\underset{\text{Fluorine-18}}{^{18}_{9}\text{F}} \quad \longrightarrow \quad \underset{\text{Oxygen-17}}{^{17}_{8}\text{O}} \quad + \quad \underset{\text{Proton}}{^{1}_{1}\text{H}}$$

Rutherford's experiment eventually led to the discovery of the proton. James Chadwick's discovery of the neutron in 1932 also involved a transmutation experiment. Neutrons were produced when beryllium-9 was bombarded with alpha particles.

$$\underset{\text{Beryllium-9}}{^{9}_{4}\text{Be}} \quad + \quad \underset{\substack{\text{Alpha} \\ \text{particle}}}{^{4}_{2}\text{He}} \quad \longrightarrow \quad \underset{\text{Carbon-12}}{^{12}_{6}\text{C}} \quad + \quad \underset{\text{Neutron}}{^{1}_{0}\text{n}}$$

✓ Checkpoint *What is transmutation?*

Figure 25.8 The first artificial transmutation reaction involved bombarding nitrogen gas with alpha particles, as illustrated here. **Interpreting Diagrams** *What particles were formed?*

The elements in the periodic table with atomic numbers above 92, the atomic number of uranium, are called the **transuranium elements.** All the transuranium elements undergo transmutation. None of them occurs in nature, and all of them are radioactive. These elements have been synthesized in nuclear reactors and nuclear accelerators. Accelerators like the one in Figure 25.9 accelerate bombarding particles to very high speeds, while reactors produce beams of low-energy particles. When uranium-238 is bombarded with relatively slow neutrons from a nuclear reactor, some uranium nuclei capture neutrons to produce uranium-239.

$$^{238}_{92}\text{U} + ^{1}_{0}\text{n} \longrightarrow ^{239}_{92}\text{U}$$

Uranium-239 is radioactive and emits a beta particle. The product is an isotope of the artificial radioactive element neptunium (atomic number 93).

$$^{239}_{92}\text{U} \longrightarrow ^{239}_{93}\text{Np} + ^{0}_{-1}\text{e}$$

Neptunium is unstable and decays, emitting a beta particle, to produce a second artificial element, plutonium (atomic number 94).

$$^{239}_{93}\text{Np} \longrightarrow ^{239}_{94}\text{Pu} + ^{0}_{-1}\text{e}$$

Plutonium and neptunium are both transuranium elements and do not occur in nature. Scientists in Berkeley, California synthesized these first artificial elements in 1940. Since that time, more than 20 additional transuranium elements have been produced artificially.

Figure 25.9 Fermilab is a major accelerator center located in Batavia, Illinois. The main accelerator is a ring that has a radius of 1.0 km.

25.2 Section Assessment

9. ⬤ **Key Concept** What determines the type of decay a radioisotope will undergo?

10. ⬤ **Key Concept** How much of a sample of radioisotope remains after one half-life? After two half-lives?

11. ⬤ **Key Concept** What are two ways that transmutation can occur?

12. Complete and balance the equations for the following nuclear reactions.

a. $^{27}_{13}\text{Al} + ^{4}_{2}\text{He} \longrightarrow ^{30}_{14}\text{Si} + ?$

b. $^{214}_{83}\text{Bi} \longrightarrow ^{4}_{2}\text{He} + ?$

c. $^{27}_{14}\text{Si} \longrightarrow ^{0}_{-1}\text{e} + ?$

d. $^{66}_{29}\text{Cu} \longrightarrow ^{66}_{30}\text{Zn} + ?$

13. A radioisotope has a half-life of 4 days. How much of a 20-gram sample of this radioisotope remains at the end of each time period?

a. 4 days

b. 8 days

14. The mass of cobalt-60 in a sample is found to have decreased from 0.800 g to 0.200 g in a period of 10.5 years. From this information, calculate the half-life of cobalt-60.

Research the methods used to date materials such as pottery, coral, and stone. Prepare a written report that summarizes your findings on the radioisotopes used, their half-lives, and their limitations.

*i*nteractive
Textbook

Assessment 25.2 Test yourself on the concepts in Section 25.2.

— with **ChemASAP**

Radioactivity and Half-Lives

Purpose
To simulate the transformation of a radioactive isotope over time and to graph the data and relate it to radioactive decay and half-lives.

Materials
- pencil
- ruler
- penny
- paper
- graph paper

Procedure
On a sheet of paper, make a data table similar to the one below. For trial number 1, flip a penny 100 times and, in your grid, record the total number of heads that result. Now flip the penny the same number of times as the number of heads that you obtained in the first 100 flips. Record the total number of flips and the number of heads that result. Continue this procedure until you obtain no more heads.

Trial #	Number of flips	Number of heads
1	100	
2		
3		
4		
5		
6		
7		

FOR REFERENCE ONLY

Analysis
Using your experimental data, record the answers to the following questions below your data table.

1. Use graph paper to plot the number of flips (*y*-axis) versus the trial number (*x*-axis). Draw a smooth line through the points.

2. Examine your graph. Is the rate of the number of heads produced over time linear or nonlinear? Is the rate constant over time or does it change?

3. Why does each trial reduce the number of heads by approximately one-half?

4. A half-life is the time required for one-half of the atoms of a radioisotope to emit radiation and to decay to products. What value represents one half-life for the process of flipping coins?

You're The Chemist
The following small-scale activities allow you to develop your own procedures and analyze the results.

1. **Design It!** Design and carry out an experiment using a single die to model radioactive decay. Plot your data.

2. **Analyze It!** Many radioisotopes undergo alpha decay. They emit an alpha particle (helium nucleus ^4_2He). For example,

$$^{222}_{86}Rn \longrightarrow \ ^{218}_{84}Po + \ ^4_2He$$

Find the half-life of radon-222 in Table 25.3 and determine how long it takes for only one eighth of a sample of radon-222 to remain.

3. **Analyze It!** Other radioisotopes undergo beta decay, emitting a beta particle (electron $^{\ 0}_{-1}e$). For example,

$$^{14}_{6}C \longrightarrow \ ^{14}_{7}N + \ ^{\ 0}_{-1}e$$

Find the half-life of carbon-14 in Table 25.3 and determine what fraction of the carbon-14 in a sample has not yet decayed by beta emission after 11,460 years.

New York Standards: 4.4b, 4.4e–f, 5.3c

Guide for Reading

Key Concepts

* What happens in a nuclear chain reaction?
* Why are spent fuel rods from a nuclear reaction stored in water?
* How do fission reactions and fusion reactions differ?

Vocabulary

fission
neutron moderation
neutron absorption
fusion

Reading Strategy

Identifying Details In the three paragraphs following the heading *Nuclear Fission,* the sentence describing a chain reaction states the main idea. List the details about energy changes in fission and chain reactions that are related to the main idea.

Connecting to Your World

The sun appears as a fiery ball in the sky—so bright it should never be viewed with unprotected eyes. Although its surface temperature is about 5800 K, the sun is not actually burning. If the energy given off by the sun were the product of a combustion reaction, the sun would have burned out approximately 2000 years after it was formed, long before today. In this section, you will learn how energy is produced in the sun.

Nuclear Fission

When the nuclei of certain isotopes are bombarded with neutrons, they undergo **fission,** the splitting of a nucleus into smaller fragments. Uranium-235 and plutonium-239 are the only fissionable isotopes. Figure 25.10 shows how a fissionable atom, such as uranium-235, breaks into two fragments of roughly the same size when struck by a slow-moving neutron. At the same time, more neutrons are released by the fission. These neutrons strike the nuclei of other uranium-235 atoms, continuing the fission by a chain reaction. **In a chain reaction, some of the neutrons produced react with other fissionable atoms, producing more neutrons which react with still more fissionable atoms.**

Nuclear fission can release enormous amounts of energy. The fission of 1 kg of uranium-235, for example, yields an amount of energy equal to that generated in the explosion of 20,000 tons of dynamite. In an uncontrolled nuclear chain reaction, the total energy release takes only fractions of a second. Atomic bombs are devices that start uncontrolled nuclear chain reactions.

Figure 25.10 In nuclear fission, a uranium-235 nucleus breaks into two smaller nuclei and releases neutrons. **Predicting** *What happens when the released neutrons strike other uranium-235 nuclei?*

Figure 25.11 A nuclear reactor uses controlled fission to produce useful energy. The illustration shows the basic components of a nuclear reactor. Energy from the fission process heats the circulating coolant. The heated coolant is used to produce steam that turns a steam-driven turbine. The turbine drives a generator to produce electrical energy.

Fission can be controlled so energy is released more slowly. Nuclear reactors, such as the one illustrated in Figure 25.11, use controlled fission to produce useful energy. In the controlled fission reaction within a nuclear reactor, much of the energy generated is in the form of heat. A coolant fluid, usually liquid sodium or water, removes the heat from the reactor core. The heat is used to generate steam, which drives a turbine that in turn generates electricity. The control of fission in a nuclear reactor involves two steps, neutron moderation and neutron absorption.

Neutron Moderation **Neutron moderation** is a process that slows down neutrons so the reactor fuel (uranium-235 or plutonium-239) captures them to continue the chain reaction. Moderation is necessary because most of the neutrons produced move so fast that they will pass right through a nucleus without being absorbed. Water and carbon in the form of graphite are good moderators.

Neutron Absorption To prevent the chain reaction from going too fast, some of the slowed neutrons must be trapped before they hit fissionable atoms. **Neutron absorption** is a process that decreases the number of slow-moving neutrons. Control rods, made of a material such as cadmium, are used to absorb neutrons. When the control rods extend almost all the way into the reactor core, they absorb many neutrons, and fission occurs slowly. As the rods are pulled out, they absorb fewer neutrons and the fission process speeds up. If the chain reaction were to go too fast, heat might be produced faster than the coolant could remove it. In this case, the reactor core would overheat, which could lead to mechanical failure and release of radioactive materials into the atmosphere. Ultimately, a meltdown of the reactor core might occur.

 Checkpoint *Why must neutrons in a reactor be slowed down?*

interactive Textbook

Animation 30 Take a close look at a nuclear fission chain reaction.

— with **ChemASAP**

Nuclear Waste

Fuel rods from nuclear power plants are one major source of nuclear waste. The fuel rods are made from a fissionable isotope, either uranium-235 or plutonium-239. The fuel rods are long and narrow—typically 3 meters long with a 0.5-cm diameter. Three hundred fuel rods are bundled together to form an assembly, and one hundred assemblies are arranged to form the reactor core. During fission, the amount of fissionable isotope in each fuel rod decreases. Eventually there is no longer enough fuel in the rods to ensure that the output of the power station remains constant. The isotope-depleted, or spent, fuel rods must be removed and replaced with new fuel rods.

Spent fuel rods are classified as high-level nuclear waste. They contain a mixture of highly radioactive isotopes, including both the fission products and what remains of the nuclear fuel. Some of these fission products have very short half-lives, on the order of fractions of seconds. Others have half-lives of hundreds or thousands of years. All nuclear power plants have holding tanks, or "swimming pools," for spent fuel rods. **Water cools the spent rods, and also acts as a radiation shield to reduce the radiation levels.** The pools, like the one shown in Figure 25.12, are typically 12 meters deep, and are filled with water. Storage racks at the bottom of these pools are designed to hold the spent fuel assemblies. The rods continue to produce heat for years after their removal from the core.

The assemblies of spent fuel rods may spend a decade or more in a holding tank. In the past, plant operators expected used fuel rods to be reprocessed to recover the remaining fissionable isotope, which would be recycled in the manufacture of new fuel rods. However, with large deposits of uranium ore available—many in the United States—it is less expensive to mine new fuel than to reprocess depleted fuel. At some nuclear plants, there is no space left in the storage pool. In order to keep these plants open, their fuel rods must be moved to off-site storage facilities.

Figure 25.12 Racks at the bottom of this pool contain spent fuel rods. The blue glow is from beta particles that the rods emit into the water.

4$^1_1$H $^4_2$He   2$^0_{+1}$e
hydrogen nuclei   helium nucleus   positrons

Figure 25.13 In solar fusion, hydrogen nuclei fuse to produce helium nuclei. **Interpreting Diagrams** *What other particles are produced by this reaction?*

Nuclear Fusion

The sun, directly and indirectly, is the source of most energy used on Earth. The energy released by the sun results from nuclear fusion. **Fusion** occurs when nuclei combine to produce a nucleus of greater mass. In solar fusion, hydrogen nuclei (protons) fuse to make helium nuclei. Figure 25.13 shows that the reaction also produces two positrons. 🔑 **Fusion reactions, in which small nuclei combine, release much more energy than fission reactions, in which large nuclei split.** However, fusion reactions occur only at very high temperatures—in excess of 40,000,000°C.

The use of controlled nuclear fusion as an energy source on Earth is appealing. The potential fuels are inexpensive and readily available. One reaction that scientists are studying is the combination of a deuterium (hydrogen-2) nucleus and a tritium (hydrogen-3) nucleus to form a helium nucleus.

$$^2_1H + {}^3_1H \longrightarrow {}^4_2He + {}^1_0n + energy$$

The problems with fusion lie in achieving the high temperatures necessary to start the reaction and in containing the reaction once it has started. The high temperatures required to initiate fusion reactions have been achieved by using a fission bomb. Such a bomb is the triggering device used for setting off a hydrogen bomb, which is an uncontrolled-fusion device. Such a process is clearly of no use, however, as a controlled generator of power.

Word *Origins*

Fusion comes from the Latin word *fusus* meaning "melt together." Fusion is the combination of two low-mass nuclei to form a nucleus of larger mass, accompanied by the release of a large amount of energy. **In politics, what might be the goal of a fusionist?**

25.3 Section Assessment

15. 🔑 **Key Concept** Explain what happens in a nuclear chain reaction.

16. 🔑 **Key Concept** Why are spent fuel rods from a nuclear reaction stored in water?

17. 🔑 **Key Concept** How are fusion reactions different from fission reactions?

18. What does nuclear moderation accomplish in a nuclear reactor?

19. What is the source of the radioactive nuclei present in spent fuel rods?

20. Assuming technical problems could be overcome, what are some advantages to using a fusion reactor to produce electricity?

Elements ▶ Handbook

Heavy Water Reactors Read the paragraph on Heavy Water Reactors on page R39 of the Elements Handbook. Use what you have learned about nuclear reactors to explain what a neutron moderator does, and then explain the advantages of using heavy water instead of ordinary water as a neutron moderator.

Interactive Textbook

Assessment 25.3 Test yourself on the concepts in Section 25.3.

—with **ChemASAP**

Dating a Fossil

Direct information about earlier life on Earth comes from fossils and artifacts. The age of an artifact of biological origin, such as bone, wood, cloth, and plant fibers, from 200 to about 50,000 years old can be determined by carbon-14 dating. All living organisms contain carbon-12 and carbon-14 in a fixed ratio. After an organism dies, the ratio of carbon-12 to carbon-14 changes. Carbon-14 is radioactive with a half-life of 5730 years and decays to nitrogen-14, while carbon-12 remains constant.

Calculating *An unearthed wooden tool was found to have only 50% of the carbon-14 content of a sample of living wood. How old is the wooden tool?*

Archaeology Archaeologists study the life and culture of the past, especially ancient peoples, by excavating ancient cities, relics, and artifacts.

The Wooly Mammoth The fossil remains of a woolly mammoth are found in Pleistocene deposits (the Pleistocene epoch was from 2,500,000 to 10,000 years ago). The abundance of well-preserved carcasses in the permanently frozen ground of Siberia have provided much information about these extinct animals.

C. 23,000 BC	**C. 17,300 BC**	**C. 11,600 BC**	**C. 5,900 BC**
At the time of death, the carbon-12 to carbon-14 ratio of the woolly mammoth was very similar to that of an animal living today.	The carbon-14 in the dead mammoth was one-half of its value in 23,000 BC.	The carbon-14 was 25% of its initial value.	After another 5,730 years, the carbon-14 is now 12.5% of its 23,000 BC value.

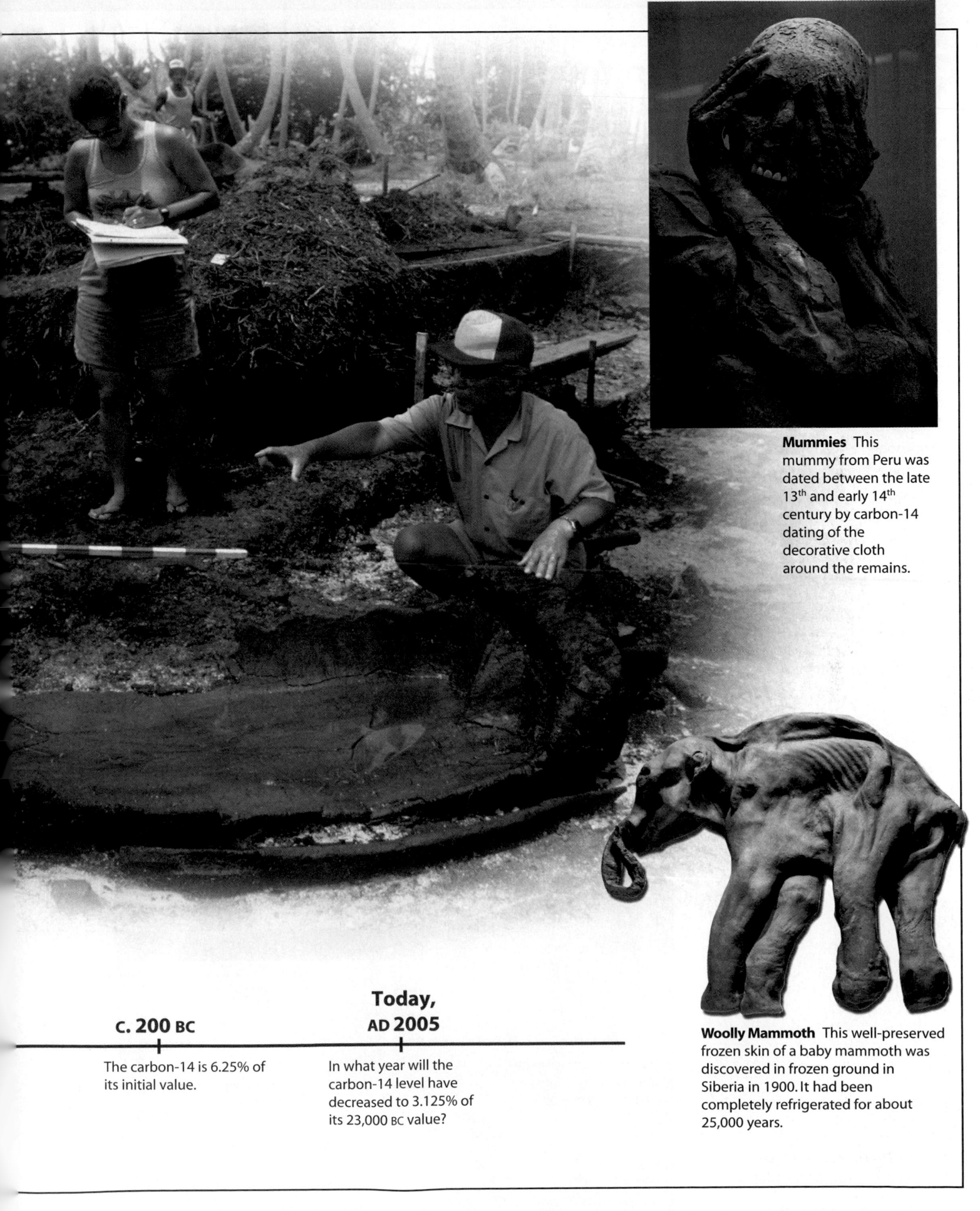

Mummies This mummy from Peru was dated between the late 13th and early 14th century by carbon-14 dating of the decorative cloth around the remains.

Today,
AD 2005

c. 200 BC

The carbon-14 is 6.25% of its initial value.

In what year will the carbon-14 level have decreased to 3.125% of its 23,000 BC value?

Woolly Mammoth This well-preserved frozen skin of a baby mammoth was discovered in frozen ground in Siberia in 1900. It had been completely refrigerated for about 25,000 years.

New York Standards: 4.4d–e

Guide for Reading

Key Concepts
- What are three devices used to detect radiation?
- How are radioisotopes used in medicine?

Vocabulary
ionizing radiation
Geiger counter
scintillation counter
film badge
neutron activation analysis

Reading Strategy
Summarizing When you summarize, you review and state, in the correct order, the main points you have read. As you read about using radiation, write a brief summary of the text following each use that is discussed. Your summary should include only the most important information.

Connecting to Your World

A common household smoke detector uses the radiation from a radioisotope. The smoke detector contains a small amount of americium, $^{241}_{95}$Am, in the form AmO_2. Radiation from the $^{241}_{95}$Am nuclei ionizes the nitrogen and oxygen in smoke-free air, allowing a current to flow. When smoke particles get in the way, they are ionized instead. The drop in current is detected by an electronic circuit, causing it to sound an alarm. In this section, you will learn about some of the other practical uses of radiation.

Detecting Radiation

Radiation emitted by radioisotopes is called ionizing radiation. **Ionizing radiation** is radiation with enough energy to knock electrons off some atoms of the bombarded substance to produce ions. Radiation cannot be seen, heard, felt, or smelled. Thus radiation detection instruments must be used to alert people to the presence of radiation and to monitor its level.

Devices such as Geiger counters, scintillation counters, and film badges are commonly used to detect radiation. These devices operate because of the effects of the radiation when it strikes atoms or molecules. For example, the radiation can produce ions, which can then be detected, or it can expose a photographic plate and produce images such as the one shown in Figure 25.14. When the plate is developed, its darkened areas show where the plate has been exposed to radiation.

 What is ionizing radiation?

Figure 25.14 Radiation can expose a photographic plate.

Geiger Counter A **Geiger counter** uses a gas-filled metal tube to detect radiation. The tube has a central wire electrode that is connected to a power supply. When ionizing radiation penetrates a thin window at one end of tube, the gas inside the tube becomes ionized. Because of the ions and free electrons produced, the gas becomes an electrical conductor. Each time a Geiger tube is exposed to radiation, current flows. The bursts of current drive electronic counters or cause audible clicks from a built-in speaker. Geiger counters can detect alpha, beta, and gamma radiation.

Geiger counter

Scintillation counter

Scintillation Counter A **scintillation counter** uses a phosphor-coated surface to detect radiation. Ionizing radiation striking the phosphor surface produces bright flashes of light, or scintillations. The number of flashes and their respective energies are detected electronically. The information is then converted into electronic pulses, which are measured and recorded. Scintillation counters have been designed to detect all types of ionizing radiation.

Film Badge A **film badge** consists of several layers of photographic film covered with black lightproof paper, all encased in a plastic or metal holder. The film badge is an important radiation detector for persons who work near any type of radiation source. The badge is worn the entire time the person is at work. At specific intervals, with the frequency depending on the type of work involved, the film is removed and developed. The strength and type of radiation exposure are determined from the darkening of the film. Records are kept of the results. Film badges do not protect a person from radiation exposure, but they do monitor the degree of exposure to radiation. Protection against radiation is achieved by keeping a safe distance from the source and by using adequate shielding.

Film badge

Studying Inverse-Square Relationships

Flashlight

1cm × 1cm
square opening

Duct tape

Purpose

To demonstrate the relationship between radiation intensity and the distance from the radiation source.

Materials

- flashlight
- strips of duct tape
- scissors
- poster board, white (50 cm × 50 cm)
- meter ruler or tape measure
- flat surface, long enough to hold the meter ruler
- loose-leaf paper
- graph paper
- pen or pencil
- light sensor (optional)

Procedure

 Probeware version available in the Probeware Lab Manual.

1. Measure and record the distance (*A*) from the bulb filament to the front surface of the flashlight.

2. Cover the end of a flashlight with tape. Leave a 1 cm × 1 cm square hole in the center.

3. Place the flashlight on its side on a flat, horizontal surface. Turn on the flashlight. Darken the room.

4. Mount a large piece of white poster board in front of the flashlight, perpendicular to the horizontal surface.

5. Move the flashlight away from the board in short increments. At each position, record the distance (*B*) from the flashlight to the board and the length (*L*) of one side of the square image on the board.

6. On a sheet of graph paper, plot *L* on the *y*-axis versus *A* + *B* on the *x*-axis. On another sheet, plot L^2 on the *y*-axis versus *A* + *B* on the *x*-axis.

Analyze and Conclude

1. As the flashlight is moved away from the board, what do you notice about the intensity of the light in the illuminated square? Use your graphs to describe the relationship between intensity and distance.

2. When the distance of the flashlight from the board is doubled and tripled, what happens to the areas and intensities of the illuminated squares?

Using Radiation

Although radiation can be harmful, it can be used safely and is important in many scientific procedures. **Neutron activation analysis** is a procedure used to detect trace amounts of elements in samples. A sample of the material to be studied is bombarded with neutrons from a radioactive source. Some atoms in the sample become radioactive. The half-life and type of radiation emitted by the radioisotopes are detected, and a computer processes this information. Because this information is characteristic for each element, scientists can determine what radioisotopes were produced and what elements were originally in the sample. Neutron activation analysis is used by museums to detect art forgeries, and by crime laboratories to analyze gunpowder residues.

Radioisotopes called tracers are used in agriculture to test the effects of herbicides, pesticides, and fertilizers. The tracer is introduced into the substance being tested to make the substance radioactive. Next, the plants are treated with the radioactively labeled substance. Then, the radioactivity of the plants is measured to find the locations of the substance. Often, the tracer is also monitored in animals that consume the plants, in water, and in soil.

Go Online
SCLINKS

For: Links on Radioactive Tracers
Visit: www.scilinks.org
Web Code: cdn-1254

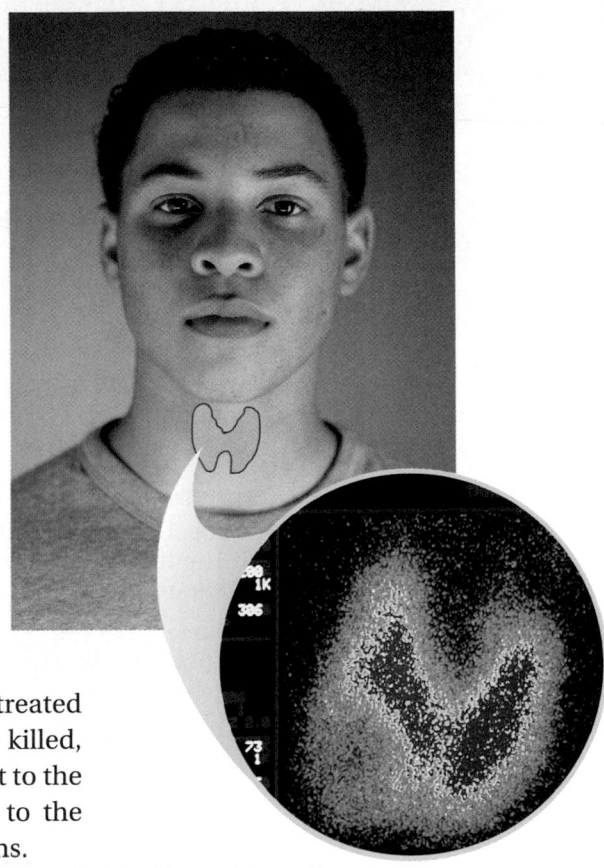

Radioisotopes can be used to diagnose medical problems and, in some cases, to treat diseases. Iodine-131, for example, is used to detect thyroid problems. The thyroid gland extracts iodide ions from the bloodstream and uses them to make the hormone thyroxine. To diagnose thyroid disease, the patient is given a drink containing a small amount of the radioisotope iodine-131. After about two hours, the amount of iodide uptake is measured by scanning the patient's throat with a radiation detector. Figure 25.15 shows the results of such a scan. In a similar way, the radioisotope technetium-99m is used to detect brain tumors and liver disorders. Phosphorus-32 is used to detect skin cancer.

Radiation has become a routine part of the treatment of some cancers. Cancer is a disease in which abnormal cells in the body are produced at a rate far beyond the rate for normal cells. The mass of cancerous tissue resulting from this runaway growth is called a tumor. Radiation therapy is often used to treat cancer because the fast-growing cancer cells are more susceptible to damage by high-energy radiation such as gamma rays than are the healthy cells. The cancerous area can be treated with radiation to kill the cancer cells. Some normal cells are also killed, however, and cancer cells at the center of the tumor may be resistant to the radiation. Therefore, the benefits of the treatment and the risks to the patient must be carefully evaluated before radiation treatment begins.

In a technique called teletherapy, a narrow beam of high-intensity gamma radiation is directed at cancerous tissue. Salts of radioisotopes can also be sealed in gold tubes and directly implanted in tumors. These seeds emit beta and gamma rays that kill the surrounding cancer cells. Because the radioisotope is in a sealed container, it is prevented from traveling throughout the body.

Pharmaceuticals containing radioisotopes of gold, iodine, or phosphorus are sometimes given in radiation therapy. For example, a dose of iodine-131 larger than that used simply to detect thyroid diseases can be given to treat the diseased thyroid. The radioactive iodine accumulates in the thyroid and emits beta and gamma rays to provide therapy.

Figure 25.15 This scanned image of a thyroid gland shows where radioactive iodine-131 has been absorbed. Doctors use these images to identify thyroid disorders.

25.4 Section Assessment

21. **Key Concept** Describe three methods of detecting radiation.

22. **Key Concept** Describe two applications of radioisotopes in medicine.

23. If you work regularly near a radiation source, why might your employer want to monitor your exposure to radiation by having you use a film badge rather than a Geiger counter?

24. What is an advantage of using a radioactive seed, consisting of a radioisotope in a small gold tube, to treat a cancerous tumor?

Writing Activity

Write a Report Research and report how technetium-99m is produced, what the letter *m* at the end of its name means, and how the isotope is used in bone imaging and other methods of medical diagnosis.

Textbook

Assessment 25.4 Test yourself on the concepts in Section 25.4.

with ChemASAP

Study Guide

Key Concepts

25.1 Nuclear Radiation
- An unstable nucleus loses energy by emitting radiation during the process of radioactive decay.
- The three main types of radiation are alpha radiation, beta radiation, and gamma radiation.

25.2 Nuclear Transformations
- The type of radioactive decay that occurs depends on the neutron-to-proton ratio of the unstable nucleus.
- After each half-life, half of the existing atoms have decayed into atoms of a new element.
- Transmutation can occur by radioactive decay, and can also occur when particles bombard the nucleus of an atom.

25.3 Fission and Fusion of Atomic Nuclei
- In a chain reaction, some of the neutrons produced react with other fissionable atoms, producing more neutrons which react with still more fissionable atoms.
- Spent fuel rods are stored in on-site pools of water to absorb the heat they continue generating and to help reduce radiation levels.
- In nuclear fusion, light nuclei fuse to make more massive nuclei. In fission, massive nuclei split apart to form less massive nuclei.

25.4 Radiation in Your Life
- Radiation may be detected with a Geiger counter or a scintillation counter. A film badge monitors radiation exposure of individuals who work with radioactive materials.
- Radioactivity and radiation are used in medical diagnosis, and in the treatment of some diseases, including some forms of cancer.

Vocabulary

- alpha particle (p. 800)
- band of stability (p. 803)
- beta particle (p. 801)
- film badge (p. 817)
- fission (p. 810)
- fusion (p. 813)
- gamma ray (p. 802)
- Geiger counter (p. 817)
- half-life (p. 804)
- ionizing radiation (p. 816)
- neutron absorption (p. 811)
- neutron activation analysis (p. 818)
- neutron moderation (p. 811)
- positron (p. 804)
- radiation (p. 799)
- radioactivity (p. 799)
- radioisotopes (p. 799)
- scintillation counter (p. 817)
- transmutation (p. 807)
- transuranium elements (p. 808)

Key Equations

- $^{238}_{92}\text{U} \xrightarrow{\text{Radioactive decay}} {}^{234}_{90}\text{Th} + {}^{4}_{2}\text{He}$

- $^{14}_{6}\text{C} \longrightarrow {}^{14}_{7}\text{N} + {}^{0}_{-1}\text{e}$

- $^{1}_{0}\text{n} \longrightarrow {}^{1}_{1}\text{H} + {}^{0}_{-1}\text{e}$

- $^{230}_{90}\text{Th} \longrightarrow {}^{226}_{88}\text{Ra} + {}^{4}_{2}\text{He} + \gamma$

Organizing Information

Use these terms to construct a concept map that organizes the major ideas of this chapter.

Concept Map 25 Solve the Concept Map with the help of an interactive guided tutorial.

—with **ChemASAP**

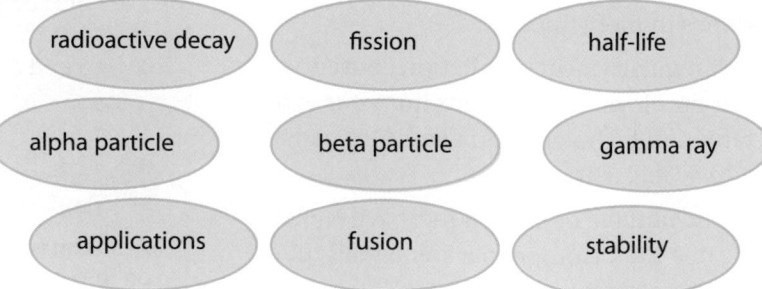

radioactive decay · fission · half-life · alpha particle · beta particle · gamma ray · applications · fusion · stability

25.1 Nuclear Radiation

25. Explain the difference between an isotope and a radioisotope.

26. The disintegration of the radioisotope radium-226 produces an isotope of the element radon and alpha radiation. The atomic number of radium (Ra) is 88; the atomic number of radon (Rn) is 86. Write a balanced equation for this transformation.

27. A radioisotope of the element lead (Pb) decays to an isotope of the element bismuth (Bi) by emission of a beta particle. Complete the equation for the decay process by supplying the missing atomic number and mass number.

$$^{210}Pb \longrightarrow\ _{83}Bi +\ _{-1}^{0}e$$

28. Write the symbol and charge for each.
a. alpha particle
b. beta particle
c. gamma ray

29. Alpha radiation is emitted during the disintegration of the following isotopes. Write balanced nuclear equations for their decay processes. Name the element produced in each case.
a. uranium-238 ($_{92}^{238}U$)   b. thorium-230 ($_{90}^{230}Th$)
c. uranium-235 ($_{92}^{235}U$)   d. radon-222 ($_{86}^{222}Rn$)

30. The following radioisotopes are beta emitters. Write balanced nuclear equations for their decay processes.
a. carbon-14 ($_{6}^{14}C$)   b. strontium-90 ($_{38}^{90}Sr$)
c. potassium-40 ($_{19}^{40}K$)   d. nitrogen-13 ($_{7}^{13}N$)

31. How are the mass number and atomic number of a nucleus affected by the loss of the following?
a. beta particle
b. alpha particle
c. gamma ray

32. The following radioactive nuclei decay by emitting alpha particles. Write the product of the decay process for each.
a. $_{92}^{238}Pu$ b. $_{83}^{210}Bi$
c. $_{84}^{210}Po$ d. $_{90}^{230}Th$

33. Complete these nuclear equations.
a. $_{15}^{32}P \longrightarrow \boxed{} +\ _{-1}^{0}e$
b. $\boxed{} \longrightarrow\ _{7}^{14}N +\ _{-1}^{0}e$
c. $_{92}^{238}U \longrightarrow\ _{90}^{234}Th + \boxed{}$
d. $_{56}^{141}Ba \longrightarrow \boxed{} +\ _{-1}^{0}e$
e. $\boxed{} \longrightarrow\ _{77}^{181}Ir +\ _{2}^{4}He$

34. Write nuclear equations for the beta decay of the following isotopes.
a. $_{38}^{90}Sr$ b. $_{6}^{14}C$ c. $_{55}^{137}Cs$ d. $_{93}^{239}Np$ e. $_{22}^{50}Ti$

35. How many protons and how many neutrons are in each of the following nuclei?
a. $_{27}^{60}Co$ b. $_{82}^{206}Pb$ c. $_{90}^{233}Th$ d. $_{1}^{3}H$

36. Write balanced nuclear equations for the alpha decay of each of the following isotopes.
a. $_{91}^{231}Pa$ b. $_{95}^{241}Am$ c. $_{88}^{226}Ra$ d. $_{99}^{252}Es$

37. Write balanced nuclear equations for the beta decay of each of the following.
a. $_{1}^{3}H$ b. $_{12}^{28}Mg$ c. $_{53}^{131}I$ d. $_{34}^{75}Se$

38. Why does the relatively large mass and charge of an alpha particle make it less penetrating than beta and gamma radiation?

39. Why might radioisotopes of C, N, and O be especially harmful to living organisms?

40. Plutonium-239 emits alpha particles and is therefore especially hazardous when inhaled or ingested. What new element is formed by this alpha emission? Write a balanced nuclear equation.

41. Bismuth-211 is a radioisotope. It decays by alpha emission to yield another radioisotope, which emits beta radiation as it decays to a stable isotope. Write equations for the nuclear reactions and name the decay products.

42. What isotope remains after three beta particles and five alpha particles are lost from a thorium-234 isotope? (Refer to the uranium-238 decay series to check your answer.)

43. Uranium has a density of 19 g/cm³. What volume does a mass of 8.0 kg of uranium occupy?

44. Element 107 is formed when nuclei of element 109 each emit an alpha particle. Nuclei of element 107, in turn, also each emit an alpha particle. Write balanced equations for these two nuclear reactions. Include the atomic number and mass number of each isotope that results in each of the two steps.

25.2 Nuclear Transformations

45. What happens to an atom with a nucleus that falls outside the band of stability?

46. Write an equation for the radioactive decay of fluorine-17 by positron emission.

47. Identify the more stable isotope in each pair.

    a. $^{14}_{6}\text{C}$, $^{13}_{6}\text{C}$ b. $^{3}_{1}\text{H}$, $^{1}_{1}\text{H}$

    c. $^{16}_{8}\text{O}$, $^{18}_{8}\text{O}$ d. $^{14}_{7}\text{N}$, $^{15}_{7}\text{N}$

48. Why is it important that radioactive isotopes used internally for diagnosis or treatment have relatively short half-lives?

49. Explain half-life.

50. A patient is administered 20 mg of iodine-131. How much of this isotope will remain in the body after 40 days if the half-life for iodine-131 is 8 days?

51. What is the difference between natural and artificial radiation?

52. What are the transuranium elements? Why are they unusual?

53. Write nuclear equations for these conversions.

    a. $^{30}_{15}\text{P}$ to $^{30}_{14}\text{Si}$

    b. $^{13}_{6}\text{C}$ to $^{14}_{6}\text{C}$

    c. $^{131}_{53}\text{I}$ to $^{131}_{54}\text{Xe}$

54. The following graph shows the radioactive decay curve for thorium-234. Use the graph to answer the questions.

Thorium-234 Decay

a. What percent of the isotope remains after 60 days?

b. How many grams of a 250-g sample of thorium-234 would remain after 40 days had passed?

c. How many days would pass while 44 g of thorium-234 decayed to 4.4 g of thorium-234?

d. What is the half-life of thorium-234?

55. Write a nuclear equation for each word equation.

    a. Radon-222 emits an alpha particle to form polonium-218.

    b. Radium-230 is produced when thorium-234 emits an alpha particle.

    c. When polonium-210 emits an alpha particle, the product is lead-206.

56. Describe the various contributions the following people made to the fields of nuclear and radiation chemistry.

    a. Marie Curie   b. Antoine Henri Becquerel

    c. James Chadwick   d. Ernest Rutherford

57. If you started with 32 million radioactive atoms, how many would you have left after five half-lives?

58. A radioactive nucleus decays to give an alpha particle and a bismuth-211 ($^{211}_{83}\text{Bi}$) nucleus. What was the original element?

59. The carbon-14 in an artifact gives 4 counts per minute per gram of carbon. Living matter has a carbon-14 content that gives 32 counts per minute per gram of carbon. What is the age of the artifact?

60. Complete the following nuclear reaction equations.

a. $^{38}_{19}\text{K} \longrightarrow {}^{38}_{18}\text{Ca} + ?$

b. $^{242}_{94}\text{Pu} \longrightarrow ? + {}^{4}_{2}\text{He}$

c. $^{68}_{31}\text{Ga} \longrightarrow ? + {}^{0}_{+1}\text{e}$

d. $^{68}_{32}\text{Ge} \longrightarrow {}^{68}_{33}\text{Ga} + ?$

61. The ratio of carbon-14 to carbon-12 in a chunk of charcoal from an archeological dig is determined to be one-half the ratio in a piece of freshly cut wood. How old is the dig site?

62. Name the elements represented by the following symbols and indicate which of them would have no stable isotopes.

a. Pt **b.** Th **c.** Fr **d.** Ti

e. Xe **f.** Cf **g.** V **h.** Pd

63. Compare the half-life of an element to a single-elimination sports tournament.

64. When neutrons bombard magnesium-24 ($^{24}_{12}\text{Mg}$), photons are ejected. What new element is formed?

65. Tritium (hydrogen-3) has a half-life of 12.3 years. How old is a bottle of wine if the tritium activity is determined to be 25% that of new wine?

66. The radioisotope cesium-137 has a half-life of 30 years. A sample decayed at the rate of 544 counts per minute in the year 1985. In what year will the decay rate be 17 counts per minute?

67. Describe the process depicted in the following graph.

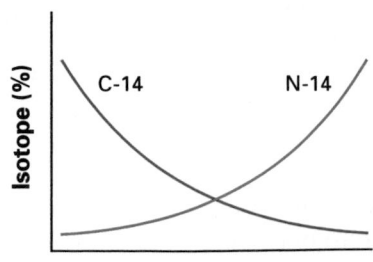

25.3 Fission and Fusion of Atomic Nuclei

68. Describe the process of nuclear fission and define a nuclear chain reaction.

69. Why are spent fuel rods removed from a reactor core? What do they contain? What happens to them after they are removed?

70. Fusion reactions produce enormous amounts of energy. Why is fusion not used to generate electrical power?

71. What is the difference between the nuclear reactions taking place in the sun and the nuclear reactions taking place in a nuclear reactor?

72. A target of bismuth-209 was bombarded with iron-58 for several days. One atom of element 109 with a mass number of 266 was produced. How many neutrons were released in the process?

$$^{209}_{83}\text{Bi} + {}^{58}_{26}\text{Fe} \longrightarrow {}^{266}_{109}X + ?\,{}^{1}_{0}\text{n}$$

73. A 0.25-mg sample of californium-249 ($^{249}_{98}\text{Cf}$) was used as the target in the synthesis of element 106. Four neutrons were emitted for each transformed $^{249}_{98}\text{Cf}$, and the result was a nucleus with 106 protons and a mass of 263 amu. What was the bombarding particle?

$$^{249}_{98}\text{Cf} + ? \longrightarrow 4\,{}^{1}_{0}\text{n} + {}^{263}_{106}X$$

25.4 Radiation in Your Life

74. Why are x-rays and the radiation emitted by radioisotopes called ionizing radiation?

75. What is the purpose of wearing a film badge when working with ionizing radiation sources?

76. Explain how iodine-131 is used in both the diagnosis and treatment of thyroid disease.

77. Write a paragraph analyzing the overall logic of the reasoning in the following argument.
(1) Radiation kills fast-growing cells.
(2) Cancer cells are fast-growing.
(3) Therefore, radiation kills only cancer cells.

Test-Taking Tip

Anticipate the Answer Use what you know to decide what you think the answer should be. Then look to see if your answer, or one much like it, is given as an option.

Regents Practice Exam

Part A

For each statement or question write the number of the word or expression that, of those given, best completes the statement or answers the question.

1. Which of the following choices is *not* a common notation of an atom with an atomic mass of 14 amu and an atomic number of 6?
   (1) carbon-14
   (2) carbon-6
   (3) $^{14}_{6}C$
   (4) C-14

2. Stability of an isotope is based on the ratio of
   (1) protons and neutrons
   (2) protons and electrons
   (3) electrons and neutrons
   (4) positive charges to negative charges

3. Spontaneous decay of isotopes can result in the release of
   (1) electromagnetic radiation only
   (2) alpha and beta particles only
   (3) alpha particles, beta particles, positrons, or gamma radiation
   (4) alpha particles, beta particles, positrons, neutrons, or gamma radiation

4. An organic compound that has a —COOH functional group is a(n)
   (1) alcohol
   (2) organic acid
   (3) ester
   (4) aldehyde

5. Nuclear reactions do *not* include
   (1) decomposition reactions
   (2) transmutations
   (3) fission
   (4) fusion

6. Nuclear reactions must balance in regard to
   (1) atomic number
   (2) charge
   (3) mass number
   (4) all of the above

Part B-1

For each statement or question write the number of the word or expression that, of those given, best completes the statement or answers the question.

7. Which of the following classes of compounds does *not* contain a carbon-oxygen double bond?
   (1) amide
   (2) ketone
   (3) aldehyde
   (4) organic acid

Use the following graph to answer Question 8.

Stable Nuclei

8. Which of the following isotopes has stable nuclei?
   (1) neodymium-130
   (2) uranium-238
   (3) iodine-131
   (4) zirconium-90

9. If a radioisotope undergoes beta emission, the
   (1) atomic number changes
   (2) number of neutrons remains constant
   (3) isotope loses a proton
   (4) mass number changes

10. The radioisotope radon-222 has a half-life of 3.8 days. How much of an initial 20.0-g sample of radon-222 would remain after 15.2 days?
    (1) 5.00 g
    (2) 12.5 g
    (3) 1.25 g
    (4) 2.50 g

11. Which of the following statements about uses of radioisotopes is *not* true?
    (1) Radioisotopes are used to treat certain cancers.
    (2) Radioisotopes can be used to treat some diseases but not diagnose them.
    (3) Certain radioisotopes are used as radioactive tracers.
    (4) Radiation therapy involves radioisotopes.

Part B-2

Answer each of the following questions.

12. How many protons, neutrons, and electrons are in an atom of each of the following isotopes?
    a. iron-59
    b. uranium-235
    c. chromium-52

13. Balance the following chemical equations.
   a. $Ca(OH)_2 + HCl \longrightarrow CaCl_2 + H_2O$
   b. $Fe_2O_3 + H_2 \longrightarrow Fe + H_2O$
   c. $NaHCO_3 + H_2SO_4 \longrightarrow Na_2SO_4 + CO_2 + H_2O$
   d. $C_2H_6 + O_2 \longrightarrow CO_2 + H_2O$

14. Identify the bonds between each of the following pairs of atoms as ionic or covalent.
   a. carbon and silicon
   b. calcium and fluorine
   c. sulfur and nitrogen
   d. bromine and cesium

15. A 10.0-mol sample of magnesium is added to sulfuric acid. If the magnesium reacts completely, how many moles of hydrogen gas are produced?

16. You have a 0.30M solution of sodium sulfate. What volume (in mL) must be measured to give 0.0020 mol of sodium sulfate?

17. Write the structural formula for each of the following compounds.
   a. 2, 2-dimethylhexane
   b. 2-methyl-2-heptene
   c. 2-butyne
   d. 3-ethyloctane

18. Name each of the following compounds.
   a. CH_3CH_2COOH
   b. CH_3CH_2CHO
   c. $CH_3CH_2CH_2OH$
   d. $CH_3CH_2CH_2NH_2$
   e. $CH_3CH_2CH_2Cl$
   f. $CH_3CH_2OCH_3$

19. What particle is needed to balance the following nuclear equation?

$$^{27}_{13}Al + {}^{4}_{2}He \longrightarrow \underline{\hspace{1.5cm}} + {}^{30}_{15}P$$

For each nuclear equation in Questions 20–22, name the particle that is being emitted.

20. $^{59}_{26}Fe \longrightarrow {}^{59}_{27}Co + {}^{0}_{-1}e$

21. $^{185}_{79}Au \longrightarrow {}^{181}_{77}Ir + {}^{4}_{2}He$

22. $^{118}_{54}Xe \longrightarrow {}^{118}_{53}I + {}^{0}_{+1}e$

Use the graph to answer Questions 23–25.

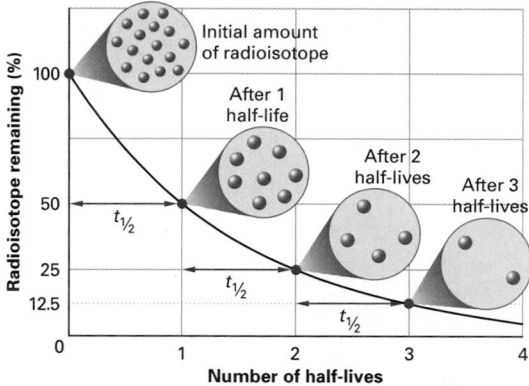

Decay Curve of a Radioactive Element

Estimate the percent remaining of the radioisotope after the given number of half-lives.

23. 0.5 $t_{1/2}$ **24.** 1.25 $t_{1/2}$ **25.** 3.75 $t_{1/2}$

26. Write the name and symbol for each of the following isotopes.

a.   **b.**   **c.**

○ Proton   ● Neutron

Part C

Answer each of the following questions.

27. Why would it be advantageous for radioactive tracers used in the study of living organisms to have a relatively short half-life?

28. Cobalt-60 is used to sterilize surgical instruments and irradiate food to help prevent spoilage. How many protons, neutrons, and electrons are in an atom of this isotope?

29. Smoke detectors commonly contain $^{241}_{95}Am$. This isotope undergoes alpha decay. What is the other product of this decay?

30. Strontium-90 is produced in small quantities in nuclear fission. Why might this isotope accumulate in the bones, possible causing bone cancer or leukemia?

Contents

Appendix A: Elements Handbook

Contents

How to Use the Elements Handbook

1. **Look for data that describes what the elements in a group have in common.**

2. **Interpret graphs to reveal trends in properties within a group.**

3. **Learn where elements exist in nature and how they are processed.**

4. **Find examples of typical chemical reactions.**

5. **Find out which compounds have important industrial uses.**

6. **Make connections between chemistry and technology.**

7. **Explore the impact of chemical reactions on the environment.**

8. **Find out the effects of certain chemicals on your health.**

9. **Discover some fun facts about elements.**

Elements Around You

Elements in Earth's Crust

Element	Parts per Million
Oxygen	466,000
Silicon	277,000
Aluminum	82,000
Iron	41,000
Calcium	41,000
Sodium	23,000
Potassium	21,000
Magnesium	21,000
Titanium	4400
Hydrogen	1400

Elements Dissolved in the Oceans

Element	Parts per Million
Chlorine	19,400
Sodium	10,800
Magnesium	1300
Sulfur	904
Calcium	411
Potassium	392
Bromine	67
Carbon	28
Strontium	8
Boron	5

Elements in the Atmosphere

Element	Parts per Million*
Nitrogen	780,900
Oxygen	209,500
Argon	9300
Neon	18
Helium	5.2
Krypton	1.14
Hydrogen	0.5
Xenon	0.086
Radon	Traces

*Data is for dry air.

Elements in the Sun

Element	Percent of Total Atoms
Hydrogen	92.1
Helium	7.8
Oxygen	0.078
Carbon	0.043
Nitrogen	0.0088
Silicon	0.0045
Magnesium	0.0038
Neon	0.0035
Iron	0.0030
Sulfur	0.0015

Elements Within You

Did You Know...

The mass of an adult's brain is about 2% of total body mass. Yet brain cells consume about 20% of the available **oxygen** when the body is at rest.

Did You Know...

Bacteria in the mouth produce **sulfur** compounds that cause bad breath. The culprits are hydrogen sulfide, H_2S, methyl mercaptan, CH_3SH, and dimethyl sulfide, $(CH_3)_2S$.

Did You Know...

The human body contains more **calcium** than any other metal. Your bones and teeth contain 99.2% of the calcium by mass.

Elements In the Human Body

Element	Percent of Total Body Mass
Oxygen	61
Carbon	23
Hydrogen	10
Nitrogen	2.6
Calcium	1.4
Phosphorus	1.1
Sulfur	0.2
Potassium	0.2
Sodium	0.14
Chlorine	0.12

Did You Know...

Although air is about 78% **nitrogen**, your body must get the nitrogen it needs from food, not from the air you inhale.

Did You Know...

There is evidence that white blood cells are able to produce toxic **chlorine** gas. The gas helps to protect against infection.

Did You Know...

Phosphorus is an important element for growth. So blood levels of the phosphate ion (PO_4^{3-}) in children are double what they are in adults.

Group 1A: Alkali Metals

Lithium | discovered in 1817 by Johan August Arfvedson

3	2 1
Li	
Lithium	
6.941	

Sodium | discovered in 1807 by Sir Humphry Davy

11	2 8 1
Na	
Sodium	
22.990	

Potassium | discovered in 1807 by Sir Humphry Davy

19	2 8 8 1
K	
Potassium	
39.098	

Rubidium | discovered in 1861 by Robert Bunsen & Gustav Kirchhoff

37	2 8 18 8 1
Rb	
Rubidium	
85.468	

Cesium | discovered in 1860 by Robert Bunsen & Gustav Kirchhoff

55	2 8 18 18 8 1
Cs	
Cesium	
132.91	

Francium | discovered in 1939 by Marguerite Perey

87	2 8 18 32 18 8 1
Fr	
Francium	
(223)	

Physical Properties

- Alkali metals are silver-gray solids that are soft enough to cut with a knife. They are soft because they have only one valence electron.

- The presence of a single valence electron also explains the low melting points and boiling points of alkali metals.

Pure alkali metals are stored under oil because they will tarnish on exposure to oxygen or moisture in air.

Melting and Boiling Points

Temperature (°C)

bp / mp

	Li	Na	K	Rb	Cs
bp	1336	883	758	700	670
mp	179	98	64	39	28

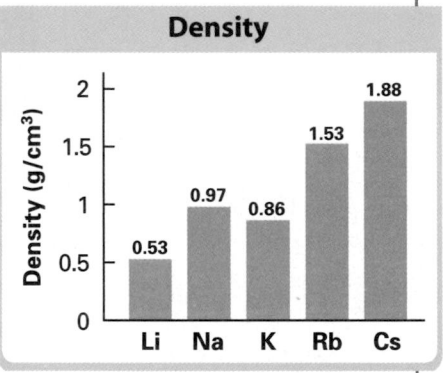

Density

Density (g/cm³)

Li	Na	K	Rb	Cs
0.53	0.97	0.86	1.53	1.88

Sources

- Alkali metals do not occur uncombined in nature because they are highly reactive.

- Sodium occurs widely as sodium chloride in underground salt and brine deposits. It is a major component of seawater.

- Sodium is the only alkali metal manufactured on a large scale. It is generally produced by the electrolysis of molten sodium chloride.

$$2NaCl(l) \longrightarrow 2Na(l) + Cl_2(g)$$

Lithium and potassium are produced by a similar process.

- The mineral sylvite, KCl, is a source of potassium.

Manufacture of Sodium

NaCl
$Cl_2(g)$
$Na(l)$
Molten NaCl
Molten Na
Steel cathode (−)
Iron screen
Graphite anode (+)

Atomic Properties

- Alkali metals have an electron configuration that ends in ns^1.
- Alkali metals form ions with a 1+ charge.
- The atoms of alkali metals are the largest in their periods.
- Cesium metal is used in photocells because its first ionization energy is very low.

First Ionization Energy

Energy (kJ/mol)

Li	Na	K	Rb	Cs
520	496	419	403	376

Electronegativity

Electronegativity

Li	Na	K	Rb	Cs	Fr
1.0	0.9	0.8	0.8	0.7	0.7

	Li	Na	K	Rb	Cs
Atomic radius (pm)	156	191	238	255	273
Ionic radius (pm)	60 Li^+	95 Na^+	133 K^+	148 Rb^+	169 Cs^+

Alkali metals can be identified by the colors produced when their compounds are heated in a flame.

Lithium   Sodium   Potassium   Rubidium   Cesium

Important Compounds and Reactions

- The alkali metals are the most reactive metals.
- All alkali metals react with water to form an alkaline solution. Example:

$$2K(s) + 2H_2O(l) \longrightarrow 2KOH(aq) + H_2(g)$$

- All alkali metals react with halogens to form an ionic halide. Example:

$$2Cs(s) + Cl_2(g) \longrightarrow 2CsCl(s)$$
$$\Delta H = -442.8 \text{ kJ/mol}$$

- Sodium hydrogen carbonate (baking soda) produces $CO_2(g)$ and steam, which causes baked goods to rise.

$$2NaHCO_3(s) \xrightarrow{\Delta} Na_2CO_3(s) + CO_2(g) + H_2O(g)$$
$$\Delta H = 129 \text{ kJ/mol}$$

- Lithium hydride is a convenient source for hydrogen.

$$LiH(s) + H_2O(l) \longrightarrow LiOH(aq) + H_2(g)$$

- Potassium superoxide, KO_2, is a source of oxygen in submarines. It removes CO_2 from the atmosphere as it produces oxygen.

$$4KO_2(s) + 2CO_2(g) \longrightarrow 2K_2CO_3(s) + 3O_2(g)$$

- Lithium carbonate, Li_2CO_3, is a prescription medicine for chronic depression.
- Sodium hypochlorite, NaOCl, is used as a bleach and to disinfect swimming pools.
- Sodium hydrogen carbonate, $NaHCO_3$, is used in fire extinguishers.
- Potassium nitrate, KNO_3, is used in matches and chemical fertilizers.
- Sodium hydroxide, NaOH, is used as a drain cleaner. It is also used to produce other chemicals and in many industrial processes.

Uses of NaOH

- 5%
- 13%
- 4%
- 14%
- 35%
- 32%

- Pulp and Paper
- Soaps and Detergents
- Petroleum
- Other Industries
- Organic Chemicals
- Inorganic Chemicals

Group 1A: Alkali Metals

Na Vapor Lamps

When streetlights have a golden glow, the source of the light is probably sodium vapor. Inside the lamp is a sealed tube containing a sodium-mercury alloy and a starter gas, such as xenon. Electrodes at each end of the tube are connected to an electric circuit. When the lamp is on, a continuous spark, or arc, forms between the electrodes. The arc produces enough heat to vaporize the sodium and mercury atoms. Within the arc, atoms ionize. Outside the arc, ions recombine with electrons and light is emitted—yellow for sodium and blue-green for mercury.

A sodium vapor lamp uses less energy than most other light sources and costs less to operate. But the lamp isn't a perfect light source.The color of an object is visible only when light of that color is reflected off the object. So yellow lines on the pavement appear yellow under a sodium vapor lamp, but a red stop sign appears gray. ■

Na K Restoring Electrolytes

"Don't sweat it" may be good advice for handling stress, but not for maintaining a healthy body. The sweat you produce on a hot day or during exercise cools your body as it evaporates. Sweat consists mainly of water, sodium chloride, and small amounts of other inorganic salts. The salts are electrolytes that help keep the volume of body fluids constant. Electrolytes produce ions when they dissolve in water.

Body fluids contain sodium ions and potassium ions. Potassium ions are the principal cations inside cells. Sodium ions are the principal cations in the fluids outside of cells. The transmission of nerve impulses depends on the movement of sodium and potassium ions across the membranes of nerve cells. Potassium ions cause the heart muscle to relax between heartbeats.

Replacing the water lost during exercise is important, but not sufficient. Electrolytes must be replaced too. Some signs of electrolyte depletion are muscle cramps, nausea, and an inability to think clearly. Many athletes use sports drinks to replace electrolytes. Some experts recommend these drinks for people who lose more than 8 liters of sweat daily or exercise continuously for more than 60 minutes.

Table salt is the chief source of sodium in the diet. But large amounts are also found in unexpected places, such as eggs. For a healthy adult, the recommended daily intake of sodium chloride is about 5 grams per day—about half the amount many people consume. The daily recommended amount of potassium is about 1 gram. The word *daily* is important because your kidneys excrete potassium even when the supply is low. Eating foods high in potassium and low in sodium is ideal. Such foods include bananas, chicken, and orange juice. ■

Cs Cesium Atomic Clock

Many watches contain a quartz crystal that vibrates at a constant rate. The vibration provides the "beat" that is translated into the time you see displayed. A clock with a quartz crystal is more accurate than a mechanical clock, which has moving parts that can be worn down by friction. But a quartz crystal isn't accurate enough for modern communication and navigation systems.

For greater accuracy, you need an atomic clock, which may gain or lose only one second in 20 million years! In most atomic clocks, cesium-133 atoms provide the "beat." Unlike quartz crystals, all cesium-133 atoms are identical and they don't wear out with use. The clock is designed so that the atoms repeatedly absorb and emit radiation. The emitted radiation has a frequency of exactly 9,192,631,770 cycles per second. The cycles are counted and translated into seconds, minutes, and hours. Since 1967, the second had been defined based on the cesium clock.

There is a standard cesium atomic clock at the National Institute of Standards and Technology in Fort Collins, Colorado. A short-wave radio station transmits accurate time signals from this clock to most of North America. Clocks and watches advertised as "atomic" or "radio controlled" contain a tiny antenna and receiver that pick up the signal and decode the information. The owner sets the time zone. The radio signal sets the time. ■

Global Positioning System (GPS) receivers can pinpoint any location on Earth to within a few meters. They depend on accurate time signals from atomic clocks in 24 Earth-orbiting satellites.

Na Salt of the Earth

In the ancient world, table salt (NaCl) was an extremely valuable commodity. Before refrigeration, salt was used to preserve foods such as meats and fish. As salt draws the water out of bacteria, they shrivel up and die. Sailors ("salty dogs") especially depended on salt pork and fish to survive long voyages.

Trade routes were established and roads were built to transport salt. In ancient China, coins were made of salt and taxes were levied on salt. Roman soldiers were paid an allotment called a *salarium argentum,* or "salt silver," from which the word *salary* is derived. ■

Li Bipolar Disorder

About two million people in the United States experience the extreme mood swings of bipolar disorder. During a manic phase, they think they can conquer the world. During a depression, they may feel hopeless. The ionic compound lithium carbonate often is used to control these symptoms. Lithium ions probably have an effect on the transmission of messages between brain cells. ■

? Did You Know...

Most alkali metals are stored under oil. But **lithium** is so light that it floats on oil. So a coat of petroleum jelly is applied to lithium before it is stored.

Group 2A: Alkaline Earth Metals

Diaphragm

Beryllium | discovered in 1798 by Nicholas Vauquelin

4
2
2
Be
Beryllium
9.0122

Magnesium | isolated in 1808 by Sir Humphry Davy

12
2
8
2
Mg
Magnesium
24.305

Calcium | discovered in 1808 by Sir Humphry Davy

20
2
8
8
2
Ca
Calcium
40.08

Strontium | discovered in 1808 by Sir Humphry Davy

38
2
8
18
8
2
Sr
Strontium
87.62

Barium | discovered in 1808 by Sir Humphry Davy

56
2
8
18
18
8
2
Ba
Barium
137.33

Radium | discovered in 1898 by Pierre Curie & Marie Curie

88
2
8
18
32
18
8
2
Ra
Radium
(226)

Physical Properties

- Alkaline earth metals are relatively soft, but harder than alkali metals.

- Alkaline earth metals have a gray white luster when freshly cut. When exposed to air, they quickly form a tough, thin oxide coating.

- Densities, melting points, and boiling points tend to be higher than for the alkali metal in the same period.

Beryllium is used as a diaphragm in speakers for accurate sound reproduction. This light but rigid metal transmits sound at 12 km/s.

- Strong, lightweight magnesium alloys are used in cameras, lawnmowers, aircraft, and automobiles.

Melting and Boiling Points

Density

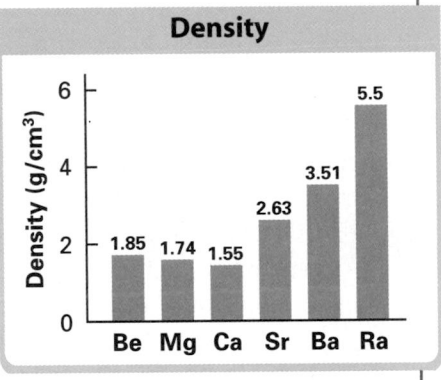

Sources

- Alkaline earth metals are not found in nature in the elemental state.

- Many mountain ranges contain alkaline earth carbonates—limestone ($CaCO_3$) and dolomite ($CaCO_3 \cdot MgCO_3$).

- Oyster shells containing $CaCO_3$ are used to extract magnesium. The chlorine gas produced as a by-product is fed back into the process.

- Barium is made by reduction of its oxide with aluminum at high temperature.

$$3BaO(s) + 2Al(s) \longrightarrow 3Ba(l) + Al_2O_3(s)$$

- Salts of highly radioactive radium are a by-product of uranium refining.

Production of Magnesium

Atomic Properties

- Alkaline earth metals have an electron configuration that ends in ns^2.

- The alkaline earth metals are strong reducing agents, losing 2 electrons and forming ions with a 2+ charge.

- Because radium is luminous, it was once used to make the hands and numbers on watches glow in the dark.

- The ratio of ^{87}Sr to ^{86}Sr varies with location. This data can be used to solve problems, such as the source of materials.

First Ionization Energy

Electronegativity

Atomic radius (pm)	Be 113	Mg 160	Ca 197	Sr 215	Ba 224	Ra 223
Ionic radius (pm)	44 Be^{2+}	66 Mg^{2+}	99 Ca^{2+}	112 Sr^{2+}	134 Ba^{2+}	143 Ra^{2+}

Calcium, strontium, and barium can be identified by the colors produced when their compounds are heated in a flame.

Calcium *Strontium* *Barium*

Important Compounds and Reactions

- Alkaline earth metals are less reactive than alkali metals.

- Alkaline earth metals react with halogens to form ionic halides. Example:

  $Mg(s) + Br_2(l) \longrightarrow MgBr_2(s)$

- All Group 2A metals (except Be) react with water to form an alkaline solution. Example:

  $Sr(s) + 2H_2O(l) \longrightarrow Sr(OH)_2(aq) + H_2(g)$

- Alkaline earth metals react with oxygen to form binary oxides. Example:

  $2Ca(s) + O_2(g) \longrightarrow 2CaO(s)$

  $\Delta H = -635.1$ kJ/mol

- Heating limestone produces lime, CaO.

  $CaCO_3(s) \xrightarrow{\Delta} CaO(s) + CO_2(g)$

  $\Delta H = 176$ kJ/mol

- Slaked lime, $Ca(OH)_2$, reacts with carbon dioxide to form limestone.

  $Ca(OH)_2(s) + CO_2(g) \longrightarrow CaCO_3(s) + H_2O(g)$

- Barium peroxide is used as a dry powdered bleach. It reacts with water to form the bleaching agent, hydrogen peroxide.

  $BaO_2(s) + 2H_2O(l) \longrightarrow$
  $\qquad\qquad H_2O_2(aq) + Ba(OH)_2(aq)$

- Gypsum, calcium sulfate dihydrate, $CaSO_4 \cdot 2H_2O$, is used to make plasterboard.

- Calcium phosphate, $Ca_3(PO_4)_2$, is the major component of bone and teeth.

Slaked lime is an ingredient in plaster, cement, and the mortar used in this stone wall.

Group 2A: Alkaline Earth Metals

Mg Chlorophyll

A plant that is deprived of magnesium will turn yellow and eventually die. The yellow color is a sign that the plant is not producing enough of the green pigment chlorophyll, which is found in structures called chloroplasts. There are about half a million chloroplasts in one square millimeter of leaf surface. In chloroplasts, light energy is changed to chemical energy.

Chlorophyll molecules absorb wavelengths of blue light and red light, and reflect green light. There is a magnesium ion at the center of each chlorophyll molecule. It is embedded like a jewel in a crown-like ring. The magnesium ion forms a bond with each nitrogen atom.

Chlorophyll a

Chlorophyll is typical of a family of compounds called porphyrins, which contain a central metal ion. In heme, the ion is Fe^{2+}. There are four heme molecules in hemoglobin, which transports oxygen in the blood. ■

Sr Ba Fireworks

Producing an aerial fireworks display requires skill and knowledge of chemistry. Shells are stored in steel pipes anchored in sand. A typical shell contains two charges, one to launch the shell and one to cause the shell to burst. When the lifting charge explodes, the shell is blown out of the pipe and the fuse attached to the bursting charge ignites. The shell travels for a few seconds before it bursts.

The name of this effect is chrysanthemum.

The explosions that launch the shells and cause them to burst are exothermic redox reactions. The reducing agent, or fuel, may be aluminum, magnesium, or sulfur. The oxidizing agent may be a nitrate, a chlorate, or a perchlorate, such as potassium perchlorate ($KClO_4$).

When a shell bursts, it releases tiny pellets called "stars," which produce the colors. Only a few elements are needed to produce these colors. Two are alkaline earth metals, strontium for bright red and barium for light green. These same colors are produced when strontium and barium compounds are heated in a flame. Flame tests can identify elements because an element emits characteristic wavelengths of light when its atoms absorb heat and then return to the ground state. ■

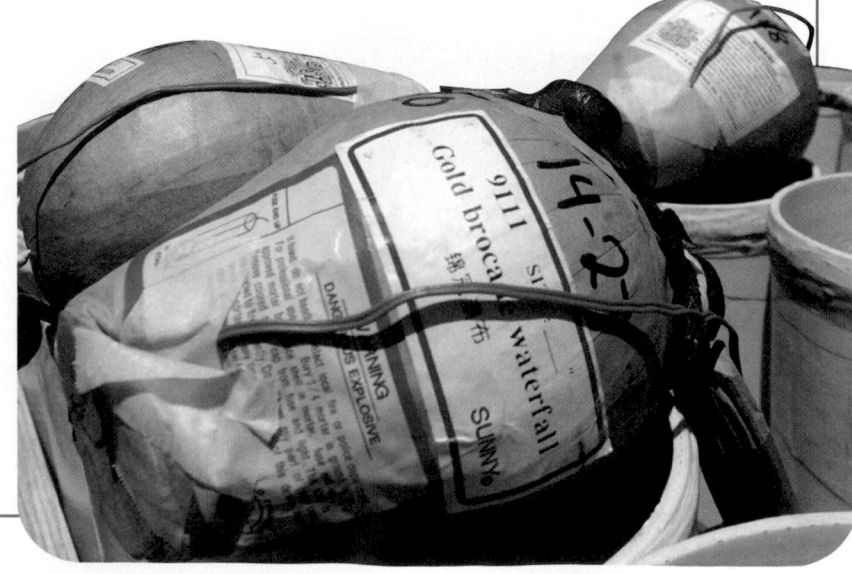

Labels for shells used in a fireworks display describe the color and the effect produced by the shell.

Ca Limestone Caves

The chemical reactions that form a limestone cave are simple. Carbon dioxide in the air dissolves in rain to form weak carbonic acid, H_2CO_3. As rain passes through soil, it dissolves carbon dioxide produced by decaying plants and becomes even more acidic. The rainwater seeps into limestone, $CaCO_3$, beneath the soil. The $CaCO_3$ dissolves in the carbonic acid, forming a solution of calcium hydrogen carbonate, $Ca(HCO_3)_2$.

$$CaCO_3(s) + H_2CO_3(aq) \longrightarrow Ca^{2+}(aq) + 2HCO_3^-(aq)$$

Over millions of years, as more and more limestone dissolves, a cave forms and slowly grows in size. Once the cave stops growing, another process may occur. Calcium hydrogen carbonate solution drips through the cave's roof. Carbon dioxide is released from solution, leaving behind a tiny deposit of solid calcium carbonate.

$$Ca^{2+}(aq) + 2HCO_3^-(aq) \longrightarrow CaCO_3(s) + CO_2(g) + H_2O(l)$$

The deposit slowly grows into a stalactite, which hangs from the ceiling like an icicle. Drops of solution that fall from the ceiling form stalagmites on the cave floor. Calcium carbonate is white. So any color in the deposits is due to traces of metal ions, such as copper (blue-green) and iron (red-brown). The growth rate of the formations depends mainly on the volume of water that drips through the roof and the concentration of calcium bicarbonate in the water. In many caves, the rate of growth is measured in centimeters per hundreds or thousands of years. ■

Stalactites and stalagmites may join together to form columns.

Ca Building Strong Bones

As a young adult, you can have a major effect on the health of your bones later in life. You acquire 90% of the bone tissue in your skeleton before age 18 as females and age 20 as males. Physical activity and the amount of calcium in your diet affect the buildup of bone mass.

To maintain a constant level of calcium in your blood, your body may release calcium from bone tissue.

If enough calcium is lost from bones, they become brittle and tend to break easily. This condition, known as osteoporosis, is most common in older people. However, it can occur in young and middle-aged adults.

The recommended daily intake of calcium from age 9 to age 18 is 1.3 g per day. This is the amount in a liter of milk.

Calcium-fortified foods, such as orange juice, are a good choice for those who cannot tolerate the lactose in milk. Vitamin D in orange juice helps you absorb calcium. ■

Did You Know...

Calcium oxide (lime) emits a bright white light when it is heated. Before electric lights, theaters used lime to focus light on a single actor. So the expression *in the limelight* describes a person in a prominent position.

Group 3A

Boron | discovered in 1808 by Sir Humphry Davy and by Joseph-Louis Gay-Lussac & Louis-Jacques Thénard

5	2 3
B	
Boron	
10.81	

Aluminum | discovered in 1825 by Hans Christian Oersted

13	2 8 3
Al	
Aluminum	
26.982	

Gallium | discovered in 1875 by Paul-Emile Lecoq de Boisbaudran

31	2 8 18 3
Ga	
Gallium	
69.72	

Indium | discovered in 1863 by Ferdinand Reich & Hieronymus T. Richter

49	2 8 18 18 3
In	
Indium	
114.82	

Thallium | discovered in 1861 by Sir William Crookes

81	2 8 18 32 18 3
Tl	
Thallium	
204.37	

Physical Properties

- Boron is a metalloid. The rest of the Group 3A elements are metals.

- Aluminum is a valuable structural material because of its strength, especially in alloys with silicon or iron. These alloys have a low density and resist corrosion.

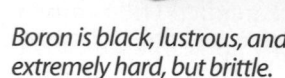

Boron is black, lustrous, and extremely hard, but brittle.

- Gallium has an extremely wide liquid temperature range (30°C to 2204°C). Solid gallium floats in liquid gallium, which is unusual for a metal.

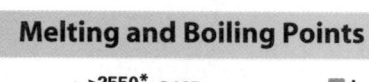

Melting and Boiling Points

Temperature (°C) — B: bp >2550* (sublimes), mp 2300; Al: bp 2467, mp 660; Ga: bp 2204, mp 30; In: bp 2080, mp 157; Ti: bp 1457, mp 304

■ bp ■ mp

*sublimes

Density

Density (g/cm³) — B: 2.35; Al: 2.7; Ga: 5.9; In: 7.31; Ti: 11.85

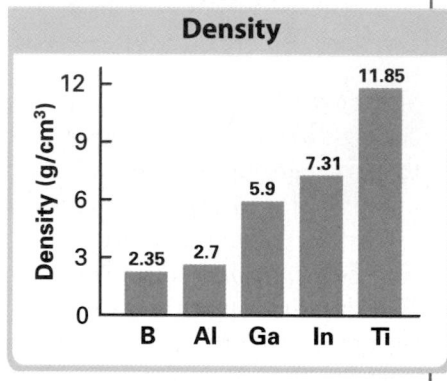

Sources

- Boron is always combined with oxygen in nature. Boron can be prepared by the reaction of its oxide with magnesium metal.

$$B_2O_3(s) + 3Mg(s) \longrightarrow 2B(s) + 3MgO(s)$$

- Bauxite is a common ore of aluminum. The primary mineral in bauxite is alumina, Al_2O_3, which is reduced to aluminum by electrolysis.

- Gallium, indium, and thorium are quite rare. They are typically extracted from ores being processed to extract other metals.

The conveyor belt is being used to unload bauxite from a train. Bauxite is a major source of aluminum. It is also a source of gallium.

Atomic Properties

First Ionization Energy

B	Al	Ga	In	Ti
801	578	579	558	589

Energy (kJ/mol)

Electronegativity

B	Al	Ga	In	Ti
2.0	1.5	1.6	1.7	1.8

- Group 3A elements have an electron configuration that ends in ns^2np^1.

- The most common oxidation number for boron, aluminum, gallium and indium is +3. For thallium, it is +1.

- Group 3A elements become more metallic from top to bottom within the group.

- Radioactive thallium-201 is injected into patients taking the stress test used in the diagnosis of heart disease.

	B	Al	Ga	In	Tl
Atomic radius (pm)	83	143	141	166	172
Ionic radius (pm)	23 B^{3+}	51 Al^{3+}	62 Ga^{3+}	81 In^{3+}	95 Ti^{3+}

Important Compounds and Reactions

- Group 3A elements react with halogens to form halides. Example:

$$2Al(s) + 3Cl_2(g) \longrightarrow 2AlCl_3(s)$$

Aluminum chloride is used as a catalyst in organic reactions.

- Group 3A elements react with oxygen to form oxides. Example:

$$4Al(s) + 3O_2(g) \longrightarrow 2Al_2O_3(s)$$
$$\Delta H = -1676 \text{ kJ/mol}$$

Because this reaction is so exothermic, powdered aluminum is a component of some explosives, fireworks, and rocket fuels.

- Aluminum sulfate (alum), $Al_2(SO_4)_3 \cdot 18H_2O$, is used in water treatment plants.

- Gallium arsenide, GaAs, converts electric current to light in light-emitting diodes (LEDs). It is produced as follows.

$$(CH_3)_3Ga(g) + AsH_3(g) \longrightarrow GaAs(s) + 3CH_4(g)$$

Corundum is a mineral form of aluminum oxide. Rubies are corundum in which a few aluminum ions are replaced by chromium ions.

- Borax, $Na_2B_4O_7 \cdot 10H_2O$, is used to soften water and is found in glasses and glazes. When a mixture of borax and hydrochloric acid is heated, boric acid is produced.

$$Na_2B_4O_7(aq) + 2HCl(aq) + 5H_2O(l) \longrightarrow$$
$$4H_3BO_3(aq) + 2NaCl(aq)$$

- Boric acid is poisonous if ingested. The solid is used as an insecticide against cockroaches. A dilute solution of boric acid is an eyewash.

- Boron carbide, B_4C, is almost as hard as diamond. It is used for items that must resist wear, such as cutting tools.

- Laboratory glassware is made of heat-resistant glass containing 12–15% boric oxide.

This LED is shown at about five times actual size.

Group 3A

In Uses of Indium

Indium is a soft metal with a low melting point of 157°C. One useful property of indium is its ability to "wet" glass. It spreads out and forms a thin layer on the glass instead of beading up. This property allows indium to be deposited on glass to make mirrors that are as reflective, but more corrosion-resistant, than silvered mirrors.

Low-melting alloys that contain indium are used as solders to join glass to glass. They also can join a metal to a metal at low temperatures. There are products, such as electronics components, that could be damaged if joined at a high temperature. The seals of some fire sprinkler heads are held in place by indium alloys. When heat from a fire melts the alloy, the seal is released, which allows water to pour from the sprinkler head. ■

Al Recycling Aluminum

Lightweight, durable aluminum has many uses. When aluminum parts replace steel parts in vehicles, less fuel is needed to travel the same distance. About 20% of the aluminum produced is used for packaging, including foil and cans.

In the United States, over 80 billion aluminum soft drink cans are sold each year. Around 50% of these cans are recycled. The energy saved by recycling just one of these cans could be used to operate a television for three hours.

Aluminum is used in durable consumer goods such as ladders.

The energy needed to recycle aluminum is 5% of the energy needed to obtain new aluminum from ore. An added benefit of recycling is a reduction in solid waste.

Recycled aluminum cans are shredded, crushed, and heated to remove materials other than aluminum. Aluminum pieces about the size of a potato chip are placed in furnaces where they are mixed with new aluminum and melted. The molten aluminum is poured into 7.6-m ingots that have a mass of about 13,600 kg. The ingots pass through rolling mills that reduce their thickness from about 0.5 m to about 0.25 mm. The thin sheets are coiled and shipped to a manufacturer who produces the bodies and tops of the cans. Aluminum from a recycled can is part of a new can within 60 days. ■

Aluminum cans are compressed before being shipped to aluminum companies for recycling.

Al Manufacturing Aluminum

Aluminum is the most abundant metal in Earth's crust (8.3% by mass). It is found in minerals such as bauxite (impure aluminum oxide, Al_2O_3). But for years after its discovery, there wasn't a practical way to extract aluminum from its ores. This rare and expensive metal was used, like gold, mainly for decoration.

A professor at Oberlin College in Ohio challenged his class to find an inexpensive way to produce aluminum. In 1885, Charles Hall responded to the challenge. He set up a laboratory in a woodshed. He knew that other chemists had tried to decompose aluminum oxide by electrolysis. This method was not practical because the melting point of aluminum oxide is quite high (2045°C). Hall found that mixing aluminum oxide with cryolite (Na_3AlF_6) produced a mixture that melted at a much lower temperature of 1012°C.

Graphite anode

Al_2O_3 dissolved in Na_3AlF_6

Graphite-lined tank (cathode)

CO_2 (g)

Al(l)

The process Hall invented is often called the Hall-Heroult process. Paul Heroult, a 23-year-old Frenchman, developed the same process almost simultaneously. It is still used today. Pure aluminum oxide is extracted from bauxite through heating to a temperature above 1000°C. The aluminum oxide is dissolved in molten cryolite and contained in a graphite-lined iron tank. The graphite rods used as an anode are consumed during the process.

Anode: $C(s) + 2O^{2-}(l) \longrightarrow CO_2(g) + 4e^-$

Cathode: $3e^- + Al^{3+}(l) \longrightarrow Al(l)$

The products are carbon dioxide and molten aluminum metal. Because the aluminum is more dense than the aluminum oxide-cryolite mixture, it collects at the bottom of the tank and is drawn off periodically. ■

Al Anodized Aluminum

If an aluminum object has a color other than silver, it was anodized before it was dyed. The main goal of anodizing is to protect the aluminum from corrosion by coating it with aluminum oxide. The ability to be dyed is an added benefit.

The aluminum object becomes the anode in an electrolytic cell. The electrolyte is a dilute acid. When an electric current flows through the cell, aluminum oxide forms on the surface of the aluminum.

The oxide layer is thin, hard, and dense. It contains tiny pores, which can absorb an organic dye. If a dyed piece is placed in boiling water, the oxide layer absorbs water and swells, which closes the pores and seals in the dye. Because the oxide layer is so thin, the silver of the aluminum base is visible through the dye and gives the object a metallic sheen. ■

Did You Know...

Indium's name comes from indigo, a bright line in its emission spectrum. Indium will emit a high-pitched sound when it is bent. Tin and gallium also "cry" when bent.

Group 4A

6	2 4
C	
Carbon	
12.011	

Carbon | known since ancient times

14	2 8 4
Si	
Silicon	
28.086	

Silicon | discovered in 1824 by Jöns Jacob Berzelius

32	2 8 18 4
Ge	
Germanium	
72.59	

Germanium | discovered in 1886 by Clemens Winkler

50	2 8 18 18 4
Sn	
Tin	
118.69	

Tin | known since ancient times

82	2 8 18 32 18 4
Pb	
Lead	
207.2	

Lead | known since ancient times

Physical Properties

- Group 4A elements are all solids at room temperature.
- The metallic properties of Group 4A elements increase from carbon to lead.
- Diamond, graphite, and buckminsterfullerene are three allotropes of carbon.

Phase Diagram of Carbon

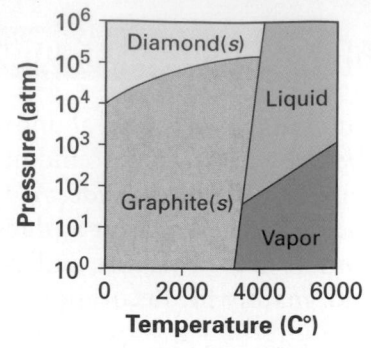

Graphite is more stable than diamond at STP, but the activation energy is too high for diamond to change to graphite at these conditions.

Melting and Boiling Points

*sublimes

Density

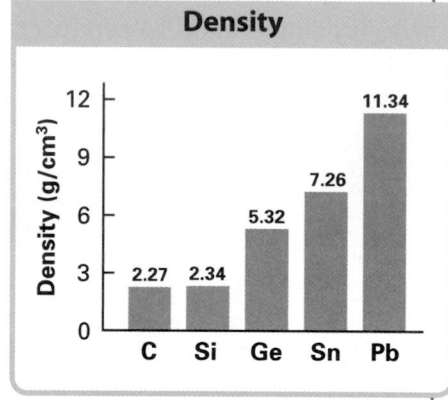

Sources

- Carbon is found in nature as an element, in Earth's atmosphere as carbon dioxide, in Earth's crust as carbonate minerals, and in organic compounds produced in cells.
- Silicon can be produced by the reduction of silicon dioxide (silica) with magnesium, carbon, or aluminum. Example:

$$SiO_2(s) + 2Mg(s) \longrightarrow Si(s) + 2MgO(s)$$

- Tin is prepared by reduction of the mineral cassiterite, SnO_2.

$$SnO_2(s) + 2C(s) \longrightarrow 2CO(g) + Sn(s)$$

- Lead is refined from the mineral galena, PbS. Galena is heated in air to form a mixture of PbO and $PbSO_4$. Lead is produced through further reaction of these compounds with PbS.

Al_2SiO_5 *andalusite*

Fe_2SiO_4 *olivine*

$AlSi_2O_5OH$ *pyrophyllite*

About 90% of the minerals in Earth's crust are silica and silicates. In silicates, each silicon atom is surrounded by three or four oxygen atoms. These units can be linked together in chains, sheets, rings, or crystals.

First Ionization Energy

Bar chart — Energy (kJ/mol):
- C: 1086
- Si: 786
- Ge: 761
- Sn: 708
- Pb: 715

Electronegativity

Bar chart — Electronegativity:
- C: 2.5
- Si: 1.8
- Ge: 1.8
- Sn: 1.8
- Pb: 1.9

Atomic Properties

- Group 4A elements have an electron configuration that ends in ns^2np^2.
- For Group 4A elements, the most common oxidation numbers are +4 and +2. For carbon, −4 is also common.
- Silicon and germanium are semiconductors.

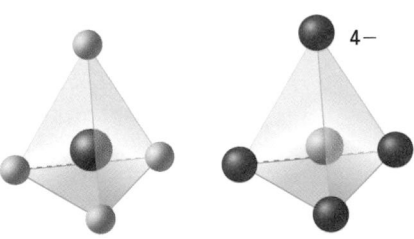

methane molecule   silicate ion

	C	Si	Ge	Sn	Pb
Atomic radius (pm)	77	109	122	139	175
Ionic radius (pm)	15 C^{4+}	41 Si^{4+}	53 Ge^{4+}	71 Sn^{4+}	84 Pb^{4+}

When carbon and silicon form four covalent bonds, there is often sp^3 hybridization. The result is compounds and ions with tetrahedral structures.

Important Compounds and Reactions

- Group 4A elements are oxidized by halogens. Example:

$$Ge(s) + 2Cl_2(g) \longrightarrow GeCl_4(l)$$

- Group 4A elements combine with oxygen to form oxides. Example:

$$Sn(s) + O_2(g) \longrightarrow SnO_2(s)$$

- Complete combustion of hydrocarbons yields carbon dioxide and water. Example:

$$CH_4(g) + 2O_2(g) \longrightarrow CO_2(g) + 2H_2O(l)$$
$$\Delta H = -890 \text{ kJ/mol}$$

- Plants use carbon dioxide to produce carbohydrates and oxygen.
- Aqueous sodium silicate, Na_2SiO_3, is used as an adhesive for paper, as a binder in cement, and to stabilize shale during oil drilling.

$$SiO_2(s) + 2NaOH(aq) \longrightarrow Na_2SiO_3(aq) + H_2O(l)$$

- Acetylene is a fuel used for welding. It forms when calcium carbide and water react.

$$CaC_2(s) + 2H_2O(l) \longrightarrow C_2H_2(g) + Ca(OH)_2(aq)$$

- Tungsten carbide, WC, is used on the cutting surfaces of drill bits and saw blades.
- Lead(IV) oxide, PbO_2, is used as electrodes in lead acid car batteries.
- Tin(II) fluoride, SnF_2, is used in toothpaste to prevent tooth decay.

Silicon dioxide, SiO_2, is the sand on many beaches and is used to make glass.

Group 4A

C | Green Chemistry

The term *green chemistry* was coined in 1992. It describes the effort to design chemical processes that don't use or produce hazardous substances. The goal is to protect the environment and conserve resources. For example, if a catalyst is used to reduce the temperature at which a reaction occurs, the process requires less energy.

Carbon dioxide is at the center of a green chemistry success story. Organic solvents are used to dissolve substances that are insoluble in water. Many of these solvents are toxic. It can be difficult to remove all traces of the toxic solvent from reaction products and safely recycle or dispose of the solvent. Supercritical carbon dioxide can replace some organic solvents.

A gas becomes a supercritical fluid at a temperature and pressure called its critical point. For carbon dioxide, this occurs at 31.1°C and about 100 atmospheres. At its critical point, carbon dioxide is in a hybrid state. It has a high density (like a liquid) but it is easily compressed (like a gas). Many organic compounds dissolve in supercritical carbon dioxide. The solvent is easily separated from a reaction mixture because it evaporates at room temperature and pressure. It is also used to separate substances from mixtures. It can extract caffeine from coffee beans, dry-clean clothes, or clean circuit boards. ■

Decaffeinating Coffee

> Caffeine dissolves inside coffee beans soaked in water.

↓ Extraction

> Caffeine diffuses into supercritical CO_2.

↓ Absorption

> Water droplets leach caffeine from CO_2.

After the caffeine is extracted, the coffee beans are dried and roasted. The aqueous solution of caffeine is sold to soft drink manufacturers.

Si | Optical Glass

Glass is a material with the structure of a liquid, but the hardness of a solid. In most solids, the particles are arranged in an orderly lattice. In solid glass, the molecules remain disordered, as in a liquid. The main ingredient in most glass is silica (SiO_2), which is one of the few substances that can cool without crystallizing.

The glass used in eyeglasses, microscopes, and telescopes is called optical glass. It is purer than window glass and transmits more light. Optical glass can be drawn into long fibers that are used like tiny periscopes to view tissues deep within the human body.

In an optical fiber, light travels through a thin glass center called the core. A second glass layer reflects light back into the core. An outer plastic layer protects the fiber from damage.

When the fibers are bundled into cables, they often replace electrical cables in computer networks. They are also used to transmit television signals and phone calls over long distances. ■

Si Semiconductors

With a cellular phone, you can call your friends from almost any location. You can play a video game, read e-mails, or get the latest news. You may even be able to take and send digital photos. How can such a complex device be small enough to fit in your pocket? Semiconductor technology is responsible.

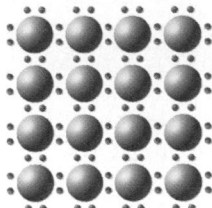

Pure silicon

Silicon is a semiconductor. In its pure form, it conducts an electric current better than most nonmetals but not as well as metals. But its ability to conduct can be changed dramatically by doping, or adding traces of other elements, to the silicon crystal.

Doping with arsenic produces a donor, or n-type, semiconductor. Each arsenic atom has five valence electrons, compared with four for silicon. So there are extra electrons in the crystal. Doping with boron produces an acceptor, or p-type, semiconductor. Because boron has only three valence electrons, there is a positive "hole" in the crystal for every boron atom. The extra electrons or holes are free to move and conduct an electric current.

N-type (with arsenic)

P-type (with boron)

Combinations of n-type and p-type semiconductors are used to build tiny electronic components. An integrated circuit containing millions of components can fit on a semiconductor wafer that is smaller than a fingernail! The resulting "chip" can control a computer, portable CD player, calculator, or cellular phone. ■

A cell phone's integrated circuit must process more and more data as features are added to the phone.

C Beyond Buckyballs

Buckminsterfullerene (C_{60}) is one member of a family of fullerenes. These structures are closed-cage spherical or nearly spherical forms of elemental carbon. The cages are networks of 20 to 600 carbon atoms.

Scientists have verified the existence of nesting spheres of fullerenes. C_{60} can be nested inside C_{240}, and this pair can be nested inside C_{540}. These nesting structures are sometimes called bucky-onions because they resemble the layers of an onion. ■

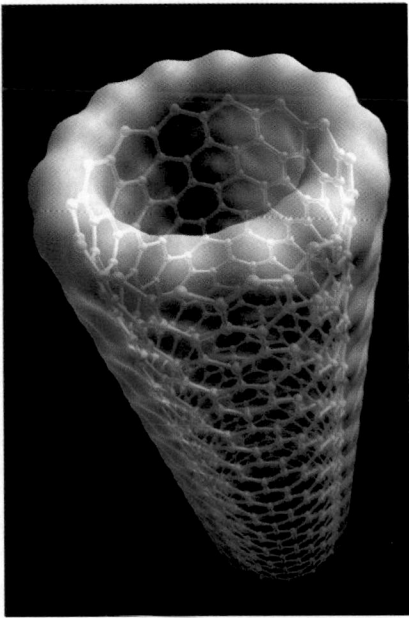

Dr. Sumio Iijima discovered a tubular fullerene, or carbon nanotube, in Japan in 1991.

Did You Know...

One name for diamonds is "ice." A diamond can quickly draw heat from your hand when you touch it. Such a high thermal conductivity is unusual for a substance containing covalent bonds.

Group 4A

C Greenhouse Gases

There are gases in Earth's atmosphere that are called greenhouse gases because they act like the glass in a greenhouse. Sunlight easily passes through these gases to Earth's surface. Some of the solar energy is reflected off the surface as infrared radiation. This radiation is absorbed by greenhouse gases and radiated back to Earth. By trapping infrared radiation, the greenhouse gases keep Earth's surface about 33°C warmer than it would be otherwise.

Carbon dioxide (CO_2) is the most abundant greenhouse gas. It is released into the air as a product of cellular respiration and removed from the air during photosynthesis. Such interactions normally keep the amount of atmospheric CO_2 in check. But the burning of fossil fuels releases more than 20 billion metric tons of CO_2 every year. Also, as forests are cleared for agriculture, the ability of plants to remove CO_2 from the atmosphere is reduced.

With an increase in greenhouse gases, more infrared radiation is trapped, causing global warming.

The glass in a greenhouse traps infrared radiation.

Scientists agree that a rise of only a few degrees in Earth's temperature could cause problems. They disagree on how severe the problems could be. Could climates change so that farmlands become deserts? Could the melting of ice caps cause sea levels to rise until coastal cities are under water? ■

Average Temperature at Earth's Surface

Si Composite Materials

Most composites contain two distinctly different materials. The materials can be arranged in layers as when a sheet of plastic is sealed between panes of glass. Or a composite may consist of a matrix in which fibers of a second material are embedded. Often, the matrix is plastic. The fibers can be carbon.

When a hockey stick has a composite shaft, there can be a quicker release of the shot.

Polycrylonitrile (PAN) is used to make some carbon fibers. PAN fibers oxidize when they are heated in air. The chains of aromatic rings that result are then heated in the absence of air. The chains fuse into long thin ribbons of almost pure carbon, which pack together in stacked layers.

Composites reinforced with carbon fibers are stronger than steel, yet light in weight. These composites are used in sports equipment, such as hockey sticks and golf clubs. It is less tiring to swing a tennis racket made from a carbon-fiber composite than one made from wood or metal. Carbon-fiber baseball bats act more like wood bats than do aluminum bats. ■

C Recycling Plastics

At about 2 kg of waste per person per day, the United States leads the world in the production of solid waste. Luckily, the United States is also a leader in recycling. It is important to recycle plastics because they are made from crude oil, a non-renewable resource. Also, some plastics release toxic gases, such as hydrogen cyanide (HCN) and hydrogen chloride (HCl), when they burn in an incinerator. Finally, plastics are used for packaging material because they do not decay when exposed to sunlight, water, or microorganisms. The downside of this resistance to decay is that plastics can remain unchanged in dumps and landfills for decades.

Plastics are usually sorted by type before they are melted and reprocessed. The plastics industry has a code to identify common types of plastics. The numeral 1 is assigned to polyethylene terephthalate (PET), which is used in soft-drink bottles. The numeral 2 refers to high-density polyethylene (HDPE), which is used in milk jugs and shampoo bottles. These are the two types in greatest demand. Carpets and clothing are made from recycled PET fibers. Recycled HDPE is used as a wood substitute for decks and benches. ■

ONLY
2
SEE SAMPLES ABOVE

Fleece clothing often contains post-consumer recycled (PCR) plastic.

Si Silicone Polymers

If you have worn hard contact lenses or used shaving cream, you have used a silicone. Silicone polymers have chains in which silicon and oxygen alternate. The properties of silicones depend on the groups bonded to the silicon atoms and the length of the chains.

In silicone rubber and resins, there are cross-links between the chains. These silicones repel water and remain elastic, even at low temperatures. They are used in space suits, as gaskets in airplane windows, and as sealants that are squeezed into place and left to harden. ■

In polydimethylsiloxane, two methyl groups are bonded to each silicon atom in the chain. Polydimethylsiloxane is used as a lubricant in skin and suntan lotions.

C Carbon Monoxide

It is hard to detect colorless, odorless carbon monoxide gas. When it is inhaled, its molecules bind to the hemoglobin in red blood cells. They bind about 200 times more effectively than oxygen molecules do. So less oxygen reaches body tissues. Headaches, dizziness, nausea, and drowsiness are symptoms of low-level carbon monoxide poisoning. Higher levels of carbon monoxide are fatal.

The incomplete combustion of fuel in gas furnaces and space heaters produces carbon monoxide. It also forms in internal combustion engines that are not well maintained. In the United States, cars have catalytic converters, which convert carbon monoxide to carbon dioxide.

Cigarette smoke contains carbon monoxide. The carbon monoxide from one cigarette can remain in a smoker's blood for several hours. Smoking increases the risk of heart attacks because the heart must pump harder to deliver oxygen to cells when the level of oxygen is reduced. ■

? Did You Know...

Members of the Scott expedition to the South Pole in 1912 may have died because of **tin**. Their supply of paraffin fuel leaked out through tiny holes in the tin-soldered joints of the storage cans because tin slowly changes to a powder below 13°C.

Group 5A

| 7 | 2 5 |
| N | |

Nitrogen | discovered in 1772 by Daniel Rutherford

Nitrogen
14.007

| 15 | 2 8 5 |
| P | |

Phosphorus | discovered in 1669 by Hennig Brand

Phosphorus
30.974

| 33 | 2 8 18 5 |
| As | |

Arsenic | discovered in 1250 by Albertus Magnus

Arsenic
74.922

| 51 | 2 8 18 18 5 |
| Sb | |

Antimony | discovered in 1600s or earlier

Antimony
121.75

| 83 | 2 8 18 32 18 5 |
| Bi | |

Bismuth | described in 1450 by Basil Valentine; shown to be a distinct element in 1753 by Claude-François Geoffroy

Bismuth
208.98

Physical Properties

- Except for nitrogen gas, Group 5A elements are solid at room temperature.

- The metallic properties of Group 5A elements increase from top to bottom within the group. N and P are nonmetals. As and Sb are metalloids. Bi is a metal.

- Liquid nitrogen is a cryogen, a liquid refrigerant that boils below −160°C.

White phosphorus is very reactive and must be stored under water. Red phosphorus is much more stable.

- The 10 allotropes of phosphorus are classified as white, red, or black.

Melting and Boiling Points

bp
mp

*sublimes   † at 28 atm

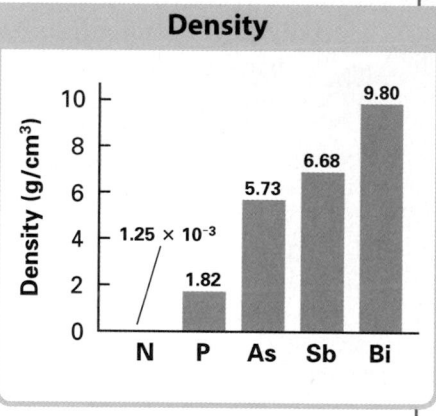

Density

Sources

- Nitrogen is obtained from the fractional distillation of liquefied air.

- Phosphorus is derived from phosphate minerals. Example:

$$Ca_3(PO_4)_2(s) + 3SiO_2(s) + 5C(s) \longrightarrow 2P(l) + 3CaSiO_3(s) + 5CO(g)$$

- Arsenic is prepared by heating a mixture of $FeAs_2$ and FeS_2 in the absence of air.

- Antimony is prepared by roasting the ore stibnite, Sb_2S_3.

Fractional Distillation of Air

Distillation column

−196°C → $N_2(g)$

Remove CO_2 and hydrocarbons

−186°C → $Ar(g)$

Compressed, cooled, and liquified air

−183°C → $O_2(l)$

Atomic Properties

- Group 5A elements have an electron configuration that ends in ns^2np^3.

- The most common oxidation numbers for Group 5A elements are +3, +5, and −3.

- Nitrogen has oxidation numbers from −3 to +5 in a variety of stable compounds.

- Elemental nitrogen, N_2, is highly unreactive due to its strong N-to-N triple bond.

First Ionization Energy

Electronegativity

	N	P	As	Sb	Bi
Atomic radius (pm)	70	109	122	137	170
Ionic radius (pm)	146 N^{3-}	212 P^{3-}	222 As^{3-}	62 Sb^{5+}	74 Bi^{5+}

Important Compounds and Reactions

- Nitrous oxide, N_2O, (laughing gas) is an anesthetic. It is made from ammonium nitrate.

$$NH_4NO_3(s) \xrightarrow{\Delta} N_2O(g) + 2H_2O(g)$$

- Nitrogen dioxide, NO_2, is an air pollutant produced when fossil fuels burn.

- Lightning causes the nitrogen and oxygen in air to react and form nitric oxide, NO.

- Poisonous hydrazine, N_2H_4, is used as a rocket fuel. It is prepared by the following reaction.

$$2NH_3(aq) + OCl^-(aq) \longrightarrow N_2H_4(aq) + Cl^-(aq) + H_2O(l)$$

The reaction is complex. One intermediate is chloramine, NH_2Cl, which is also poisonous. If you ignore the warning against mixing household ammonia and chlorine bleach, chloramine will be produced.

- Nitric acid, HNO_3, is used in fertilizers and explosives. Nitric acid is made by the Ostwald process.

- Phosphoric acid is used in soft drinks and fertilizers. It is made by a double-replacement reaction.

$$Ca_3(PO_4)_2(s) + 3H_2SO_4(aq) \longrightarrow 3CaSO_4(aq) + 2H_3PO_4(aq)$$

Dentists use phosphoric acid to etch the exposed dentine layer of a drilled tooth to help a filling adhere to the tooth.

- Ammonia is synthesized directly from its elements by the Haber-Bosch process.

$$3H_2(g) + N_2(g) \longrightarrow 2NH_3(g)$$
$$\Delta H = 46.19 \text{ kJ/mol}$$

- Amino acids such as glycine, H_2NCHCO_2H, are the building blocks of proteins.

- Bismuth subsalicylate, $BiO(C_7H_5O_3)$, is the active ingredient of a pink liquid antacid.

- Arsenic trioxide, As_2O_3, is powerful poison. It is used as a weed killer and insecticide.

- Antimony is added to alloys to increase their hardness.

Ostwald Process

Ammonia is oxidized to nitrogen dioxide in two stages. The nitrogen dioxide forms nitric acid as it passes through warm water.

Group 5A

N Ammonia

The nitrogen in air is not in a form that is useful for plants. Natural sources of usable nitrogen in soil aren't sufficient to support current levels of crop production. A German chemist named Fritz Haber came up with a solution. He figured out how to convert atmospheric nitrogen into ammonia. In the Haber process, nitrogen and hydrogen are heated under pressure in the presence of iron.

$$N_2(g) + 3H_2(g) \longrightarrow 2NH_3(g)$$

The ammonia is liquefied. Liquid ammonia, aqueous solutions of ammonia, and ammonium salts are used as fertilizers. Liquid ammonia is also used as a refrigerant. Many cleaning products contain aqueous ammonia, which is a weak base. Ammonia is also used to manufacture explosives. ■

Haber Process

$N_2(g) + H_2(g)$ → **Compressor** → **Reaction chamber** $T = 500°C$ $P = 10^5$ kPa

unreacted $N_2(g) + H_2(g)$

Cooling unit

$NH_3(l)$ **storage tank**

When the reaction mixture is cooled, the ammonia is liquefied and separated from the reactants.

N Explosives

Explosions are extremely rapid exothermic reactions that produce gaseous products. The most forceful explosions occur when the reactants are liquids or solids. Pressure builds up as the reactants are converted to gases, especially if the gases are confined. When the gases expand, the resulting release of pressure causes a shock wave. The kinetic energy of this wave, the wind that follows it, and the heat is the destructive force of the explosion.

An explosion requires fuel and an oxidizer. If the oxidizer and fuel are separate, the reaction is a combustion reaction. This type of explosion could occur if natural gas leaking in a building was ignited by a spark or flame.

$$CH_4 + 2O_2(g) \longrightarrow CO_2(g) + 2H_2O(g) \qquad \Delta H = 890 \text{ kJ/mol}$$

If the fuel is its own oxidizer, a decomposition reaction takes place. Nitroglycerine, $C_3H_5(NO_3)_3$, is a thick, pale, oily liquid. It decomposes to form a mixture of gaseous products.

$$4C_3H_5(NO_3)_3(l) \longrightarrow 6N_2(g) + O_2(g) + 12CO_2(g) + 10H_2O(g)$$
$$\Delta H = -1427 \text{ kJ/mol}$$

Self-oxidizing explosives are often unstable. Jarring them may be enough to cause detonation. Alfred Nobel, a Swedish chemist and inventor, found a way to use nitroglycerine with less risk. After his family's nitroglycerine factory exploded in 1864, he moved his experiments to a barge in the middle of a lake. One day he found a cask of nitroglycerine that had leaked. Luckily, the diatomaceous earth in which the cask was packed had absorbed the liquid. Nobel found that the mixture was stable until detonated by a blasting cap. Plus, the mixture was as explosive as the pure liquid. Nobel named his invention dynamite. ■

In his will, Nobel established a fund to provide annual prizes in chemistry, physics, physiology and medicine, literature, and peace.

N Acid Rain

Normal rainfall has a pH of about 5.6. It is mildly acidic because carbon dioxide in the air dissolves in tiny water droplets and forms carbonic acid (H_2CO_3). In acid rain, the pH is lower due to the emission of nitrogen oxides and sulfur oxides into the atmosphere. Some natural sources, such as volcanoes, emit these oxides. But most come from power plants that burn fossil fuels. In the atmosphere, the oxides form nitric acid (HNO_3) and sulfuric acid (H_2SO_4), which fall to Earth in rain or snow.

Because acid rain leaches nutrients from soil, trees are dying in the Appalachian Mountains. Because aquatic species are highly sensitive to changes in pH, some lakes once full of fish and frogs are nearly lifeless.

Power plants are a main source of sulfur and nitrogen oxides. Chemists developed devices called scrubbers that remove these pollutants from smoke. In one type of scrubber, smoke passes through an aqueous suspension of lime (CaO). The lime reacts with SO_2 to form solid calcium sulfite ($CaSO_3$).

Another type of scrubber is used to remove nitrogen oxides. Ammonia is sprayed onto a surface covered with a mixture of catalysts. As smoke passes over the surface, nitrogen oxides react with ammonia and oxygen, forming nitrogen and water.

Researchers have developed some methods for removing both types of oxides at the same time. For example, the smoke can be passed through an alkaline suspension of yellow phosphorus. The chemical reactions that occur convert almost all the oxides into valuable by-products, including some of the plant nutrients used in fertilizers. ■

pH ranges

> 5.3	4.7 - 4.8
5.2 - 5.3	4.6 - 4.7
5.1 - 5.2	4.5 - 4.6
5.0 - 5.1	4.4 - 4.5
4.9 - 5.0	4.3 - 4.4
4.8 - 4.9	< 4.3

This map is based on pH data collected at about 175 field stations in 2002.

N P Fertilizers

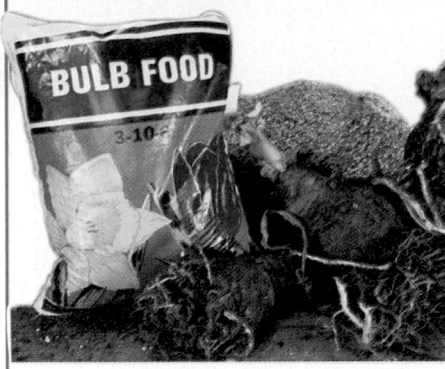

Most fertilizers contain salts of nitrogen, phosphorus, and potassium. These elements are essential to plant growth. On the label, the percents by mass of these nutrients are always listed in the order N-P-K.

Because the salts in a fertilizer can vary, there are rules for reporting the content. Nitrogen is always reported as the percent by mass of elemental nitrogen. Phosphorus and potassium are reported as the percent by mass of phosphorus pentoxide, P_2O_5, and potassium oxide, K_2O.

This system makes it easy to compare the nutrient content of fertilizers. For example, a fertilizer labeled 20-10-10 has twice the mass of nitrogen as a fertilizer labeled 10-10-10. But they both contain the same mass of phosphorus and potassium. The numbers may not add up to 100% because fertilizers can contain ingredients not included in the N-P-K analysis. ■

Did You Know...

If nail polish or lipstick contain **bismuth** oxychloride (BiOCl), they appear lustrous and pearly.

Group 6A

8	2 6
O	
Oxygen	
15.999	

Oxygen | discovered in 1772 by Carl Scheele and in 1774 by Joseph Priestly

16	2 8 6
S	
Sulfur	
32.06	

Sulfur | known since ancient times

34	2 8 18 6
Se	
Selenium	
78.96	

Selenium | discovered in 1817 by Jöns Jacob Berzelius

52	2 8 18 18 6
Te	
Tellurium	
127.60	

Tellurium | discovered in 1782 by Franz Joseph Müller van Reichenstein

84	2 8 18 32 18 6
Po	
Polonium	
(209)	

Polonium | discovered in 1898 by Marie Curie

Physical Properties

- Except for oxygen gas, O_2, Group 6A elements are solid at room temperature.
- The metallic properties of Group 6A elements increase from top to bottom within the group.
- Polonium is a radioactive metal (half-life = 140 days).

monoclinic   *rhombic*

The unit cell in crystalline sulfur is an S_8 molecule.

Melting and Boiling Points

Temperature (°C)

bp
mp

990   962
685   452   254
445
113   217
−183
−219

O   S   Se   Te   Po

Density

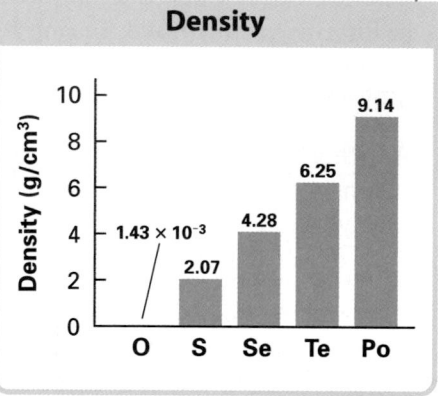

Density (g/cm³)

9.14
6.25
4.28
2.07
1.43 × 10⁻³

O   S   Se   Te   Po

Sources

- Large-scale production of oxygen is by fractional distillation of liquid air. Liquid oxygen is stored and shipped at its boiling point of −183°C in vacuum-walled bottles.
- The Frasch process is used to mine sulfur from underground deposits. A well is drilled into a sulfur bed and a set of concentric tubes installed. Superheated water melts the sulfur. Compressed air forces it to the surface.
- Sulfur is also produced from hydrogen sulfide, H_2S, and sulfur dioxide, SO_2.

$$2H_2S(g) + SO_2(g) \longrightarrow 2H_2O(l) + 3S(s)$$

- Selenium and tellurium are by-products of the processing of sulfide ores for other metals.
- Polonium is formed by the radioactive decay of radium in minerals such as pitchblende.

The Frasch Process

Compressed air →
Hot sulfur froth
Hot Water (180°C) →
Quicksand
Sulfur-bearing rock
Hot water
Air
Solid Sulfur
Liquid Sulfur (119°C)

Atomic Properties

- Group 6A elements have an electron configuration that ends in ns^2np^4.
- For Group 6A elements, the most common oxidation numbers are +4, +6, and −2.
- Oxygen is paramagnetic because there are unpaired electrons in O_2 molecules.

First Ionization Energy

Energy (kJ/mol)

O	S	Se	Te	Po
1314	999	941	869	813

Electronegativity

Electronegativity

O	S	Se	Te	Po
3.5	2.5	2.4	2.1	2.0

	O	S	Se	Te	Po
Atomic radius (pm)	66	105	120	139	168
Ionic radius (pm)	140 O^{2-}	184 S^{2-}	198 Se^{2-}	221 Te^{2-}	94 Po^{4+}

Liquid oxygen is held between the poles of a magnet because of its attraction to the magnet.

Important Compounds and Reactions

- Oxygen reacts with almost all other elements to form oxides. Example:

$$4K(s) + O_2(g) \longrightarrow 2K_2O(s)$$
$$\Delta H = -363.2 \text{ kJ/mol}$$

- Ozone, O_3, is produced directly from oxygen, O_2, during lightening strikes.

$$3O_2(g) \longrightarrow 2O_3(g) \qquad \Delta H = +285 \text{ kJ/mol}$$

- Oxygen is necessary for releasing energy from fuels, such as glucose, in organisms.

$$C_6H_{12}O_6(s) + 6O_2(g) \longrightarrow 6CO_2(g) + 6H_2O(g)$$
$$\Delta H = -2808 \text{ kJ/mol}$$

- Oxygen is used to produce steel and to oxidize hydrogen in fuel cells.
- Sulfur compounds often have unpleasant odors. Hydrogen sulfide, H_2S, smells like a rotten egg. It forms when metallic sulfides and hydrochloric acid react. Example:

$$FeS(s) + 2HCl(aq) \longrightarrow H_2S(g) + FeCl_2(aq)$$

When concentrated sulfuric acid is added to sucrose, water vapor (steam) and carbon are produced. The release of the vapor causes the carbon to expand.

- Concentrated sulfuric acid, H_2SO_4, is a strong dehydrating agent. Example:

$$C_{12}H_{22}O_{11}(s) \xrightarrow{H_2SO_4} 12C(s) + 11H_2O(g)$$

- So people will know when there is a natural gas leak, ethyl mercaptan, CH_3CH_2SH, is added to supplies of odorless natural gas.
- Sodium thiosulfate, $Na_2S_2O_3$, also known as *hypo*, is used in the development of film.
- The addition of cadmium selenide, $CdSe$, gives glass a beautiful ruby color.

Group 6A

Se Selenium In Food

Selenium is an antioxidant that protects cell membranes from damage. In the United States, grain is grown on selenium-rich soils. Livestock and people who eat those grains are unlikely to be deficient in selenium.

An essential nutrient may be harmful in large doses. Too much selenium can damage the nervous system. It may also cause anxiety and fatigue.

This milkvetch (Astragalus bisulcatus) accumulates high levels of selenium.

Soils in the Great Plains and Rocky Mountain regions often contain high levels of selenium. If cattle graze on plants that grow in those soils, they may develop chronic selenium poisoning. The symptoms include loss of hair, sore hoofs, lameness, and a lack of energy.

Acute selenium poisoning causes cattle to lose their vision and stumble aimlessly before dying from respiratory failure. Cowboys called this condition the "blind staggers." ∎

S Sulfuric Acid

Pure sulfuric acid is a dense, colorless, oily liquid. Concentrated sulfuric acid is 98% H_2SO_4 and 2% H_2O. Dilute sulfuric acid reacts with metals, oxides, hydroxides, or carbonates to form sulfates. The reaction with metals also releases hydrogen gas. Sulfuric acid can be used to produce other acids from their salts. For example, hydrogen chloride can be produced from sulfuric acid and sodium chloride.

$$H_2SO_4(l) + 2NaCl(s) \longrightarrow Na_2SO_4(s) + 2HCl(g)$$

Sulfuric acid is produced mainly from sulfur dioxide. The process is called the contact process because the key reaction takes place when the reactants are in contact with the surface of the solid catalyst.

(1) Melted sulfur is burned in air.

$$S(l) + O_2(g) \longrightarrow SO_2(g)$$

(2) Sulfur dioxide is oxidized in the presence of a vanadium oxide catalyst, V_2O_5.

$$2SO_2(g) + O_2(g) \xrightarrow{V_2O_5} 2SO_3(g)$$

(3) Sulfur trioxide dissolves in water and forms sulfuric acid.

Much of the sulfuric acid produced in North America is used to make fertilizers. Sulfuric acid is also used in petroleum refining, the production of other chemicals, and for pickling iron and steel. During pickling, oxides are removed from the surface of a metal. ∎

When sulfur burns in air, the product is the irritating gas sulfur dioxide, SO_2.

This sidegill slug produces sulfuric acid, which discourages predators.

O Ozone

Near Earth's surface, ozone (O_3) is a pollutant. In the stratosphere, ozone is literally a lifesaver. The ozone layer in the stratosphere absorbs 99% of the sun's harmful ultraviolet (UV) radiation. In the 1970s, scientists began to suspect that the ozone layer might be threatened. They based their concerns on laboratory models. In 1985, their suspicions were confirmed when British researchers discovered a "hole" in the ozone layer over Antarctica. In the winter, the amount of ozone was reduced by almost one half.

The scientists traced the thinning of the ozone layer to chlorofluorocarbons (CFCs). These chemicals were used mainly as propellants in aerosol spray cans and as coolants in refrigerators and air conditioners. CFCs are highly stable and inert in the lower atmosphere. Over time, they drift up into the stratosphere, where they are broken down by solar radiation. Through a repeated cycle of reactions (2) and (3), a single chlorine atom can destroy as many as 100,000 molecules of ozone.

$$(1) \quad CCl_3F \longrightarrow Cl\cdot + \cdot CCl_2F$$

$$(2) \quad Cl\cdot + O_3 \longrightarrow ClO\cdot + O_2$$

$$(3) \quad ClO\cdot + O \longrightarrow Cl\cdot + O_2$$

In 1978, the United States banned the use of CFCs in aerosols. By 1990, 40 nations had agreed to eliminate production of CFCs. The ban has had an effect. Concentrations of CFCs have begun to level off in the stratosphere and even decline in the lower atmosphere. ■

Scientists estimate that it may take decades for the ozone layer to reach pre-1980 levels. On September 9, 2000, the "hole" over Antarctica was record size. The amount of ozone is low in the blue areas.

S O Sulfites

Ancient Egyptians and Romans used sulfur dioxide (SO_2) to preserve food. When SO_2 reacts with water, hydrogen sulfite ions (HSO_3^-) and sulfite ions (SO_3^{2-}) form. The food industry uses the term *sulfite* to describe sulfur-based preservatives. Sulfites are antioxidants that slow down the discoloration or deterioration of food.

Restaurants used to spray fruit and lettuce in salad bars with sulfites to maintain the color of the fruit and keep the lettuce from wilting. Sulfites can cause asthma attacks and headaches. After some people died from severe reactions, the Food and Drug Administration banned the use of sulfites on fresh produce. Sulfites must be listed on the food label if a processed food contains at least 10 parts per million. ■

Did You Know...

Organic compounds containing **sulfur** give onions their taste and smell. When an onion is cut, reactions occur that produce propanethial-S-oxide. When receptors in your eyes are exposed to this irritating gas, they trigger the production of tears.

Group 7A: Halogens

9	2 7
F	
Fluorine	
18.998	

Fluorine | discovered in 1886 by Henri Moissan

17	2 8 7
Cl	
Chlorine	
35.453	

Chlorine | discovered in 1774 by Carl Wilhelm Scheele

35	2 8 18 7
Br	
Bromine	
79.904	

Bromine | discovered in 1826 by Antoine-Jérôme Balard

53	2 8 18 18 7
I	
Iodine	
126.90	

Iodine | discovered in 1811 by Bernard Courtois

85	2 8 18 32 18 7
At	
Astatine	
(210)	

Astatine | discovered in 1940 by Dale R. Corson, K. R. Mackenzie, & Emilio Segrè

Physical Properties

- Halogens are nonmetals. At room temperature, fluorine and chlorine are gases and bromine is a liquid. Iodine and astatine are solids.

- Halogens are very reactive. The reactivity decreases from fluorine to astatine. Halogens do not exist in the elemental form in nature.

- Astatine isotopes are radio-active with short half-lives.

There are vapors in the bromine and iodine tubes because bromine is volatile and iodine sublimes easily at room temperature.

Melting and Boiling Points

Temperature (°C): F −188, −220; Cl −35, −101; Br 59, −7; I 184, 114

bp
mp

Density

Density (g/cm³): F 1.81×10^{-3}; Cl 3.21×10^{-3}; Br 3.12; I 4.93

Sources

- Chlorine gas is made commercially by the electrolysis of brine.

$$2NaCl(aq) + 2H_2O(l) \longrightarrow Cl_2(g) + H_2(g) + 2NaOH(aq)$$

- Bromine is obtained from seawater by a displacement reaction with chlorine.

$$2NaBr(aq) + Cl_2(g) \longrightarrow 2NaCl(aq) + Br_2(l)$$

- Iodine is found in brine and in sodium iodate, $NaIO_3$, in deposits of sodium nitrate. Iodine is produced from $NaIO_3$ by this redox reaction.

$$2NaIO_3(aq) + 5NaHSO_3(aq) \longrightarrow$$
$$I_2(g) + 2Na_2SO_4(aq) + 3NaHSO_4(aq) + H_2O(l)$$

- Fluorine is made by the electrolysis of potassium fluoride, KF, dissolved in liquid hydrogen fluoride, HF.

Fluorite, CaF_2, is the principal mineral of fluorine. The term fluorescent comes from this mineral, which glows in the presence of UV radiation.

Atomic Properties

First Ionization Energy

Electronegativity

- Group 7A elements have an electron configuration that ends in ns^2np^5.

- Halogens exist as diatomic molecules.

- Each halogen has the highest electronegativity in its period.

- The most common ionic charge for halogens is $1-$. Except for fluorine, halogens also have positive oxidation numbers of $+1$, $+3$, $+5$, and $+7$.

	F	Cl	Br	I	At
Atomic radius (pm)	62	102	120	140	140
Ionic radius (pm)	133 F^-	181 Cl^-	196 Br^-	220 I^-	

Chlorine forms four anions with oxygen. The oxidation number of chlorine is different in each anion.

Hypochlorite   Chlorite   Chlorate   Perchlorate

Important Compounds and Reactions

- Halogens form metal halides. Example:

$$2Na(s) + Cl_2(g) \longrightarrow 2NaCl(s)$$
$$\Delta H = -411 \text{ kJ/mol}$$

- Halogens form hydrogen halides. Example:

$$H_2(g) + Cl_2(g) \longrightarrow 2HCl(g)$$
$$\Delta H = -92.3 \text{ kJ/mol}$$

- Dry bleach is a mixture of compounds represented by the formula $CaCl(ClO)$. Dry bleach is used to bleach paper and textiles. It also removes stains and disinfects laundry.

$$Ca(OH)_2(aq) + Cl_2(g) \longrightarrow$$
$$CaCl(ClO)(aq) + H_2O(l)$$

- Small amounts of oxygen are produced in the laboratory by heating potassium chlorate, $KClO_3$. Potassium chlorate is an oxidizing agent in fireworks, matches, and explosives.

$$2KClO_3(s) \longrightarrow 2KCl(s) + 3O_2(g)$$

- Canisters of sodium chlorate are used on submarines to produce oxygen. They are carried on airplanes in case of an emergency.

- Chlorine is used to make the monomer vinyl chloride, $CH_2 = CHCl$, which reacts to form the polymer polyvinyl chloride (PVC).

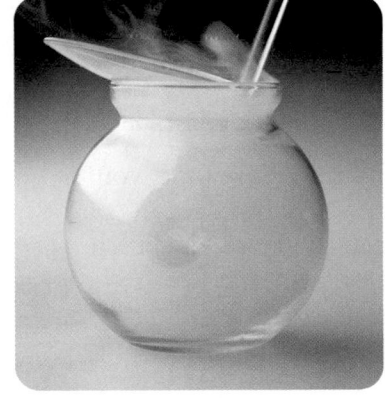

Chlorine reacts vigorously with sodium to form solid sodium chloride.

- Hydrofluoric acid (HF) is made from the mineral fluorite and sulfuric acid. Although HF is extremely dangerous, it has many uses, including cleaning metals and frosting glass.

$$CaF_2(s) + H_2SO_4(aq) \longrightarrow 2HF(g) + CaSO_4(s)$$

- Nonstick pans are coated with a polymer of tetrafluoroethene, $F_2C = CF_2$.

- Tincture of iodine is a solution of iodine, I_2, and potassium iodide, KI, in alcohol. It is an example of an iodine-based skin disinfectant.

Group 7A: Halogens

F Tooth Decay

Your teeth have a hard outer layer called enamel. Enamel is mainly calcium carbonate, $CaCO_3$, and hydroxyapatite, $[Ca_3(PO_4)_2]_3 \cdot Ca(OH)_2$. Lactic acid, $C_3H_6O_3$, is the main cause of tooth decay. It forms when bacteria in saliva feed on sugars present in the sticky plaque on tooth surfaces. An increase in H^+ concentration causes the minerals in tooth enamel to decay faster.

Fluoride ions are added to the water supply in many cities. Most toothpastes contain fluoride ions. The ions replace hydroxide ions in hydroxyapatite to form fluoroapatite, $[Ca_3(PO_4)_2]_3 \cdot CaF_2$. This replacement makes the enamel more resistant.

Fluoride ions alone won't prevent tooth decay. You need to vigorously brush your teeth and floss to keep plaque from building up on tooth enamel. ■

Cl Swimming Pool Chemistry

The person who maintains a swimming pool has two main goals. Prevent the growth of bacteria that cause diseases. Prevent the growth of algae that can foul the water and clog the filters. Chlorine compounds are used to disinfect pool water. "Liquid chlorine" contains sodium hypochlorite, $NaClO$. "Dry chlorine" is calcium hypchlorite, $Ca(ClO)_2$. When hypochlorite ions dissolve in water, hydrolysis occurs and weak hypochlorous acid, $HClO$, is produced.

$$ClO^-(aq) + H_2O(l) \rightleftharpoons HOCl(aq) + OH^-(aq)$$

The amount of undissociated hypochlorous acid in the pool water depends on the pH. If the pH is too high, the hydrolysis reaction will shift toward the reactants and reduce the concentration of $HClO$. If the pH is too low, too much acid will form. A high concentration of acid can cause eye irritation, damage plaster, and corrode the metal piping and filters in the pool.

If the pH of the pool water is too high, solid sodium hydrogen sulfate can be used to react with the OH^- ions.

$$NaHSO_4(s) + OH^-(aq) \longrightarrow Na^+(aq) + SO_4^{2-}(aq) + H_2O(l)$$

If the pH is too low, sodium carbonate can be used to neutralize some of the acid.

$$Na_2CO_3(s) + 2H^+(aq) \longrightarrow 2Na^+(aq) + H_2O(l) + CO_2(aq)$$

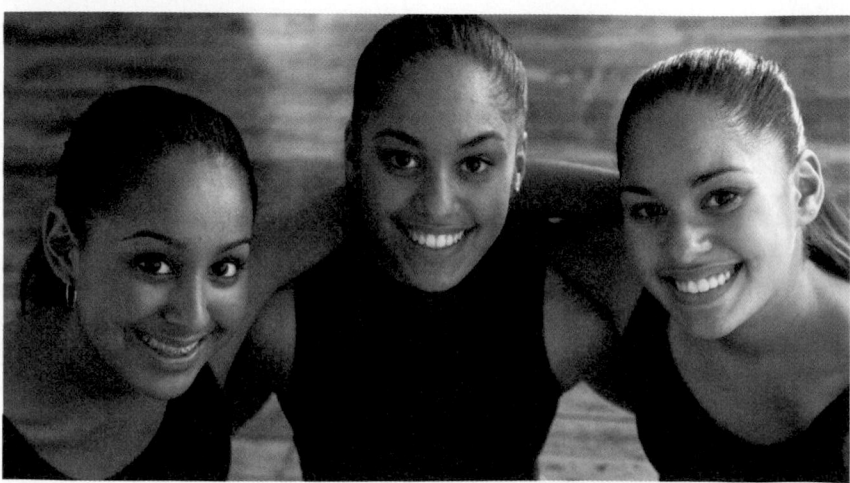

The use of fluorides in drinking water and toothpastes has caused such a drastic reduction in tooth decay that many young adults have never had a cavity.

F Artificial Blood

The most important function of blood is its ability to deliver oxygen from the lungs to cells throughout the body, and carry carbon dioxide from the cells to the lungs. Blood transfusions have been the traditional response to blood loss due to severe injuries or surgery. Blood transfusions have saved millions of lives. But it takes time to determine the recipient's blood type and less common blood types may not be available. Also, blood can carry disease-causing bacteria and viruses.

Some artificial blood contains perfluorocarbons (PFCs). PFCs are organic compounds in which all the hydrogen has been replaced by fluorine. PFCs can dissolve and transport large quantities of oxygen. PFCs are mixed with emulsifiers and salts that mimic the composition of blood, minus the cells.

Large amounts of PFCs can be manufactured and their purity controlled. PFCs can deliver oxygen to areas where blood flow is restricted by narrowed arteries or tumors. In current trials, artificial blood is used to delay the need for blood transfusions during surgery. Because PFCs carry less oxygen than hemoglobin does, the patient must breathe oxygen-rich air.

Because blood is so complex, scientists may never find a substitute to perform all its functions. Therefore, there is still a great need for donations of human blood. ■

The liquid in the beaker is a perfluorocarbon that is saturated with oxygen. The mouse survived by absorbing oxygen from the liquid in its lungs.

I Iodized Salt

The thyroid gland produces hormones that help to control the body's growth and the energy produced by cells. Trace amounts of iodine are needed to produce thyroid hormones. An adult needs about 150 mg of iodine daily.

Ocean fish are a good source of iodine. When people used to get most of their food from local sources, a person who lived far from the ocean often had an iodine deficiency.

To compensate for the lack of iodine, the thyroid gland might enlarge. A severe deficiency could cause mental retardation. Adding potassium iodide to table salt proved to be a simple solution to this public health problem.

In the United States, iodized salt was first sold in 1924. There is about 400 mg of iodine in a teaspoon of iodized salt.

The use of iodized salt has virtually eliminated the problem of iodine deficiency in the United States. ■

? Did You Know...

The purple dye prized by Roman emperors and other rulers contains **bromine**. The dye was extracted from the mollusk *Murex brandaris*, which lives in the Mediterranean Sea.

Group 8A: Noble Gases

Helium | discovered in 1868 by Pierre Janssen

2	2
He	
Helium	
4.0026	

Neon | discovered in 1898 by Sir William Ramsay & Morris Travers

10	2 8
Ne	
Neon	
20.179	

Argon | discovered in 1894 by Lord Rayleigh & Sir William Ramsay

18	2 8 8
Ar	
Argon	
39.948	

Krypton | discovered in 1898 by Sir William Ramsay & Morris Travers

36	2 8 18 8
Kr	
Krypton	
83.80	

Xenon | discovered in 1898 by Sir William Ramsay & Morris Travers

54	2 8 18 18 8
Xe	
Xenon	
131.30	

Radon | discovered in 1900 by Friedrich E. Dorn

86	2 8 18 32 18 8
Rn	
Radon	
(222)	

Physical and Chemical Properties

- All Group 8A elements are monatomic gases at STP.

- Noble gases are colorless, odorless, and tasteless.

- The first compound of a noble gas, $XePtF_6$, was made in 1962. There are now more than 100 known compounds of fluorine and xenon.

Incandescent light bulbs are filled with argon instead of air to extend the life of the filament.

- In 2000, chemists in Finland made a compound of argon, HArF, that exists only at temperatures below −246°C.

Melting and Boiling Points

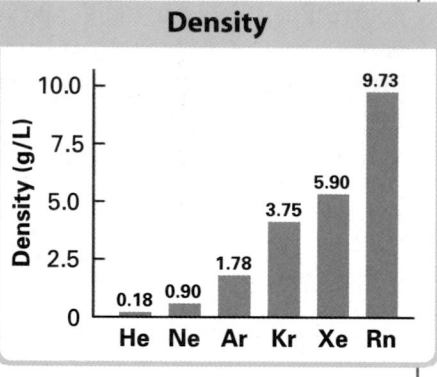
Density

Sources

- Helium is separated from natural gas deposits. Neon, argon, krypton, and xenon are separated from air by fractional distillation.

- Because of its low density, helium is used in weather balloons and airships.

- In addition to "neon" lights, noble gases are used in fluorescent bulbs, strobe lights, and headlights.

- Liquid helium cools the magnets used for magnetic resonance imaging (MRI).

Atomic Properties

- Noble gases have an electron configuration that ends in ns^2np^6. Helium ($1s^2$) is an exception.

- Noble gases rarely form compounds. When they do, the most common oxidation number is +2.

- Each noble gas emits a characteristic color in a gas discharge tube.

First Ionization Energy

Noble gases have the highest ionization energies because their highest occupied energy levels are filled.

Helium *Neon* *Argon* *Krypton* *Xenon*

Ne Neon Lights

By 1855, scientists could produce light by passing an electric current through a gas under low pressure in a sealed glass tube. With the discovery of the noble gases, a new technology emerged. In 1910, George Claude displayed the first neon lamp in Paris, France.

In 1923, a car dealer from Los Angeles bought two signs that spelled out "Packard" for $24,000 (about $250,000 in today's dollars). When he displayed the signs in Los Angeles, people described the light as "liquid fire." By the 1930s, businesses were using neon lights to draw the attention of customers.

Although all noble gases emit visible light when their atoms are excited, neon and argon are the gases most often used in neon lights. Orange-red lights contain only neon. Other colors are produced by adding a bit of mercury to the noble gas. The tube is coated with a material that glows when exposed to UV light emitted by mercury vapor. ■

Ar Taken For a Ride By Argon

Whether riding on a paved city street or on an unpaved mountain trail, a bicyclist is likely to find rough patches. When faced with rough terrain, the cyclist may worry about the tires, but probably not about the bicycle frame. The frame is made of steel or aluminum alloy tubes that are joined together.

The tubes are joined together by Gas Tungsten Arc Welding (GTAW). An electric arc is struck between a tungsten electrode and the parts to be welded. Heat from the arc melts the ends of the tubes and fuses them together. Filler may be placed between the ends of the tubes to increase the strength of the joint or to produce a smoother joint.

During welding in air, there is a danger that the metal tubes or electrode will oxidize. To prevent oxidation, the area around the arc is filled with an inert gas, most often argon. Welding with argon has an added benefit. Because argon is a poor conductor of heat, the arc that forms is narrow. This narrow arc produces a weld that is both neat in appearance and mechanically strong. ■

Xe Xenon-Ion Engines

The signals for a television program may bounce off a communication satellite. The satellite is in orbit above the equator. The position of the satellite may be maintained by a xenon-ion propulsion system.

When electrons strike xenon atoms in a xenon-ion engine, the atoms lose electrons and form positive ions. The ions are accelerated by a charged grid and shot from the engine at about 105 km/h. This action pushes, or thrusts, the satellite in the opposite direction. With multiple engines facing in different directions, a satellite can be moved in any direction.

Although a xenon-ion engine produces a relatively small amount of thrust, it can provide thrust for months or years. This makes xenon-ion engines a good choice for lengthy space missions. In addition, an inert gas poses no hazard for the satellite or the people who handle the propellant tanks. ■

 Did You Know...

When liquid **helium** is cooled to below 2 K, its viscosity drops to zero. It will escape from an unsealed container by flowing up the sides of the container.

Hydrogen

Hydrogen | discovered in 1766 by Henry Cavendish

1	1
H	
Hydrogen	
1.0079	

Sources

- Hydrogen is rarely found on Earth in an uncombined state.

- Electrolysis of water produces the purest hydrogen, but the process requires too much energy to be economical.

$$2H_2O(l) \longrightarrow 2H_2(g) + O_2(g)$$
$$\Delta H = +572 \text{ kJ}$$

- Hydrogen is produced when methane and steam react at 1100°C over a nickel catalyst.

$$H_2O(g) + CH_4(g) \xrightarrow{\text{Ni}}$$
$$CO(g) + 3H_2(g)$$
$$\Delta H = +206 \text{ kJ}$$

The products pass over a metal oxide catalyst at 400°C. More hydrogen is produced as carbon monoxide reacts with added steam.

$$CO(g) + H_2O(g) \longrightarrow$$
$$CO_2(g) + H_2(g)$$
$$\Delta H = -41 \text{ kJ}$$

Carbon dioxide is removed as the gases flow through a basic solution.

$$CO_2(g) + 2OH^-(aq) \longrightarrow$$
$$CO_3^{2-}(aq) + H_2O(l)$$

Atomic and Physical Properties

- Hydrogen has an electron configuration of $1s^1$.

- The most common oxidation numbers for hydrogen are +1 and −1.

- Most hydrogen (99.985%) is protium, or hydrogen-1.

- The other stable isotope is deuterium (hydrogen-2), which has the symbol D. Harold Urey discovered heavy hydrogen, D_2, in 1931.

- Tritium (hydrogen-3) was discovered in 1934. Its half-life is 12.3 years.

Properties of Hydrogen

Property	Value
Density at STP	0.09 g/L
Melting point	−259°C
Boiling point	−253°C
Ionization energy	1.312×10^3 kJ/mol
Electronegativity	2.1

Atomic radius (pm)	H	30
Ionic radius (pm)	1.2 H^+	

Important Compounds and Reactions

- Hydrogen forms covalent binary hydrides with nonmetals. Example:

$$H_2(g) + Cl_2(g) \longrightarrow 2HCl(g)$$

- Two thirds of the hydrogen produced in the U.S. is used to synthesize the covalent binary compound ammonia.

- Hydrogen forms ionic hydrides with alkali metals and alkaline earth metals. These hydrides are powerful reducing agents. Example:

$$Ca(s) + H_2(g) \longrightarrow CaH_2(s)$$

- Hydrogen is used to make methanol, CH_3OH. The reaction takes place at 200–300 atm and 400°C in the presence of a metal oxide catalyst.

$$CO(g) + 2H_2(g) \longrightarrow$$
$$CH_3OH(g)$$

Methanol is an industrial solvent. It is used to make formaldehyde, CH_2O, which is used to make plastics.

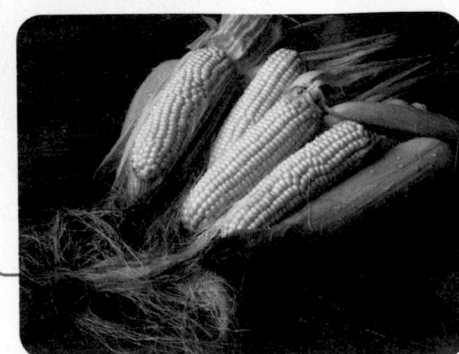

Hydrogen is used to turn liquid oils such as corn oil into solid margarine. Hydrogen is added to carbon–carbon double bonds during hydrogenation.

H   Heavy Water Reactors

Because 1 in 6000 hydrogen atoms is deuterium, 1 in 20,000,000 water molecules is D_2O. D_2O is called heavy water because it is about 10% heavier than ordinary "light" water. In heavy water nuclear reactors, D_2O is used in place of H_2O as a neutron moderator. Both types of water are good moderators, but D_2O is more efficient than H_2O because D_2O absorbs fewer neutrons. So in a heavy water reactor, the uranium used to make the fuel doesn't have to be enriched. The initial cost of separating the heavy water from light water is offset by the lower cost of the uranium fuel. ■

Lake water passes through a series of extraction towers in which D_2O is separated from H_2O.

H   A Hydrogen Economy

Hydrogen is a pollution-free fuel. When it burns in air, the only product is water with trace amounts of nitrogen oxides. No carbon dioxide, carbon monoxide, oxides of sulfur, or unburned hydrocarbons are emitted. In a *hydrogen economy*, hydrogen would replace fossil fuels as the energy source for heating, transportation, and industrial processes. Achieving this goal will require new technology for the production, distribution, and storage of hydrogen.

Large-scale production of hydrogen currently begins with fossil fuels. The process emits CO_2, unless money is spent to trap the CO_2. Some hydrogen is extracted from biomass sources such as wood chips. In the future, green algae may produce hydrogen in the presence of sunlight. Liquid hydrogen may be shipped in vacuum-insulated tanks or through underground pipes.

Cars that run on hydrogen fuel are being built. One challenge is storing the hydrogen. On the space shuttle, it is stored as a liquid. In some vehicles, it is produced from fossil fuels as needed. One promising technology is storage of solid hydrogen in metal hydrides. ■

This is a model of a vehicle in which hydrogen is stored in a metal hydride at low pressure. When the hydride is heated, the hydrogen is released.

H   Hydrogen Peroxide

The strips used to whiten teeth usually contain hydrogen peroxide, H_2O_2. It is a powerful oxidizer that doesn't produce toxic gases or unwanted residues. A 3% aqueous solution is safe for use at home. Stronger concentrations are used to treat wastewater, bleach paper, and produce detergents.

Hydrogen peroxide can inhibit the growth of bacteria in water pipes and increase the growth of bacteria that clean up polluted soils. How is this possible? The answer is *selectivity*. Scientists can adjust variables such as pH, temperature, and concentration so that hydrogen peroxide oxidizes one pollutant and not another. ■

? Did You Know...

Hydrogen in the center of the sun has a density of about 200 g/mL. The temperature is about 13 million degrees Celsius. Radiation released when hydrogen nuclei fuse takes about a million years to reach the sun's surface.

Hydrogen   **R39**

Transition Metals

Physical Properties

- Most transition metals are ductile, malleable, and good conductors of heat and electric current.

- For transition metals, density and melting point tend to increase across a series or increase to a peak in Group 6B and then decrease.

Except for copper and gold, transition metals, including platinum, have a silvery luster.

- Compounds of transition metals tend to have color.

Before 1700
Au gold
Ag silver
Cu copper
Fe iron
Hg mercury
Zn zinc

1700–1799
Co cobalt ~1735
Pt platinum 1735
Ni nickel 1751
Mn manganese 1774
Mo molybdenum 1778
W tungsten 1783
Ti titanium 1791
Y yttrium 1794
Cr chromium 1797

1800–1899
V vanadium 1801
Nb niobium 1801
Ta tantalum 1802
Pd palladium 1803
Rh rhodium 1803
Os osmium 1803
Ir iridum 1803
Cd cadmium 1817
Zr zirconium 1824
Ru ruthenium 1844
Sc scandium 1878

After 1900
Lu lutetium 1907
Hf hafnium 1923
Re rhenium 1925

Density and Melting Points of Period 4 Transition Metals

Density (g/L):
Sc 2.99, Ti 4.51, V 6.0, Cr 7.15, Mn 7.3, Fe 7.87, Co 8.86, Ni 8.90, Cu 8.96, Zn 7.14

Temperature (°C):
Sc 1541, Ti 1668, V 1910, Cr 1907, Mn 1246, Fe 1538, Co 1495, Ni 1455, Cu 1084, Zn 420

Sources

- Transition metals come from mineral deposits in Earth's crust. Minerals that are used for the commercial production of metals are called ores.

- For centuries, people have developed techniques for separating metals from ores. The ore is concentrated and the metal removed by reduction. Then the metal is refined and purified.

Gold exists as an element in nature. But its ore needs to be concentrated before the gold can be extracted and purified.

Atomic Properties

- Among the transition metals, as atomic number increases, there is an increase in the number of electrons in the second-to-highest occupied energy level.

- In periods 5 and 6, transition metals in the same group have identical or almost identical atomic radii. Consequently, these pairs of elements have very similar chemical properties. They tend to occur together in nature and are difficult to separate.

Trends in Atomic Size for Transition Metals

Chemical Properties

- There is great variation in reactivity among transition metals. Scandium and yttrium are similar to Group 1A and 2A metals. They are easily oxidized on exposure to air and react with water to release hydrogen. Platinum and gold are extremely unreactive and resist oxidation.

- In general, transition metals have multiple oxidation states. Compounds in which the elements are in their highest oxidation states are powerful oxidizing agents.

- Most transition metals form compounds with distinctive colors. The color of a transition metal compound or solution can indicate the oxidation state of the metal.

Oxidation Numbers of Period 4 Transition Metals

● most common

The oxidation number of vanadium is +5 in the yellow solution, +4 in the blue solution, +3 in the green solution, and +2 in the purple solution.

VO_4^{3-}

$Cr_2O_7^{2-}$

MnO_4^-

In these aqueous solutions, vanadium, chromium, and manganese are in their highest oxidation states.

Transition Metals

Catalytic Converters

In an internal combustion engine, some hydrocarbon molecules aren't completely oxidized. They form carbon monoxide instead of carbon dioxide. Some hydrocarbon molecules even pass into the exhaust without reacting. At the high temperature and pressure inside an engine's cylinders, some nitrogen from the air reacts with oxygen to produce irritating nitrogen oxides.

A catalytic converter keeps these pollutants from being released into the air. Inside the converter is a porous ceramic cylinder with a honeycomb structure. The ceramic absorbs particles of rhodium and platinum. The metals are catalysts for reactions that occur as exhaust gases pass through channels in the converter. Rhodium helps convert nitrogen oxides to nitrogen. Platinum helps convert hydrocarbons and carbon monoxide to carbon dioxide and water. ■

Ceramic with Pt and Rh

Cu Copper Alloys

Copper was one of the first metals to be widely used. It is found uncombined in nature or easily reduced from its ores. The Roman supply of copper came mainly from Cyprus and was known as *aes Cyprium* (metal of Cyprus). This name evolved to *cyprium* and then *cuprium*, which is why copper has the symbol Cu. Pure copper is valued both for its ability to conduct an electric current and its ability to resist corrosion.

When a bronze bell is struck, the clear, loud tone lasts for several seconds.

Around 3500 BC, people began to add tin to copper to form bronze. This alloy is harder than pure copper and easier to melt for casting. Metalworkers could produce bronze with different properties by varying the amount of tin. Bronze used to make statues might contain as little as 10% tin by mass. Bronze used to make bells would contain 13–25% tin. Most copper coins are bronze with 4% tin and 1% zinc.

Brass is an alloy of copper and zinc. Brass is harder than pure copper and more malleable than bronze. Brass containing at least 65% copper can be worked when it is cold. Brass with 55–65% copper can be worked when it is hot. Before large amounts of gold and silver reached Europe in the 1500s, brass was the metal used for decorative items.

Copper that is exposed to oxygen and water forms a patina of basic copper salts. This thin film protects the underlying metal from further oxidation. The composition of the patina, its color, and the rate at which it forms vary with the climate. The rate is faster near the ocean. ■

Historically, brass was used to make high-quality scientific instruments. This microscope was made in 1765.

Fe Iron and Steel

Carbon is used to extract iron from its ores. At first, people used charcoal from burnt wood. In 1709, Abraham Darby invented a process that used coke instead of charcoal. Coke is almost pure carbon. It is produced when coal is heated and the impurities removed as gases. With coke, the production of iron became less expensive and more efficient.

Iron ore is reduced to metallic iron in a blast furnace. Ore, coke, and limestone are added at the top of the furnace. Molten iron and slag collect at the bottom. The "pig" iron produced contains 3–5% carbon and smaller amounts of other impurities, which make the iron brittle. Pig iron can't be rolled or welded, but it can be cast. Cast iron is used to make stoves and engine blocks for cars.

Most pig iron is used to make steel. The methods for making steel differ, but they all lower the carbon content to less than 2% and remove other impurities. About 90% of the steel produced is carbon steel, which contains no other metals. Mild steel, which is malleable and ductile, contains less than 0.2% carbon. Medium steel (0.2% to 0.6% carbon) is used for structural components, such as beams and girders. Because high-carbon steel (0.8% to 1.5% carbon) is harder than other carbon steels, it is used to make items such as drill bits and knives.

Transition metals are used to produce alloy steels with a specific set of properties. The most common stainless steel contains about 18% chromium and 8% nickel. ∎

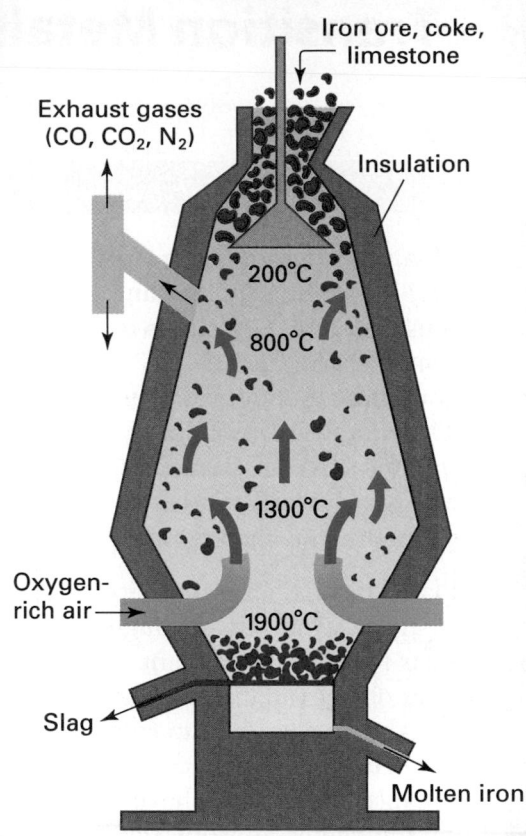

Blast Furnace

Iron ore, coke, limestone

Exhaust gases (CO, CO_2, N_2)

Insulation

200°C

800°C

1300°C

Oxygen-rich air

1900°C

Slag

Molten iron

Iron ore typically contains Fe_2O_3, and SiO_2. When heated, limestone produces CaO, which reacts with SiO_2 to form slag. Slag is used to manufacture Portland cement.

In 1779, Abraham Darby III built the world's first cast-iron bridge across the River Severn in England. The bridge is still used by pedestrians.

? Did You Know...

Swords made with Damascus steel were highly valued. The source of this quality was the 0.02% **vanadium** in the iron ore that the steel makers used. When they began to use a different source of iron ore, the quality of their steel declined.

Transition Metals

Fe Ni Co

Phytoremediation uses plants such as sunflowers, Indian mustard, and dandelions to remove pollutants from contaminated soil and water. The contaminants include organic solvents, pesticides, and toxic metals such as cadmium and chromium.

Plants have a natural ability to absorb nutrients through their roots. Often a plant does not distinguish a toxic metal such as cadmium from a nutrient such as zinc because these metals have similar chemical properties. So cadmium is absorbed and transported to the leaves and stems, where it accumulates. The plants are composted or burned after harvesting. The metal residues are buried in an approved landfill or recovered through smelting. ■

Refrigerator magnets contain a barium ferrite, $BaO \cdot 6Fe_2O_3$, or strontium ferrite, $SrO \cdot 6Fe_2O_3$, powder, which is embedded in plastic or rubber. Horseshoe magnets usually contain an alloy of aluminum, nickel, and cobalt.

Iron, nickel, and cobalt are strongly attracted to magnetic fields. When these metals are exposed to a magnetic field, their cations line up in an orderly arrangement. When the field is removed, the ions remain lined up, and the material can act as a magnet. This type of magnetism is called ferromagnetism.

A magnet retains its strength unless it is heated past a point called the Curie temperature. For iron, this temperature is 1043 K. For cobalt, it is 1388 K. For nickel, it is 627 K.

Magnets made from a neodymium, boron, and iron alloy are very powerful. If they are allowed to fly together, they will shatter. They are used to check for counterfeit bills because they can detect tiny magnetic particles placed in the ink of genuine bills. ■

The wrench is strongly attracted to the tiny neodymium-iron-boron cube.

Au

Gold occurs chiefly as small flecks of free metal in veins of quartz. About 5 g of gold is produced from a metric ton (10^6 g) of gold-bearing rock.

Gold can be pounded into sheets so thin that they will transmit light. These sheets, called gold leaf, are used for lettering and decoration in general. Gold is used on the outside surfaces of satellites because it resists corrosion. Its high electrical and thermal conductivity make gold a good choice to plate contacts in microcircuits.

Pure gold is alloyed to make it harder and more durable. Gold alloys are safe to use as fillings for teeth because gold is highly unreactive.

Units called karats (k) are used to describe the purity of gold. Pure gold is 24k or 100% gold. Gold in coins is usually 22k or 92% gold. Gold in rings is often 14k (58%). ■

Micronutrients

Trace amounts of some transition metals are essential for human health.

Iron is found mainly in hemoglobin and myoglobin. Hemoglobin is the protein that transports oxygen in blood. Myoglobin is the protein that stores oxygen in muscle tissue. Vitamin C helps the absorption of iron by promoting the reduction of Fe^{3+} ions to Fe^{2+} ions.

Zinc is a cofactor in many enzymes. It helps protect the immune system. Hormones that control growth and reproduction do not function properly without zinc. A lack of zinc impairs the sense of taste and reduces the appetite.

Copper is a component of enzymes that control the synthesis of melanin, hemoglobin, and phospholipids in the sheath that protects nerves.

Molybdenum affects the absorption of copper. It is also needed for the oxidation of lipids and the metabolism of sulfur and nitrogen.

Chromium assists in the metabolism of glucose and may help to control adult-onset diabetes. A lack of chromium may affect growth.

Manganese is required for the proper function of the nervous system and the thyroid gland. It is needed for glucose metabolism. It helps maintain healthy bones and cartilage.

Cobalt is a component of vitamin B12, which is required for the synthesis of red blood cells. ∎

Transition Metal Micronutrients

Element	RDA or AI*	Dietary Sources
Iron	10 mg RDA (M) 20 mg RDA (F)	liver, green vegetables, egg yolk, fish, whole wheat, nuts, oatmeal, molasses, and beans
Zinc	11 mg RDA (M) 8 mg RDA (F)	liver, eggs, meat, milk, whole grains, and shellfish
Copper	900 μg RDA	beans, peas, and shellfish
Molybdenum	45 μg RDA	beans, peas, and whole grains
Chromium	35 μg AI (M) 25 μg AI (F)	meat and whole grains
Manganese	2.3 mg AI (M) 1.8 mg AI (F)	nuts, whole grains, dried fruits, and green leafy vegetables

*Recommended Dietary Allowance or Adequate Intake

Ti Suncreens

You need some exposure to sunlight so your skin cells can make vitamin D, which is needed for healthy bones and teeth. Yet the UV radiation in sunlight can damage skin cells and even lead to skin cancer. The best way to protect your skin is to limit your time in the sun. The next best way is to use a sunscreen.

All the active ingredients in sunscreens protect against UVB light (280–320 nm), which is the primary cause of sunburn. Some protect against UVA light (320–400 nm), which penetrates deeper and causes long-term damage. A sun protective factor rating (SPF) measures only how effective a sunscreen is against UVB, not UVA.

Titanium dioxide, TiO_2, can reflect and scatter UV light. This stable and nonirritating oxide has one drawback. It looks like white paint on the skin. One manufacturer has addressed this problem by decreasing the size of the TiO_2 particles to a diameter of about 21 nm. At this size, TiO_2 appears transparent because its particles are smaller than wavelengths of visible light and light isn't reflected by the particles. ∎

Did You Know...

An octopus has blood that is blue, not red, because the compound that transports oxygen in an octopus contains **copper,** not iron. Snails, oysters, and spiders are also bluebloods.

Appendix B: Reference Tables

CONTENTS

Table B.1

SI Units and Conversion Factors

Length	SI Unit: meter (m)	Mass	SI Unit: kilogram (kg)
	1 meter = 1.0936 yards		1 kilogram = 1000 grams
	1 centimeter = 0.39370 inch		= mass weighing 2.2046 lbs
	1 inch = 2.54 centimeters		1 amu = 1.66057×10^{-27} kilograms
	1 mile = 5280 feet	**Time**	**SI Unit: second (s)**
	= 1.6093 kilometers		1 hour = 60 minutes
Volume	**SI Unit: cubic meter (m³)**		1 hour = 3600 seconds
	1 liter = 10^{-3} m³	**Energy**	**SI Unit: joule (J)**
	= 1.0567 quarts		1 joule = 1 kg · m²/s² (exact)
	1 gallon = 4 quarts		1 joule = 0.23901 calorie
	= 8 pints		1 calorie = 4.184 joules
	= 3.7854 liters	**Pressure**	**SI Unit: Pascal (Pa)**
	1 quart = 32 fluid ounces		1 atmosphere = 101.3 kilopascals
	= 0.94635 liter		= 760 mm Hg (torr)
Temperature	**SI Unit: kelvin (K)**		= 14.70 pounds per square inch
	1 kelvin = 1 Celsius degree		
	°C = (5/9) (°F − 32)		
	kelvin temperature = °C + 273.15		

Table B.2

Some Properties of the Elements

Element	Symbol	Atomic number	Atomic mass	Melting point (°C)	Boiling point (°C)	Density (g/cm³) (gases at STP)	Oxidation numbers
Actinium	Ac	89	(227)	1050	3200	10.07	+3
Aluminum	Al	13	26.98154	660.37	2467	2.6989	+3
Americium	Am	95	243	994	2607	13.67	+3, +4, +5, +6
Antimony	Sb	51	121.75	630.74	1950	6.691	−3, +3, +5
Argon	Ar	18	39.948	−189.2	−185.7	0.0017837	
Arsenic	As	33	74.9216	817	613	5.73	−3, +3, +5
Astatine	At	85	(210)	302	337	—	
Barium	Ba	56	137.33	725	1640	3.5	+2
Berkelium	Bk	97	(247)	986	—	14.78	
Beryllium	Be	4	9.01218	1278	2970	1.848	+2
Bismuth	Bi	83	208.9804	271.3	1560	9.747	+3, +5
Bohrium	Bh	107	(264)	—	—	—	
Boron	B	5	10.81	2079	3675	2.34	+3
Bromine	Br	35	79.904	−7.2	58.78	3.12	−1, +1, +5
Cadmium	Cd	48	112.41	320.9	765	8.65	+2
Calcium	Ca	20	40.08	839	1484	1.55	+2
Californium	Cf	98	(251)	900	—	14	
Carbon	C	6	12.011	3550	4827	2.267	−4, +2, +4
Cerium	Ce	58	140.12	799	3426	6.657	+3, +4
Cesium	Cs	55	132.9054	28.40	669.3	1.873	+1
Chlorine	Cl	17	35.453	−100.98	−34.6	0.003214	−1, +1, +5, +7
Chromium	Cr	24	51.996	1857	2672	7.18	+2, +3, +6
Cobalt	Co	27	58.9332	1495	2870	8.9	+2, +3
Copper	Cu	29	63.546	1083.4	2567	8.96	+1, +2
Curium	Cm	96	(247)	1340	—	13.51	+3
Darmstadtium	Ds	110	(269)	—	—	—	
Dubnium	Db	105	(262)	—	—	—	
Dysprosium	Dy	66	162.50	1412	2562	8.550	+3
Einsteinium	Es	99	(252)	—	—	—	
Erbium	Er	68	167.26	159	2863	9.066	+3
Europium	Eu	63	151.96	822	1597	5.243	+2, +3
Fermium	Fm	100	(257)	—	—	—	
Fluorine	F	9	18.998403	−219.62	−188.54	0.001696	−1
Francium	Fr	87	(223)	27	677	—	+1
Gadolinium	Gd	64	157.25	1313	3266	7.9004	+3
Gallium	Ga	31	69.72	29.78	2204	5.904	+3
Germanium	Ge	32	72.59	937.4	2830	5.323	+2, +4
Gold	Au	79	196.9665	1064.43	3080	19.3	+1, +3
Hafnium	Hf	72	178.49	2227	4602	13.31	+4
Hassium	Hs	108	(265)	—	—	—	
Helium	He	2	4.00260	−272.2	−268.934	0.001785	
Holmium	Ho	67	164.9304	1474	2695	8.795	+3
Hydrogen	H	1	1.00794	−259.14	−252.87	0.00008988	−1, +1
Indium	In	49	114.82	156.61	2080	7.31	+1, +3
Iodine	I	53	126.9045	113.5	184.35	4.93	−1, +1, +5, +7
Iridium	Ir	77	192.22	2410	4130	22.42	+3, +4

Table B.2

Some Properties of the Elements (cont.)

Element	Symbol	Atomic number	Atomic mass	Melting point (°C)	Boiling point (°C)	Density (g/cm³) (gases at STP)	Oxidation numbers
Iron	Fe	26	55.847	1535	2750	7.874	+2, +3
Krypton	Kr	36	83.80	−156.6	−152.30	0.003733	
Lanthanum	La	57	138.9055	921	3457	6.145	+3
Lawrencium	Lr	103	(262)	—	—	—	+3
Lead	Pb	82	207.2	327.502	1740	11.35	+2, +4
Lithium	Li	3	6.941	180.54	1342	0.534	+1
Lutetium	Lu	71	174.967	1663	3395	9.840	+3
Magnesium	Mg	12	24.305	648.8	1090	1.738	+2
Manganese	Mn	25	54.9380	1244	1962	7.32	+2, +3, +4, +7
Meitnerium	Mt	109	(268)	—	—	—	
Mendelevium	Md	101	257	—	—	—	+2, +3
Mercury	Hg	80	200.59	−38.842	356.58	13.55	+1, +2
Molybdenum	Mo	42	95.94	2617	4612	10.22	+6
Neodymium	Nd	60	144.24	1021	3068	6.90	+3
Neon	Ne	10	20.179	−248.67	−246.048	0.0008999	
Neptunium	Np	93	(237)	640	3902	20.25	+3, +4, +5, +6
Nickel	Ni	28	58.69	1453	2732	8.902	+2, +3
Niobium	Nb	41	92.9064	2468	4742	8.57	+3, +5
Nitrogen	N	7	14.0067	−209.86	−195.8	0.0012506	−3, +3, +5
Nobelium	No	102	(259)	—	—	—	+2, +3
Osmium	Os	76	190.2	3045	5027	22.57	+3, +4
Oxygen	O	8	15.9994	−218.4	−182.962	0.001429	−2
Palladium	Pd	46	106.42	1554	2970	12.02	+2, +4
Phosphorus	P	15	30.97376	44.1	280	1.82	−3, +3, +5
Platinum	Pt	78	195.08	1772	3627	21.45	+2, +4
Plutonium	Pu	94	(244)	641	3232	19.84	+3, +4, +5, +6
Polonium	Po	84	(209)	254	962	9.32	+2, +4
Potassium	K	19	39.0982	63.25	760	0.862	+1
Praseodymium	Pr	59	140.9077	931	3512	6.64	+3
Promethium	Pm	61	(145)	1168	2460	7.22	+3
Protactinium	Pa	91	231.0359	1560	4027	15.37	+4, +5
Radium	Ra	88	(226)	700	1140	5.5	+2
Radon	Rn	86	(222)	−71	−61.8	0.00973	
Rhenium	Re	75	186.207	3180	5627	21.02	+4, +6, +7
Rhodium	Rh	45	102.9055	1966	3727	12.41	+3
Rubidium	Rb	37	85.4678	38.89	686	1.532	+1
Ruthenium	Ru	44	101.07	2310	3900	12.41	+3
Rutherfordium	Rf	104	(261)	—	—	—	
Samarium	Sm	62	150.36	1077	1791	7.520	+2, +3
Scandium	Sc	21	44.9559	1541	2831	2.989	+3
Seaborgium	Sg	106	(263)	—	—	—	
Selenium	Se	34	78.96	217	684.9	4.79	−2, +4, +6
Silicon	Si	14	28.0855	1410	2355	2.33	−4, +2, +4
Silver	Ag	47	107.8682	961.93	2212	10.50	+1
Sodium	Na	11	22.98977	97.81	882.9	0.971	+1

Table B.2

Element	**Symbol**	**Atomic number**	**Atomic mass**	**Melting point (°C)**	**Boiling point (°C)**	**Density (g/cm³) (gases at STP)**	**Oxidation numbers**

Some Properties of the Elements (cont.)

Element	Symbol	Atomic number	Atomic mass	Melting point (°C)	Boiling point (°C)	Density (g/cm³) (gases at STP)	Oxidation numbers
Strontium	Sr	38	87.62	769	1384	2.54	+2
Sulfur	S	16	32.06	112.8	444.7	2.07	−2, +4, +6
Tantalum	Ta	73	180.9479	2996	5425	16.654	+5
Technetium	Tc	43	(98)	2172	4877	11.50	+4, +6, +7
Tellurium	Te	52	127.60	449.5	989.8	6.24	−2, +4, +6
Terbium	Tb	65	158.9254	1356	3123	8.229	+3
Thallium	Tl	81	204.383	303.5	1457	11.85	+1, +3
Thorium	Th	90	232.0381	1750	4790	11.72	+4
Thulium	Tm	69	168.9342	1545	1947	9.321	+3
Tin	Sn	50	118.69	231.968	2270	7.31	+2, +4
Titanium	Ti	22	47.88	1660	3287	4.54	+2, +3, +4
Tungsten	W	74	183.85	3410	5660	19.3	+6
Ununbium	Uub	112	(277)	—	—	—	
Ununquadium	Uuq	114	—	—	—	—	
Unununium	Uuu	111	(272)	—	—	—	
Uranium	U	92	238.0289	1132.3	3818	18.95	+3, +4, +5, +6
Vanadium	V	23	50.9415	1890	3380	6.11	+2, +3, +4, +5
Xenon	Xe	54	131.29	−111.9	−107.1	0.005887	
Ytterbium	Yb	70	173.04	819	1194	6.965	+2, +3
Yttrium	Y	39	88.9059	1522	3338	4.469	+3
Zinc	Zn	30	65.38	419.58	907	7.133	+2
Zirconium	Zr	40	91.22	1852	4377	6.506	+4

Table B.3

Physical Constants	
Atomic mass unit	$1 \text{ amu} = 1.6605 \times 10^{-24} \text{ g}$
Avogadro's number	$N = 6.0221 \times 10^{23} \text{ particles/mol}$
Gas constant	$R = 8.31 \text{ L·kPa/K·mol}$
Ideal gas molar volume	$V_m = 22.414 \text{ L/mol}$
Masses of subatomic particles	
Electron (e^-)	$m_e = 0.0005486 \text{ amu} = 9.1096 \times 10^{-28} \text{g}$
Proton (p^+)	$m_p = 1.007277 \text{ amu} = 1.67261 \times 10^{-24} \text{g}$
Neutron (n^0)	$m_n = 1.008665 \text{ amu} = 1.67492 \times 10^{-24} \text{g}$
Speed of light (in vacuum)	$c = 2.997925 \times 10^8 \text{ m/s}$

Table B.4

Electron Configurations of the Elements

Elements		1s	2s	2p	3s	3p	3d	4s	4p	4d	4f	5s	5p	5d	5f	6s	6p	6d	7s	7p
1	Hydrogen	1																		
2	Helium	2																		
3	Lithium	2	1																	
4	Beryllium	2	2																	
5	Boron	2	2	1																
6	Carbon	2	2	2																
7	Nitrogen	2	2	3																
8	Oxygen	2	2	4																
9	Fluorine	2	2	5																
10	Neon	2	2	6																
11	Sodium	2	2	6	1															
12	Magnesium	2	2	6	2															
13	Aluminum	2	2	6	2	1														
14	Silicon	2	2	6	2	2														
15	Phosphorus	2	2	6	2	3														
16	Sulfur	2	2	6	2	4														
17	Chlorine	2	2	6	2	5														
18	Argon	2	2	6	2	6														
19	Potassium	2	2	6	2	6		1												
20	Calcium	2	2	6	2	6		2												
21	Scandium	2	2	6	2	6	1	2												
22	Titanium	2	2	6	2	6	2	2												
23	Vanadium	2	2	6	2	6	3	2												
24	Chromium	2	2	6	2	6	5	1												
25	Manganese	2	2	6	2	6	5	2												
26	Iron	2	2	6	2	6	6	2												
27	Cobalt	2	2	6	2	6	7	2												
28	Nickel	2	2	6	2	6	8	2												
29	Copper	2	2	6	2	6	10	1												
30	Zinc	2	2	6	2	6	10	2												
31	Gallium	2	2	6	2	6	10	2	1											
32	Germanium	2	2	6	2	6	10	2	2											
33	Arsenic	2	2	6	2	6	10	2	3											
34	Selenium	2	2	6	2	6	10	2	4											
35	Bromine	2	2	6	2	6	10	2	5											
36	Krypton	2	2	6	2	6	10	2	6											
37	Rubidium	2	2	6	2	6	10	2	6			1								
38	Strontium	2	2	6	2	6	10	2	6			2								
39	Yttrium	2	2	6	2	6	10	2	6	1		2								
40	Zirconium	2	2	6	2	6	10	2	6	2		2								
41	Niobium	2	2	6	2	6	10	2	6	4		1								
42	Molybdenum	2	2	6	2	6	10	2	6	5		1								
43	Technetium	2	2	6	2	6	10	2	6	5		2								
44	Ruthenium	2	2	6	2	6	10	2	6	7		1								
45	Rhodium	2	2	6	2	6	10	2	6	8		1								
46	Palladium	2	2	6	2	6	10	2	6	10										

Electron Configurations of the Elements (cont.)

Elements		1s	2s	2p	3s	3p	3d	4s	4p	4d	4f	5s	5p	5d	5f	6s	6p	6d	7s	7p
47	Silver	2	2	6	2	6	10	2	6	10		1								
48	Cadmium	2	2	6	2	6	10	2	6	10		2								
49	Indium	2	2	6	2	6	10	2	6	10		2	1							
50	Tin	2	2	6	2	6	10	2	6	10		2	2							
51	Antimony	2	2	6	2	6	10	2	6	10		2	3							
52	Tellurium	2	2	6	2	6	10	2	6	10		2	4							
53	Iodine	2	2	6	2	6	10	2	6	10		2	5							
54	Xenon	2	2	6	2	6	10	2	6	10		2	6							
55	Cesium	2	2	6	2	6	10	2	6	10		2	6			1				
56	Barium	2	2	6	2	6	10	2	6	10		2	6			2				
57	Lanthanum	2	2	6	2	6	10	2	6	10		2	6	1		2				
58	Cerium	2	2	6	2	6	10	2	6	10	1	2	6	1		2				
59	Praseodymium	2	2	6	2	6	10	2	6	10	3	2	6			2				
60	Neodymium	2	2	6	2	6	10	2	6	10	4	2	6			2				
61	Promethium	2	2	6	2	6	10	2	6	10	5	2	6			2				
62	Samarium	2	2	6	2	6	10	2	6	10	6	2	6			2				
63	Europium	2	2	6	2	6	10	2	6	10	7	2	6			2				
64	Gadolinium	2	2	6	2	6	10	2	6	10	7	2	6	1		2				
65	Terbium	2	2	6	2	6	10	2	6	10	9	2	6			2				
66	Dysprosium	2	2	6	2	6	10	2	6	10	10	2	6			2				
67	Holmium	2	2	6	2	6	10	2	6	10	11	2	6			2				
68	Erbium	2	2	6	2	6	10	2	6	10	12	2	6			2				
69	Thulium	2	2	6	2	6	10	2	6	10	13	2	6			2				
70	Ytterbium	2	2	6	2	6	10	2	6	10	14	2	6			2				
71	Lutetium	2	2	6	2	6	10	2	6	10	14	2	6	1		2				
72	Hafnium	2	2	6	2	6	10	2	6	10	14	2	6	2		2				
73	Tantalum	2	2	6	2	6	10	2	6	10	14	2	6	3		2				
74	Tungsten	2	2	6	2	6	10	2	6	10	14	2	6	4		2				
75	Rhenium	2	2	6	2	6	10	2	6	10	14	2	6	5		2				
76	Osmium	2	2	6	2	6	10	2	6	10	14	2	6	6		2				
77	Iridium	2	2	6	2	6	10	2	6	10	14	2	6	7		2				
78	Platinum	2	2	6	2	6	10	2	6	10	14	2	6	9		1				
79	Gold	2	2	6	2	6	10	2	6	10	14	2	6	10		1				
80	Mercury	2	2	6	2	6	10	2	6	10	14	2	6	10		2				
81	Thallium	2	2	6	2	6	10	2	6	10	14	2	6	10		2	1			
82	Lead	2	2	6	2	6	10	2	6	10	14	2	6	10		2	2			
83	Bismuth	2	2	6	2	6	10	2	6	10	14	2	6	10		2	3			
84	Polonium	2	2	6	2	6	10	2	6	10	14	2	6	10		2	4			
85	Astatine	2	2	6	2	6	10	2	6	10	14	2	6	10		2	5			
86	Radon	2	2	6	2	6	10	2	6	10	14	2	6	10		2	6			
87	Francium	2	2	6	2	6	10	2	6	10	14	2	6	10		2	6		1	
88	Radium	2	2	6	2	6	10	2	6	10	14	2	6	10		2	6		2	
89	Actinium	2	2	6	2	6	10	2	6	10	14	2	6	10		2	6	1	2	
90	Thorium	2	2	6	2	6	10	2	6	10	14	2	6	10		2	6	2	2	
91	Protactinium	2	2	6	2	6	10	2	6	10	14	2	6	10	2	2	6	1	2	
92	Uranium	2	2	6	2	6	10	2	6	10	14	2	6	10	3	2	6	1	2	

Table B.4

Electron Configurations of the Elements (cont.)

Elements		1s	2s	2p	3s	3p	3d	4s	4p	4d	4f	5s	5p	5d	5f	6s	6p	6d	7s	7p
93	Neptunium	2	2	6	2	6	10	2	6	10	14	2	6	10	4	2	6	1	2	
94	Plutonium	2	2	6	2	6	10	2	6	10	14	2	6	10	6	2	6		2	
95	Americium	2	2	6	2	6	10	2	6	10	14	2	6	10	7	2	6		2	
96	Curium	2	2	6	2	6	10	2	6	10	14	2	6	10	7	2	6	1	2	
97	Berkelium	2	2	6	2	6	10	2	6	10	14	2	6	10	9	2	6		2	
98	Californium	2	2	6	2	6	10	2	6	10	14	2	6	10	10	2	6		2	
99	Einsteinium	2	2	6	2	6	10	2	6	10	14	2	6	10	11	2	6		2	
100	Fermium	2	2	6	2	6	10	2	6	10	14	2	6	10	12	2	6		2	
101	Mendelevium	2	2	6	2	6	10	2	6	10	14	2	6	10	13	2	6		2	
102	Nobelium	2	2	6	2	6	10	2	6	10	14	2	6	10	14	2	6		2	
103	Lawrencium	2	2	6	2	6	10	2	6	10	14	2	6	10	14	2	6	1	2	
104	Rutherfordium	2	2	6	2	6	10	2	6	10	14	2	6	10	14	2	6	2	2	
105	Dubnium	2	2	6	2	6	10	2	6	10	14	2	6	10	14	2	6	3	2	
106	Seaborgium	2	2	6	2	6	10	2	6	10	14	2	6	10	14	2	6	4	2	
107	Bohrium	2	2	6	2	6	10	2	6	10	14	2	6	10	14	2	6	5	2	
108	Hassium	2	2	6	2	6	10	2	6	10	14	2	6	10	14	2	6	6	2	
109	Meitnerium	2	2	6	2	6	10	2	6	10	14	2	6	10	14	2	6	7	2	
110	Darmstadium	2	2	6	2	6	10	2	6	10	14	2	6	10	14	2	6	9	1	
111	Unununium	2	2	6	2	6	10	2	6	10	14	2	6	10	14	2	6	10	1	
112	Ununbium	2	2	6	2	6	10	2	6	10	14	2	6	10	14	2	6	10	2	
114	Ununquadium	2	2	6	2	6	10	2	6	10	14	2	6	10	14	2	6	10	2	2

Table B.5

Common Ions

Positive Ions (Cations)

1+ charge		2+ charge		3+ charge	
H^+	hydrogen	Mg^{2+}	magnesium	Al^{3+}	aluminum
Na^+	sodium	Fe^{2+}	iron(II)	Fe^{3+}	iron(III)
K^+	potassium	Co^{2+}	cobalt(II)	Co^{3+}	cobalt(III)
NH_4^+	ammonium	Ni^{2+}	nickel(II)	Ni^{3+}	nickel(III)
Li^+	lithium	Ca^{2+}	calcium		
Ag^+	silver	Zn^{2+}	zinc		
Cu^+	copper(I)	Cu^{2+}	copper(II)		

Negative Ions (Anions)

1− charge		2− charge		3− charge	
F^-	fluoride	O^{2-}	oxide	N^{3-}	nitride
Cl^-	chloride	S^{2-}	sulfide	P^{3-}	phosphide
Br^-	bromide	SO_4^{2-}	sulfate	PO_4^{3-}	phosphate
OH^-	hydroxide	CO_3^{2-}	carbonate		

Table B.6

Other Symbols and Abbreviations

Symbol	Meaning	Symbol	Meaning	Symbol	Meaning
α	alpha rays	H_f	heat of formation	m	molality
β	beta rays	h	hour	mL	milliliter (*volume*)
γ	gamma rays	h	Planck's constant	mm	millimeter (*length*)
Δ	change in	Hz	hertz (*frequency*)	mol	mole (*amount*)
$\delta+, \delta-$	partial ionic charge	J	joule (*energy*)	mp	melting point
λ	wavelength	K	kelvin (*temperature*)	N	normality
π	pi bond	K_a	acid dissociation constant	n^0	neutron
σ	sigma bond	K_b	base dissociation constant	n	number of moles
ν	frequency	K_b	molal boiling point elevation constant	n	principal quantum number
amu	atomic mass unit			P	pressure
(*aq*)	aqueous solution	K_{eq}	equilibrium constant	p^+	proton
atm	atmosphere (*pressure*)	K_f	molal freezing point depression constant	Pa	pascal (*pressure*)
bp	boiling point			R	ideal gas constant
°C	degree Celsius (*temperature*)	K_w	ion product constant for water	S	entropy
c	speed of light in a vacuum			s	second
cm	centimeter (*length*)	K_{sp}	solubility product constant	(*s*)	solid
E	energy	kcal	kilocalorie (*energy*)	SI	International System of Units
e^-	electron	kg	kilogram (*mass*)		
fp	freezing point	kPa	kilopascal (*pressure*)	STP	standard temperature and pressure
G	Gibb's free energy	L	liter (*volume*)		
g	gram (*mass*)	(*l*)	liquid	T	temperature
(*g*)	gas	M	molarity	$t_{\frac{1}{2}}$	half-life
gfm	gram formula mass	m	meter (length)	V	volume
H	enthalpy	m	mass	v	velocity, speed

Table B.7

Symbols of Common Elements

Symbol	Element	Symbol	Element	Symbol	Element
Ag	silver	Cu	copper	O	oxygen
Al	aluminum	F	fluorine	P	phosphorus
As	arsenic	Fe	iron	Pb	lead
Au	gold	H	hydrogen	Pt	platinum
Ba	barium	Hg	mercury	S	sulfur
Bi	bismuth	I	iodine	Sb	antimony
Br	bromine	K	potassium	Sn	tin
C	carbon	Mg	magnesium	Sr	strontium
Ca	calcium	Mn	manganese	Ti	titanium
Cl	chlorine	N	nitrogen	U	uranium
Co	cobalt	Na	sodium	W	tungsten
Cr	chromium	Ni	nickel	Zn	zinc

Table B.8

Names and Charges of Polyatomic Ions

1− charge		2− charge		3− charge	
Name	**Formula**	**Name**	**Formula**	**Name**	**Formula**
Chlorate	ClO_3^-	Carbonate	CO_3^{2-}	Phosphate	PO_4^{3-}
Chlorite	ClO_2^-	Chromate	CrO_4^{2-}	Phosphite	PO_3^{3-}
Cyanide	CN^-	Dichromate	$Cr_2O_7^{2-}$		
Dihydrogen phosphate	$H_2PO_4^-$	Oxalate	$C_2O_4^{2-}$	**1+ charge**	
Ethanoate	CH_3COO^-	Peroxide	O_2^{2-}	**Name**	**Formula**
Thiosulfate	$S_2O_3^{2-}$	Silicate	SiO_3^{2-}	Ammonium	NH_4^+
Hydroxide	OH^-	Sulfate	SO_4^{2-}		
Hydrogen carbonate	HCO_3^-	Sulfite	SO_3^{2-}		
Hydrogen sulfate	HSO_4^-				
Hydrogen sulfite	HSO_3^-				
Hypochlorite	ClO^-				
Nitrate	NO_3^-				
Nitrite	NO_2^-				
Perchlorate	ClO_4^-				
Permanganate	MnO_4^-				
Thiocyanate	SCN^-				

Table B.9

Solubilities of Compounds at 25°C and 101.3 kpa

	acetate	bromide	carbonate	chlorate	chloride	hydroxide	iodide	nitrate	oxide	perchlorate	phosphate	sulfate	sulfide
aluminum	S	S	X	S	S	I	S	S	I	S	I	S	d
ammonium	S	S	S	S	S	X	S	S	X	S	S	S	S
barium	S	S	I	S	S	S	S	S	sS	S	I	I	d
calcium	S	S	I	S	S	S	S	S	sS	S	I	sS	I
copper(II)	S	S	X	S	S	I	S	S	I	S	I	S	I
iron(II)	S	S	I	S	S	I	S	S	I	S	I	S	I
iron(III)	S	S	X	S	S	I	S	S	I	S	I	sS	d
lithium	S	S	sS	S	S	S	S	S	S	S	sS	S	S
magnesium	S	S	I	S	S	I	S	S	I	S	I	S	d
potassium	S	S	S	S	S	S	S	S	S	S	S	S	S
silver	sS	I	I	S	I	X	I	S	I	S	I	sS	I
sodium	S	S	S	S	S	S	S	S	S	S	S	S	S
strontium	S	S	I	S	S	S	S	S	S	S	I	I	I
zinc	S	S	I	S	S	I	S	S	I	S	I	S	I

Key: S = soluble   d = decomposes in water

sS = slightly soluble   X = no such compound

I = insoluble

Rules for Naming Ions

Positive Ions (Cations)

Rule	Example	Name
1. Cations formed from metallic elements have the same name as the element.	Na^+	sodium ion
2a. For a cation that can have different charges, indicate the charge by Roman numerals in parentheses.	Fe^{3+} Fe^{2+}	iron (III) ion iron (II) ion
2b. Or, instead of 2a., use the ending *-ic* to denote the ion whose positive charge is larger, and *ous* to denote the ion whose positive charge is smaller.	Fe^{3+} Fe^{2+}	ferric ion ferrous ion
3. Cations formed from nonmetals end in *-ium.*	NH_4^+	ammonium ion

Negative Ions (Anions)

Rule	Example	Name
1. For single-atom ions, replace the end of the element's name with *-ide.*	H^-	hydride ion
2. A few simple polyatomic anions have names ending in *-ide.*	OH^-	hydroxide ion
3. For polyatomic ions containing oxygen, or *oxions,* the most common form of the ion has a name ending in *-ate.*	CO_3^{2-} ClO_3^-	carbonate ion chlorate ion
4. Use the ending *-ite* to indicate one less oxygen than for the *-ate* ending.	ClO_2^-	chlorite ion
5. Use the prefix *hypo-* to indicate one less oxygen atom than for the *-ite* ending.	ClO^-	hypochlorite ion
6. Use the prefix *per-* to indicate one more oxygen than for the *-ate* ending.	ClO_4^-	perchlorate ion
7. Use the prefix *thio-* to indicate a sulfur atom has replaced an oxygen atom.	SO_4^{2-} $S_2O_3^{2-}$	sulfate ion thiosulfate ion
8. Use *bi-* before the anion name to indicate the presence of a replaceable hydrogen.	CO_3^{2-} HCO_3^-	carbonate ion bicarbonate ion

Scientific Notation

Scientists use photonic lattices to trap or bend light within extremely tiny spaces. The micrograph above shows a photonic lattice made of silicon rods. Each rod is 1.2 microns, or 1.2×10^{-6} meter, wide.

Very large and very small numbers are often expressed in scientific notation (also known as exponential form). In scientific notation, a number is written as the product of two numbers: a coefficient, and 10 raised to a power. For example, the number 84,000 written in scientific notation is 8.4×10^4. The coefficient in this number is 8.4. In scientific notation, the coefficient is always a number greater than or equal to one and less than ten. The power of ten, or exponent, in this example is 4. The exponent indicates how many times the coefficient 8.4 must be multiplied by 10 to equal the number 84,000.

$$8.4 \times 10^4 = 8.4 \times 10 \times 10 \times 10 \times 10 = 84,000$$

exponential form
(scientific notation)   standard form

When writing numbers greater than ten in scientific notation, the exponent is equal to the number of places that the decimal point has been moved to the left.

$$6,300,000 = 6.3 \times 10^6 \qquad 94,700 = 9.47 \times 10^4$$

6 places   4 places

Numbers less than one have a negative exponent when written in scientific notation. For example, the number 0.000 25 written in scientific notation is 2.5×10^{-4}. The negative exponent -4 indicates that the coefficient 2.5 must be divided four times by 10 to equal the number 0.000 25, as shown below.

$$2.5 \times 10^{-4} = \frac{2.5}{10 \times 10 \times 10 \times 10} = 0.000\ 25$$

exponential form
(scientific notation)   standard form

When writing numbers less than one in scientific notation, the value of the exponent equals the number of places the decimal has been moved to the right. The sign of the exponent is negative.

$$0.000\ 008 = 8 \times 10^{-6} \qquad 0.00736 = 7.36 \times 10^{-3}$$

6 places   3 places

If your calculator has an exponent key, you can enter numbers in scientific notation when doing calculations. See the section on using a calculator (pages R62–R65) for more information on calculator operations that involve scientific notation.

Multiplication and Division

To multiply numbers written in scientific notation, multiply the coefficients and add the exponents.

$(3 \times 10^4) \times (2 \times 10^2) = (3 \times 2) \times 10^{4+2} = 6 \times 10^6$
$(2.1 \times 10^3) \times (4.0 \times 10^{-7}) = (2.1 \times 4.0) \times 10^{3+(-7)} = 8.4 \times 10^{-4}$

To divide numbers written in scientific notation, divide the coefficients and subtract the exponent in the denominator from the exponent in the numerator.

$$\frac{3.0 \times 10^5}{6.0 \times 10^2} = \left(\frac{3.0}{6.0}\right) \times 10^{5-2} = 0.5 \times 10^3 = 5.0 \times 10^2$$

Addition and Subtraction

If you want to add or subtract numbers expressed in scientific notation and you are not using a calculator, then the exponents must be the same. For example, suppose you want to calculate the sum of 5.4×10^3 and 8.0×10^2. First, rewrite the second number so that the exponent is a 3.

$$8.0 \times 10^2 = 0.80 \times 10^3$$

Now add the numbers.

$$(5.4 \times 10^3) + (0.80 \times 10^3) = (5.4 + 0.80) \times 10^3 = 6.2 \times 10^3$$

Follow the same rule when you subtract numbers expressed in scientific notation without the aid of a calculator.

$$(3.42 \times 10^{-5}) - (2.5 \times 10^{-6}) = (3.42 \times 10^{-5}) - (0.25 \times 10^{-5})$$
$$= (3.42 - 0.25) \times 10^{-5} = 3.17 \times 10^{-5}$$

SAMPLE PROBLEM MH-1

Using Scientific Notation in Arithmetic Operations
Solve each problem, and express your answer in correct scientific notation.

a. $(8.0 \times 10^{-2}) \times (7.0 \times 10^{-5})$
b. $(7.1 \times 10^{-2}) + (5 \times 10^{-3})$

Solution

Follow the rules described above for multiplying and adding numbers expressed in scientific notation.

a. $(8.0 \times 10^{-2}) \times (7.0 \times 10^{-5}) = (8.0 \times 7.0) \times 10^{-2+(-5)}$
$$= 56 \times 10^{-7} = 5.6 \times 10^{-6}$$
b. $(7.1 \times 10^{-2}) + (5 \times 10^{-3}) = (7.1 \times 10^{-2}) + (0.5 \times 10^{-2})$
$$= (7.1 + 0.5) \times 10^{-2} = 7.6 \times 10^{-2}$$

Practice the Math

1. Express each number in scientific notation
   a. 500,000
   b. 285.2
   c. 0.000 000 042
   d. 0.0002
   e. 0.030 06
   f. 83,700,000

2. Write each number in standard form.
   a. 4×10^{-3}
   b. 3.4×10^5
   c. 0.045×10^4
   d. 5.9×10^{-6}

3. Solve each problem and express your answer in scientific notation.
   a. $(2 \times 10^9) \times (4 \times 10^3)$
   b. $(6.2 \times 10^{-3}) \times (1.5 \times 10^1)$
   c. $(10^{-4}) \times (10^8) \times (10^{-2})$
   d. $(3.4 \times 10^{-3}) \times (2.5 \times 10^{-5})$

4. Solve each problem and express your answer in scientific notation.
   a. $(9.4 \times 10^{-2}) - (2.1 \times 10^{-2})$
   b. $(6.6 \times 10^{-8}) + (5.0 \times 10^{-9})$
   c. $(6.7 \times 10^{-2}) - (3.0 \times 10^{-3})$

5. Solve each problem and express your answer in scientific notation.

   a. $\dfrac{(3.8 \times 10^{-3}) \times (1.2 \times 10^6)}{8 \times 10^4}$

   b. $(1.4 \times 10^2) \times (2 \times 10^8) \times (7.5 \times 10^{-4})$

   c. $\dfrac{6.6 \times 10^6}{(8.8 \times 10^{-2}) \times (2.5 \times 10^3)}$

   d. $\dfrac{(1.2 \times 10^{-3})^2}{(10^{-2})^3 \times (2.0 \times 10^{-3})}$

6. Express each measurement in scientific notation.
   a. The length of a football field: 91.4 m.
   b. The diameter of a carbon atom: 0.000 000 000 154 m.
   c. The diameter of a human hair: 0.000 008 m.
   d. The average distance between the centers of the sun and Earth: 149,600,000,000 m.

Applying Scientific Notation to Chemistry

7. The following expressions are solutions to typical chemistry problems. Calculate the answer for each expression. Make sure to cancel units as you write your solutions.

   a. $5.6 \times 10^3 \text{ mm} \times \left(\dfrac{1 \text{ m}}{10^3 \text{ mm}} \right) \times \left(\dfrac{10^9 \text{ nm}}{1 \text{ m}} \right) = ?$

   b. $6.8 \times 10^4 \text{ cg H}_2\text{O} \times \left(\dfrac{1 \text{ g H}_2\text{O}}{10^2 \text{ cg H}_2\text{O}} \right) \times \left(\dfrac{1 \text{ mL H}_2\text{O}}{1 \text{ g H}_2\text{O}} \right) \times \left(\dfrac{1 \text{ L H}_2\text{O}}{10^3 \text{ mL H}_2\text{O}} \right) = ?$

   c. $4.0 \times 10^2 \text{ mL NaOH} \times \left(\dfrac{1 \text{ L NaOH}}{10^3 \text{ mL NaOH}} \right) \times \left(\dfrac{6.5 \times 10^{-2} \text{ mol NaOH}}{1 \text{ L NaOH}} \right) = ?$

8. A cube of aluminum measures 1.50×10^{-2} m on each edge. Use the following expression to calculate the surface area of the cube.

   $$\text{Surface area} = 6 \times (1.50 \times 10^{-2} \text{ m})^2 = ?$$

9. A small gold (Au) nugget has a mass of 3.40×10^{-3} kg. Use the following expression to calculate the number of gold atoms contained in the nugget.

   $3.40 \times 10^{-3} \text{ kg Au} \times \left(\dfrac{10^3 \text{ g Au}}{1 \text{ kg Au}} \right) \times \left(\dfrac{1 \text{ mol Au}}{197.0 \text{ g Au}} \right) \times \left(\dfrac{6.02 \times 10^{23} \text{ atoms Au}}{1 \text{ mol Au}} \right) = ?$

10. The volume of a sphere is given by the formula $V = \frac{4}{3}\pi r^3$, where $\pi = 3.14$ and $r = $ radius. What is the volume of a spherical drop of water with a radius of 2.40×10^{-3} m?

Significant Figures

The significant figures of a measurement are those digits known with certainty plus the rightmost digit that is estimated. Every measurement has a certain number of significant figures. For instance, if you measure the air temperature to be 21°C, this measurement has two significant figures.

Counting Significant Figures

Every nonzero digit in a measurement is significant. For example, the measurement 831 g has three significant figures. The rules for when to count zeros in measurements as significant are as follows:

- Zeros in the middle of a number are always significant. A length that measures 507 m has three significant figures.
- Zeros at the beginning of a number are not significant. The measurement 0.0056 m has two significant figures.
- Zeros at the end of a number are only significant if they follow a decimal point. The measurement 35.00 g has four significant figures; the measurement 2400 g has two significant figures.

Counted values (17 beakers) and the numbers in defined relationships (100 cm = 1 m) are exact numbers and are considered to have an unlimited number of significant figures. Exact numbers never affect the number of significant figures in the results of a calculation.

Each of the measurements listed below has three significant figures. The significant figures are underlined.

<u>456</u> mL	0.<u>305</u> g
<u>70.4</u> mg	0.000<u>457</u> g
<u>5.64</u> × 10³ km	<u>444</u>,000 ng
<u>1.30</u> × 10⁻² m	0.00<u>406</u> dm

The mass of this bowl of candy is 298.8 grams. The measurement has four significant figures.

SAMPLE PROBLEM MH-2

Counting Significant Figures in Measurements

How many significant figures are in each measurement?

a. 3300°C **b.** 110.5 kJ
c. 0.000 0176 g **d.** 210,000 kcal
e. 5 notebooks **f.** 0.90 lb

Solution

Follow the rules described above for counting significant figures.

a. 2 **b.** 4
c. 3 **d.** 2
e. unlimited **f.** 2

Significant Figures in Calculations

When measurements are used in a calculation, the answer you calculate must be rounded to the correct number of significant figures. How you round your answer depends on the mathematical operation used in the calculation.

- In multiplication and division, the answer can have *no more significant figures* than the least number of significant figures in any measurement in the problem.
- In addition and subtraction, the answer can have *no more decimal places* than the least number of decimal places in any measurement in the problem.

When a calculated answer must be rounded to the appropriate number of significant figures, use the following rules:

- If the first nonsignificant digit is less than 5, drop all nonsignificant digits.
- If the first nonsignificant digit is 5, or greater than 5, increase the last significant digit by one and drop all nonsignificant digits.

The Sample Problem below illustrates how to apply these rules when performing calculations involving measurements.

SAMPLE PROBLEM MH-3

Rounding Calculated Answers
Solve each problem, and round your answer to the correct number of significant figures.

a. $(5.3 \text{ m}) \times (1.54 \text{ m})$
b. $23.5 \text{ m} + 2.1 \text{ m} + 7.26 \text{ m}$
c. $189.427 \text{ g} - 19.00 \text{ g}$
d. $\dfrac{0.497 \text{ m}^2}{1.50 \text{ m}}$

Solution

Follow the rules described above for rounding calculated answers to the appropriate number of significant figures.

a. $(5.3 \text{ m}) \times (1.54 \text{ m}) = 8.162 \text{ m}^2 = 8.2 \text{ m}^2$
  (5.3 m has two significant figures.)
b. $23.5 \text{ m} + 2.1 \text{ m} + 7.26 \text{ m} = 32.86 \text{ m} = 32.9 \text{ m}$
  (2.1 has one decimal place.)
c. $189.427 \text{ g} - 19.00 \text{ g} = 170.427 \text{ g} = 170.43 \text{ g}$
  (19.00 has two decimal places.)
d. $\dfrac{0.497 \text{ m}^2}{1.50 \text{ m}} = 0.3313333 \text{ m} = 0.331 \text{ m}$
  (0.497 and 1.50 each have three significant figures.)

Practice the Math

1. How many significant figures are in each measurement?
   a. 0.723 m
   b. 14.0 g
   c. 123,000 m
   d. 6.00×10^{-2} g
   e. 0.005 12 kg
   f. 1050 cm

2. Round each of the measurements in Question 1 to two significant figures.

3. Multiply or divide the following measurements, and round your answer to the correct number of significant figures.
   a. 3.4 m × 7.8 m
   b. 7.00 cm × 9.8 cm
   c. 1.56 mm × 0.864 mm × 14.00 mm
   d. 6.88 m² ÷ 2.6 m
   e. 52.98 g ÷ 1.8 mL
   f. 0.14 kg ÷ 0.0131 L

4. Add or subtract the following measurements, and round your answer to the correct number of significant figures.
   a. 2.34 m + 18.28 m
   b. 828.2 g − 134 g
   c. 0.278 cm + 0.0832 cm + 0.15 cm
   d. 54.2 mg − 12.66 mg
   e. 6.40 ng + 0.450 ng + 1.001 ng
   f. $(5.2 \times 10^{-2}$ dg$) + (1.82 \times 10^{-3}$ dg$)$

Applying Significant Figures to Chemistry

5. Determine the number of significant figures in each measurement.
   a. The density of mercury (Hg): 13.55 kg/L
   b. The number of milligrams (mg) in one gram (g): 1000 mg = 1 g
   c. The number of protons in an atom of copper (Cu): 29 protons
   d. The mass of a silver (Ag) atom: 1.792×10^{-22} g
   e. The melting point of gallium: 29.8°C
   f. The concentration of a water solution of NaCl: 24% (m/v).

6. The data from Question 5 has been used to set up a solution to each of the following problems. Calculate each answer, and express each answer to the correct number of significant figures. Make sure to cancel units where appropriate.
   a. Calculate the mass of 0.45 L of mercury.

   $$0.45 \text{ L Hg} \times \frac{13.55 \text{ kg Hg}}{1 \text{ L Hg}} = ?$$

   b. How many milligrams are in 6.321 grams?

   $$6.321 \text{ g} \times \frac{1000 \text{ mg}}{1 \text{ g}} = ?$$

   c. How many protons are in 7 copper atoms?

   $$7 \text{ Cu atoms} \times \frac{29 \text{ protons}}{1 \text{ Cu atom}} = ?$$

   d. What is the mass of 35 silver atoms?

   $$35 \text{ Ag atoms} \times \frac{1.792 \times 10^{-22} \text{ g Ag}}{1 \text{ Ag atom}} = ?$$

   e. What is the melting point of gallium in kelvins (K)?
   K = °C + 273 = 29.8 + 273 = ?

   f. How many grams of NaCl are in 25.8 mL of a 24% (m/v) NaCl solution?

   $$25.8 \text{ mL solution} \times \frac{24 \text{ g NaCl}}{100 \text{ mL solution}} = ?$$

7. Calculate the perimeter ((2 × length) + (2 × width)) and the area (length × width) of a garden plot that measures 32.8 m by 15 m. Round each answer to the correct number of significant figures.

Using a Calculator

A scientific calculator has specialized function keys that you can use to manipulate numbers and perform arithmetic operations.

You can readily solve chemistry problems involving numeric calculations with the aid of a hand-held scientific calculator. As you know, a calculator has various keys used for entering numbers and performing operations with those numbers. In the following text, calculator keys are indicated by boldfaced square brackets. As you work out each problem, press the calculator keys that match the operations or numbers within the brackets.

Arithmetic Operations

A scientific calculator has operator keys for basic arithmetic operations such as addition [+], subtraction [−], multiplication [×], and division [÷]. To complete an arithmetic operation, you must press the operator key for an equals sign, [=].

A different set of keys is used for entering numbers. For example, to enter the number 27.2 on your calculator, press the numeric entry keys [2][7][.][2].

Try the following arithmetic operations on your calculator. Be sure to clear the calculator using the [ON/C], [C/CE], or [AC] key before entering any numbers.

	Numeric Entry Keys	Operator Key	Numeric Entry Keys	Operator Key	Display
a. 94.2 + 71.32	[9][4][.][2]	[+]	[7][1][.][3][2]	[=]	*165.52*
b. 301.6 − 58.98	[3][0][1][.][6]	[−]	[5][8][.][9][8]	[=]	*242.62*
c. 15.72 × 14.23	[1][5][.][7][2]	[×]	[1][4][.][2][3]	[=]	*223.6956*
d. 331.72 ÷ 78.23	[3][3][1][.][7][2]	[÷]	[7][8][.][2][3]	[=]	*4.240317014*

If we assume that all the digits in each of the numbers entered are significant figures, then the answers displayed by the calculator have more digits than can be justified as significant. Thus, you must round each calculated answer to the appropriate number of significant figures.

For the addition problem **a**, the displayed value of 165.52 must be rounded to 165.5 (no more than 1 decimal place). For the subtraction problem **b**, the displayed value of 242.62 must be rounded to 242.6 (no more than one decimal place). The answers to multiplication problem **c** and division problem **d** should each be reported to four significant figures (the least number of significant figures in either of the numbers used in each calculation). For **c**, the answer should be reported as 223.7. For **d**, the answer should be reported as 4.240.

For more help with significant figures and rounding, go to page R59.

Exponential Numbers

To enter very large or very small numbers on a scientific calculator, use the exponential key. The exponential key on your calculator may be labeled [EE], [EXP], or [EEX]. In the Math Handbook, the exponential key will be represented by [EE].

Suppose you want to enter the exponential number 2.94×10^{24} on your calculator. First enter the coefficient [2][.][9][4]. Then press [EE] and enter the exponent [2][4]. The display reads 2.94^{24}. Notice that the "×10" part of the exponential form is not entered on (or displayed by) the calculator. Pressing the exponential key indicates to the calculator that the next number entered is a power of 10.

If a number written in exponential form has a negative exponent, use the sign-change key [+/−] (not the subtraction key!) to make the sign of the exponent negative. For example, to enter the number 3.08×10^{-12} on your calculator, first enter the coefficient [3][.][0][8]. Then press [EE] followed by [+/−]. Notice how the display changes from 3.08^{00} to 3.08^{-00}. Lastly, enter [1][2], the value of the exponent. The display now reads 3.08^{-12}.

You can practice entering exponential numbers on a calculator by trying the following examples. The keystrokes are listed after each exponential number. The numbers displayed by your calculator should match those in the last column.

		Numeric Entry Keys			Display
a.	2.79×10^4	[2][.][7][9] [EE]		[4]	2.79^{04}
b.	7.43×10^{18}	[7][.][4][3] [EE]		[1][8]	7.43^{18}
c.	6.89×10^{-22}	[6][.][8][9] [EE]	[+/−]	[2][2]	6.89^{-22}
d.	1.11×10^{-5}	[1][.][1][1] [EE]	[+/−]	[5]	1.11^{-05}

The next two examples show operations involving exponential numbers. For simplification, only the exponential and operator keystrokes are shown. The answer that should appear on your calculator display is written in italics.

e. Given expression: $[2.43 \times 10^{23}] \times 7.30 = 1.77 \times 10^{24}$
     Using a calculator: 2.43 [EE] 23 [×] 7.30 [=] *1.7739^{24}*

f. Given expression: $9.93 \times 10^{15} \div 2.56 \times 10^{13} = 3.88 \times 10^2$
     Using a calculator: 9.33 [EE] 15 [÷] 2.56 [EE] 13 [=] *3.87890625^{02}*

The answer for **e** displayed by the calculator is 1.7739×10^{24}. This number must be rounded to 1.77×10^{24}, according to the rules for significant figures in calculations.

The calculated answer for **f** must be rounded to three significant figures. Note that the final answer on the display of your calculator may be in scientific notation as *3.87890625^{02}* or in decimal form as *387.890625*, depending on your calculator settings. If you obtained the latter result, you may be able to set the calculator's display mode so that it automatically converts answers to scientific notation by using the key labeled [SCI] or [MODE].

Chain Calculations

Calculations that require more than one arithmetic operation are called chain calculations. Examples of chain calculations are shown below.

a. $2.58 + 7.12 + 9.30 = 19.00$

b. $6.3 \times \left(\dfrac{7.4 \times 10^{-2}}{1.0 \times 10^{2}} \right) \times \left(\dfrac{2.79 \times 10^{3}}{1.9 \times 10^{-7}} \right) = 6.8 \times 10^{7}$

c. $2.98 + \left(\dfrac{8.76 \times 10^{-3}}{6.22 \times 10^{-3}} \right) = 4.39$

To solve problem **a**, enter the following sequence of calculator keystrokes:

2.58 [+] 7.12 [+] 9.30 [=] *19.*

Note that the calculator keystrokes are exactly as they appear in reading the equation from left to right. Also notice that the calculated answer should have two decimal places, but the calculator has dropped these digits in the displayed answer because they are zeros. You must add them in reporting the correct answer, 19.00.

Problem **b** illustrates a kind of problem that comes up with startling regularity in chemistry-related dimensional analysis. The correct calculator keystrokes are as follows.

6.3 [×] 7.4 [EE][+/−] 2 [÷] 1.0 [EE] 2 [×] 2.79 [EE] 3 [÷] 1.9

[EE][+/−] 7 [=] *6.845778947*[07]

Note that each operation is performed in the order it appears in the equation. The calculated answer must be rounded to two significant figures.

In problem **c**, however, performing the operations in the order they appear will *not* yield a correct answer. Instead, try completing the division operation within the parentheses first, and then add 2.98 to the result. The calculator keystrokes are as follows.

8.76 [EE][+/−] 3 [÷] 6.22 [EE][+/−] 3 [+] 2.98 [=] *4.388360129*

The calculated answer must be rounded to two decimal places.

Alternatively, you can use the open-parenthesis [(] and closed-parenthesis [)] keys. The [(] and [)] keys allow you to key in equation **c** as written, using the following keystrokes.

2.98 [+][(] 8.76 [EE][+/−] 3 [÷] 6.22 [EE][+/−] 3 [)][=] *4.388360129*

SAMPLE PROBLEM MH-4

Arithmetic Operations with Exponential Numbers
Use a calculator to obtain the answer shown below.

$$\frac{2.88 \times 10^{7}}{5.98 \times 10^{-3}} = 4.82 \times 10^{9}$$

Solution

Use the following keystroke sequence:

2.88 [EE] 7 [÷] 5.98 [EE][+/−] 3 [=] *4.816053512*[09]

The calculated answer must be rounded to three significant figures, yielding the result 4.82×10^{9}.

Practice the Math

Use your calculator to solve for x *in each problem. Express your answer in scientific notation and report it to the correct number of significant figures.*

1. $x = 5467.4 \div 2.7$

2. $x = 26.54 + 26.8 + 58.33 + 10.00 + 87.3$

3. $x = 3.75 \times 10^{-5} + 7.00 \times 10^{-5}$

4. $x = \left(\dfrac{6.02 \times 10^{23}}{4.77 \times 10^{17}} \right)$

5. $x = 8.73 + \left(\dfrac{4.17 \times 10^{-3}}{5.27 \times 10^{-4}} \right)$

6. $x = \left(\dfrac{3.98 \times 10^{5}}{7.215 \times 10^{13}} \right) \times \left(\dfrac{6.21 \times 10^{14}}{5.123 \times 10^{12}} \right)$

7. $x = 2.45 \div 0.49$

8. $x = 273.0 - 42.6 + 7.0$

9. $x = \left(\dfrac{5.44 \times 10^{6}}{6.98 \times 10^{4}} \right) \times 3.89$

Applying Calculator Operations to Chemistry

Use your calculator and the given expression to solve each problem. Make sure to cancel units where appropriate.

10. A gold necklace found in an Egyptian pyramid has a volume of 27.5 cm³ and a mass of 530.0 g. What is the density of the gold?

$$\text{density} = \frac{\text{mass}}{\text{volume}} = \frac{530.0 \text{ g}}{27.5 \text{ cm}^3} = ?$$

11. A magnesium atom has a diameter of 3.20×10^{-10} meter. What would be the length in meters (m) of 1 mole of magnesium atoms (6.02×10^{23} atoms) laid end-to-end in a straight line?

$$\frac{3.20 \times 10^{-10} \text{ m}}{1 \text{ Mg atom}} \times \frac{6.02 \times 10^{23} \text{ Mg atoms}}{1 \text{ mol Mg}} = ?$$

12. The molecular formula of the sugar glucose is $C_6H_{12}O_6$. The molar masses of the constituent elements of glucose are: carbon, 12.011 g/mol; hydrogen, 1.0079 g/mol; and oxygen, 15.999 g/mol. What is the molar mass of glucose to three decimal places?

$$(6 \times 12.011 \text{ g}) + (12 \times 1.0079 \text{ g}) + (6 \times 15.999 \text{ g}) = ?$$

13. The compound benzene, C_6H_6, has a molar mass of 78.11 g/mol, of which 72.00 g is carbon. What percent of the molar mass of benzene is carbon?

$$\frac{72.00 \text{ g C}}{78.11 \text{ g C}_6\text{H}_6} \times 100\% = ?$$

14. A gaseous compound has a density of 1.37 g/L at STP and 1 mol occupies 22.4 L at STP. What is the molar mass of the compound?

$$\frac{1.37 \text{ g}}{1 \text{ L}} \times \frac{22.4 \text{ L}}{1 \text{ mol}} = ?$$

15. How many moles of Fe_2O_3 are in 50.0 g?

$$50.0 \text{ g Fe}_2\text{O}_3 \times \frac{1.00 \text{ mol Fe}_2\text{O}_3}{159.6 \text{ g Fe}_2\text{O}_3} = ?$$

16. The formation of copper(II) sulfide (CuS) from its component elements is given below.

$$\text{Cu}(s) + \text{S}(s) \longrightarrow \text{CuS}(s)$$

How many grams of CuS are produced when 2.73 mol Cu reacts with an excess of sulfur?

$$2.73 \text{ mol Cu} \times \frac{1 \text{ mol CuS}}{1 \text{ mol Cu}} \times \frac{95.6 \text{ g CuS}}{1 \text{ mol CuS}} = ?$$

17. The ideal gas constant, R, is calculated from the relationship given below. What is the value of R in units of (L•kPa)/(K•mol)?

$$R = \frac{101.3 \text{ kPa} \times 22.4 \text{ L}}{273 \text{ K} \times 1.00 \text{ mol}} = ?$$

18. A student sets up the following relationship to calculate the number of moles/liter of sodium chloride, NaCl, in 100 mL of an aqueous salt solution containing 0.50 g of NaCl. How many moles/liter of sodium chloride does the solution contain?

$$\frac{0.50 \text{ g NaCl}}{100 \text{ mL}} \times \frac{1 \text{ mol NaCl}}{58.5 \text{ g NaCl}} \times \frac{1000 \text{ mL}}{1 \text{ L}} = ?$$

Conversion Problems and Dimensional Analysis

A person's height can be measured in units such as feet, inches, or meters. Conversion factors allow you to convert from one unit to another.

Many problems in both everyday life and in the sciences involve converting measurements. These problems may be simple conversions between the same kinds of measurement. For example:

a. A person is five and one-half feet tall. Express this height in inches.
b. A flask holds 0.575 L of water. How many milliliters of water is this?

In other cases, you may need to convert between different kinds of measurements.

c. How many gallons of gasoline can you buy for $15.00 if gasoline costs $1.42/gallon?
d. What is the mass of 254 cm³ of gold if the density of gold is 19.3 g/cm³?

More complex conversion problems may require conversions between measurements expressed as ratios of units. Consider the following examples.

e. A car is traveling at 65 miles/hour. What is the speed of the car expressed in feet/second?
f. The density of nitrogen gas is 1.17 g/L. What is the density of nitrogen expressed in micrograms/deciliter (μg/dL)?

Problems **a** through **f** can be solved using a method that is known by a few different names—dimensional analysis, factor label, and unit conversion. These names emphasize the fact that the dimensions, labels, or units of the measurements in a problem—the units in the given measurement(s) as well as the units desired in the answer—can help you write the solution to the problem.

Dimensional analysis makes use of ratios called conversion factors. A conversion factor is a ratio of two quantities equal to one another. For example, to work out problem **a**, you must know the relationship 1 ft = 12 in. The two conversion factors derived from this equality are shown below.

$$\frac{1 \text{ ft}}{12 \text{ in}} = 1 \text{ (unity)} = \frac{12 \text{ in}}{1 \text{ in}}$$

To solve problem **a** by dimensional analysis, you must multiply the given measurement (5.5 ft) by a conversion factor that allows the *feet* units to cancel, leaving the unit *inches*—the unit of the requested answer.

$$5.5 \text{ ft} \times \frac{12 \text{ in}}{1 \text{ ft}} = 66 \text{ in}$$

Carefully study the solutions to the remaining five example problems below. Notice that in each solution, the conversion factors are written so that the unit of the given measurement cancels, leaving the correct unit for each answer. When working conversion problems, the equalities needed to write the conversion factor may be given in the problem. This is true in examples **c** and **d**. In other problems, you need to either know or look up the necessary equalities, as in examples **b**, **e**, and **f**.

b. $0.575 \text{ L} \times \dfrac{10^3 \text{ mL}}{1 \text{ L}} = 575 \text{ mL}$

c. $\$15.00 \times \dfrac{1 \text{ gal}}{\$1.42} = 10.6 \text{ gal}$

d. $254 \text{ cm}^3 \times \dfrac{19.3 \text{ g}}{1 \text{ cm}^3} = 4.90 \times 10^3 \text{ g}$

e. $\dfrac{65 \text{ mi}}{1 \text{ h}} \times \dfrac{5280 \text{ ft}}{1 \text{ mi}} \times \dfrac{1 \text{ h}}{3600 \text{ s}} = 95 \text{ ft/s}$

f. $\dfrac{1.17 \text{ g}}{1 \text{ L}} \times \dfrac{10^6 \text{ } \mu\text{g}}{1 \text{ g}} \times \dfrac{1 \text{ L}}{10 \text{ dL}} = 1.17 \times 10^5 \text{ } \mu\text{g/dL}$

Based on the prices advertised below, you can derive conversion factors that relate cost to a certain amount of produce. For example, you can write $0.75/2 Italian artichokes or $0.79/zuchini.

SAMPLE PROBLEM MH-5

Applying Dimensional Analysis

A grocer is selling oranges at "3 for $1." How much would it cost to buy a dozen oranges?

Solution

The following equality is given in the problem.

$$3 \text{ oranges} = \$1$$

You can write two conversion factors based on this relationship.

$$\dfrac{\$1}{3 \text{ oranges}} \quad \text{and} \quad \dfrac{3 \text{ oranges}}{\$1}$$

The given unit is oranges; the desired unit is dollars. Thus, use the conversion factor on the left to convert from oranges to dollars. One dozen equals 12, so you can start the calculation with the measurement 12 oranges.

$$12 \text{ oranges} \times \dfrac{\$1}{3 \text{ oranges}} = \$4$$

The given unit (oranges) cancels, leaving the desired unit (dollars) in the answer.

Practice the Math

Use the following equalities for Questions 1–3.

60 s = 1 min	5.50 yd = 1 rod
12 in = 1 ft	7 days = 1 wk
60 min = 1 h	5280 ft = 1 mi
3 ft = 1 yd	365 days = 1 yr
24 h = 1 day	

1. Write the conversion factor need for each unit conversion.

  a. feet → yards   **b.** years → days

  c. yards → rods   **d.** days → hours

  e. feet → miles   **f.** seconds → minutes

2. Solve each problem by dimensional analysis.

  a. How many feet long is the 440-yard dash?

  b. Calculate the number of minutes in two weeks.

  c. Calculate the number of days in 1800 h.

  d. How many miles is 660 ft?

  e. How many inches long is a 100-yd football field?

  f. Calculate the number of hours in one year.

  g. How many rods are in 12 miles?

  h. Calculate the number of minutes in 7 days.

3. Solve each problem by dimensional analysis.

  a. A student walks at a brisk 3.50 mi/h. Calculate the student's speed in yards/minute.

  b. Water runs through a hose at the rate of 2.5 gal/min. What is the rate of water flow in units gallons/day?

  c. A clock gains 2.60 s each hour (2.6 s gained/h.) What is the rate of time gained in minutes/week?

  d. A spider travels 115 in. in 1 min (speed = 115 in/min). What is the speed of the spider in miles/hour?

Applying Dimensional Analysis to Chemistry

Use the following metric relationships to work out Questions 4 and 5.

10^3 m = 1 km	10^9 nm = 1 m
10 dm = 1 m	10^{12} pm = 1 m
10^2 cm = 1 m	10^3 cm^3 = 1 L
10^3 mm = 1 m	1 mL = 1 cm^3
10^6 μm = 1 m	1 g H$_2$O = 1 mL H$_2$O

4. Perform the following conversions.

  a. 45 m to kilometers

  b. 4×10^7 nm to meters

  c. 8.5 dm to millimeters

  d. 8.2×10^{-4} μm to centimeters

  e. 0.23 km to decimeters

  f. 865 cm^3 to liters

  g. 7.28×10^2 pm to micrometers

  h. 56 g H$_2$O to L H$_2$O

5. Perform the following conversions.

  a. 4.5 m/s to millimeters/minute

  b. 7.9×10^{-2} km/h to decimeters/minute

  c. 77 mL H$_2$O/s to liters H$_2$O/hour

  d. 3.34×10^4 nm/min to centimeters/second

Algebraic Equations

Many relationships in chemistry can be expressed as simple algebraic equations. However, the equation given is not always in the form that is most useful in figuring out a particular problem. In such a case, you must first solve the equation for the unknown quantity; this is done by rearranging the equation so that the unknown is on one side of the equation, and all the known quantities are on the other side.

Solving Simple Equations

An equation is solved using the laws of equality. The laws of equality are summarized as follows: *If equals are added to, subtracted from, multiplied by, or divided by equals, the results are equal.* In other words, you can perform any of these mathematic operations on an equation and not destroy the equality, *as long as you do the same thing to both sides of the equation.* The laws of equality apply to any legitimate mathematic operation, including squaring, taking square roots, and taking the logarithm.

Consider the following equation, which states the relationship between the Kelvin and Celsius temperature scales.

$$K = {}^{\circ}C + 273$$

Can this equation be used to find the Celsius-temperature equivalent of 400 K? Yes, it can, if the equation is first solved for the unknown quantity, °C.

In the above example, to solve for °C, subtract 273 from both sides of the equation.

$$K = {}^{\circ}C + 273$$
$$K - 273 = {}^{\circ}C + 273 - 273$$
$$^{\circ}C = K - 273$$

Now you have solved the equation for the unknown quantity. To calculate its value, substitute the known quantity into the solved equation.

$$^{\circ}C = K - 273$$
$$= 400 - 273$$
$$= 127{}^{\circ}C$$

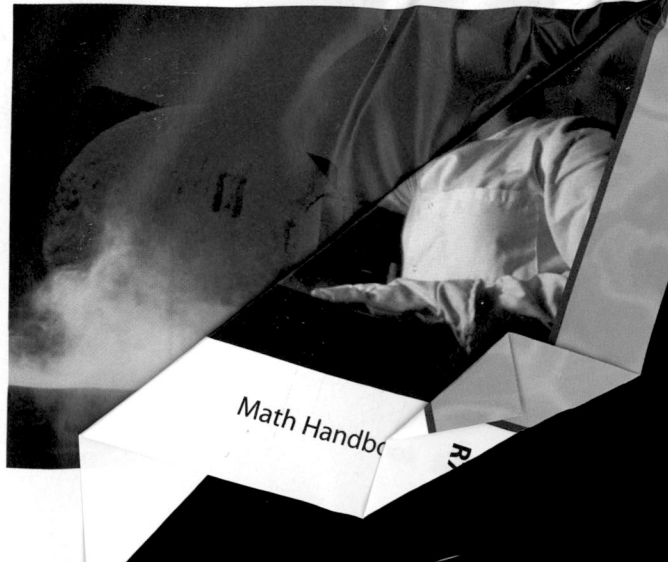

A technician in a genetic research lab removes frozen cell samples from cryostorage. The cells are stored in liquid nitrogen at −196°C. What is this temperature in kelvins?

Math Handb

R

This thermometer shows both the Fahrenheit and Celsius temperature scales. What temperature in Celsius corresponds to −40°F? Verify the conversion by performing a calculation.

Another commonly used temperature scale is the Fahrenheit scale. The relationship between the Fahrenheit and Celsius temperature scales is given by the following equation.

$$°F = (1.8 \times °C) + 32$$

Suppose you want to use this equation to convert 365°F into degrees Celsius. To solve for °C, you must isolate it on one side of the equation. Since the right side of the equation has 32 added to the quantity (1.8 × °C), first subtract 32 from both sides of the equation, and then divide each side by 1.8.

$$°F = (1.8 \times °C) + 32$$
$$°F - 32 = (1.8 \times °C) + 32 - 32$$
$$°F - 32 = (1.8 \times °C)$$
$$\frac{°F - 32}{1.8} = \frac{1.8 \times °C}{1.8}$$
$$\frac{(°F - 32)}{1.8} = °C$$

Now that you have solved the equation for the unknown quantity (°C), you can substitute the known quantity (365°F) into the equation and calculate the answer.

$$°C = \frac{(°F - 32)}{1.8} = \frac{(365 - 32)}{1.8} = \frac{333}{1.8} = 185°C$$

SAMPLE PROBLEM MH-6

Solving Algebraic Equations

The heat (q) absorbed by the water in a calorimeter can be calculated using the following relationship.

$$q = m \times C \times \Delta T$$

In this expression, m is the mass of the water; C is the specific heat of water (4.18 J/g ·°C); and ΔT is the change in temperature. If 120 g of water absorb 3500 J of heat, by how much will the temperature of the water increase?

Solution

First solve the equation for the unknown quantity, ΔT.

$$q = m \times C \times \Delta T$$
$$\frac{q}{m \times C} = \frac{m \times C \times \Delta T}{m \times C}$$
$$\frac{q}{m \times C} = \Delta T$$

Now substitute the known values for q, m, and C.

$$\Delta T = \frac{q}{m \times C}$$
$$= \frac{3500 \text{ J}}{(120 \text{ g} \times 4.18 \text{ J/g·°C})} = 7.0°C$$

Practice the Math

1. Solve each equation for z.

   a. $xy + z = 5$

   b. $\dfrac{z}{a-4} = t$

   c. $\dfrac{b}{d} = \dfrac{2a}{z}$

   d. $\sqrt{z} = 2b$

2. Solve each equation for a. Then calculate a value for a if $b = 4$, $c = 10$, and $d = 2$.

   a. $bd = ac$

   b. $a + b = cd$

   c. $c + b = \dfrac{a}{d}$

   d. $\dfrac{bd}{a} = c^2$

3. Solve each equation for h. Then calculate a value for h if $g = 12$, $k = 0.4$, and $m = 1.5$.

   a. $kh = \dfrac{g}{m}$

   b. $\dfrac{(g-m)}{h} = k$

   c. $gh - k = m$

   d. $\dfrac{mk}{(g+h)} = 2$

Applying Algebra to Chemistry

4. Solve for v in the following equation.

$$d = \dfrac{m}{v}$$

   Let d = density, m = mass, and v = volume. What is the volume of 642 g of gold if the density of gold is 19.3 g/cm³?

5. Solve for n in the following equation.

$$P \times V = n \times R \times T$$

   How many moles (n) of helium gas fill a 6.45-L (V) balloon at a pressure (P) of 105 kPa and a temperature (T) of 278 K?
   ($R = 8.31$ (L·kPa)/(K·mol))

6. Solve for V_2 in the following equation.

$$\dfrac{P_1 \times V_1}{T_1} = \dfrac{P_2 \times V_2}{T_2}$$

   A 2.50-L (V_1) sample of nitrogen gas at a temperature (T_1) of 308 K has a pressure (P_1) of 1.15 atm. What is the new volume (V_2) of the gas if the pressure (P_2) is increased to 1.80 atm and the temperature (T_2) decreased to 286 K?

7. Solve for P_{He} in the following equation.

$$P_{total} = P_{Ar} + P_{He} + P_{Kr}$$

   A mixture of gases has a total pressure (P_{total}) of 376 kPa. What is the partial pressure of helium (P_{He}), if $P_{Ar} = 92$ kPa and $P_{Kr} = 144$ kPa?

8. Solve for T_2 in the following equation.

$$\dfrac{V_1}{T_1} = \dfrac{V_2}{T_2}$$

   What is the value of T_2 when $V_1 = 5.0$ L, $V_2 = 15$ L, and $T_1 = 200$ K?

Percents

The grade of a road is the slope expressed as a percent. A downhill 6% grade means that for every 100 units of horizontal distance traveled, there is a corresponding 6-unit descent.

A percent is a ratio that compares a number to 100. The word *percent* (%) means "parts of 100" or "per 100 parts." Another way to think of a percent is a part of a whole expressed in hundredths. Thus, the number 0.52 ("52 hundredths") can also be expressed as 52%, or "52 per 100 parts."

You should be familiar with percents. For example, test scores are often expressed as percents. Suppose you answer 24 questions correctly on a 30-question exam. The part out of the whole, expressed as a percent, can be calculated as follows.

$$\frac{\text{Part}}{\text{Whole}} = \frac{\text{number of correctly answered questions}}{\text{number of questions asked}}$$

$$= \frac{24}{30}$$

$$= 0.80 = \frac{80}{100} = 80\%$$

Note that 0.80, 80/100, and 80% all express the same value: 80 hundredths (or "80 per 100 parts").

Another way to calculate a percent is to multiply the ratio of the part to the whole by 100%.

$$\text{Percent} = \frac{\text{part}}{\text{whole}} \times 100\%$$

Suppose a high school science club consists of 27 boys and 23 girls. What percent of the club is made up of boys?

$$\text{Percent} = \frac{\text{number of boys}}{\text{number of total members}} \times 100\%$$

$$= \frac{27}{27 + 23} \times 100\%$$

$$= \frac{27}{50} \times 100\%$$

$$= 0.54 \times 100\%$$

$$= 54\%$$

Because a percent represents a relationship between two quantities, it can be used as a conversion factor. For example, suppose a friend tells you that she got a score of 95% on a 40-question exam. How many questions did she answer correctly? A score of 95% means 95 correctly answered questions for every 100 questions asked. By expressing this relationship as a conversion factor, you can calculate the number of correctly answered questions.

$$40 \text{ questions asked} \times \left(\frac{95 \text{ correctly answered questions}}{100 \text{ questions asked}} \right)$$

$$= 38 \text{ correctly answered questions}$$

Using Percents as Conversion Factors

Six students are absent from their class one day. If 80% of the students in the class are present, what is the total class enrollment?

Solution

Because 80% of the class is present, the six absent students make up 20% of the class. If 20% of the students are absent, this means that 20 students are absent for every 100 students enrolled. Use dimensional analysis to calculate the total class enrollment.

$$6 \text{ students absent} \times \left(\frac{100 \text{ students enrolled}}{20 \text{ students absent}} \right)$$

$$= \frac{600}{20} \text{ students enrolled}$$

$$= 30 \text{ students enrolled}$$

Practice the Math

1. Write each fraction as a percent.
   a. $\frac{3}{4}$ b. $\frac{1}{5}$ c. $\frac{7}{10}$ d. $\frac{5}{8}$
2. Write each decimal as a percent.
   a. 0.39   b. 0.08   c. 4.2   d. 0.5
3. Calculate a score for each exam expressed as a percent.
   a. Sixteen questions correctly answered on a 25-question exam.
   b. Forty-one questions correctly answered on a 50-question exam.
   c. Sixty-eight questions correctly answered on an 85-question exam.

4. A quality control inspector found that 7 out of every 200 flashlights produced were defective. What percent of the flashlights were not defective?
5. A student answered 57 questions correctly on an exam and received a score of 95%. How many questions were on the exam?
6. During a flu epidemic, 28% of the students were absent. If 238 students were absent, what is this school's enrollment?

Applying Percents to Chemistry

7. A mining company is abstracting silver from an ore is that 0.014% silver (by mass). How many kilograms of ore must be processed to yield 0.7 kg of silver?
8. A fertilizer is 12.0% (by mass) nitrogen and 5.5% (by mass) phosphorus. How many grams of each element are in 140 g of this fertilizer?
9. A compound is broken down into 34.5 g of element A, 18.2 g of element B, and 2.6 g of element C. What is the percent (by mass) of each element in this compound?

10. What is the percent by mass of sodium chloride (NaCl) in each of the following solutions?
    a. 44 g NaCl dissolved in 756 g of water
    b. 15 g NaCl dissolved in 485 g of w...
    c. 135 g NaCl dissolved in 765...
11. The antiseptic hydrogen peroxide ...being as a 3.0% (by mass) sol... water. How many g...22% alcohol (by are in 250 g of th... alcohol are in a ...icine?
12. A nighttime c... volume). ... 250 m...

Math Handbook

Graphing

A line graph can be used to show the relationship between two variables. The manipulated variable is plotted on the x-axis. The responding variable is plotted on the y-axis.

The relationship between two variables in an experiment is often determined by graphing the experimental data. A graph is a "picture" of the data. Once a graph is constructed, additional information can be derived about the variables.

In constructing a graph, you must first label the axes. The manipulated variable (also known as the independent variable) is plotted on the *x*-axis. This is the horizontal axis. The manipulated variable is controlled by the experimenter. When the independent variable is changed, a corresponding change in the responding variable (also known as the dependent variable) is measured. The responding variable is plotted on the *y*-axis. This is the vertical axis. The label on each axis should include the unit of the quantity being graphed.

Before data can be plotted on a graph, each axis must be scaled. Each interval on the scale must represent the same amount. To make it easy to find numbers along the scale, the interval chosen is usually a multiple of 1, 2, 5, or 10. Although each scale can start at zero, this is not always practical.

Data are plotted by putting a point at the intersection of corresponding values of each pair of measurements. Once the data has been plotted, the points are connected by a smooth curve. A smooth curve comes as close as possible to all the plotted points. It may in fact not touch any of them.

Inverse and Direct Proportionalities

Depending on the relationship between two variables, a plotted curve may or may not be a straight line. Two common curves are shown below.

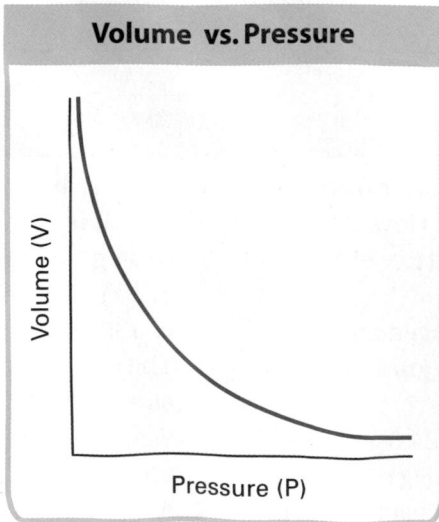

Volume vs. Pressure

Volume (V) — Pressure (P)

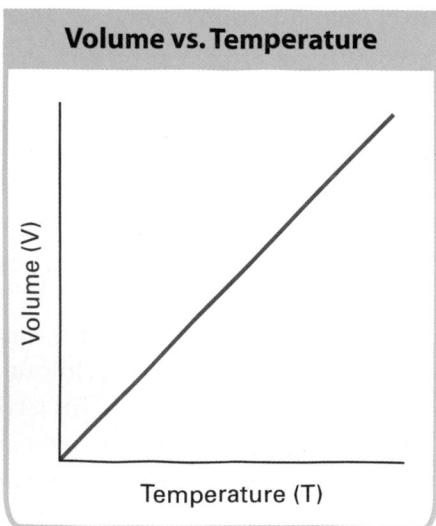

Volume vs. Temperature

Volume (V) — Temperature (T)

Algebraic Equations

Many relationships in chemistry can be expressed as simple algebraic equations. However, the equation given is not always in the form that is most useful in figuring out a particular problem. In such a case, you must first solve the equation for the unknown quantity; this is done by rearranging the equation so that the unknown is on one side of the equation, and all the known quantities are on the other side.

Solving Simple Equations

An equation is solved using the laws of equality. The laws of equality are summarized as follows: *If equals are added to, subtracted from, multiplied by, or divided by equals, the results are equal.* In other words, you can perform any of these mathematic operations on an equation and not destroy the equality, *as long as you do the same thing to both sides of the equation.* The laws of equality apply to any legitimate mathematic operation, including squaring, taking square roots, and taking the logarithm.

Consider the following equation, which states the relationship between the Kelvin and Celsius temperature scales.

$$K = °C + 273$$

Can this equation be used to find the Celsius-temperature equivalent of 400 K? Yes, it can, if the equation is first solved for the unknown quantity, °C.

In the above example, to solve for °C, subtract 273 from both sides of the equation.

$$K = °C + 273$$
$$K - 273 = °C + 273 - 273$$
$$°C = K - 273$$

Now you have solved the equation for the unknown quantity. To calculate its value, substitute the known quantity into the solved equation.

$$°C = K - 273$$
$$= 400 - 273$$
$$= 127°C$$

A technician in a genetic research lab removes frozen cell samples from cryostorage. The cells are stored in liquid nitrogen at −196°C. What is this temperature in kelvins?

This thermometer shows both the Fahrenheit and Celsius temperature scales. What temperature in Celsius corresponds to −40°F? Verify the conversion by performing a calculation.

Another commonly used temperature scale is the Fahrenheit scale. The relationship between the Fahrenheit and Celsius temperature scales is given by the following equation.

$$°F = (1.8 \times °C) + 32$$

Suppose you want to use this equation to convert 365°F into degrees Celsius. To solve for °C, you must isolate it on one side of the equation. Since the right side of the equation has 32 added to the quantity (1.8 × °C), first subtract 32 from both sides of the equation, and then divide each side by 1.8.

$$°F = (1.8 \times °C) + 32$$
$$°F - 32 = (1.8 \times °C) + 32 - 32$$
$$°F - 32 = (1.8 \times °C)$$
$$\frac{°F - 32}{1.8} = \frac{1.8 \times °C}{1.8}$$
$$\frac{(°F - 32)}{1.8} = °C$$

Now that you have solved the equation for the unknown quantity (°C), you can substitute the known quantity (365°F) into the equation and calculate the answer.

$$°C = \frac{(°F - 32)}{1.8} = \frac{(365 - 32)}{1.8} = \frac{333}{1.8} = 185°C$$

SAMPLE PROBLEM MH-6

Solving Algebraic Equations

The heat (q) absorbed by the water in a calorimeter can be calculated using the following relationship.

$$q = m \times C \times \Delta T$$

In this expression, m is the mass of the water; C is the specific heat of water (4.18 J/g ·°C); and ΔT is the change in temperature. If 120 g of water absorb 3500 J of heat, by how much will the temperature of the water increase?

Solution

First solve the equation for the unknown quantity, ΔT.

$$q = m \times C \times \Delta T$$
$$\frac{q}{m \times C} = \frac{m \times C \times \Delta T}{m \times C}$$
$$\frac{q}{m \times C} = \Delta T$$

Now substitute the known values for q, m, and C.

$$\Delta T = \frac{q}{m \times C}$$
$$= \frac{3500 \text{ J}}{(120 \text{ g} \times 4.18 \text{ J/g·°C})} = 7.0°C$$

Practice the Math

1. Solve each equation for z.

   a. $xy + z = 5$

   b. $\dfrac{z}{a - 4} = t$

   c. $\dfrac{b}{d} = \dfrac{2a}{z}$

   d. $\sqrt{z} = 2b$

2. Solve each equation for a. Then calculate a value for a if $b = 4$, $c = 10$, and $d = 2$.

   a. $bd = ac$

   b. $a + b = cd$

   c. $c + b = \dfrac{a}{d}$

   d. $\dfrac{bd}{a} = c^2$

3. Solve each equation for h. Then calculate a value for h if $g = 12$, $k = 0.4$, and $m = 1.5$.

   a. $kh = \dfrac{g}{m}$

   b. $\dfrac{(g - m)}{h} = k$

   c. $gh - k = m$

   d. $\dfrac{mk}{(g + h)} = 2$

Applying Algebra to Chemistry

4. Solve for v in the following equation.

$$d = \frac{m}{v}$$

Let d = density, m = mass, and v = volume. What is the volume of 642 g of gold if the density of gold is 19.3 g/cm^3?

5. Solve for n in the following equation.

$$P \times V = n \times R \times T$$

How many moles (n) of helium gas fill a 6.45-L (V) balloon at a pressure (P) of 105 kPa and a temperature (T) of 278 K?
($R = 8.31$ (L·kPa)/(K·mol))

6. Solve for V_2 in the following equation.

$$\frac{P_1 \times V_1}{T_1} = \frac{P_2 \times V_2}{T_2}$$

A 2.50-L (V_1) sample of nitrogen gas at a temperature (T_1) of 308 K has a pressure (P_1) of 1.15 atm. What is the new volume (V_2) of the gas if the pressure (P_2) is increased to 1.80 atm and the temperature (T_2) decreased to 286 K?

7. Solve for P_{He} in the following equation.

$$P_{total} = P_{Ar} + P_{He} + P_{Kr}$$

A mixture of gases has a total pressure (P_{total}) of 376 kPa. What is the partial pressure of helium (P_{He}), if $P_{Ar} = 92$ kPa and $P_{Kr} = 144$ kPa?

8. Solve for T_2 in the following equation.

$$\frac{V_1}{T_1} = \frac{V_2}{T_2}$$

What is the value of T_2 when $V_1 = 5.0$ L, $V_2 = 15$ L, and $T_1 = 200$ K?

Percents

The grade of a road is the slope expressed as a percent. A downhill 6% grade means that for every 100 units of horizontal distance traveled, there is a corresponding 6-unit descent.

A percent is a ratio that compares a number to 100. The word *percent* (%) means "parts of 100" or "per 100 parts." Another way to think of a percent is a part of a whole expressed in hundredths. Thus, the number 0.52 ("52 hundredths") can also be expressed as 52%, or "52 per 100 parts."

You should be familiar with percents. For example, test scores are often expressed as percents. Suppose you answer 24 questions correctly on a 30-question exam. The part out of the whole, expressed as a percent, can be calculated as follows.

$$\frac{\text{Part}}{\text{Whole}} = \frac{\text{number of correctly answered questions}}{\text{number of questions asked}}$$

$$= \frac{24}{30}$$

$$= 0.80 = \frac{80}{100} = 80\%$$

Note that 0.80, 80/100, and 80% all express the same value: 80 hundredths (or "80 per 100 parts").

Another way to calculate a percent is to multiply the ratio of the part to the whole by 100%.

$$\text{Percent} = \frac{\text{part}}{\text{whole}} \times 100\%$$

Suppose a high school science club consists of 27 boys and 23 girls. What percent of the club is made up of boys?

$$\text{Percent} = \frac{\text{number of boys}}{\text{number of total members}} \times 100\%$$

$$= \frac{27}{27 + 23} \times 100\%$$

$$= \frac{27}{50} \times 100\%$$

$$= 0.54 \times 100\%$$

$$= 54\%$$

Because a percent represents a relationship between two quantities, it can be used as a conversion factor. For example, suppose a friend tells you that she got a score of 95% on a 40-question exam. How many questions did she answer correctly? A score of 95% means 95 correctly answered questions for every 100 questions asked. By expressing this relationship as a conversion factor, you can calculate the number of correctly answered questions.

$$40 \text{ questions asked} \times \left(\frac{95 \text{ correctly answered questions}}{100 \text{ questions asked}} \right)$$

$$= 38 \text{ correctly answered questions}$$

SAMPLE PROBLEM MH-7

Using Percents as Conversion Factors

Six students are absent from their class one day. If 80% of the students in the class are present, what is the total class enrollment?

Solution

Because 80% of the class is present, the six absent students make up 20% of the class. If 20% of the students are absent, this means that 20 students are absent for every 100 students enrolled. Use dimensional analysis to calculate the total class enrollment.

$$6 \text{ students absent} \times \left(\frac{100 \text{ students enrolled}}{20 \text{ students absent}} \right)$$

$$= \frac{600}{20} \text{ students enrolled}$$

$$= 30 \text{ students enrolled}$$

Practice the Math

1. Write each fraction as a percent.
   a. $\frac{3}{4}$ b. $\frac{1}{5}$ c. $\frac{7}{10}$ d. $\frac{5}{8}$
2. Write each decimal as a percent.
   a. 0.39   b. 0.08   c. 4.2   d. 0.5
3. Calculate a score for each exam expressed as a percent.
   a. Sixteen questions correctly answered on a 25-question exam.
   b. Forty-one questions correctly answered on a 50-question exam.
   c. Sixty-eight questions correctly answered on an 85-question exam.

4. A quality control inspector found that 7 out of every 200 flashlights produced were defective. What percent of the flashlights were not defective?
5. A student answered 57 questions correctly on an exam and received a score of 95%. How many questions were on the exam?
6. During a flu epidemic, 28% of the students were absent. If 238 students were absent, what is this school's enrollment?

Applying Percents to Chemistry

7. A mining company is abstracting silver from an ore is that 0.014% silver (by mass). How many kilograms of ore must be processed to yield 0.7 kg of silver?
8. A fertilizer is 12.0% (by mass) nitrogen and 5.5% (by mass) phosphorus. How many grams of each element are in 140 g of this fertilizer?
9. A compound is broken down into 34.5 g of element A, 18.2 g of element B, and 2.6 g of element C. What is the percent (by mass) of each element in this compound?

10. What is the percent by mass of sodium chloride (NaCl) in each of the following solutions?
    a. 44 g NaCl dissolved in 756 g of water
    b. 15 g NaCl dissolved in 485 g of water
    c. 135 g NaCl dissolved in 765 g of water
11. The antiseptic hydrogen peroxide is often sold as a 3.0% (by mass) solution, the rest being water. How many grams of hydrogen peroxide are in 250 g of this solution?
12. A nighttime cold medicine is 22% alcohol (by volume). How many mL of alcohol are in a 250 mL bottle of this medicine?

Graphing

A line graph can be used to show the relationship between two variables. The manipulated variable is plotted on the x-axis. The responding variable is plotted on the y-axis.

The relationship between two variables in an experiment is often determined by graphing the experimental data. A graph is a "picture" of the data. Once a graph is constructed, additional information can be derived about the variables.

In constructing a graph, you must first label the axes. The manipulated variable (also known as the independent variable) is plotted on the *x*-axis. This is the horizontal axis. The manipulated variable is controlled by the experimenter. When the independent variable is changed, a corresponding change in the responding variable (also known as the dependent variable) is measured. The responding variable is plotted on the *y*-axis. This is the vertical axis. The label on each axis should include the unit of the quantity being graphed.

Before data can be plotted on a graph, each axis must be scaled. Each interval on the scale must represent the same amount. To make it easy to find numbers along the scale, the interval chosen is usually a multiple of 1, 2, 5, or 10. Although each scale can start at zero, this is not always practical.

Data are plotted by putting a point at the intersection of corresponding values of each pair of measurements. Once the data has been plotted, the points are connected by a smooth curve. A smooth curve comes as close as possible to all the plotted points. It may in fact not touch any of them.

Inverse and Direct Proportionalities

Depending on the relationship between two variables, a plotted curve may or may not be a straight line. Two common curves are shown below.

Volume vs. Pressure

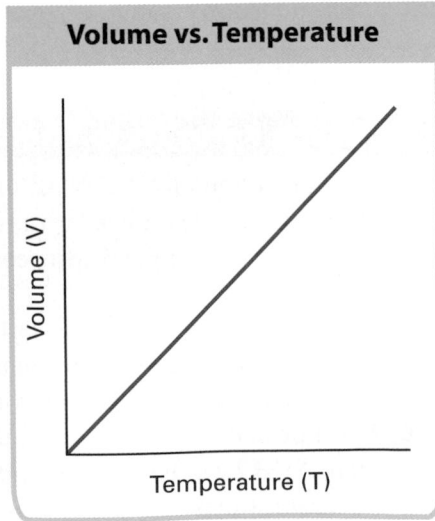

Volume vs. Temperature

The volume- vs. -pressure curve is typical of an inverse proportionality. As the manipulated variable (P) increases, the responding variable (V) decreases. The product of the two variables at any point on the curve of an inverse proportionality is a constant. Thus, $V \times P = $ constant.

The straight line in the volume- vs. -temperature graph is typical of a direct proportionality. As the manipulated variable (T) increases, there is a corresponding increase in the responding variable (V). A straight line can be represented by the following general equation.

$$y = mx + b$$

The variables y and x are plotted on the vertical and horizontal axes, respectively. The y-intercept, b, is the value of y when x is zero. The slope, m, is the ratio of the change in y (Δy) for a corresponding change in x (Δx).

$$m = \frac{\Delta y}{\Delta x}$$

Plotting and Interpreting Graphs

Consider the following set of data about a bicyclist's trip. Assume that the bicyclist rode at a constant speed.

Distance from home (km)	15	25	35	50	75
Time (h)	1	2	3	4.5	7

Graph these data using time as the manipulated variable, and then use the graph to answer the following questions.

a. How far from home was the bicyclist at the start of the trip?
b. How long did it take for the bicyclist to get 40 km from home?

The plotted points are shown in the graph below. Each point was plotted by finding the value of time on the x-axis, then moving up vertically to the value of the other variable (distance). A smooth curve (in this case a straight line), has been drawn through the points.

Figure 1

Distance vs. Time

Figure 2

To answer problem **a**, extend the curve so that it intersects the *y*-axis, as in the graph above. The graph shows that the bicyclist started the trip 5 km from home. This is the value of the vertical axis (distance) when the time elapsed is zero (point *a* on the graph).

For problem **b**, find the value 40 km on the *y*-axis of the graph. Move to the right (horizontally) in the graph until you reach the line. Drop down vertically and read the value of time at this point (point *b*). It takes the bicyclist 3.5 h to get 40 km from home.

SAMPLE PROBLEM MH-8

Interpreting Graphs
Use the distance- vs. -time graph above to calculate the bicyclist's average speed in kilometers per hour (km/h).

Solution

Speed is distance/time. The average speed of the bicyclist is the slope of the line in the graph. Calculate the slope using the values for time and distance corresponding to points *c* and *d*.

$$m = \frac{\Delta y}{\Delta x} = \frac{55 \text{ km} - 40 \text{ km}}{5 \text{ h} - 3.5 \text{ h}} = \frac{15 \text{ km}}{1.5 \text{ h}} = 10 \text{ km/h}$$

You can now write an equation for the line.

$$y = mx + b$$
$$\text{Distance} = (10 \text{ km/h})(\text{time}) + 5 \text{ km}$$

Practice the Math

1. A bicyclist wants to ride 100 kilometers. The data below show the time required to ride 100 kilometers at different average speeds.

Time (h)	4	5	8	10	15	20
Avg speed (km/h)	25	20	12.5	10	6.7	5

a. Graph the data, using average speed as the independent variable.
b. Is this a direct or inverse proportionality?
c. What average speed must be maintained to complete the ride in 12 hours?
d. If a bicyclist's average speed is 18 km/h, how long does it take to ride 100 km?

2. The data below shows how the mass of a baby varies with its age during its first year of life.

Age(days)	40	110	200	270	330
Mass (kg)	4.0	5.4	7.3	8.6	9.9

a. Graph the data, using age as the independent variable.
b. Derive an equation in the form of $y = mx + b$. Include units on the values of y and b.
c. Why would the values of y and b be of interest to both the baby's parents and physician?

Applying Graphs to Chemistry

3. Use the following data to draw a graph that shows the relationship between the Fahrenheit and Celsius temperature scales. Make °F the responding variable. Use the graph to derive an equation relating °F and °C. Then use the graph or the equation to find values for y_1, x_2, and x_3.

Temperature (°F)	50	212	356	−4	y_1	70	400
Temperature (°C)	10	100	180	−20	70	x_2	x_3

4. Different volumes of the same liquid were added to a graduated cylinder sitting on a balance. After each addition of liquid the total volume of liquid and mass of the liquid-filled graduated cylinder was recorded in the table below.

Total volume of liquid (mL)	10	25	45	70	95
Mass of liquid and cylinder (g)	138	159	187	222	257

a. Graph the data, using volume as the manipulated variable.
b. What is the y-intercept of the line? Make sure to include the unit.
c. What does the value of the y-intercept represent?
d. Calculate the slope of the line, and make sure to include the unit.
e. What does the slope of the line represent for this liquid?
f. Write a general equation that represents the line in your graph.

5. A student collected the following data or a fixed volume of gas.

Temperature (ºC)	10	20	40	70	100
Pressure (mm Hg)	726	750	800	880	960

a. Graph the data, using pressure as the responding variable.
b. Is this a direct or inverse proportionality?
c. At what temperature is the gas pressure 822 mm Hg?
d. What is the pressure of the gas at a temperature of 0°C?
e. How does the pressure of the gas change with a change in temperature?
f. Write an equation relating the pressure and temperature of the gas.

Logarithms

The acidity of a solution is measured with a pH meter. The pH scale is a logarithmic scale based on the relationship pH = −log[H⁺].

Certain scales of measurement are based on logarithms, including the pH scale (used to measure acidity) and the decibel scale (used to measure the relative loudness of sounds). Because the pH scale is a logarithmic scale, it allows a vast range of values (from 1.0 to 10^{-14}) to be expressed simply as a number between 1 and 14.

The common logarithm (*log*) of a number is the exponent to which 10 must be raised to produce that number. If $x = 10^y$, then $\log x = y$. Thus, since $0.01 = 10^{-2}$, it follows that $\log 0.01 = -2$. Likewise, $\log 10{,}000 = 4$, because $10{,}000 = 10^4$.

Using a Calculator to Compute Logarithms

You can determine the logarithm of a number by using the **[log]** key on a calculator. (Do not confuse the **[log]** key with the **[ln]** key.) If you are calculating the logarithm of a measured value, then the number of decimal places in the logarithm must be rounded to equal the number of significant figures in the measurement. For example, to calculate the logarithm of 3.45, enter the keystrokes shown below.

$$\log 3.45 = \text{[3][.][4][5] [log]} = 0.5378191 = 0.538$$

The number in the display (the logarithm) is *0.5378191*. This value must be rounded to three decimal places so as to equal the number of significant figures in the original number. (3.45 has three significant figures.)

Practice using the logarithm function on your calculator by working out problems **a** and **b**. For simplification, only the **[log]** keystrokes are indicated. Make sure to round your answers to the correct number of decimal places.

a. $\log 0.0087 = 0.0087$ **[log]** $= -2.0604807 = -2.06$
(0.0087 has two significant figures, so round to two decimal places.)
b. $\log 3.11 \times 10^{-5} = 3.11 \times 10^{-5}$ **[log]** $= -4.5072396 = -4.507$
(3.11×10^{-5} has three significant figures, so round to three decimal places.)

Antilogarithms

The reverse process of converting a logarithm into a number is referred to as obtaining the antilogarithm. The antilogarithm of the logarithm of number x is the number x itself.

$$\text{antilog} (\log x) = x$$

If $\log 10^{-7} = -7$, then antilog $(-7) = 10^{-7}$. Likewise, if $\log 10^2 = 2$, then antilog $(2) = 10^2$.

You can calculate the antilog of a number by using the **[10ˣ]** key on your calculator. To find the antilogarithm of 0.538, enter **[.][5][3][8]** followed by the **[10ˣ]** key. (Depending on your calculator, you may need to press the **[2nd]** or **[INV]** key first.) The number in the display (the antilogarithm) is *3.45143734*. This value must be reported to three significant figures (as 3.45), because the original number (0.538) was reported to three decimal places.

Practice using the **[10ˣ] key** on your calculator by working out the antilogarithms of the logarithms you calculated earlier.

a. antilog $(-2.06) = -2.06$ **[10ˣ]** $= 0.0087096 = 0.0087$
    $(-2.06$ has two decimal places, so round to two significant figures)
b. antilog $(-4.507) = -4.507$ **[10ˣ]** $= 0.000031117 = 3.11 \times 10^{-5}$
    $(-4.507$ has three decimal places, so round to three significant figures)

SAMPLE PROBLEM MH-9

Logarithms and Antilogarithms
Use your calculator to find the logarithm of 8.10×10^3. Check your answer by computing its antilogarithm.

Solution

$\log 8.10 \times 10^3 = 8.10 \times 10^3$ **[log]** $= 3.9084850 = 3.908$
antilog $(3.908) = 3.908$ **[10ˣ]** $= 8090.9590 = 8.09 \times 10^3$

Notice that because you rounded the logarithm to three decimal places, the calculated antilog (8.09×10^3) is not exactly the same as the original number given (8.10×10^3).

Practice the Math

1. Calculate the logarithms of the following numbers.

a. 7.56   **b.** 0.000678
c. 456   **d.** 4.27×10^3
e. 1.485×10^{-6} **f.** 1×10^{-12}

2. Calculate the antilogarithms of the following numbers.

a. 2.56   **b.** 6.111
c. -3.55 **d.** 1.138
e. 0.962   **f.** -0.864

Applying Logarithms to Chemistry

3. The hydrogen ion concentration, [H⁺], of an aqueous solution can be expressed as a pH value according to the following relationship.

$$pH = -\log [H^+]$$

Determine pH values for solutions having the following [H⁺] values. The symbol *M* represents molarity, a unit of concentration.

a. $1 \times 10^{-8} M$ **b.** $1 \times 10^{-1} M$
c. $4.8 \times 10^{-7} M$ **d.** 0.0034 M

4. The relationship between pH and [H⁺] can also be expressed as follows.

$$[H^+] = \text{antilog } (-pH)$$

Determine [H⁺] values for aqueous solutions having the following pH values.

a. 14.0   **b.** 7.0
c. 7.86   **d.** 4.05
e. 11.65   **f.** 2.945
g. 3.68   **h.** 12.850

Appendix D: Safety In the Chemistry Lab

The experiments in this book have been carefully designed to minimize the risk of injury. However, safety is also your responsibility. The following rules are essential for keeping you safe in the laboratory. The rules address pre-lab preparation, proper laboratory practices, and post-lab procedures.

Pre-Lab Preparation

1. Read the entire procedure before you begin. Listen to all of your teacher's instructions. When in doubt about a procedure, ask your teacher.

2. Do only the assigned experiments. Do any experiment only when your teacher is present and has given you permission to work.

3. Know the location and operation of the following safety equipment: fire extinguisher, fire blanket, emergency shower, and eye wash station.

4. Know the location of emergency exits and escape routes. To make it easy to exit quickly, do not block walkways with furniture. Keep your work area orderly and free of personal belongings such as coats and backpacks.

5. Protect your clothing and hair from chemicals and sources of heat. Tie back long hair and roll up loose sleeves when working in the laboratory. Avoid wearing bulky or loose-fitting clothing. Remove dangling jewelry. Wear closed-toe shoes at all times in the laboratory.

Proper Laboratory Practices

6. Even with well-designed and tested laboratory procedures, an accident may occur while you are working in the lab.

   ⚠ Report any accident, no matter how minor, to your teacher.

7. Wear chemical splash goggles at all times when working in the laboratory. These goggles are designed to protect your eyes from injury. While working in the lab, do not rub your eyes, because chemicals are easily transferred from your hands to your eyes.

   ⚠ If, despite these precautions, a chemical gets in your eye, remove any contact lenses and immediately wash your eye with a continuous stream of lukewarm water for at least 15 minutes.

8. To reduce danger, waste, and cleanup, always use the minimal amounts of chemicals specified for an experiment.

9. Never taste any chemical used in the laboratory, including food products that are the subject of an investigation. Treat all items as though they are contaminated with unknown chemicals that may be toxic. Keep all food and drink that is not part of an experiment out of the laboratory. Do not eat, drink, or chew gum in the laboratory.

   ⚠ If you accidentally ingest a substance, notify your teacher immediately.

10. Don't use chipped or cracked glassware. Don't handle broken glass. If glassware breaks, tell your teacher and nearby classmates. Discard broken glass as instructed by your teacher.

    ⚠ If, despite these precautions, you receive a minor cut, allow it to bleed for a short time. Wash the injured area under cold running water and notify your teacher. More serious cuts or puncture wounds require immediate medical attention.

11. Do not handle hot glassware or equipment. You can prevent burns by being aware that hot and cold equipment can look exactly the same.

    ⚠ If you are burned, immediately run cold water over the burned area for several minutes until the pain is reduced. Cooling helps the burn heal. Ask a classmate to notify your teacher.

12. Recognize that the danger of an electrical shock is greater in the presence of water. Keep electrical appliances away from sinks and faucets to minimize the risk of electrical shock. Be careful not to spill water or other liquids in the vicinity of an electrical appliance.

    ⚠ If, despite these precautions, you spill water near an electrical appliance, stand back, notify your teacher, and warn other students in the area.

13. Report any chemical spills immediately to your teacher. Follow your teacher's instructions for cleaning up spills. Warn other students about the identity and location of spilled chemicals.

    ⚠ If, despite these precautions, a corrosive chemical gets on your skin or clothing, notify your teacher. Then wash the affected area with cold running water for several minutes.

Post-Lab Procedures

14. Dispose of chemicals in a way that protects you, your classmates, and the environment. Always follow your teacher's directions for cleanup and disposal. Clean your small-scale reaction surface by draining the contents onto a paper towel. Then wipe the surface with a damp paper towel and dry the surface completely. Dispose of the paper towels in the waste bin.

15. Wash your hands thoroughly with soap and water before leaving the laboratory.

Take appropriate precautions when any of the following safety symbols appears in an experiment.

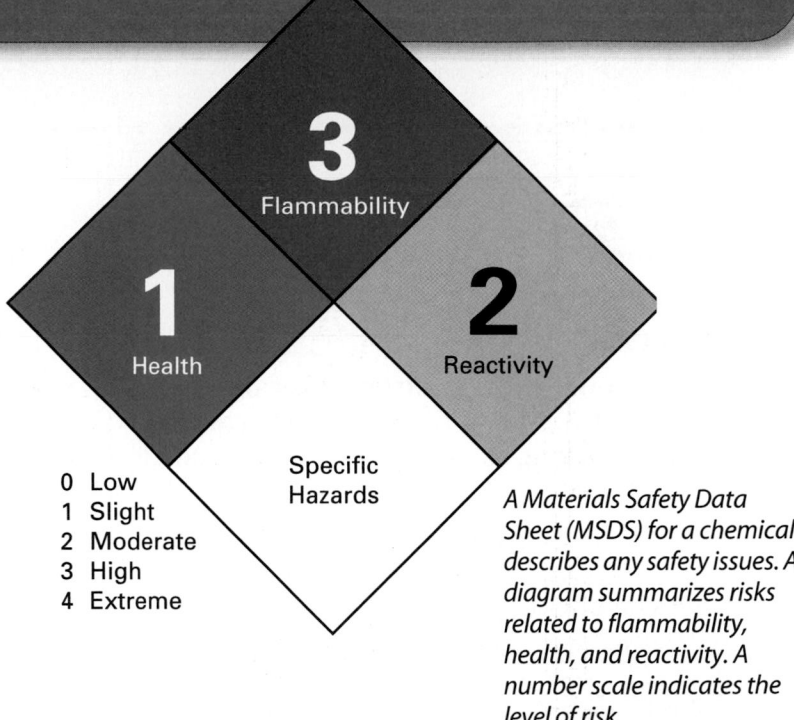

0 Low
1 Slight
2 Moderate
3 High
4 Extreme

A Materials Safety Data Sheet (MSDS) for a chemical describes any safety issues. A diagram summarizes risks related to flammability, health, and reactivity. A number scale indicates the level of risk.

Safety Symbols

 Eye Safety
Wear safety goggles.

 Clothing Protection
Wear a lab coat or apron when using corrosive chemicals or chemicals that can stain clothing.

 Skin Protection
Wear plastic gloves when using chemicals that can irritate or stain your skin.

 Broken Glass
Do not use chipped or cracked glassware. Do not heat the bottom of a test tube.

 Open Flame
Tie back hair and loose clothing. Never reach across a lit burner.

 Flammable Substance
Do not have a flame near flammable materials.

 Corrosive Substance
Wear safety goggles, an apron, and gloves when working with corrosive chemicals.

 Poison
Don't chew gum, drink, or eat in the laboratory. Never taste a chemical in the laboratory.

 Fume
Avoid inhaling substances that can irritate your respiratory system.

 Thermal Burn
Do not touch hot glassware or equipment.

 Electrical Equipment
Keep electrical equipment away from water or other liquids.

 Sharp Object
To avoid a puncture wound, use scissors or other sharp objects only as intended.

 Disposal
Dispose of chemicals only as directed.

 Hand Washing
Wash your hands thoroughly with soap and water.

Chapter 1

26. 24 short blocks

27. 24 minutes

28. The order of the morning errands cannot vary, but the order of the afternoon errands can vary, as long as the haircut takes place before 3 pm.

29. Possible answers are to do an errand during his lunch hour or to extend the hours during which he does errands.

35. Chemistry concerns the changes that matter undergoes.

37. Carothers did pure chemistry when he tested the proposal of another chemist. However, his results led to applied chemistry.

39. A firefighter needs to know the chemistry of what happens when something burns and what chemically needs to be done to put out the fire. A reporter needs to know chemistry when interviewing chemists or reporting on happenings that involve chemistry.

41. Answers will vary.

43. In a macroscopic view you can see an object like a burr with the unaided eye. The tiny hooks on the surface of the burr require a microscopic view because it requires magnification to view them.

45. Biochemists study composition of and changes in living organisms.

47. Testing soil reveals its composition. Chemicals that are needed in the soil and are not there can be added.

49. Lead poisoning can cause nervous system damage in young children.

51. New materials were developed and used in the prosthetic limb.

53. They based their conclusions on experimental evidence.

55. to test a hypothesis

57. The independent variable is changed by the person performing the experiment. The dependent variable changes as a result of changing the independent variable.

59. A theory is tested by many experiments and modified if necessary. A scientific law summarizes the results of many observations and experiments.

61. The doctor's hypothesis is that your sore throat is caused by strep throat. She tests the hypothesis with an experiment, a throat culture.

63. **a.** The independent variable is the temperature of the basketball. The dependent variable is the height of the bounce.
    b. Answers might include the methods of dropping the basketball and measuring the height of the bounce.

65. **a.** the amount of salt added
    b. the freezing point
    c. There can be only one independent variable; all other factors must be constant.
    d. The hypothesis is supported, but the freezing point seems to level off.

67. The person who is educated in the theories and practice of chemistry is more likely to recognize the significance of an accidental discovery and be able to develop that discovery into an important scientific contribution.

69. Diagrams should show one string that is threaded through both holes A and C. The string through hole B is a separate string.

71. **b., c.,** and **d.**

73. step 1, analyze

75. 4,320 times an hour, 103,680 times a day

77. 300 miles

79. The particles in choice B are oxygen and nitrogen particles, and they are in a 1:4 ratio, as indicated by the percent of each present in air.

81. 144,000 eggs

83. **a.** $1.00 per package
    b. number of envelopes in a package

9. Iron is magnetic; table salt is not. Table salt will dissolve in water; iron will not.

10. By lowering the temperature to below the boiling point of each gas, you could condense each substance and separate the gases.

18. Liquid A is probably a substance. Liquid B is a mixture.

19. The liquid was not an element because a solid was left when the liquid evaporated. A physical process, such as evaporation, cannot be used to break down a compound. Therefore, the liquid was a mixture.

35. An extensive property depends on the amount of matter in a sample; an intensive property depends on the type of matter in a sample. Extensive properties include mass and volume. Intensive properties include color, hardness, melting point, and boiling point.

37. Answers could include reddish color, conductor of heat and electricity, malleable, and its melting and boiling points.

39. Answers might include the state at room temperature.

41. Gaseous acetone is a vapor. Vapors are normally liquid or solid at room temperature.

43. Chlorine condenses, and mercury, bromine, and water freeze.

45. Mass is an extensive property and does not depend on composition.

47. ethanol

49. sulfur

51. State is usually given as the state at room temperature, usually 20°C.

53. Particles in a gas are free to move, so a container is needed. Particles in a solid do not move relative to each other, so solids have a definite shape and volume without a container.

55. a. mercury and sulfur
   b. For both elements, 125°C is between the melting point and the boiling point.
   c. Ethanol, mercury, bromine, and water would be in a different order, and gold and copper would be switched.

57. Solutions are homogeneous mixtures, which means that they consist of one phase.

59. Sample answer: Dissolve the sugar in the water and decant the liquid. Depending on the size of the charcoal pieces, they could be separated from the sand by filtration or burning the charcoal. Sand and charcoal can also be separated by color.

61. a. Hydrogen and oxygen are the elements that make up the compound water.
   b. Nitrogen and oxygen are elements present in the mixture air.
   c. Sodium and chlorine are elements in the compound table salt.
   d. The compound table sugar contains the element carbon and the elements in the compound water.

63. Accept any answers students can justify.

65. With heat, iron and sulfur change into a new substance, iron sulfide. In a chemical change, such as this, composition changes. In a physical change, chemical composition remains the same.

67. 18 g of water

69. In photograph A, bubbles form. In photograph B, a red solid forms.

1. a. 4   **b.** 4   **c.** 2   **d.** 5

2. a. 3   **b.** 2   **c.** 4   **d.** 4

3. a. 8.71×10^1 m   **b.** 4.36×10^8 m
   c. 1.55×10^{-2} m   **d.** 9.01×10^3 m
   e. 1.78×10^{-3} m   **f.** 6.30×10^2 m

4. a. 9×10^1 m   **b.** 4×10^8 m
   c. 2×10^{-2} m   **d.** 9×10^3 m
   e. 2×10^{-3} m   **f.** 6×10^2 m

5. a. 79.2 m   **b.** 7.33 m
   c. 11.53 m   **d.** 17.3 m

6. 23.8 g

7. a. 1.8×10^1 m^2
   b. 6.75×10^2 m
   c. 5.87×10^{-1} min

8. 1.3×10^3 m^3

16. -196°C

17. melting point = 1234 K; boiling point = 2485 K

28. 1.0080×10^4 min

29. 1.44000×10^5 s

30. 67 students

31. 86.4°F

32. a. 44 m
   b. 4.6×10^{-3} g
   c. 10.7 cg

33. a. 1.5×10^{-2} L   **b.** 7.38×10^{-3} kg
   c. 6.7×10^3 ms   **d.** 9.45×10^7 μg

34. 2.27×10^{-8} cm

35. 1.3×10^8 dm

36. 1.93×10^4 kg/m^3

37. 7.0×10^{12} RBC/L

46. density = 2.50 g/cm^3; no

47. 10.5 cm^3

48. a. 6.32 cm^3
   b. 0.342 cm^3

49. See answers for problem 48.

57. Lissa: inaccurate and imprecise
   Lamont: accurate and precise
   Leigh Anne: inaccurate and precise

59. a. 98.5 L   **b.** 0.000 763 cg
   c. 57.0 m   **d.** 12.2°C

61. (59) **a.** 9.85×10^1 L
   b. 7.63×10^{-4} cg
   c. 5.70×10^1 m
   d. $1.22 \times 10^{1\circ}$C
   (60) **a.** 4.3×10^1 g
   b. 2.258×10^2 L
   c. 9.20×10^1 kg
   d. 3.24×10^1 m^3

63. Results can be close to each other without being close to the actual value.

65. e., d., c., f., b., a.

67. Yes, the mass of an object is constant, but its weight varies with location.

69. a. second   **b.** meter
   c. kelvin   **d.** kilogram

71. a. mm   **b.** cm   **c.** cm

73. °F = 1.8°C + 32

75. conversion factor

77. It must be identical to the unit in the given measurement or in the numerator of the previous conversion factor.

79. a. 7.3 μL/s
   b. 78.6 mg/mm^2
   c. 1.54 g/cm^3

81. 2.83×10^2 mg, 0.283 g, 2.83×10^{-4} kg
   6.6 g, 6.6×10^2 cg, 6.6×10^{-3} kg
   2.8×10^{-1} mg, 2.8×10^{-2} cg, 2.8×10^{-7} kg

83. 1 g/10^2 cg, 10^2 cg/1 g, 1 g/10^3 mg, 10^3 mg/1 g, 10^3 mg/10^2 cg, 10^2 cg/10^3 mg

85. 31.1 m/s

87. Yes; neither mass nor volume of a solid or a liquid changes appreciably with location.

89. 5 dL

91. 4.20×10^4 cm^3

93. 73 g

95. volume of iron = 45.1 cm^3
   mass of lead = 514 g Pb

Chapter 4

15. a. 19   **b.** B   **c.** 5   **d.** 5
   e. 16   **f.** 16   **g.** 23   **h.** 23

16. a. 9 protons and 9 electrons
   b. 20 protons and 20 electrons
   c. 13 protons and 13 electrons

17. a. 8   **b.** 16   **c.** 61   **d.** 45   **e.** 125

18. a. $^{12}_{6}$C   **b.** $^{19}_{9}$F   **c.** $^{9}_{4}$Be

19. $^{16}_{8}$O, $^{17}_{8}$O, $^{18}_{8}$O

20. Chromium-50 has 26 neutrons, chromium-52 has 28 neutrons, and chromium-53 has 29 neutrons.

21. boron-11

22. Silicon-28 must be by far the most abundant. The other two isotopes must be present in very small amounts.

23. 63.6 amu

24. 79.90 amu

35. Democritus's ideas were not helpful in explaining chemical behavior because they lacked experimental support.

37. Atoms can be separated from each other, joined together, or rearranged.

39. No; in general Dalton proposed a valid atomic theory that was in line with the experimental evidence available to him.

41. a. A beam of electrons (cathode rays) is deflected by an electric field toward a positively charged plate.
   b. The cathode rays were always composed of electrons regardless of the metal used in the electrodes or the gas used in the cathode ray tube.

43. Atoms contain equal numbers of protons, which are positively charged, and electrons, which are negatively charged. When an electron is lost, the atom contains more protons than electrons, which leaves it with a positive charge.

45. The atom contains a dense, positively charged nucleus, but the atom is mostly empty space.

47. protons and neutrons

49. 5 protons and 6 neutrons

51. Millikan used the quantity of charge value and the charge-to-mass ratio measured by Thomson.

53. They were attracted to a positively charged plate.

55. Change the metal used as a target and account for differences in deflection patterns.

57. 4×10^{-25} g

59. the number of protons in the nucleus

61. The atomic number is the number of protons in the atom. The mass number is the total number of protons and neutrons.

63. because of the existence of isotopes

65. Average atomic mass is the arithmetic mean of the isotopes. Weighted average atomic mass considers both the mass and the relative abundance of the isotopes.

67. according to increasing atomic number

69. They are the same number.

71. 207 amu

73. Accept any answer students can justify.

Chapter 5

8. a. $1s^2 2s^2 2p^2$
  b. $1s^2 2s^2 2p^6 3s^2 3p^6$
  c. $1s^2 2s^2 2p^6 3s^2 3p^6 3d^8 4s^2$

9. a. $1s^2 2s^2 2p^1$; one unpaired electron
  b. $1s^2 2s^2 2p^6 3s^2 3p^2$ two unpaired electrons

14. 2.00×10^{-5} m; longer wavelength than red light

15. 6.00×10^{15} s^{-1}; ultraviolet

23. In Rutherford's model, negatively charged electrons surround a dense, positively charged nucleus. In Bohr's model, the electrons are assigned to concentric circular orbits of fixed energy.

25. a region in space around the nucleus in which there is a high probability of finding an electron

27. a. 1   **b.** 2   **c.** 3   **d.** 4

29. Each electron in an atom has its own, unique energy, but the energies of some electrons are extremely close.

31. An orbit confines the electron to a fixed circular path around the nucleus. An orbital is a region around the nucleus in which electrons are likely to be found.

33. Aufbau principle: electrons occupy the lowest possible energy levels; Pauli exclusion principle: an atomic orbital can hold at most two electrons; Hund's rule: one electron occupies each of a set of orbitals with equal energies before any pairing of electrons occurs.

35. The p orbitals in the third quantum level contain three electrons.

37. b. and **c.**

39. $2s$, $3p$, $4s$, $3d$

41. a. $1s^2 2s^2 2p^6 3s^2 3p^6 3d^{10} 4s^2 4p^4$ (2-8-18-6)
  b. $1s^2 2s^2 2p^6 3s^2 3p^6 3d^3 4s^2$ (2-8-11-2)
  c. $1s^2 2s^2 2p^6 3s^2 3p^6 3d^8 4s^2$ (2-8-16-2)
  d. $1s^2 2s^2 2p^6 3s^2 3p^6 4s^2$ (2-8-8-2)

43. $1s^2 2s^2 2p^6 3s^2 3p^6 3d^{10} 4s^2 4p^3$ (2-8-18-5) The fourth energy level is not full.

45. $1s^2 2s^2 2p^3$ (2-5); nitrogen; 3 unpaired electrons

47. 2

49. a.

51. The electrons obey Hund's rule.

53. Classical physics views energy changes as continuous. In the quantum concept, energy changes occur in tiny discrete units called quanta.

55. The electron of the hydrogen atom is raised (excited) to a higher energy level.

57. Energy from the flame excites electrons in the sodium atoms. When the electrons drop back to the ground state, the atoms give off energy in the form of yellow light.

59. 5.890×10^{-5} cm and 5.896×10^{-5} cm

61. a.

63. Answers might include that the model of the atom is based on the abstract idea of probability. Light is considered a particle and a wave at the same time. Atoms and light cannot be compared to familiar objects or observations because humans cannot experience atoms or photons directly and because matter and energy behave differently at the atomic level than at the level humans can observe directly.

65. **a.** the first atom
b. the second atom
c. the second atom
d. the first atom

67. **a.** Frequency (s^{-1})
5.20×10^{12}
4.40×10^{13}
9.50×10^{13}
1.70×10^{14}
2.20×10^{14}
4.70×10^{14}

b.

c. 6.62×10^{-34} joule • second
d. The slope is Planck's constant.

69. 2.18×10^{-18} J; 5.45×10^{-19} J; 1.96×10^{-17} J

Chapter 6

8. **a.** $1s^2 2s^2 2p^2$
b. $1s^2 2s^2 2p^6 3s^2 3p^6 3d^{10} 4s^2 4p^6 5s^2$
c. $1s^2 2s^2 2p^6 3s^2 3p^6 3d^3 4s^2$

9. **a.** B, Al, Ga, In, Tl
b. F, Cl, Br, I, At
c. Ti, Zr, Hf, Rf

25. Its actual properties agreed with the predicted properties, and Mendeleev's table gained wider acceptance.

27. Yes, both carbon and silicon are in Group 4A (14), and each has four valence electrons.

29. Metalloids have properties that are intermediate between those of metals and nonmetals.

31. **a.** C, Si
b. La
c. B, Ne, P, Br, At
d. Sb, Bi

33. Yes; 113 is the lowest atomic number yet to be discovered.

35. Group 8A (18)

37. helium

39. **a.** $1s^2 2s^2 2p^1$ (2-3)
b. $1s^2 2s^2 2p^6 3s^2 3p^6 3d^{10} 4s^2 4p^3$ (2-8-18-5)
c. $1s^2 2s^2 2p^5$ (2-7)
d. $1s^2 2s^2 2p^6 3s^2 3p^6 3d^{10} 4s^2$ (2-8-18-2)
e. $1s^2 2s^2 2p^6 3s^2 3p^1$ (2-8-3)

41. **a.** H, Li, Na, K, Rb, Cs, Fr
b. O, S, Se, Te, Po
c. Zn, Cd, Hg, Uub

43. **a.** Possible positive ions are Rb$^+$ and Sr^{2+}. Possible negative ions are Br$^-$, Se^{2-}, and As^{3-}.
b. No; a positive ion is isoelectronic with the noble gas in the preceding period, and a negative ion is isoelectronic with the noble gas in the same period.

45. The first ionization energy is the energy needed to remove the outermost electron. The second ionization energy is the energy needed to remove the second-outermost electron.

47. **a.** Se, Mg, Be **b.** Cs, Ba, Bi **c.** Na, Al, S

49. It is smaller.

51. **a.** F **b.** N **c.** Mg **d.** As

53. **a.** O **b.** F **c.** O **d.** S

55. Nonmetals; nuclear charge is greater for nonmetals, and no energy levels are added. Thus, electrons are pulled closer to the nucleus in nonmetals, and more energy is required to remove them.

57. 170 pm

59. Magnesium achieves a stable electron configuration by losing two electrons. Aluminum achieves a stable electron configuration by losing three electrons.

61. **a.** The first ionization energy increases as electronegativity increases.
b. Going across a period, nuclear charge increases, causing the nucleus to attract the electrons more. The outer electrons are closer to the nucleus because the nuclear pull is stronger and the shielding effect does not increase because there is no change in number of energy levels. The closer the electrons are held by the nucleus, the more energy required to remove an electron from an atom.

63. **a.** Calcium is a Group 2A (2) metal, so it is easy to remove its second outer electron.

Potassium contains only one outer electron. It loses this one electron easily, but it takes much more energy to remove another electron from this noble gas configuration.

b. Aluminum is a Group 3A (3) metal, so it has three valence electrons, and it is relatively easy to remove them. Magnesium is a Group 2A (2) metal. It loses two electrons readily, but the third electron requires a large amount of energy because it is being removed from a noble gas configuration.

65. Mg^{2+} has more protons in its nucleus, so the attraction between the nucleus and the electrons is greater, and thus it has a smaller radius.

67. The largest increase is between ionization numbers 4 and 5 because carbon easily loses its four valence electrons. The fifth electron is removed from a full energy level.

Chapter 7

1. a. sulfide ion, S^{2-}
   b. aluminum ion, Al^{3+}

2. a. 2 electrons lost
   b. 3 electrons gained
   c. 2 electrons lost

12. a. KI   **b.** Al_2O_3

13. $CaCl_2$

31. a. gain of 1 electron
   b. loss of 1 electron
   c. gain of 3 electrons
   d. loss of 2 electrons
   e. loss of 1 electron
   f. gain of 1 electron

33. electrons in the highest occupied energy level

35. a. $:\overset{\cdot}{\underset{\cdot}{\ddot{C}l}}\cdot$ **b.** $:\ddot{S}\cdot$ **c.** $\cdot \dot{Al}\cdot$ **d.** $Li\cdot$

37. a. Al^{3+} **b.** Li^+ **c.** Ba^{2+}
   d. K^+ **e.** Ca^{2+} **f.** Sr^{2+}

39. a. S^{2-} **b.** Na^+ **c.** F^- **d.** P^{3-}

41. c.

43. a. $\cdot \dot{C}\cdot$ **b.** $\cdot Be\cdot$ **c.** $:\ddot{O}\cdot$
   d. $:\ddot{F}\cdot$ **e.** $Na\cdot$ **f.** $\cdot \dot{P}\cdot$

45. They have lost valence electrons.

47. a. oxygen atom, sulfur atom, oxide ion, sulfide ion

b. sodium ion, potassium ion, sodium atom, potassium atom

49. a. $1s^2 2s^2 2p^6 3s^2 3p^6 3d^3$ (2-8-11)
   b. $1s^2 2s^2 2p^6 3s^2 3p^6 3d^4$ (2-8-12)
   c. $1s^2 2s^2 2p^6 3s^2 3p^6 3d^5$ (2-8-13)

51. a. Br^- **b.** H^-
   c. As^{3-} **d.** Se^{2-}

53. All have the configuration of Ne, $1s^2 2s^2 2p^6$ (2-8).

55. a. All have the noble-gas configuration of $1s^2 2s^2 2p^6 3s^2 3p^6$ (2-8-8).
   b. All have the noble-gas configuration of $1s^2 2s^2 2p^6$ (2-8).

57. By gaining or losing electrons atoms of elements achieve a noble-gas electron configuration.

59. a. positive ion, lose $1e^-$
   b. positive ion, lose $1e^-$
   c. unreactive
   d. negative ion, gain $1e^-$
   e. positive ion, lose $2e^-$

61. a. and **b.**

63. The positive charges balance the negative charges.

65. a. K^+, Cl^- **b.** Ba^{2+}, SO_4^{2-}
   c. Mg^{2+}, Br^- **d.** Li^+, CO_3^{2-}

67. Ions are free to move in molten $MgCl_2$, but they are held in place in the solid compound.

69. a., c., e., and **f.**

71. Hexagonal close-packed unit cells have 12 neighbors for every atom or ion. Face-centered cubic unit cells also have 12 neighbors for every atom or ion, with an atom or ion in the center of each face. Body-centered cubic unit cells have 8 neighbors for every atom or ion, with an atom or ion at the center of each cube.

73. In sodium chloride crystals the sodium and chloride ions vibrate about fixed points; in the molten state, the ions are free to move.

75. Na^+ and Cs^+ differ greatly in size. Na^+ and Cl^- are similar in size to Mn^{2+} and S^{2-}.

77. body-centered cubic: Na, K, Fe, Cr, W; face-centered cubic: Cu, Ag, Au, Al, Pb; hexagonal close-packed: Mg, Zn, Cd

79. Steel is a mixture and will vary in composition. Its properties depend on its composition. In addition to iron, steel can contain varying amounts of carbon and other metals.

81. Brass is a mixture of copper and zinc. The properties of a particular sample of brass vary with the relative proportions of the two metals.

83. 0.1445 nm

Chapter 8

7. a. :Cl:Cl: **b.** :Br:Br: **c.** :I:I:

8. a. H:O:O:H   **b.** :Cl:P:Cl:
                                :Cl:

9. $\left[\text{H:O:}\right]^-$

10. $\left[\begin{array}{c}\text{F}\\ \text{F:B:F}\\ \text{F}\end{array}\right]^-$

11. $\left[\begin{array}{c}\text{:O:}\\ \text{:O:S:O:}\\ \text{:O:}\end{array}\right]^{2-}$ $\left[\begin{array}{c}\text{:O:}\\ \text{:O:C:}\\ \text{:O}\end{array}\right]$

12. $\left[\text{H:O:C}\begin{array}{c}\text{O}\\ \text{:O:}\end{array}\right]$

30. a. moderately polar covalent
  b. ionic
  c. moderately to very polar covalent
  d. moderately to very polar covalent
  e. ionic
  f. nonpolar covalent

31. c, d, b, a

39. ionic

41. An atom is stable when its outer energy level contains an octet, as it does in a neon atom. A chlorine atom achieves an octet by sharing an electron with another chlorine atom.

43. Ionic bonds depend on electrostatic attraction between oppositely charged ions. Covalent bonds involve attractions that occur when electrons are shared by two atoms.

45. a. :I:I: **b.** :F:O:F:
  c. H:S:H   **d.** :I:N:I:
                                        :I:

47. Atoms in C—N and C—O single bonds contain unshared pairs of electrons, which are needed for coordinate covalent bonds. Atoms in C—H and C—C single bonds do not.

49. b. and c.; assuming only single bonds, the P and S atoms in these compounds each have 10 valence electrons.

51. The greater the bond dissociation energy, the lower the chemical reactivity.

53. a. Carbon does not have an octet.
    $\left[\text{:C::N:}\right]^-$
  b. A fluorine atom has 10 electrons.
    :F:P:F:
      :F:

55. C, O, H, S, N, F, Cl; they are all nonmetals.

57.

:Cl   :Cl:
:Cl\\P/:Cl: :F\\S/:F: :F—I—F:
:Cl: :Cl: :F /|\\ :F:

P forms 5 hybrid orbitals (dsp^3), S forms 6 hybrid orbitals (d^2sp^3), and I forms 7 hybrid orbitals (d^3sp^3).

59. H:N:N::N: ⟷ H:N::N::N:

61. a. linear
  b. tetrahedral
  c. trigonal planar
  d. bent
  e. linear
  f. bent

63. a. sp^3 **b.** sp^2 **c.** sp **d.** sp

65. a. tetrahedral
  b. tetrahedral
  c. bent

67. a. trigonal planar
  b. pyramidal
  c. linear
  d. tetrahedral

69. a. bent
  b. tetrahedral
  c. pyramidal

71. The electronegativities of the two atoms will differ by about 0.4 to 2.0.

73. an intermolecular force caused by an electrostatic interaction between a hydrogen atom that is covalently bonded to an electronegative atom and an unshared electron pair of a nearby atom

75. More energy is required to separate the molecules.

77. 1.6

79. Answers will vary. Table 8.3 suggests that there is no clear difference. Students' argu-

ments could be based on chemical properties, such as conductivity of the compound
in the liquid state.

81. hydrogen bonding

Chapter 9

1. a. anion, selenide ion
   b. cation, barium ion
   c. anion, phosphide ion

2. a. three electrons lost
   b. two electrons gained
   c. one electron lost

10. a. BaS **b.** Li_2O **c.** Ca_3N_2 **d.** CuI_2

11. a. NaI **b.** $SnCl_2$ **c.** K_2S **d.** CaI_2

12. a. $(NH_4)_2SO_3$
   b. $Ca_3(PO_4)_2$

13. a. $(NH_4)_2SO_3$
   b. $Cr(NO_2)_3$

34. 2:1

43. a. 2+   **b.** 2+   **c.** 3+   **d.** 1+

45. cyanide, CN^- and hydroxide, OH^-

47. For the representative metals, ionic charge
can be determined by the group the metal is
in. For transition metals, it is more difficult to
predict ionic charge from the periodic table.

49. For formulas, symbols for the ions are written, and the charges are balanced with subscripts. For naming, the name of the cation is
followed by the name of the anion.

51. For formulas, symbols of the ions are written,
and the charges are balanced with subscripts. Parentheses are used around the
polyatomic ion if a subscript is needed. For
naming, the name of the positive ion is followed by the name of the negative ion.

53. when more than a single polyatomic ion is
needed to balance the formula

55. a. $KMnO_4$
   b. $Ca(HCO_3)_2$
   c. Cl_2O_7
   d. Si_3N_4
   e. NaH_2PO_4
   f. PBr_5
   g. CCl_4

57. a. sodium chlorate
   b. mercury(I) bromide
   c. potassium chromate
   d. perchloric acid

e. tin(IV) oxide
   f. iron(III) acetate
   g. potassium hydrogen sulfate
   h. calcium hydroxide
   i. barium sulfide

59. $SnCl_4$

61. Possible answers include that cations are
named before anions. When the ion of a
metal has more than one possible charge,
the charge is shown by a Roman numeral.
Monatomic anions have an –ide ending.
Possible purposes include that knowing
ionic charge is necessary because it determines how many ions are in the formula of
the compound.

63. a. The charges do not total zero.
   b. The charges do not total zero.
   c. Neon is a noble gas and does not form
   compounds.
   d. The subscripts are not in the lowest,
   whole-
   number ratio.

65. a. K_2CO_3 is more soluble in water than
   $CaCO_3$ is.
   b. The copper compound is blue; the iron
   compound is white.
   c. Add water to dissolve the NH_4Cl; then filter out the insoluble $BaSO_4$.
   d. chlorine (nonmetal), sulfur (nonmetal),
   bromine (nonmetal), barium (metal),
   iodine (nonmetal), mercury (metal)
   e. barium sulfate, calcium carbonate, potassium carbonate, copper(II) sulfate pentahydrate, iron(II) sulfate pentahydrate,
   ammonium chloride
   f. 639 g
   g. 7.54 cm^3
   h. color, density, melting point, or boiling
   point

67. a. tri-   **b.** mono-   **c.** di-
   d. hexa-   **e.** penta-   **f.** tetra-

69. a. BCl_3 **b.** dinitrogen pentoxide
   c. N_2H_4 **d.** carbon tetrachloride

71. a. magnesium permanganate
   b. beryllium nitrate
   c. potassium carbonate
   d. dinitrogen tetrahydride
   e. lithium hydroxide
   f. barium fluoride
   g. phosphorus triiodide
   h. zinc oxide
   i. phosphorous acid

73. A molecular formula shows the number of each kind of atom in a molecule of the compound. The formula unit shows the lowest whole-number ratio of ions in a compound.

75. a. N_2O, dinitrogen monoxide
  b. NO_2, nitrogen dioxide
  c. NO, nitrogen monoxide
  d. N_2O_4, dinitrogen tetroxide

77. No; to be an acid, the compound must produce H^+ ions in water.

79. a. $Fe(OH)_2$ **b.** lead(II) hydroxide
  c. $Cu(OH)_2$ **d.** cobalt(II) hydroxide

81. In any sample of the same chemical compound, the masses of the elements are always in the same proportions.

83. No; the simplest ratio of nitrogen to oxygen in the compound is 21:13, which is not a 7:4 ratio.

85. Common names vary in different languages and are difficult to remember and convert to formulas.

Chapter 10

1. 5.0 kg

2. 672 seeds

3. 4.65 mol Si

4. 0.360 mol

5. 2.75×10^{24} atoms

6. 7.72 mol NO_2

7. 137.5 g/mol

8. 84.0 g $NaHCO_3$

16. 1.27 g $C_{20}H_{42}$

17. 225 g $Fe(OH)_2$

18. 3.43×10^{-2} mol B

19. 0.987 mol N_2O_3

20. a. 7.17×10^{-2} L CO_2 **b.** 82.9 L N_2

21. a. 28.0 L He   **b.** 7.50 L C_2H_6

22. 80.2 g/mol

23. 3.74 g/L

32. 72.2% Mg, 27.8% N

33. 93.0% Hg, 7.0% O

34. a. 80.0% C, 20.0% H
  b. 19.2% Na, 0.83% H, 26.7% S, 53.3% O

35. a. 82.4% N   **b.** 35.0% N

36. a. OH   **b.** $HgSO_4$

37. C_3H_8N

38. $C_2H_6O_2$

39. a. same empirical formula
  b. different

47. Count, mass, or volume; examples will vary.

49. a. 3   **b.** 2   **c.** 9   **d.** 10

51. 1.00 mol C_2H_6

53. a. 98.0 g   **b.** 76.0 g   **c.** 100.1 g
  d. 132.1 g   **e.** 89.0 g   **f.** 159.8 g

55. Answers should include determining the moles of each atom from the formula, finding the atomic mass of each element, multiplying the number of moles of each atom times its atomic mass, and summing these products.

57. Answers might include finding the mass or volume of Avogadro's number of an item of a known mass or volume.

59. 3.01×10^{13} km

61. One mol of carbon and 1 mol of sulfur contain the same number of atoms, but each sulfur atom has a mass greater than the mass of a carbon atom. The most common isotope of sulfur contains 16 each of protons, neutrons, and electrons, and carbon contains 6 of each particle.

63. 3.54×10^{23} O_2 molecules

65. 6.025×10^{23} formula units/mol

67. a. 0.258 mol SiO_2
  b. 4.80×10^{-4} mol AgCl
  c. 1.12 mol Cl_2
  d. 0.106 mol KOH
  e. 5.93 mol $Ca(C_2H_3O_2)_2$
  f. 2.00×10^{-2} mol Ca

69. a. 170 L Ar   **b.** 9.9 L C_2H_6

71. a. 234 L SO_3
  b. 2.99×10^{-22} g $C_9H_8O_4$
  c. 3.13×10^{25} atoms

73. c.

75. 0.982 g He

77. a. 5.9% H, 94.2% S
  b. 22.6% N, 6.5% H, 19.4% C, 52.6% O
  c. 41.7% Mg, 54.9% O, 3.4% H
  d. 42.1% Na, 18.9% P, 39.0% O

79. d.

81. a. molecular **b.** molecular **c.** empirical

83. a. H_2O_2 **b.** $C_6H_6O_4$

85. a. CO   **b.** $C_2O_2NH_5$ **c.** Cl_2OC

87. a. $CuBr_2$ **b.** CH_3

89. C_2H_6O

91. a. $C_9H_{11}O_2N$ **b.** $C_9H_{11}O_2N$

Chapter 11

1. When solid sodium is dropped into water, hydrogen gas and aqueous sodium hydroxide are produced.

2. $S(s) + O_2(g) \longrightarrow SO_2(g)$

3. a. $2AgNO_3 + H_2S \longrightarrow Ag_2S + 2HNO_3$

  b. $3Zn(OH)_2 + 2H_3PO_4 \longrightarrow$
    $Zn_3(PO_4)_2 + 6H_2O$

4. a. $H_2 + S \longrightarrow H_2S$

  b. $2FeCl_3 + 3Ca(OH)_2 \longrightarrow$
    $2Fe(OH)_3 + 3CaCl_2$

5. a. $FeCl_3 + 3NaOH \longrightarrow Fe(OH)_3 + 3NaCl$

  b. $CS_2 + 3Cl_2 \longrightarrow CCl_4 + S_2Cl_2$

6. $Ca(OH)_2 + H_2SO_4 \longrightarrow CaSO_4 + 2H_2O$

13. $2Be + O_2 \longrightarrow 2BeO$

14. $3Mg + N_2 \longrightarrow Mg_3N_2$

15. $2HI \longrightarrow H_2 + I_2$

16. HBr

17. a. $Fe(s) + Pb(NO_3)_2(aq) \longrightarrow$
    $Fe(NO_3)_2(aq) + Pb(s)$

  b. $Cl_2(g) + 2NaI(aq) \longrightarrow 2NaCl(aq) + I_2(aq)$

  c. $Ca(s) + 2H_2O(l) \longrightarrow$
    $Ca(OH)_2(aq) + H_2(g)$

18. a. $3NaOH(aq) + Fe(NO_3)_3(aq) \longrightarrow$
    $Fe(OH)_3(s) + 3NaNO_3(aq)$

  b. $3Ba(NO_3)_2(aq) + 2H_3PO_4(aq) \longrightarrow$
    $Ba_3(PO_4)_2(s) + 6HNO_3(aq)$

19. a. $3KOH(aq) + H_3PO_4(aq) \longrightarrow$
    $K_3PO_4(aq) + 3H_2O(l)$

  b. $3H_2SO_4(aq) + 2Al(OH)_3(aq) \longrightarrow$
    $Al_2(SO_4)_3(aq) + 6H_2O(l)$

20. a. $2HCOOH + O_2 \longrightarrow 2CO_2 + 2H_2O$

  b. $C_7H_{16} + 11O_2 \longrightarrow 7CO_2 + 8H_2O$

21. $C_6H_{12}O_6 + 6O_2 \longrightarrow 6CO_2 + 6H_2O$

28. $H^+(aq) + OH^-(aq) \longrightarrow H_2O(l)$

29. complete ionic equation: $3Ca^{2+}(aq) +$
    $6OH^-(aq) + 6H^+(aq) + 2PO_4^{3-}(aq) \longrightarrow$
    $3Ca^{2+}(aq) + 2PO_4^{3-}(aq) + 6H_2O(l);$
  net ionic equation: $H^+(aq) + OH^-(aq) \longrightarrow$
    $H_2O(l)$

37. Dalton said that the atoms of reactants are rearranged to form new substances as products.

39. a. Gaseous ammonia and oxygen react in the presence of a platinum catalyst to produce nitrogen monoxide gas and water vapor.

  b. Aqueous solutions of sulfuric acid and barium chloride are mixed to produce a precipitate of barium sulfate and aqueous hydrochloric acid.

  c. The gas dinitrogen trioxide reacts with water to produce an aqueous solution of nitrous acid.

41. a. $C + 2F + 2G \longrightarrow CF_2G_2$

  b. $F + 3W + S + 2P \longrightarrow FW_3SP_2$

43. a. $2PbO_2 \longrightarrow 2PbO + O_2$

  b. $2Fe(OH)_3 \longrightarrow Fe_2O_3 + 3H_2O$

  c. $(NH_4)_2CO_3 \longrightarrow 2NH_3 + H_2O + CO_2$

  d. $2NaCl + H_2SO_4 \longrightarrow Na_2SO_4 + 2HCl$

45. a. $Cl_2(g) + 2KI(aq) \longrightarrow I_2(aq) + 2KCl(aq)$

  b. $2Fe(s) + 6HCl(aq) \longrightarrow 2FeCl_3(aq) + 3H_2(g)$

  c. $P_4O_{10}(s) + 6H_2O(l) \longrightarrow 4H_3PO_4(aq)$

47. a. $2K(s) + 2H_2O(l) \longrightarrow 2KOH(aq) + H_2(g)$

  b. $C_2H_5OH(l) + 3O_2(g) \longrightarrow$
    $2CO_2(g) + 3H_2O(g)$

  c. $2Bi(NO_3)_3(aq) + 3H_2S(g) \longrightarrow$
    $Bi_2S_3(s) + 6HNO_3(aq)$

  d. $2Al(s) + 3Br_2(l) \longrightarrow 2AlBr_3(s)$

  e. $2HNO_3(aq) + Ba(OH)_2(aq) \longrightarrow$
    $Ba(NO_3)_2(aq) + 2H_2O(l)$

49. a. $2Mg + O_2 \longrightarrow 2MgO$

  b. $4P + 5O_2 \longrightarrow 2P_2O_5$

  c. $Ca + S \longrightarrow CaS$

51. a. $2Ag_2O(s) \xrightarrow{\Delta} 2Ag(s) + O_2(g)$

  b. $NH_4NO_3(s) \xrightarrow{\Delta} N_2O(g) + 2H_2O(g)$

53. a. $H_2C_2O_4(aq) + 2KOH(aq) \longrightarrow$
    $K_2C_2O_4(aq) + 2H_2O(l)$

  b. $CdBr_2(aq) + Na_2S(aq) \longrightarrow$
    $CdS(s) + 2NaBr(aq)$

55. a. $C_4H_8 + 6O_2 \longrightarrow 4CO_2 + 4H_2O$

  b. $C_3H_6O + 4O_2 \longrightarrow 3CO_2 + 3H_2O$

57. a. $Na_2O(s) + H_2O(l) \longrightarrow 2NaOH(aq)$

  b. $H_2(g) + Br_2(g) \longrightarrow 2HBr(g)$

59. a. tube A

  b. $2Na(s) + 2H_2O(l) \longrightarrow 2NaOH(aq) + H_2(g);$
  single-replacement

61. a. $2Al_2O_3 \xrightarrow{energy} 4Al + 3O_2$

  b. $Sn(OH)_4 \xrightarrow{\Delta} SnO_2 + 2H_2O$

  c. $Ag_2CO_3 \xrightarrow{\Delta} Ag_2O + CO_2$

63. Smoking is not permitted near an oxygen source because a fire will burn faster in an area of high oxygen concentration. However, if a match were struck in a room full of oxygen and isolated from combustible material, the match would only burn more vigorously.

65. a. $3NaI + H_3PO_4 \longrightarrow 3HI + Na_3PO_4$; double-replacement

b. $K_2O + H_2O \longrightarrow 2KOH$; combination (synthesis)

c. $2H_2SO_4 \xrightarrow{\Delta} 2H_2O + O_2 + 2SO_2$; decomposition

d. $2Al + 3H_2SO_4 \longrightarrow 3H_2 + Al_2(SO_4)_3$; single-replacement

e. $C_5H_{12} + 8O_2 \longrightarrow 5CO_2 + 6H_2O$; combustion

67. a. single-replacement

b. $Cl_2(g) + 2I^-(aq) \longrightarrow I_2(aq) + 2Cl^-(aq)$

69. a. $2HCl(aq) + Ca(OH)_2(aq) \longrightarrow$
$$CaCl_2(aq) + 2H_2O(l)$$

b. $2HCl(aq) + Ba(OH)_2(aq) \longrightarrow$
$$BaCl_2(aq) + 2H_2O(l)$$

71. a. $ZnS(aq) + H_2SO_4(aq) \longrightarrow$
$$H_2S(g) + ZnSO_4(aq)$$

b. $NaOH(aq) + HNO_3(aq) \longrightarrow$
$$H_2O(l) + NaNO_3(aq)$$

c. $2KF(aq) + Ca(NO_3)_2(aq) \longrightarrow$
$$CaF_2(s) + 2KNO_3(aq)$$

Chapter 12

1. 288 seats, 864 wheels, 576 pedals

2. Answers will vary but should include the correct number of parts to make the product.

3. 2 molecules H_2 + 1 molecule $O_2 \longrightarrow$
$$2 \text{ molecules } H_2O;$$
2 mol H_2 + 1 mol $O_2 \longrightarrow$ 2 mol H_2O;
44.8 L H_2 + 22.4 L $O_2 \longrightarrow$ 44.8 L H_2O;
4. 2 mol C_2H_2 + 5 mol $O_2 \longrightarrow$
$$4 \text{ mol } CO_2 + 2 \text{ mol } H_2O;$$
44.8 L C_2H_2 + 112 L $O_2 \longrightarrow$
$$89.6 \text{ L } CO_2 + 44.8 \text{ L } H_2O;$$
212 g reactants $\longrightarrow$ 212 g products

4. 2 mol C_2H_2 + 5 mol $O_2 \longrightarrow$
$$4 \text{ mol } CO_2 + 2 \text{ mol } H_2O;$$
44.8 L C_2H_2 + 112 L $O_2 \longrightarrow$
$$89.6 \text{ L } CO_2 + 44.8 \text{ L } H_2O;$$
212 g reactants $\longrightarrow$ 212 g products

11. a. $\dfrac{4 \text{ mol Al}}{3 \text{ mol O}_2}, \dfrac{3 \text{ mol O}_2}{4 \text{ mol Al}}, \dfrac{4 \text{ mol Al}}{2 \text{ mol Al}_2O_3},$
$\dfrac{2 \text{ mol Al}_2O_3}{4 \text{ mol Al}}, \dfrac{2 \text{ mol Al}_2O_3}{3 \text{ mol O}_2}, \dfrac{3 \text{ mol O}_2}{2 \text{ mol Al}_2O_3}$

b. 7.4 mol

12. a. 11.1 mol   **b.** 0.52 mol

13. 2.03 g C_2H_2

14. 1.36 mol CaC_2

15. 4.82×10^{22} molecules O_2

16. 11.5 g NO_2

17. 1.93 L O_2

18. 0.28 L PH_3

19. 18.6 mL SO_2

20. 1.9 dL CO_2

25. O_2 is the limiting reagent.

26. HCl is the limiting reagent.

27. a. 5.40 mol O_2 required, C_2H_4 is limiting;
b. 5.40 mol H_2O

28. 43.2 g H_2O

29. 59.3 g Fe

30. 17.0 g Ag

31. 83.5%

32. 57.7%

35. a. Two moles of $KClO_3$ decompose to form two moles of KCl and three moles of O_2.

b. Four moles of NH_3 react with six moles of NO to form five moles of N_2 and six moles of H_2O.

c. Four moles of K react with one mole of O_2 to form two moles of K_2O.

37. Yes; a net ionic equation is balanced and thus obeys the law of conservation of mass.

39. Acceptable answers should include the idea of writing a ratio using the coefficients of two substances from a balanced equation as the number of moles of each substance reacting or being formed.

41. the relative number of moles or particles of reactants and products

43. a. 1.21×10^{-2} mol of calcium phosphate
b. 2.42×10^{-2} mol of phosphoric acid
c. 2.37 g phosphoric acid

45. a. 7.0×10^2 L N_2
b. no reagent in excess

47. a. Initially, the amount of NaCl formed increases as the amount of Na used increases. Beyond a mass of about 2.5 g Na, the chlorine is used up, so no more NaCl forms.
b. 0.109 mol Na
c. 0.0545 mol Cl_2
d. 3.85 g Cl_2

49.
  a. 174 mol alcohol
  b. 87.0 mol glucose
  c. 13 days

51.
  a. 0.843 mol $CaCO_3$
  b. 0.843 mol $CaCl_2$
  c. 93.6 g $CaCl_2$
  d. Answers might include that not all the $CaCO_3$ reacts or that the limestone contained other materials.

53.
  a. 0.803 mol SiC   **b.** 0.803 mol SiO_2
  c. 48.3 g SiO_2

55.
  a. Al   **b.** 3.0 mol $AlCl_3$
  c. 0.8 mol Cl_2

57. 10.7 kg $CaSO_4$

59. The percent yield is 115%; such a yield could be attributed to experimenter error or to outside materials contaminating the product.

Chapter 13

1. 51.3 kPa, 0.507 atm

2. 33.7 kPa is greater than 0.25 atm

25. An elastic collision transfers energy from one particle to another. There is no change in the total kinetic energy.

27. pascal (Pa), the SI unit; millimeters of mercury (mm Hg); atmosphere (atm)

29. **a.** 25 kPa,   **b.** 0.25 atm

31. If the temperature does not change, the average kinetic energy is not affected.

33. At absolute zero, the motion of particles would cease.

35. Atmospheric pressure is caused by the mass of the air pressing on the molecules below it. The mass of air above a mountain is less than the mass above sea level.

37. No. Collisions between objects other than at the atomic level involve the transformation of kinetic energy into heat energy.

39. In both cases, particles with sufficient kinetic energy move from the liquid to the vapor phase. In a closed container, a dynamic equilibrium is set up between the contained liquid and its vapor.

41. More molecules have enough energy to escape attractions within the liquid.

43. It increases the kinetic energy, which increases the vapor pressure.

45. **a.** about 50 mm Hg
  b. about 94°C
  c. 760 mm Hg is standard pressure.

47. Vapor pressure is lower in flask (a) because the level of mercury in the left arm of (a) is higher, which indicates less pressure on the mercury.

49. by measuring the difference in heights between the two arms

51. Evaporation is the conversion of a liquid to a gas or vapor when the liquid is below the boiling point. The vapor pressure is the force per unit area exerted by the vaporized particles on the walls of a sealed container. The boiling point is the temperature at which the vapor pressure of the liquid becomes equal to the external pressure.

53. Net amounts of vapor molecules and liquid molecules remain constant, but there is an ongoing exchange of particles.

55. Possible answers include that because the beaker is an open container the water should boil at 100°C, if you are at or close to sea level; your partner probably misread the thermometer and should recheck the value.

57. Some compounds have stronger intermolecular attractions than others.

59. The kinetic energy of the escaping molecules is the same, and so the vapor pressure is the same.

61. Answers might include condensation of the water vapor on a cold surface.

63. It is more than atmospheric pressure because the reading includes air pressure plus the vapor pressure of the mercury.

65. The molecules or ions or atoms have sufficient kinetic energy to overcome the attractive forces holding them in place.

67. **a.** liquid
  b. vapor (gas)
  c. liquid
  d. vapor (gas)
  e. solid
  f. solid

69. Particles have the same kinetic energy when the temperature is the same.

71. **a.** eight   **b.** one-eighth
  c. eight   **d.** nine
  e. 14

73. Molecules use the added heat to escape the liquid. The average kinetic energy remains the same.

75. a. Graphs should show a steeply rising smooth curve when temperature is plotted on the x-axis and vapor pressure on the y-axis.
   b. 80°C
   c. 100°C

Chapter 14

7. 6.48 L

8. 68.3 kPa

9. 3.39 L

10. 8.36 L

11. 2.58 kPa

12. 341 K (68°C)

13. 0.342 L

14. 54.8 kPa

23. 2.51×10^2 mol He(g)

24. 2.5 g air

31. 93.4 × kPa

32. 3.3 kPa

39. The gas particles become closer together.

41. The volume decreases. The molecules have less kinetic energy, so they cause less pressure on the inside of the balloon.

43. The pressure quadruples.

45. Gases are easily compressed because there is a lot of space between the particles.

47. 2 mol KNO_3 for each 1 mol O_2

49. 1.00×10^2 kPa

51. 18 L

53. $T_2 = P_2 V_2 T_1 / P_1 V_1$

55. $\dfrac{P_1 \times V_1}{T_1} = \dfrac{P_2 \times V_2}{T_2}$

When the volume is constant, $V_1 = V_2$, so the volume terms cancel, leaving an equation that relates temperature and pressure.

57. Temperatures measured on the Kelvin scale are always positive and directly proportional to the average kinetic energy of the gaseous particles.

59. The variables are directly proportional.

61. There could be different amounts of gas or they could be at different pressures.

63. Its particles have no volume, no forces between them, and elastic collisions. It follows the gas laws at all temperatures and pressures.

65. 33.0 L

67. 3.60×10^2 kPa

69. The particles in a real gas have a finite volume and are attracted to one another.

71. Because attractions between molecules in gases such as nitrogen and oxygen are insignificant, these gases have the molar volume of an ideal gas, 22.41 L at STP. Based on their molar volumes at STP, attractions between molecules increase in strength and effect from methane to carbon dioxide to ammonia.

73. At any temperature hydrogen gas diffuses faster than chlorine gas by an approximate factor of six.

75. 2.25:1

77. c. NH_3

79. 46% CH_4

81. Helium atoms have a smaller molar mass than the oxygen and nitrogen molecules in air and diffuse faster through the balloon.

83. 2.0×10^2 g

85. The partial pressure of oxygen would be greater than at sea level because the atmospheric pressure would be greater than at sea level.

Chapter 15

6. 36.1% H_2O

7. 49.3% H_2O

23. Surface molecules are attracted to molecules below but not above. Molecules inside the liquid are attracted in all directions.

25. A surfactant is a wetting agent that physically interferes with hydrogen bonding between water molecules and reduces surface tension.

27. Water has a low vapor pressure.

29. Bodies of water would freeze from the bottom up, killing many forms of aquatic life.

31. hexane, ethanol, water

33. a. 1.00 g/mL
   b. 4°C
   c. No; the curve breaks at 0°C as liquid water at 0°C changes to ice at 0°C.

35. The container would break because water expands as it freezes.

37. The blood and all of the body's cells contain large amounts of water. Most of the important chemical reactions of life take place in aqueous solutions inside cells.

39. A surfactant helps to wet the burning material, so less water rolls off. Less water used means that less water that carries pollutants enters the environment. In addition, the water will carry off less debris due to reduced surface tension.

41. Water enters cracks in pavement and expands when it freezes, creating larger cracks. Continuous freeze-thaw cycles cause pavement to break up.

43. Solutions are homogeneous mixtures in which a solute is dissolved in a solvent. Aqueous solutions specifically have water as the solvent.

45. Polar water molecules electrostatically attract ions and polar covalent molecules. Nonpolar compounds have no charges.

47. a. HCl and **c.** NH_3 are polar and will dissolve. **b.** NaI, and **d.** $MgSO_4$ are ionic and will dissolve. **e.** CH_4 (nonpolar) will not dissolve. **f.** $CaCO_3$ (strong ionic forces) will not dissolve.

49. ions

51. An aqueous solution of a strong electrolyte is almost totally ionized.

53. a. $Na_2SO_4 \cdot 10H_2O$
  b. $CaCl_2 \cdot 2H_2O$
  c. $Ba(OH)_2 \cdot 8H_2O$

55. $MgSO_4 \cdot 7H_2O \longrightarrow MgSO_4 \cdot H_2O + 6H_2O$

57. They absorb water vapor from air.

59. a. gasoline
  b. water
  c. gasoline
  d. water

61. a. No, both form a colorless solution in water.
  b. Answers include drying to examine the crystals, testing for electrical conductivity, doing a flame test.

63. No; nonpolar molecules and polar molecules do not dissolve in each other.

65. a. sodium carbonate monohydrate, 14.5% H_2O

b. magnesium sulfate heptahydrate, 51.2% H_2O

67. 24.5% H_2O; 75.5% $CaCl_2$

69. The nonpolar liquid would form a layer on top of the water if its density were less than that of water and on the bottom if its density were greater. A temporary emulsion would form if the mixture were shaken.

71. In a solution, particles stay suspended indefinitely. Particles in muddy water will settle out.

73. scattering of visible light by colloids and suspensions

75. The molecules of the dispersing medium collide with the small, dispersed colloidal particles.

77. the addition of ions having a charge opposite that of the colloidal particles

79. a. (1), (3), (6), (8)
  b. (1), (2), (5), (6), (7), (9)
  c. (2), (4), (5)

Chapter 16

1. 4.4×10^{-1} g/L

2. 2.6 atm

8. $1.0 \times 10^{-1} M$

9. $2.8 M$

10. 1.42×10^{-1} mol NH_4NO_3

11. 5.0×10^{-1} mol $CaCl_2$; 5.6×10^1 g $CaCl_2$

12. 47.5 mL

13. Use a pipet to transfer 5.0×10^1 mL of the $1.0 M$ solution to a 250-ml volumetric flask. Then add distilled water up to the mark.

14. 5.0% v/v

15. 1.2×10^1 mL

29. 1.26×10^1 g NaF

30. $2.85 \times 10^{-1} m$ NaCl

31. $X_{C_2H_5OH} = 0.190$; $X_{H_2O} = 0.810$

32. $X_{CCl_4} = 0.437$; $X_{CHCl_3} = 0.563$

33. 2.06°C

34. 44.1°C

35. 101.37°C

36. 114 g NaCl

43. Collisions of the solvent molecules with the solute particles provide enough force to overcome gravity.

45. Particles of solute crystallize.

47. 5.55×10^2 g $AgNO_3$

49. a. 1.6×10^{-2} g/L
b. 4.7×10^{-2} g/L

51.

53. unsaturated

55. a. 76°C: 15 mol/kg; 33°C: 5 mol/kg
b. 82°C
c. 30°C

57. a. $1.3M$ KCl
b. $3.3 \times 10^{-1}M$ $MgCl_2$

59. a. 5.0×10^{-1} mol NaCl, 29 g NaCl
b. 1.0 mol KNO_3, 1.0×10^2 g KNO_3
c. 2.5×10^{-2} mol $CaCl_2$, 2.8 g $CaCl_2$

61. a. 16% (v/v) ethanol
b. 63.6% (v/v) isopropyl alcohol

63. $1.2 \times 10^{-1}M$ HCl

65. a. $Na_2SO_4(aq) + BaCl_2(aq) \longrightarrow$
$$BaSO_4(s) + 2NaCl(aq)$$

b. 2.26×10^{-2} mol $BaSO_4$
c. 2.26×10^{-2} mol Na_2SO_4
d. $9.0 \times 10^{-2}M$ Na_2SO_4

67. a. sea water **b.** $1.5M$ KNO_3 **c.** $0.100M$ $MgCl_2$

69. More energy must be supplied to reach the boiling point; therefore the boiling point is increased relative to pure solvent.

71. a. 0.30 mol **b.** 0.40 mol
c. 0.50 mol **d.** 0.20 mol

73. $1M$ solution: 1 mol of solute in 1 L of solution; $1m$ solution: 1 mol of solute in 1000 g of solvent

75. a. 100.26°C **b.** 101.54°C

77. a. -1.1°C **b.** -0.74°C **c.** -1.5°C

79. $\Delta T_f = -9.60$°C; $\Delta T_b = +4.74$°C

81. The mole fraction of $NaHCO_3$ is 0.020. The solution is $1.1m$.

83. a. about 1.14 **b.** about -7.2°C
c. about -9.5°C

85. mole fraction $C_2H_5OH = 0.20$; mole fraction $H_2O = 0.80$

87. 100.680°C

89. mole fraction water $= 0.972$; mole fraction sugar $= 0.028$

91. Dissolve a known mass of the unknown molecular compound (g solute) in a known mass of a suitable solvent (g solvent). Determine the freezing points of the pure solvent and the solution with a thermometer in an insulated cup. Calculate the freezing point depression. Use $\Delta T_f = K_f \times m$ to find the molality (1 mol solute/1 kg solvent) of the solution. Use the molality to find the molar mass of the solute in g/mol. The molar mass obtained is valid only for an undissociating molecular solute.

$$\frac{\text{g solute}}{\text{g solvent}} \times \frac{100 \text{ g solvent}}{1 \text{ kg solvent}} \times \frac{1 \text{ kg solvent}}{1 \text{ mol solute}}$$

$$= \frac{\text{g solute}}{1 \text{ mol solute}}$$

Chapter 17

1. Heat flows from the system (paraffin) to the surroundings (air). The process is exothermic.

2. Since the beaker becomes cold, heat is absorbed by the system (chemicals within the beaker) from the surroundings (beaker and surrounding air). The process is endothermic.

3. $2.0 \text{ J}/(\text{g} \cdot °\text{C})$

4. 1.8 kJ

12. 1.46 kJ

13. 146 J

14. 6.63 kJ

15. 89.4 kJ

21. 3.34 kJ

22. 1.20 g ice

23. $1.44 \times 10^2 \text{ kJ}$

24. $1.9 \times 10^{-1} \text{ kJ}$

25. $-3.01 \times 10^2 \text{ kJ}$

26. $3.42 \text{ mol NH}_4\text{NO}_3(s)$

32. a. $-3.091 \times 10^1 \text{ kJ}$ **b.** $1.784 \times 10^2 \text{ kJ}$
     c. $-1.130 \times 10^2 \text{ kJ}$

33. CO is a compound and not an element in its standard state.

39. Potential energy is energy stored in a substance because of its chemical composition.

41. $1 \text{ Cal} = 1000 \text{ cal}$

43. Answers will vary, but should mention that thermochemistry measures heat flow across the boundary between the system and the surroundings.

45. a. exothermic
     b. The immediate surroundings are the glass beaker and the air. If one or more of the substances is in water, the water is also considered part of the surroundings.

47. Substance B; for equal masses, the substance with the greater heat capacity undergoes the smaller temperature change.

49. enthalpy

51. The foam cup will absorb heat. Some heat will be lost to the air. If the reactants are not completely mixed, temperature measurements will not be accurate.

53. one atmosphere pressure (101.3 kPa); all reactants and products in their normal physical state at 25°C

55. $1.42 \times 10^3 \text{ g}$

57. Heat is being used to melt (break down the structure of) the ice.

59. increase

61. $1.02 \times 10^5 \text{ J}$

63. a. $1.34 \times 10^4 \text{ J}$; $1.34 \times 10^1 \text{ kJ}$
     b. $1.28 \times 10^2 \text{ g H}_2\text{O}$

65. $6.71 \times 10^1 \text{ kJ}$

67. When the vapor condenses to a liquid, the heat of vaporization is released. Therefore, the energy content of the vapor must have been higher than that of the liquid. The statement is incorrect.

69. ΔH_{vap} for water at 70°C is approximately 42 kJ/mol. 1 L of water (1000 mL) has a mass of 1000 g and contains 55.6 mol water. Therefore, the amount of heat required is 42 kJ/mol $\times$ 55.6 mol = $2.34 \times 10^3 \text{ kJ}$

71. a. $-1.676 \times 10^3 \text{ kJ}$ **b.** exothermic

73. zero

75. a. $-7.50 \times 10^2 \text{ kJ}$ **b.** exothermic

77. The standard heat of formation ($\Delta H°_f$) of a compound is the change in enthalpy that accompanies the formation of one mole of a compound from its elements with all substances in their standard states at 25°C.

79. $-6.66 \times 10^3 \text{ kJ}$

81. a. -184.8 kJ
     b. -138.6 kJ
     c. -46.19 kJ

83. -2816 kJ

Chapter 18

6. a. reactants favored   **b.** reactants favored
     c. products favored   **d.** products favored

7. $K_{\text{eq}} = 12$

8. $K_{\text{eq}} = 8.3 \times 10^{-2}$; one is the inverse of the other.

9. $K_{\text{eq}} = 1.6 \times 10^{-3}$

10. $K_{\text{eq}} = 0.79$

17. $2 \times 10^{-14} M$

18. $6.7 \times 10^{-5} M$

19. $2 \times 10^{-17} M$

20. $3.2 \times 10^{-6} M$

36. Rate = $k[\text{A}]$; rate is moles per liter per second. [A] is moles per liter. $k = \text{rate}/[\text{A}]$. $k = 1/\text{s} = \text{s}^{-1}$

37. 0.25 mol/L s; 0.125 mol/L s

43. Chemical reactions require collisions with sufficient energy to break and form bonds.

45. A catalyst increases the rate of reaction by providing an alternative reaction mechanism with a lower activation energy.

47. A catalyst provides a pathway by which particles can collide at lower energy than is usually required for reaction to occur.

49. They are equal.

51. a. $K_{eq} = \dfrac{[H_2S]^2 \times [CH_4]}{[H_2]^4 \times [CS_2]}$

    b. $K_{eq} = \dfrac{[PCl_3] \times [Cl_2]}{[PCl_5]}$

53. 25 kJ

55. increase in products

57. $K_{eq} = 6.59 \times 10^{-1}$

59. a. favors products
    b. favors reactants
    c. favors reactants
    d. no effect

61. a. $[Ni^{2+}][S^{2-}]$
    b. $[Ba^{2+}][CO_3^{2-}]$

63. c., b., d., a.

65. The product of the concentrations of the ions must be greater than the ion-product constant (K_{sp}).

67. $2.0 \times 10^{-8}M$

69. a measure of the disorder of a system

71. a. ice
    b. sodium chloride crystals

73. No; some endothermic processes are spontaneous because of their favorable change in entropy.

75. the enthalpy change and the entropy change

77. a. yes   **b.** yes
    c. no   **d.** yes

79. Possible answers include drying hair, mowing the lawn, boiling water, burning gas in a car, and sharpening a pencil.

81. 100 minutes

83. a. 1.22×10^{-4} mol/(L·s)
    b. 1.94×10^{-4} mol/(L·s)

85. a.

    b. The rate when $t = 100$ s is 8×10^{-4} mol/L·s. The rate when $t = 250$ s is 4×10^{-4} mol/L·s.

87. a. 3 g   **b.** 1.3 g   **c.** It decreases.

Chapter 19

1. a Lewis base; it has a non-bonding pair of electrons that it can donate.

2. a. H^+ is the Lewis acid; H_2O is the Lewis base.
    b. $AlCl_3$ is the Lewis acid; Cl^- is the Lewis base.

8. a. diprotic, two ionizable hydrogens
    b. triprotic; three ionizable hydrogens
    c. monoprotic; one ionizable hydrogen
    d. diprotic; two ionizable hydrogens

9. a. basic   **b.** basic   **c.** acidic   **d.** neutral

10. $1.0 \times 10^{-11}M$; basic

11. a. 4.0   **b.** 2.82

12. a. 12.00   **b.** 1.35

13. a. $1.0 \times 10^{-5}M$ **b.** $1.5 \times 10^{-13}M$

14. a. $1.0 \times 10^{-4}M$ **b.** $2.8 \times 10^{-12}M$

15. a. 9.63   **b.** 3.65

16. a. 4.30   **b.** 9.08

22. 1.8×10^{-4}

23. 4.89×10^{-6}

30. 4.68 mol KOH

31. 0.20 mol NaOH

32. 56 mL HCl

33. $0.128M$

38. a. $HPO_4^{2-} + H^+ \longrightarrow H_2PO_4^-$
    b. $H_2PO_4^- + OH^- \longrightarrow HPO_4^{2-} + H_2O$

39. $CH_3COO^- + H^+ \longrightarrow CH_3COOH$

45. a. base   **b.** acid   **c.** base
    d. acid   **e.** acid   **f.** acid

47. a. $2Li + 2H_2O \longrightarrow 2LiOH + H_2$
    b. $Ba + 2H_2O \longrightarrow Ba(OH)_2 + H_2$

49. a. HNO_3 with NO_3^-, H_2O with H_3O^+
    b. CH_3COOH with CH_3COO^-, H_2O with H_3O^+

c. H_2O with OH^-, NH_3 with NH_4^+
d. H_2O with OH^-, CH_3COO^- with CH_3COOH

51. $HPO_4^{2-} \longrightarrow H^+ + PO_4^{3-}$ (acting as an acid);
$HPO_4^{2-} + H^+ \longrightarrow H_2PO_4^-$ (acting as a base)

53. a. KOH is the base; HBr is the acid.
b. HCl is the acid; H_2O is the base.

55. a. Answers will vary; students are likely to consider the Arrhenius theory the easiest to understand, and the Lewis theory the best because it is the most general. All three theories are accepted behavior of a certain group of compounds. The Brønsted-Lowry theory includes a greater number of compounds than the Arrhenius theory because it is more general, and the Lewis theory includes the greatest number of compounds because it is the most general.
b. Each theory has advantages in certain circumstances.

57. $1.0 \times 10^{-7} M$ for both H^+ and OH^-

59. The hydrogen ion concentration of pure water at 25°C is $1.0 \times 10^{-7} M$. The negative logarithm, or pH, of this concentration is 7.0.

61. a. $1.0 \times 10^{-10} M$
b. $1.0 \times 10^{-6} M$
c. $1.0 \times 10^{-2} M$

63. a., c., b.

65. The y–axis might correspond to concentration of H^+ because HCl is a strong acid.

67. pH = 10.66

69. a. strong base
b. strong acid
c. weak base
d. strong acid

71. a. $K_a = \dfrac{[H^+][F^-]}{[HF]}$
b. $K_a = \dfrac{[H^+][HCO_3^-]}{[H_2CO_3]}$

73. $4.6 \times 10^{-4} M$

75. a. In order, pH = 7.4721, 7.2675, 7.0835, 6.9165, 6.7675, 6.6310

b. 7.37   **c.** 35°C

77. a. $HNO_3 + KOH \longrightarrow KNO_3 + H_2O$
b. $2HCl + Ca(OH)_2 \longrightarrow CaCl_2 + 2H_2O$
c. $H_2SO_4 + 2NaOH \longrightarrow Na_2SO_4 + 2H_2O$

79. a. $1.40 M$ **b.** $2.61 M$

81. a. 8.73
b. phenolphthalein or thymol blue

83. The reaction is complete where the graph starts to plateau because no more water forms from that point.

85. 1.8×10^{-3} mol HCl

87. $0.72 M$ NaOH

89. 4.00×10^{-3} mol Na_2CO_3

91. $5.00 \times 10^{-2} M H_2SO_4$

93. $HCO^{3-}(aq) + H_2O\,(l) \longrightarrow$
$\qquad\qquad\qquad H_2CO_3(aq) + OH^-(aq)$;
hydroxide ions are produced.

95. $H_2PO_4^- + OH^- \longrightarrow H_2O + HPO_4^{2-}$
$HPO_4^{2-} + H^+ \longrightarrow H_2PO_4^-$
Added OH^- is neutralized by $H_2PO_4^-$, and added acid is neutralized by HPO_4^{2-}.

97. $NaC_2H_3O_2 + H_2O \longrightarrow Na^+ + HC_2H_3O_2 + OH^-$

Chapter 20

1. a. Na: oxidized (reducing agent); S: reduced (oxidizing agent)
b. Al: oxidized (reducing agent); O_2: reduced (oxidizing agent)

2. a. oxidation   **b.** reduction

9. a. S, +3; O, −2
b. Na, +1; O, −1
c. P, +5; O, −2
d. N, +5; O, −2

10. a. +5   **b.** 0   **c.** +7   **d.** +1

11. a. H_2 oxidized, O_2 reduced
b. N reduced, O oxidized

12. a. H_2 reducing agent, O_2 oxidizing agent
b. N oxidizing agent, O reducing agent

17. a. redox reaction; Mg is oxidized, Br_2 is reduced.
b. not a redox reaction

18. a. not a redox reaction
b. redox reaction; H_2 is oxidized, Cu is reduced.

19. a. 2, 2, 3
b. 2, 2, 2, 1, 2

20. a. 1, 8, 2, 2, 3, 4
b. 1, 2, 1, 2, 1

21. $4Zn + NO_3^- + 6H_2O + 7OH^- \longrightarrow$
$\qquad\qquad\qquad 4Zn(OH)_4^{2-} + NH_3$

25. oxidation

27. a. $2Ba(s) + O_2(g) \longrightarrow 2BaO(s)$; barium is oxidized.
b. $CuO(s) + H_2(g) \longrightarrow Cu(s) + H_2O(l)$; copper is reduced.
c. $C_2H_4(g) + 3O_2(g) \longrightarrow 2CO_2(g) + 2H_2O(l)$; carbon is oxidized.
d. $3CaO(s) + 2Al(s) \longrightarrow Al_2O_3(s) + 3Ca(s)$; calcium is reduced.

29. a. oxidizing agent **b.** reducing agent
c. oxidizing agent **d.** oxidizing agent

31. a. H_2 is the reducing agent; S is the oxidizing agent.
b. N_2 is the oxidizing agent; H_2 is the reducing agent.
c. S is the reducing agent; O_2 is the oxidizing agent.
d. H_2 is the reducing agent; O_2 is the oxidizing agent.

33. Lead atoms are oxidized by losing 2 electrons to form Pb^{2+} ions. Oxygen atoms are reduced by gaining 2 electrons to form O^{2-} ions.

35. When one reactant loses electrons another reactant must gain them.

37. Double replacement reactions never involve the transfer of electrons; instead they involve the transfer of positive ions in aqueous solution.

39. a. SO_4^{2-} **b.** H_2O_2 **c.** NO_3^-
d. $Cr_2O_7^{2-}$ **e.** H_2O

41. Rhenium is oxidized and selenium is reduced because the bonded electrons would shift toward the more electronegative element, selenium.

43. the charge an atom would have if the electrons in each bond were assigned to the atoms of the more electronegative element

45. c. is false

47. a. +4 **b.** +5 **c.** +5
d. +3 **e.** +5 **f.** +3

49. a. reactant, 0; product, +3
b. reactant, −2; product, −2
c. X
d. H

51. Nitride ion has the minimum oxidation number of −3, so it cannot gain additional electrons and be an oxidizing agent. It can lose electrons however, and be a reducing agent. Nitrogen in the nitrate ion has the maximum oxidation number of +5, so it can-

not lose additional electrons and be a reducing agent. It can gain electrons however, and be an oxidizing agent.

53. a. $2Al(s) + 3Cl_2(g) \longrightarrow 2AlCl_3(s)$
b. $2Al(s) + Fe_2O_3(s) \longrightarrow Al_2O_3(s) + 2Fe(s)$
c. $3Cl_2(g) + 6KOH(aq) \longrightarrow$
$KClO_3(aq) + 5KCl(aq) + 3H_2O(l)$
d. $2HNO_3(aq) + 3H_2S(aq) \longrightarrow$
$3S(s) + 2NO(g) + 4H_2O(l)$
e. $KIO_4(aq) + 7KI(aq) + 8HCl(aq) \longrightarrow$
$8KCl(aq) + 4I_2(s) + 4H_2O(l)$

55. a. $2Li(s) + 2H_2O(l) \longrightarrow 2LiOH(aq) + H_2(g)$
b. $K_2Cr_2O_7(aq) + 14HCl(aq) \longrightarrow$
$2KCl(aq) + 2CrCl_3(aq) + 7H_2O(l) + 3Cl_2(g)$
c. $2Al(s) + 6HCl(aq) \longrightarrow$
$2AlCl_3(aq) + 3H_2(g)$
d. $Cl_2(g) + H_2O(l) \longrightarrow HCl(aq) + HClO(aq)$
e. $I_2O_5(s) + 5CO(g) \longrightarrow I_2(s) + 5CO_2(g)$
f. $H_2O(l) + SO_3(g) \longrightarrow H_2SO_4(aq)$

57. a. $WO_3(s) + 3H_2(g) \longrightarrow W(s) + 3H_2O(g)$
b. H_2
c. W

59. $N_2O_4(l) + 2N_2H_4(l) \longrightarrow 3N_2(g) + 4H_2O(g)$
Based on oxidation number changes, nitrogen atoms from N_2O_4 gain electrons in forming N_2 and nitrogen atoms from N_2H_4 lose electrons in forming N_2.

61. 0.405 g Cu

63. a. $5CO + I_2O_5 \longrightarrow I_2 + 5CO_2$
b. C is oxidized; I is reduced.
c. 0.23 g CO

65. a. $3Hg^{2+} + 2Al \longrightarrow 3Hg + 2Al^{3+}$
b. $MnO_2 + 4H^+ + Fe \longrightarrow$
$Mn^{2+} + 2H_2O + Fe^{2+}$
c. $2Fe^{3+} + Cd \longrightarrow 2Fe^{2+} + Cd^{2+}$

Chapter 21

9. nonspontaneous; $E^0_{cell} = -0.02\,V$

10. yes; $E^0_{cell} = +0.16\,V$

11. $2Al(s) + 3Cu^{2+}(aq) \longrightarrow 2Al^{3+}(aq) + 3Cu(s)$

12. $Cu(s) + 2Ag^+(aq) \longrightarrow Cu^{2+}(aq) + 2Ag(s)$

13. $E^0_{cell} = +2.00\,V$

14. $E^0_{cell} = +0.46\,V$

23. an equation that represents the oxidation or the reduction in a redox reaction

25. nothing

27. cathode

29. anode: zinc, cathode: carbon (graphite)

31. $Pb(s)|PbSO_4(aq)||PbO_2(s)|PbSO_4(s)$

33. A fuel cell needs no recharging, does not produce toxic wastes if the fuel is hydrogen gas, and it is lighter.

35. Some of the iron dissolves, and the nail becomes coated with copper.
Oxidation: $Fe \longrightarrow Fe^{2+} + 2e^-$
Reduction: $Cu^{2+} + 2e^- \longrightarrow Cu$
$Fe(s) + CuSO_4(aq) \longrightarrow FeSO_4(aq) + Cu(s)$

37. It will be the reaction that has the larger cell potential, or more readily oxidized or reduced.

39. The chemists' definition focuses on the electrons that are produced by oxidation at the anode of a voltaic cell; the dictionary definition is probably based on an electrolytic cell, whose electrodes are defined by the battery terminals to which they are attached.

41. a. The iron electrode is the anode; the nickel electrode is the cathode.
b. The anode is negative; the cathode is positive.
c. Anode: $Fe(s) \longrightarrow Fe^{2+}(aq) + 2e^-$
Cathode: $Ni^{2+}(aq) + 2e^- \longrightarrow Ni(s)$
d. $E^0_{cell} = +0.19\,V$

43. a. Anode undergoes oxidation; cathode undergoes reduction.
b. The electrolytes remain fairly constant.
c. electrode reactions
d. decreases

45. the ability of a voltaic cell to produce a current

47. Connect the aluminum half–cell to a standard hydrogen half–cell and use a voltmeter. The indicated voltage is the standard reduction potential for the aluminum half–cell.

49. a. 1.61 V   **b.** 0.94 V

51. a. Li^+ **b.** Fe^{3+} **c.** Cu^{2+} **d.** I_2

53. It will not work as a battery.

55. a. $2AgCl + Ni \longrightarrow$
$2Ag + NiCl_2$; $E^0_{cell} = +0.47\,V$
b. $3Cl_2 + 2Al \longrightarrow 2AlCl_3$; $E^0_{cell} = +3.02\,V$

57. a., e., and **f.** are spontaneous; **b., c.,** and **d.** are nonspontaneous.

59. a. $Zn + Pb^{2+} \longrightarrow Zn^{2+} + Pb$
e. $Fe + Pb^{2+} \longrightarrow Fe^{2+} + Pb$
f. $2Na + Cl_2 \longrightarrow 2Na^+ + 2Cl^-$

61. The teaspoon is the cathode in an electrolytic cell with silver cyanide as the electrolyte. When the DC current flows, the silver ions deposit as silver on the teaspoon.

63. electrode A

65. Voltaic cells convert chemical energy into electrical energy. Electrolytic cells use electrical energy to cause a chemical reaction.

67. a. oxidation: $6Cl^-(l) \longrightarrow 3Cl_2(g) + 6e^-$
(anode) reduction:
$2Al(l) + 6e^- \longrightarrow 2Al(l)$ (cathode)
b. overall reaction:
$2AlCl_3(l) \longrightarrow 2Al(l) + 3Cl_2(g)$
c. anode, chlorine gas; cathode, liquid aluminum

69. a. $2Cl^-(aq) \longrightarrow Cl_2(g) + 2e^-$
b. $Na^+(aq) + e^- \longrightarrow Na(s)$

Chapter 22

1.

2. 10

3. a. 3-ethylhexane
b. 2-methylbutane

4. a. 2,3-dimethylpentane
b. 2-methylpentane

5.
$$\begin{array}{c} CH_3 \\ | \\ CH_3CHCHCH_2CH_2CH_3 \\ | \\ CH_3 \end{array}$$

6.

18. Both a and b have an asymmetric carbon, denoted as C*.

$$\begin{array}{cc} CH_3\overset{*}{C}HCHO & CH_3\overset{*}{C}HOH \\ | & | \\ Cl & CH_3 \end{array}$$

19. a. The asymmetric carbon is denoted as C*.

$$\begin{array}{c} CH_3 \\ | \\ CH_3CH_2-\overset{*}{C}-Br \\ | \\ F \end{array}$$

b. no asymmetric carbon

35. a. propane   **b.** octane   **c.** pentane

37. a. 2-methylbutane
b. 2,3-dimethylbutane
c. 3-methylhexane

39. a. Only one of two methyl substituents has been numbered; 2,2-dimethylpentane.
b. Propane was not the longest continuous chain; pentane.
c. Substituent was not given the lowest number; 2-methylbutane.
d. Butane was not the longest continuous chain; 3-methylpentane.

41. No; an addition reaction requires a double or triple bond.

43. a. propene
b. *trans*-2-pentene
c. 4-methyl-1-pentene
d. 3-ethyl-2-methyl-2-pentene

45. a. single bonds and triple bond; ethyne (acetylene)
b. single bonds; propane

47. $H_2C{=}C{=}CH_2$

49. Five structural isomers of molecular formula C_6H_{14} exist.

$$C-C-C-C-C-C$$
hexane

$$C-\overset{\overset{\displaystyle C}{|}}{\underset{\underset{\displaystyle C}{|}}{C}}-C-C$$
2, 2-dimethylbutane

$$C-\overset{\overset{\displaystyle C}{|}}{C}-C-C-C$$
2-methylpentane

$$C-\overset{\overset{\displaystyle C}{|}}{C}-\overset{\overset{\displaystyle C}{|}}{C}-C$$
2, 3-dimethylbutane

$$C-C-\overset{\overset{\displaystyle C}{|}}{C}-C-C$$
3-methylpentane

51. a.
trans-2-pentene   or   *cis*-2-pentene

b.
2-methyl-2-pentene

c.
3-ethyl-2-pentene

53. No; no carbon atom in hexane can be bonded to four different groups.

55. If rotation occurred around a carbon-carbon double bond, both of the following compounds would be the same, CH_3 CH 5 CH CH_2 CH_3.

trans-2-pentene   *cis*-2-pentene

57. a. $C_6 = 5$, $C_7 = 9$, $C_8 = 18$, $C_9 = 35$, $C_{10} = 75$
b. As the size of the alkane molecule gets larger, the number of ways that the carbon atoms can be bonded together (structural isomers) increases dramatically.

59. Two different structural formulas are possible because this compound exhibits resonance.

61. a. $H{:}\overset{H}{\underset{}{C}}{::}\overset{H}{\underset{}{C}}{:}H$ **b.** $H{:}\overset{H}{\underset{H}{C}}{:}\overset{H}{\underset{H}{C}}{:}\overset{H}{\underset{H}{C}}{:}H$

c. $H{:}C{:::}C{:}H$ **d.** $H{:}\overset{H}{\underset{}{C}}{:}\overset{H}{\underset{}{C}}{:}H$ $H{:}\overset{}{\underset{H}{C}}{:}\overset{}{\underset{H}{C}}{:}H$

63. a. 9.6 billion
b. 81% (m/m)

65. Cyclic hydrocarbons are more structurally rigid, so their van der Waals forces are stronger. Thus, it takes more energy (a higher temperature) to liberate these molecules from the liquid state.

67. An aromatic compound contains a benzene ring, which contains resonating bonds. Cycloalkanes contain only single bonds.

63. a. single bonds
b. double bond
c. benzene ring
d. ring, single bonds

71. $2C_8H_{18} + 25O_2 \longrightarrow 16CO_2 + 18H_2O$

73. Coal is mostly large aromatic rings.

75. The amount of heat per carbon is higher for methane (-890 kJ/mole for one mole of carbon burned) than for benzene (-3268 kJ/6 =

-545 kJ/ mole for one mole of carbon burned). Methane undergoes complete combustion if sufficient air is present:

$$CH_4(g) + 2O_2 \longrightarrow CO_2(g) + 2H_2O(g).$$

Because of a deficiency of hydrogens, benzene burns with an undesirable sooty flame in air:

$$C_6H_6(l) + 6O_2(g) \longrightarrow$$
$$4CO_2(g) + CO(g) + C(s) + 3H_2O(g).$$

Benzene is obtained from coal tar obtained by the destructive distillation of coal. The amount of energy required to produce benzene offsets any benefit obtained from its combustion. Benzene is a known carcinogen (cancer-causing agent).

Chapter 23

27. a. Cl

ClCH$_2$CCH$_2$CH$_3$
Cl

b. Br

Br   Br

c. Cl

Cl

29.

a. Cl

CH—CH$_2$—CH$_3$
Cl

1, 1-dichloropropane

Cl   Cl

CH$_2$—CH—CH$_3$

1, 2-dichloropropane

Cl   Cl

CH$_2$—CH$_2$—CH$_2$

1, 3-dichloropropane

Cl

CH$_3$—C—CH$_3$
Cl

2, 2-dichloropropane

b. Br

CH$_3$—CH$_2$—CH$_2$—CH$_2$

1-bromobutane

Br

CH$_3$—CH$_2$—CH—CH$_3$

2-bromobutane

CH$_3$ Br

CH$_3$—CH —CH$_2$

1-bromo-2-methylpropane

CH$_3$

CH$_3$—C—CH$_3$
Br

2-bromo-2-methylpropane

31. Both atoms in a carbon-carbon double bond have the same electronegativity, so the bond is nonpolar. Because oxygen is considerably more electronegative than carbon, a carbon-oxygen bond is very polar.

33. Substitution of an alkane by a halogen, for example, usually gives a mixture of products. Addition to a double bond or a triple bond can give a single addition product.

35. a. 2-propanol
b. 1,2-propanediol

37. a. H   Br

CH$_2$—CH$_2$

bromoethane

b. Cl   Cl

CH$_2$—CH$_2$

1, 2-dichloroethane

c. H   OH

CH$_2$—CH$_2$

ethanol

d. H   H

CH$_2$—CH$_2$

ethane

e. H   Cl

CH$_2$—CH$_2$

chloroethane

39. a. phenol
 b. ether
 c. alcohol
 d. phenol
 e. alcohol

41. The alcohol molecules form hydrogen bonds with one another, resulting in a higher boiling point. They also form hydrogen bonds with water molecules, causing 1-butanol to be more soluble than diethyl ether. (Although diethyl ether is polar, 1-butanol has greater polarity.)

43. $H_2C = CH_2(g) + Br_2(l) \longrightarrow CH_2BrCH_2Br(l)$
$CH_2BrCH_2Br(l) + 2NaOH(aq) \longrightarrow$
$\qquad\qquad CH_2OHCH_2OH(l) + 2NaBr(aq)$

45. a. CH_3OH
   methanol

 b.
$$\overset{\displaystyle OH}{\underset{\displaystyle |}{CH_3-CH-CH_3}}$$
   2-propanol

 c.
$$\overset{\displaystyle CH_3\ \ H}{\underset{\displaystyle |\ \ \ \ |}{\underset{\displaystyle \underset{|}{H}}{CH_3-CH-C-OH}}}$$
   2-methyl-1-propanol

 d.
   [cyclohexane ring with OH and H]

   cyclohexanol

47. a. $CH_3-\overset{\displaystyle O}{\overset{\displaystyle \|}{C}}-OCH_3 + H_2O$

 b. $CH_3CH_2CH_2-\overset{\displaystyle O}{\overset{\displaystyle \|}{C}}-O^-Na^+ + CH_3CH_2OH$

 c. $CH_3-\overset{\displaystyle O}{\overset{\displaystyle \|}{C}}-H$

49. a. carboxyl group, ethanoic acid (acetic acid)
 b. ketone (carbonyl group), propanone (acetone)
 c. ether, diethyl ether (ethyl ether)
 d. alcohol (hydroxyl group), ethanol (ethyl alcohol)

51. a. $CH_3CH_2COO^-Na^+$, CH_3CH_2OH

 b. $CH_3COO^-K^+$, [benzene ring]—OH

 c. CH_3CH_2COOH, CH_3CHCH_2OH

53. The chemical properties (and toxicity) of organic compounds are determined by the compound as a whole. As a substituent in a molecule, a phenyl group ring does not have the same properties as benzene.

55. The short-chain ethanoic acid has higher water solubility.

57. a. $-CH_2-CH-$
        $\quad\quad\quad |$
        $\quad\quad\quad CH_2$
        $\quad\quad\quad |$
        $\quad\quad\quad CH_3$
    b. $-CH-CH-$
        $\quad\quad |\quad\ |$
        $\quad\quad Cl\ \ Cl$

Chapter 24

35. Photosynthetic organisms use energy from the sun to synthesize glucose and oxygen from carbon dioxide and water.

37. Answers might include mitochondria (source of cellular energy), lyosomes (site of cellular digestion), endoplasmic reticulum (attachment site for ribosomes), and ribosomes (site for making proteins).

39. Evidence from fossilized bacteria indicates that prokaryotic cells are older.

41. Nutrients supply carbon compounds, ions, and energy needed for growth. When nutrients are limited, they are used for energy needed to sustain the cell, not for growth.

43. Glucose is found in blood, corn, and grapes. Fructose is found in honey and many fruits.

45. glucose and fructose

47. glucose

49. Monosaccharides are single simple sugars (glucose and fructose). Disaccharides are two linked monosaccharide units (sucrose). Polysaccharides have many linked monosaccharide units (starch, glycogen, cellulose).

51. sucrose and water

53. two

55. Both tripeptides contain the same peptides, but the sequences are different.

57. complex formed then an enzyme and substrate bind to each other

59. A substrate molecule or molecules binds to the active site of the enzyme.

61. All amino acids contain an amino group, a carboxylic group, and a hydrogen atom bonded to a central carbon atom. Amino acids differ in the side chain also bonded to the central carbon atom.

63. hydrogen bonds between adjacent parts of the chains and covalent bonds between side-chain groups

65. triester of glycerol and fatty acids

67. two

69. Both tripeptides contain the same peptides, but the sequences are different.

71. complex formed then an enzyme and substrate bind to each other

73. A substrate molecule or molecules binds to the active site of the enzyme.

75. a phosphate group, a five-carbon sugar unit, and a nitrogen base

77. hydrogen bonding

79. three

81. DNA sequences are unique for each individual.

83. a. Arg-Gly-Cys-Asn
   b. Arg-Gly-Cys-Asn

85. C-G-x-C-C-x-T-C-A(or G) or -A-G-x; there are multiple codes for the same amino acid.

87. a. amino acid
   b. monosaccharide (simple sugar)
   c. nucleotide

89. many applications in medicine and agriculture

91. Mutations could occur that would change how the organism constructs a protein.

93. inside the helix; strands must unwind

95. Bacteria necessary for nitrogen fixation might be killed by sterilization of the soil.

97. a. peptides and proteins
   b. polysaccharides
   c. polynucleotides (RNA and DNA)

99. A-C-C-T-A-C-T-A-C; no, Leu has six possible code words.

101. foods or existing body tissues

103. Nitrogen is converted (fixed) to ammonia and ammonium ions. Plants make nitrogen-containing compounds. Animals eat nitrogen-containing plants and other animals. Plants and animals die. Decay of the dead plants and animals returns nitrogen to the atmosphere.

105. Atmospheric nitrogen is reduced to ammonia by industrial processes.

107. More oxygen is needed for energy-producing processes; it rids the body of excess CO_2.

109. about 275 mol ATP

111. CO_2 cannot produce energy through oxidation, but glucose can be oxidized to CO_2.

Chapter 25

7. 0.063 mg Mn-56

8. No; one forth of the sample will remain.

25. Each isotope of an element has the same atomic number but a different atomic mass. A radioisotope is an isotope that is radioactive.

27. $^{210}_{82}Pb \longrightarrow \ ^{210}_{83}Bi + \ ^{0}_{-1}e$

29. a. $^{238}_{92}U \longrightarrow \ ^{234}_{90}Th + \ ^{4}_{2}He$; thorium-234
   b. $^{230}_{90}Th \longrightarrow \ ^{226}_{88}Ra + \ ^{4}_{2}He$; radium-226
   c. $^{235}_{92}U \longrightarrow \ ^{231}_{90}Th + \ ^{4}_{2}He$; thorium-231
   d. $^{222}_{86}Rn \longrightarrow \ ^{218}_{84}Po + \ ^{4}_{2}He$; polonium-218

31. a. mass number: unchanged; atomic number: increases by 1
   b. mass number: decreases by 4; atomic number: decreases by 2
   c. Mass number and atomic number are both unchanged.

33. a. $^{32}_{16}S$ **b.** $^{14}_{6}C$ **c.** $^{4}_{2}He$ **d.** $^{141}_{57}La$ **e.** $^{185}_{79}Au$

35. a. 27 protons and 33 neutrons
   b. 82 protons and 124 neutrons
   c. 90 protons and 143 neutrons
   d. 1 proton and 2 neutrons

37. a. $^{3}_{1}H \longrightarrow \ ^{3}_{2}He + \ ^{0}_{-1}e$
   b. $^{28}_{12}Mg \longrightarrow \ ^{28}_{13}Al + \ ^{0}_{-1}e$
   c. $^{131}_{53}I \longrightarrow \ ^{131}_{54}Xe + \ ^{0}_{-1}e$
   d. $^{75}_{34}Se \longrightarrow \ ^{75}_{35}Br + \ ^{0}_{-1}e$

39. Radioactive isotopes of these elements can be incorporated into the body tissue of organisms. When the isotopes decay they can damage tissue very easily.

41. $^{211}_{83}Bi \longrightarrow \ ^{207}_{81}Tl + \ ^{4}_{2}He$; thallium-207
   $^{207}_{81}Tl \longrightarrow \ ^{207}_{82}Pb + \ ^{0}_{-1}e$; lead-207

43. $4.2 \times 10^2 \ cm^3$

45. It undergoes radioactive decay.

47. a. $^{13}_{6}C$ **b.** $^{1}_{1}H$
   c. $^{16}_{8}O$ **d.** $^{14}_{7}N$

49. One half-life is the time required for one-half of the atoms of a radioisotope to emit radiation and decay.

51. Natural radioactivity comes from elements in nature. Artificial radioactivity comes from elements created in nuclear reactors and accelerators.

53. a. $^{30}_{15}P + ^{0}_{-1}e \longrightarrow ^{30}_{14}Si$

  b. $^{13}_{6}C + ^{1}_{0}n \longrightarrow ^{14}_{6}C$

  c. $^{131}_{53}I \longrightarrow ^{131}_{54}Xe + ^{0}_{-1}e$

55. a. $^{222}_{86}Rn \longrightarrow ^{218}_{84}Po + ^{4}_{2}He$

  b. $^{234}_{90}Th \longrightarrow ^{230}_{88}Ra + ^{4}_{2}He$

  c. $^{210}_{84}Po \longrightarrow ^{206}_{82}Pb + ^{4}_{2}He$

57. 1 million

59. 1.72×10^4

61. 5730 years

63. In every round of the tournament, one-half the teams are eliminated; in every half-life one-half the substance decays. In the tournament a single team eventually emerges as the winner and the tournament stops, but radioactive decay continues (almost) indefinitely.

65. 24.6 yr

67. This graph shows the radioactive decay of carbon-14, along with the increase of the nitrogen-14 product.

69. A power plant cannot maintain a constant output of electricity with spent fuel rods, which contain depleted fissionable isotopes and fission products. The rods are stored in pools of water.

71. Nuclear fusion takes place in the sun. A nuclear reactor utilizes nuclear fission.

73. $^{18}_{8}O$

75. The film badge measures radiation exposure; an exposed film badge indicates how much radiation a worker has received.

77. The reasoning is not sound. Cells other than cancer cells may be fast-growing and therefore killed by radiation as well.

Glossary

A

absolute zero the zero point on the Kelvin temperature scale, equivalent to −273.15°C *(3.2)*

accepted value a quantity used by general agreement of the scientific community *(3.1)*

accuracy the closeness of a measurement to the true value of what is being measured *(3.1)*

acid a compound that produces hydrogen ions in solution; *see also* hydrogen-ion donor, Lewis acid *(9.4)*

acid dissociation constant (K_a) the ratio of the concentration of the dissociated form of an acid to the undissociated form; stronger acids have larger K_a values than weaker acids *(19.3)*

acidic solution any solution in which the hydrogen-ion concentration is greater than the hydroxide-ion concentration *(19.2)*

activated complex an unstable arrangement of atoms that exists momentarily at the peak of the activation-energy barrier; an intermediate or transitional structure formed during the course of a reaction *(18.1)*

activation energy the minimum energy colliding particles must have in order to react *(18.1)*

active site a groove or pocket in an enzyme molecule into which the substrate (reactant molecule) fits; where the substrate is converted to products *(24.3)*

activity series a list of elements in order of decreasing activity; the activity series of halogens is Fl, Cl, Br, I *(11.2)*

actual yield the amount of product that forms when a reaction is carried out in the laboratory *(12.3)*

addition reaction a reaction in which a substance is added at the double bond of an alkene or at the triple bond of an alkyne *(23.2)*

adenosine triphosphate (ATP) a molecule that transmits the energy needed by cells of all living things *(24.6)*

alcohol an organic compound having an —OH (hydroxyl) group; the general structure is R—OH *(23.2)*

aldehyde an organic compound in which the carbon of the carbonyl group is joined to at least one hydrogen; the general formula is RCHO *(23.3)*

aliphatic hydrocarbon any straight-chain or branched-chain alkane, alkene, or alkyne *(22.3)*

alkali metal any metal in Group 1A of the periodic table *(6.2)*

alkaline earth metal any metal in Group 2A of the periodic table *(6.2)*

alkaline solution a basic solution *(19.2)*

alkane a hydrocarbon containing only single covalent bonds; alkanes are saturated hydrocarbons *(22.1)*

alkene a hydrocarbon containing one or more carbon–carbon double bonds; alkenes are unsaturated hydrocarbons *(22.2)*

alkyl group a hydrocarbon substituent; the methyl group (—CH₃) is an alkyl group *(22.1)*

alkyl halide a halocarbon in which one or more halogen atoms are attached to the carbon atoms of an aliphatic chain *(23.1)*

alkyne a hydrocarbon containing a carbon–carbon triple bond; alkynes are unsaturated hydrocarbons *(22.2)*

allotrope one of two or more different molecular forms of an element in the same physical state; oxygen (O_2) and ozone (O_3) are allotropes of the element oxygen *(13.3)*

alloy a mixture composed of two or more elements, at least one of which is a metal *(7.3)*

alpha particle a positively charged particle emitted from certain radioactive nuclei; it consists of two protons and two neutrons and is identical to the nucleus of a helium atom *(25.1)*

amino acid an organic compound having amino (—NH₂) and carboxyl (—COOH) groups in the same molecule; proteins are made from the 20 naturally occurring amino acids *(24.3)*

amorphous solid describes a solid that lacks an ordered internal structure; denotes a random arrangement of atoms *(13.3)*

amphoteric a substance that can act as both an acid and a base *(19.1)*

amplitude the height of a wave's crest *(5.3)*

anabolism synthesis processes in the metabolism of cells; these processes usually require the expenditure of energy *(24.6)*

analytical chemistry the area of chemistry that focuses on the composition of matter *(1.1)*

anion any atom or group of atoms with a negative charge *(6.3)*

anode the electrode at which oxidation occurs *(21.1)*

applied chemistry research that is directed toward a practical goal or application *(1.1)*

aqueous solution water that contains dissolved substances *(15.2)*

aromatic compound an organic compound that contains a benzene ring or other ring in which the bonding is like that of benzene; aromatic compounds are also known as arenes *(22.4)*

aryl halide a halocarbon in which one or more halogens are attached to the carbon atoms of an arene ring *(23.1)*

asymmetric carbon a carbon atom that has four different atoms or groups attached *(22.3)*

atmospheric pressure the pressure exerted by atoms and molecules in the atmosphere surrounding Earth, resulting from collisions of these particles with objects *(13.1)*

atom the smallest particle of an element that retains its identity in a chemical reaction *(4.1)*

atomic emission spectrum the pattern formed when light passes through a prism or diffraction grating to separate it into the different frequencies of light it contains *(5.3)*

atomic mass the weighted average of the masses of the isotopes of an element *(4.3)*

atomic mass unit (amu) a unit of mass equal to one-twelfth the mass of a carbon-12 atom *(4.3)*

atomic number the number of protons in the nucleus of an atom of an element *(4.3)*

atomic orbital a mathematical expression describing the probability of finding an electron at various locations; usually represented by the region of space around the nucleus where there is a high probability of finding an electron *(5.1)*

atomic radius one-half the distance between the nuclei of two atoms of the same element when the atoms are joined *(6.3)*

aufbau principle the rule that electrons occupy the orbitals of lowest energy first *(5.2)*

Avogadro's hypothesis equal volumes of gases at the same temperature and pressure contain equal numbers of particles *(10.2)*

Avogadro's number the number of representative particles contained in one mole of a substance; equal to 6.02×10^{23} particles *(10.1)*

B

balanced equation a chemical equation in which mass is conserved; each side of the equation has the same number of atoms of each element *(11.1)*

band of stability the location of stable nuclei on a neutron-vs.-proton plot *(25.2)*

barometer an instrument used to measure atmospheric pressure *(13.1)*

base a compound that produces hydroxide ions in solution; *see also* hydrogen-ion acceptor, Lewis base *(9.4)*

base dissociation constant (K_b) the ratio of the concentration of the conjugate acid times the concentration of the hydroxide ion to the concentration of the conjugate base *(19.3)*

basic solution any solution in which the hydroxide-ion concentration is greater than the hydrogen-ion concentration *(19.2)*

battery a group of voltaic cells that are connected to one another *(21.1)*

beta particle an electron resulting from the breaking apart of neutrons in an atom *(25.1)*

binary compound a compound composed of two elements; NaCl and Al_2O_3 are binary compounds *(9.2)*

biochemistry the areas of chemistry that focus on processes that take place in organisms *(1.1)*

biotechnology the field that applies science to the production of biological products or processes *(1.2)*

boiling point (bp) the temperature at which the vapor pressure of a liquid is just equal to the external pressure on the liquid *(13.2)*

boiling-point elevation the difference in temperature between the boiling point of a solution and the boiling point of the pure solvent *(16.3)*

bond dissociation energy the energy required to break the bond between two covalently bonded atoms; this value is usually expressed in kJ per mol of substance *(8.2)*

bonding orbital a molecular orbital that can be occupied by two electrons of a covalent bond *(8.3)*

Boyle's law for a given mass of gas at constant temperature, the volume of the gas varies inversely with pressure *(14.2)*

branched-chain alkane an alkane with one or more alkyl groups attached to the parent structure *(22.1)*

Brownian motion the chaotic movement of colloidal particles, caused by collision with particles of the solvent in which they are dispersed *(15.3)*

buffer a solution in which the pH remains relatively constant when small amounts of acid or base are added; a buffer can be either a solution of a weak acid and the salt of a weak acid or a solution of a weak base with the salt of a weak base *(19.5)*

buffer capacity a measure of the amount of acid or base that may be added to a buffer solution before a significant change in pH occurs *(19.5)*

C

calorie (cal) the quantity of heat needed to raise the temperature of 1 g of pure water 1°C *(3.2)*

calorimeter an insulated device used to measure the absorption or release of heat in chemical or physical processes *(17.2)*

calorimetry the precise measurement of heat flow out of a system for chemical and physical processes *(17.2)*

carbohydrate the name given to monomers and polymers of aldehydes and ketones that have numerous hydroxyl groups; sugars and starches are carbohydrates *(24.2)*

carbonyl group a functional group having a carbon atom and an oxygen atom joined by a double bond; it is found in aldehydes, ketones, esters, and amides *(23.3)*

carboxyl group a functional group consisting of a carbonyl group attached to a hydroxyl group; it is found in carboxylic acids *(23.3)*

carboxylic acid an organic acid containing a carboxyl group; the general formula is RCOOH *(23.3)*

catabolism the reactions in living cells in which substances are broken down and energy is produced *(24.6)*

catalyst a substance that increases the rate of reaction by lowering the activation-energy barrier; the catalyst is not used up in the reaction *(11.1)*

cathode the electrode at which reduction occurs *(21.1)*

cathode ray a stream of electrons produced at the negative electrode (cathode) of a tube containing a gas at low pressure *(4.2)*

cation any atom or group of atoms with a positive charge *(6.3)*

cell potential the difference between the reduction potentials of two half-cells *(21.2)*

Celsius scale the temperature scale on which the freezing point of water is 0°C and the boiling point is 100°C *(3.2)*

Charles's law the volume of a fixed mass of gas is directly proportional to its Kelvin temperature if the pressure is kept constant *(14.2)*

chemical change a change that produces matter with a different composition than the original matter *(2.3)*

chemical equation an expression representing a chemical reaction; the formulas of the reactants (on the left) are connected by an arrow with the formulas for the products (on the right) *(11.1)*

chemical equilibrium a state of balance in which the rates of the forward and reverse reactions are equal; no net change in the amount of reactants and products occurs in the chemical system *(18.2)*

chemical formula an expression that indicates the number and type of atoms present in the smallest representative unit of a substance *(7.2)*

chemical potential energy energy stored in chemical bonds *(17.1)*

chemical property the ability of a substance to undergo a specific chemical change *(2.4)*

chemical reaction a change in which one or more reactants change into one or more products; characterized by the breaking of bonds in reactants and the formation of bonds in products *(2.4)*

chemical symbol a one- or two-letter representation of an element *(2.3)*

chemistry the study of the composition of matter and the changes that matter undergoes *(1.1)*

cis **configuration** the configuration in which substituent groups are on the same side of a double bond *(22.3)*

coefficient a small whole number that appears in front of a formula in a balanced chemical equation *(11.1)*

coenzyme a small organic molecule or metal ion necessary for an enzyme's biological activity *(24.3)*

colligative property a property of a solution that depends only upon the number of solute particles, and not upon their identities; boiling-point elevation, freezing-point depression, and vapor-pressure lowering are colligative properties *(16.3)*

collision theory atoms, ions, and molecules can react to form products when they collide, provided that the particles have enough kinetic energy *(18.1)*

colloid a mixture whose particles are intermediate in size between those of a suspension and a solute solution *(15.3)*

combination reaction a chemical change in which two or more substances react to form a single new substance; also called a synthesis reaction *(11.2)*

combined gas law the law that describes the relationship among the pressure, temperature, and volume of an enclosed gas *(14.2)*

combustion reaction a chemical change in which an element or a compound reacts with oxygen, often producing energy in the form of heat and light *(11.2)*

common ion an ion that is common to both salts in a solution; in a solution of silver nitrate and silver chloride, Ag^+ would be a common ion *(18.3)*

common ion effect a decrease in the solubility of an ionic compound caused by the addition of a common ion *(18.3)*

complete ionic equation an equation that shows dissolved ionic compounds as dissociated free ions *(11.3)*

compound a substance that contains two or more elements chemically combined in a fixed proportion *(2.3)*

compressibility a measure of how much the volume of matter decreases under pressure *(14.1)*

concentrated solution a solution containing a large amount of solute *(16.2)*

concentration a measurement of the amount of solute that is dissolved in a given quantity of solvent; usually expressed as mol/L *(16.2)*

condensed structural formula a structural formula that leaves out some bonds and/or atoms; the presence of these atoms or bonds is understood *(22.1)*

conjugate acid the particle formed when a base gains a hydrogen ion; NH_4^+ is the conjugate acid of the base NH_3 *(19.1)*

conjugate acid-base pair two substances that are related by the loss or gain of a single hydrogen ion; ammonia (NH_3) and the ammonium ion (NH_4^+) are a conjugate acid-base pair *(19.1)*

conjugate base the particle that remains when an acid has donated a hydrogen ion; OH^- is the conjugate base of the acid water *(19.1)*

conversion factor a ratio of equivalent measurements used to convert a quantity from one unit to another *(3.3)*

coordinate covalent bond a covalent bond in which one atom contributes both bonding electrons *(8.2)*

coordination number the number of ions of opposite charge that surround each ion in a crystal *(7.2)*

covalent bond a bond formed by the sharing of electrons between atoms *(8.1)*

cracking the controlled process by which hydrocarbons are broken down or rearranged into smaller, more useful molecules *(22.5)*

crystal a solid in which the atoms, ions, or molecules are arranged in an orderly, repeating, three-dimensional pattern called a crystal lattice *(13.3)*

cyclic hydrocarbon an organic compound that contains a hydrocarbon ring *(22.4)*

Dalton's atomic theory the first theory to relate chemical changes to events at the atomic level *(4.1)*

Dalton's law of partial pressures at constant volume and temperature, the total pressure exerted by a mixture of gases is equal to the sum of the partial pressures of the component gases *(14.4)*

decomposition reaction a chemical change in which a single compound is broken down into two or more simpler products *(11.2)*

dehydrogenation reaction a reaction in which hydrogen is lost *(23.3)*

deliquescent describes a substance that removes sufficient water from the air to form a solution; the solution formed has a lower vapor pressure than that of the water in the air *(15.2)*

denatured alcohol ethanol to which a poisonous substance has been added to make it toxic *(23.2)*

density the ratio of the mass of an object to its volume *(3.4)*

dependent variable *see* responding variable

desiccant a hygroscopic substance used as a drying agent *(15.2)*

diatomic molecule a molecule consisting of two atoms *(8.1)*

diffusion the tendency of molecules to move toward areas of lower concentration until the concentration is uniform throughout *(14.4)*

dilute solution a solution that contains a small amount of solute *(16.2)*

dimensional analysis a technique of problem-solving that uses the units that are part of a measurement to help solve the problem *(3.3)*

dipole a molecule that has two poles, or regions with opposite charges *(8.4)*

dipole interactions intermolecular forces resulting from the attraction of oppositely charged regions of polar molecules *(8.4)*

diprotic acid any acid that contains two ionizable protons (hydrogen ions); sulfuric acid (H_2SO_4) is a diprotic acid *(19.1)*

disaccharide a carbohydrate formed from two monosaccharide units; common table sugar (sucrose) is a disaccharide *(24.2)*

dispersion forces attractions between molecules caused by the electron motion on one molecule affecting the electron motion on the other through electrical forces; these are the weakest interactions between molecules *(8.4)*

displacement reaction *see* single-replacement reaction

distillation a process used to separate dissolved solids from a liquid, which is boiled to produce a vapor that is then condensed into a liquid *(2.2)*

double covalent bond a bond in which two atoms share two pairs of electrons *(8.2)*

double-replacement reaction a chemical change that involves an exchange of positive ions between two compounds *(11.2)*

dry cell a commercial voltaic cell in which the electrolyte is a moist paste; despite their name, the compact, portable batteries used in flashlights are dry cells *(21.1)*

effloresce to lose water of hydration; the process occurs when the hydrate has a vapor pressure higher than that of water vapor in the air *(15.2)*

effusion the process that occurs when a gas escapes through a tiny hole in its container *(14.4)*

electrical potential the ability of a voltaic cell to produce an electric current *(21.2)*

electrochemical cell any device that converts chemical energy into electrical energy or electrical energy into chemical energy *(21.1)*

electrochemical process the conversion of chemical energy into electrical energy or electrical energy into chemical energy; all electrochemical processes involve redox reactions *(21.1)*

electrode a conductor in a circuit that carries electrons to or from a substance other than a metal *(21.1)*

electrolysis a process in which electrical energy is used to bring about a chemical change; the electrolysis of water produces hydrogen and oxygen *(21.3)*

electrolyte a compound that conducts an electric current when it is in an aqueous solution or in the molten state; all ionic compounds are electrolytes, but most covalent compounds are not *(15.2)*

electrolytic cell an electrochemical cell used to cause a chemical change through the application of electrical energy *(21.3)*

electromagnetic radiation energy waves that travel in a vacuum at a speed of 2.998×10^8 m/s; includes radio waves, microwaves, infrared waves, visible light, ultraviolet waves, X-rays, and gamma rays *(5.3)*

electron a negatively charged subatomic particle *(4.2)*

electron configuration the arrangement of electrons of an atom in its ground state into various orbitals around the nuclei of atoms *(5.2)*

electron dot structure a notation that depicts valence electrons as dots around the atomic symbol of the element; the symbol represents the inner electrons and atomic nucleus; also called Lewis dot structure *(7.1)*

electronegativity the ability of an atom to attract electrons when the atom is in a compound *(6.3)*

element the simplest form of matter that has a unique set of properties; an element cannot be broken down into simpler substances by chemical means *(2.3)*

elementary reaction a reaction in which reactants are converted to products in a single step *(18.5)*

empirical formula a formula with the lowest whole-number ratio of elements in a compound; the empirical formula of hydrogen peroxide (H_2O_2) is HO *(10.3)*

emulsion the colloidal dispersion of one liquid in another *(15.3)*

endothermic process a process that absorbs heat from the surroundings *(17.1)*

end point the point in a titration at which the indicator changes color *(19.4)*

energy the capacity for doing work or producing heat *(3.2)*

energy level the specific energies an electron in an atom or other system can have *(5.1)*

enthalpy (*H*) the heat content of a system at constant pressure *(17.2)*

entropy (*S*) a measure of the disorder of a system; systems tend to go from a state of order (low entropy) to a state of maximum disorder (high entropy) *(18.4)*

enzyme a protein that acts as a biological catalyst *(24.3)*

enzyme–substrate complex the structure formed when a substrate molecule joins an enzyme at its active site *(24.3)*

equilibrium constant (K_{eq}) the ratio of product concentrations to reactant concentrations at equilibrium, with each concentration raised to a power equal to the number of moles of that substance in the balanced chemical equation *(18.2)*

equilibrium position the relative concentrations of reactants and products of a reaction that has reached equilibrium; indicates whether the reactants or products are favored in the reversible reaction *(18.2)*

equivalence point the point in a titration where the number of moles of hydrogen ions equals the number of moles of hydroxide ions *(19.4)*

error the difference between the accepted value and the experimental value *(3.1)*

ester a derivative of a carboxylic acid in which the —OH of the carboxyl group has been replaced by the —OR from an alcohol; the general formula is RCOOR *(23.3)*

ether an organic compound in which oxygen is bonded to two carbon groups; the general formula is R—O—R *(23.2)*

evaporation vaporization that occurs at the surface of a liquid that is not boiling *(13.2)*

excess reagent a reagent present in a quantity that is more than sufficient to react with a limiting reagent; any reactant that remains after the limiting reagent is used up in a chemical reaction *(12.3)*

exothermic process a process that releases heat to its surroundings *(17.1)*

experiment a repeatable procedure that is used to test a hypothesis *(1.3)*

experimental value a quantitative value measured during an experiment *(3.1)*

extensive property a property that depends on the amount of matter in a sample *(2.1)*

F

fatty acid the name given to continuous-chain carboxylic acids that were first isolated from fats *(23.3)*

fermentation the production of ethanol from sugars by the action of yeast or bacteria *(23.2)*

film badge a radiation detection device that consists of several layers of photographic film covered with black lightproof paper, all encased in a plastic or metal holder *(25.4)*

filtration a process that separates a solid from the liquid in a heterogeneous mixture *(2.2)*

first-order reaction a reaction in which the reaction rate is proportional to the concentration of only one reactant *(18.5)*

fission the splitting of a nucleus into smaller fragments, accompanied by the release of neutrons and a large amount of energy *(25.3)*

formula unit the lowest whole-number ratio of ions in an ionic compound; in magnesium chloride, the ratio of magnesium ions to chloride ions is 1:2 and the formula unit is $MgCl_2$ *(7.2)*

free energy the energy available to do work *(18.4)*

freezing-point depression the difference in temperature between the freezing point of a solution and the freezing point of the pure solvent *(16.3)*

frequency (v) the number of wave cycles that pass a given point per unit of time; frequency and wavelength are inversely proportional to each other *(5.3)*

fuel cell a voltaic cell that does not need to be recharged; the fuel is oxidized to produce a continuous supply of electrical energy *(21.1)*

functional group a specific arrangement of atoms in an organic compound that is capable of characteristic chemical reactions; the chemistry of an organic compound is determined by its functional groups *(23.1)*

fusion the process of combining nuclei to produce a nucleus of greater mass *(25.3)*

G

gamma ray a high-energy photon emitted by a radioisotope *(25.1)*

gas a form of matter that takes the shape and volume of its container; a gas has no definite shape or volume *(2.1)*

gas pressure results from the force exerted by a gas per unit surface area of an object; due to collisions of gas particles with the object *(13.1)*

Gay-Lussac's law the pressure of a gas is directly proportional to the Kelvin temperature if the volume is constant *(14.2)*

Geiger counter a device that uses a gas-filled metal tube to detect radiation *(25.4)*

gene a segment of DNA that codes for a single peptide chain *(24.5)*

genetic code the arrangement of bases in the code words in DNA; there are 61 triplet code words used to specify the amino acids in proteins plus 3 triplet code words that signal "stop" after the protein synthesis is complete *(24.5)*

geometric isomers compounds that have atoms in the same order, but differ in the orientation of groups around a double bond *(22.3)*

Gibbs free-energy change (ΔG) the maximum amount of energy that can be coupled to another process to do useful work *(18.4)*

glass transparent fusion product of inorganic materials that have cooled to a rigid state without crystallizing *(13.3)*

Graham's laws of effusion the rate of effusion of a gas is inversely proportional to the square root of its molar mass; this relationship is also true for the diffusion of gases *(14.4)*

gram (g) a metric mass unit equal to the mass of 1 cm^3 of water at 4°C *(3.2)*

ground state the lowest possible energy of an electron described by quantum mechanics *(5.3)*

group a vertical column of elements in the periodic table; the constituent elements of a group have similar chemical and physical properties *(4.3)*

H

half-cell the part of a voltaic cell in which either oxidation or reduction occurs; it consists of a single electrode immersed in a solution of its ions *(21.1)*

half-life ($t_{1/2}$) the time required for one-half of the nuclei of a radioisotope sample to decay to products *(25.2)*

half-reaction an equation showing either the oxidation or the reduction that takes place in a redox reaction *(20.3)*

half-reaction method a method of balancing a redox equation by balancing the oxidation and reduction half-reactions separately before combining them into a balanced redox equation *(20.3)*

halide ion a negative ion formed when a halogen atom gains an electron *(7.1)*

halocarbon any member of a class of organic compounds containing covalently bonded fluorine, chlorine, bromine, or iodine *(23.1)*

halogen a nonmetal in Group 7A of the periodic table *(6.2)*

heat (q) energy that transfers from one object to another because of a temperature difference between the objects *(17.1)*

heat capacity the amount of heat needed to increase the temperature of an object exactly 1°C *(17.1)*

heat of combustion the heat of reaction for the complete burning of one mole of a substance *(17.2)*

heat of reaction the enthalpy change for a chemical equation exactly as it is written *(17.2)*

Heisenberg uncertainty principle it is impossible to know exactly both the velocity and the position of a particle at the same time *(5.3)*

Henry's law at a given temperature the solubility of a gas in a liquid is directly proportional to the pressure of the gas above the liquid *(16.1)*

hertz (Hz) the unit of frequency, equal to one cycle per second *(5.3)*

Hess's law of heat summation if you add two or more thermochemical equations to give a final equation, then you also add the heats of reaction to give the final heat of reaction *(17.4)*

heterogeneous mixture a mixture that is not uniform in composition; components are not evenly distributed throughout the mixture *(2.2)*

homogeneous mixture a mixture that is uniform in composition; components are evenly distributed and not easily distinguished *(2.2)*

homologous series a group of compounds in which there is a constant increment of change in molecular structure from one compound in the series to the next *(22.1)*

Hund's rule electrons occupy orbitals of the same energy in a way that makes the number or electrons with the same spin direction as large as possible *(5.2)*

hybridization the mixing of several atomic orbitals to form the same total number of equivalent hybrid orbitals *(8.3)*

hydrate a compound that has a specific number of water molecules bound to each formula unit *(15.2)*

hydration reaction a reaction in which water is added to an alkene *(23.2)*

hydrocarbon an organic compound that contains only carbon and hydrogen *(22.1)*

hydrogenation reaction a reaction in which hydrogen is added to a carbon–carbon double bond to give an alkane *(23.2)*

hydrogen bonds attractive forces in which a hydrogen covalently bonded to a very electronegative atom is also weakly bonded to an unshared electron pair of another electronegative atom *(8.4)*

hydrogen-ion acceptor a base, according to the Brønsted-Lowry theory; ammonia acts as a base when it accepts hydrogen ions from water *(19.1)*

hydrogen-ion donor an acid, according to the Brønsted-Lowry theory *(19.1)*

hydronium ion (H_3O^+) the positive ion formed when a water molecule gains a hydrogen ion *(19.1)*

hydroxide ion (OH^-) the negative ion formed when a water molecule loses a hydrogen ion *(19.1)*

hydroxyl group the —OH functional group present in alcohols *(23.2)*

hygroscopic a term describing salts and other compounds that remove moisture from the air *(15.2)*

hypothesis a proposed explanation for an observation *(1.3)*

ideal gas constant the constant in the ideal gas law with the symbol R and the value 8.31 (L·kPa)/(K·mol) *(14.3)*

ideal gas law the relationship $PV = nRT$, which describes the behavior of an ideal gas *(14.3)*

immiscible describes liquids that are insoluble in one another; oil and water are immiscible *(16.1)*

inhibitor a substance that interferes with the action of a catalyst *(18.1)*

independent variable *see* manipulated variable

inner transition metal an element in the lanthanide or actinide series; the highest occupied *s* sublevel and nearby *f* sublevel of its atoms generally contain electrons; also called inner transition element *(6.2)*

inorganic chemistry the study of substances that, in general, do not contain carbon *(1.1)*

intensive property a property that depends on the type of matter in a sample, not the amount of matter *(2.1)*

intermediate a product of one of the steps in a reaction mechanism; it becomes a reactant in the next step *(18.5)*

International System of Units (SI) the revised version of the metric system, adopted by international agreement in 1960 *(3.2)*

ion an atom or group of atoms that has a positive or negative charge *(6.3)*

ionic bond the electrostatic attraction that binds oppositely charged ions together *(7.2)*

ionic compound a compound composed of positive and negative ions *(7.2)*

ionization energy the energy required to remove an electron from an atom in its gaseous state *(6.3)*

ionizing radiation radiation with enough energy to knock electrons off some atoms of a bombarded substance to produce ions *(25.4)*

ion-product constant for water (K_w) the product of the concentrations of hydrogen ions and hydroxide ions in water; it is 1×10^{-14} at 25°C *(19.2)*

isomers compounds that have the same molecular formula but different molecular structures *(22.3)*

isotopes atoms of the same element that have the same atomic number but different atomic masses due to a different number of neutrons *(4.3)*

joule (J) the SI unit of energy; 4.184 J equal one calorie *(3.2)*

Kelvin scale the temperature scale in which the freezing point of water is 273 K and the boiling point is 373 K; 0 K is absolute zero *(3.2)*

ketone an organic compound in which the carbon of the carbonyl group is joined to two other carbons; the general formula is RCOR *(23.3)*

kilogram (kg) the mass of 1 L of water at 4°C; it is the base unit of mass in SI *(3.2)*

kinetic energy the energy an object has because of its motion *(13.1)*

kinetic theory a theory explaining the states of matter, based on the concept that all matter consists of tiny particles that are in constant motion *(13.1)*

L

law of conservation of energy in any chemical or physical process, energy is neither created nor destroyed *(17.1)*

law of conservation of mass in any physical change or chemical reaction, mass is conserved; mass can be neither created nor destroyed *(2.4)*

law of definite proportions in samples of any chemical compound, the masses of the elements are always in the same proportion *(9.5)*

law of disorder it is a natural tendency of systems to move in the direction of maximum chaos or disorder *(18.4)*

law of multiple proportions whenever two elements form more than one compound, the different masses of one element that combine with the same mass of the other element are in the ratio of small whole numbers *(9.5)*

Le Châtelier's principle when a stress is applied to a system in dynamic equilibrium, the system changes in a way that relieves the stress *(18.2)*

Lewis acid any substance that can accept a pair of electrons to form a covalent bond *(19.1)*

Lewis base any substance that can donate a pair of electrons to form a covalent bond *(19.1)*

limiting reagent any reactant that is used up first in a chemical reaction; it determines the amount of product that can be formed in the reaction *(12.3)*

lipid a member of a large class of relatively water-insoluble organic compounds; fats, oils, and waxes are lipids *(24.4)*

liquid a form of matter that flows, has a fixed volume, and an indefinite shape *(2.1)*

liter (L) the volume of a cube measuring 10 centimeters on each edge (1000 cm³); it is the common unprefixed unit of volume in the metric system *(3.2)*

M

macroscopic describes the world of objects that are large enough to see with the unaided eye *(1.2)*

manipulated variable the variable that is changed during an experiment; also called independent variable *(1.3)*

mass a measure of the amount of matter that an object contains; the SI base unit of mass is the kilogram *(2.1)*

mass number the total number of protons and neutrons in the nucleus of an atom *(4.3)*

matter anything that has mass and occupies space *(1.1)*

measurement a quantitative description that includes both a number and a unit *(3.1)*

melting point (mp) the temperature at which a substance changes from a solid to a liquid; the melting point of water is 0°C *(13.3)*

metabolism all the chemical reactions carried out by an organism; includes energy-producing (catabolism) reactions and energy-absorbing (anabolism) reactions *(24.6)*

metal one of a class of elements that are good conductors of heat and electric current; metals tend to be ductile, malleable, and shiny *(6.1)*

metallic bond the force of attraction that holds metals together; it consists of the attraction of free-floating valence electrons for positively charged metal ions *(7.3)*

metalloid an element that tends to have properties that are similar to those of metals and nonmetals *(6.1)*

meter (m) the base unit of length in SI *(3.2)*

microscopic describes the world of objects that can be seen only under magnification *(1.2)*

miscible describes liquids that dissolve in one another in all proportions *(16.1)*

mixture a physical blend of two or more substances that are not chemically combined *(2.2)*

molal boiling-point elevation constant (K_b) the change in boiling point for a 1-molal solution of a nonvolatile molecular solute *(16.4)*

molal freezing-point depression constant (K_f) the change in freezing point for a 1-molal solution of a nonvolatile molecular solute *(16.4)*

molality (m) the concentration of solute in a solution expressed as the number of moles of solute dissolved in 1 kilogram (1000 g) of solvent *(16.4)*

molar heat of condensation (ΔH_{cond}) the amount of heat released by one mole of a vapor as it condenses to a liquid at a constant temperature *(17.3)*

molar heat of fusion (ΔH_{fus}) the amount of heat absorbed by one mole of a solid substance as it melts to a liquid at a constant temperature *(17.3)*

molar heat of solidification (ΔH_{solid}) the amount of heat lost by one mole of a liquid as it solidifies at a constant temperature *(17.3)*

molar heat of solution (ΔH_{soln}) the enthalpy change caused by the dissolution of one mole of a substance *(17.3)*

molar heat of vaporization (ΔH_{vap}) the amount of heat absorbed by one mole of a liquid as it vaporizes at a constant temperature *(17.3)*

molarity (M) the concentration of solute in a solution expressed as the number of moles of solute dissolved in 1 liter of solution *(16.2)*

molar mass a term used to refer to the mass of a mole of any substance *(10.1)*

molar volume the volume occupied by 1 mole of a gas at standard temperature and pressure (STP); 22.4 L *(10.2)*

mole (mol) the amount of a substance that contains 6.02×10^{23} representative particles of that substance *(10.1)*

molecular compound a compound that is composed of molecules *(8.1)*

molecular formula a chemical formula of a molecular compound that shows the kinds and numbers of atoms present in a molecule of a compound *(8.1)*

molecular orbital an orbital that applies to the entire molecule *(8.3)*

molecule a neutral group of atoms joined together by covalent bonds *(8.1)*

mole fraction the ratio of the moles of solute in solution to the total number of moles of both solvent and solute *(16.4)*

mole ratio a conversion factor derived from the coefficients of a balanced chemical equation interpreted in terms of moles *(12.2)*

monatomic ion a single atom with a positive or negative charge resulting from the loss or gain of one or more valence electrons *(9.1)*

monomer a simple molecule that repeatedly combines to form a polymer *(23.4)*

monoprotic acid any acid that contains one ionizable proton (hydrogen ion); nitric acid (HNO_3) is a monoprotic acid *(19.1)*

monosaccharide a carbohydrate consisting of one sugar unit; also called a simple sugar *(24.2)*

N

net ionic equation an equation for a reaction in solution showing only those particles that are directly involved in the chemical change *(11.3)*

network solid a solid in which all of the atoms are covalently bonded to each other *(8.4)*

neutralization reaction a reaction in which an acid and a base react in an aqueous solution to produce a salt and water *(19.4)*

neutral solution an aqueous solution in which the concentrations of hydrogen and hydroxide ions are equal; it has a pH of 7.0 *(19.2)*

neutron a subatomic particle with no charge and a mass of 1 amu; found in the nucleus of an atom *(4.2)*

neutron absorption a process that decreases the number of slow-moving neutrons in a nuclear reactor; this is accomplished by using control rods made of a material such as cadmium, which absorbs neutrons *(25.3)*

neutron activation analysis a procedure used to detect trace amounts of elements in samples by bombarding the sample with neutrons from a radioactive source *(25.4)*

neutron moderation a process used in nuclear reactors to slow down neutrons so the reactor fuel captures them to continue the chain reaction *(25.3)*

noble gas an element in Group 8A of the periodic table; the *s* and *p* sublevels of the highest occupied energy level are filled *(6.2)*

nonelectrolyte a compound that does not conduct an electric current in aqueous solution or in the molten state *(15.2)*

nonmetal an element that tends to be a poor conductor of heat and electric current; nonmetals generally have properties opposite to those of metals *(6.1)*

nonpolar covalent bond a covalent bond in which the electrons are shared equally by the two atoms *(8.4)*

nonspontaneous reaction a reaction that does not favor the formation of products at the specified conditions *(18.4)*

normal boiling point the boiling point of a liquid at a pressure of 101.3 kPa or 1 atm *(13.2)*

nucleic acid a polymer of ribonucleotides (RNA) or deoxyribonucleotides (DNA) found primarily in cell nuclei; nucleic acids play an important role in the transmission of hereditary characteristics, protein synthesis, and the control of cell activities *(24.5)*

nucleotide one of the monomers that make up DNA and RNA; it consists of a nitrogen-containing base (a purine or pyrimidine), a sugar (ribose or deoxyribose), and a phosphate group *(24.5)*

nucleus the tiny, dense central portion of an atom, composed of protons and neutrons *(4.2)*

observation information obtained through the senses; observation in science often involves a measurement *(1.3)*

octet rule atoms react by gaining or losing electrons so as to acquire the stable electron structure of a noble gas, usually eight valence electrons *(7.1)*

optical isomers molecules that differ from one another in the way that four different groups are arranged around a carbon atom *(22.3)*

organic chemistry the study of compounds containing carbon *(1.1)*

oxidation a process that involves complete or partial loss of electrons or a gain of oxygen; it results in an increase in the oxidation number of an atom *(20.1)*

oxidation number a positive or negative number assigned to an atom to indicate its degree of oxidation or reduction; the oxidation number of an uncombined element is zero *(20.2)*

oxidation-number-change method a method of balancing a redox equation by comparing the increases and decreases in oxidation numbers *(20.3)*

oxidation-reduction reaction a reaction that involves the transfer of electrons between reactants *(20.1)*

oxidizing agent the substance in a redox reaction that accepts electrons; in the reaction, the oxidizing agent is reduced *(20.1)*

partial pressure the contribution each gas in a mixture of gases makes to the total pressure *(14.4)*

pascal (Pa) the SI unit of pressure *(13.1)*

Pauli exclusion principle an atomic orbital may describe at most two electrons, each with opposite spin direction *(5.2)*

peptide an organic compound formed by a combination of amino acids in which the amino group of one acid is united with the carboxyl group of another through an amide bond *(24.3)*

peptide bond the bond between the carbonyl group of one amino acid and the nitrogen of the next amino acid in the peptide chain; the structure is

(24.3)

percent composition the percent by mass of each element in a compound *(10.3)*

percent error the percent that a measured value differs from the accepted value *(3.1)*

percent yield the ratio of the actual yield to the theoretical yield for a chemical reaction expressed as a percentage; a measure of the efficiency of a reaction *(12.3)*

period a horizontal row of elements in the periodic table *(4.3)*

periodic law when the elements are arranged in order of increasing atomic number, there is a periodic repetition of their physical and chemical properties *(6.1)*

periodic table an arrangement of elements in which the elements are separated into groups based on a set of repeating properties *(4.3)*

pH a number used to denote the hydrogen-ion concentration, or acidity, of a solution; it is the negative logarithm of the hydrogen-ion concentration of a solution *(19.2)*

phase any part of a sample with uniform composition and properties *(2.2)*

phase diagram a graph showing the conditions at which a substance exists as a solid, liquid, or vapor *(13.4)*

phospholipid a lipid that contains a phosphate group; because phospholipids have hydrophilic heads and hydrophobic tails, they form the lipid bilayers found in cell membranes *(24.4)*

photon a quantum of light; a discrete bundle of electromagnetic energy that interacts with matter similarly to particles *(5.3)*

photosynthesis the process by which green plants and algae use radiant energy from the sun to synthesize glucose from carbon dioxide and water *(24.1)*

physical change a change during which some properties of a material change, but the composition of the material does not change *(2.1)*

physical chemistry the area of chemistry that deals with the mechanism, the rate, and the energy transfer that occurs when matter undergoes a change *(1.1)*

physical property a quality or condition of a substance that can be observed or measured without changing the substance's composition *(2.1)*

pi bond (π bond) a covalent bond in which the bonding electrons are most likely to be found in sausage-shaped regions above and below the bond axis of the bonded atoms *(8.3)*

polar covalent bond (polar bond) a covalent bond between atoms in which the electrons are shared unequally *(8.4)*

polar molecule a molecule in which one side of the molecule is slightly negative and the opposite side is slightly positive *(8.4)*

pollutant a material found in air, water, or soil that is harmful to humans and other organisms *(1.2)*

polyatomic ion a tightly bound group of atoms that behaves as a unit and has a positive or negative charge *(8.2)*

polymer a very large molecule formed by the covalent bonding of repeating small molecules, known as monomers *(23.4)*

polypeptide a peptide with more than 10 amino acids *(24.3)*

polysaccharide a complex carbohydrate polymer formed by the linkage of many monosaccharide monomers; starch, glycogen, and cellulose are polysaccharides *(24.2)*

positron a particle with the mass of an electron but a positive charge *(25.2)*

precipitate a solid that forms and settles out of a liquid mixture *(2.4)*

precision describes the closeness, or reproducibility, of a set of measurements taken under the same conditions *(3.1)*

product a substance produced in a chemical reaction *(2.4)*

protein any peptide with more than 100 amino acids *(24.3)*

proton a positively charged subatomic particle found in the nucleus of an atom *(4.2)*

pure chemistry the pursuit of chemical knowledge for its own sake *(1.1)*

pure substance *see* substance

quantum the amount of energy needed to move an electron from one energy level to another *(5.1)*

quantum mechanical model the modern description, primarily mathematical, of the behavior of electrons in atoms *(5.1)*

radiation the penetrating rays and particles emitted by a radioactive source *(25.1)*

radioactivity the process by which nuclei emit particles and rays *(25.1)*

radioisotope an isotope that has an unstable nucleus and undergoes radioactive decay *(25.1)*

rate describes the speed of change over an interval of time *(18.1)*

rate law an expression relating the rate of a reaction to the concentration of the reactants *(18.5)*

reactant a substance present at the start of a reaction *(2.4)*

reaction mechanism a series of elementary reactions that take place during the course of a complex reaction *(18.5)*

redox reaction another name for an oxidation-reduction reaction *(20.1)*

reducing agent the substance in a redox reaction that donates electrons; in the reaction, the reducing agent is oxidized *(20.1)*

reduction a process that involves a complete or partial gain of electrons or the loss of oxygen; it results in a decrease in the oxidation number of an atom *(20.1)*

reduction potential a measure of the tendency of a given half-reaction to occur as a reduction (gain of electrons) in an electrochemical cell *(21.2)*

representative element an element in an "A" group in the periodic table; as a group these elements display a wide range of physical and chemical properties. In their atoms, the *s* and *p* sublevels in the highest occupied energy level are partially filled *(6.2)*

representative particle the smallest unit into which a substance can be broken down without a change in composition, usually atoms, molecules, or ions *(10.1)*

resonance structure one of the two or more equally valid electron dot structures of a molecule or polyatomic ion *(8.2)*

responding variable the variable that is observed during an experiment; also called dependent variable *(1.3)*

reversible reaction a reaction in which the conversion of reactants into products and the conversion of products into reactants occur simultaneously *(18.2)*

S

salt bridge a tube containing a strong electrolyte used to separate the half-cells in a voltaic cell; it allows the passage of ions from one half-cell to the other but prevents the solutions from mixing completely *(23.1)*

salt hydrolysis a process in which the cations or anions of a dissociated salt accept hydrogen ions from water or donate hydrogen ions to water *(19.5)*

saponification the hydrolysis of fats or oils by a hot aqueous alkali-metal hydroxide; soaps are made by saponification *(24.4)*

saturated compound an organic compound in which all carbon atoms are joined by single covalent bonds; it contains the maximum number of hydrogen atoms *(22.2)*

saturated solution a solution containing the maximum amount of solute for a given amount of solvent at a constant temperature and pressure; an equilibrium exists between undissolved solute and ions in solution *(16.1)*

scientific law a concise statement that summarizes the results of many observations and experiments *(1.3)*

scientific method a logical, systematic approach to the solution of a scientific problem; steps in the scientific method include making observations, testing hypotheses, and developing theories *(1.3)*

scientific notation an expression of numbers in the form $m \times 10^n$ where m is equal to or greater than 1 and less than 10, and n is an integer *(3.1)*

scintillation counter a device that uses a phosphor-coated surface to detect radiation *(25.4)*

self-ionization a term describing the reaction in which two water molecules react to produce ions *(19.2)*

sigma bond (σ bond) a bond formed when two atomic orbitals combine for form a molecular orbital that is symmetrical around the axis connecting the two atomic nuclei *(8.3)*

significant figures all the digits that can be known precisely in a measurement, plus a last estimated digit *(3.1)*

single covalent bond a bond formed when two atoms share a pair of electrons *(8.2)*

single-replacement reaction a chemical change in which one element replaces a second element in a compound; also called a displacement reaction *(11.2)*

skeleton equation a chemical equation that does not indicate the relative amounts of reactants and products *(11.1)*

solid a form of matter that has a definite shape and volume *(2.1)*

solubility the amount of a substance that dissolves in a given quantity of solvent at specified conditions of temperature and pressure to produce a saturated solution *(16.1)*

solubility product constant (K_{sp}) an equilibrium constant applied to the solubility of electrolytes; it is equal to the product of the concentrations of the ions each raised to a power equal to the coefficient of the ion in the dissociation equation *(18.3)*

solute dissolved particles in a solution *(15.2)*

solution a homogeneous mixture; consists of solutes dissolved in a solvent *(2.2)*

solvation a process that occurs when an ionic solute dissolves; in solution, solvent molecules surround the positive and negative ions. *(15.2)*

solvent the dissolving medium in a solution *(15.2)*

specific heat the amount of heat needed to increase the temperature of 1 g of a substance 1°C; also called specific heat capacity *(17.1)*

specific rate constant a proportionality constant relating the concentrations of reactants to the rate of the reaction *(18.5)*

spectator ion an ion that is not directly involved in a chemical reaction; an ion that does not change oxidation number or composition during a reaction *(11.3)*

spectrum wavelengths of visible light that are separated when a beam of light passes through a prism; range of wavelengths of electromagnetic radiation *(5.3)*

spontaneous reaction a reaction that favors the formation of products at the specified conditions; spontaneity depends on enthalpy and entropy changes *(18.4)*

standard atmosphere (atm) a unit of pressure; it is the pressure required to support 760 mm of mercury in a mercury barometer at 25°C *(13.1)*

standard cell potential (E^0_{cell}) the measured cell potential when the ion concentration in the half-cells are $1.00M$ at 1 atm of pressure and 25°C *(21.2)*

standard entropy (S^0) the entropy of a substance in its stable state at 25°C and 1 atm *(18.4)*

standard heat of formation (ΔH_f^0) the change in enthalpy that accompanies the formation of one mole of a compound from its elements with all substances in their standard states at 25°C *(17.4)*

standard hydrogen electrode an arbitrary reference electrode (half-cell) used with another electrode (half-cell) to measure the standard reduction potential of that cell; the standard reduction potential of the hydrogen electrode is assigned a value of 0.00 V *(21.2)*

standard solution a solution of known concentration used in carrying out a titration *(19.4)*

standard temperature and pressure (STP) the conditions under which the volume of a gas is usually measured; standard temperature is 0°C, and standard pressure is 101.3 kPa, or 1 atmosphere (atm) *(10.2)*

stereoisomers molecules that have atoms in the same order, but which differ in the arrangement of the atoms in space *(22.3)*

stoichiometry that portion of chemistry dealing with numerical relationships in chemical reactions; the calculation of quantities of substances involved in chemical equations *(12.1)*

straight-chain alkane a saturated hydrocarbon that contains any number of carbon atoms arranged one after the other in a chain *(22.1)*

strong acid an acid that is completely (or almost completely) ionized in aqueous solution *(19.3)*

strong base a base that completely dissociates into metal ions and hydroxide ions in aqueous solution *(19.3)*

strong electrolyte a solution in which a large portion of the solute exists as ions *(15.2)*

structural formula a chemical formula that shows the arrangement of atoms in a molecule or a polyatomic ion; each dash between a pair of atoms indicates a pair of shared electrons *(8.2)*

structural isomers compounds that have the same molecular formula, but whose atoms are bonded in a different order *(22.3)*

sublimation the process in which a solid changes to a gas or vapor without passing through the liquid state *(13.4)*

substance matter that has a uniform and definite composition; either an element or a compound; also called pure substance *(2.1)*

substituent an atom or group of atoms that can take the place of a hydrogen atom on a parent hydrocarbon molecule *(22.1)*

substitution reaction a common type of organic reaction; involves the replacement of an atom or group of atoms by another atom or group of atoms *(23.1)*

substrate a molecule on which an enzyme acts *(24.3)*

supersaturated solution a solution that contains more solute than it can theoretically hold at a given temperature; excess solute precipitates if a seed crystal is added *(16.1)*

surface tension an inward force that tends to minimize the surface area of a liquid; it causes the surface to behave as if it were a thin skin *(15.1)*

surfactant any substance that interferes with the hydrogen bonding between water molecules and thereby reduces surface tension; soaps and detergents are surfactants. *(15.1)*

surroundings everything in the universe outside of the system *(17.1)*

suspension a mixture from which some of the particles settle out slowly upon standing *(15.3)*

synthesis reaction *see* combination reaction

system a part of the universe on which you focus your attention *(17.1)*

technology the means by which a society provides its members with those things needed and desired *(1.1)*

temperature a measure of the average kinetic energy of particles in matter; temperature determines the direction of heat transfer *(3.2)*

tetrahedral angle a bond angle of 109.5° that results when a central atom forms four bonds directed toward the center of a regular tetrahedron *(8.3)*

theoretical yield the amount of product that could form during a reaction calculated from a balanced chemical equation; it represents the maximum amount of product that could be formed from a given amount of reactant *(12.3)*

theory a well-tested explanation for a broad set of observations *(1.3)*

thermochemical equation a chemical equation that includes the enthalpy change *(17.2)*

thermochemistry the study of energy changes that occur during chemical reactions and changes in state *(17.1)*

titration process used to determine the concentration of a solution (often an acid or base) in which a solution of known concentration (the standard) is added to a measured amount of the solution of unknown concentration until an indicator signals the end point *(19.4)*

trans configuration the configuration in which substituent groups are on the opposite sides of a double bond *(22.3)*

transition metal one of the Group B elements in which the highest occupied *s* sublevel and a nearby *d* sublevel generally contain electrons *(6.2)*

transition state a term sometimes used to refer to the activated complex *(18.1)*

transmutation the conversion of an atom of one element to an atom of another element *(25.2)*

transuranium element any elements in the periodic table with atomic number above 92, the atomic number of uranium *(25.2)*

triglyceride an ester in which all three hydroxyl groups on a glycerol molecule have been replaced by long-chain fatty acids; fats are triglycerides *(24.4)*

triple covalent bond a covalent bond in which three pairs of electrons are shared by two atoms *(8.2)*

triple point the point on a phase diagram that represents the only set of conditions at which all three phases exist in equilibrium with one another *(13.4)*

triprotic acid any acid that contains three ionizable protons (hydrogen ions); phosphoric acid (H_3PO_4) is a triprotic acid *(19.1)*

Tyndall effect scattering of light by particles in a colloid or suspension, which causes a beam of light to become visible *(15.3)*

unit cell the smallest group of particles within a crystal that retains the geometric shape of the crystal *(13.3)*

unsaturated solution a solution that contains less solute than a saturated solution at a given temperature and pressure *(16.1)*

unsaturated compound an organic compound with one or more double or triple carbon–carbon bonds *(22.2)*

unshared pair a pair of valence electrons that is not shared between atoms *(8.2)*

vacuum a space where no particles of matter exist *(13.1)*

valence electron an electron in the highest occupied energy level of an atom *(7.1)*

van der Waals forces the two weakest intermolecular attractions—dispersion interactions and dipole forces *(8.4)*

vapor describes the gaseous state of a substance that is generally a liquid or solid at room temperature *(2.1)*

vaporization the conversion of a liquid to a gas or a vapor *(13.2)*

vapor pressure a measure of the force exerted by a gas above a liquid in a sealed container; a dynamic equilibrium exists between the vapor and the liquid *(13.2)*

voltaic cell an electrochemical cell used to convert chemical energy into electrical energy; the energy is produced by a spontaneous redox reaction *(21.1)*

volume a measure of the space occupied by a sample of matter *(2.1)*

VSEPR theory valence-shell electron-pair repulsion theory; because electron pairs repel, molecules adjust their shapes so that valence electron pairs are as far apart as possible *(8.3)*

water of hydration water molecules that are an integral part of a crystal structure *(15.2)*

wavelength (λ) the distance between adjacent crests of a wave *(5.3)*

wax an ester of a long-chain fatty acid and a long-chain alcohol *(24.4)*

weak acid an acid that is only slightly ionized in aqueous solution *(19.3)*

weak base a base that reacts with water to form the hydroxide ion and the conjugate acid of the base *(19.3)*

weak electrolyte a solution that conducts electricity poorly because only a fraction of the solute exists as ions *(15.2)*

weight a force that measures the pull of gravity on a given mass *(3.2)*

Spanish Glossary

A

absolute zero/cero absoluto punto cero de la escala Kelvin de temperatura; equivale a −273.15°C *(3.2)*

accepted value/valor aceptado cantidad que se usa por acuerdo general de la comunidad científica *(3.1)*

accuracy/exactitud qué tan cerca está una medición del valor real de lo que se mide *(3.1)*

acid/ácido compuesto que, en solución, produce iones hidrógeno, cede iones hidrógeno o acepta pares de electrones *(9.4)*

acid dissociation constant (K_a)/constante de disociación ácida (K_a) razón de la concentración de la forma disociada de un ácido a la concentración de la forma no disociada; los ácidos fuertes tienen valores K_a más altos que los ácidos débiles *(19.3)*

acidic solution/solución ácida cualquier solución en la que la concentración de iones hidrógeno es mayor que la de iones hidróxido *(19.2)*

activated complex/complejo activado acomodo inestable de átomos que existe momentáneamente en el punto más alto de la barrera de energía de activación; estructura intermedia o de transición que se forma en el curso de una reacción *(18.1)*

activation energy/energía de activación energía mínima que deben tener las partículas para que, al chocar, reaccionen *(18.1)*

active site/sitio activo hendidura o bolsa en una molécula de enzima, en la que embona el sustrato (molécula que reacciona); donde el sustrato se convierte en productos *(24.3)*

activity series/serie de actividad lista de elementos en orden de actividad decreciente; la serie de actividad de los halógenos es F, Cl, Br, I *(11.2)*

actual yield/rendimiento real cantidad de producto que se forma cuando se lleva a cabo una reacción en el laboratorio *(12.3)*

addition reaction/reacción de adición reacción en la que una sustancia se añade al doble enlace de un alqueno o al triple enlace de un alquino *(23.2)*

adenosine triphosphate (ATP)/trifosfato de adenosina (ATP) molécula que transmite la energía que necesitan las células de todos los seres vivos *(24.6)*

alcohol/alcohol compuesto orgánico que posee un grupo —OH (hidroxilo); su estructura general es R—OH *(23.2)*

aldehyde/aldehído compuesto orgánico en el que el carbono del grupo carbonilo está unido a por lo menos un hidrógeno; su fórmula general es RCHO *(23.3)*

aliphatic hydrocarbon/hidrocarburo alifático cualquier alcano, alqueno o alquino de cadena lineal o cadena ramificada *(22.3)*

alkali metal/metal alcalino cualquier metal del grupo 1A de la tabla periódica *(6.2)*

alkaline earth metal/metal alcalinotérreo cualquier metal del grupo 2A de la tabla periódica *(6.2)*

alkaline solution/solución alcalina solución básica *(19.2)*

alkane/alcano hidrocarburo que sólo contiene enlaces covalentes sencillos; los alcanos son hidrocarburos saturados *(22.1)*

alkene/alqueno hidrocarburo que contiene uno o más enlaces dobles carbono–carbono; los alquenos son hidrocarburos insaturados *(22.2)*

alkyl group/grupo alquilo un hidrocarburo sustituto; el grupo metilo (—CH_3) es un grupo alquilo *(22.1)*

alkyl halide/haluro de alquilo compuesto halocarbonado en el que uno o más átomos de halógeno están unidos a los átomos de carbono de una cadena alifática *(23.1)*

alkyne/alquino hidrocarburo que contiene un triple enlace carbono–carbono; los alquinos son hidrocarburos insaturados *(22.2)*

allotrope/alótropo una de dos o más formas moleculares distintas de un elemento en el mismo estado físico; el oxígeno (O_2) y el ozono (O_3) son alótropos del elemento oxígeno *(13.3)*

alloy/aleación mezcla formada por dos o más elementos, donde al menos uno de ellos es un metal *(7.3)*

alpha particle/partícula alfa partícula con carga positiva emitida por ciertos núcleos radiactivos; consta de dos protones y dos neutrones, y es idéntica al núcleo de un átomo de helio *(25.1)*

amino acid/aminoácido compuesto orgánico que posee grupos amino (—NH_2) y carboxilo (—COOH) en la misma molécula; las proteínas se forman a partir de los 20 aminoácidos naturales *(24.3)*

amorphous solid/sólido amorfo describe un sólido que carece de una estructura interna ordenada; denota un acomodo aleatorio de átomos *(13.3)*

amphoteric/anfótero cifra que describe una sustancia que puede actuar como ácido y también como base *(19.1)*

amplitude/amplitud altura de la cresta de una onda *(5.3)*

anabolism/anabolismo procesos de síntesis dentro del metabolismo de las células; por lo regular, esos procesos requieren gasto de energía *(24.6)*

analytical chemistry/química analítica rama de la química que se concentra en la composición de la materia *(1.1)*

anion/anión cualquier átomo o grupo de átomos que posee carga negativa *(6.3)*

anode/ánodo electrodo en el que hay oxidación *(21.1)*

applied chemistry/química aplicada investigaciones que tienen una meta o aplicación práctica *(1.1)*

aqueous solution/solución acuosa agua que contiene sustancias disueltas *(15.2)*

aromatic compound/compuesto aromático compuesto orgánico que contiene un anillo bencénico u otro anillo con enlaces similares a los del benceno; los compuestos aromáticos también se conocen como arenos *(22.4)*

aryl halide/haluro de arilo compuesto en el que uno o más átomos de halógeno están unidos a átomos de carbono de un anillo de areno *(23.1)*

asymmetric carbon/carbono asimétrico átomo de carbono unido a cuatro átomos o grupos distintos *(22.3)*

atmospheric pressure/presión atmosférica presión ejercida por átomos y moléculas de la atmósfera que rodea a la Tierra y que resulta de los choques de dichas partículas con los objetos *(13.1)*

atom/átomo partícula más pequeña de un elemento que conserva su identidad en una reacción química *(4.1)*

atomic emission spectrum/espectro de emisión atómica patrón que se forma cuando la luz atraviesa un prisma o una rejilla de difracción que la separa en las diferentes frecuencias de luz que contiene *(5.3)*

atomic mass/masa atómica promedio ponderado de las masas de los isótopos de un elemento *(4.3)*

atomic mass unit (amu)/unidad de masa atómica (uma) unidad de masa igual a un doceavo de la masa de un átomo de carbono 12 *(4.3)*

atomic number/número atómico número de protones que hay en el núcleo del átomo de un elemento *(4.3)*

atomic orbital/orbital atómico expresión matemática que describe la probabilidad de hallar un electrón en diversos lugares; se suele representar como la región del espacio en torno al núcleo donde hay una probabilidad elevada de hallar un electrón *(5.1)*

atomic radius/radio atómico mitad de la distancia entre los núcleos de dos átomos del mismo elemento cuando dichos átomos están unidos *(6.3)*

aufbau principle/principio de aufbau regla según la cual los electrones primero ocupan los orbitales de energía más baja *(5.2)*

Avogadro's hypothesis/hipótesis de Avogadro volúmenes iguales de gases a la misma temperatura y presión contienen el mismo número de partículas *(10.2)*

Avogadro's number/número de Avogadro número de partículas representativas contenidas en un mol de una sustancia; es igual a 6.02×10^{23} partículas *(10.1)*

B

balanced equation/ecuación balanceada ecuación química en la que se conserva la masa; cada lado de la ecuación tiene el mismo número de átomos de cada elemento *(11.1)*

band of stability/banda de estabilidad región ocupada por los núcleos estables en un diagrama neutrones-protones *(25.2)*

barometer/barómetro instrumento que sirve para medir la presión atmosférica *(13.1)*

base/base compuesto que, en solución, produce iones hidróxido, acepta iones hidrógeno o cede pares de electrones *(9.4)*

base dissociation constant (K_b)/constante de disociación básica (K_b) razón de la concentración del ácido combinado multiplicada por la concentración del ion hidróxido, a la concentración de la base conjugada *(19.3)*

basic solution/solución básica cualquier solución en la que la concentración de ion hidróxido es mayor que la concentración de ion hidrógeno *(19.2)*

battery/batería grupo de celdas voltaicas conectadas entre sí *(21.1)*

beta particle/partícula beta electrón que se produce al descomponerse los neutrones de un átomo *(25.1)*

binary compound/compuesto binario compuesto integrado por dos elementos; $NaCl$ y Al_2O_3 son compuestos binarios *(9.2)*

biochemistry/bioquímica rama de la química que se concentra en los procesos que se dan en los organismos *(1.1)*

biotechnology/biotecnología campo que aplica la ciencia a la realización de productos o procesos biológicos *(1.2)*

boiling point (bp)/punto de ebullición (p. eb.) temperatura en la que la presión de vapor de un líquido es apenas igual a la presión externa sobre el líquido *(13.2)*

boiling-point elevation/incremento del punto de ebullición diferencia de temperatura entre el punto de ebullición de una solución y el punto de ebullición del disolvente puro *(16.3)*

bond dissociation energy/energía de disociación de enlaces energía requerida para romper el enlace entre dos átomos unidos de forma covalente; este valor suele expresarse en kJ por mol de sustancia *(8.2)*

bonding orbital/orbital de enlace orbital molecular que puede ser ocupado por los dos electrones de un enlace covalente *(8.3)*

Boyle's law/ley de Boyle para una masa dada de gas a temperatura constante, el volumen del gas varía en proporción inversa con la presión *(14.2)*

branched-chain alkane/alcano de cadena ramificada alcano con uno o más grupos alquilo unidos a la estructura madre *(22.1)*

Brownian motion/movimiento browniano movimiento caótico de partículas coloidales, debido a los choques con las partículas del disolvente en el que están dispersas *(15.3)*

buffer/solución amortiguadora solución cuyo pH permanece relativamente constante si se le añaden pequeñas cantidades de ácido o base; una solución amortiguadora puede ser una solución de un ácido débil y la sal de un ácido débil o una solución de una base débil y la sal de una base débil *(19.5)*

buffer capacity/capacidad amortiguadora medida de la cantidad de ácido o base que se puede añadir a una solución amortiguadora sin que haya un cambio importante del pH *(19.5)*

C

calorie (cal)/caloría (cal) cantidad de calor necesaria para elevar 1°C la temperatura de 1 g de agua pura *(3.2)*

calorimeter/calorímetro aparato con material aislante que sirve para medir la absorción o desprendimiento de calor durante procesos químicos o físicos *(17.2)*

calorimetry/calorimetría medición precisa del cambio del calor durante procesos químicos y físicos *(17.2)*

carbohydrate/carbohidrato nombre dado a monómeros y polímeros de aldehídos y cetonas que tienen muchos grupos hidroxilo; los azúcares y almidones son carbohidratos *(24.2)*

carbonyl group/grupo carbonilo grupo funcional que consiste en un átomo de carbono y uno de oxígeno unidos por un doble enlace; se le encuentra en aldehídos, cetonas, ésteres y amidas *(23.3)*

carboxyl group/grupo carboxilo grupo funcional que consiste en un grupo carbonilo unido a un grupo hidroxilo; se le encuentra en los ácidos carboxílicos *(23.3)*

carboxylic acid/ácido carboxílico ácido orgánico que contiene un grupo carboxilo; su fórmula general es RCOOH *(23.3)*

catabolism/catabolismo reacción, dentro de las células vivas, por la que diversas sustancias se descomponen y producen energía (24.6)

catalyst/catalizador sustancia que aumenta la velocidad de reacción disminuyendo la barrera de energía de activación; el catalizador no se consume en la reacción (11.1)

cathode/cátodo electrodo en el que hay reducción (21.1)

cathode ray/rayo catódico haz de electrones producido en el electrodo negativo (cátodo) de un tubo que contiene un gas a baja presión (4.2)

cation/catión cualquier átomo o grupo de átomos que posee carga positiva (6.3)

cell potential/potencial de celda diferencia entre los potenciales de reducción de dos medias celdas (21.2)

Celsius scale/escala Celsius escala de temperatura en la que el punto de congelación del agua es 0°C y el punto de ebullición del agua es 100°C (3.2)

Charles's law/ley de Charles el volumen de una masa fija de gas es directamente proporcional a su temperatura Kelvin si la presión se mantiene constante (14.2)

chemical change/cambio químico cambio que produce materia con una composición diferente que la de la materia original (2.3)

chemical equation/ecuación química expresión que representa una reacción química; las fórmulas de los reactantes (a la izquierda) se unen mediante una flecha a las fórmulas de los productos (a la derecha) (11.1)

chemical equilibrium/equilibrio químico estado de equilibrio en el que las velocidades de la reacción hacia adelante y la reacción inversa son iguales; no hay un cambio total en la cantidad de reactantes y productos en el sistema químico (18.2)

chemical formula/fórmula química expresión que indica el número y tipo de átomos que están presentes en la unidad más pequeña representativa de una sustancia (7.2)

chemical potential energy/energía potencial química energía almacenada en los enlaces químicos (17.1)

chemical property/propiedad química capacidad de una sustancia para sufrir un cambio químico específico (2.4)

chemical reaction/reacción química cambio en el que uno o más reactantes se convierten en uno o más productos; se caracteriza por la ruptura de enlaces en los reactantes y la formación de enlaces en los productos (2.4)

chemical symbol/símbolo químico representación de un elemento que emplea una o dos letras (2.3)

chemistry/química estudio de la composición de la materia y los cambios que ésta sufre (1.1)

cis **configuration/configuración** *cis* configuración en la cual los grupos sustitutos están del mismo lado de un doble enlace (22.3)

coefficient/coeficiente número entero pequeño que aparece antepuesto a una fórmula en una ecuación química balanceada (11.1)

coenzyme/coenzima pequeña molécula orgánica o ion metálico que se requiere para que una enzima tenga actividad biológica (24.3)

colligative property/propiedad coligativa propiedad de una solución que depende únicamente del número de partículas de soluto, y no de su identidad; el incremento del punto de ebullición, la disminución del punto de congelación y el descenso de la presión de vapor son propiedades coligativas (16.3)

collision theory/teoría de choques los átomos, iones y moléculas pueden reaccionar para formar productos cuando chocan, siempre que las partículas tengan suficiente energía cinética (18.1)

colloid/coloide mezcla cuyas partículas tienen un tamaño intermedio entre las de una suspensión y las de soluto de una solución (15.3)

combination reaction/reacción de combinación cambio químico en el que dos o más sustancias reaccionan para formar una sola sustancia nueva; también llamado reacción de síntesis (11.2)

combined gas law/ley combinada de los gases ley que describe las relaciones entre la presión, la temperatura y el volumen de un gas encerrado (14.2)

combustion reaction/reacción de combustión cambio químico en el que un elemento o un compuesto reacciona con oxígeno y por lo regular produce energía en forma de luz y calor (11.2)

common ion/ion común ion que es común a dos sales disueltas en una solución; en una solución de nitrato de plata y cloruro de plata, Ag^+ sería un ion común (18.3)

common ion effect/efecto de ion común disminución en la solubilidad de un compuesto iónico debida a la adición de un ion común (18.3)

complete ionic equation/ecuación iónica completa ecuación que muestra los compuestos iónicos disueltos en forma de iones disociados libres (11.3)

compound/compuesto sustancia que contiene dos o más elementos combinados químicamente en una proporción fija (2.3)

compressibility/compresibilidad medida de cuánto disminuye el volumen de la materia cuando se le aplica presión (14.1)

concentrated solution/solución concentrada solución que contiene una gran cantidad de soluto (16.2)

concentration/concentración medida de la cantidad de soluto que está disuelto en una cantidad específica de disolvente; suele expresarse en mol/L (16.2)

condensed structural formula/fórmula estructural condensada fórmula estructural que no muestra algunos enlaces y/o átomos; la presencia de estos enlaces o átomos se sobreentiende (22.1)

conjugate acid/ácido conjugado partícula que se forma cuando una base gana un ion hidrógeno; NH_4^+ es el ácido conjugado de la base NH_3 (19.1)

conjugate acid-base pair/par conjugado ácido-base dos sustancias relacionadas entre sí por la pérdida o ganancia de un solo ion hidrógeno; el amoniaco (NH_3) y el ion amonio (NH_4^+) son un par conjugado ácido-base (19.1)

conjugate base/base conjugada partícula que queda cuando un ácido transfiere un ion hidrógeno; OH^- es la base conjugada del ácido agua (19.1)

conversion factor/factor de conversión razón de medidas equivalentes usadas para convertir una cantidad de una unidad a otra (3.3)

coordinate covalent bond/enlace covalente coordinado enlace covalente en el que un átomo aporta dos electrones de enlace (8.2)

coordination number/número de coordinación número de iones de carga opuesta que rodean a cada ion en un cristal (7.2)

covalent bond/enlace covalente enlace que se forma cuando dos átomos comparten electrones (8.1)

cracking/pirólisis proceso controlado por el cual los hidrocarburos se descomponen o reacomodan para obtener moléculas más pequeñas y útiles *(22.5)*

crystal/cristal sólido en el que los átomos, iones o moléculas están dispuestos en un patrón tridimensional ordenado y repetitivo llamado red cristalina *(13.3)*

cyclic hydrocarbon/hidrocarburo cíclico compuesto orgánico que contiene un anillo de hidrocarburo *(22.4)*

Dalton's atomic theory/teoría atómica de Dalton primera teoría en relacionar los cambios químicos con sucesos a nivel atómico *(4.1)*

Dalton's law of partial pressures/teoría de Dalton de las presiones parciales a volumen y temperatura constantes, la presión total ejercida por una mezcla de gases es igual a la suma de las presiones parciales de los gases componentes *(14.4)*

decomposition reaction/reacción de descomposición cambio químico en el que un solo compuesto se descompone en dos o más productos más simples *(11.2)*

dehydrogenation reaction/reacción de deshidrogenación reacción en la que se pierde hidrógeno *(23.3)*

deliquescent/delicuescente término que describe una sustancia que absorbe suficiente humedad del aire como para formar una solución; la solución formada tiene una presión de vapor más baja que la de la humedad del aire *(15.2)*

denatured alcohol/alcohol desnaturalizado etanol al que se ha añadido una sustancia venenosa para hacerlo tóxico *(23.2)*

density/densidad razón de la masa de un objeto a su volumen *(3.4)*

dependent variable/variable dependiente *véase* variable de respuesta

desiccant/desecante sustancia higroscópica empleada como agente secante *(15.2)*

diatomic molecule/molécula diatómica molécula que consta de dos átomos *(8.1)*

diffusion/difusión tendencia de las moléculas a moverse hacia áreas de concentración más baja hasta que la concentración es uniforme en todo el medio *(14.4)*

dilute solution/solución diluida solución que contiene muy poco soluto *(16.2)*

dimensional analysis/análisis dimensional técnica para resolver problemas que se apoya en las unidades de las mediciones para resolver el problema *(3.3)*

dipole/dipolo molécula que tiene dos polos o regiones de carga opuesta *(8.4)*

dipole interaction/interacción dipolar fuerzas intermoleculares que resultan de la atracción de regiones de moléculas polares que tienen cargas opuestas *(8.4)*

diprotic acid/ácido diprótico cualquier ácido que contenga dos protones (iones hidrógeno) ionizables; el ácido sulfúrico (H_2SO_4) es un ácido diprótico *(19.1)*

disaccharide/disacárido carbohidrato formado por dos unidades de monosacárido; el azúcar de mesa común (sacarosa) es un disacárido *(24.2)*

dispersion forces/fuerzas de dispersión atracciones entre moléculas que se dan cuando el movimiento de los electrones de una molécula afecta el movimiento de los electrones de la otra mediante fuerzas eléctricas; se trata de las interacciones más débiles entre moléculas *(8.4)*

displacement reaction/reacción de desplazamiento *véase* reacción de sustitución sencilla

distillation/destilación proceso empleado para separar sólidos disueltos de un líquido, el cual se hace hervir para producir un vapor que después se condensa para convertirlo en líquido *(2.2)*

double covalent bond/enlace covalente doble enlace en el que dos átomos comparten dos pares de electrones *(8.2)*

double-replacement reaction/reacción de sustitución doble cambio químico que implica un intercambio de iones positivos entre dos compuestos *(11.2)*

dry cell/pila seca celda voltaica comercial en la que, a pesar del nombre, el electrolito es una pasta húmeda; las baterías compactas y portátiles que se usan en las linternas son pilas secas *(21.1)*

effloresce/eflorecerse perder agua de hidratación; el proceso se presenta cuando la presión de vapor del hidrato es más alta que la del vapor de agua en el aire *(15.2)*

effusion/efusión proceso en el cual un gas escapa por un agujero diminuto en su recipiente *(14.4)*

electrical potential/potencial eléctrico capacidad de una celda voltaica para producir corriente eléctrica *(21.2)*

electrochemical cell/celda electroquímica cualquier dispositivo que convierte energía química en energía eléctrica o energía eléctrica en energía química *(21.1)*

electrochemical process/proceso electroquímico conversión de energía química en energía eléctrica o energía eléctrica en energía química; en todos los procesos electroquímicos intervienen reacciones redox *(21.1)*

electrode/electrodo en un circuito, un conductor que transporta electrones hacia o desde una sustancia que no es un metal *(21.1)*

electrolysis/electrolisis proceso en el que se usa energía eléctrica para realizar un cambio químico; la electrolisis del agua produce hidrógeno y oxígeno *(21.3)*

electrolyte/electrolito compuesto que conduce una corriente eléctrica cuando está en solución acuosa o derretido; todos los compuestos iónicos son electrolitos, pero muy pocos compuestos covalentes lo son *(15.2)*

electrolytic cell/celda electrolítica celda electroquímica que se usa para efectuar un cambio químico mediante la aplicación de energía eléctrica *(21.3)*

electromagnetic radiation/radiación electromagnética ondas de energía que viajan en el vacío a una velocidad de 2.998×10^8 m/s; incluye las ondas de radio, microondas, ondas infrarrojas, luz visible, ondas ultravioleta, rayos X y rayos gamma *(5.3)*

electron/electrón partícula subátomica con carga negativa *(4.2)*

electron configuration/configuración electrónica distribución de los electrones de un átomo en su estado basal, en diversos orbitales alrededor del núcleo del átomo *(5.2)*

electron dot structure/estructura electrón-punto notación que muestra los electrones de valencia como puntos alrededor del símbolo atómico del elemento; el símbolo representa los electrones internos y el núcleo atómico; también se conoce como estructura de puntos de Lewis *(7.1)*

electronegativity/electronegatividad capacidad de un átomo para atraer electrones cuando el átomo está en un compuesto *(6.3)*

element/elemento forma más simple de materia que posee un conjunto único de propiedades; un elemento no puede descomponerse en sustancias más simples usando métodos químicos *(2.3)*

elementary reaction/reacción básica reacción en la que los reactantes se convierten en productos en un solo paso *(18.5)*

empirical formula/fórmula empírica fórmula que muestra las proporciones de los elementos en un compuesto con los números enteros más pequeños posibles; la fórmula empírica del peróxido de hidrógeno (H_2O_2) es HO *(10.3)*

emulsion/emulsión dispersión coloidal de un líquido en otro *(15.3)*

endothermic process/proceso endotérmico proceso en el que se absorbe calor del entorno *(17.1)*

end point/punto final punto de una valoración química en que el indicador cambia de color *(19.4)*

energy/energía capacidad para efectuar trabajo o producir calor *(3.2)*

energy level/nivel energético las energías específicas que puede tener un electrón en un átomo u otro sistema *(5.1)*

enthalpy (*H*)/entalpía (*H*) cantidad de calor en un sistema a presión constante *(17.2)*

entropy (*S*)/entropía (*S*) medida del desorden de un sistema; los sistemas tienden a pasar de un estado ordenado (baja entropía) a un estado de máximo desorden (alta entropía) *(18.4)*

enzyme/enzima proteína que actúa como catalizador biológico *(24.3)*

enzyme–substrate complex/complejo enzima-sustrato estructura que se forma cuando una molécula de sustrato se une a una enzima en su sitio activo *(24.3)*

equilibrium constant (*K*eq)/constante de equilibrio (*K*eq) razón de las concentraciones de los productos a las concentraciones de los reactantes en el equilibrio, con cada concentración elevada a una potencia igual al número de moles de esa sustancia en la ecuación química balanceada *(18.2)*

equilibrium position/posición de equilibrio las concentraciones relativas de reactantes y productos de una reacción que ha alcanzado el equilibrio; indica si se favorecen los reactantes o productos en la reacción reversible *(18.2)*

equivalence point/punto de equivalencia punto de una valoración química en la que el número de moles de iones hidrógeno es igual al número de moles de iones hidróxido *(19.4)*

error/error diferencia entre el valor aceptado y el valor experimental *(3.1)*

ester/éster derivado de un ácido carboxílico en el que el —OH del grupo carboxilo ha sido sustituido por el —OR de un alcohol; la fórmula general es RCOOR *(23.3)*

ether/éter compuesto orgánico en el que el oxígeno está unido a dos grupos carbono; la fórmula general es R—O—R *(23.2)*

evaporation/evaporación vaporización que se da en la superficie de un líquido que no está en ebullición *(13.2)*

excess reagent/reactivo excesivo reactivo que está presente en una cantidad más que suficiente para reaccionar con un reactivo limitante; cualquier reactante que queda después de que se ha usado todo el reactivo limitante en una reacción química *(12.3)*

exothermic process/proceso exotérmico proceso en el que se desprende calor hacia el entorno *(17.1)*

experiment/experimento procedimiento repetido que sirve para probar una hipótesis *(1.3)*

experimental value/valor experimental valor cuantitativo que se mide durante un experimento *(3.1)*

extensive property/propiedad extensiva propiedad que depende de la cantidad de materia en una muestra *(2.1)*

fatty acid/ácido graso nombre que se da a los ácidos carboxílicos de cadena continua que se aislaron originalmente de las grasas *(23.3)*

fermentation/fermentación producción de etanol a partir de azúcares por la acción de levaduras o bacterias *(23.2)*

film badge/placa de película dispositivo para detectar radiación que consta de varias capas de película fotográfica cubiertas con papel negro opaco, todo envuelto en un estuche de plástico o metal *(25.4)*

filtration/filtración proceso para separar un sólido de un líquido en una mezcla heterogénea *(2.2)*

first-order reaction/reacción de primer orden reacción cuya velocidad de reacción es proporcional a la concentración de un solo reactante *(18.5)*

fission/fisión división de un núcleo en fragmentos más pequeños, acompañada por desprendimiento de neutrones y una gran cantidad de energía *(25.3)*

formula unit/unidad de fórmula razón más baja, expresada en números enteros, de los iones de un compuesto iónico; en el cloruro de magnesio, la razón de iones magnesio a iones cloruro es de 1:2, así que la unidad de fórmula es $MgCl_2$ *(7.2)*

free energy/energía libre energía que está disponible para realizar trabajo *(18.4)*

freezing-point depression/disminución del punto de congelación diferencia de temperatura entre el punto de congelación de una solución y el del disolvente puro *(16.3)*

frequency (*v*)/frecuencia (*v*) número de ciclos de onda que pasan por un punto específico en la unidad de tiempo; la frecuencia y la longitud de onda son inversamente proporcionales *(5.3)*

fuel cell/celda de combustible celda voltaica que no necesita recargarse; el combustible se oxida para producir un suministro continuo de energía eléctrica *(21.1)*

functional group/grupo funcional distribución específica de átomos en un compuesto orgánico que puede participar en reacciones químicas características; la química de un compuesto orgánico está determinada por sus grupos funcionales *(23.1)*

fusion/fusión proceso en el que se combinan núcleos para producir un núcleo con mayor masa *(25.3)*

G

gamma ray/rayo gamma fotón de alta energía emitido por un radioisótopo *(25.1)*

gas/gas estado de la materia que adopta la forma y el volumen del recipiente que la contiene; los gases no tienen forma ni volumen definidos *(2.1)*

gas pressure/presión de gas resultado de fuerza que ejerce un gas por unidad de área total de un objeto; se debe a los choques de las partículas de gas contra el objeto *(13.1)*

Gay-Lussac's law/ley de Gay-Lussac la presión de un gas es directamente proporcional a su temperatura Kelvin si se mantiene constante el volumen *(14.2)*

Geiger counter/contador Geiger dispositivo que usa un tubo de metal lleno de gas para detectar radiación *(25.4)*

gene/gen segmento de ADN que contiene el código para una sola cadena péptida *(24.5)*

genetic code/código genético distribución de bases en las palabras de código del ADN; se usan 61 tripletes de palabras de código para especificar los aminoácidos de las proteínas, además de 3 tripletes de palabras de código que indican "parar" una vez que termina la síntesis de proteínas *(24.5)*

geometric isomers/isómeros geométricos compuestos que tienen átomos en el mismo orden, pero difieren en la orientación de los grupos alrededor de un enlace doble *(22.3)*

Gibbs free-energy change (ΔG)/cambio de energía libre de Gibbs (ΔG) cantidad máxima de energía que se puede acoplar a otro proceso para efectuar trabajo útil *(18.4)*

glass/vidrio producto transparente que resulta de la fusión de materiales inorgánicos que se han enfriado hasta solidificarse sin cristalizarse *(13.3)*

Graham's laws of effusion/leyes de efusión de Graham la velocidad de efusión de un gas es inversamente proporcional a la raíz cuadrada de su masa molar; esta relación también se cumple en la difusión de gases *(14.4)*

gram (g)/gramo (g) unidad métrica de masa igual a la masa de 1 cm^3 de agua a 4°C *(3.2)*

ground state/estado fundamental energía más baja que puede tener un electrón descrito por la mecánica cuántica *(5.3)*

group/grupo columna vertical de elementos en la tabla periódica; los elementos de un grupo tienen propiedades físicas y químicas similares *(4.3)*

H

half-cell/semicelda parte de una celda voltaica en la que se lleva a cabo la oxidación o reducción; consta de un solo electrodo sumergido en una solución de sus iones *(21.1)*

half-life ($t_{1/2}$)/semivida ($t_{1/2}$) tiempo que tarda en desintegrarse la mitad de los núcleos de una muestra de un radioisótopo *(25.2)*

half-reaction/semirreacción ecuación que muestra la oxidación o bien la reducción que se da en una reacción redox *(20.3)*

half-reaction method/método de semirreacción método para balancear una ecuación redox equilibrando por separado las semirreacciones de oxidación y reducción antes de combinarlas para obtener una ecuación redox balanceada *(20.3)*

halide ion/ion haluro ion negativo que se forma cuando un átomo de halógeno gana un electrón *(7.1)*

halocarbon/compuesto halocarbonado cualquier miembro de una clase de compuestos orgánicos que contienen flúor, cloro, bromo o yodo unidos mediante enlaces covalentes *(23.1)*

halogen/halógeno no metal del grupo 7A de la tabla periódica *(6.2)*

heat (q)/calor (q) energía que fluye de un objeto a otro debido a la diferencia de temperaturas entre los objetos *(17.1)*

heat capacity/capacidad calorífica cantidad de calor necesaria para elevar exactamente 1°C la temperatura de un objeto *(17.1)*

heat of combustion/calor de combustión calor de reacción al quemarse totalmente un mol de una sustancia *(17.2)*

heat of reaction/calor de reacción cambio de calor correspondiente a una ecuación química en la forma exacta en que está escrita *(17.2)*

Heisenberg uncertainty principle/principio de incertidumbre de Heisenberg es imposible conocer con exactitud la velocidad y la posición de una partícula al mismo tiempo *(5.3)*

Henry's law/ley de Henry a una temperatura determinada, la solubilidad de un gas en un líquido es directamente proporcional a la presión del gas sobre el líquido *(16.1)*

hertz (Hz)/hertz (Hz) unidad de frecuencia, igual a un ciclo por segundo *(5.3)*

Hess's law of heat summation/ley de Hess de la suma de los calores ley según la cual, si se suman dos o más ecuaciones termoquímicas para obtener una ecuación final, también se suman los calores de reacción para obtener el calor de reacción final *(17.4)*

heterogeneous mixture/mezcla heterogénea mezcla cuya composición no es uniforme; sus componentes no están distribuidos de forma equitativa en toda la mezcla *(2.2)*

homogeneous mixture/mezcla homogénea mezcla cuya composición es uniforme; sus componentes están distribuidos de forma equitativa y no es fácil distinguirlos *(2.2)*

homologous series/serie homóloga grupo de compuestos en el que se observa un incremento constante de cambio en la estructura molecular de un compuesto al siguiente *(22.1)*

Hund's rule/regla de Hund los electrones ocupan orbitales de la misma energía haciendo que el número de electrones cuyo espín tiene la misma dirección sea lo más grande posible *(5.2)*

hybridization/hibridización combinación de varios orbitales atómicos para formar el mismo número total de orbitales híbridos equivalentes *(8.3)*

hydrate/hidrato compuesto que tiene un número específico de moléculas de agua unidas a cada unidad de fórmula *(15.2)*

hydration reaction/reacción de hidratación reacción en la que se añade agua a un alqueno *(23.2)*

hydrocarbon/hidrocarburo compuesto orgánico que contiene sólo carbono e hidrógeno *(22.1)*

hydrogenation reaction/reacción de hidrogenación reacción en la que se añade hidrógeno a un doble enlace carbono–carbono para dar un alcano *(23.2)*

hydrogen bonds/enlaces de hidrógeno fuerzas de atracción en las que un átomo de hidrógeno, unido por un enlace covalente a un átomo muy electronegativo, también se une débilmente a un par no compartido de electrones de otro átomo electronegativo *(8.4)*

hydrogen-ion acceptor/receptor de iones hidrógeno una base, según la teoría de Brønsted-Lowry; el amoniaco actúa como base cuando acepta iones hidrógeno del agua *(19.1)*

hydrogen-ion donor/donador de iones hidrógeno un ácido, según la teoría de Brønsted-Lowry *(19.1)*

hydronium ion (H₃O⁺)/ion hidronio (H₃O⁺) ion positivo que se forma cuando una molécula de agua gana un ion hidrógeno *(19.1)*

hydroxide ion (OH⁻)/ion hidróxido (OH⁻) ion negativo que se forma cuando una molécula de agua pierde un ion hidrógeno *(19.1)*

hydroxyl group/grupo hidroxilo grupo funcional —OH presente en los alcoholes *(23.2)*

hygroscopic/higroscópico se llama así a las sales y otros compuestos que absorben humedad del aire *(15.2)*

hypothesis/hipótesis explicación propuesta para una observación *(1.3)*

ideal gas constant/constante del gas ideal constante de la ley del gas ideal; se representa con el símbolo R y tiene un valor de 8.31 (L·kPa)/(K·mol) *(14.3)*

ideal gas law/ley del gas ideal relación $PV = nRT$, que describe el comportamiento del gas ideal *(14.3)*

immiscible/inmiscible se dice de los líquidos que son insolubles uno en el otro; el aceite y el agua son inmiscibles *(16.1)*

inhibitor/inhibidor sustancia que interfiere la acción de un catalizador *(18.1)*

independent variable/variable independiente *véase* variable manipulada

inner transition metal/metal interno de transición elemento de las series de los lantánidos o los actínidos; el subnivel s más alto ocupado y el subnivel f cercano de sus átomos contienen electrones; también se llama elemento interno de transición *(6.2)*

inorganic chemistry/química inorgánica estudio de sustancias que, en general, no contienen carbono *(1.1)*

intensive property/propiedad intensiva propiedad que depende del tipo de materia de una muestra, no de la cantidad de materia *(2.1)*

intermediate/intermediario producto de uno de los pasos de un mecanismo de reacción; se convierte en reactante en el siguiente paso *(18.5)*

International System of Units (SI)/Sistema Internacional de Unidades (SI) versión modificada del sistema métrico, adoptada por acuerdo internacional en 1960 *(3.2)*

ion/ion átomo o grupo de átomos que tiene carga positiva o negativa *(6.3)*

ionic bond/enlace iónico atracción electrostática que une a iones con carga opuesta *(7.2)*

ionic compound/compuesto iónico compuesto formado por iones positivos y negativos *(7.2)*

ionization energy/energía de ionización energía necesaria para sacar un electrón de un átomo en su estado gaseoso *(6.3)*

ionizing radiation/radiación ionizante radiación que tiene la energía suficiente para desprender electrones de algunos átomos de una sustancia bombardeada, produciendo así iones *(25.4)*

ion-product constant for water (K�w)/constante de producto de iones del agua (K�w) producto de las concentraciones de iones hidrógeno y de iones hidróxido del agua; es 1×10^{-14} a 25°C *(9.2)*

isomers/isómeros compuestos que tienen la misma fórmula molecular, pero diferentes estructuras moleculares *(22.3)*

isotopes/isótopos átomos del mismo elemento que tienen el mismo número atómico pero diferentes masas atómicas porque tienen distinto número de neutrones *(4.3)*

joule (J)/julio (J) unidad de energía en el SI; 4.184 J equivalen a una caloría *(3.2)*

Kelvin scale/escala Kelvin escala de temperatura en la que el punto de congelación del agua es 273 K, y el de ebullición, 373 K; 0 K es el cero absoluto *(3.2)*

ketone/cetona compuesto orgánico en el que el carbono del grupo carbonilo está unido a otros dos carbonos: la fórmula general es RCOR *(23.3)*

kilogram (kg)/kilogramo (kg) masa de 1 L de agua a 4°C; es la unidad base de masa en el SI *(3.2)*

kinetic energy/energía cinética energía que tienen los objetos de acuerdo con su movimiento *(13.1)*

kinetic theory/teoría cinética teoría que explica los estados de la materia basándose en el concepto de que toda la materia está formada por pequeñas partículas que están en constante movimiento *(13.1)*

law of conservation of energy/ley de conservación de la energía ley según la cual en ningún proceso químico o físico se crea ni se destruye energía *(17.1)*

law of conservation of mass/ley de conservación de la masa en cualquier cambio físico o reacción química, la masa se conserva; la masa no puede crearse ni destruirse *(2.4)*

law of definite proportions/ley de las proporciones definidas en muestras de cualquier compuesto químico, las masas de los elementos siempre están en la misma proporción *(9.5)*

law of disorder/ley del desorden tendencia natural de los sistemas a desplazarse en la dirección de máximo caos o desorden *(18.4)*

law of multiple proportions/ley de las proporciones múltiples siempre que dos elementos forman más de un compuesto, las diferentes masas de un elemento que se combinan con la misma masa del otro elemento están en razón de números enteros pequeños *(9.5)*

Le Châtelier's principle/principio de Le Châtelier cuando se aplica una tensión a un sistema que está en equilibrio dinámico, el sistema cambia a modo de aliviar dicha tensión *(18.2)*

Lewis acid/ácido de Lewis cualquier sustancia capaz de aceptar un par de electrones para formar un enlace covalente *(19.1)*

Lewis base/base de Lewis cualquier sustancia capaz de ceder un par de electrones para formar un enlace covalente *(19.1)*

limiting reagent/reactivo limitante cualquier reactante que se haya consumido primero en una reacción química; determina la cantidad de producto que se puede formar en la reacción *(12.3)*

lipid/lípido miembro de una clase amplia de compuestos orgánicos relativamente insolubles en agua; las grasas, aceites y ceras son lípidos *(24.4)*

liquid/líquido forma de materia que fluye; tiene volumen fijo pero forma indefinida *(2.1)*

liter (L)/litro (L) volumen de un cubo cuyas aristas miden 10 centímetros cada una ($1000 cm^3$); es la unidad común de volumen en el sistema métrico *(3.2)*

M

macroscopic/macroscópico término que describe el mundo de los objetos suficientemente grandes como para verse a simple vista *(1.2)*

manipulated variable/variable manipulada variable que cambia durante un experimento; también se llama variable independiente *(1.3)*

mass/masa medida de la cantidad de materia contenida en un objeto; la unidad base de masa en el SI es el kilogramo *(2.1)*

mass number/número de masa número total de protones y neutrones que contiene el núcleo de un átomo *(4.3)*

matter/materia todo lo que tiene masa y ocupa espacio *(1.1)*

measurement/medición descripción cuantitativa que incluye tantos números como unidades *(3.1)*

melting point (mp)/punto de fusión (p.f.) temperatura a la que una sustancia cambia del estado sólido al líquido; el punto de fusión del agua es 0°C *(13.3)*

metabolism/metabolismo todas las reacciones químicas llevadas a cabo por los organismos; incluyen reacciones que producen energía (catabolismo) y reacciones que consumen energía (anabolismo) *(24.6)*

metal/metal miembro de una clase de elementos que son buenos conductores del calor y la electricidad; los metales suelen ser dúctiles, maleables y brillantes *(6.1)*

metallic bond/enlace metálico fuerza de atracción que mantiene unidos los átomos de un metal; se debe a la atracción entre los electrones de valencia, que flotan libremente, y los iones metálicos de carga positiva *(7.3)*

metalloid/metaloide elemento cuyas propiedades son similares a las de los metales y de los no metales *(6.1)*

meter (m)/metro (m) unidad base de longitud en el SI *(3.2)*

microscopic/microscópico término que describe el mundo de los objetos que sólo pueden verse con instrumentos amplificadores *(1.2)*

miscible/miscible se les llama así a los líquidos que se disuelven uno en el otro en todas las proporciones *(16.1)*

mixture/mezcla incorporación física de dos o más sustancias que no se combinan químicamente *(2.2)*

molal boiling-point elevation constant (K_b)/constante molal de incremento del punto de ebullición (K_b) cambio en el punto de ebullición de una solución 1-molal de un soluto molecular no volátil *(16.4)*

molal freezing-point depression constant (K_f)/constante molal de disminución del punto de congelación (K_f) cambio en el punto de congelación de una solución 1-molal de un soluto molecular no volátil *(16.4)*

molality (m)/molalidad (m) concentración de soluto en una solución expresada como el número de moles de soluto disueltos en 1 kilogramo (1000 g) de disolvente *(16.4)*

molar heat of condensation (ΔH_{cond})/calor molar de condensación (ΔH_{cond}) cantidad de calor que un mol de vapor desprende al condensarse, convirtiéndose en líquido, a temperatura constante *(17.3)*

molar heat of fusion (ΔH_{fus})/calor molar de fusión (ΔH_{fus}) cantidad de calor que un mol de una sustancia sólida absorbe al fundirse, convirtiéndose en líquido, a temperatura constante *(17.3)*

molar heat of solidification (ΔH_{solid})/calor molar de solidificación (ΔH_{solid}) cantidad de calor que un mol de un líquido pierde al solidificarse a temperatura constante *(17.3)*

molar heat of solution (ΔH_{soln})/calor molar de disolución (ΔH_{soln}) cambio de calor debido a la disolución de un mol de una sustancia *(17.3)*

molar heat of vaporization (ΔH_{vap})/calor molar de vaporización (ΔH_{vap}) cantidad de calor absorbida por un mol de un líquido al evaporarse a temperatura constante *(17.3)*

molarity (M)/molaridad (M) concentración de soluto en una solución expresada como el número de moles de soluto disueltos en 1 litro de solución *(16.2)*

molar mass/masa molar término empleado para referirse a la masa de un mol de cualquier sustancia *(10.1)*

molar volume/volumen molar volumen ocupado por 1 mol de un gas a temperatura y presión estándar (TPE); 22.4 L *(10.2)*

mole (mol)/mol cantidad de una sustancia que contiene 6.02×10^{23} partículas representativas de esa sustancia *(10.1)*

molecular compound/compuesto molecular compuesto formado por moléculas *(8.1)*

molecular formula/fórmula molecular fórmula química de un compuesto molecular que indica los tipos y números de átomos presentes en una molécula de un compuesto *(8.1)*

molecular orbital/orbital molecular orbital que abarca toda la molécula *(8.3)*

molecule/molécula grupo neutro de átomos unidos por enlaces covalentes *(8.1)*

mole fraction/fracción molar razón de los moles de soluto en solución al número total de moles de disolvente y soluto *(16.4)*

mole ratio/razón molar factor de conversión derivado de los coeficientes de una ecuación química equilibrada interpretada en términos de moles *(12.2)*

monatomic ion/ion monoatómico un solo átomo con carga positiva o negativa debida a la pérdida o ganancia de uno o más electrones de valencia *(9.1)*

monomer/monómero molécula sencilla que se combina repetidamente para formar un polímero *(23.4)*

monoprotic acid/ácido monoprótico ácido que sólo contiene un protón (ion hidrógeno) ionizable; el ácido nítrico (HNO_3) es un ácido monoprótico *(19.1)*

monosaccharide/monosacárido carbohidrato que consta de una sola unidad de azúcar; también llamado azúcar simple *(24.2)*

net ionic equation/ecuación iónica neta ecuación de una reacción en solución que sólo muestra las partículas que intervienen directamente en el cambio químico *(11.3)*

network solid/sólido en cadena sólido en el que todos los átomos están unidos entre sí por enlaces covalentes *(8.4)*

neutralization reaction/reacción de neutralización reacción en la que un ácido y una base reaccionan en solución acuosa para producir una sal y agua *(19.4)*

neutral solution/solución neutral solución acuosa en la que las concentraciones de iones hidrógeno y iones hidróxido son iguales; tiene un pH de 7.0 *(19.2)*

neutron/neutrón partícula subatómica sin carga que tiene una masa de 1 uma; se le encuentra en el núcleo de los átomos *(4.2)*

neutron absorption/absorción de neutrones proceso que reduce el número de neutrones lentos en un reactor nuclear; esto se logra mediante el uso de varillas de control hechas con un material como el cadmio, que absorbe neutrones *(25.3)*

neutron activation analysis/análisis por activación de neutrones procedimiento en el que se bombardea una muestra con neutrones de una fuente radiactiva para detectar cantidades muy pequeñas de elementos en la muestra *(25.4)*

neutron moderation/moderación de neutrones proceso empleado en reactores nucleares para frenar los neutrones de modo que el combustible del reactor los capture para continuar la reacción en cadena *(25.3)*

noble gas/gas noble elemento del grupo 8A de la tabla periódica; los subniveles *s* y *p* del nivel energético ocupado más alto están totalmente llenos *(6.2)*

nonelectrolyte/no electrolito compuesto que no conduce una corriente eléctrica en solución acuosa ni en estado fundido *(15.2)*

nonmetal/no metal elemento que suele ser mal conductor del calor y la electricidad; las propiedades de los no metales generalmente son opuestas a las de los metales *(6.1)*

nonpolar covalent bond/enlace covalente no polar enlace covalente en el que los dos átomos comparten equitativamente los electrones *(8.4)*

nonspontaneous reaction/reacción no espontánea reacción que no favorece la formación de productos en las condiciones especificadas *(18.4)*

normal boiling point/punto normal de ebullición el punto de ebullición de un líquido a una presión de 101.3 kPa o 1 atm *(13.2)*

nucleic acid/ácido nucleico polímero de ribonucleótidos (ARN) o desoxirribonucleótidos (ADN) que se encuentra primordialmente en el núcleo de las células; los ácidos nucleicos desempeñan un papel importante en la transmisión de las características hereditarias, en la síntesis de proteínas y en el control de las actividades celulares *(24.5)*

nucleotide/nucleótido uno de los monómeros que constituyen el ADN y el ARN; consiste en una base nitrogenada (una purina o una pirimidina), un azúcar (ribosa o desoxirribosa) y un grupo fosfato *(24.5)*

nucleus/núcleo la diminuta porción central densa de un átomo; se compone de protones y neutrones *(4.2)*

observation/observación información obtenida a través de los sentidos; en la ciencia, la observación suele implicar la medición *(1.3)*

octet rule/regla del octeto los átomos reaccionan ganando o perdiendo electrones a modo de adquirir la estructura electrónica estable de un gas noble, que por lo regular consta de ocho electrones de valencia *(7.1)*

optical isomers/isómeros ópticos moléculas que se diferencian entre ellas por la manera como se distribuyen cuatro grupos distintos en torno a un átomo de carbono *(22.3)*

organic chemistry/química orgánica estudio de los compuestos que contienen carbono *(1.1)*

oxidation/oxidación proceso que implica la pérdida total o parcial de electrones o la ganancia de oxígeno; conduce a un aumento en el número de oxidación de un átomo *(20.1)*

oxidation number/número de oxidación número positivo o negativo que se asigna a un átomo para indicar su grado de oxidación o reducción; el número de oxidación de un elemento no combinado es cero *(20.2)*

oxidation-number-change method/método de cambio del número de oxidación método para balancear una ecuación redox comparando los incrementos y reducciones de los números de oxidación *(20.3)*

oxidation–reduction reaction/reacción de oxidación–reducción reacción en la que hay transferencia de electrones entre los reactantes *(20.1)*

oxidizing agent/agente oxidante en una reacción redox, la sustancia que acepta electrones; en la reacción, el agente oxidante se reduce *(20.1)*

partial pressure/presión parcial contribución de cada gas de una mezcla de gases a la presión total *(14.4)*

pascal (Pa)/pascal (Pa) unidad de presión en el SI *(13.1)*

Pauli exclusion principle/principio de exclusión de Pauli orbital atómico puede describir como máximo a dos electrones, los cuales deben tener espín opuesto *(5.2)*

peptide/péptido compuesto orgánico formado por la combinación de aminoácidos de modo que el grupo amino de un ácido se une al grupo carboxilo de otro creando un enlace amida *(24.3)*

peptide bond/enlace péptido enlace que hay entre el grupo carbonilo de un aminoácido y el nitrógeno del siguiente aminoácido de la cadena péptida; la estructura es

(24.3)

percent composition/composición porcentual porcentaje en masa de cada elemento de un compuesto *(10.3)*

percent error/error porcentual porcentaje en que un valor medido difiere del valor aceptado *(3.1)*

percent yield/rendimiento porcentual razón del rendimiento real al rendimiento teórico de una reacción química, expresando como porcentaje; es una medida de la eficiencia de la reacción *(12.3)*

period/periodo fila horizontal de elementos en la tabla periódica *(4.3)*

periodic law/ley periódica si los elementos se acomodan en orden de menor a mayor número atómico, se observa una repetición periódica de sus propiedades físicas y químicas *(6.1)*

periodic table/tabla periódica distribución de los elementos dividiéndolos en grupos según un conjunto de propiedades repetidas *(4.3)*

pH/pH número empleado para denotar la concentración de ion hidrógeno (acidez) de una solución; es el logaritmo negativo de la concentración de ion hidrógeno en una solución *(19.2)*

phase/fase cualquier parte de una muestra que tiene composición y propiedades uniformes *(2.2)*

phase diagram/diagrama de fases gráfica que muestra las condiciones en las que una sustancia existe como sólido, líquido o vapor *(13.4)*

phospholipid/fosfolípido lípido que contiene un grupo fosfato; como los fosfolípidos tienen una cabeza hidrofílica y una cola hidrofóbica, pueden formar las bicapas lípidas de las membranas celulares *(24.4)*

photon/fotón cuanto de luz; paquete discreto de energía electromagnética que interactúa con la materia de forma similar a como lo hacen las partículas *(5.3)*

photosynthesis/fotosíntesis proceso por el cual las plantas y algas verdes aprovechan la energía radiante del sol para sintetizar glucosa a partir de dióxido de carbono y agua *(24.1)*

physical change/cambio físico cambio durante el cual se alteran algunas propiedades de un material, pero sin que se altere la composición del material *(2.1)*

physical chemistry/fisicoquímica área de la química que se relaciona con el mecanismo, la velocidad y la transferencia de energía que ocurre cuando la materia sufre un cambio *(1.1)*

physical property/propiedad física cualidad o condición de una sustancia que se puede observar o medir sin alterar la composición de la sustancia *(2.1)*

pi bond (π bond)/enlace pi (enlace π) enlace covalente en el que hay una alta probabilidad de encontrar los electrones de enlace en regiones alargadas que están arriba y abajo del eje de enlace de los átomos enlazados *(8.3)*

polar covalent bond (polar bond)/enlace covalente polar (enlace polar) enlace covalente entre átomos que no comparten equitativamente sus electrones *(8.4)*

polar molecule/molécula polar molécula que tiene un lado ligeramente negativo y el otro ligeramente positivo *(8.4)*

pollutant/contaminante material presente en el aire, agua o suelos y que es perjudicial para el ser humano y otros organismos *(1.2)*

polyatomic ion/ion poliatómico grupo fuertemente enlazado de átomos, que se comporta como una unidad y tiene carga positiva o negativa *(8.2)*

polymer/polímero molécula muy grande formada por la unión, mediante enlaces covalentes, de moléculas pequeñas repetidas, llamadas monómeros *(23.4)*

polypeptide/polipéptido péptido que tiene más de 10 aminoácidos *(24.3)*

polysaccharide/polisacárido carbohidrato complejo formado por el encadenamiento de muchos monómeros de monosacárido; el almidón, el glucógeno y la celulosa son polisacáridos *(24.2)*

positron/positrón partícula con la misma masa que un electrón pero con carga positiva *(25.2)*

precipitate/precipitado sólido que se forma a partir de una mezcla líquida y se asienta *(2.4)*

precision/precisión cifra que describe la variabilidad de una serie de mediciones efectuadas en las mismas condiciones *(3.1)*

product/producto sustancia que se obtiene en una reacción química *(2.4)*

protein/proteína cualquier péptido que tiene más de 100 aminoácidos *(24.3)*

proton/protón partícula subatómica con carga positiva que se encuentra en el núcleo de los átomos *(4.2)*

pure chemistry/química pura búsqueda de conocimientos químicos por sí mismos *(1.1)*

pure substance/sustancia pura *véase* sustancia

quantum/cuanto cantidad de energía necesaria para desplazar un electrón de un nivel energético a otro *(5.1)*

quantum mechanical model/modelo según la mecánica cuántica descripción moderna, primordialmente matemática, del comportamiento de los electrones en los átomos *(5.1)*

radiation/radiación rayos y partículas penetrantes emitidos por una fuente radiactiva *(25.1)*

radioactivity/radiactividad proceso por el cual los núcleos emiten partículas y rayos *(25.1)*

radioisotope/radioisótopo isótopo cuyo núcleo es inestable y sufre desintegración radiactiva *(25.1)*

rate/velocidad (de reacción) cifra que describe la velocidad de cambio a lo largo de un intervalo de tiempo *(18.1)*

rate law/ley de velocidad de reacción expresión que relaciona la velocidad de una reacción con la concentración de los reactantes *(18.5)*

reactant/reactante sustancia presente al principio de una reacción *(2.4)*

reaction mechanism/mecanismo de reacción serie de reacciones básicas que se dan durante el curso de una reacción compleja *(18.5)*

redox reaction/reacción redox otro nombre que se da a la reacción de oxidación-reducción *(20.1)*

reducing agent/agente reductor en una reacción redox, la sustancia que cede electrones; en la reacción, el agente reductor se oxida *(20.1)*

reduction/reducción proceso que implica una ganancia total o parcial de electrones o pérdida de oxígeno; provoca una disminución en el número de oxidación de un átomo *(20.1)*

reduction potential/potencial de reducción medida de la tendencia que tiene una semirreacción específica de efectuarse como reducción (con ganancia de electrones) en una celda electroquímica *(21.2)*

representative element/elemento representativo elemento de un grupo "A" de la tabla periódica; en conjunto, estos elementos exhiben una amplia gama de propiedades físicas y químicas. En sus átomos, los subniveles s y p del nivel energético ocupado más alto están parcialmente llenos *(6.2)*

representative particle/partícula representativa unidad más pequeña en que puede dividirse una sustancia sin que cambie su composición; por lo regular es un átomo, molécula o ion *(10.1)*

resonance structure/estructura de resonancia de las dos o más estructuras electrón-punto igualmente válidas de una molécula o ion poliatómico *(8.2)*

responding variable/variable de respuesta variable que se observa durante un experimento; también llamada variable dependiente *(1.3)*

reversible reaction/reacción reversible reacción en la que se da en forma simultánea la conversión de reactantes en productos y la conversión de productos en reactantes *(18.2)*

S

salt bridge/puente salino tubo que contiene un electrolito fuerte y se usa para separar las semiceldas de una celda voltaica; permite el paso de iones de una semicelda a la otra, pero impide que las soluciones se mezclen totalmente *(23.1)*

salt hydrolysis/hidrólisis de sales proceso por el cual los cationes o aniones de una sal disociada aceptan iones hidrógeno del agua o ceden iones hidrógeno al agua *(19.5)*

saponification/saponificación hidrólisis de grasas o aceites con una solución acuosa caliente de un hidróxido de metal alcalino; los jabones se hacen mediante la saponificación *(24.4)*

saturated compound/compuesto saturado compuesto orgánico en el que todos los átomos de carbono están unidos unos a otros por enlaces covalentes sencillos; contiene el número máximo de átomos de hidrógeno *(22.2)*

saturated solution/solución saturada solución que contiene la cantidad máxima de soluto para una cantidad dada de disolvente a temperatura y presión constantes; existe equilibrio entre el soluto no disuelto y los iones en solución. *(16.1)*

scientific law/ley científica expresión concisa que resume los resultados de muchas observaciones y experimentos *(1.3)*

scientific method/método científico enfoque lógico y sistemático para resolver un problema científico; los pasos del método científico incluyen hacer observaciones, probar hipótesis y desarrollar teorías *(1.3)*

scientific notation/notación científica convención por la cual los números se expresan en la forma $m \times 10^n$, donde m es un número mayor o igual que 1 y menor que 10, y n es un entero *(3.1)*

scintillation counter/contador de centelleo dispositivo que utiliza una superficie recubierta con un material fosforescente para detectar radiación *(25.4)*

self-ionization/autoionización reacción en la que dos moléculas de agua reaccionan para producir iones *(19.2)*

sigma bond (σ bond)/enlace sigma (enlace σ) enlace que se forma cuando dos orbitales atómicos se combinan para formar un orbital molecular que es simétrico respecto al eje que conecta a los dos núcleos atómicos *(8.3)*

significant figures/dígitos significativos todos los dígitos de una medición que se pueden conocer con precisión, más un último dígito estimado *(3.1)*

single covalent bond/enlace covalente sencillo enlace que se forma cuando dos átomos comparten un par de electrones *(8.2)*

single-replacement reaction/reacción de sustitución sencilla cambio químico en el que un elemento reemplaza a un segundo elemento en un compuesto; también llamado reacción de desplazamiento *(11.2)*

skeleton equation/ecuación esqueleto ecuación química que no indica las cantidades relativas de los reactantes y productos *(11.1)*

solid/sólido estado de la materia que tiene forma y volumen definidos *(2.1)*

solubility/solubilidad cantidad de una sustancia que se disuelve en una cantidad dada de disolvente en condiciones específicas de temperatura y presión para producir una solución saturada *(16.1)*

solubility product constant (K_{sp})/constante del producto de solubilidad (K_{sp}) constante de equilibrio aplicada a la capacidad disoluble de electrolitos; es igual al producto de las concentraciones de los iones, cada una elevada a una potencia igual al coeficiente que tiene ese ion en la ecuación de disociación *(18.3)*

solute/soluto partículas disueltas en una solución *(15.2)*

solution/solución mezcla homogénea que consiste en solutos disueltos en un disolvente *(2.2)*

solvation/solvatación proceso que tiene lugar cuando se disuelve un soluto iónico; en solución, las moléculas de disolvente rodean a los iones positivos y negativos *(15.2)*

solvent/disolvente medio dispersor en una solución *(15.2)*

specific heat/calor específico cantidad de calor requerida para elevar 1°C la temperatura de 1 g de una sustancia *(17.1)*

specific rate constant/constante específica de velocidad de reacción constante de proporcionalidad que relaciona las concentraciones de los reactantes con la velocidad de la reacción *(18.5)*

spectator ion/ion espectador ion que no interviene directamente en una reacción química; ion que no cambia de número de oxidación ni de composición durante una reacción *(11.3)*

spectrum/espectro longitudes de onda de la luz visible que se separan cuando un haz de luz atraviesa un prisma; gama de longitudes de onda de radiación electromagnética *(5.3)*

spontaneous reaction/reacción espontánea reacción que favorece la formación de productos en las condiciones especificadas; la espontaneidad depende de los cambios de entalpía y de entropía *(18.4)*

standard atmosphere (atm)/atmósfera estándar (atm) unidad de presión; es la presión necesaria para sostener 760 mm de mercurio en un barómetro de mercurio a 25°C *(13.1)*

standard cell potential (E_{cel}^0)/potencial estándar de celda (E_{cel}^0) potencial de celda que se mide cuando las concentraciones de los iones en las semiceldas son $1.00M$ a 1 atm de presión y 25°C *(21.2)*

standard entropy (S^0)/entropía estándar (S^0) entropía de una sustancia en su estado estable a 25°C y 1 atm *(18.4)*

standard heat of formation (ΔH_f^0)/calor estándar de formación (ΔH_f^0) cambio de entalpía que acompaña a la formación de un mol de un compuesto a partir de sus elementos, estando todas las sustancias en su estado estándar a 25°C *(17.4)*

standard hydrogen electrode/electrodo estándar de hidrógeno electrodo (semicelda) arbitrario de referencia que se usa junto con otro electrodo (semicelda) para medir el potencial estándar de reducción de esa celda; se asigna al potencial estándar de reducción del electrodo de hidrógeno el valor de 0.00 V *(21.2)*

standard solution/solución estándar solución cuya concentración se conoce; se usa para efectuar valoraciones químicas *(19.4)*

standard temperature and pressure (STP)/temperatura y presión estándar (TPE) las condiciones en las que normalmente se mide el volumen de un gas; la temperatura estándar es 0°C y la presión estándar es 101.3 kPa, o sea, 1 atmósfera (atm) *(10.2)*

stereoisomers/estereoisómeros moléculas cuyos átomos están en el mismo orden, pero que difieren en la distribución de los átomos en el espacio *(22.3)*

stoichiometry/estequiometría rama de la química que se ocupa de las relaciones numéricas en las ecuaciones químicas; el cálculo de las cantidades de sustancias presentes en las ecuaciones químicas *(12.1)*

straight-chain alkane/alcano de cadena lineal hidrocarburo saturado que contiene cualquier número de átomos de carbono acomodados uno tras otro en una cadena *(22.1)*

strong acid/ácido fuerte ácido que se ioniza casi totalmente en solución acuosa *(19.3)*

strong base/base fuerte base que se disocia totalmente en una solución acuosa para dar iones metálicos y iones hidróxido *(19.3)*

strong electrolyte/electrolito fuerte solución en la que una porción considerable del soluto existe en forma de iones *(15.2)*

structural formula/fórmula estructural fórmula química que indica la distribución de los átomos en una molécula o ion poliatómico; cada raya entre un par de átomos indica un par de electrones compartidos *(8.2)*

structural isomers/isómeros estructurales compuestos que tienen la misma fórmula molecular, aunque sus átomos están enlazados en un orden distinto *(22.3)*

sublimation/sublimación proceso por el cual un sólido cambia a gas o vapor sin pasar por el estado líquido *(13.4)*

substance/sustancia materia que tiene una composición uniforme y definida; puede ser un elemento o un compuesto; también llamada sustancia pura *(2.1)*

substituent/sustituto átomo o grupo de átomos que puede ocupar el lugar de un átomo de hidrógeno en una molécula precursora de hidrocarburo *(22.1)*

substitution reaction/reacción de sustitución tipo común de reacción orgánica; implica el reemplazo de un átomo o grupo de átomos por otro átomo o grupo de átomos *(23.1)*

substrate/sustrato molécula sobre la que actúa una enzima *(24.3)*

supersaturated solution/solución sobresaturada solución que contiene más soluto del que en teoría puede contener a una temperatura específica; el soluto en exceso se precipita si se añade un cristal que actúa como semilla *(16.1)*

surface tension/tensión superficial fuerza que tiende a reducir al mínimo la superficie total de un líquido y actúa hacia el seno de éste; hace que la superficie se comporte como si fuera una membrana elástica *(15.1)*

surfactant/tensoactivo cualquier sustancia que perturba la formación de enlaces de hidrógeno entre las moléculas de agua y así reduce la tensión superficial; los jabones y detergentes son tensoactivos *(15.1)*

surroundings/entorno todo lo que no forma parte del sistema, es decir, el resto del universo *(17.1)*

suspension/suspensión mezcla de la que se separan lentamente algunas partículas por asentamiento cuando no se agita *(15.3)*

synthesis reaction/reacción de síntesis *véase* reacción de combinación

system/sistema parte del universo en la que centramos nuestra atención *(17.1)*

technology/tecnología los medios por los cuales una sociedad proporciona a sus miembros las cosas que necesitan y desean *(1.1)*

temperature/temperatura medida de la energía cinética promedio de las partículas de la materia; la temperatura determina la dirección de la transferencia de calor *(3.2)*

tetrahedral angle/ángulo tetraédrico ángulo de enlace de 109.5° que se forma cuando un átomo central forma cuatro enlaces dirigidos hacia el centro de un tetraedro regular *(8.3)*

theoretical yield/rendimiento teórico cantidad de producto que podría formarse durante una reacción, calculada a partir de una ecuación química balanceada; representa la cantidad máxima de producto que podría formarse a partir de una cantidad determinada de reactantes *(12.3)*

theory/teoría explicación, probada exhaustivamente, de un conjunto amplio de observaciones *(1.3)*

thermochemical equation/ecuación termoquímica ecuación química que incluye el cambio de calor *(17.2)*

thermochemistry/termoquímica estudio de los cambios de calor que acompañan a las reacciones químicas y a los cambios de estado físico *(17.1)*

titration/valoración química proceso empleado para determinar la concentración de una solución (a menudo un ácido o base) por el cual una solución de concentración conocida (solución estándar) se añade a una cantidad medida de una solución cuya concentración se desconoce, hasta que un indicador marca el punto final *(19.4)*

trans* configuration/configuración *trans configuración en la que los grupos sustitutos están en lados opuestos de un doble enlace *(22.3)*

transition metal/metal de transición uno de los elementos del grupo B en el que el subnivel *s* ocupado más alto y un subnivel *d* cercano generalmente contienen electrones *(6.2)*

transition state/estado de transición término empleado ocasionalmente para referirse al complejo activado *(18.1)*

transmutation/transmutación conversión de un átomo de un elemento en un átomo de otro elemento *(25.2)*

transuranium element/elemento transuránico cualquier elemento de la tabla periódica cuyo número atómico es mayor que 92, el número atómico del uranio *(25.2)*

triglyceride/triglicérido éster en el que los tres grupos hidroxilo de una molécula de glicerol han sido sustituidos por ácidos grasos de cadena larga; las grasas son triglicéridos *(24.4)*

triple covalent bond/enlace covalente triple enlace covalente en el que dos átomos comparten tres pares de electrones *(8.2)*

triple point/punto triple punto de un diagrama de fases que representa el único conjunto de condiciones en el que las tres fases existen en equilibrio *(13.4)*

triprotic acid/ácido triprótico ácido que contiene tres protones (iones hidrógeno) ionizables; el ácido fosfórico (H_3PO_4) es un ácido triprótico *(19.1)*

Tyndall effect/efecto Tyndall dispersión de la luz por las partículas de un coloide o una suspensión, que hace que un haz de luz se vuelva visible *(15.3)*

unit cell/celda unitaria grupo más pequeño de partículas dentro de un cristal que conserva la forma geométrica del cristal *(13.3)*

unsaturated solution/solución insaturada se dice de una solución que contiene menos soluto que una solución saturada a una temperatura y presión específicas *(16.1)*

unsaturated compound/compuesto insaturado compuesto orgánico que tiene uno o más dobles o triples enlaces carbono–carbono *(22.2)*

unshared pair/par no compartido par de electrones de valencia que no es compartido por dos átomos *(8.2)*

vacuum/vacío espacio en el que no existen partículas de materia *(13.1)*

valence electron/electrón de valencia electrón que está en el nivel energético ocupado más alto de un átomo *(7.1)*

van der Waals forces/fuerzas de van der Waals las dos atracciones intermoleculares más débiles —interacciones de dispersión y fuerzas dipolares *(8.4)*

vapor/vapor estado gaseoso de una sustancia que suele ser líquida o sólida a temperatura ambiente *(2.1)*

vaporization/vaporización conversión de un líquido en gas o vapor *(13.2)*

vapor pressure/presión de vapor medida de la fuerza que ejerce un gas sobre un líquido en un contenedor sellado; equilibrio dinámico que existe entre el vapor y el líquido *(13.2)*

voltaic cell/celda voltaica celda electroquímica empleada para convertir energía química en energía eléctrica; la energía se produce por una reacción redox espontánea *(21.1)*

volume/volumen medida del espacio ocupado por una muestra de materia *(2.1)*

VSEPR theory/teoría RPENV teoría de repulsión de pares de electrones del nivel de valencia; como los pares de electrones se repelen, las moléculas ajustan su forma de modo que los pares de electrones de valencia estén lo más alejados posible entre sí *(8.3)*

water of hydration/agua de hidratación moléculas de agua que forman parte integral de una estructura cristalina *(15.2)*

wavelength (λ)/longitud de onda (λ) distancia entre crestas adyacentes de una onda *(5.3)*

wax/cera éster de un ácido graso de cadena larga y un alcohol de cadena larga *(24.4)*

weak acid/ácido débil ácido que se ioniza poco en solución acuosa *(19.3)*

weak base/base débil base que reacciona con agua para formar el ion hidróxido y el ácido combinado de la base *(19.3)*

weak electrolyte/electrolito débil solución que apenas conduce la electricidad porque sólo una fracción del soluto existe en forma de iones *(15.2)*

weight/peso fuerza que mide la atracción de la gravedad sobre una masa específica *(3.2)*

Index

The page on which a term is defined is indicated in **boldface** type.

absolute zero **77,** 389
accelerator, nuclear 808
accepted value **65**
accuracy **64**
acetic acid. *See* **ethanoic acid**
acetone (propanone) 740
acetylene. *See* **ethyne**
acid-base indicators 600, 601–602
acid-base theories 587–593
   Arrhenius 588–589, 592
   Brønsted-Lowry **590**–592
   Lewis **592**–593
acid dissociation constant 606–**607**
acidic solution **595**
acidity. *See* **pH**
acidity of paper 623
acid rain R27
acids **271**–272, 588
   Arrhenius 588–589, 592
   Brønsted-Lowry **590**–592
   concentration of 609, 614
   conjugate **591**–592
   diprotic **588**
   formulas for 272
   Lewis **592**–593
   monoprotic **588**
   naming 271–272
   properties of 587
   strong **605**–607
   triprotic **588**
   uses of 595, R25, R30, R33
   weak **605**–607
activated complex 543, **544**
activation energy **543**
   catalysts and 547
active site **772**–773
activity series **333**
actual yield **372**–373
addition polymer 747–749
addition reactions **733**–735
adenine 778, 779
adenosine diphosphate (ADP) 786, 787
adenosine triphosphate (ATP) **786**–788
adhesives 242
aerosol cans 417
agriculture
   chemistry and 15
   industrial nitrogen fixation in 790
   recombinant DNA and 784, 785
air
   composition of dry 432, R4
   compressed 430, 433
   fractional distillation of R24

air bags 359, 376–377, 413
alchemy 20, 645
alcohols **730**–733
   naming 731
   properties of 732–733
   substitution reaction to produce 729
aldehydes **737**–740
   common 738
   naming 738
   primary alcohols oxidized to 744, 745
   properties of 739
   tests for 745
   uses of 739–740
algebraic equations 140, R69–R71
aliphatic alcohols 730
   structural formulas for 731
aliphatic carboxylic acids 741
aliphatic hydrocarbons **703**
alkali metals **161,** R6–R9
alkaline batteries 667, 668
alkaline earth metals **161,** R10–R13
alkaline solutions **595**
alkanes **694**–701
   branched-chain 697, **698**–699
   naming 696, 698–699
   oxidation of 744–745
   properties of 700
   straight-chain **695**
   structural formulas for 696–697
alkenes **702**
   addition reactions of 733–734
alkyl group **698,** 727
alkyl halides **727**
alkynes **703**
allotropes **398**
   of carbon 398–399
   of phosphorus R24
   of sulfur R28
alloys **203**
   building with 204
   of copper R42
   of indium R16
   of iron R43
   types of 203
alpha emission 804
alpha particles 107, **800,** 802
alpha radiation 800, 801
aluminum 195, 253
   anodized R17
   extraction from bauxite 682, R17
   properties of 159, R14–R15
   recycling R16
   resistance to corrosion 298, 636
amazonite 397
amide 751
amino acids **769**–773
   abbreviations for 770
   DNA codes for 781
   enzymes and 772–773
   peptides and 770
   proteins and 770–771
   side chains 769
amino acid sequence 770, 771

ammonia 215, 361, 608
   aqueous solution of 453, 592
   as base 590–591
   in bat's urine 587
   from distilled coal 715
   as fertilizer 557, R26
   molecule 219, 232
   in Ostwald Process R25
   production of 357, 359, 549, R26
   reduction of nitrogen to 789
ammonium chloride hydrolysis 619–620
ammonium ion 223, 257, 266
ammonium nitrate cold pack 525
ammonium sulfate 613
amorphous solids **399**
amphoteric substance **592**
amplitude, of wave **138**
amu **114**–115
anabolism **788**
analytical chemistry **8**
analytical chemists 93
andalusite R18
anesthetics 727, 736, R25
anions **172,** 192, 194
   formation of 172, 191–192
   naming 254
   size of 175, 176
anode **665**
antacids 14, 612
anthracite coal 714
antifreeze 489, 492, 493
   natural 487
antioxidants 548
ants, poisonous 271
applied chemistry **9**
aqueous solution(s) **450**–458
   electrolytes and nonelectrolytes **452**–453, 458, R8
   hydrates **454**–457
   reactions in 342–345
   of sodium chloride 487–488
   solution process 451
   solvents and solutes **450**
aqueous systems 450–463
   heterogeneous 459–462
      colloids 459, **460**–462
      suspensions **459,** 461, 462
   homogeneous. *See* **aqueous solution(s)**
aragonite 197
archaeologists 119
arene. *See* **aromatic hydrocarbon**
Arfvedson, Johan August R6
argon, uses of R36, R37
Aristotle 101
aromatic aldehydes 739
aromatic hydrocarbons **710**–711
   in coal 715
   substituted 711
aromatic substitution reactions 728–729
Arrhenius, Svante 588
Arrhenius acids 588–589, 592
Arrhenius bases 589–590

Acknowledgments

Photographs

Table of Contents iiiMR, © Charles O'Rear/CORBIS; iiiBR, © Geoffrey Nilsen Photography/Addison-Wesley; vTR, © James Soots Lawrence/Livermore National Laboratory; vB, © Richard Megna/Fundamental Photographs; viL, © Kevin R. Morris/CORBIS; viR, © Douglas E. Walker/ Masterfile; vii, © Runk/Schoenberger/Grant Heilman Photography; viii, © Ken Karp/Addison-Wesley; ixT, © David Bishop/Phototake; ixB, © Jens J. Jensen/CORBIS; x, © Robert George Young/Masterfile; xii, xiii, © Ken O'Donoghue/Prentice Hall; xiv, © Mitch Hrdlicka/Getty Images; xviiiT, © Lon C Diehl/PhotoEdit; xviiiT(inset), © RAL Studio/Stock Connection/PictureQuest; xviiiM, © Derek Berwin/Getty Images; xviiiB, © Michael & Patricia Fogden/ CORBIS; xixT, © Royalty-Free/PictureQuest; xixBL, © Bob Handelman/Getty Images; xixBR, © George Haling/ Photo Researchers

Chapter 1 6, © Andrew Brookes/CORBIS; 7T, Courtesy of NASA; 7B, © George Ranalli/Photo Researchers; 8C, © Mike Powell/Getty Images; 8TR, © Michelle Joyce/Index Stock Imagery; 8MR, © Tom McCarthy/Rainbow; 8BR, © Michael Abbey/Photo Researchers; 8TL, © Alfred Pasieka/ Photo Researchers; 8BL, © Nicholas Veasey/Getty Images; 9L © Tom Bochsler Photography/ Prentice Hall; 9R, © Stewart Cohen/Index Stock Imagery; 10L, © John Lund/Getty Images; 10R, © Raeanne Rubenstein/IndexStock Imagery; 11, © Marc Pokempner/Getty Images; 12T, © Michael Brohm/Courtesy of the Illinois State Museum; 12B, © Dr. Jeremy Burgess/Photo Researchers; 13T, © James Soots Lawrence/Livermore National Laboratory; 13B, 13B (inset), © Thomas Hovland/Grant Heilman Photography; 14, © Alfred Pasieka/Photo Researchers; 15T, © Andy Caulfield/Getty Images; 15B, © Courtesy of Maggie Sliker; 16, Courtesy of U.S. Environmental Protection Agency; 17ALL, Courtesy of NASA; 18C, © Larry Lefever/Grant Heilman Photography; 18TR, © Dorling Kindersley; 18BR, © Arthur C. Smith III/Grant Heilman Photography; 18BL, © Wally Eberhart/Visuals Unlimited; 19TL, © Gustav Verderber/Visuals Unlimited; 19TR, © Doug Wechsler/Animals Animals; 19M, © Norbert Wu/Minden Pictures; 19BL, © Michael & Patricia Fogden/CORBIS; 19BR, © Jack M. Bostrack/Visuals Unlimited; 20T, © Jack M. Bostrack/ Visuals Unlimited; 20B, © Chassenet Bsip/Photo Researchers; 21BOTH, The Art Archive; 22, © Peter Gregoire/IndexStock Imagery; 23, © Ken O'Donoghue/Prentice Hall; 24T, © AFP/CORBIS; 24B, © J. Nouvok/PhotoEdit; 25, © John Abbott Photography; 26-27, © Ken O'Donoghue/Prentice Hall; 26BR, © Richard Megna/ Fundamental Photographs; 28T © Pat Kepic/Addison-Wesley; 28B, © Amy Etra/PhotoEdit; 30, © Andre Jenny/Alamy Images; 35, © Robert E. Daemmrich/Getty Images

Chapter 2 38, © Wendy Chan/Getty Images; 39T, © BananaStock/PictureQuest; 39B, © Prentice Hall; 40L, © Graham Tim/CORBIS SYGMA; 40R, © Sandro Vannini/CORBIS; 41, © Geoffrey Nilsen Photography/Addison-Wesley; 42, © Lawrence Migdale/Photo Researchers; 43TR, © Dennis Kunkel/Phototake; 43BL&BKGD, © Walter Bibikow/Getty Images; 43BR, © Royalty Free/Getty Images; 44T, © Dorling Kindersley; 44B, © David Young-Wolff/PhotoEdit/PictureQuest; 45, © Ken O'Donoghue/Prentice Hall; 46T, © Cheyenne Rouse/IndexStock Imagery; 46B, © John A. Rizzo/PhotoDisc/PictureQuest; 48T, © Evan Sklar/FoodPix/Getty Images; 48B, © David Lawrence/Addison-Wesley; 49L, © Rich Treptow/Photo Researchers; 49L (inset), © David Lawrence/Addison-Wesley; 49M, © Mike Hewitt/Getty Images; 49M (inset), © Yoav Levy/Phototake; 49R, © Art Stein/Photo Researchers; 49R (inset), © Michael Newman/PhotoEdit; 50L, © E. R. Degginger/Color-Pic; 50ML, © Coco McCoy/Rainbow; 50MR, © PhotoDisc/Getty Images; 50R, © Paul Conklin, 51, © Clive Streeter/Dorling Kindersley; 53T, © Cameron Davidson/Getty Images; 53B, © Tom Bochsler/Prentice Hall; 54L, © Chris Pellant/Dorling Kindersley; 54M, © Saturn Stills/Photo Researchers; 54R, Courtesy of Dr. David Fankhauser; 55, © Richard Megna/Fundamental Photographs; 56, © Ken O'Donoghue/Prentice Hall; 59, © Richard Megna/Fundamental Photographs

Chapter 3 62, © Daryl Benson/Masterfile; 63T, Courtesy of NASA; 63B, © Peter Arnold; 64, © Randy Faris/CORBIS; 65, © Richard Hutchings/Addison-Wesley; 66, © PhotoDisc/Getty Images; 68, © PhotoDisc/Getty Images; 69, © F. Hirdes/Masterfile; 70, © Jeff Greenberg/PhotoEdit; 71, © Andy Sacks/Getty Images; 72, © Ken O'Donoghue/Prentice Hall; 73T, © David McLain/Aurora & Quanta Productions; 74, © David Zimmerman/CORBIS; 75L, © Ken Karp/Addison-Wesley; 75M, 75R, © David Lawrence/Addison-Wesley; 76, Courtesy of NASA; 77L, © W. Geiersperger/CORBIS; 77M, ©Eric O'Connell/Getty Images; 77R, © Richard Megna/Fundamental Photographs; 78, © Pierre Arsenault/Masterfile; 79, © Phototake; 80T, © William Whitehurst/CORBIS; 81B, © Fran Heyl Associates; 82, © Tony Freeman/Photo Researchers; 84, © Digital Vision/Getty Images; 85, © Topham/The Image Works; 86, © Yorgos Nikas/Getty Images; 87, © Ken O'Donoghue/Prentice Hall; 88ML, R, © Fox & Fowle Architects; 88M, © Andres Groden Photography, Couresty of Fox & Fowle Architects; 88BL, © Alan Levenson/Getty Images; 88BKGD, © Royalty Free/Getty Images ; 89T, © IFA/eStock Photo/PictureQuest; 90, © Clive Streeter/Dorling Kindersley; 91, © Nancy Richmon/The Image Works; 92T, © PhotoDisc/Getty Images; 92B, © Matthew Donaldson/ImageState/PictureQuest; 93, © TEK Image/Photo Researchers; 94, © Ken O'Donoghue/ Prentice Hall

Chapter 4 100, Courtesy of IBM Research, Almaden Reserch Center; 101T, © V.C.L./Getty Images; 101B, © Archivo Iconografico,S.A./CORBIS; 103, Courtesy of IBM Research,

Almaden Research Center; 104T, © G. Schuster/Masterfile; 105, © Richard Megna/Fundamental Photographs; 106, © G.R. "Dick" Roberts Photo Library; 108, © Ken O'Donoghue/Prentice Hall; 109TR, © Volker Steger/Peter Arnold; 109MR, © IBMRL-LBI/Visuals Unlimited; 109BR, © K.H. Kjeldsen/Photo Researchers; 109BL, © Andrew Syred/Photo Researchers; 110T, © Royalty-Free/CORBIS; 111T, © Tom Bochsler/Prentice Hall; 111B, © Malcolm Piers/Getty Images; 113T, © John Maher/IndexStock Imagery; 113B, © L. Clarke/CORBIS; 114, © Barry L. Runk/Grant Heilman Photography; 115, © Mike Powell/Getty Images; 116, 117, © Charles D. Winters/Photo Researchers; 119, © James L. Amos/CORBIS; 120, © Ken O'Donoghue/Prentice Hall; 122, © Richard Megna/Fundamental Photographs

Chapter 5 126, © David Parker/Photo Researchers; 129T, © Embry Riddle Aeronautical University; 129B, © Phil Degginger/Color-Pic; 130, © Jim Sugar/CORBIS; 133T, © Joe Bator/CORBIS; 135, © Gary Morrison/Getty Images; 136, © Tony Freeman/PhotoEdit; 137, © Ken O'Donoghue/Prentice Hall; 138T, © Richard Pasley/Stock Boston; 140, © Walter Bibikow/Getty Images; 141, 142, © Richard Megna/Fundamental Photographs; 144, © Oliver Meckes/Photo Researchers; 146, © Mauritius, GMBH/Phototake; 147TL, © PhotoDisc/Getty Images; 147TR, © V.C.L./Getty Images; 147B, © Chris Barry/Phototake; 150, © Richard Megna/Fundamental Photographs; 152, © Carolina Biological Supply Company/Phototake

Chapter 6 154, © James Leynse/CORBIS; 155T, © Glamour International/AGE Fotostock America; 155B, © Carey B. Van Loon; 156T, © Gary J. Shulfer/C. Marvin Lang; 156B, © The Granger Collection, New York; 159BL, © David Muench/CORBIS; 159M, © Ken Davies/Masterfile; 159R, © Dorling Kindersley; 160L, Courtesy of Texas Instruments Incorporated; 160R, © Paul Chesley/Getty Images; 161T, © Susan Van Etten/PhotoEdit; 164, © Woodward Payne/Royalty-Free/PictureQuest; 165T, © PhotoDisc/Getty Images; 165T(inset), © John Durham/Photo Researchers; 165B, © U.S. Geological Survey, Denver; 165B (inset), © Color-Pic/Earth Scenes; 167, © Richard L. Carlton/Visuals Unlimited; 168T, © Roy Rainford/Robert Harding World Imagery; 168ML, © Geoff Dann/Dorling Kindersley; 168MM, © Harry Taylor/Dorling Kindersley; 168MR, © Mike Dunning/Dorling Kindersley; 168B, © Robert Frerck/Getty Images; 169T (inset), © Vital Pictures/Getty Images; 169T, © Ken O'Donoghue/Prentice Hall; 169BL, Jacob Lawrence/Spike Mafford/Francine Seders Gallery; 169BR, © Jeff Greenberg/PhotoEdit; 170T, © SuperStock; 179, Ken O'Donoghue/Prentice Hall

Chapter 7 186, © Scott Camazine/Photo Researchers; 187T, © Robert Maier/Earth Scene; 187BL, © Steve Dunwell/Getty Images; 187BM, © Kelly Harriger/CORBIS; 187BR, © Geoff Dann/Dorling Kindersley; 189, © PhotoDisc/Getty Images; 190, © Louis B. Wallach/Getty Images; 192, © David Samuel Robbins/CORBIS; 193, © Richard Megna/Fundamental Photographs; 194T, © Erwin C. Nielsen/Visuals Unlimited; 195T, © Ken Karp/Addison-Wesley; 195B, © Bruce Iverson/Photo Researchers; 196, © Kevin R. Morris/CORBIS; 197TL, © Runk/Schoenberger/Grant Heilman Photography; 197TM, © Gim Media/Gemological Institute of America; 197TCL, © Breck P. Kent; 197TCM, © J&L Weber/Peter Arnold; 197TCR, © Jeffrey A. Scovil; 197BCL, © J&L Weber/Peter Arnold; 197BCM, © Breck P. Kent/Earth Scenes; 197BCR, © Grace Davies/Omni-Photo Communications; 197BL, © George Whiteley/Photo Researchers; 197BM, © Tomisch/Photo Researchers; 197BL, © Paul Silverman/Fundamental Photographs; 199, 200, © Ken O'Donoghue/Prentice Hall; 201T, © Lowell Georgia/CORBIS; 202T, © Steve Elmore/CORBIS; 202BL, © Paul Silverman/Fundamental Photographs; 202BM, © Digital Vision/PictureQuest; 202BR, © Clive Streeter/Dorling Kindersley; 203, © David Young-Wolff/PhotoEdit; 204BL, © J. Lawrence/ImageState/PictureQuest; 204BM, © Digital Vision/Getty Images; 204TR, © AFP/CORBIS; 205BL, © Nicolas Russell/Getty Images; 205, © EyeWire Collection/Getty Images

Chapter 8 212, © Brett Baunton/Getty Images; 213T, © Ken O'Donoghue/Prentice Hall; 213BL, © Ken Karp/Addison-Wesley; 213BR, © Patti McConville/Getty Images; 214BL, © Robert Frerck/Woodfin Camp; 214BR, © Garry Hunter/Getty Images; 215TL, © David Young-Wolff/PhotoEdit; 217T, © NASA/Photo Researchers; 220, © Tony Freeman/PhotoEdit; 221, © EyeWire Collection/Getty Images; 222, © Davies & Starr/Getty Images; 223, © Michael Newman/PhotoEdit; 225, © G. Biss/Masterfile; 226, © Ken O'Donoghue/Prentice Hall; 227, © Ulf Wallin/Getty Images; 228, © Douglas E. Walker/ Masterfile; 230T, © Andrew Sacks/Getty Images; 237T, © Allan Davey/Masterfile; 237B, © David Young-Wolff/PhotoEdit; 239, © Richard Hutchings/PhotoEdit; 241, © Craig Tuttle/CORBIS; 243, © Leloup Vincent/CORBIS; 242TR, © Araldite/Advertising Archives; 242MR, © Davies & Starr/Getty Images; 245, © Ken O'Donoghue/Prentice Hall

Chapter 9 252, © Brian Pieters/Masterfile; 253T, © John Michael/ImageState; 254, Tom Pantages; 255, © Ken Karp/Addison-Wesley; 256T, © Bill Aron/PhotoEdit; 256B, © Brian Hagiwara/Getty Images; 258L, © Alastair Laidlaw/Getty Images; 258M, © Steve Kahn/Getty Images; 258R, © Jack Fields/Photo Researchers; 259L, © Lon C Diehl/PhotoEdit; 259 (inset), © RAL Studio/Stock Connection/PictureQuest; 260T, © Brian Leatart/Getty Images; 260B, © Lawrence Migdale/Stock Boston; 261L, © Michael Prince/CORBIS; 261R, © PhotoDisc/Getty Images; 262, © William Traufic/CORBIS; 263, © José Manuel Sanchis Calvete/CORBIS; 264L, © Andreas Einsiedel/Dorling Kindersley; 264M, © Tony Freeman/PhotoEdit; 264R, 265, © Richard Megna/Fundamental Photographs; 266, © Yoav Lev/Phototake; 267, © Ken O'Donoghue/Prentice Hall; 268T, © DigitalVision/PictureQuest; 268BL, © Kennan

Harvey/Getty Images; 268BR, © Lowell Georgia/CORBIS; 270, © Victor Paris/Getty Images; 271T, © James Robinson/Animals Animals; 271B, © Richard Megna/Fundamental Photographs; 273L, © Joel Benard/ Masterfile; 273M, ©Royalty-Free/CORBIS; 273R, © Rosemary Weller/Getty Images, 274T, © Kathleen Finlay/Masterfile; 274R, © Ken Karp/Addison-Wesley; 276T, © Jonathan Nourok/PhotoEdit; 276B, © Kelly-Mooney Photography/CORBIS; 277, © Richard Megna/Fundamental Photographs; 279, © Ken O'Donoghue/Prentice Hall

Chapter 10 286, © Francis Dean/The Image Works; 287T, © Peter Gridley/Getty Images; 287B, © Steve Gorton/Dorling Kindersley; 288, © Jon Chomitz/Photo Researchers; 289T, © James Stevenson/Dorling Kindersley; 289B, © Sally Boon/FoodPix/Getty Images;290T,M, ©David Lawrence/Addison-Wesley; 290B, ©Richard Hutchins/Addison-Wesley; 291, © Ken Karp/Addison-Wesley; 292, © Lon C Diehl/PhotoEdit; 293, © ZEFA-Lange/CORBIS; 294, 295, © Tom Pantages; 296, Courtesy of NASA; 297T, © Evan Sklar/Getty Images; 298, © Jean Miele/Bettmann/CORBIS; 299, © Tom Schierlitz/Getty Images; 300BL, © Richard Megna/Fundamental Photographs; 300BR, © Tom Pantages; 301, 304, © Ken O'Donoghue/Prentice Hall; 305T, © David Lawrence/Addison-Wesley; 306B, © Digital Vision; 306B (inset), ©Jack Wilburn/EarthScenes, 308, © Ken O'Donoghue/Prentice Hall; 309T,©Bill Barley/SuperStock; 309B, © Royalty-Free/CORBIS; 311, © Tom Pantages; 313TR, © Dennis O'Clair/Getty Images; 318, © Thomas Brase/Getty Images

Chapter 11 320, © Lewis Kemper/Phototake Photos/Getty Images, 321B, © Ken O'Donoghue/Prentice Hall; 322L, © Terry Why/Phototake; 322M, © Michael Dalton/Fundamental Photographs; 322R, © Phil Degginger/Color-Pic; 323, © Ken Karp/Addison-Wesley; 324, © Richard Megna/Fundamental Photographs; 325, © Jeff Greenberg/Omni-Photo Communications; 326, © Ken O'Donoghue/Prentice Hall; 327, © EAC Images/NASA/Aurora & Quanta Productions;328,© Peter DeLory/Getty Images; 329, © Digital Vision/PictureQuest; 330T, © Charles O'Rear/CORBIS; 331T, David Lawrence/Addison-Wesley; 331B, © Tom Pantages; 332T, © Ken Karp/Addison-Wesley; 332B, © Reuters NewMedia Inc./CORBIS; 333, David Lawrence/Addison-Wesley; 334, © Runk/Schoenberger/Grant Heilman Photography; 335, 336, © Richard Megna/Fundamental Photographs; 337, © Runk/Schoenberger/Grant Heilman Photography; 338T, © David Lawrence/Addison-Wesley; 338M, © Ken Karp/Addison-Wesley; 338B, © David Lawrence/Addison-Wesley; 339, © Richard Megna/Fundamental Photographs; 340, © Bill Stormont/CORBIS; 341T, © Patrick Durand/CORBIS SYGMA; 341BL, © David Job/Getty Images; 341BL (inset), © Tony Freeman/PhotoEdit; 341BR, © Prentice Hall; 341BR (inset), ©Ana/The Image Works; 342T, © Demetrio Carrasco/Getty Images; 342B, 343, © Richard Megna/Fundamental Photographs; 345, © Ken O'Donoghue/Prentice Hall; 348, © Ken Karp/Addison-Wesley; 349TL, © Carey B. Van Loon; 349TR, © Stephen Frisch/Stock Boston; 349BL, 349BR, © Richard Megna/Fundamental Photographs

Chapter 12 352, © Mitch Hrdlicka/Getty Images; 353T, © Noriyuki Yoshida/SuperStock; 353B, © Michael Newman/PhotoEdit; 355, © AP/Wide World Photos; 356, © Bill Ross/CORBIS; 358, © D. Cavagnaro/DRK Photo; 359T, © David Woods/CORBIS; 359B, © Grant Heilman Photography; 360, © Richard Hutchings/Addison-Wesley; 362, © Courtesy NASA; 364, © Runk/Schoenberger/Grant Heilman Photography; 365, © Steve Craft/Masterfile; 367, © Jon Chomitz/Prentice Hall; 368T, © Patrick Ramsey/ImageState; 368B, © Ken O'Donoghue/Prentice Hall; 370, © Ken Karp/Addison-Wesley; 371, © Peter Christopher/Masterfile; 372, © Ken O'Donoghue/Prentice Hall; 373TL, © Courtesy of The Topps Company, Inc.; 373TR, © Blank Archives/Getty Images; 373B, © Richard Hutchings/Addison-Wesley; 374, © PhotoDisc/Getty Images; 381, © AP/Wide World Photos

Chapter 13 384, © Fukuhara/CORBIS; 385T, © Daniel J Cox/Getty Images; 386TR, © Leonard Arnold; 389, © Wolfgang Ketterle/Courtesy of Ketterle Lab; 390T, © G. Brad Lewis/Getty Images; 390B, © Richard Megna/Fundamental Photographs, 391TL, © Phil Degginger/Color-Pic; 391TR, © Dave King/Dorling Kindersley; 396T, © Scott Camazine/Photo Researchers; 397TL, © Joe McDonald/Earth Scene; 397TM, © Arthur R. Hill/Visuals Unlimited; 397TR, © Mark A. Schneider/Photo Researchers; 397BL, 397BML, © Mark A. Schneider/Visuals Unlimited; 397BMR, © Mark A. Schneider/Photo Researchers; 397BR, © Mark A. Schneider/Visuals Unlimited; 400, © Ken O'Donoghue/Prentice Hall; 401T, © Breck P. Kent/Earth Scenes; 403, © Ken Karp/Addison-Wesley; 404, © John Madere/CORBIS; 405TR, © Mason Morfit/Getty Images; 405ML, © AP/Wide World Photos; 405MR, © PhotoDisc/Getty Images; 405BL, © Peter Dazeley/Getty Images; 405BR, © Thinkstock/PictureQuest; 408, © Richard Megna/Fundamental Photographs

Chapter 14 412, © Federico Cabello/SuperStock; 413T, © Mike Hewitt/Getty Images; 413B, © Romilly Lockyer/Getty Images; 415, © EyeWire Collection/Getty Images; 418T, © Trevor Collens-Pool/Getty Images; 420, © Ken Karp/Addison-Wesley; 422, © Bonnie Kamin/PhotoEdit; 425, © NASA/Photo Researchers; 426T, © Charles D. Winters/Photo Researchers; 427, © Robert Garvey/CORBIS; 428T, © Ken O'Donoghue/Prentice Hall; 428B, © Richard Megna/Fundamental Photographs; 430B, © Wayne Levin/Getty Images; 431TR, Courtesy of NAUI; 432T, © Davis Barber/PhotoEdit; 433, © Galen Rowell/CORBIS; 434, © Derek Berwin/Getty Images; 435, © Ken Karp/Addison-Wesley; 436, © Joseph Sohm/ChromoSohm/CORBIS; 437, © Ken O'Donoghue/Prentice Hall; 440L, © Robert Brenner/PhotoEdit; 440R, © Andrew Lambert Photography /Photo Researchers

Chapter 15 444, © Brian Sytnyk/Masterfile; 445T, © Frank Rossotto/CORBIS; 445B, © Jeremy Woodhouse/Digital Vision; 447, © Hermann Eisenbeiss/Photo Researchers; 448, © Ken O'Donoghue/Prentice Hall; 449, © Richard Walters/Visuals Unlimited; 450B, © Russ Lappa/Addison-Wesley; 451, © Eunice Harris/Photo Researchers; 452, © David Wasserman/Brand X Pictures/PictureQuest; 453, 454T, © Richard Megna/Fundamental Photographs; 454BL, © Kristen Brochman/Fundamental Photographs; 455, © Tom Pantages; 457, © Ken Karp/Addison-Wesley; 458, © Ken O'Donoghue/Prentice Hall; 459T, © Paul Poplis/Foodpix; 459B, © Russ Lappa/Addison-Wesley; 460(2nd from B), © Johnathan T. Wright/Bruce Coleman; 460

ALL OTHER, © Ken Karp/Addison-Wesley; 461, © Sanford/Agliolo/CORBIS; 462, © Jon Chomitz/Prentice Hall; 463TR, © Ian O'Leary/Dorling Kindersley; 463ML, © David Wasserman/ Brand X Pictures /PictureQuest; 463MM, © Biophoto Associates/Photo Researchers; 463MR, © Flip Chalfant/Getty Images; 463B, © Frank Pedrick/The Image Works; 467, © Walter Hodges/CORBIS

Chapter 16 470, © Paul Edmondson/Getty Images; 471T, © St. Petersburg Times/Getty Images; 471B, © Ken Karp/Addison-Wesley; 473L, © Tony Craddock/Photo Researchers; 473R, © Ken O'Donoghue/Prentice Hall; 474, © John Lamb/Getty Images; 475, © Richard Megna/Fundamental Photographs; 479TR, © National Cancer Institute/NIBSC/Photo Researchers; 479BR, © Hank Morgan/Photo Researchers; 481T, ©Jeff Greenberg/The Image Works; 481, 483T, © Ken Karp/Addison-Wesley; 483B, © Richard Hutchings/Addison-Wesley; 484, © Ken O'Donoghue/Prentice Hall; 485, © Tom Pantages; 487T, © Zig Leszczynski/Animals Animals; 488, © Ken Karp/Addison-Wesley; 489T, © Richard Megna/Fundamental Photographs; 489B, © AP/Wide World Photos; 490, © Tom Pantages; 491T, © Jose Azel/Aurora Photos; 493, © Dan McCoy/ Rainbow; 497, © Ken O'Donoghue/Prentice Hall; 502, © Ken O'Donoghue

Chapter 17 504, © Phil Degginger/Color-Pic; 505T, © Royalty-Free/CORBIS; 505B, © Rich Graves/Getty Images; 506L, © Michael Jones/Alaska Stock Images; 506R, © Pete Saloutos/CORBIS; 507, © Mary Steinbacher/PhotoEdit; 508, © Paul A. Souders/CORBIS; 509L, © AP/Wide World Photos; 509R, © Jon Chomitz/Prentice Hall; 510, © Clive Streeter/Dorling Kindersley; 511T, © Lee Snyder/Photo Researchers; 512TL, © Michael Newman/PhotoEdit; 513, © Tom Pantages; 514, © Alyx Kellington/IndexStock Imagery; 517, © Royalty-Free/CORBIS; 518-519, © Royalty-Free/CORBIS; 518TR, © Richard Cummins/CORBIS; 519BR, © PhotoDisc/Getty Images; 520, © AFP/CORBIS; 521, © PhotoDisc/Getty Images; 522, 525, © Ken O'Donoghue/Prentice Hall; 527T, © Dave King/Dorling Kindersley; 527B, © Horst Klemm/Masterfile; 528L, © Charles D. Winters/Photo Researchers; 528R, © E. R. Degginger/Color-Pic; 531, © 1998 Ben S. Kwiatkowski/Fundamental Photographs; 533, © Jonnie Miles/Getty Images; 538, © Pete Turner/Getty Images

Chapter 18 540, © AP/Wide World Photos; 541T, © Alpine Aperture; 541BL, © Orban Thierry/CORBIS SYGMA; 5410BR, © Dave King/Dorling Kindersley; 542L, © Barry Runk/Grant Heilman Photography; 542M, © Erika Stone/Peter Arnold; 542R, © G. I. Bernard/Earth Scenes; 544, © Ken O'Donoghue/Prentice Hall; 545, © Ken Karp/Addison-Wesley; 546, © Bettman/CORBIS; 548, © Ken O'Donoghue/Prentice Hall; 549T, © PhotoDisc/Getty Images; 551, © Dennis MacDonald/PhotoEdit; 552-553, © Empics/SportsChrome; 555, © Dominic Rouse/Getty Images; 556, © Geoffrey Nilsen/Addison-Wesley; 557, © Thomas Hovland/Grant Heilman Photography; 559, © Yoav Levy/Phototake; 560T, © CNRI/Photo Researchers; 560B, © Ken Karp/Addison-Wesley; 561, © Tony Freeman/PhotoEdit; 562, © Richard Megna/Fundamental Photographs; 563, © Ken Karp/Addison-Wesley; 564, © David Bishop/Phototake; 565, © Michael Dalton/Fundamental Photographs; 566T, © Franz-Marc Frei/CORBIS; 567T, © Annie Griffiths Belt/Getty Images; 567B, © Ken Karp/Addison-Wesley; 568T, © Ron Watts/CORBIS; 569B, © Richard Hutchings/Addison-Wesley; 569R, © Ken O'Donoghue/Prentice Hall; 573, © Leonard Lessin/Peter Arnold; 574, © Ken O'Donoghue/Prentice Hall; 575T, © Robert Laberge/Getty Images; 576L, © Tom Bean/CORBIS; 576-577, © Photo Disc/Getty Images; 579, ©Bob Handelman/Getty Images

Chapter 19 586, © Jose Azel/Aurora Photos; 587T, © Virginia Weinland/Photo Researchers; 587BL, © Ken Karp/Addison-Wesley; 258BML, © Richard Megna/Fundamental Photographs, 587BMR, © Russ Lappa/Addison-Wesley, 587BR, © PhotoDisc/Getty Images; 590T, © Leonard Lessin/Peter Arnold, 590B, © Ken Karp/Addison-Wesley; 593, © Scott T. Smith/CORBIS; 594T, © Brian Pieters/Masterfile; 595T, © E.R. Degginger/Color-Pic; 595B, © Ken Karp/Addison-Wesley; 596, © Michael Newman/PhotoEdit; 598, © PhotoDisc/Getty Images, 600, 602, © Richard Megna/Fundamental Photographs, 603TL, © Royalty-Free/CORBIS; 603TR, © Patrick Johns/CORBIS; 603ML, © Robert Mackinlay/Peter Arnold; 603MR, © Phil Schermeister/CORBIS; 603B, © Richard Megna/Fundamental Photographs; 604, © Ken O'Donoghue/Prentice Hall; 605T, © PhotoDisc/Getty Images; 607, © David Young-Wolff/PhotoEdit; 608, © Paul J. Richards/AFP /Getty Images; 611, © Franco Origlia/Getty Images; 612T, © PhotoDisc/Getty Images; 612B, © Garry Black/Masterfile; 614, © Ken Karp/Addison-Wesley; 615T, © Richard Megna/Fundamental Photographs; 615B, © Ken Karp/Addison-Wesley; 617, © Jon Chomitz/Prentice Hall; 618T, © Andrew Syred/Getty Images; 619T, © Richard Megna/Fundamental Photographys; 619B, 620, © Ken Karp/Addison-Wesley; 622, © Charles D. Winters/Photo Researchers; 623TL, © Silver Burdett Ginn; 623TR, © Dorling Kindersley; 623 M, 623B, Library of Congress

Chapter 20 630, © Sandi and Bill Langley/IndexStock Imagery; 631T, © Christian Michaels/Getty Images; 631B, © Richard Megna/Fundamental Photographs; 632T, © PhotoDisc/Getty Images; 632BL, 632BR, © E.R. Degginger/Color-Pic; 633L, © Paul Silverman/Fundamental Photographs; 633M, 633R, © Ken Karp/Addison-Wesley; 634, © Dorling Kindersley; 635, © Jens J. Jensen/CORBIS; 636, © Richard Hamilton Smith/CORBIS; 637T, © Phil Degginger/Color-Pic; 637BL, © Michael Newman/PhotoEdit; 637BR, © Julie Houck/Stock Boston; 638, © Annette Price - H2O Photography/Alamy Photography; 639T, © Ross M. Horowitz/Getty Images; 640ALL, 642ALL, © Ken Karp/Addison-Wesley; 643, © Tom Pantages; 644TR, © Ken O'Donoghue/Prentice Hall; 644B, Courtesy of National Association of Underwater Instructors; 645T, The Granger Collection, New York; 645B, © Richard Megna/Fundamental Photographs; 646A, © Adam Jones/Visuals Unlimited; 646B, © E.R. Degginger/Color-Pic; 647, © Charles D. Winters/Photo Researchers; 648, © Photo Researchers; 649, © Ken Karp/Addison-Wesley; 653, © Ken O'Donoghue/Prentice Hall; 654, © George Haling/Photo Researchers; 655, © Richard Megna/Fundamental Photographs; 658, 660, © Ken Karp/Addison-Wesley

Chapter 21 662, © ThinkStock/IndexStock Imagery; 663T, © HBOI/Visuals Unlimited; 663B, © Richard Megna/Fundamental Photographs; 665BOTH, The

Granger Collection, New York; 668, © Tim Boyle/Getty Images; 670, © D. Ducros/ Photo Researchers; 671T, © Jeremy Maude/Masterfile; 671B, © Paul Silverman/ Fundamental Photographs; 677, © Prentice Hall; 678T, © Chris Collins/CORBIS; 678BL, © Markku Lahdesmaki/CORBIS; 678BR, © Occidental Chemical Corp.; 680, © Charles D. Winters/Photo Researchers; 682, © Russ Lappa/Prentice Hall; 683, © Christian Sarramon/CORBIS; 684, 685TR, © Ken O'Donoghue/Prentice Hall

Chapter 22 692, © Berry Bingel/Getty Images; 693T, © Richard Hansen/Photo Researchers; 695TL, © Paul Fusco/Magnum Photos; 695TR, © Leonard Lessin/Peter Arnold; 697, 699, © Ken O'Donoghue/Prentice Hall; 700T, © Davis Barber/PhotoEdit; 700B, © Simon Fraser/Photo Researchers; 701, © Royalty-Free/PictureQuest; 702T, © Gusto/Photo Researchers; 702B, © Alan & Linda Detrich/Photo Researchers; 704T, © Benelux Press/IndexStock Imagery; 706, © Yoav Levy/Phototake; 707, 708, © Ken O'Donoghue/Prentice Hall; 709T, © Barry Runk/Grant Heilman Photography; 711, © Patricia Jordan/Peter Arnold; 712T, Courtesy of NASA; 714BKGD, Earth History Hall, American Museum of Natural History; 714BL, © Bob O'Shaughnessy/CORBIS; 714ML, © E. R. Degginger/Color-Pic; 714MR, © Carolina Biological Supply Company/Phototake; 714BR, © E. R. Degginger/Color-Pic; 715, © Allen Oddie/ PhotoEdit; 716-717, © James Nelson/Getty Images; 716TR, ©Syracuse Newspapers/ Logan Wallace/The Image Works; 717T, © Keith Wood/Getty Images

Chapter 23 724, © Neil Fletcher/Dorling Kindersley; 725T, © AP/Wide World Photos; 725B, © Ken O'Donoghue/Prentice Hall; 727, © John Greim/Photo Researchers; 730T, The Granger Collection, New York; 731, © Ken O'Donoghue/Prentice Hall; 732L, © Michael Keller/ CORBIS; 732M, © Bob Daemmrich/Stock Boston; 732R, © Michael Groen/Addison-Wesley; 733L, © Barry Runk/Grant Heilman Photography; 733R, © Felica Martinez/PhotoEdit; 734, © Richard Megna/Fundamental Photographs; 736, © Hulton-Deutsch Collection/CORBIS; 737, © Ken Karp/Addison-Wesley; 740TL, © Ken O'Donoghue/Prentice Hall; 740TR, © Clayton Sharrard/PhotoEdit; 740B, © Michael Groen/Addison-Wesley; 742L, © Dorling Kindersley; 742M, © Alan & Linda Detrick/Grant Heilman Photography; 742R, © Barry L. Runk/Grant Heilman Photography; 744T, © SuperStock/PictureQuest; 744B, © PhotoDisc/Getty Images; 745, 746, © Richard Megna/Fundamental Photographs; 747T, © William McKellar/ Brand X Pictures/PictureQuest; 747B, © Ken O'Donoghue/Prentice Hall; 748L, © Alan Schein/CORBIS; 748R, © Bud Freund/Index Stock Imagery/PictureQuest; 749T, © Stephen Frisch/Stock Boston/PictureQuest; 749BL, © Richard Choy/Peter Arnold; 749MM, © Garry Gay/Getty Images,749MB, © Chris Sorensen/CORBIS; 749BR, © Michel Tcherevkoff/Getty Images; 750BOTH, © Michael English/Custom Medical Stock Photo; 751L, © Paul Souders/Getty Images; 751R, © Amy and Chuck Wiley/Wales/Index Stock Imagery; 752, © Bob Daemmrich/Stock Boston; 753, © Ken O'Donoghue/Prentice Hall; 754-755, © Andrea Pistolesi/Getty Images; 754TR, © Peter Angelo Simon/CORBIS; 754ML, © David McLain/Aurora Photos; 754MR, © Neil Fletcher & Matthew Ward/Dorling Kindersley; 754ML&MR (inset), © Courtesy Louet Sales; 755TL, © Dorling Kindersley; 755TM, © Richard Shiell/Earth Scenes; 755TR, © Howard Rice/Dorling Kindersley; 755TL,TM,TR (inset), © Courtesy Louet Sales

Chapter 24 762, © Laureen March/CORBIS; 763T, © Dr. Dennis Kunkel/Visuals Unlimited; 764, © Dr. George Chapman/Visuals Unlimited; 765, © Cornelia Doerr/AGE Fotostock America; 766T, © Bill Beatty/Visuals Unlimited; 766M, © Maximilian Stock Ltd./Photo Researchers; 766B, © Brian Hagiwara/FoodPix/Getty Images; 769T, © Tony Garcia/Getty Images; 771BL, © Dennis Kunkel/Phototake; 773, © Dr. Hans Gelderblom/Visuals Unlimited; 774, © Ken O'Donoghue/Prentice Hall; 775T, © Jennifer Cheung/Getty Images; 775B, © John E. Kelly/FoodPix/Getty Images; 776T, © Richard Hutchings/Addison-Wesley; 777T, © Dennis Kunkel/Phototake; 778T, © Ariel Skelley/CORBIS; 778B, © Phil A. Harrington/Peter Arnold; 780, © Ken O'Donoghue/Prentice Hall; 781, © Tony Freeman/PhotoEdit; 782, © Ken Edward/Photo Researchers; 783, © Dan McCoy/Rainbow; 785TL, © Calgene/Peter Arnold; 785BR, © Reuters/Ho/Archive Photo/Getty Images; 786T, © Alison Wright/ CORBIS; 787, © John Shaw/Photo Researchers; 789L, © Bojan Brecelj/CORBIS; 789M, © Jim Strawer/Grant Heilman Photography; 789R, © Royalty-Free/CORBIS; 790, © Wally Eberhart/Visuals Unlimited; 791TR, © Phototake; 791ML, © Mark Maio/Phototake; 791MR, © Lippincott Williams & Wilkins; 791BL, © Derek Berwin/Getty Images; 791BR, © James Balog/Getty Images; 797, © Leonard Lessin/Peter Arnold

Chapter 25 798, © W. Deuter/Masterfile; 799T, The Granger Collection, New York; 803T, © Steven Cole/Getty Images; 806, © David McNew/Getty Images; 808, CERN/Photo Researchers; 809, © Ken O'Donoghue/Prentice Hall; 810T, © Robert George Young/Masterfile; 811T, © Dr. Jeremy Burgess/Photo Researchers; 812, © Roger Ressmeyer/CORBIS; 816T, © Stephen Marks/Getty Images; 816B, © Royalty-Free/CORBIS; 814BL, © Jonathan Blair/CORBIS; 814-815, © Nicholas Devore III/Photographers/Aspen/PictureQuest; 815TR, © Eduardo Gill/BlackStar Publishing/ PictureQuest; 815BR, © Dave King/Dorling Kindersley; 816T, © Stephen Marks/Getty Images; 816B, © Royalty-Free/CORBIS; 817T, © Mauritius/GMBH/PhotoTake; 817M, © Kevin Schafer/Peter Arnold; 817R, © Yoav Levy/Phototake; 819T, © Ryan McVay/Getty Images; 819B, © CNRI/Phototake

Elements Handbook 826T, © Tom Bochsler/Prentice Hall; 826M2, © Richard Megna/ Fundamental Photographs; 826B2, © Lester V. Bergman/CORBIS; R1, © PhotoDisc/ Getty Images; R2TR, © Rich Treptow/Visuals Unlimited; R2BL, © Phil Silverman/ Fundamental Photographs; R2BR, © Gunter Marx Photography/CORBIS; R4T, R4M, © Corbis Images/ PictureQuest; R4B, © Joe Sohm/ Visions Of America, LLC/ PictureQuest; R5, © Royalty-Free/CORBIS; R6T, © Runk/Schoenberger/Grant Heilman Photography; R7L, © Tom Bochsler/Prentice Hall; R7B2, © Richard Megna/ Fundamental Photographs; R7B2, © Lester V. Bergman/ CORBIS; R8T, © PhotoDisc/ Getty Images; R8B, © Park Street/PhotoEdit; R9T, © Jon Chomitz/Prentice Hall; R9B, © Bruce Forster/Getty Images; R10, © Reg Charity/CORBIS; R11B, © Lester V. Bergman/CORBIS; R11B, © Image Farm/Alamy Images; R12T, © Peter Bowater/Photo Researchers; R12B, © David Greedy/Getty Images; R13, © Jules Cowan/ImageState;

PictureQuest; R14T, © Lester V. Bergman/CORBIS; R14B, © Doug Steley/Alamy Images; R15M, © Phil Silverman/Fundamental Photographs; R15B, © Andrew Syred/ Photo Researchers; R16T, © Tomi/ PhotoLink/PhotoDisc/PictureQuest; R16B, © Jose Fuste Raga/CORBIS; R17, © Ed Degginger/Color-Pic; R18M, © M. Claye/Photo Researchers; R18BL, © Mark A. Schneider/Photo Researchers; R18BR, © Harry Taylor/Dorling Kindersley; R19, © Gabe Palmer/CORBIS; R20, © Elizabeth Simpson/Getty Images; R21BL, © 2003 Jeff J. Daly/Fundamental Photographs; R21MR, © Alfred Pasieka/Photo Researchers; R22T, © Nigel Cattlin/Photo Researchers; R22B, © Stockbyte/PictureQuest; R23T, © Alan Detrick/Photo Researchers; R23M, © PhotoDisc/Getty Images; R24, © Richard Megna/Fundamental Photographs; R26T, © David Harvey/Woodfin Camp; R26B, © Ted Spiegel/CORBIS; R27, Barry L. Runk/Grant Heilman Photography; R28TL, © Prentice Hall, Inc.; R28TR, © Jeffrey A. Scovil; R29TL, © Yoav Levy/Phototake; R29M, © Ken Karp/Addison-Wesley; R30ML, Colin Ladyka; R30MR, © Richard Megna/Fundamental Photographs; R30B, Photo Massimo Boyer/edge-of-reef.com; R31TR, © Dave King/Dorling Kindersley; R31B, Courtesy of NASA; R32T, © Richard Megna/Fundamental Photographs; R32, ©1987 Paul Silverman/Fundamental Photographs; R33, © Richard Megna/Fundamental Photographs; R34T, © Royalty-Free/CORBIS; R34B, © Jose Luis Pelaez/CORBIS; R35T, © Gwen Rosenberg /Alliance Pharmaceutical Corp.; R35B, © Carolina Biological Supply Company/Phototake; R36T, © Dominic Episcopo/ImageState; R36B, © Al Fenn/Time Life Pictures/Getty Images; R37B, © Paul A. Souders/CORBIS; R37B, © Tim McGuire/ CORBIS; R38, ©Micjael Gadomski/Earthscenes; R39T, Courtesy of AECL (Atomic Energy of Canada Limited); R39B, © AFP/Getty Images; R40T, © Harry Taylor/Dorling Kindersley; R40B, © Layne Kennedy/CORBIS; R41BL, © Stephen Frisch; R41BR, © Richard Megna/Fundamental Photographs; R42TR, R42BR, © Burstein Collection/CORBIS; R42BL, © Document General Motors/Reuter/CORBIS; R43, © Robert Estall/CORBIS; R44TR, © Phil Degginger/Color-Pic; R44B, © Gunter Marx Photography/CORBIS; R45, © Microzoa/Getty Images

Math Handbook R56, © SNL/DOE/Photo Researchers; R59, © Richard Megna/ Fundamental Photographs; R62, © Paul Silverman/Fundamental Photographs; R66, © Michelle D. Bridwell/PhotoEdit; R67, © Matthew McVay/Stock Boston; R69, © James King-Holmes/Photo Researchers; R70, © Robert Brenner/PhotoEdit; R72, © Tony Freeman/PhotoEdit; R74, © Syracuse Newspapers /Stephen D. Cannerelli/The Image Works; R78, © Charles D. Winters/Photo Researchers

Illustrations

Ron Carboni 519

Stephen Durke 141, 300, 386T, 391, 442, 443B, 447, 476, 511, 512, 666, 672, 673, 681, 687, 689BOTH, 713, 818, R6B, R17

GTS Companies xv, 16, 22, 29, 31, 32, 34, 37, 50, 51, 56, 60, 81, 89, 118, 120, 124, 128-129, 133, 138, 143, 145, 153, 157, 162-163, 165, 166, 171, 174, 175, 176, 178, 182, 183, 184, 189, 190, 191, 192, 200, 201, 211, 217, 218, 219, 221, 222, 223, 228, 232, 233, 245, 248, 253, 254, 267, 275, 277, 278, 293, 303, 304, 305, 316, 325, 345, 349, 350, 354, 357, 362, 363, 369, 380, 388, 394, 397, 400, 403, 407, 411, 418, 420, 429, 437, 441, 442, 443, 458, 466, 468, 474, 492, 500, 506, 515, 520, 523, 528, 529, 530, 532, 537, 539, 542, 543, 547, 550, 556, 572, 576, 578, 582, 583, 597, 598, 602, 606, 615, 617, 618, 621, 626, 627, 655, 684, 689, 708, 721, 765, 768, 771, 772, 778, 779, 784, 786, 788, 789, 803, 804, 805, 809, 822, 823, 825, R6T, R7, R10, R11, R12, R14, R15, R18, R19, R20, R22, R23, R24, R25, R26, R28, R29, R32, R33T, R36, R38, R40, R40, R43

Trevor Johnston 313, 376-377

Rob Kemp 716-717

George Ladas xviii, 259

Richard McMahon 44, 47, 64, 67, 78, 81, 89, 104, 105, 184, 198, 351T, 372, 386B, 393, 394T, 402, 411R, 461, 472, 487, 491, 570, 636, 667, 668, 669, 670

Precision Graphics iii, vii, x, 36B, 41, 43, 61, 99, 102, 107, 113, 115, 123, 125, 128-129, 129B, 130, 131, 132, 139, 153, 161, 170, 172, 175, 176, 185, 195, 198, 202, 208, 209, 214, 215, 216, 217, 218, 219, 221, 222, 223, 228, 229, 230, 231, 234, 235, 236, 237, 238, 239, 240, 241, 243, 248, 251, 257, 274, 283, 284, 285, 295, 309, 311, 319, 325, 326, 327, 331, 332, 333, 335, 336, 351, 357, 364, 369, 383, 386TR, 396B, 398, 399, 401, 414, 415, 416, 417, 418, 420, 422, 430, 431, 433, 439, 446, 449, 451, 453, 469, 478, 479, 483, 487, 488, 503, 543, 549, 554, 560, 568, 573, 585, 588, 591, 592, 594, 613, 618, 629, 631, 632, 633, 661, 663, 680, 694, 695, 698, 702, 703, 704, 705, 708, 709, 710, 720, 723, 726, 732, 735, 737, 741, 743, 758, 759, 761, 763, 771B, 773, 776, 777, 782, 791, 797, 800, 801, 802, 804, 807, 810, 811, 813, 824, 825, R21, R27, R28B, R33M

Prentice Hall 137, 392, 396M, 409, 691, R74, R75, R76, R84, R86, R91

Neil Stewart 242, 644

Nina Wallace 712

Bob Young 685